Atomic Masses of the Elements

Name	Symbol	Atomic Number	Atomic Mass[a]	Name	Symbol	Atomic Number	Atomic Mass[a]
Actinium	Ac	89	(227)	Mendelevium	Md	101	(258)
Aluminum	Al	13	26.98	Mercury	Hg	80	200.6
Americium	Am	95	(243)	Molybdenum	Mo	42	95.94
Antimony	Sb	51	121.8	Moscovium	Mc	115	(289)
Argon	Ar	18	39.95	Neodymium	Nd	60	144.2
Arsenic	As	33	74.92	Neon	Ne	10	20.18
Astatine	At	85	(210)	Neptunium	Np	93	(237)
Barium	Ba	56	137.3	Nickel	Ni	28	58.69
Berkelium	Bk	97	(247)	Nihonium	Nh	113	(284)
Beryllium	Be	4	9.012	Niobium	Nb	41	92.91
Bismuth	Bi	83	209.0	Nitrogen	N	7	14.01
Bohrium	Bh	107	(264)	Nobelium	No	102	(259)
Boron	B	5	10.81	Oganesson	Og	118	(294)
Bromine	Br	35	79.90	Osmium	Os	76	190.2
Cadmium	Cd	48	112.4	Oxygen	O	8	16.00
Calcium	Ca	20	40.08	Palladium	Pd	46	106.4
Californium	Cf	98	(251)	Phosphorus	P	15	30.97
Carbon	C	6	12.01	Platinum	Pt	78	195.1
Cerium	Ce	58	140.1	Plutonium	Pu	94	(244)
Cesium	Cs	55	132.9	Polonium	Po	84	(209)
Chlorine	Cl	17	35.45	Potassium	K	19	39.10
Chromium	Cr	24	52.00	Praseodymium	Pr	59	140.9
Cobalt	Co	27	58.93	Promethium	Pm	61	(145)
Copernicium	Cn	112	(285)	Protactinium	Pa	91	231.0
Copper	Cu	29	63.55	Radium	Ra	88	(226)
Curium	Cm	96	(247)	Radon	Rn	86	(222)
Darmstadtium	Ds	110	(271)	Rhenium	Re	75	186.2
Dubnium	Db	105	(262)	Rhodium	Rh	45	102.9
Dysprosium	Dy	66	162.5	Roentgenium	Rg	111	(272)
Einsteinium	Es	99	(252)	Rubidium	Rb	37	85.47
Erbium	Er	68	167.3	Ruthenium	Ru	44	101.1
Europium	Eu	63	152.0	Rutherfordium	Rf	104	(261)
Fermium	Fm	100	(257)	Samarium	Sm	62	150.4
Flerovium	Fl	114	(289)	Scandium	Sc	21	44.96
Fluorine	F	9	19.00	Seaborgium	Sg	106	(266)
Francium	Fr	87	(223)	Selenium	Se	34	78.96
Gadolinium	Gd	64	157.3	Silicon	Si	14	28.09
Gallium	Ga	31	69.72	Silver	Ag	47	107.9
Germanium	Ge	32	72.64	Sodium	Na	11	22.99
Gold	Au	79	197.0	Strontium	Sr	38	87.62
Hafnium	Hf	72	178.5	Sulfur	S	16	32.07
Hassium	Hs	108	(265)	Tantalum	Ta	73	180.9
Helium	He	2	4.003	Technetium	Tc	43	(99)
Holmium	Ho	67	164.9	Tellurium	Te	52	127.6
Hydrogen	H	1	1.008	Tennessine	Ts	117	(294)
Indium	In	49	114.8	Terbium	Tb	65	158.9
Iodine	I	53	126.9	Thallium	Tl	81	204.4
Iridium	Ir	77	192.2	Thorium	Th	90	232.0
Iron	Fe	26	55.85	Thulium	Tm	69	168.9
Krypton	Kr	36	83.80	Tin	Sn	50	118.7
Lanthanum	La	57	138.9	Titanium	Ti	22	47.87
Lawrencium	Lr	103	(262)	Tungsten	W	74	183.8
Lead	Pb	82	207.2	Uranium	U	92	238.0
Lithium	Li	3	6.941	Vanadium	V	23	50.94
Livermorium	Lv	116	(293)	Xenon	Xe	54	131.3
Lutetium	Lu	71	175.0	Ytterbium	Yb	70	173.0
Magnesium	Mg	12	24.31	Yttrium	Y	39	88.91
Manganese	Mn	25	54.94	Zinc	Zn	30	65.41
Meitnerium	Mt	109	(268)	Zirconium	Zr	40	91.22

[a]Values in parentheses are the mass number of the most stable isotope.

Letter to Professors

Dear Professor,

Thank you for considering or choosing to use our new product, General, Organic, & Biological Chemistry: An Interactive Approach. We're so excited to have this chance to share it with you.

Together with Pearson and literally hundreds of reviewers and class testers, we've worked hard to create a product that truly meets your needs, as well as the needs of this generation of digital students. We know that like us, you care deeply about the success of all your students. Like us, we know you've seen many of those magical "a-ha" moments in your classroom when students finally make sense of a complex concept, or truly see why chemistry matters in their daily lives, their communities, and their future careers. With this project, we've created a learning tool that brings the engagement and inspiration of the classroom to the work students do when they're not in your class.

Like all scientists, we take the process of peer review seriously. Our project has been informed and improved by both science education literature as well as contributions from hundreds of faculty and students throughout its development. The comments, suggestions, and feedback have been used to help hone this new learning resource. We've leveraged this feedback to help us design the most engaging, effective, integrated chemistry learning experience we can so that all students have the chance to both master this essential content as well as fully appreciate the role of chemistry in their everyday lives and their future careers.

We know that caring about students and their long-term success is at the core of what we all do as faculty. We thank you for collaborating with us to craft this new learning resource for this inspiring group of students. If you ever want to chat about curriculum or have any comments about the book that you'd like to share, please do not hesitate to reach out to us.

Sincerely,
Kalyn Shea Owens, PhD
Jeff Owens, PhD
Ann J. Murkowski, MS
Next.Gen.GOB@gmail.com

Letter to Students

Dear Student,

We are so excited for you to start your journey into the world of chemistry. While it might not feel like it at this moment, chemistry is a foundational science that truly touches all our lives. As authors and classroom educators, we have focused our efforts on your needs and worked hard to produce a highly contextualized and engaging learning resource that consistently shows you the connections between chemistry and your everyday life and future career. Importantly, our project has been shaped by the feedback of hundreds of students that have class tested this learning resource and provided valuable feedback for improvement.

Your authors are an interdisciplinary team with decades of teaching experience as well as experience in the healthcare and biopharmaceutical industry. And importantly, we're a team that loves being in the classroom—loves the energy, dedication, and passion that our students bring with them. We know the power of seeing connections between disciplines, of watching a video explaining a key concept, and of getting detailed feedback right when you need it. We wrote this book to support you, to help you not just survive but thrive as you move through your chemistry.

On the screens that follow, you'll find clear, concise explanations of chemistry consistently contextualized to help you see how and why every topic matters. Every section contains multiple opportunities for you to practice what you're learning and check your understanding. Detailed feedback helps confirm that you're on the right track or provides a hint if you need it. And we've taken the most challenging concepts from each chapter and developed them into our VisibleChem Videos. These aren't sleek, polished productions read by robotic voices. They're us—explaining key concepts just like we would if you'd stopped by our office hours, and we sat down together with a whiteboard.

We hope you find this new, digital-first learning resource to be a powerful tool as you move through general, organic, and biochemistry. We know you have an amazing future putting your chemistry to use to improve not just your own life but the lives of your family and communities. It's a profound privilege to provide this resource in support of your journey.

Sincerely,
Kalyn Shea Owens, PhD
Jeff Owens, PhD
Ann J. Murkowski, MS
Next.Gen.GOB@gmail.com

General, Organic, & Biological Chemistry

An Interactive Approach

Kalyn Shea Owens
North Seattle College

Jeff Owens
Cardinal Health and Edmonds College

Ann J. Murkowski
North Seattle College

 Pearson

Content Strategy & Management: Jeanne Zalesky, Elizabeth Ellsworth Bell
Content Development: Matthew Walker, Erin Mulligan, Becky Contos Oles
Content Production: Kristen Flathman, Brett Coker, Mary Tindle, Keri Rand, Jayne Sportelli, Meaghan Fallano, Margaret Trombley
Product Management: Christopher Hess, Jessica Moro
Product Marketing: Candice Madden
Rights and Permissions: Ben Ferrini, Matthew Perry

Please contact https://support.pearson.com/getsupport/s/ with any queries on this content.

Cover Image by *watchara/Shutterstock*

Library of Congress Cataloging-in-Publication Data
Cataloging-in-Publication Data is available on file at the Library of Congress.

KD 09.21.2022 1902

4 2022

Access Code Card
ISBN-10: 0-137-83732-1
ISBN-13: 978-0-137-83732-8

Rental Edition
ISBN-10: 0-137-65136-8
ISBN-13: 978-0-137-65136-8

Pearson's Commitment to Diversity, Equity, and Inclusion

Pearson is dedicated to creating bias-free content that reflects the diversity, depth, and breadth of all learners' lived experiences.

We embrace the many dimensions of diversity, including but not limited to race, ethnicity, gender, sex, sexual orientation, socioeconomic status, ability, age, and religious or political beliefs.

Education is a powerful force for equity and change in our world. It has the potential to deliver opportunities that improve lives and enable economic mobility. As we work with authors to create content for every product and service, we acknowledge our responsibility to demonstrate inclusivity and incorporate diverse scholarship so that everyone can achieve their potential through learning. As the world's leading learning company, we have a duty to help drive change and live up to our purpose to help more people create a better life for themselves and to create a better world.

Our ambition is to purposefully contribute to a world where:

- Everyone has an equitable and lifelong opportunity to succeed through learning.
- Our educational content accurately reflects the histories and lived experiences of the learners we serve.
- Our educational products and services are inclusive and represent the rich diversity of learners.
- Our educational content prompts deeper discussions with students and motivates them to expand their own learning (and worldview).

Accessibility

We are also committed to providing products that are fully accessible to all learners. As per Pearson's guidelines for accessible educational Web media, we test and retest the capabilities of our products against the highest standards for every release, following the WCAG guidelines in developing new products for copyright year 2022 and beyond.

 You can learn more about Pearson's commitment to accessibility at
https://www.pearson.com/us/accessibility.html

Contact Us

While we work hard to present unbiased, fully accessible content, we want to hear from you about any concerns or needs with this Pearson product so that we can investigate and address them.

 Please contact us with concerns about any potential bias at
https://www.pearson.com/report-bias.html

 For accessibility-related issues, such as using assistive technology with Pearson products, alternative text requests, or accessibility documentation, email the Pearson Disability Support team at **disability.support@pearson.com**

v

About the Authors

KALYN SHEA OWENS earned her undergraduate degree in Chemistry from the University of California, San Diego, and her Ph.D. in Organic Chemistry from the University of California, Davis. She then transitioned to chemical education research as a National Science Foundation (NSF) funded Postdoctoral Fellow at the University of Washington, College of Education. This transition to education research was the point in her pathway that she found her true passion and calling. Combining chemistry content knowledge with the tools to investigate how people learn chemistry is her life-long mission, and she is particularly interested in how diverse student populations can thrive and find success in early gateway courses. Owens is currently a professor at North Seattle College where she teaches a range of chemistry courses. She and co-author Murkowski have collaborated for years to conduct research that focuses on designing and assessing interdisciplinary STEM curriculum, investigating students' conceptions of the representational nature of chemistry, and exploring how early research experiences promote equity and inclusion. Owens has received three awards for innovation and excellence in teaching and continues to obtain funding from the NSF to transform the chemistry learning experience to be inclusive and engaging. Owens enjoys spending time outdoors with her family and inspiring students from all walks of life to learn and love chemistry.

JEFF OWENS received his B.S. degree in chemistry from the University of California, Santa Barbara in the College of Creative Studies, and his Ph.D. in Chemistry and Biochemistry from the University of California, Davis and the National Institute of Genetics, Japan. After conducting post-doctoral research at the Fred Hutchinson Cancer Research Center in Seattle, he helped start a successful biotech company that was acquired by Axis-Shield and is currently owned by Abbott Labs. He then worked on process development of antibody-based drugs in support of clinical trials at Lilly ICOS and Biogen IDEC. Owens returned to academics and taught allied health GOB courses and organic chemistry for STEM majors as a tenured faculty member and department head in Seattle area colleges for 16 years. He is now a Senior Scientist at Cardinal Health and remains engaged in chemistry education. In his spare time, he enjoys a range of outdoor activities in the Pacific Northwest with his friends and family.

ANN J. MURKOWSKI earned her B.S. degree in Biology from the University of Puget Sound and her M.S. in Molecular and Evolutionary Biology from Western Washington University. She spent seven years working in biotechnology for both the University of Washington and a private start-up before returning to her first love, teaching. Murkowski is currently a faculty member at North Seattle College in Seattle Washington where she teaches a broad range of biology courses for both majors and non-majors. Murkowski is passionate about the power of interdisciplinary teaching and learning to engage all students and promote equity in all STEM disciplines. She and Kalyn Owens have been teaching integrated biology and chemistry classes in a variety of formats since 2005. She also believes in the transformative power of early research experiences for science students and manages two NSF-funded programs to provide research experiences and support to early-stage science students. In her spare time, Murkowski loves to hike, bike, and explore the great outdoors.

Preface

Our interdisciplinary author team is composed of passionate educators and education researchers with decades of experience putting students at the center of everything we do. Our team also brings years of experience in the biopharmaceutical and health care industry, allowing us to further contextualize the General, Organic, and Biochemisty content for the student. We are committed to ensuring that every student has access to high-quality, effective, engaging learning materials that allow them to successfully learn the abstract chemical concepts needed to move forward in their academic paths. Equally importantly, we strive to ensure that diverse student populations begin to think of themselves as capable scientists and see the multitude of ways chemistry impacts and informs their daily lives and future careers.

In our work in the classroom, we designed active learning spaces and developed evidence-based curriculum centered on compelling applications to motivate students to explore how chemistry connects to other disciplines, their daily lives and the issues they care about. With this text, we were inspired to bring these innovations to students learning outside the classroom. Our aim was to create a dynamic resource that specifically targets this new generation of technology savvy students in the learning process through pedagogical strategies that motivate, engage, and provide opportunities for application of new knowledge to real world examples. We are particularly passionate about creating interdisciplinary learning opportunities for students that are relevant, interactive, visual, and provide ongoing just-in-time feedback. More than ever, this generation of students seeks engaging, interactive learning experiences that are the hallmarks of effective classroom learning environments.

About the Product

Despite all we know about how to support students in the classroom, we still send them home to read from static pages, alone, for hours on end. With this digital first product, we reimagine how students engage with their texts. Each unit is introduced with a current health or environmental topic purposefully written to inspire students to see the interdisciplinary nature of science and to learn the chemistry found in the unit chapters. Applications to biology, healthcare, and the environment are consistently woven throughout each chapter. Key concepts are presented visually and reinforced with multiple opportunities for students to practice new skills and assess their learning. These opportunities include embedded videos of key concepts which provide visual and engaging explanations of each chapter's most challenging topics and just-in-time, detailed feedback, which helps reinforce student progress and address alternative conceptions early in the learning process.

Key Features of *General, Organic, & Biological Chemistry: An Interactive Approach* include:

> **Learn** tutorials are designed to help solve the most challenging problems in each chapter and guide students through practice questions. The tutorials include guided problem-solving sessions, sample problems, and step-by-step guides that continuously engage students in self-evaluation.

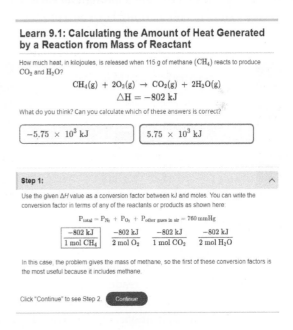

Learn 9.1: Calculating the Amount of Heat Generated by a Reaction from Mass of Reactant

How much heat, in kilojoules, is released when 115 g of methane (CH_4) reacts to produce CO_2 and H_2O?

$$CH_4(g) + 2O_2(g) \rightarrow CO_2(g) + 2H_2O(g)$$
$$\triangle H = -802 \text{ kJ}$$

What do you think? Can you calculate which of these answers is correct?

| -5.75×10^3 kJ | 5.75×10^3 kJ |

Step 1:

Use the given ΔH value as a conversion factor between kJ and moles. You can write the conversion factor in terms of any of the reactants or products as shown here:

$$P_{total} = P_{N_2} + P_{O_2} + P_{other\ gases\ in\ air} = 760\ mmHg$$

| $\dfrac{-802\ kJ}{1\ mol\ CH_4}$ | $\dfrac{-802\ kJ}{2\ mol\ O_2}$ | $\dfrac{-802\ kJ}{1\ mol\ CO_2}$ | $\dfrac{-802\ kJ}{2\ mol\ H_2O}$ |

In this case, the problem gives the mass of methane, so the first of these conversion factors is the most useful because it includes methane.

Click "Continue" to see Step 2. [Continue]

> **BioConnects** are woven throughout each chapter to provide students with a deeper appreciation of the connection between chemistry and biology. They combine text and graphics that are often specific to the biology in the human body—showing how relevant

and useful their chemistry knowledge will be in the real world.

⟨ **Back** Page 4 of 5 **Next** ⟩

VisibleChem Videos are inviting, short video clips designed to help students focus on the most challenging chemistry concepts in each chapter. These videos provide a way to reduce text throughout each chapter to focus students on learning key concepts and skills in a more engaging format.

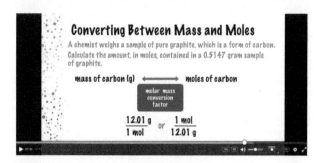

Unit Introductions and Conclusions contextualize chemistry concepts in current medical research as a method for making learning relevant. These modern research "hooks" pull the reader in, allow students to immediately grasp exactly how the unit topics relate to modern research applications, and motivate students to want to learn the chemistry concepts within each unit. Key ideas from each chapter are revisited in the Unit Conclusions providing an important opportunity for students to apply their new knowledge and interpret scientific data presented in real-world examples.

Practice exercises leverage the interactivity of the digital platform, allowing students to engage with new concepts, solve problems, and immediately assess their understanding of the content. Both the questions and answers probe common misconceptions; detailed

feedback provides targeted responses that guide students through each problem.

The end of section **Check** questions provide students with a series of 3–4 quick questions to provide instant, detailed feedback to students, helping them monitor and assess their learning.

The **End-of-Chapter Quiz** allows students to assess their basic comprehension across the entire chapter. Detailed feedback for each question provides students with just-in-time instruction for further self-evaluation of their own understanding.

Mastering Chemistry and Instructor Resources

Mastering Chemistry offers a wide variety of problems, ranging from multi-step tutorials with extensive hints and feedback to multiple-choice End-of-Chapter Problems and Test Bank questions. To provide additional scaffolding for students moving from Tutorials Problems to End-of-Chapter Problems, we created Enhanced End-of-Chapter Problems that contain specific wrong-answer feedback.

Pearson eText is an easy-to-use digital textbook available within Mastering that lets students read, highlight, take notes, and review key vocabulary all in one place. If you're not using Mastering, students can purchase the Pearson eText on their own or you can assign it as a course to schedule readings, view student usage analytics, and share your own notes with students. Learn more about Pearson eText.

- **NEW-Analytics Dashboard.** Use the dashboard to gain insight into how students are working in their eText to plan more effective instruction in and out of class.

- **Scheduled Reading.** Assign a chapter or specific section to hold students accountable for their reading and help them prep for lecture, homework, and quizzes. Scheduled Readings populate to each student's assignment page, and you can now link readings directly to a Mastering assignment.

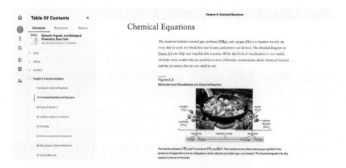

Enhanced End-of-Chapter Problems provide instructional support when and where students need it, and include links to the eText, math remediation, and wrong-answer feedback for homework assignments.

GapFinder Diagnostic Modules assess students' prerequisite knowledge such as study skills, foundational science, and math concepts, and then recommend **GapFinder Study Modules** with personalized remediation specific to the student's individual knowledge gaps. GapFinder Modules are assignable in Mastering as Dynamic Study Modules, but are completed and graded differently, and available to students for self-study in Mastering.

Dynamic Study Modules are assignable modules that pose a series of question sets about a course topic. Questions adapt to each student's performance and offer personalized, targeted feedback to help them master key concepts. Students can use their computer or the MyLab and Mastering app to access Dynamic Study Modules.

General, Organic, & Biological Chemistry includes a full suite of instructor support materials in the Instructor Resources area in Mastering Chemistry. Resources include customizable **lecture PowerPoint presentations**; **image PowerPoint presentations**; **all images and worked examples** from the text; a **test bank**; and an **instructor's solutions manual**.

Student Class Tests

General, Organic, and Biological Chemistry students across the country have contributed to the development of *General, Organic, & Biological Chemistry: An Interactive Approach.* Students were asked to use chapters in place of, or alongside, their current textbook during their course and provide feedback to the authors and editorial team.

What Students are Saying:

"I think these sample chapters make me want to switch to an online textbook. It has resources like the videos and models which helped explain the content. Traditional textbooks just don't have the same features."

Hanna Capps,
Lander University

"The thing I liked the most about the sample chapters were the Learn Tutorials, VisibleChems, and BioConnects. These gave me useful methods to check my comprehension of the chapter material and different review methods help view concepts in different ways."

Alexander Johnson,
University of Mary

"I feel like this sample chapter gave the same amount of information as our regular textbook but did so in a more simplified way. This sample chapter helped me to understand the more difficult parts of this chapter faster."

Gerard O'Reilly,
Binghamton University

" . . . Easy to read and understand . . . I felt more comfortable practicing the problems. I love this textbook and I would use it every day if I could."

Caroline Rumph,
Lander University

"I thought the book did a great job connecting the material to real world applications. I think the connections helped me better understand the chemistry."

Rylee Spitz,
Delta College

"Most of the time when I open my chemistry book, I expect to be overwhelmed by explanations and confusion. The features in this book like the practice problems and VisibleChems really help the development of ideas and understandings. I also loved the layout and design of this book. It never felt overwhelmingly cluttered and was very clean. Lastly, I absolutely loved the notes section where it allowed me to highlight things in the text that I either had questions on, wanted to make a note of, or thought was a main idea. Especially with the ability to look at them in a separate section organized. Great idea for students that really want to understand and dig deep into the reading! The interactive online book is great."

Kayla Walsh,
Mankato State University

Brief Contents

Contents

Videos, BioConnects, and Learns

Media assets are listed by unit or section number.

Unit Videos

VisibleChem Videos

Nomenclature Videos

Videos

BioConnects

Learns

Acknowledgments

Developing a new text book is an extraordinarily long and complex process. We will always be profoundly grateful to Jeanne Zalesky and Christopher Hess for their early support and insights as we developed our vision for this integrated, interactive, digital-first learning resource. These two amazing individuals guided us throughout this journey and have shown unwavering support through the duration of this project. But we owe perhaps our deepest gratitude to Erin Mulligan, our tireless developmental editor. Erin is an amazing writer, an unrelenting advocate for the student experience, a powerful mentor, and just a lovely human being. Her deep expertise and constant encouragement made this book so much more effective and the process of creating it so much more enjoyable.

It has been a true joy to discover the extraordinary commitment, talent, and professionalism of the team behind Pearson's products. Both Scott Dustan and Barbara Yien brought knowledge, encouragement, and guidance to us as new authors on an unfamiliar and often overwhelming journey. Matt Walker always had a smile and a kind word while tirelessly working to help us develop and curate our content along the way. We owe an especially deep debt to both Elizabeth Ellsworth Bell and Jessica Moro for guiding us through this process and bringing all the pieces to life, often in the nick of time. They are optimistic, creative problem-solvers—exactly who you want on your team when the path gets challenging. Becky Contos Oles did an amazing job of bringing our art program to life from our notes and scribbles. Keri Rand worked with seemingly endless patience to help us produce, improve, and launch over a hundred videos. Candice Madden graciously introduced us to the very foreign world of marketing. And Brett Coker somehow managed to keep everything moving through production without ever losing his patience or his sense of humor. Thank you Brett, and the rest of the content production group. We are deeply grateful to all these folks, and the entire Pearson team, for their hard work, consistent support, commitment to quality, and, on a journey like this, friendship.

We would also like to thank the thousands of students who have passed through our classrooms. They continue to inspire us with their curiosity, passion, and commitment to learning. A huge thank you also goes to each and every one of the faculty reviewers, focus group participants, as well as the hundreds of student and faculty class testers that provided such valuable and guiding feedback to us along the way.

And lastly, we'd like to thank our family and friends for sticking with us. We never dreamed this project would take so long or prove so all-consuming. We are grateful for your support and patience, and look forward to spending more time together.

Reviewers

Jo Nell Aarons Gillings, *Miami Dade College*
Samuel Abegaz, *Columbus State University*
Leslie Adamczyk, *Pellissippi State Community College*
Mamta Agarwal, *Chaffey College*
Edward Alexander, *San Diego Mesa College*
Zahra Alghoul, *Georgia State University*
Vera Alino, *Cosumnes River College*
Leonard Anagho, *Georgia Gwinnett College*
Dani Anthony, *Butler Community College*
Melissa Armstrong, *Gaston College*
Andrea Ashley-Oyewole, *Prairie View A&M University*
Maher Atteya, *Georgia State University*
Sahar Atwa, *University of Louisiana, Monroe*
Christy Bagwill, *Saint Louis University*
Mohammad Bahrami, *California State University, Los Angeles*
Alla Bailey, *Rochester Institute of Technology*
David Baker, *Delta College*
Daniel Bamper, *Oklahoma State University, Oklahoma City*
Sangita Baniya, *Bunker Hill Community College*
Felicia Barbieri, *Gwynedd Mercy University*
Rebecca Barlag, *Ohio University*
Judit Beagle, *University of Dayton*
Moriah Beck, *Wichita State University*
Thomas Bertolini, *University of Southern California*
Stephen Block, *University of Wisconsin, Madison*
Glenn Allen Bobo, *Bevill State Community College*
John Bonte, *Clinton Community College*
Matthew Bork, *Rockford University*
Dina Borysenko, *Milwaukee Area Technical College*
Laura Boyd, *University of Texas, Tyler*
Rebecca Bozym, *La Roche College*
Corina Brown, *University of Northern Colorado*
Jeff Browning, *University of Mary Hardin-Baylor*
John Bumpus, *University of Northern Iowa*
Dennis Burns, *Wichita State University*
Holly Carmichael, *Nash Community College*
Don Carpenetti, *Craven Community College*
Pete Carpico, *Stark State College*
Angie Carraway, *Meridian Community College*
Kathy Carrigan, *Portland Community College*
Malak Charara, *Nevada State College*
LIheng Chen, *Aquinas College*
Nestor Chevere, *American International College*
Ronald Choppi, *Chaffey College*
Emma Chow, *Palm Beach State College*
Travis Clark, *Wright State University*
Jacquelyn Cole, *Shepherd University*
Bernadette Corbett, *Metropolitan Community College*

Wyatt Cotton, *Cincinnati State College*
Kyle Craig, *Walla Walla University*
Jesse Crandall, *University of Saint Joseph*
Susan Crane, *Mount Saint Joseph University*
Michael Cross, *Northern Essex Community College*
Mark Cubberley, *Wright State University, Lake Campus*
Rajeev Dabke, *Columbus State University*
Julian Davis, *University of the Incarnate Word*
Duane DeSpain, *Eastern Arizona College*
Badrinath Dhakal, *Vance-Granville Community College*
Jean Dupon, *Coastline Community College*
Subodh K. Dutta, *East Carolina University*
Sara Egbert, *Walla Walla Community College*
Doug Engel, *Seminole College of Florida*
Dan Esterline, *University of Cincinnati, Blue Ash*
Louis Fadel, *Ivy Tech Community College, Lake Count*
Michael Ferguson, *University of Hawaii*
Theodore E. Fickel, *Los Angeles Valley College*
Vicki Flaris, *Bronx Community College*
Douglas Flournoy, *Indian Hills Community College*
George Flowers, *Albany State University, West*
Chris Fowler, *High Point University*
Eden Francis, *Clackamas Community College*
Andrew Frazer, *University of Central Florida*
Peter Friedman, *San Diego City College*
Don Fujito, *La Roche College*
Shamus Funk, *Chippewa Valley Tech College*
Jason Furrer, *University of Missouri*
Connie Gabel, *Metropolitan State University of Denver*
August Gallo, *University of Louisiana, Lafayette*
Fred Garces, *San Diego Miramar College*
Phillip Brady, *Garrett Itawamba Community College*
Norma Gatica, *Cuyahoga Community College, Western Campus*
Dixie Gautreaux, *Franciscan Missionaries of Our Lady University*
Zewdu Gebeyehu, *Columbus State University*
Denise M. Gigante, *Onondaga Community College*
Marcia Gillette, *Indiana University, Kokomo*
Cynthia Gilley, *Miramar College*
Deepa Godambe, *William Rainey Harper College*
Stephen Z. Goldberg, *Adelphi University*
Farai Gombedza, *Purdue University, North West*
Aaron Goodpaster, *Ivy Tech Community College, Muncie*
Alexandra Gorgevsky, *Palm Beach State College*
Etta Gravely, *North Carolina A&T State University*
Bobbie Grey, *Riverside City College*
Anthony Guerra, *Des Moines Area Community College*

Fenghai Guo, *Winston-Salem State University*
Midge Hall, *Clark State Community College*
Mildred Hall, *Northern Kentucky University*
Robert Hammond, *Central Carolina Community College*
Michele Hargittai, *Saint Francis University*
Karin Hassenrueck, *California State University, Northridge*
Bruce Hathaway, *LeTourneau University*
Jack Hayes, *State Fair Community College*
Lance Hellman, *Nevada State College*
John Hershberger, *North Dakota State University*
Megan Hess, *Pierce College*
Jason Holland, *University of Central Missouri*
Heather D. Hollandsworth, *Harding University*
Heather Hopgood, *Ohio University*
Amber Howerton, *Nevada State College*
Huiyuan Hu, *University of North Carolina, Greensboro*
Ling Huang, *Sacramento City College*
Sara Hubbard, *Ouachita Baptist University*
Jason Hudzik, *County College of Morris*
Kate Huisinga, *Malone University*
Thottala Jayaraman, *University of Pittsburgh*
Ryan Jeske, *Ball State University*
Melody Jewell, *South Dakota State University*
Miguel Jimenez, *El Camino College*
Peng Jing, *Purdue University, Fort Wayne*
Shell Joe, *Santa Ana College*
Lauren Johnson, *University of Texas, Tyler*
Ara Kahyaoglu, *Bergen Community College*
Sriram Kasturi, *Notre Dame College*
Stephanie Katz, *Villanova University*
Colleen Kelley, *Pima Community College*
Pamela Kerrigan, *College of Mount St. Vincent*
Renat Khatmullin, *Middle Georgia State University*
John R Kiser, *Western Piedmont Community College*
JoDe Knutson-Person, *Bismarck State College*
Rebecca Laird, *University of Iowa*
Mary Lamar, *Eastern Kentucky University*
Richard Lavallee, *Santa Monica College*
Yu Kay Law, *Indiana University, East*
Ralph Layland, *Lander University*
Katherine Leigh, *Dixie State University*
Chuck Leland, *Black Hawk College*
Andrea Leonard, *University of Louisiana, Lafayette*
Diana Leung, *University of Alabama*
Aiye Liang, *Charleston Southern University*
Scott Luaders, *Quincy University*
Theresa Luersen, *Quinnipiac University*
Amy Lumley, *Coffeyville Community College*
Sudha Madhugiri, *Collin College*
Virginie Maggiotti, *Gaston College*
Angela Mahaffey, *Loyola University, Chicago*
Alison Maley-Eady, *Cambrian College*
Raffi Manjikian, *William Paterson University*

Anna Manukyan, *Hostos Community College*
Janet Marshall, *Miami University, Middletown*
Bonnie Martinez, *Marietta College*
Joseph Mastone, *Middlesex Community College*
Hisako Masuda, *Indiana University, Kokomo*
Vivian Mativo, *Georgia State University*
Kent McCorkle, *MiraCosta College*
Lisa McGaw, *Northern Oklahoma College*
Charlene McMahon, *Milwaukee Area Technical College*
Scott Melideo, *Bucks County Community College*
Jonathan Meyers, *Columbus State University*
Mitchel Millan, *Casper College*
Kenneth Milliken, *Holmes Community College*
Susan Mircovich, *Kenai Peninsula College*
Vinod Mishra, *Snead State Community College*
Katie Mitchell-Koch, *Wichita State University*
Rebecca Moen, *Minnesota State University, Mankato*
Steven Mullen, *Parkland College*
Nixon Mwebi, *Jacksonville State University*
Subhalakshmi Nagarajan, *Bowling Green State University*
Sri Kamesh Narasimhan, *SUNY Corning Community College*
Sara Narayan, *Stevenson University*
Thong Nguyen, *Miramar College*
H Nguyen, *Highline Community College*
Jodi Noble, *Messiah College*
Daphne Norton, *University of Georgia*
Janice O'Donnell, *Henderson State University*
Susan Oliver, *Central Community College*
Thomas Olmstead, *Grossmont College*
Tanesha Osborne, *Georgia Southern University*
Kim Pamplin, *Abilene Christian University*
Giordano Paniconi, *Marymount University*
S. Shanaka Paranahewage, *Carl Albert State College*
Ernest Pascoe, *College of Coastal Georgia*
Chris Patridge, *D'Youville College*
John Patton, *Southwest Baptist University*
Richard Pennington, *Georgia Gwinnett College*
Ivana Peralta, *Vincennes University*
Joshua Perry, *Navarro College*
Donna Perygin, *Jacksonville State University*
Greg Phelan, *SUNY College at Cortland*
Patrick Pierce, *California State University, Long Beach*
Lawrence Pilgram, *Missouri Western University*
Polina Pine, *Loyola University, Chicago*
Christine Piva, *University of Massachusetts, Dartmouth*
Elizabeth Pulliam, *Tallahassee Community College*
Harry Pylypiw, *Quinnipiac University*
Ria Ramoutar, *Georgia Southern University*
Tanea Reed, *Eastern Kentucky University*
Michael Rennekamp, *Columbus State Community College*
Krysta Riel Maas, *College of St. Scholastica*
Samantha Robinson, *University of Washington*

Marisol Rodriguez, *University of Puerto Rico, Carolina*
Kristopher Roeske, *Wesley College/ DSU Downtown*
Amy Rogers, *Palm Beach State College*
Matthieu Rouffet, *Point Loma Nazarene University*
Matthew Rowley, *Southern Utah University*
Gillian Rudd, *Georgia Gwinnett College*
Michael Russell, *Mt. Hood Community College*
Raymond Sadeghi, *University of Texas, San Antonio*
Seema Saiyed, *Amarillo College*
Michael Sakuta, *Georgia Perimeter College*
Julia Saloni, *Jackson State University*
Hussein Samha, *Southern Utah University*
Jacopo Samson, *Hunter College of CUNY*
Douglas Schauer, *Southwestern Michigan College*
Doug Schirch, *Goshen College*
Bryan Schmidt, *Minot State University*
Melissa Schoene, *Georgia State University*
Lisa Selchau, *MiraCosta College*
Victor Selchau, *MiraCosta College*
Nawal Sharma, *Houston Community College*
Timothy Shelton, *Shasta College*
Tammy Siciliano, *Ohio State University, Mansfield*
Regan Silvestri, *Lorain County Community College*
Crystal Sims, *University of Arkansas, Cossatot Community College*
John Singer, *Jackson Community College*
Joseph Sloop, *Georgia Gwinnett College*
Sally Ann Smesko, *Daemen College*
Mary Ann Veronica Smith, *Marywood University*
Michele Smith, *Georgia Southwestern State University*
Mary Snow, *University of Alabama, Huntsville*
Patricia Snyder, *Florida Atlantic University*
Kyung-ae Son-Guidry, *Lamar State College*
Jie Song, *University of Michigan, Flint*

Allison Soult, *University of Kentucky*
Richard Spinney, *Ohio State University*
Carol Stallworth, *Hillsborough Community College*
Ron Stamper, *Mott Community College*
Shuai Sun, *Haskell Indian Nations University*
Stan Svojanovsky, *Missouri Western University*
Blair Szymczyna, *Boston University*
Amy Taketomo, *Hartnell College*
María Tarafa, *Miami Dade College*
Kerri Taylor, *Columbus State University*
Susan Thomas, *University of Texas, San Antonio*
Simon Tong, *Binghamton University*
Forrest Towne, *Central Oregon Community College*
Allison Tracy, *University of Maryland, Baltimore County*
Jennifer Van Wyk, *Southwestern Illinois University*
Dennis Viernes, *University of Mary*
Elena Viltchinskaia, *New Mexico Military Institute*
Thottumkara Vinod, *Western Illinois University*
Patricia Visser, *Jackson College*
Anne Vonderheide, *University of Cincinnati*
Grady Wann, *University of California, Davis*
Lisa Webb, *Christopher Newport University*
Karen Wesenberg-Ward, *Montana Tech*
Cindy White, *Harding University*
Kenneth White, *Elgin Community College*
Richard Wilkosz, *Northcentral Tech College*
Scott Witherow, *University of Tampa*
Steven Wood, *Brigham Young University*
Stephen Woski, *University of Alabama*
Shahla Yekta, *University of Rhode Island*
Amy Young, *Dominican University*
Meishan Zhao, *University of Chicago*
Susan Zirpili, *Slippery Rock University*
Jim Zubricky, *University of Toledo*

Unit 1
Introduction
Atoms, Measurement, and Nuclear Chemistry

Chapter 1: Introduction to Chemistry

Chapter 2: Measurement in Science and Medicine

Chapter 3: Atoms: The Building Blocks of Chemistry

Chapter 4: Nuclear Chemistry

Over two million positron emission tomography (PET) scans are done in the U.S. each year (Figure U1.1). This powerful technology allows healthcare providers to use radioactive molecules to see specific regions of the body and assess their function. PET scans help diagnose and treat a wide array of diseases including cancer and Alzheimer's disease.

Figure U1.1 Positron Emission Tomography (PET).

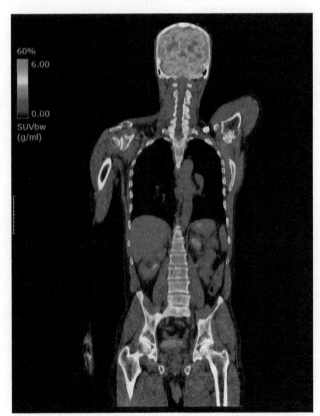

Unit 1: Introduction

Diagnosing Disease: How Can We use Atoms and Nuclear Chemistry to Find and Treat Disease?

 To learn more about how nuclear chemistry helps healthcare providers visualize and diagnose disease through the use of Positron Emission Tomography (PET), watch **Video U1.1** in the Pearson eText.

Video U1.1 provides a striking illustration of how scientists are able to use radioactive probes to visualize specific regions of the body. These methods are used to image, diagnose, and treat a variety of diseases (Figure U1.2). All these approaches require a deep understanding of the structure of the atom, its components, and isotopes.

In this unit, we will learn more about the structure of the atom and take a closer look at the nature of these radioactive pharmaceuticals. In Chapter 1, we'll get more familiar with how chemists think and ask questions about the world as well as begin to explore the elements that make up our world. As we move into Chapter 2, we'll learn critical information about how scientists and healthcare providers measure and quantify the world around them. Chapter 3 will allow us to look more closely at the structure of the atom before we explore the various types of radiation and their applications in Chapter 4. At the end of this unit, we'll return to this use of radioactive probes to treat disease and apply some of the chemistry we've been learning to better understand these types of applications.

Figure U1.2 A Patient Entering a PET Scan.

PET scanners rely on the detection of particles released from radioactive pharmaceuticals to provide an image of a particular region of the body.

Unit 1 Chemistry Application: Pinpointing Disease in the Pancreas

Congenital hyperinsulinism (HI) is the most common cause of persistent low blood sugar or hypoglycemia in children, affecting an estimated one in 40,000 infants. Prompt diagnosis and treatment is critical as untreated HI can result in permanent brain damage or even death. There are two common forms of the disease, diffuse and focal. Both forms involve cells in the pancreas that produce insulin, a hormone that regulates blood sugar (Figure U1.3). In diffuse HI, many of the cells in the pancreas are affected. In focal HI, in contrast, only a small region of the pancreas is affected. Distinguishing between these two forms is critical as surgically removing the affected areas usually provides a cure for focal HI cases.

Healthcare providers are able to distinguish the two forms through the use of a compound known as Fluorodopa F18 (Figure U1.4). This radioactive drug closely resembles the structure of a naturally occurring molecule taken up by many cells in the pancreas. If concentrated focal disease is present, the overactive cells will take up a larger amount of the drug and emit radiation that is detectable by a Positron Emission Tomography (PET) scan.

A PET scan is a common form of nuclear medicine. Prior to the scan, the patient receives an injection of a radioactive compound that is targeted specifically to the area of the body to be imaged. As the compound decays, specific types of particles are released and detected by the scanner. A PET scan, in particular, detects the emission of a particle known as a positron. The resulting image can often be used to diagnose disease or help guide a surgeon if removal of the affected tissue is necessary.

Figure U1.3 The Location of the Pancreas.

The pancreas is a large gland found next to the stomach. In addition to producing digestive juices, it makes the hormones that regulate blood sugar levels.

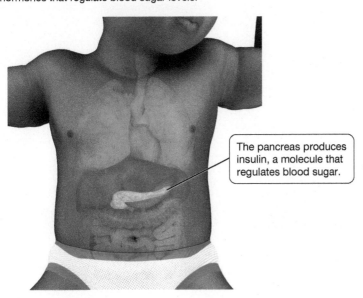

The pancreas produces insulin, a molecule that regulates blood sugar.

Figure U1.4 The Atoms in Fluorodopa F18, the Compound Used to Visualize the Pancreas.

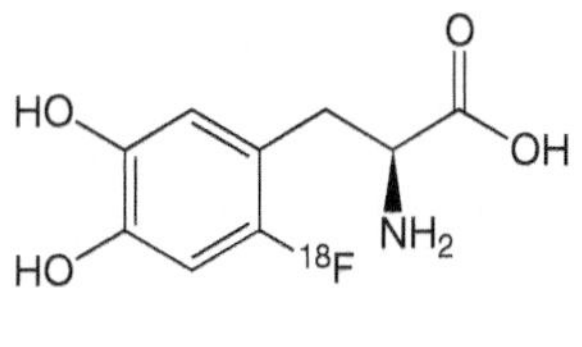

Questions to Think About

What chemistry do we need to know to understand this diagnostic approach? Here are some questions to consider as you move through this unit:

- What is an atom made of and how does one atom differ from another?
- What specific elements from the periodic table are involved in PET?
- How do scientists measure and quantify the correct dose for a treatment like this?
- Why are some atoms radioactive? What are the different types of radioactivity?

What chemistry would you like to know in order to more fully understand this approach?

Now that we have an overview of this unit, let's step into Chapter 1 and begin to think like chemists!

Chapter 1
Introduction to Chemistry

Chemistry is a central science and helps us understand our world.

 ## Chapter Outline

1.1 What is Chemistry?

1.2 Matter

1.3 Elements and Compounds

1.4 The Periodic Table

Learning Objectives

1.1 Recognize chemistry as the central science that studies matter on the atomic level.

1.2 Describe matter by its composition and physical state.

1.3 Describe elements and explain how they differ from compounds.

1.4 Explain the general characteristics and organization of the periodic table.

Introduction

Humans have a deep curiosity about what things are made of and how the world works. Our desire to understand is an important aspect of human nature and a foundation of scientific thought. Over time, scientists have learned a great deal about the properties of materials and the mechanisms that govern natural processes.

As human understanding of the natural world continues to grow, new questions emerge just as fast, or even faster. Attempting to answer these questions, scientists combine information and ideas from different disciplines to address complex global challenges, such as how to provide effective heath care, cleaner energy, and access to safe drinking water (Figure 1.1).

At the very core of human knowledge is an understanding of chemistry. Chemistry provides us with the ability to advance technology and improve the human condition in powerful ways.

1.1 What is Chemistry?

Chemistry is the study of the properties, structure, and transformations of matter. The term **matter** describes anything that has mass and takes up space. So, chemistry is the study of anything we can touch, smell, feel, see, or taste. This may seem like a tall order for chemists–to study and know about all of matter—but it is also what makes chemistry such an exciting discipline.

The fundamental building blocks of matter—*atoms*—determine the way matter operates in the world. **Atoms** are extremely tiny particles that are the basic units of matter. Everything around us is composed of atoms. For this reason, chemists spend their time probing the world at the **atomic level**, on the size scale of a single atom.

Exploring the world at this level provides tools and ideas for new technologies, new medical treatments (Figure 1.2), and new strategies for solving complex environmental problems. A fundamental understanding of chemistry and the atomic level of matter is the basis for all these endeavors.

How Does Chemistry Relate to Other Disciplines?

People sometimes call chemistry the *central science*. This is because understanding the properties of matter on the atomic level contributes to our knowledge of medicine, biology, environmental science, geology, physics, and much more (Figure 1.3). Significant scientific research typically involves bringing together more than one discipline

---

Figure 1.1 Chemistry in our Lives.

A) The development of high-tech health care tools, such as this ultrasound scanner, is based on an understanding of chemistry. **B)** To design solar panels, scientists seek out the best materials for trapping and storing energy from the sun. **C)** Chemistry can help ensure that communities have access to safe drinking water.

A   B   C

Figure 1.2 Understanding Atomic Level Structure is Critical to Developing New Medical Treatments.

A) A scientist uses a technique called X-ray crystallography to understand how atoms connect to one another. **B)** Scientists used this technique to better understand the atomic level structure of SARS-CoV-2, the virus responsible for the CoViD-19 pandemic, in order to rapidly develop effective vaccines.

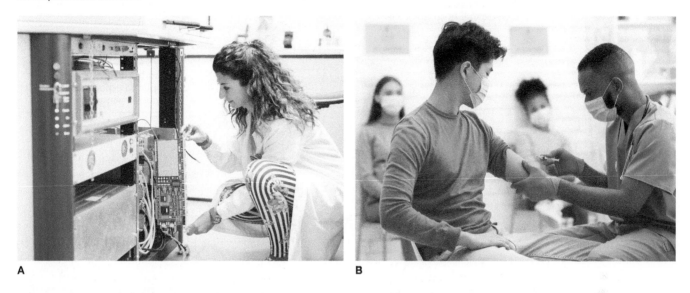

A

B

Figure 1.3 Chemistry as the Central Science.

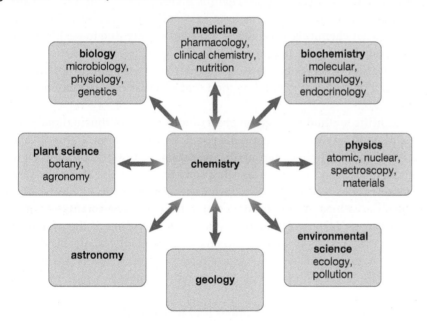

to solve a problem. Understanding how disciplines overlap helps us develop a more holistic view of complex systems and solve challenging problems.

Applying what we learn in chemistry to other courses, such as biology, both reinforces our knowledge of chemistry and deepens our understanding of biology. A strong foundation in chemistry also helps when we practice careers in the sciences. Success in medical fields, for example, requires an understanding of chemical principles and how they apply to the human body.

Scientific Method

When children are growing up, they often ask questions about how the world works. Why is the sky blue? What is snow made of? How salty is the ocean? Children also

Figure 1.4 The Scientific Method to Knowledge.

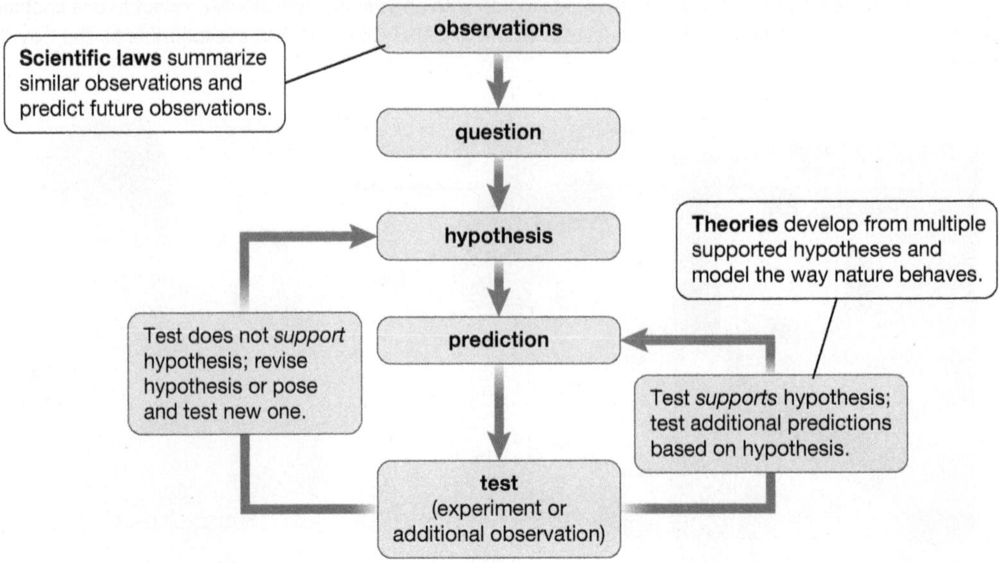

tend to explore our world through experimentation mostly by touching, observing, and tasting. These natural tendencies to question and explore are fundamental to how chemists think and carry out a scientific investigation. As adults, we are also curious about many things, such as how medications work, why the climate is changing, or what chemicals are entering our food supply due to pesticide use. We may be interested in the development of new technologies for alternative energy or water purification. Everyone is curious in their own way about how the world works and can relate to the general method that scientists use to carry out a scientific investigation.

The **scientific method** is based on observations and experimentation. Scientists observe and perform experiments on the physical world to find out more about it (Figure 1.4). Some of these experiments are *qualitative* (describing how a process occurs); others are *quantitative* (measuring something specific about the physical world). Observations lead scientists to formulate a **hypothesis**, a tentative explanation of the observations. A hypothesis is tested through **experiments**—highly controlled procedures designed to gain a better understanding of the system under investigation. The results of experiments may support the hypothesis or prove it wrong. If the hypothesis is wrong, the scientists may revise or discard it and start again. Scientists can reject even widely accepted hypotheses when new evidence becomes available.

In some cases, a series of observations lead to a **scientific law**, a statement that summarizes similar observations and predicts future ones. In other cases, one or more well-established hypotheses can form the basis for a **theory**, a model of the way nature behaves and why. Scientific theories provide the foundation for all scientific knowledge.

Visualizing Chemistry

Much of what scientists do involves observing and explaining those observations. Scientists have always drawn pictures of what they observe and their ideas and hypotheses (Figure 1.5). Charles Darwin (1809–1882), the famous biologist, created a drawing of the *tree of life* as he formulated his ideas about how organisms are related (Figure 1.5A). Although this is a historical example of a drawing, it still provides insight into how scientists express new ideas. It also illustrates how scientists refine

Figure 1.5 **A)** Charles Darwin's Early Sketch of the Tree of Life. **B)** Linus Pauling's Drawing Representing Part of a Protein.

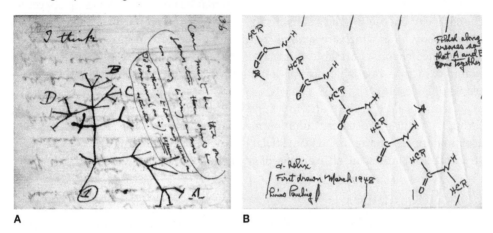

A   B

and use drawings to communicate. The renowned Nobel Prize- winning chemist, Linus Pauling (1901–1994) drew the sketch in Figure 1.5B when he was working to gain a better understanding of how the human body functions.

The atoms that chemists study are so small that there is no practical and easy way to directly observe them. We also cannot directly observe how these particles interact. In fact, atoms are so tiny that the period at the end of this sentence is as wide as about twenty million atoms. Chemists therefore must rely on drawings, symbols, diagrams, models, and computer visualizations to communicate ideas. Students must also learn how to interpret these representations. New technologies continue to provide the scientific community and the public with better ways to visualize the atomic level (Figure 1.6). Keep the atomic level in mind when we explore other ways that chemistry impacts our lives as described in BioConnect 1.1 (contains Figures 1.7–1.15).

Figure 1.6 Student Visualizing Gold Particles in Solution Using a *Hybrid Reality Environment* in the Department of Chemistry at the University of Illinois at Chicago.

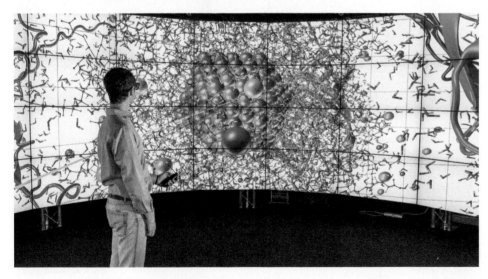

Explore how Chemistry and Biology connect: **BioConnect 1.1:** Chemistry in Our Lives in the Pearson eText.

Quiz yourself on the content of this section: **Check 1.1** in the Pearson eText.

1.2 Matter

Recall from Section 1.1 that matter is anything that has mass and takes up space. A chemist may choose to study salts, rocks, plants, or the matter that makes up the human body, all of which are *naturally occurring*. A **naturally occurring substance** is a substance chemists are able to isolate from a source that exists in nature. For example, sucrose, raw table sugar, is a naturally occurring substance found in many plants (Figure 1.16).

Chemists also produce and investigate **synthetic substances**, materials made through chemical processes. Common medications and medical materials such as acetaminophen, vitamin tablets, artificial sweeteners, and the plastics used to construct artificial hearts, are all examples of synthetic substances (Figure 1.16).

Pure Substances

In addition to separating matter into naturally occurring and synthetic substances, chemists separate all matter into two categories—*pure substances* and *mixtures*.

A **pure substance** is matter that is composed of a single component and has a constant composition regardless of where it is found. In other words, every sample of a pure substance has the same composition.

A pure substance can be either an individual element or a compound. An **element** is a pure substance that cannot be broken down chemically into simpler substances. Hydrogen (H), oxygen (O) and copper (Cu) are examples of elements (Figure 1.17). The **periodic table**, which we discuss in more detail in Section 1.4, is a list of all the elements.

Figure 1.16 A Collection of Natural (Left) and Synthetic (Right) Substances.

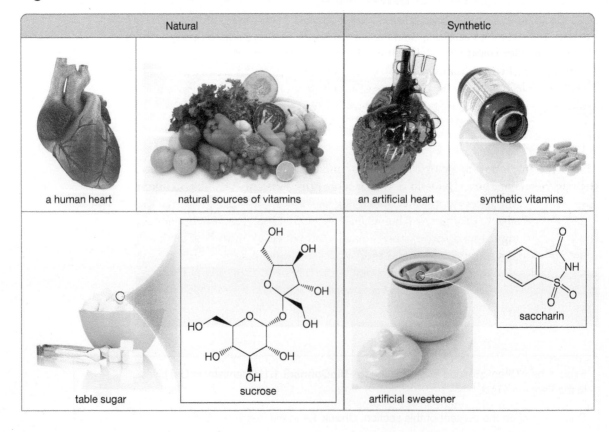

Figure 1.17 Pure Substances May be Elements or Compounds.

Copper is a pure substance composed of copper atoms. Water is also a pure substance composed of the compound H_2O.

A **compound** is a pure substance that forms when two or more elements combine in constant proportions to make a new substance. Water, for example, is a pure substance that is also a compound. Water is always made up of the same proportion of the elements hydrogen and oxygen. The ratio of elements in the compound water is given by its **chemical formula**, H_2O. This formula indicates that water contains two atoms of the element hydrogen and one atom of the element oxygen. As we discuss in more detail in Section 1.4, each element is represented by a one or two letter abbreviation; in this case H represents hydrogen and O represents oxygen.

Mixtures

A **mixture**, in contrast to a pure substance, is composed of more than one substance. A **homogeneous mixture** is a blend of two or more pure substances that has a uniform composition. Salt dissolved in water is a homogeneous mixture (Figure 1.18). It is generally not possible to distinguish a homogeneous mixture from a pure substance simply by observing the mixture. Salt water may look identical to pure water but is very different in terms of composition and properties. A **heterogeneous mixture** is a mixture that does *not* have uniform composition. A mixture of oil and water is a heterogeneous mixture because the oil does not mix with the water and forms a top layer over a bottom layer of water (Figure 1.18).

Separation of Mixtures

Another difference between a pure substance and a mixture is that a mixture can be separated into its individual components without altering the chemical composition of the individual components. We can separate salt, for example, from the water in a

Figure 1.18 Homogeneous and Heterogeneous Mixtures.

A) Salt dissolved in water is a homogeneous mixture because of its uniform composition. **B)** Oil and water, in contrast, is a heterogeneous mixture. This allows some of the oil to be removed from the surface after an oil spill.

Figure 1.19 Substances in Mixtures Can Be Separated.

This worker in Thailand is collecting sea salt from shallow pools where the water in the homogeneous saltwater mixture is allowed to evaporate.

salt-water sample by evaporating the water, leaving the salt behind (Figure 1.19). We can even more easily separate oil from water in the oil-water mixture by removing the top oil layer. There are many strategies for separating mixtures, some of which we will encounter in later chapters.

Figure 1.20 summarizes the classification of matter.

Figure 1.20 The Classification of Matter into Pure Substances and Mixtures.

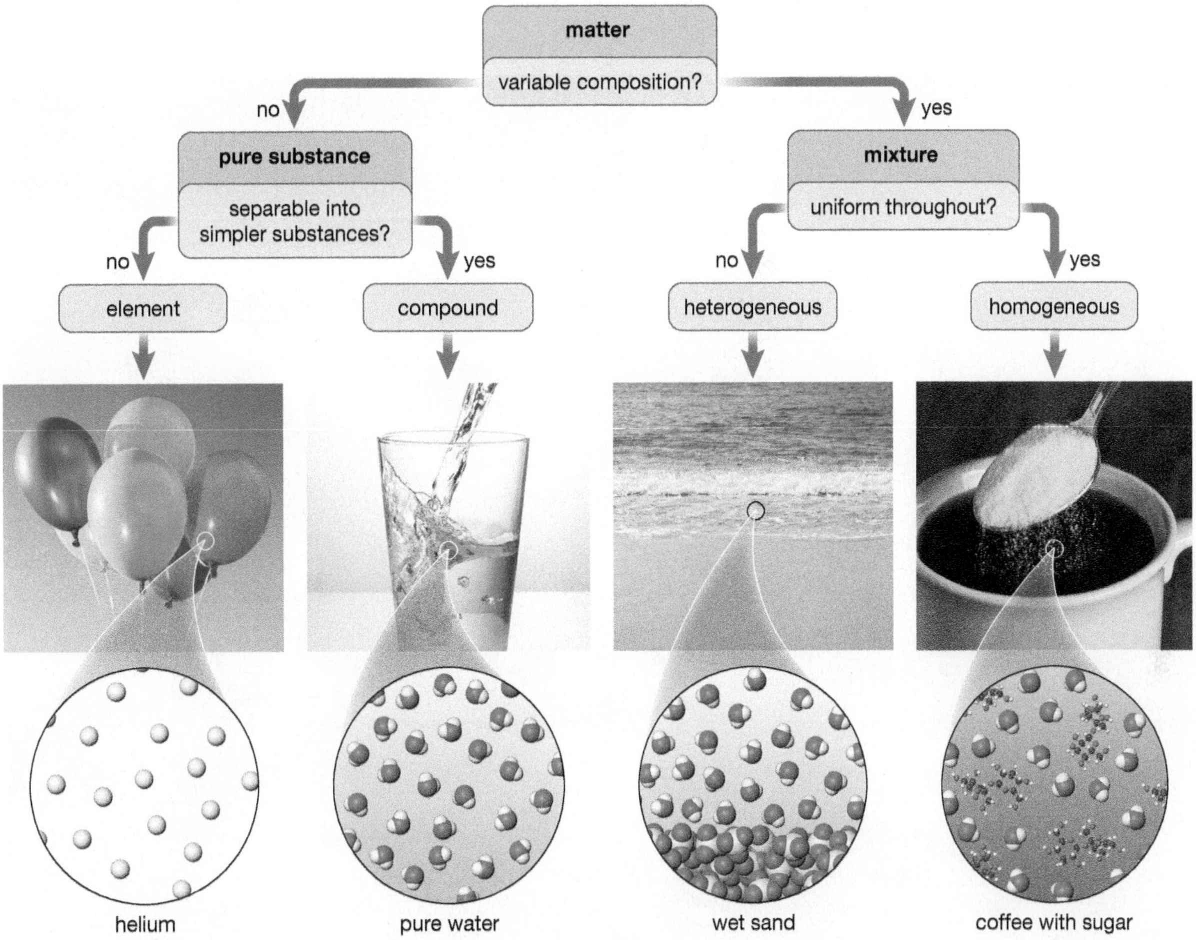

matter
variable composition?

no →
yes →

pure substance
separable into simpler substances?

mixture
uniform throughout?

no → element
yes → compound

no → heterogeneous
yes → homogeneous

helium

pure water

wet sand

coffee with sugar

Apply what you have just learned: **Practice 1.1–1.4** in the Pearson eText.

States of Matter

A **state of matter** is one of the distinct forms in which matter can exist. Matter exists in three common states—solid, liquid, and gas. A **solid** has a definite volume and retains its shape regardless of its container. On the atomic level, the particles in a solid are packed close to each other; they can vibrate but they do not move around each other (Figure 1.21). There are numerous examples of solids all around us, such as the table you may be sitting at or the hard shell of your computer.

A **liquid** has a definite volume, but not a definite shape. The particles in a liquid touch but they are free to move around each other. When we pour coffee from the pot to the cup or when we fill a water bottle, the liquids take the shape of the specific container.

A **gas** does not have a definite shape or volume. The particles of a gas move randomly and are much further apart than the particles in liquids and solids. A gas fills the volume and shape of whatever container it occupies.

Figure 1.21 States of Matter.

Solids, such as ice, have a definite volume and retain their shape. Liquids, such as water, have a definite volume but not a definite shape. Gasses, such as those in the atmosphere, have neither a definite volume nor shape.

Apply what you have just learned: **Practice 1.5 and 1.6** in the Pearson eText.

Physical Properties and Physical Changes

Figure 1.22 Copper Tubing.

Matter is characterized by its physical properties and chemical properties. Any characteristic that we use to describe or identify a substance is a **property**. More specifically, **physical properties** are characteristics that we can measure or observe without altering the composition of the substance. Physical properties include color, odor, and the temperature at which substances melt or boil. For example, if a scientist were to make a list of the physical properties of a piece of copper in the laboratory, the list would include things such as, orange color, solid state, and shiny surface (Figure 1.22).

When matter undergoes a **physical change,** the substance changes without altering the composition of the substance. For example, melting an ice cube to form liquid water and boiling liquid water to form steam are both physical changes (Figure 1.23). Water has the same composition before and after these physical changes.

Chemical Properties and Chemical Changes

Chemical properties are properties we observe when the chemical composition of a substance is converted to another substance. A **chemical change**—more commonly referred to as a **chemical reaction**—converts one substance to another. The conversion

Figure 1.23 Water Boiling is a Physical Change.

A physical change: Water molecules change from a liquid to a gaseous state when water boils.

$H_2O(g)$

$H_2O(l)$

Figure 1.24 Chemical Change.

Hydrogen and oxygen undergo a chemical change that produces water.

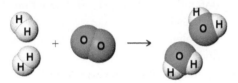

of hydrogen (H_2) and oxygen (O_2) to water (H_2O) is a chemical reaction because the composition of the substances in the beginning is different from the composition of the substances at the end (Figure 1.24). We study chemical reactions in more detail in Chapter 8. For now, explore VisibleChem Videos 1.1 and 1.2 to find more examples of physical and chemical changes.

Watch this concept come to life: **VisibleChem Video 1.1:** Physical Changes and **VisibleChem Video 1.2:** Chemical Changes in the Pearson eText.

Apply what you have just learned: **Practice 1.7–1.9** in the Pearson eText.

Quiz yourself on the content of this section: **Check 1.2** in the Pearson eText.

1.3 Elements and Compounds

An element is a pure substance that cannot be broken down chemically into simpler substances. Common elements include oxygen, helium, iron, and gold. Currently, scientists have identified 118 elements, most of which exist naturally on Earth. The other

Figure 1.25 Periodic Table of the Elements.

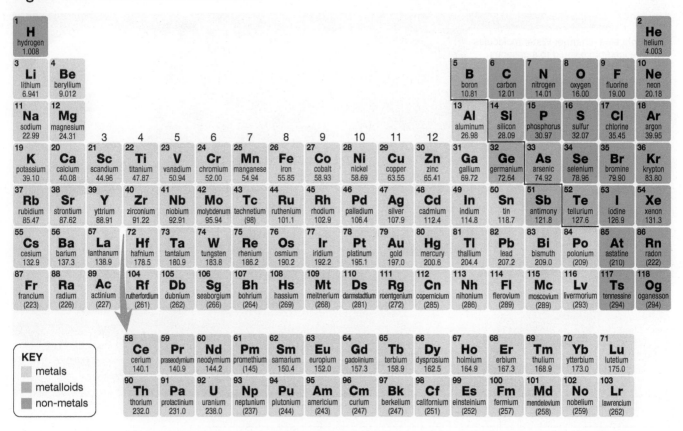

KEY
metals
metalloids
non-metals

elements have been synthesized in laboratories across the world. Some elements are considered rare and are unfamiliar to most people. These rare elements are difficult to find on earth and have few uses in society.

The periodic table of the elements (Figure 1.25) lists all the elements. The position of an element in the periodic table indicates a lot about its chemical properties. We explore the organization of the periodic table in Section 1.4.

Element Symbols

As we mentioned in Section 1.2, each element has a name and a chemical symbol. Each **chemical symbol** contains either one or two letters. Elements that have a chemical symbol that is only one letter are represented with a single upper-case letter. For example, the letter C symbolizes Carbon. We represent elements that have a two-letter chemical symbol with an upper-case letter followed by a lower-case letter. Magnesium, for example, has the chemical symbol Mg. Some chemical symbols are derived from the original Latin names, and therefore have a chemical symbol that may not be easily recognized. Sodium is a good example of this; its chemical symbol is Na, which comes from its Latin name, *natrium*.

Name	Chemical Symbol
magnesium	Mg
carbon	C
sodium	Na

Common Earth Elements

While there are over one hundred known elements, there are only five elements that make up the majority of the outer layer of planet Earth (Figure 1.26). This layer, referred to as the crust, is primarily made up of the elements oxygen (O), silicon (Si), aluminum (Al), iron (Fe), and calcium (Ca). Becoming familiar with these common elements can provide a new view of the world we live in. Explore Figure 1.26 to learn more about these commonly found elements.

Figure 1.26 Elements in Earth's Crust.

Hover on the sections of the pie chart to learn more about these elements.

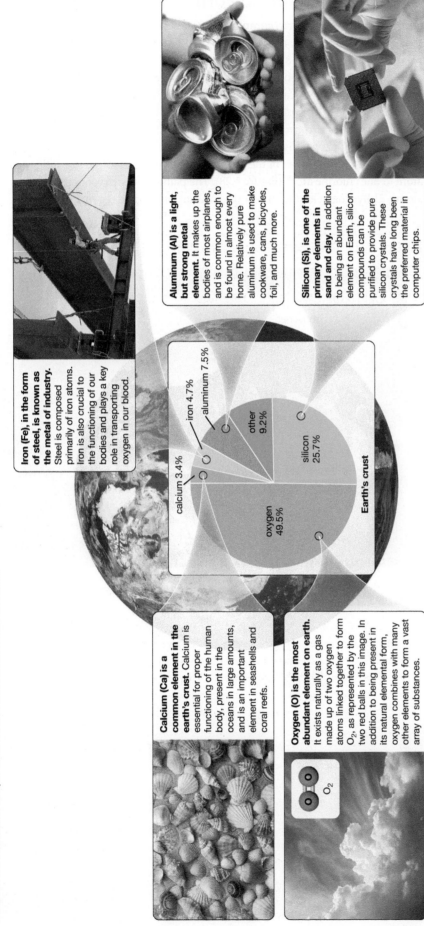

Iron (Fe), in the form of steel, is known as the metal of industry. Steel is composed primarily of iron atoms. Iron is also crucial to the functioning of our bodies and plays a key role in transporting oxygen in our blood.

Aluminum (Al) is a light, but strong metal element. It makes up the bodies of most airplanes, and is common enough to be found in almost every home. Relatively pure aluminum is used to make cookware, cans, bicycles, foil, and much more.

Silicon (Si), is one of the primary elements in sand and clay. In addition to being an abundant element on Earth, silicon compounds can be purified to provide pure silicon crystals. These crystals have long been the preferred material in computer chips.

Calcium (Ca) is a common element in the earth's crust. Calcium is essential for proper functioning of the human body, present in the oceans in large amounts, and is an important element in seashells and coral reefs.

Oxygen (O) is the most abundant element on earth. It exists naturally as a gas made up of two oxygen atoms linked together to form O_2, as represented by the two red balls in this image. In addition to being present in its natural elemental form, oxygen combines with many other elements to form a vast array of substances.

O_2

iron 4.7%
aluminum 7.5%
other 9.2%
silicon 25.7%
calcium 3.4%
oxygen 49.5%

Earth's crust

Elements Combine to Form Compounds

Elements combine to form compounds. Glucose is a compound that is composed of the elements carbon (C), hydrogen (H), and oxygen (O). To represent this compound, we include the chemical symbol of each element, along with a subscript to indicate the ratio of elements in the compound. Recall from earlier in the chapter that this notation is referred to as a chemical formula.

The chemical formula for glucose is $C_6H_{12}O_6$. The subscript numbers indicate that there are six carbon atoms, 12 hydrogen atoms, and six oxygen atoms in each compound of glucose (Figure 1.27).

Table salt is composed of the elements sodium and chlorine in a ratio of one sodium atom to one chlorine atom (Figure 1.28). The pain reliever oxycodone contains 18 carbon atoms, 21 hydrogen atoms, one nitrogen atom, and four oxygen atoms (Figure 1.29).

Figure 1.27 Chemical Formulas for the Common Sugar, Glucose.

Figure 1.28 Chemical Formula for Table Salt (NaCl).

Figure 1.29 Chemical Formula for the Medication, Oxycodone.

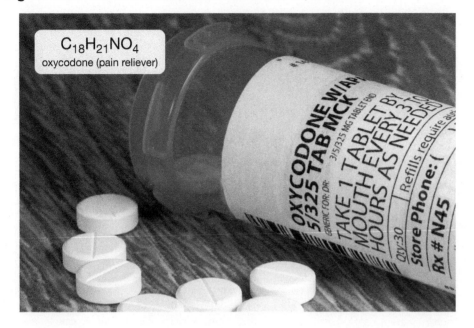

$C_{18}H_{21}NO_4$
oxycodone (pain reliever)

Predict answers and see step-by-step solutions: **Learn 1.1:** Identifying Elements in Chemical Formulas in the Pearson eText.

Explore how Chemistry and Biology connect: **BioConnect 1.2:** Elements in the Human Body in the Pearson eText.

Apply what you have just learned: **Practice 1.10 and 1.11** in the Pearson eText.

Quiz yourself on the content of this section: **Check 1.3** in the Pearson eText.

A chemical formula provides the identity and ratio of elements in a compound but *does not* reveal how each individual atom connects to the other atoms in the compound. We cover this topic in Unit 2.

1.4 The Periodic Table

An early version of the periodic table of elements was suggested by Russian chemist and inventor Dmitri Mendeleev in the year 1869 (Figure 1.35). Since then it has been revised and updated. We will encounter an updated periodic table throughout our study of chemistry. The table organizes all the elements based on their properties. In other words, the position an element occupies in the table provides information about its properties and behavior. This allows us to make predictions about how elements and compounds will react under a variety of conditions.

Periods and Groups

The periodic table of the elements lists all known elements. The table features periods and groups (Figure 1.36). Each horizontal row is a **period**. Periods are labeled from Period 1 to Period 7. The first period contains only the elements hydrogen (H) and helium (He). Period 2 begins with the element lithium (Li) and progresses across to neon (Ne).

Each vertical column is a **group** (or family). The elements in each group have similar properties. There are two numbering systems for groups. The first system is older and uses a number followed by either an A or a B. The elements in groups number 1A–8A are the **main group elements**. The elements with a B after their group numbers are the **transition metals**. Providing a simpler numbering of groups, the newer numbering system spans from group 1–18.

Metals, Metalloids, and Nonmetals

Chemists commonly categorize an element on the periodic table based on whether it is a metal, metalloid, or nonmetal. A **metal** is a

Figure 1.35 A Monument to Dmitri Mendeleev, Author of the Periodic Table, in Saint Petersburg Russia.

Figure 1.36 Periods and Groups on the Periodic Table of the Elements.

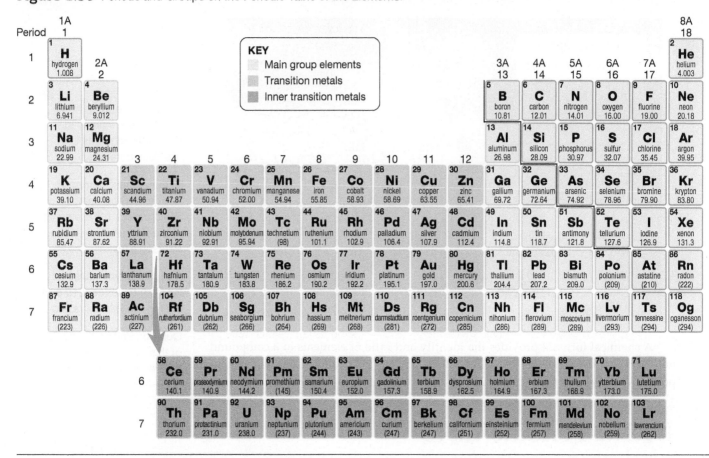

Figure 1.37 Common Groups in the Periodic Table.

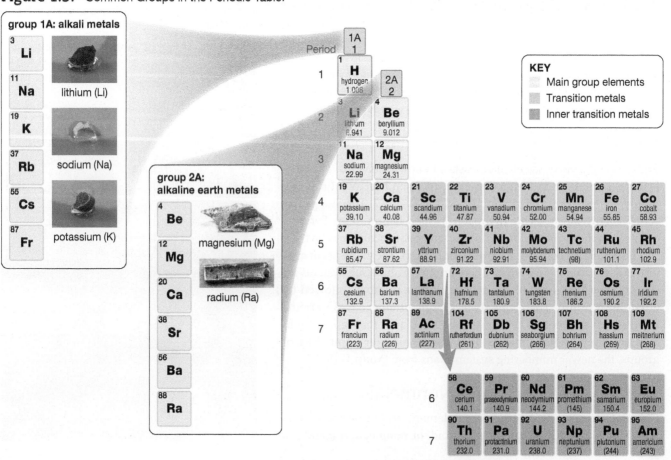

shiny substance that conducts electricity. Metals can be drawn into wires (they are *ductile*) and hammered into shapes (they are *malleable*).

The solid bold line on the periodic table in Figure 1.36 separates the metals from the other elements with the exception of hydrogen (H). The line starts at boron (B) and steps down, forming a staircase shape, to the element astatine (At). Generally speaking, the elements to the left of this line are the metals. The elements to the right are the nonmetals.

Unlike metals, **nonmetals** do not have a shiny appearance. Nonmetals are also poor conductors of heat and electricity. Some examples of nonmetals are oxygen (O), chlorine (Cl), and helium (He). Nonmetals typically have low boiling and melting points. We find them on the far-right side of the periodic table.

We find the **metalloids** along the staircase line on the periodic table. As we might expect, the metalloids have properties intermediate between metals and nonmetals. There are just six agreed upon metalloids: boron (B), silicon (Si), germanium (Ge), arsenic (As), antimony (Sb), and tellurium (Te). Some scientists also include polonium (Po), astatine (As), and tennessine (Ts) on the list of metalloids. More research is needed to classify these elements into one of these three categories.

Common Groups on the Periodic Table

The elements within a group usually have similar properties. Each group has a family name.

The group 1A elements are the **alkali metals**. These elements are metals, such as sodium and potassium, which react violently when placed in water (Figure 1.37). The group 2A elements are the **alkaline earth metals.** They are also reactive. Calcium and magnesium are common alkaline earth metals.

On the other side of the periodic table are the group 7A elements, the **halogens**. The halogens are very reactive nonmetals. Chlorine and fluorine are the most common halogens.

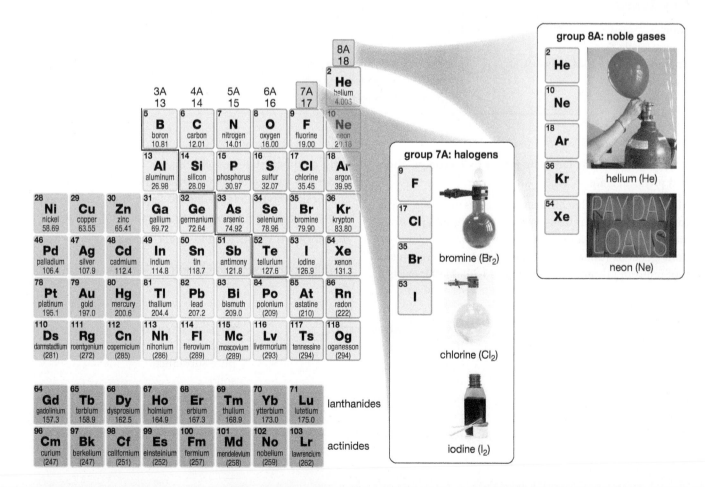

Group 8A is the **noble gas** family. Unlike the other families we have introduced, the noble gases are generally unreactive. Helium is the most common noble gas. It, like the other noble gasses, does not easily combine with other elements to form compounds.

Explore VisibleChem Video 1.3 to learn more about how the periodic table is organized.

 Watch this concept come to life: **VisibleChem Video 1.3:** Tour of the Periodic Table in the Pearson eText.

Apply what you have just learned: **Practice 1.12 and 1.13** in the Pearson eText.

Quiz yourself on the content of this section: **Check 1.4** in the Pearson eText.

Chapter Summary

1.1 What is Chemistry?

Learning Objective: Recognize chemistry as the central science that studies matter on the atomic level.

Chemistry is the study of the properties, structure, and transformation of matter. Chemists examine the world at the atomic level—on the scale of a single atom–to understand matter and provide tools and ideas to build new technologies, develop new medical treatments, and propose solutions to complex environmental problems. Chemistry is known as the central science (Figure 1.3). The scientific method is the established approach to developing new knowledge(Figure 1.4).

BioConnect 1.1: Chemistry in Our Lives

Key Terms

atom	hypothesis	scientific law
atomic level	matter	scientific method
carcinogen (from BioConnect 1.1)	nuclear chemistry (from BioConnect 1.1)	theory
chemistry	positron emission tomography (PET)	
experiment	(from BioConnect 1.1)	

1.2 Matter

Learning Objective: Describe matter by its composition and physical state.

Matter is anything that has mass and takes up space. Matter can be classified as pure substance or mixture. A pure substance can be an element or a compound. Mixtures are homogeneous (uniform in composition) or heterogeneous (not uniform in composition) (Figure 1.20). Matter exists in three common states—solid, liquid, or gas. When matter undergoes a physical change, the substance is altered but its chemical composition remains the same. A chemical change, in contrast, affects a substance's chemical composition.

VisibleChem Video 1.1: Physical Changes

VisibleChem Video 1.2: Chemical Changes

Key Terms

chemical change	heterogeneous mixture	physical property
chemical formula	homogeneous mixture	property
chemical property	liquid	pure substance
chemical reactions	mixture	solid
compound	naturally occurring substance	state of matter
element	periodic table	synthetic substance
gas	physical change	

1.3 Elements and Compounds

Learning Objective: Describe elements and explain how they differ from compounds.

An element is a pure substance that cannot be broken down chemically into simpler substances. To represent elements, we use chemical symbols. For example, C is the symbol for the element carbon. Elements combine to form compounds, which are represented by a chemical formula. A chemical formula includes each element in the compound along with a subscript to indicate the ratio of elements in the compound. There are 118 elements known. However just four elements (oxygen, silicon, aluminum, iron, and calcium) compose most of Earth's crust. The human body is composed primarily of carbon, hydrogen, oxygen, and nitrogen.

BioConnect 1.2: Elements in the Human Body

Key Term

chemical symbol

1.4 The Periodic Table

Learning Objective: Explain the general characteristics and organization of the periodic table.

The periodic table organizes all the elements based on their properties (Figure 1.36). A row on the periodic table is a period; columns are groups. Elements in the same group share similar properties. Examples of groups include the alkali metals, alkaline earth metals, halogens, and noble gases. The elements on the periodic table can also be organized into the larger categories of metals, nonmetals, and metalloids.

VisibleChem Video 1.3: Tour of the Periodic Table

Key Terms

alkali metal	main-group element	nonmetal
alkaline earth metal	metal	period
group	metalloid	transition metal
halogen	noble gas	

The **End-of-Chapter Problems** are located in the back of the book in Appendix A.

 End-of-Chapter Quiz   Have you mastered the content of this chapter? Try the **End-of-Chapter Quiz** in the Pearson eText.

1. Which of the following statements is true?
   a) Chemistry is the study of atoms that make up toxic chemicals and does not relate directly to biological processes.
   b) Biology and chemistry are closely related, but chemistry does not relate to physics or engineering.
   c) Chemistry and medicine are directly related, but chemistry does not relate directly to astronomy or geology.
   d) Chemistry is directly connected with a broad range of scientific disciplines.

2. Select the pure substance.
   a) air
   b) ocean water
   c) water (H_2O)
   d) smoke from a fire

3. Select the homogeneous mixture.
   a) a mixed green salad
   b) a mixture of alcohol and water
   c) a handful of dirt from the ground
   d) a bag of trash

4. Identify the process that is a transition from the liquid to solid state.
   a) ice melting
   b) breaking a piece of ice
   c) water evaporating in the hot sun
   d) water freezing to ice

5. Which pair of elements are very abundant in the human body?
   a) C and Ba   b) Cu and O
   c) C and H   d) N and Co

6. Select the chemical element.

a) Al   b) NH_3

c) CH_3OH d) HCl

7. Identify the compound(s) with the chemical formula C_2H_6O. Be sure to consider each example before answering the question.

a)

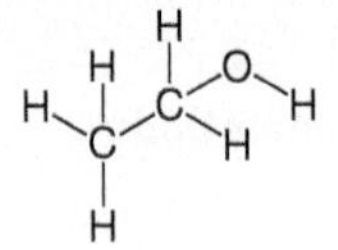

b)

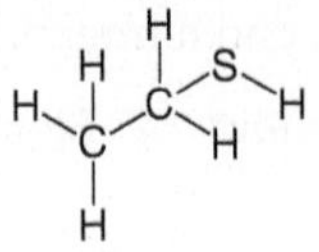

c)

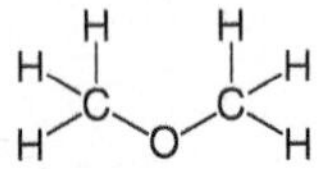

d) both A and C

8. What is the correct chemical formula for the given compound?

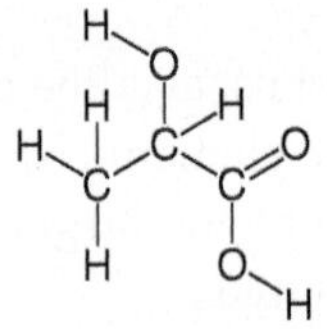

a) $C_3H_6O_2$ b) $C_3H_6O_3$

c) $C_3H_5O_3$ d) $C_2H_6O_3$

9. Which statement about the periodic table is correct?

a) Nonmetal elements are on the far left of the periodic table in Groups 1 and 2.

b) Alkali earth metals are in the middle of the periodic table.

c) Alkali metals are located in Group 1A.

d) Halogens are located in Group 6A.

10. Which two elements are in the same period?

a) calcium (Ca) and strontium (Sr)

b) sodium (Na) and aluminum (Al)

c) boron (B) and chlorine (Cl)

d) potassium (K) and palladium (Pd)

11. Identify the transition metal.

a) Mg   b) Na

c) Ni   d) Kr

12. Identify the nonmetal atom that is a common element in the human body?

a) He   b) N

c) K   d) Co

Chapter 2
Measurement in Science and Medicine

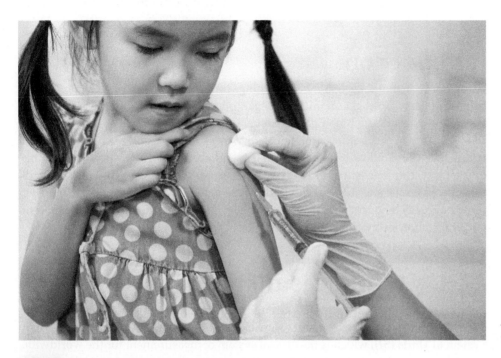

Accurate measurements are essential in science and medicine.

Chapter Outline

Learning Objectives

2.1 Report measurements of length, mass, and volume in metric units.

2.2 Use scientific notation and significant figures when problem-solving and communicating about measurements.

2.3 Use conversion factors to convert between units.

2.4 Apply ratio and proportion conversion factors for medical dosage calculations.

2.5 Solve problems with conversion factors and units commonly used in environmental science.

2.6 Convert temperature measurements from one scale to another.

2.7 Explain the concept of density and specific gravity, and solve problems involving density, mass, and volume measurements.

Introduction

Without a systematic way to measure things and communicate with others about values humans could not manufacture cell phones, build the international space station, or measure the blood glucose level of a patient with diabetes (Figure 2.1). Today, more than ever before in human history, measurements and calculations impact our daily lives and allow us to use an amazing number of tools. As we will see in this chapter, scientific measurements involve uncertainty and many different units of measure. Scientific and medical communities around the world work together, using agreed-upon methods to measure and calculate values to produce and use the tools of modern science, technology, and medicine.

2.1 Units of Measurement

Health professionals and scientists around the world rely on the **metric system** to communicate about measurement. Metric units are the basis of the **International System of Units (SI),** which is the official system of measurement for the worldwide scientific community. In the United States, in contrast, most people use the *English system*, using units such as gallon (gal.), pound (lb.), ounce (oz.), and mile (mi.). Although the English system is familiar to most people living in the U.S., the English system makes communicating effectively with the rest of the world somewhat challenging. For example, most car speedometers include both miles/hour and kilometers/hour to make it easier to convert between the two systems. Another disadvantage of the English system is that units in this system, unlike the units in the metric system, are not systematically related to one another and therefore are more difficult to master.

Figure 2.1 Technology and Medicine Demand Accurate, Consistent Measurements.

A) A student uses a smartphone. **B)** An astronaut works at the International Space Station. **C)** A healthcare worker monitors a patient's oxygen levels.

A   B   C

Table 2.1 Units of Measurement

Measurement	Metric	SI
length	meter (m)	meter (m)
volume	liter (L)	cubic meter (m³)
mass	gram (g)	kilogram (kg)
temperature	degree Celsius (°C)	kelvin (K)
time	second (s)	second (s)

In chemistry, we use the metric system, which features **base units** for each type of measurement (Table 2.1). Base units include the meter (m) for length, gram (g) for mass, and liter (L) for volume.

Metric Prefixes

In the metric system, prefixes indicate how much larger or smaller a measurement is in relation to the base unit (Table 2.2; Figure 2.2). For example, the prefix *kilo-* means 1,000 times as large. We can use any metric prefix with all the metric base units to express a measurement on the scale that is most convenient.

$$1 \, \textbf{\textit{kilo}}\text{gram} = 1000 \text{ grams}$$
$$1 \, \textbf{\textit{kilo}}\text{meter} = 1000 \text{ meters}$$

A metric system prefix can also make the unit smaller than the base unit. For example, the prefix *milli-* means one thousandth as large.

$$1 \, \textbf{\textit{milli}}\text{gram} = 0.001 \text{ grams}$$
$$1 \, \textbf{\textit{milli}}\text{meter} = 0.001 \text{ meters}$$

We report most measurements in this text using the metric system. Learning to convert between the metric system and the English system is an essential skill that we discuss in Section 2.3.

Apply what you have just learned: **Practice 2.1** in the Pearson eText.

Table 2.2 Metric Prefixes

Prefixes indicate how much smaller or larger than the base unit a measurement is.

Prefix	Symbol	Meaning	Numerical Value	Scientific Notation[b]
giga-	G	billion	1,000,000,000.	10^9
mega-	M	million	1,000,000.	10^6
kilo-	k	thousand	1000.	10^3
deci-	d	tenth	0.1	10^{-1}
centi-	c	hundredth	0.01	10^{-2}
milli-	m	thousandth	0.001	10^{-3}
micro-	μ[a]	millionth	0.000001	10^{-6}
nano-	n	billionth	0.000000001	10^{-9}

[a]This symbol is the lowercase Greek letter mu.
[b]Scientific notation is explained in Section 2.2.

Figure 2.2 Student Inserting a Flash Drive.

Many disciplines use the metric system. You may have noticed that the memory on your computer or storage device, for example, is measured in gigabytes (GB).

Figure 2.3 The Base Unit for Length is the Meter (m).

Length

The base unit for length in the metric system is the **meter (m)**. Stating that a destination is one thousand meters away is the same as stating that it is one kilometer away. This illustrates a conversion from one unit in the metric system to another unit in the metric system (meters to kilometers). The kilometer is much too large for most measurements in chemistry. More common units of length in the lab are the centimeter (cm), millimeter (mm), and nanometer (nm). In the medical field, however, professionals commonly measure human height using the meter (Figure 2.3).

$$1 \text{ m} = 100 \text{ cm}$$
$$1 \text{ m} = 1000 \text{ mm}$$
$$1 \text{ m} = 1,000,000,000 \text{ nm}$$

Mass

The **mass** of an object is a measure of the amount of matter it contains. Weight, in contrast, is the measure of how strongly gravity pulls on the matter. If you are on Earth and not moving, your weight and mass are the same.

The base unit for measuring mass in the metric system is the **gram (g)**. Compared to the English pound (lb.), the gram is quite small. There are 454 grams in one pound. The most common mass units used in chemistry are the gram (g), kilogram (kg) and milligram (mg). Typically, when you go to the doctor for an exam, a nurse records your mass in kilograms (Figure 2.4).

$$1 \text{ kg} = 1000 \text{ g}$$
$$1 \text{ g} = 1000 \text{ mg}$$

Volume

Volume is the amount of space a substance occupies. Volume measurements are common in both the chemistry laboratory and in the medical field so there are many specialized tools for doing this work. In the laboratory, a chemist may use a piece of glassware designed to measure liquids in specific amounts (Figure 2.5). In the

Figure 2.4 The Base Unit for Mass is the Gram (g).
A nurse, however, usually records a patient's weight in kilograms (kg).

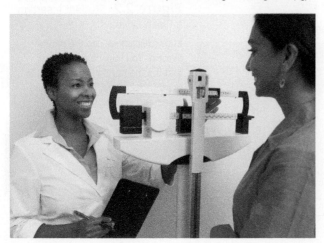

Figure 2.5 A Chemistry Student Measures the Volume of a Reagent in the Lab.

hospital, medical professionals often use syringes to dispense liquids (Figure 2.6). Although it is possible to measure volumes of solids and gases, in both chemistry and medicine we more commonly measure volumes of liquids.

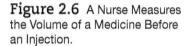

Figure 2.6 A Nurse Measures the Volume of a Medicine Before an Injection.

The base unit of volume in the metric system is the **liter (L)**. One liter is slightly larger than the English quart (1 liter = 1.06 quarts). In chemistry, the volume units we use most commonly are the deciliter (dL), milliliter (mL), and microliter (μL).

$$1 \text{ L} = 10 \text{ deciliter}$$
$$1 \text{ L} = 1000 \text{ milliliter}$$
$$1 \text{ L} = 1,000,000 \text{ microliter}$$

Healthcare providers often measure liquids in **cubic centimeters** (cc or cm^3). A cubic centimeter is equivalent to a milliliter (mL).

$$1 \text{ mL} = 1 \text{ cm}^3 = 1 \text{ cc}$$

Apply what you have just learned: **Practice 2.2 and 2.3** in the Pearson eText.

Quiz yourself on the content of this section: **Check 2.1** in the Pearson eText.

2.2 Communicating About Measurements

Measuring and recording measurements are important responsibilities for both scientists (Figure 2.7) and health care workers (Figure 2.8). A reliable measurement has both a number and a unit:

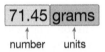

A number alone is usually meaningless without a unit. If we were asked how much medication we gave to a patient, the answer "fifty" would not mean anything to the person who asked the question. The answer "50.0 milligrams," gives the person we are speaking to much more information.

In this section we investigate the shorthand notation called **scientific notation.** We use scientific notation to communicate effectively when reporting the number part

---

Figure 2.7 A Scientists Measures Water Clarity in Antarctica.

Figure 2.8 A Nurse Weighs an Infant.

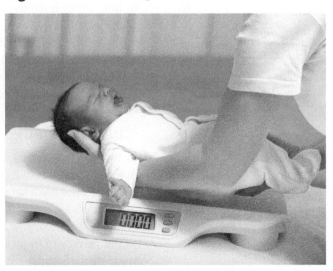

Figure 2.9 An Insect Trap in Ensenada, Mexico.

The trap uses insect sex hormones to lure insects into the trap. Researchers record the exact number of insects caught in the trap to monitor the abundance of insect pests in the vineyard.

Figure 2.10 The Width of This Mole is a Measured Number.

Measured numbers are sometimes called inexact numbers.

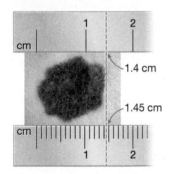

Watch this concept come to life:
VisibleChem
Video 2.1: Measuring Length, Volume, and Mass in the Pearson eText.

of a measurement. Scientific notation is useful when measurements are very large or very small. In addition, we explore the rules about how many digits to write down when taking measurements and doing calculations using measurements.

Significant Figures

We use two types of numbers in chemistry measurements: exact numbers and measured numbers. We obtain **exact numbers** from counting items. Exact numbers can also be part of a definition that compares two units in the same measuring system as this sentence illustrates: A human has two legs and one heart. There are sixteen moths in the trap in Figure 2.9. There are exactly 1000 meters in a kilometer. These are examples of exact numbers.

   Measured numbers are measurements or estimates that contain some uncertainty that must be communicated. When taking a measurement, for example, we write down a specific number of digits based on the limits of the measuring device. For instance, when measuring the length of a possible melanoma on a patient using the two measuring instruments shown in Figure 2.10, we could write the measurement as either 1.4 cm or 1.45 cm depending on which tool is used.

   When recording measurements, scientists write down all the digits that are possible to determine from the measuring device and then estimate one additional digit. **Significant figures** (which are also referred to as **significant digits**) are all the digits in a measured number including the one estimated digit. For example, the length measurement 1.4 has two significant figures and the length 1.45 has three significant figures.

   Explore VisibleChem 2.1 to learn how to record measurements using the correct number of significant figures.

Rules for Using Significant Figures

In addition to recording our own measurements correctly, we also must determine the number of significant figures present in measurements we encounter from others. Fortunately, there are a set of rules for this (Table 2.3). The rules for determining significant figures are focused on the zeros in a measurement. Generally, the rules are used to determine whether a zero in a measurement is significant.

   In many situations it is necessary to reduce the number of digits in a numerical value. To accomplish this, we round. To round, find the number to the right of the last

Table 2.3 Rules for Determining the Number of Significant Figures in a Measured Number

Rule 1: A number is a significant figure if it is:	Example	Number of significant figures
a. not a zero	3.9 g	2
	1.24 km	3
b. a zero between two nonzero digits	9008 mm	4
	3.07 m	3
c. a zero at the end of a number with a decimal point	30.0 °C	3
	22.000 g	5
Rule 2: A zero is not significant if it is:	**Example**	**Number of significant figures**
a. at the beginning of a number	0.00032 cm	2
	0.05 mL	1
b. at the end of a large number that does not have a decimal point	380,000 m	2
	1100 g	2

significant figure. Round the number up if the number to its right is five or greater. Do not round up if the last significant digit to its right is four or less. For example, to round number 3.547 to three significant figures, we round to 3.55. The number 3.543, in contrast, is rounded to 3.54.

Scientific Notation

Scientists often deal with very small and very large numbers. A geologist might discuss the age of the earth (4,600,000,000 years; Figure 2.11). A chemist may be interested in the diameter of a copper (Cu) atom (0.000000000128 m). The large number of zeros in both numbers makes them difficult to record and interpret. To make this more convenient, scientists use scientific notation for writing large and small numbers.

Using Scientific Notation

The diameter of a typical coronavirus is typically 0.000000125 m (Figure 2.12). It is much more convenient, however, to express this number in scientific notation. When using scientific notation, we write a number as the product of a number between one and ten and the number 10 raised to a power. When numbers are much smaller than one, as is the case with this measurement of the COVID-19 virus, the exponent is a negative number. For example, we record 0.000000125 m as 1.25×10^{-7} m. This

Apply what you have just learned: **Practice 2.4 and 2.5** in the Pearson eText.

Figure 2.12 An Artist's Representation of a Corona Virus.

A corona virus called SARS-CoV-2 caused the global pandemic of COVID-19 disease.

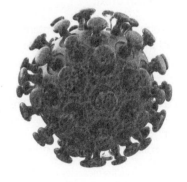

Figure 2.11 Scientific Notation for Large and Small Numbers.

A) Geologists estimate that Earth is 4,600,000,000 years old. **B)** A copper atom is 0.000000000128 m in diameter. **C)** We can express both these numbers are more clearly and efficiently in scientific notation.

A

B

Predict answers and see step-by-step solutions: **Learn 2.1:** Converting Large and Small Numbers to Scientific Notation in the Pearson eText.

Apply what you have just learned: **Practice 2.6–2.8** in the Pearson eText.

Predict answers and see step-by-step solutions: **Learn 2.2:** Determining Significant Figures in Calculations—Multiplication and Division and **Learn 2.3:** Determining Significant Figures in Calculations—Addition and Substraction in the Pearson eText.

Apply what you have just learned: **Practice 2.9** in the Pearson eText.

Quiz yourself on the content of this section: **Check 2.2** in the Pearson eText.

negative number tells us how many times we must move the decimal to the right until we reach a number between one and ten:

$$0.000000125 \text{ m} = 1.25 \times 10^{-7} \text{ m}$$

Move decimal seven places to the right.

If a number is much larger than one, the exponent is a positive number. Studies of viruses indicate that a single cough can contain up to 200,000,000 virus particles, allowing the virus to spread rapidly between individuals. Using scientific notation, we can express the number 200,000,000 as 2.0×10^8 virus particles. The positive number tells us how many times we must move the decimal to the left until we reach a number between one and ten:

$$200000000 \text{ viruses} = 2.0 \times 10^8 \text{ viruses}$$

Move decimal eight places to the left.

Significant Figures in Calculations

We often use measurements in calculations. By following established rules and paying attention to the significant figures and decimal places in the original measurement, we can determine how many digits a calculated result must contain. A calculator can help us do this work faster, but it cannot determine the correct way to report the final results. Fortunately, the rules for using significant figures in calculations provide a guide for reporting results with the correct number of significant figures (Table 2.4).

Table 2.4 Rules for using Significant Figures in Calculations

Rules	Examples
1. In multiplication and division, the result contains the same number of significant figures as the measurement that has the fewest significant figures.	$\underset{\text{(5 sig. figures)}}{1.3514 \text{ g/mL}} \times \underset{\text{(2 sig. figures)}}{0.34 \text{ mL}} = 0.459476 = \underset{\text{(2 sig. figures)}}{0.46 \text{ g}}$ Round to two significant figures *to reflect the measurement with the fewest number of significant figures.* $\underset{\text{(5 sig. figures)}}{2.4462 \text{ g}} \div \underset{\text{(3 sig. figures)}}{1.44 \text{ mL}} = 1.69875 = \underset{\text{(3 sig. figures)}}{1.70 \text{ g/mL}}$ Round to three significant figures *to reflect the measurement with the fewest number of significant figures.*
2. In addition and subtraction, the result contains the same number of decimal places as the quantity that has the fewest decimal places. We underline the last significant figure for clarity.	$\begin{array}{r} 1.493 \text{ cm} \\ 0.3 \ \ \text{ cm} \\ + \ 4.33 \ \ \text{ cm} \\ \hline 6.1\underline{2}3 \text{ cm} = 6.1 \text{ cm} \end{array}$ $\begin{array}{r} 20.456 \text{ mL} \\ - \ \ 2.15 \ \ \text{ mL} \\ \hline 18.0\underline{3}6 \text{ mL} = 18.04 \text{ mL} \end{array}$ Round to hundredths place for four significant figures to *reflect the measurement with the fewest number of decimal places.* Round to tenths place for two significant figures to *reflect the measurement with the fewest number of decimal places.*
3. When rounding to the correct number of significant figures, round down if the last digit dropped is 4 or less. Round up if the last digit dropped is 5 or more.	Round to two significant figures: 7.284 *rounds to* 7.3 7.241 *rounds to* 7.2 7.251 *rounds to* 7.3 7.249 *rounds to* 7.2
4. In multistep calculations, round *only* the final answer. We underline the least significant figure (see Rule 2) to keep track of significant figures throughout the calculation.	$(5.781 - 2.1) \times 7.193 \times 3.32$ $= 3.\underline{6}81 \times 7.193 \times 3.32$ $= 87.90507756$ $= 88$

2.3 Unit Conversions

To solve problems in chemistry and the health sciences we often need to convert a measurement from one set of units to another. For example, converting from milliliters to liters is common practice in the chemistry laboratory. Medical professionals often must convert ounces of medication to milliliters to correctly dose a patient. Converting units can also be a part of our everyday lives. For example, if we are asked the number of minutes we worked on our lab report, we can quickly convert the hours worked to minutes to answer the question in the specific units. So, how do we convert units using a systematic approach?

To convert one unit to another, we use one or more conversion factors. A **conversion factor** is an equality that is expressed as a ratio and used to convert units. For example, there are 60 seconds in 1 minute, which we express as 60 seconds = 1 minute. We can write this as a conversion factor in two different ways:

$$\frac{60 \text{ seconds}}{1 \text{ minute}} \quad \text{or} \quad \frac{1 \text{ minute}}{60 \text{ seconds}}$$

When performing calculations, we can flip the fraction to cancel units. Another example that we use as a conversion factor is the number of milliliters in a liter, 1000 mL = 1 L:

$$\frac{1000 \text{ mL}}{1 \text{ L}} \quad \text{or} \quad \frac{1 \text{ L}}{1000 \text{ mL}}$$

Converting between the English and metric measurement systems is common practice. Table 2.5 lists some common conversion factors.

> Apply what you have just learned: **Practice 2.10** in the Pearson eText.

Problem Solving using Conversion Factors

To convert quantities from one set of units to another requires we use a method called **dimensional analysis** (Figure 2.13). In this approach, we use the conversion factors so that units cancel. To accomplish this, we begin with the original quantity and multiply by a conversion factor in a way that leaves the desired units in our answer.

| original value with original units | × | unit conversion factor | = | new value with desired units |

If we want to convert 162 pounds (lb.) to kilograms (kg), for example, we first need to find a conversion factor that applies, and then set up the problem such that units cancel and we are left with kilograms, which are the desired units. In this case, we write the conversion factor in one of the following ways:

$$\frac{2.20 \text{ lb}}{1 \text{ kg}} \quad \text{or} \quad \frac{1 \text{ kg}}{2.20 \text{ lb}}$$

Table 2.5 Conversion Factors for Common Unit Conversion Calculations

Quantity	Metric (SI)	U.S.	Metric–U.S.
length	1 km = 1000 m 1 m = 1000 mm 1 cm = 10 mm	1 ft = 12 in. 1 yd = 3 ft 1 mi = 5280 ft	2.54 cm = 1 in. (exact) 1 m = 39.4 in. 1 km = 0.621 mi
volume	1 L = 1000 mL 1 dL = 100 mL 1 mL = 1 cm³	1 qt = 4 cups 1 qt = 2 pt 1 gal = 4 qt	946 mL = 1 qt 1 L = 1.06 qt
mass	1 kg = 1000 g 1 g = 1000 mg	1 lb = 16 oz	1 kg = 2.20 lb 454 g = 1 lb
time	1 h = 60 min 1 min = 60 s	1 h = 60 min 1 min = 60 s	

Figure 2.13 Blood Plasma. Hospitals use plasma to treat patients. It often comes in pint-sized bags but is administered in units of liters. Using dimensional analysis to convert units is common practice in a hospital.

The original quantity is in pounds (lb), so we choose the second ratio above so that units cancel as follows:

$$162 \, \cancel{lb} \times \frac{1 \, kg}{2.20 \, \cancel{lb}} = 73.6 \, kg$$

When doing dimensional analysis, we must remember to always choose a conversion factor that 1) relates the two units involved, and 2) cancels out the unwanted unit. To explore more examples of unit conversion problems, click on VisibleChem Videos 2.2–2.4.

Watch this concept come to life: **VisibleChem Videos 2.2–2.4:** Unit Conversion Problem Solving in the Pearson eText.

Predict answers and see step-by-step solutions: **Learn 2.4:** Solving Unit Conversion Problems in the Pearson eText.

Apply what you have just learned: **Practice 2.11** in the Pearson eText.

Predict answers and see step-by-step solutions: **Learn 2.5:** Using Two or More Conversion Factors When Converting Units in the Pearson eText.

Apply what you have just learned: **Practice 2.12** in the Pearson eText.

Quiz yourself on the content of this section: **Check 2.3** in the Pearson eText.

2.4 Dosage Calculations

Have you ever thought about the amount of trust people place in medical professionals? What if someone made a mistake in giving you or a loved one a prescription drug dosage? Most of us take a prescribed drug at some point in our lives. Errors can be made during many steps: 1) prescribing a drug, 2) transcribing a drug order, or 3) administering the drug to a patient.

Although nurses do not prescribe drugs directly, they play critical roles in identifying errors that are sometimes made in patient prescriptions. In addition, nurses can either create or prevent errors while transcribing a drug order or administering drugs to a patient (Figure 2.14). The National Academies Institute of Medicine reports that at least 1.5 million preventable adverse drug events (ADEs) occur in the United States each year. Some evidence indicated that the actual number might be much higher. The report also concludes that between 44,000 and 98,000 deaths in U.S. hospitals each year are the result of preventable medical errors. The frequency of medication errors not only affects the health and well-being of patients, but also the cost of health care. With this in mind, let's practice using unit conversions to calculate dosage amounts.

Figure 2.14 A Nurse Administers Oral Drugs to an Infant (left) and an IV Drug to a Patient (right).

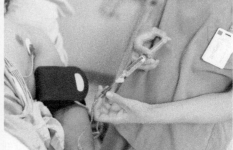

Practicing Dosage Calculations with Unit Conversions

Consider a prescription order for levothyroxine sodium, which is given to patients with hypothyroidism (a condition where the thyroid gland does not produce enough thyroid hormone). If we know that the patient requires 75 micrograms (μg) per day of the medication, and that each tablet contains 0.025 milligrams (mg), we can use unit conversion to determine the number of tablets a patient must take each day.

We first convert from micrograms (μg) to milligrams (mg) to determine the amount of medication in each tablet. We can use this information to figure out the number of tablets needed:

$$\left[\frac{75. \; \mu g}{day}\right]\left[\frac{1 \; mg}{1000 \; \mu g}\right]\left[\frac{1 \; tablet}{0.0250 \; mg}\right] = 3.0 \; tablets \; per \; day$$

Learn 2.6 provides additional practice in determining dosage amounts for drugs in tablet form. Other dosage calculations involve injections of medications in liquid form, usually in milliliters (mL). Continue on to Learn 2.7 for an example of this type of dosage calculation.

Predict answers and see step-by-step solutions: **Learn 2.6:** Calculating Dosage of an Oral Tablet and **Learn 2.7:** Calculating Dosage of a Liquid Medication Based on Body Weight in the Pearson eText.

Apply what you have just learned: **Practice 2.13 and 2.14** in the Pearson eText.

Explore how Chemistry and Biology connect: **BioConnect 2.1:** Infectious Doses in the Pearson eText.

Quiz yourself on the content of this section: **Check 2.4** in the Pearson eText.

2.5 Common Units in Environmental Science

The quality of drinking water is a primary determinant of health for the world's population. Air quality is similarly important. Air pollution increases the risk of developing a wide range of diseases, such as respiratory and heart disease, and even lung cancer (Figure 2.22). In this section, we look at how scientific measurements of some important environmental contaminants can be useful in monitoring human and environmental health.

As the human population of Earth continues to grow, so do the challenges and opportunities we face as a global community. Have you ever wondered what happens to all of the old computers, TVs, and cell phones when newer devices are purchased by hundreds of millions of people on the planet? You might be relieved to know that much of the so-called global "e-waste" is recycled, but this is often done under very unhealthy conditions for those living around the recycling sites (Figure 2.23). The process of electronic recycling produces environmental contaminants such as mercury, lead, and arsenic. Environmental scientists and public health workers study the effects

Figure 2.22 A Woman Monitors Air Pollution Levels on her Phone.

Figure 2.23 Electronic Waste Recycling Releases Toxins Such as Mercury, Lead, and Arsenic.

of these toxins on humans and the environment. Measuring and monitoring their levels is an important application of our study of units and unit conversion.

PPM and PPB

In everyday life, we use the term "percent" to indicate a certain number "out of a hundred." For example, a 10% off sale means a $100 pair of shoes on sale costs $90; the discount is ten dollars out of 100. In a similar way, **parts per million (ppm)** *means a number of something "out of a million"* (1×10^6). Likewise, **parts per billion (ppb)** *means a number of something "out of a billion"* (1×10^9).

For example, by mass, one milligram is a thousandth of a gram. One milligram is a thousandth of a thousandth of a kilogram, which is the same as a millionth (1 ppm). By volume, a liter of water weighs 1000 grams, or 1 million milligrams; so, *1 mg/L is 1 ppm*. Environmental scientists and toxicologists often use ppm and ppb to describe the concentration of a substance in water or soil.

To put these numbers in perspective, one ppm is similar to one minute out of two years. One ppb is like one square in a roll of toilet paper that stretches from New York to London. Despite the small size of these numbers, the impact of toxins in the ppm to ppb range can be significant. For example, the **U.S. Environmental Protection Agency (EPA)** currently sets acceptable levels of mercury contamination at 0.002 ppm. Mercury levels higher than this can cause severe neurological impacts and kidney damage. Unfortunately, a 2014 analysis of the mercury levels in hair from workers at an e-waste site in Guiyu, China (Figure 2.24) found that 48% of the workers had levels above EPA limits[2].

Limits on Environmental Toxins

Arsenic is a naturally occurring substance found in rocks, soil, and water. It can also be produced during industrial activities and then released into the environment. The majority of industrial arsenic in the U.S. is used as a wood preservative, but arsenic is also contained in some paints, dyes, metals, drugs, fertilizers, soaps, and semiconductors. In addition, practices such as copper mining and coal burning also release arsenic into our environment (Figure 2.25).

Figure 2.24 Children Living Near an E-Waste Dumpsite in Guiyu, China.

Elevated levels of mercury and other toxins have been gaining increased attention at e-waste dumpsites such as this one in China.

Figure 2.25 Wastewater From an Abandoned Mine in Colorado.

Wastewater from mining often contains a variety of toxins including arsenic. Arsenic levels in drinking water are carefully regulated. Exposure can lead to a variety of health problems including skin damage and increased cancer risk.

Table 2.6 The Maximum Contaminant Level (MCL) of Some Common Toxins

In the U.S., the EPA establishes these limits.

Toxin	MCL Level	Common Sources	Toxic Effects
mercury (Hg)	0.002 ppm	erosion of natural deposits; discharge from refineries and factories; run off from landfills & croplands, electronics production and recycling	kidney and neurological damage
lead (Pb)	0.015 ppm	corrosion of household plumbing; erosion of natural deposits; electronics production and recycling	impaired neurological and kidney function; reduced fertility
arsenic (As)	0.010 ppm	erosion of natural deposits; runoff from glass and electronics production and recycling	skin damage, problems with circulatory system; increased cancer risk
PCBs (polychlorinated biphenyls)	0.0005 ppm	runoff from landfills; discharge of waste chemicals	skin changes; impacts reproductive, immune, and nervous systems, increased risk of cancer
dioxins	0.00000003 ppm	emissions from waste incineration and other combustion; discharge of waste chemicals	reduced fertility; increased risk of cancer

In the U.S., the EPA sets limits for the Maximum Contamination Level (MCL) for a wide range of contaminants, including arsenic (Table 2.6). The MCL values are the highest level of a contaminant that is allowed in drinking water.

Measuring Concentrations of Airborne Substances

Scientists measure the concentrations of a variety of airborne substances, such as carbon dioxide (CO_2). Atmospheric levels of carbon dioxide (CO_2) fluctuate naturally over time, but a large body of scientific evidence suggests that human activity has been significantly increasing atmospheric CO_2 levels (Figure 2.26).

Figure 2.26 Measurements of Carbon Dioxide at Mauna Loa Observatory.

Scientists began measuring the carbon dioxide levels at Mauna Loa in 1958. Levels have been rising in the decades since monitoring began. The smaller variations seen each year are due to the seasonal shifts in the amount of carbon dioxide plants take in during their growing seasons.

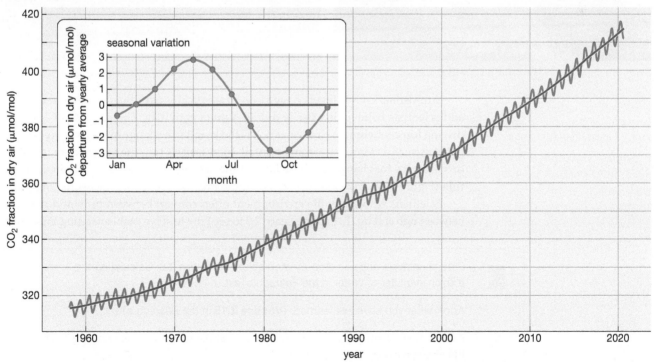

data: Dr. Pieter Tans, NOAA/ESRL (www.esrl.noaa.gov/gmd/ccgg/trends/) and Dr. Ralph Keeling, Scripps Institution of Oceanography (scrippsco2.ucsd.edu/), accessed 2020-10-31

Figure 2.27 Impacts of Increase CO_2.

As global temperatures rise as a result of climate change, glaciers such as the Triftgletscher glacier in Switzerland have begun to recede rapidly. Left: 2002, right: 2003. Photos J. Alean. http://www.swisseduc.ch/glaciers/glossary/glacier-recession-en.html

Atmospheric CO_2 levels have risen dramatically over the last several decades, and scientists believe this rise is due to human activities. The increased CO_2 is the driving force for **climate change** which is the long-term change in the average weather patterns such as temperature and rainfall. Increased CO_2 in the atmosphere is also the driving force for changes in the acidity of the oceans, a process called **ocean acidification** (Figure 2.27). Like many other contaminants, CO_2 levels are measured in ppm.

Scientists who study the environment often convert between ppm and mg/L, or between ppb and ug/L. Explore Learn 2.8 to see how to solve problems using these units.

Predict answers and see step-by-step solutions: **Learn 2.8:** Calculating the Amount of a Toxin in a Liter of Water in the Pearson eText.

Apply what you have just learned: **Practice 2.15** in the Pearson eText.

Explore how Chemistry and Biology connect: **BioConnect 2.2:** Determining Toxicity in the Pearson eText.

Quiz yourself on the content of this section: **Check 2.5** in the Pearson eText.

2.6 Measuring Temperature

Temperature is a measure of how hot or cold an object is. We can report temperature using the **Fahrenheit temperature scale** (°F), the **Celsius temperature scale** (°C), or the **Kelvin temperature scale (K)**. When we use the metric system, we measure temperature almost exclusively using the Celsius scale. The SI unit for reporting temperature, however, is the kelvin (K).

Notice the relationship between the three temperature scales (Figure 2.34). Kelvin and Celsius degrees are the same size. These two scales both have the same number of degrees between the boiling and freezing points of water: exactly one hundred degrees. Water freezes at 0 °C and boils at 100 °C. The only difference between the Celsius and Kelvin scale is the zero point. On the Celsius scale, 0 °C is the freezing point of water, and on the Kelvin scale 273 K is the freezing point of water and 0 K is the coldest possible temperature, also known as **absolute zero**.

The size of the degrees on the Fahrenheit scale differs from the degrees on the other two scales. There is a 180-degree difference between the boiling and freezing of water on the Fahrenheit scale.

To convert from one temperature scale to another, we us the following equations:

$$°F = 1.8(°C) + 32$$
$$°C = (°F - 32)/1.8$$

Because a temperature of −273 °C corresponds to 0 K, converting between these two scales requires adding or subtracting 273 depending on the original unit.

$$K = °C + 273$$
$$°C = K - 273$$

Predict answers and see step-by-step solutions: **Learn 2.9:** Converting Temperatures in the Pearson eText.

Apply what you have just learned: **Practice 2.16** in the Pearson eText.

Quiz yourself on the content of this section: **Check 2.6** in the Pearson eText.

Figure 2.34 Fahrenheit, Celsius, and Kelvin Temperature Scales and Conversions. Note that measurements in Kelvin do not include the degree sign.

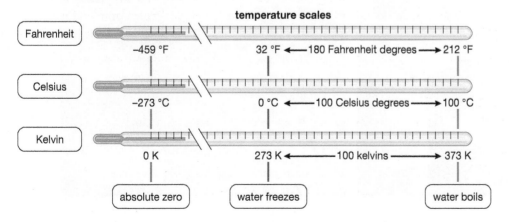

Table 2.7 Density of Common Substances

Substance	Density (g/cm³)
charcoal (from oak)	0.57
ethanol	0.789
ice	0.917 (at 0 °C)
water	1.00 (at 4 °C)
sugar (sucrose)	1.58
table salt (sodium chloride)	2.16
glass	2.6
aluminum	2.70
titanium	4.51
iron	7.86
copper	8.96
lead	11.4
mercury	13.55
gold	19.3
platinum	21.4

 Apply what you have just learned: **Practice 2.17** in the Pearson eText.

2.7 Density and Specific Gravity

A physical property that we use to characterize different substances is density. The **density** (d) of a substance is the ratio of its mass (m) to its volume (V).

$$\text{Density} = \frac{\text{mass}}{\text{volume}} \qquad d = \frac{m}{V}$$

Imagine holding a rock in one hand and a cotton ball in the other. The rock has a greater mass per volume ratio, so we say it has a greater density than the cotton ball. Bone density is another example of density that comes up in our everyday lives. As people age, our bone density tends to decrease, making bones more fragile and likely to break.

We typically report density values in grams per milliliter (g/mL), but occasionally we use other units, such as grams per cubic centimeter (g/cm³). Every substance has a unique density that is generally determined in a laboratory setting. Gold, for example, has a density of 19.3 g/cm³, whereas aluminum has a density of just 2.70 g/cm³. Table 2.7 lists the densities of a variety of substances.

Problem Solving with Density

Density is important in chemistry and medicine for many reasons (Figure 2.35). Determining a substance's density and comparing it to known values, for example, can help us identify unknown substances. To do this, we use the density and laboratory measurements of mass and volume. For example, if the mass of a solid is 67.90 grams and its volume is 9.6 milliliters, we can calculate this solid's density as follows:

$$\text{Density} = \frac{67.90 \text{ g}}{9.6 \text{ mL}} = 7.1 \text{ g/mL}$$

We can also use density as a conversion factor. If we are given the density and mass, we can calculate volume. If we are given the density and volume, we can calculate mass. Click on Learn 2.10 to see how to do these calculations.

 Predict answers and see step-by-step solutions: **Learn 2.10:** Problem Solving with Density in the Pearson eText.

Apply what you have just learned: **Practice 2.18 and 2.19** in the Pearson eText.

Figure 2.35 Bone Density Scanning.

A) Bone density scanning, also called dual-energy x-ray absorptiometry (DEXA) or bone densitometry, is a form of x-ray technology used to measure bone loss. **B)** DEXA is most often used to diagnose osteoporosis, a gradual loss of calcium that causes bones to become thinner, more fragile, and more likely to break.

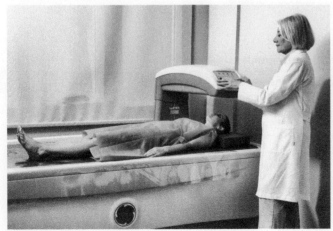

A

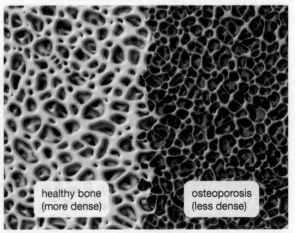

healthy bone (more dense)

osteoporosis (less dense)

B

Figure 2.36 Urine Sample.

The specific gravity of urine is measured to determine if a patient has an imbalance in metabolism.

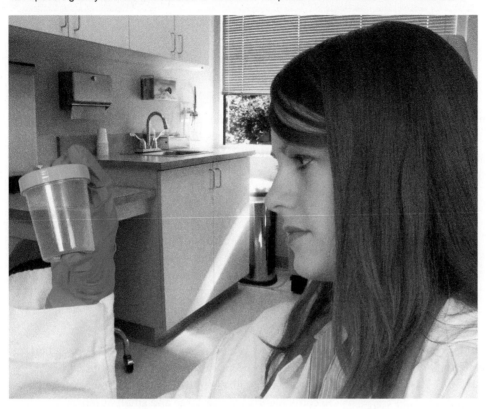

Specific Gravity

In medicine, health care professionals often determine the density of urine through an indirect measurement that compares the density of urine to the density of water (Figure 2.36). **Specific gravity** *(sp gr) is a relationship between the density of a substance and the density of water at* 4 °C.

$$\text{Specific gravity} = \frac{\text{density of substance}}{\text{density of water}}$$

Because the density of water is 1.00g/mL and is in the denominator of the equation, the specific gravity of a substance is equal to its density. Note that all the units cancel out when we use this equation, so specific gravity is a unitless quantity.

The specific gravity test involving urine is called *urine specific gravity*. The results of this test indicate to health care workers whether the patient has a healthy amount of compounds dissolved in the urine, or if the amount is elevated. The range of specific gravity for normal urine is between 1.005 − 1.030. There are several conditions involving imbalances in metabolism that can cause an elevated urine specific gravity. One very common condition that does this is diabetes mellitus. An elevated urine specific gravity can result when a patient has excess sugar in the urine. The sugars cause the density of urine to increase above healthy levels.

Apply what you have just learned: **Practice 2.20** in the Pearson eText.

Quiz yourself on the content of this section: **Check 2.7** in the Pearson eText.

Chapter Summary

2.1 Units of Measurement

Learning Objective: Report measurements of length, mass, and volume in metric units.

The metric system and the International System of Units (SI units) are used globally. The United States is one of the few countries still using the English System of measurements. Metric prefixes indicate the magnitude of a number; this indicates the location of the decimal point in the number Table 2.2.

Key Terms

base unit	International System of Units (SI)	meter (m)
cubic centimeters (cc or cm^3)	liter (L)	metric system
gram (g)	mass	volume

2.2 Communication about Measurements

Learning Objective: Use scientific notation and significant figures when problem-solving and communicating about measurements.

A measurement has both a number value and a unit associated with it. We must take the rules of significant figures into account when considering measured (or inexact) values because all measurements have uncertainty (Table 2.3 and Table 2.4). We also must pay special attention to the type of zero found in a number (leading, between numbers, or trailing). Scientific notation helps us to conveniently express large and small numbers.

VisibleChem Video 2.1: Measuring Length, Volume, and Mass

Key Terms

exact number
measured numbers
scientific notation
significant figures (digits)

2.3 Unit Conversions

Learning Objective: Use conversion factors to convert between units.

The ability to convert between different units is a critical skill in science. Conversion factors are ratios between different units and are simple fractions that we can flip in order to cancel units Table 2.5. We can perform multiple conversions and unit cancelations to complete a multi-step unit conversion. If units cancel correctly so we end up with the desired units, we know each step has been chosen correctly.

VisibleChem Video 2.2: Metric System Unit Conversion Problem Solving

VisibleChem Video 2.3: Metric-English System Unit Conversion Problem Solving

VisibleChem Video 2.4: Problem Solving Using Conversion Factors Composed of Two Units

Key Terms

conversion factor
dimensional analysis

2.4 Dosage Calculations

Learning Objective: Apply ratio and proportion conversion factors for medical dosage calculations.

Dosage calculations are medical applications of unit conversions that ensure that the correct amounts of medicines are administered to patients. As with any unit conversion, in dosage calculations, we must take care to set up the proportions as fractions with units. We can then cancel units to confirm the dosage calculation is performed correctly. Dosage calculations often involve the patient's weight, an IV flow rate, or an amount of medicine per unit of time.

BioConnect 2.1: Infectious Doses

Key Terms

bacteria
infectious dose (ID)

minimum infectious dose
(from BioConnect 2.1)

virion (from BioConnect 2.1)
virus (from BioConnect 2.1)

2.5 Common Units in Environmental Science

Learning Objective: Solve problems with conversion factors and units commonly used in environmental science.

The ability to measure and understand the amounts of substances in our environment is critical to science, health, and environmental sustainability. Common examples include concentrations of various toxins in our air, water, and the soil expressed as parts per million (ppm) or parts per billion (ppb). Fortunately, we have methods to test and monitor our environment and toxin concentration calculations generally involve straightforward unit conversions. Parts per million (ppm) is a number of something "out of a million" (1×10^6). Parts per billion (ppb) is a number of something "out of a billion" (1×10^9). One ppm is equivalent to one milligram of a substance per liter of water (mg/L), or one milligram of a substance per kilogram of soil (mg/kg).

BioConnect 2.2: Determining Toxicity

Key Terms

climate change
LD50 (from BioConnect 2.2)
ocean acidification

parts-per-billion (ppb)
parts-per-million (ppm)

U.S. Environmental Protection Agency
(EPA)

2.6 Measuring Temperature

Learning Objective: Convert temperature measurements from one scale to another.

The three commonly used temperature scales are Celsius (°C), Kelvin (K), and Fahrenheit (°F) Figure 2.34. In science and medicine, the most common are Celsius and Kelvin. Kelvins and Celsius degrees are the same size, but the scales are offset by 273°(0 °C $=$ 273 K). The coldest theoretical temperature possible, known as "absolute zero" is 0 K (which corresponds to −273 °C). We convert among the temperature scales using the following formulas:

$$T_K = T_C + 273 \qquad T_C = \frac{T_F - 32}{1.8} \qquad T_F = 1.8(T_C) + 32$$

Key Terms

absolute zero
Celsius (°C) temperature scale

Fahrenheit temperature scale (°F)
Kelvin (K) temperature scale

temperature

2.7 Density

Learning Objective: Explain the concept of density and specific gravity, and solve problems involving density, mass, and volume measurements.

The density of an object or substance is the ratio of the mass to the volume it occupies $\left(d = \frac{m}{v}\right)$. Common units of density are g/mL or g/cm³. We can use density values as conversion factors to solve problems. The specific gravity of a substance is equal to the density of that substance divided by the density of water (1.00 g/mL). Specific gravity measurements are unitless numbers. Urine specific gravity provides medical professionals with information about possible health issues.

Key Terms

density
specific gravity

Key Equations

$$\text{Density} = \frac{\text{mass}}{\text{volume}}$$

$$\text{Specific gravity} = \frac{\text{density of substance}}{\text{density of water}}$$

The **End-of-Chapter Problems** are located in the back of the book in Appendix A.

 End-of-Chapter Quiz   Have you mastered the content of this chapter? Try the **End-of-Chapter Quiz** in the Pearson eText.

1. Which measurement is equivalent to 1.35×10^{-4} L?
   a) 1,350 mL
   b) 0.00135 L
   c) 0.135 mL
   d) 1,350 L

2. Which unit is the most convenient unit to describe the volume of a mouthful of water?
   a) nL
   b) m
   c) g
   d) mL

3. Write the number 5.70 million, an estimate of the total population of people living in Singapore, in standard scientific notation.
   a) 5.70×10^5
   b) 5.70×10^6
   c) 5.70×10^{-6}
   d) 5,700,000

4. Select the correct answer to this calculation expressed to the appropriate number of significant figures?
   $$\frac{(2.468 + 0.61)(2.1)}{1.2 \times 10^{-1}}$$
   a) 53.865
   b) 54
   c) 53.9
   d) 0.54

5. A nurse draws 12.5 mL of blood from a patient for a blood test. How many cc is this? (A cc is a common abbreviation for a cubic centimeter: one cc = 1 cubic centimeter = 1 cm³ = 1 mL.)
   a) 12.5 cc
   b) 1953.125 cc
   c) 0.125 cc
   d) 2.321 cc

6. The "calorie" is a common unit used to measure the energy value of food. The unit we refer to as the "dietary calorie" or "large calorie" and abbreviate as kcal represents one thousand calories (1 kcal = 1000 cal). Another energy term used quite often in science is the Joule (J). By definition, 1 cal = 4.184 J. If a bowl of rice and vegetables contains 425 "dietary calories" (kcals), how many Joules is this? Express your answer in scientific notation to three significant figures.
   a) 1778.2 J
   b) 1.7782×10^6 J
   c) 1.78×10^3 J
   d) 1.78×10^6 J

7. The total annual generation of Municipal Solid Waste (MSW, also known as garbage) in the U.S. has increased by over 65% since 1980, to a current level of over 250 million US short tons per year. (1 short ton = 2000 pounds = 907.185 kilograms). An average American weighing 180 pounds generates approximately their own weight in Municipal Solid Waste every 41 days! Calculate the total number of kilograms of Municipal Solid Waste the US generates each year. Express your answer in scientific notation to three significant figures.
   a) 2.26×10^{11} kg
   b) 2.27×10^{11} kg
   c) 2.27×10^9 kg
   d) 4.08×10^{13} kg

8. The drug Herceptin® is used in breast cancer treatment. A vial of the drug contains 150 mg Herceptin that a nurse dissolves in 20 mL before administering it to the patient. What is the concentration of the dissolved drug solution in mg/mL?
   a) 0.75 mg/mL
   b) 75 mg/mL
   c) 7.5 mg/mL
   d) 3000 mg/mL

9. The drug Rituxan® is used in cancer treatment for non-Hodgkin's lymphoma and chronic lymphocytic leukemia. The dosage for a particular patient is 375 mg/m², If a 62-year-old female cancer patient is 158 cm tall, how many mL of a 10 mg/mL solution of the drug is the correct dose for her? Express your answer in standard form to two significant figures.
   a) 59 mL
   b) 94 mL
   c) 0.94 mL
   d) 936 mL

10. Blood transfusions are common and often life-saving procedures. Over four million Americans need blood transfusions each year. Medical professionals perform transfusions to replace blood lost during surgery or in the case of serious injury, severe infection, liver disease, and other conditions where the body is unable to produce enough healthy blood. If a patient in the hospital requires a transfusion of one 500-cc (cubic centimeter) unit of whole blood every two hours, at what flow rate (mL/min) should the transfusion be performed? The delivery pump requires the nurse to input the flow rate in decimal form to two significant figures ($1 \text{ cc} = 1 \text{ cm}^3 = 1 \text{ mL}$).
    a) 8.3 mL/min
    b) 250 mL/min
    c) 4.1 mL/min
    d) 4.2 mL/min

11. Green chemistry is an increasingly common approach to manufacturing materials and products in an environmentally friendly way. The green chemistry movement is evolving and improving as business and regulatory agencies refine their pollution-prevention initiatives. As green chemists work to improve farming methods, commercial products, and medicines to support the growing population on our planet, they are also focusing on reducing the environmental impact of these efforts. A plastics manufacturer makes 145,000 metric tons (1 metric ton = 1000 kilogram) of biodegradable plastic per year. Plastic water bottles each weigh 18 grams on average. Approximately how many biodegradable water bottles could be produced each year by this one manufacturer in an effort to replace non-biodegradable bottles? Express your answer in standard scientific notation to three decimal places.
    a) 8.06×10^9 bottles/yr
    b) 8.06×10^6 bottles/yr
    c) 8.05×10^9 bottles/yr
    d) 8.06×10^3 bottles/yr

12. Tuberculosis (TB) is a disease caused by the bacterium *Mycobacterium tuberculosis*. TB usually affects the lungs, but can also attack the kidneys, spine, and brain. According to the World Health Organization (WHO), there are over eight million cases of TB globally and around one million of those cases result in death. The infectious dose (ID) of the bacterium is very low (estimated at around 10 organisms), and the disease is usually spread through the air when an infected person coughs or sneezes. If a child with TB sneezes in a crowd of people and spreads 840 TB bacterium into the air, and one out of every four people becomes infected, how many newly infected people could result?
    a) 840 possible new cases
    b) 84 possible new cases
    c) 21 possible new cases
    d) 4 possible new cases

13. Aflatoxins are naturally occurring mycotoxins (poisons produced by fungi). Aflatoxins, produced by certain species of fungi, are a highly toxic class of compounds that are among the most carcinogenic substances known. The fungi that produce aflatoxins can colonize and contaminate grain before harvest, or during storage. In order to protect human and animal health, the United States Food and Drug Administration (FDA) has determined that if levels of more than 20 ppb of aflatoxins in food or feed are detected, action must be taken. A bag of rice is tested, and the results indicate a contamination level of 4.8×10^{-7} g/100 g rice. What is this level expressed in ppb? Is it below the tolerance level requiring action? One ppb = one microgram per kilogram (μg/kg). Express your answer in standard decimal notation to two significant figures.
    a) The level is 480 ppb; this is above the action level established by the FDA.
    b) The level is 4.8 ppb; this is below the action level established by the FDA.
    c) The level is 0.48 ppb; this is below the action level established by the FDA.
    d) The level is 48 ppb; this is above the action level established by the FDA.

14. You are telling a friend who is living in Korea how to cook a favorite dish that you cook in your oven in the U.S. at a setting of 375 °F. What temperature in Celsius should you tell him to set his oven at to cook the food? Express your answer in standard decimal form to three significant figures.
    a) 191 °C
    b) 226 °C
    c) 208 °C
    d) 343 °C

15. Organisms known as extremophiles have adapted to thrive under conditions that most other organisms would find very harsh, or uninhabitable. For example, the thermophilic bacterium, *Phormidium,* found in the hot springs and geyser basins of Yellowstone National Park, can thrive in temperatures up to 57.0 °C. Convert this temperature to Fahrenheit. (As a reference, you might enjoy a 102 °F hot bath at the end of a long day.) Express your answer in standard decimal form to three significant figures with the correct units.

   a) 103 °F
   b) 89.0 °F
   c) 135
   d) 135 °F

16. If the density of human skeletal muscle is 1.06 g/cm^3. What is the volume of a 312.8 g muscle? Be sure to express your answer with the correct number of significant figures and appropriate units.

   a) 295.09 cm^3
   b) 295 cm^3
   c) 332 cm^3
   d) 3.39 × 10^{-3} cm^3

17. An overweight man has an initial body volume of 113.4 L (as measured by water displacement) before he begins to eat more healthy foods and exercise regularly. After one year, his doctor determines his new body volume is 89.3 L. The density of body fat is 0.9196 kg/L. Assuming that a loss of body fat was the only change that took place, how many kg of body fat did the man lose? In this problem, we ignore the increase in muscle mass and other changes that certainly occurred during a one-year fitness program. Be sure to express your answer with the correct number of significant figures and appropriate units.

   a) 82.1 kg
   b) 24.1 kg
   c) 22.2 kg
   d) 104 kg

18. Carbon fiber materials are used to replace steel and aluminum in a wide range of manufactured products worldwide because carbon fiber is very strong and "light" (less dense) than traditional metals. For example, the Boeing Company has incorporated carbon fiber composites into parts of the Boeing 787 passenger aircraft in order to make the plane lighter. If a bicycle frame made of steel weighs 2.31 kg, and it is replaced with a carbon fiber frame of the same size, how much lighter is the new carbon fiber bicycle frame? Assume the density of the carbon fiber material is 1.58 kg/L, and the density of the steel bicycle frame is 7.7 kg/L. Hint: First find the volume of the bicycle frame.

   a) 1.84 kg
   b) 0.47 kg
   c) 0.30 kg
   d) 6.12 kg

19. A surgeon removes a tumor with a volume of 4.6 cm^3 during surgery. The weight of the tumor is 4.210 g. What is the density of the tumor?

   a) 1.1 g/cm^3
   b) 0.92 g/cm^3
   c) 0.9152 g/cm^3
   d) 19.4 g/cm^3

References

1. Towner J S, Rollin P E, Bausch D G, Sanchez A, Crary S M, Vincent M, Lee W F, Spiropoulou C F, Ksiazek T G, Lukwiya M, Kaducu F, Downing R, Nichol S T. (2004) Rapid Diagnosis of Ebola Hemorrhagic Fever by Reverse Transcription-PCE in an Outbreak Setting and Assessment of Patient Viral Load as a Predictor of Outcome. Journal of Virology. 78: 4330–4341.

2. Ni W, Chen Y, Huang Y, Wang X, Zhang G, Luo J, Wu K. (2014) Hair Mercury Concentrations and Associated Factors in an Electronic Waste Recycling Area, Guiyu, China. *Environ Res.* 128: 84–91.

Chapter 3
Atoms: The Building Blocks of Chemistry

Atoms are the building blocks of all materials on Earth.

⌄ Chapter Outline

3.1 The Atom

3.2 Isotopes

3.3 Electron Arrangements

3.4 Valence Electrons

3.5 How Electrons Fill Orbitals

Learning Objectives

3.1 Identify and describe the structure of atoms.

3.2 Determine the number of subatomic particles present in specific isotopes and define the atomic mass of elements.

3.3 Describe the arrangement of electrons in atoms.

3.4 Identify valence electrons and represent them using electron-dot symbols.

3.5 Write electron configurations for elements.

Introduction

The things we encounter in the world are all made up of atoms. Atoms are the basic building blocks of all materials on Earth and are the foundation of chemistry. The bark of trees, for example, is composed of cellulose, a compound made up of carbon, hydrogen, and oxygen atoms (Figure 3.1A). Similarly, acetaminophen–a common medication–is made of carbon, hydrogen, oxygen, and nitrogen atoms (Figure 3.1B). We can explore everything in the world around us at the atomic level. And this exploration ultimately helps us to better understand why matter behaves the way it does.

So, what do atoms look like? What are they composed of? How does an atom of one element differ from the atom of another element? We explore these questions in this chapter with the goal of gaining a deeper understanding of a world that is so small, yet provides so much fundamental information about everything around us.

3.1 The Atom

If we were to take a piece of silver and divide it into smaller and smaller pieces, how far could we go? Could this go on forever? Philosophers contemplated this for many thousands of years but only relatively recently (200 years ago) have scientists begun to answer the question. What we now know is that we would eventually end up with a single silver atom (Figure 3.2).

All matter is composed of the building blocks called atoms. An atom *is the basic unit of a chemical element*. Atoms are the smallest component of an element that maintains the chemical properties of that element.

Subatomic Particles

In the past 100 years, further experimentation has revealed that atoms are composed of even smaller, more fundamental particles called **subatomic particles**.

Figure 3.1 Atoms Are the Building Blocks of all Materials.

A) The cellulose that makes up much of the structure of a tree is composed of carbon, hydrogen, and oxygen atoms. **B)** The drug acetaminophen is carbon, hydrogen, oxygen, and nitrogen atoms.

A   cellulose

B   acetaminophen

Figure 3.2 Atoms Are the Smallest Particles of an Element.

silver

Figure 3.3 Properties of Electrical Charge.

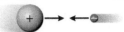

Positive (orange) and negative (blue) electrical charges attract one another.

Positive charges repel one another. Negative charges repel one another.

All atoms are composed of three subatomic particles: protons, neutrons, and electrons. **Electrical charge**, a fundamental property of subatomic particles, results in attractive and repulsive forces between the subatomic particles (Figure 3.3). **Protons** (p) are positively charged particles with a very small mass (Table 3.1). **Neutrons** (n) are charge-neutral (they are not positive or negative) and have a similar mass to protons. **Electrons** (e) are negatively charged particles that have a mass much smaller than protons and neutrons. The atoms of each element have a different number of subatomic particles and the atoms of each element are unique for this reason. In this chapter you will learn to use the periodic table to determine how many subatomic particles of each type are in the atoms of each element.

Structure of Atoms

Let's explore subatomic particles and learn how they form an atom. Through a series of experiments, scientists determined that in addition to subatomic particles, all atoms contain a **nucleus**, a small, densely packed, positively charged, region located at the center of the atom. The nucleus contains the atoms' protons and the neutrons. The electrons form an **electron cloud** around the nucleus and make up most of the volume of an atom.

Given that there are both positive charges and negative charges in the atom, how does the atom stay together as one unit? The structure of the atom is dependent on the attractive and repulsive forces of the subatomic particles. Unlike charges attract, so the negatively charged electrons are held closely to the positive protons. In contrast, like charges repel one another, so the electrons move as far apart from one another as possible. Electrons are located around the nucleus in a way that minimizes electron-electron repulsion. The positively charged protons in the nucleus also repel one another, but are held together by strong forces, the nature of which is beyond the scope of this chapter.

Table 3.1 Summary of the Subatomic Particles.

	Mass (kg)	Mass (amu)	Charge (relative)	
Proton	1.67262×10^{-27}	1.00727	+1	
Neutron	1.67493×10^{-27}	1.00866	0	
Electron	0.00091×10^{-27}	0.00055	−1	

Size of Atoms

The entire mass of an atom is very small (on order of 10^{-24} grams). Although the electrons occupy the majority of space, most of the mass of an atom is in the nucleus, where the protons and neutrons are found. Protons and neutrons have a greater mass than electrons and they are packed very closely together in the nucleus. The electrons, on the other hand, occupy a vast amount of space.

Because the mass of individual atoms is so small, chemists use a unit called an **atomic mass unit (amu)** for atoms and subatomic particles. An amu is equal to one-twelfth the mass of a carbon atom. In grams, one amu is equal to 1.661×10^{-24} grams.

To illustrate the size of the nucleus compared to the region the electrons occupy, consider the following analogy. If the nucleus were the size of a soccer ball, an atom would be the size of a large stadium (Video 3.1).

Video 3.1:
Just How Small is an Atom?

Apply what you have just learned: **Practice 3.1–3.4** in the Pearson eText.

Atomic Number

All atoms are composed of the same subatomic particles. So, what makes the atoms of one element different from those of another? To answer this question, we compare the number of subatomic particles in the atoms of different elements. All the atoms of a given element have the same number of protons in the nucleus. For example, an atom with two protons is a helium (He) atom, and an atom with six protons is a carbon (C) atom (Figure 3.4). The number of protons in the nucleus is unique to each element. This number distinguishes an atom of one element from an atom of another element.

The **atomic number** (Z) is the number of protons in an atom of a specific element.

$$\text{atomic number (Z)} = \text{number of protons}$$

Figure 3.4 The Number of Protons Uniquely Identifies each Element.

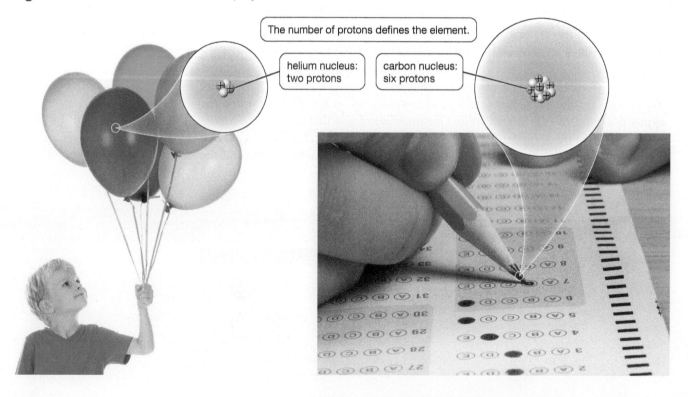

The number of protons defines the element.

helium nucleus: two protons

carbon nucleus: six protons

Equal Number of Protons and Electrons

The elements in the periodic table (see Section 1.4) are arranged by increasing atomic number. Each element's atomic number is written above its chemical symbol in the periodic table. For example, lithium (Li) has the number 3 above its chemical symbol. This atomic number tells us a lithium atom contains three protons (Figure 3.5).

Figure 3.5 Lithium's Atomic Number is 3.

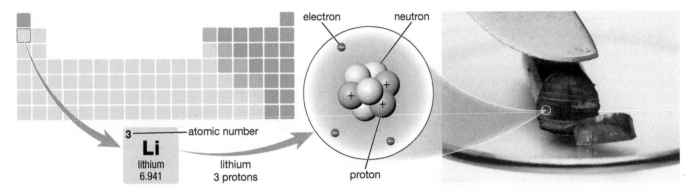

Atoms typically have an equal number of protons and electrons. This results in electrically neutral atoms with an overall charge of zero (Figure 3.6). For example, lithium (Li) has an atomic number of 3, indicating that an electrically neutral lithium atom has three positively charged protons and three negatively charged electrons. Similarly, carbon (C) has six protons and therefore has six electrons and an overall charge of zero.

Apply what you have just learned: **Practice 3.5** in the Pearson eText.

Mass Number

We now know how to determine the number of protons and electrons in an atom of a specific element from the periodic table, but what about the neutrons? Recall that the majority of the mass of an atom is in the nucleus where the protons and neutrons are located. The **mass number** (A) of an element is equal to the total number of protons and neutrons.

mass number (A) = number of protons + number of neutrons

The number of neutrons and the mass number are not listed on the periodic table, but we can determine both. If the number of neutrons is given, we calculate the mass number using the atomic number, which is listed on the periodic table. For example, a lithium (Li) atom with four neutrons and three protons has a mass number equal to seven (Figure 3.7):

mass number (A) of lithium: 4 neutrons + 3 protons = 7

Figure 3.6 Neutral Atoms have Equal Number of Protons and Electrons.

Lithium has three protons and three electrons.

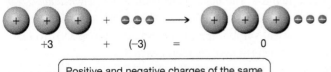

Figure 3.7 A Lithium Nucleus with Three Protons and Four Neutrons.

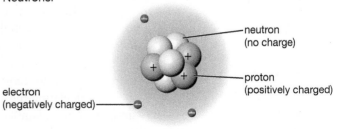

Apply what you have just learned: **Practice 3.6** in the Pearson eText.

Quiz yourself on the content of this section: **Check 3.1** in the Pearson eText.

Figure 3.8 Isotopes of Carbon.

A) Carbon occurs in several isotopes, including C-12, C-13, and C-14. **B) The Tollund Man.** Because the amount of carbon-14 in tissues decreases over time, carbon isotopes can often be used to estimate the age of biological remains, like this mummified man. The Tollund man lived during the 4th century BCE in Scandinavia. Carbon dating will be discussed in more detail in Chapter 4.

carbon-12	carbon-13	carbon-14
98.9%	1.1%	<0.0001%
6 protons	6 protons	6 protons
6 neutrons	7 neutrons	8 neutrons

If the mass number is given, we can also determine the number of neutrons. For example, a cobalt (Co) atom has a mass number of sixty and an atomic number of twenty-seven so it must contain thirty-three neutrons:

$$\text{neutrons} = \text{mass number} - \text{protons}$$
$$\text{neutrons} = 60 - 27 = 33 \text{ neutrons}$$

3.2 Isotopes

In Section 3.1, we learned that atoms with the same number of protons by definition are atoms of the same element. However, it is possible for atoms of the same element with the same number of protons to have a different number of neutrons. **Isotopes** are exactly that, atoms of the same element that have the same atomic number (and therefore the same number of protons), but different number of neutrons. For example, all atoms of carbon (C) have six protons, but some carbon atoms have six neutrons, some have seven neutrons, and some have eight neutrons (Figure 3.8). Recall that an element's mass number is equal to the total number of protons and neutrons. The different number of neutrons changes the mass number of each carbon isotope, but the atomic number and the chemical behavior of the various isotopes generally remain the same.

To differentiate between isotopes of the same element, we use isotope symbol notation.

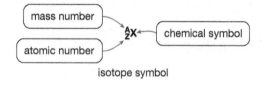

isotope symbol

The isotope symbol is the chemical symbol of the element with the atomic number as a subscript to the left of the symbol and the mass number as a superscript.

Sometimes we write isotopes using the element name followed by the mass number, such as carbon-12, carbon-13, or carbon-14 (Figure 3.8).

$$^{12}_{6}C = \text{carbon-12}$$

Atomic Mass

Most elements exist in nature as isotopes. Different isotopes are typically not present in equal abundance. For example, chlorine has two naturally existing isotopes, chlorine-35 (containing 17 protons and 18 neutrons) and chlorine-37 (containing 17 protons and 20 neutrons). Chemists have determined experimentally that any given large sample of chlorine typically is 75.77% chlorine-35 and 24.23% chlorine-37.

The difference in mass of isotopes affects how chemists determine an average mass for each element, called the **atomic mass**. *The atomic mass value is the weighted average of the mass of all the naturally occurring isotopes of an element.* The atomic mass is listed on the periodic table below the chemical symbol for each element (Figure 3.9). To learn more about how the atomic mass is determined, click on Learn 3.1.

Try calculating the atomic mass for copper in Practice 3.7 before exploring the structure of some familiar atoms in VisibleChem 3.1.

Figure 3.9 Atomic Mass of Chlorine.

U.S. industries produce about 25 billion pounds of the element chlorine each year. Communities add chlorine to swimming pools and public water supplies to kill bacteria.

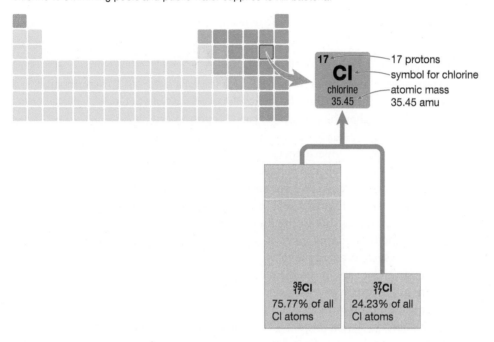

Predict answers and see step-by-step solutions: **Learn 3.1:** Calculating Atomic Mass in the Pearson eText.

Apply what you have just learned: **Practice 3.7** in the Pearson eText.

Watch this concept come to life: **VisibleChem Video 3.1:** The Atomic Structure of Common Elements in the Pearson eText.

Apply what you have just learned: **Practice 3.8 and 3.9** in the Pearson eText.

Explore how Chemistry and Biology connect: **BioConnect 3.1:** Cells are the Building Blocks of Life in the Pearson eText.

Quiz yourself on the content of this section: **Check 3.2** in the Pearson eText.

3.3 Electron Arrangements

While the number of protons uniquely identifies an atom from a specific element, it is primarily the electrons that determine the properties and chemical behavior of elements. Recall that the electrons in an atom occupy the large space outside of the nucleus. In this section, we study the defined organization of the electrons in atoms, which ultimately will help you gain a better understanding of how atoms react.

So, how do chemists describe the location of electrons? Instead of pinpointing the exact location of an electron at any given moment, chemists discuss and define the regions of space, or electron clouds, where electrons are most likely to be found. We describe the space outside the nucleus where electrons are located in terms of *energy levels, sublevels, and orbitals.* The first three **energy levels** are illustrated in Figure 3.14. The

Figure 3.14 Electron Energy Levels.

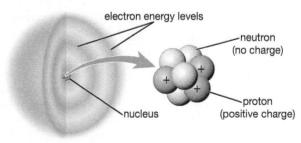

lowest energy level is found closest to the nucleus. The second and third energy levels are further from the nucleus and higher in energy. The higher energy electrons (outer electrons) are key to understanding how an atom interacts with other atoms.

Let's explore energy levels in more detail.

Energy Levels, Sublevels, and Orbitals

Electron energy levels are represented by a lowercase "n" and are numbered 1, 2, 3, 4 and so forth. The farther the energy level is from the nucleus, the larger the n value and the higher the energy. We can compare energy levels to steps in a staircase—the energy levels (or steps) have distinct values (Figure 3.15). In general, electrons occupy the lowest energy step first and are only found at energy levels represented by each step, not between the steps.

Within each energy level are **sublevels**. We identify the sublevels with the letters s, p, d, and f (Figure 3.16). There are a greater number of sublevels in the higher energy levels due to the increased amount of space available for more electrons. The first energy level ($n = 1$), for example, has only one sublevel (s), whereas the second energy level ($n = 2$) has two sublevels (s and p). Three sublevels (s, p, and d) are in the third energy level ($n = 3$) and four sublevels (s, p, d, f) are in the fourth energy level.

Notice that the number of spaces, which are each referred to as an **orbital**, in each sublevel varies (Figure 3.16). There is one s orbital (yellow box), three p orbitals (green boxes), five d orbitals (orange boxes) and seven f orbitals (purple boxes). Each orbital can contain a maximum of two electrons. Electrons fill orbitals beginning with the lowest orbital (1s) and progress up from there. Click on VisibleChem 3.2 to explore the arrangement of electrons in more detail.

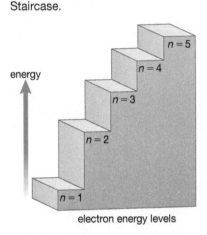

Figure 3.15 Electron Energy Levels Shown as Steps in a Staircase.

electron energy levels

Figure 3.16 Electron Sublevels Within Each Level.

Energy level	Number of sublevels	Types of sublevels			
		s	p	d	f
$n = 4$	4	□	▢▢▢	▢▢▢▢▢	▢▢▢▢▢▢▢
$n = 3$	3	□	▢▢▢	▢▢▢▢▢	
$n = 2$	2	□	▢▢▢		
$n = 1$	1	□			

Watch this concept come to life: **VisibleChem Video 3.2:** Organization of Electrons into Energy Levels, Sublevels and Orbitals in the Pearson eText.

Apply what you have just learned: **Practice 3.10 and 3.11** in the Pearson eText.

Explore how Chemistry and Biology connect: **BioConnect 3.2:** Microscopes Help Us Explore in the Pearson eText.

Quiz yourself on the content of this section: **Check 3.3** in the Pearson eText.

3.4 Valence Electrons

The way that an atom reacts with other atoms depends on the electrons in each atom's outermost energy level (the level furthest from the nucleus), or **valence shell**. The electrons in an atom's valence shell are **valence electrons**. Identifying the number and specific location of valence electrons for each element allows us to make predictions about how atoms react with each other to form compounds, which we will learn more about in Unit 2.

We use the periodic table to predict how many valence electrons an atom has and in which levels and sublevels those valence electrons are located. Conveniently, the group number for elements in groups 1A–8A is the same as the number of valence electrons (Figure 3.25). For example, all the group 1A alkali metals have one valence electron and all the group 2A elements have two valence electrons. Group 3A elements have three valence electrons and so on across the periodic table.

Figure 3.25 Valence Electrons and Group Number.

Elements in the same group have the same number of valence electrons. The number of valence electrons in each element's valence shell is the same as the element's group number.

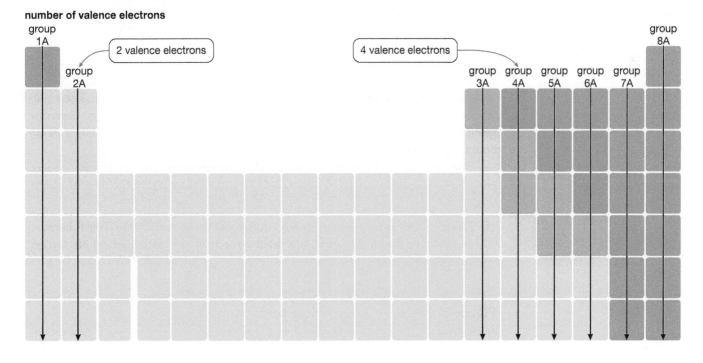

Apply what you have just learned: **Practice 3.12** in the Pearson eText.

Electron-Dot Symbols

We use **electron-dot symbols** to represent valence electrons. Electron-dot symbols feature the chemical symbol of the element along with the valence electrons, which are represented by dots. Each dot in an atom's symbol represents an electron. When we are drawing one to four valence electrons, we place a single dot on each side of the chemical symbol. When an element has more than four valence electrons, we pair dots. For example, boron (B) is in group 3A and it has three valence electrons (Figure 3.26). We represent each with a dot on each of three sides of the chemical symbol. Phosphorus (P) is in group 5A with five valence electrons. In this case, we place four dots on each side of the element symbol and pair the fifth electron with one of the single electrons. Click on Learn 3.2 to learn more about drawing electron-dot symbols.

Figure 3.26 Electron-Dot Symbols for Main Group Elements.

Valence electrons are represented by dots. Dots are placed one at a time on each of the four sides of the chemical symbol for the element. Any additional valence electrons are added to form pairs on each side of the chemical symbol.

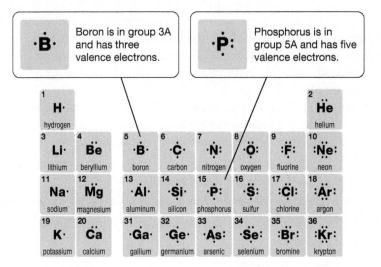

Boron is in group 3A and has three valence electrons.

Phosphorus is in group 5A and has five valence electrons.

Predict answers and see step-by-step solutions: **Learn 3.2:** Writing Electron-dot Symbols in the Pearson eText.

Apply what you have just learned: **Practice 3.13** in the Pearson eText.

Periodic Trends

Several properties of atoms show specific patterns across the periodic table. These patterns are **periodic trends**. Periodic trends often involve a regular change from one group to the next and similar changes across a period. *Atomic size* and *ionization energy* both follow periodic trends.

The size of an atom, or **atomic size**, is determined by the distance of the valence electrons from the nucleus. Two periodic trends characterize the size of atoms (Figure 3.27):

1. The size of an atom increases down a column of the periodic table. This is because as we move down a column, the valence electrons for each element are farther from the nucleus.

Figure 3.27 Atomic Size, a Periodic Trend.

Atoms get smaller as we move across a row in the periodic table, and larger as we move down a column.

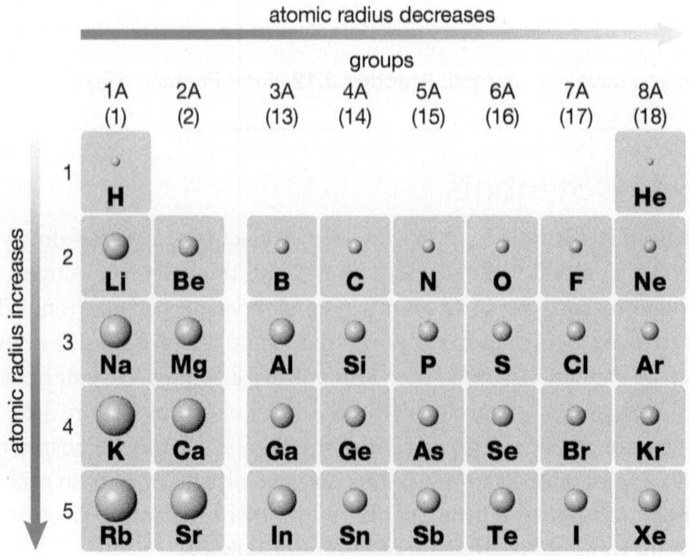

atomic radius decreases →

groups

		1A (1)	2A (2)	3A (13)	4A (14)	5A (15)	6A (16)	7A (17)	8A (18)
1		H							He
2		Li	Be	B	C	N	O	F	Ne
3		Na	Mg	Al	Si	P	S	Cl	Ar
4		K	Ca	Ga	Ge	As	Se	Br	Kr
5		Rb	Sr	In	Sn	Sb	Te	I	Xe

atomic radius increases ↓

2. The size of atoms decreases across a row of the periodic table as the number of protons increases. A greater number of protons have a stronger attraction to the electrons, pulling them closer to the nucleus and making the atom smaller.

Ionization Energy

Given that electrons are attracted to protons, it requires energy to remove an electron from a neutral atom. The energy required to remove an electron is **ionization energy**. Removing an electron from a neutral atom creates a **cation**, which is a positively charged atom. When one electron is removed from a sodium atom, for example, a $+1$ charge is formed on the newly formed sodium cation. We explore the formation of ions in more detail in Chapter 5.

$$\underset{\substack{\text{neutral} \\ \text{atom}}}{\text{Na}} + \underset{\substack{\text{ionization} \\ \text{energy}}}{\text{energy}} \longrightarrow \underset{\text{cation}}{\text{Na}^+} + e^-$$

The stronger the attraction between the electrons and protons, the more energy is required to remove an electron. Two periodic trends characterize ionization energy values (Figure 3.28):

1. Ionization energy decreases as we move down a column of the periodic table. This is because as we move down a column the valence electrons for each element are farther from the positively charged nucleus.

2. As we move across the periodic table, however, ionization energy increases. This is because the number of protons increases from left to right on the periodic table so there is a stronger pull on the valence electrons in the elements on the right side of the table.

Figure 3.28 Ionization Energy, a Periodic Trend.

The amount of energy required to remove an electron decreases as we move down a column. Ionization energy increases as we move from left to right across the periodic table.

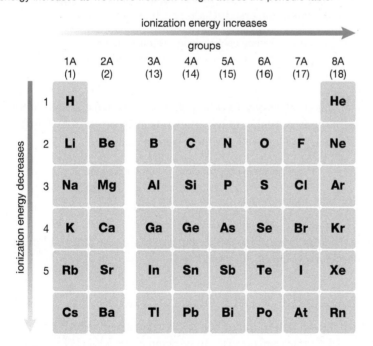

Apply what you have just learned: **Practice 3.14 and 3.15** in the Pearson eText.

Quiz yourself on the content of this section: **Check 3.4** in the Pearson eText.

3.5 How Electrons Fill Orbitals: Electron Configurations

Figure 3.29 Helium Weather Balloon Released.

Helium gas is often used in weather balloons that collect weather and atmospheric data for scientists. Helium atoms have two electrons, both of which are found in the 1s orbital as shown here.

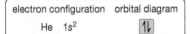

We now turn our attention to how electrons are arranged in specific atoms. **Orbital diagrams** and **electron configurations** are useful representations that show how electrons fill in specific orbitals in order of increasing energy. Recall that we discussed the organization of electrons into levels, sublevels, and orbitals in VisibleChem Video 3.2. As you saw in the VisibleChem Video, an orbital diagram includes a box to represent each orbital. An electron configuration similarly shows the placement of electrons by using numbers, letters, and superscripts.

For example, helium atoms have two electrons both of which are found in the 1s orbital (Figure 3.29).

The rules we include here provide guidance for both orbital energy diagrams and electron configurations to describe the electronic structure of atoms:

RULE 1: Electrons fill the lowest energy orbitals available first beginning with 1s, which is closest to the nucleus. Energy of the sublevels increase in the following order: $s \rightarrow p \rightarrow d \rightarrow f$

RULE 2: Each orbital can hold two electrons, but the electrons in the same orbital must have opposite orientations, as illustrated by the two electrons in the orbital diagram for helium.

RULE 3: When orbitals are equal in energy, one electron fills each orbital before electrons pair up.

Electron Configuration for Specific Elements

Lithium (Li), for example, has three electrons. To draw the orbital diagram for lithium, we pair up the first two electrons in the 1s orbital and place the third electron in the 2s orbital. To show the electron arrangement using an electron configuration, we include the number of electrons as superscripts after each orbital:

Carbon (C) has six electrons. Its orbital diagram has two electrons in the 1s orbital, two electrons in the 2s orbital, and two electrons in 2p orbitals. Notice that one electron is placed in a separate p orbital before electrons pair up:

VisibleChem Video 3.3: Electron Arrangements

Click on VisibleChem Video 3.3 to explore more examples of how orbital diagrams and electron configurations are related.

Abbreviating Electron Configurations

We can shorten the electron configuration of elements using a shorthand notation to create an *abbreviated electron configuration*. To write an *abbreviated electron configuration*, we use the chemical symbol of the noble gas that directly precedes the element of interest as a substitute for the electron configuration of the inner electrons. We do this in two steps:

- We write the symbol for the preceding noble gas in brackets.
- We follow that bracketed symbol with the electron configuration of the outer electrons.

Figure 3.30 Abbreviated Electron Configuration for Chlorine.

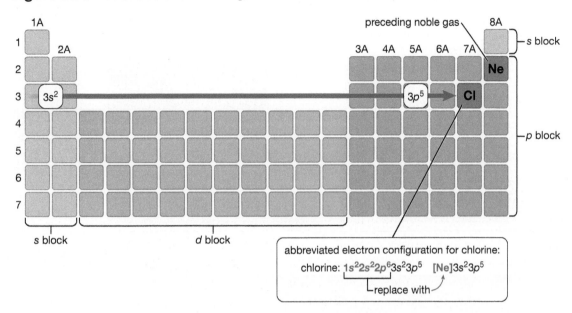

abbreviated electron configuration for chlorine:

chlorine: $1s^2 2s^2 2p^6 3s^2 3p^5$ [Ne]$3s^2 3p^5$

replace with

For example, consider the second-row element carbon. Each second-row element has a filled first level. We write this as $1s^2$. Note that this is the same as the electron configuration of the noble gas helium (He). Because $1s^2$ is also the electron configuration of helium, we replace carbon's inner $1s^2$ electrons with the symbol for helium in brackets [He]. The result is the configuration $[He]2s^2 2p^2$.

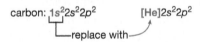

carbon: $1s^2 2s^2 2p^2$ [He]$2s^2 2p^2$

replace with

As a second example, consider chlorine (Cl). The noble gas that precedes chlorine (Cl) is neon (Ne). In the abbreviated electron configuration for chlorine, the symbol for neon (Ne) in brackets replaces the electron configuration for chlorine's inner electrons (Figure 3.30).

Click on Learn 3.3 to learn more about orbital diagrams, electron configurations, and noble gas notation.

> Predict answers and see step-by-step solutions: **Learn 3.3:** Orbital Diagrams and Electron Configurations in the Pearson eText.
>
> Apply what you have just learned: **Practice 3.16 and 3.17** in the Pearson eText.

Electron Configurations and the Periodic Table

Each of the elements on the periodic table has its own electron configuration. To easily determine what an element's electron configuration is, it is useful to explore how the location of an element on the periodic table is related to its electron configuration.

The periodic table contains four regions that correspond to the four sublevels ($s, p, d,$ and f). We refer to these regions as blocks (Figure 3.37). The name of each block is based on the last sublevel that fills for each group of elements:

The s block is group 1A and 2A and the element helium (He).

The p block is groups 3A–8A.

The d block is the 10 columns of transition metals.

The f block is the two groups of inner transition metals.

For example, recall that lithium (Li) has three electrons with the final electron located in the $2s$ sublevel (Figure 3.31). Carbon (C) is in the p block. Predictably the carbon $2p$ sublevel fills last.

Figure 3.31 Regions of the Periodic Table by Sublevel.

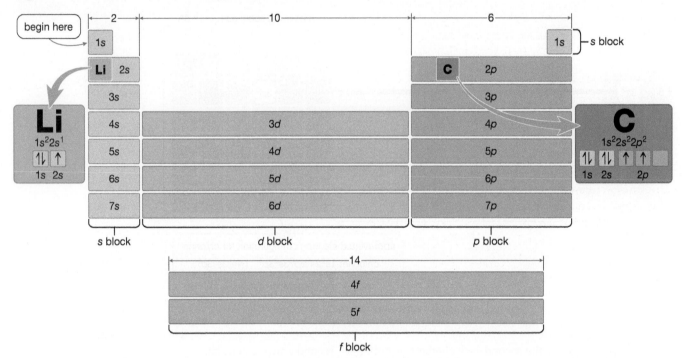

Electron Configurations for Elements 11–18

We can predict the electron configurations of all the elements based on their locations in the periodic table. Keep in mind that knowing how electrons are arranged in atoms is ultimately useful for predicting how atoms react.

Figure 3.32 describes the orbital diagrams and electron configurations for elements 11-18. Notice the block location of each of these elements and how the block correlates to the last electrons added to each atom. Chlorine, for example, is in the *p block* and has five electrons in the 3p sublevel. Similarly, for the other elements in the *p block*, the 3p sublevel is the last to fill.

Figure 3.32 Orbital Diagrams and Electron Configurations for Elements 11–18.

Atomic number	Element	Orbital diagram (3s and 3p orbitals only) 3s	3p	Electron configuration	Abbreviated electron configuration	Block designation
11	Na	[Ne] ↑	☐☐☐	$1s^2 2s^2 2p^6 3s^1$	$[Ne]3s^1$	s block
12	Mg	[Ne] ↑↓	☐☐☐	$1s^2 2s^2 2p^6 3s^2$	$[Ne]3s^2$	s block
13	Al	[Ne] ↑↓	↑ ☐☐	$1s^2 2s^2 2p^6 3s^2 3p^1$	$[Ne]3s^2 3p^1$	p block
14	Si	[Ne] ↑↓	↑ ↑ ☐	$1s^2 2s^2 2p^6 3s^2 3p^2$	$[Ne]3s^2 3p^2$	p block
15	P	[Ne] ↑↓	↑ ↑ ↑	$1s^2 2s^2 2p^6 3s^2 3p^3$	$[Ne]3s^2 3p^3$	p block
16	S	[Ne] ↑↓	↑↓ ↑ ↑	$1s^2 2s^2 2p^6 3s^2 3p^4$	$[Ne]3s^2 3p^4$	p block
17	Cl	[Ne] ↑↓	↑↓ ↑↓ ↑	$1s^2 2s^2 2p^6 3s^2 3p^5$	$[Ne]3s^2 3p^5$	p block
18	Ar	[Ne] ↑↓	↑↓ ↑↓ ↑↓	$1s^2 2s^2 2p^6 3s^2 3p^6$	$[Ne]3s^2 3p^6$	p block

Click on Learn 3.4 to learn more about how to determine electron configurations for elements 11–18.

Predict answers and see step-by-step solutions: **Learn 3.4:** Electron Configurations and the Periodic Table in the Pearson eText.

Apply what you have just learned: **Practice 3.18 and 3.19** in the Pearson eText.

Electron Configurations and Valence Electrons

Electron configurations are a very useful tool for identifying an element's valence electrons. Recall that valence electrons are those in the outermost (highest) energy level of an atom. For example, the electron configuration of lithium (Li; $1s^2 2s^1$) indicates that there is one electron in the outer energy level ($n = 2$). This means that lithium has one valence electron. Carbon has a total of four valence electrons in the second energy level.

Lithium
$1s^2 2s^1$
1 valence electron

Carbon
$1s^2 2s^2 2p^2$
4 valence electrons

Elements in the same group on the periodic table have the same number of valence electrons and similar electron configurations. For example, the alkali metals (Group 1A) have a valence shell electron configuration of ns^1 and have one valence electron. Similarly, the group 2A elements have a common valence shell electron configuration of ns^2 with two valence electrons as Figure 3.33 illustrates. Group 3A elements have the common valence shell electron configuration of $ns^2 np^1$ with three valence electrons.

Click on Learn 3.5 to learn more about how to identify valence electrons from electron configurations.

Figure 3.33 Valence Electrons and Group Number.

Elements in the same group have the same number of valence electrons and similar electron configurations.

group 2A

Be	[He]2s^2
Mg	[Ne]3s^2
Ca	[Ar]4s^2
Sr	[Kr]5s^2
Ba	[Xe]6s^2
Ra	[Rn]7s^2

$-ns^2$

Predict answers and see step-by-step solutions: **Learn 3.5:** Identifying Valence Electrons from Electron Configurations in the Pearson eText.

Apply what you have just learned: **Practice 3.20** in the Pearson eText.

Quiz yourself on the content of this section: **Check 3.5** in the Pearson eText.

Chapter Summary

3.1 The Atom

Learning Objective: Identify and describe the structure of atoms.

An atom is the basic unit of a chemical element. Atoms are composed of subatomic particles, including positively-charged protons, neutral neutrons, and negatively-charged electrons (Table 3.1). Protons and neutrons have a similar mass and are both found in the nucleus of an atom.

Electrons have negligible mass and are located outside the nucleus. Elements are described by their atomic number (Z), which is equal to the number of protons in an atom, a defining feature of every element. An element's mass number (A) is equal to the number of protons plus the number of electrons in one atom.

Video 3.1: Just How Small is an Atom?

Key Terms

atomic mass unit (amu)
atomic number (Z)
electrical charge
electron

electron cloud
mass number (A)
neutron

nucleus
proton
subatomic particle

3.2 Isotopes

Learning Objective: Determine the number of subatomic particles present in specific isotopes and define the atomic mass of elements.

Isotopes are atoms of the same element that have the same number of protons, but a different number of neutrons. For example, fluorine-18 is a synthetic isotope containing nine protons and nine neutrons. Most elements exist as a combination of naturally occurring isotopes. The atomic mass of an element represents the weighted average mass based on the ratio of naturally occurring isotopes. The number of neutrons of any given isotope is found by subtracting the element's atomic number (Z) from the mass number (A).

VisibleChem Video 3.1: The Atomic Structure of Common Elements

BioConnect 3.1: Cells are the Building Blocks of Life

Key Terms

atomic mass
cell (from BioConnect 3.1)
isotope

3.3 Electron Arrangements

Learning Objective: Describe the arrangement of electrons in atoms.

Electrons fill regions around the nucleus in numbered energy levels. Within each level, we label sublevels with the letters s, p, d, and f. Within each of these sublevels are regions of space called orbitals. Orbitals have varying shapes, but each can contain a maximum of two electrons. Orbitals closest to the nucleus are occupied by electrons first because they are lower in energy than orbitals farther from the nucleus.

VisibleChem Video 3.2: Organization of Electrons into Energy Levels, Sublevls, and Orbitals

BioConnect 3.2: Microscopes Help Us Explore

Key Terms

energy level
orbital
sublevel

3.4 Valence Electrons

Learning Objective: Identify valence electrons and represent them using electron-dot symbols.

The chemical behavior of elements depends on the electrons in their outermost energy level, known as the valence shell. The periodic table helps us to predict the number and location of valence electrons (Figure 3.25). Elements in the same group have the same number of valence electrons. Electron-dot symbols are a convenient way to show the number and location of an element's valence electrons (Figure 3.26). Elements with the same number of valence electrons share similar patterns of chemical reactivity.

Key Terms

atomic size
cation
electron-dot symbol

ionization energy
periodic trends

valence electrons
valence shell

3.5 Electron Configurations

Learning Objective: Write electron configurations for elements.

Orbital energy diagrams and electron configurations illustrate electrons in specific orbitals. Electrons fill the lowest energy orbitals first. Each orbital can hold a maximum of two electrons, but the orientation of the two electrons must be opposite. If orbitals are at equal energy levels, a single electron is added to each orbital before pairing two electrons in the same orbital. We can abbreviate electron configurations using noble gas notation. We can predict an element's electron configuration from its location on the periodic table.

VisibleChem Video 3.3: Electron Arrangements

Key Terms

electron configuration
orbital diagram

The **End-of-Chapter Problems** are located in the back of the book in Appendix A.

 End-of-Chapter Quiz   Have you mastered the content of this chapter? Try the **End-of-Chapter Quiz** in the Pearson eText.

1. Which term refers to the number of protons in the nucleus of an atom?
  a) group number **b)** mass number
  c) atomic number **d)** period number

2. Which statement is true about the atom?
  a) Electrons are located outside the nucleus and are repelled by other electrons.
  b) Electrons are positively charged and located in the nucleus of the atom.
  c) Protons and electrons are repelled by each other.
  d) Protons, neutrons, and electrons occupy the space around the outside of the nucleus.

3. Which statement about isotopes is true?
  a) Isotopes of the same element have the same mass number, but different atomic numbers.
  b) Isotopes of the same element weigh the same but have different numbers of protons.
  c) Isotopes of the same element have different mass numbers and atomic numbers because they have different numbers of neutrons in the nucleus.
  d) Isotopes of the same element have the same atomic number, but different mass numbers.

4. How does fluorine-19 differ from fluorine-18?
  a) Fluorine-19 contains 19 protons, and fluorine-18 contains 18 protons.
  b) Fluorine-19 contains 19 neutrons, and fluorine-18 contains 18 neutrons.
  c) Fluorine-19 contains 19 electrons, and fluorine-18 contains 18 electrons.
  d) Fluorine-19 contains 10 neutrons, and fluorine-18 contains 9 neutrons.

5. How many protons, neutrons, and electrons does the Cl-37 isotope have?
  a) 37 protons, 37 neutrons, and 37 electrons
  b) 17 protons, 37 neutrons, and 17 electrons
  c) 17 protons, 20 neutrons, and 17 electrons
  d) 17 protons, 17 neutrons, and 20 electrons

6. Select the true statement about the following isotopes: ^{72}Zn, ^{75}As, and ^{74}Ge.
  a) They have the same number of electrons.
  b) They have the same number of protons.
  c) They have the same number of protons and neutrons.
  d) They all have the same number of neutrons.

7. Which statement is correct about atomic mass?
  a) We do not consider isotopes when calculating atomic mass, only atomic number is considered.
  b) We determine the atomic mass by calculating the percentage of mass contributed by each isotope using a weighted average.
  c) If an atom has two isotopes, we add the mass of each and divide by two in order to obtain an average atomic mass.
  d) We divide the heaviest isotope by the mass of the lightest isotope to obtain the overall atomic mass of an element.

8. Which sublevel of the aluminum atom contains only one electron?
  a) $2s$ **b)** $2p$ **c)** $3p$ **d)** $3s$

9. How many electrons does krypton have in its $4p$ sublevel?
  a) 6   **b)** 8   **c)** 16   **d)** 36

10. Which statement is correct about orbitals?
    a) Orbitals can hold either zero, one, two, or three electrons depending on energy level.
    b) Each orbital can only hold one electron and electrons in neighboring orbitals must have opposite orientations.
    c) Each orbital can hold eight electrons and all electrons must have the same orientation.
    d) Each orbital can hold a maximum of two electrons and electrons in the same orbital must have opposite orientations.

11. How many valence electrons do the elements of alkaline earth metals (Group 2A) have?
    a) one
    b) two
    c) three
    d) four

12. Which of the following statements is true about valence electrons?
    a) All elements have different numbers of valence electrons because they are all unique from each other.
    b) The number of valence electrons an atom has is equal to the atomic number of that element.
    c) Elements in the same group on the periodic table have the same number of valence electrons.
    d) Valence electrons are always located in orbitals within the p or d sublevels because these sublevels are higher energy and farther from the nucleus than the s sublevel orbitals.

13. What is the correct order of increasing energy for the first three sublevels?
    a) $d < s < p$
    b) $s < p < d$
    c) $s < d < p$
    d) $p < d < s$

14. Which electron-dot symbol corresponds to the element with the electron configuration $1s^2 2s^2 2p^6 3s^2 3p^2$?
    a) $\cdot\overset{\cdot}{S}i\cdot$
    b) $\cdot\overset{\cdot}{C}\cdot$
    c) $\cdot Si\cdot$
    d) $\cdot\overset{\cdot}{P}\cdot$

15. How many valence electrons are represented in the following electron configuration: $1s^2 2s^2 2p^6 3s^2 3p^4$? Which element does this electron configuration belong to?
    a) four valence electrons; silicon (Si)
    b) three valence electrons; sulfur (S)
    c) six valence electrons; sulfur (S)
    d) four valence electrons; oxygen (O)

16. Choose the correct electron configuration and abbreviated noble gas notation for the element aluminum (Al).
    a) $1s^2 2s^2 2p^6 3s^2 3p^1$ and $[Ne]3s^2 3p^1$
    b) $1s^2 2s^2 2p^6 3s^2 3p^3$ and $[Ne]3s^2 3p^3$
    c) $1s^2 2s^2 2p^6 3s^2 3d^1$ and $[Ne]3s^2 3d^1$
    d) $1s^2 2s^2 2p^4 3s^2 3p^1$ and $[Ar]3s^2 3p^1$

17. What is the correct number of valence electrons *and* the correct element symbol for the element with this electron configuration: $1s^2 2s^2 2p^6 3s^2 3p^6$?
    a) six valence electrons; O
    b) six valence electrons; Si
    c) eight valence electrons; S
    d) eight valence electrons; Ar

Chapter 4
Nuclear Chemistry

The energy released from radioactive atoms can be used to treat disease and produce energy.

 ## Chapter Outline

Learning Objectives

4.1 Define radioactivity and represent radioisotopes with correct atomic symbols.

4.2 Identify the types of radioactivity and common nuclear reactions using nuclear equations.

4.3 Describe how scientists detect and measure radiation and recognize the common units used in nuclear chemistry.

4.4 Calculate the amount of radioisotope remaining after one or more half-life.

4.5 Explain how nuclear chemistry is used in medicine.

4.6 Describe nuclear fission and fusion.

Introduction

When some people hear the word radioactivity, they have a negative association and think of nuclear weapons or dangerous accidents at nuclear power plants. If you have known people with these impressions, or been one of them yourself, you might be pleasantly surprised to learn that tens of millions of patients around the world actually *benefit* from diagnostic and therapeutic doses of radioactivity each year in a hospital setting (Figure 4.1). Radioactivity is used for treatment of medical conditions such as thyroid disease, cancer, and heart disease. In this chapter, we will define and explore the different types of radioactivity and gain a better understanding of nuclear chemistry, both of which involve changes within the nuclei of atoms.

4.1 Radioactivity

Radioactivity is the release of subatomic particles or high-energy radiation by the nuclei of some atoms. **Radiation**, in contrast, is a more general term that describes energy that travels through space. Sunshine, for example, is a form of low energy radiation. In this chapter, we focus on a specific type of radiation: the radiation that is released from radioactive atoms.

Atoms that are **radioactive** are unstable and spontaneously decompose by releasing small particles. Emission of these particles is one way that an unstable atom transforms into a more stable one. Many atoms in nature naturally remain intact indefinitely. For example, the first 19 elements on the periodic table are considered stable. As atoms get larger, however, the likelihood of their nuclei being unstable increases. The elements with atomic numbers 20 and above generally have one or more isotopes with unstable nuclei that naturally release radioactivity.

Figure 4.1 Radioactivity is a Powerful Tool in Medicine.

A) Nuclear medicine uses small doses of radioactive materials to treat and diagnose a variety of diseases. **B)** Thyroid cancer, for example, can often be treated with radioactive iodine therapy. **C)** Imaging using radioactive tracer molecules provides a powerful tool to visualize tumors.

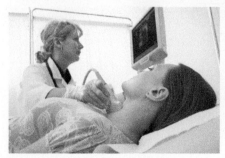
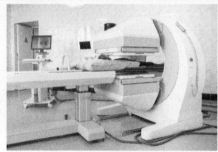
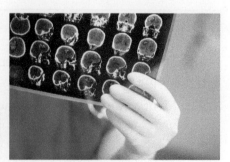

A
B
C

Radioactivity was discovered in 1896 when scientists observed that the element uranium emitted particles that could be detected. Marie Curie (Figure 4.2) continued this work by searching for other elements that release radioactivity. Curie was awarded the Nobel prize in physics for her work on radioactivity and a second Nobel prize in chemistry for the discovery of two new elements.

Radioisotopes

A **radioisotope** is an isotope that is radioactive and spontaneously emits particles or high-energy radiation. Approximately three hundred naturally occurring isotopes are radioactive. Researchers in laboratories have synthesized an even larger number of radioactive isotopes.

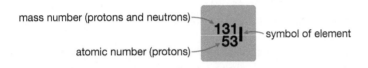

Recall from Section 3.2 that we write isotopes using a chemical symbol, mass number (A) and atomic number (Z). The same is true for radioisotopes. For example, cobalt-60 is a radioisotope used to sterilize an array of consumer products and medical equipment (Figure 4.3). This specific isotope of cobalt contains 27 protons and 33 neutrons with a mass number equal to 60. Recall that the number of neutrons is the difference between the atomic number and mass number.

Apply what you have just learned: **Practice 4.1–4.3** in the Pearson eText.

Quiz yourself on the content of this section: **Check 4.1** in the Pearson eText.

Figure 4.2 Marie Curie.

Marie Curie (1867–1934) was the first woman to be awarded the Nobel prize, and the first person to be awarded two Nobel prizes.

Figure 4.3 The Radioisotope, Cobalt-60 is used to Sterilize Food and Consumer Products.

The radiation released by cobalt-60 is routinely used to sterilize medical equipment and household products such as Band Aids. Cobalt-60 is also used to sterilize some food products, dramatically reducing the risk of food-borne illness. Irradiation kills bacteria and mold spores but does not make the sterilized products radioactive.

4.2 Nuclear Reactions

A **nuclear reaction** is the spontaneous change in the nucleus of an atom that emits radioactivity. This process is often referred to as **radioactive decay**. We can represent a nuclear reaction using a **nuclear equation**. In a nuclear equation, the atomic symbol of the radioisotope is on the left side of the arrow and the new isotope that forms and the particles that are emitted are on the right side of the arrow:

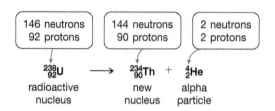

In this example of a nuclear reaction, uranium-238 decomposes to thorium-234 by emitting an **alpha particle**. An alpha particle is composed of two protons and two neutrons. Since two protons and two neutrons combined are identical to a helium-4 nucleus, we often use the ^4_2He symbol for an alpha particle. We can also represent alpha particles as $^4_2\alpha$.

A nuclear reaction that releases an alpha particle is **alpha emission**. In alpha emission a radioisotope decays to a new isotope that has two fewer protons and two fewer neutrons, and an alpha particle is released. In the example above, uranium-238 (92 protons) undergoes alpha emission to form thorium-234 (90 protons) and an alpha particle (2 protons).

Balancing Nuclear Reactions

Predict answers and see step-by-step solutions: **Learn 4.1:** Writing a Nuclear Equation in the Pearson eText.

Apply what you have just learned: **Practice 4.4** in the Pearson eText.

In a nuclear equation, the sum of both the mass numbers (A) and the atomic numbers (Z) must be equal on both sides. Notice that in the equation shown in Figure 4.4 the uranium-238 loses two protons, (changing from 92 protons to 90 protons) and becomes the element thorium. The mass number also decreases to 234. The total mass number values and the atomic number values must be equal on both sides of the equation. Recognizing this criterion for a correctly written nuclear equation allows us to predict what products form in nuclear reactions. Learn 4.1 illustrates how to write nuclear equations making sure that the total mass number values and the atomic number values are equal on both sides of the equation.

Figure 4.4 Thorium Metal.

The decay of uranium-238 results in thorium-234 and an alpha particle. Thorium is used in a variety of scientific instruments and as fuel in specialized nuclear reactors. Many countries, including the Netherlands and China, are developing thorium reactors as thorium reactors can be much safer and harder to weaponize than uranium reactors.

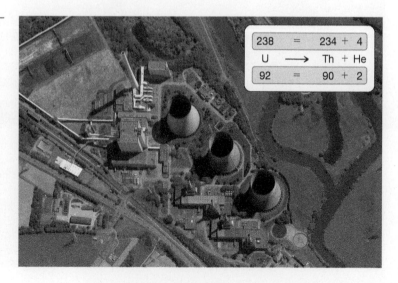

Table 4.1 Common Types of Nuclear Reactions.

Type of nuclear reaction	Process	Type of radioactivity	Example
alpha emission	decay of an unstable nucleus, in which an **alpha particle** is released and a new isotope forms	alpha particle ^4_2He or $^4_2\alpha$	$^{210}_{84}Po \rightarrow \: ^{206}_{82}Pb \: + \: ^4_2He$
beta emission	decay of an unstable nucleus, in which a **beta particle** is released and a new isotope forms	beta particle $^0_{-1}\beta$ or $^0_{-1}e$	$^{14}_6C \rightarrow \: ^{14}_7N \: + \: ^0_{-1}\beta$
positron emission	decay of an unstable nucleus, in which a **positron** is released and a new isotope forms	positron $^0_{+1}\beta$ or $^0_{+1}e$	$^{40}_{19}K \rightarrow \: ^{40}_{18}Ar \: + \: ^0_{+1}\beta$
gamma emission	decay of an unstable nucleus by releasing high energy **gamma rays**	gamma ray $^0_0\gamma$ or γ	$^{99m}_{43}Tc \rightarrow \: ^{99}_{43}Tc \: + \: ^0_0\gamma$

Types of Nuclear Reactions

We categorize nuclear reactions based on the radioactivity that the reaction releases. The following four types of nuclear reactions are common: *alpha emission (described previously), beta emission, positron emission, and gamma emission* (Table 4.1).

A **beta particle** is a high-energy electron with a negative one charge. Because the mass of an electron is negligible, the mass number of a beta particle is zero. We represent beta particles with the Greek letter ($^0_{-1}\beta$) or by the symbol of an electron including the mass number and the charge ($^0_{-1}e$). A nuclear reaction that releases a beta particle is **beta emission**.

A **positron** is similar to a beta particle but has a positive one charge. We sometimes represent the positron with the Greek symbol beta with a superscripted positive charge (β^+). But you may see it represented as the symbol for an electron with the mass number and charge indicated ($^0_{+1}e$ or $^0_{+1}\beta$). A nuclear reaction that releases a positron is **positron emission**.

Gamma rays are a form of high-energy radiation often released along with other forms of radioactivity. We use the Greek letter gamma ($^0_0\gamma$) to represent gamma rays. Note that gamma rays have no mass and no charge. A nuclear reaction that releases gamma rays is **gamma emission**. Gamma emission often accompanies alpha or beta emission.

Explore VisibleChem 4.1 to learn more about these types of nuclear reactions.

Watch this concept come to life: **VisibleChem Video 4.1:** Nuclear Reactions in the Pearson eText.

Apply what you have just learned: **Practice 4.5–4.8** in the Pearson eText.

Quiz yourself on the content of this section: **Check 4.2** in the Pearson eText.

4.3 Detecting and Measuring Radioactivity

The most common tool for detecting radioactivity is the **Geiger counter**, a portable device that produces an electrical current when it encounters radioactivity. When it detects radioactivity, the instrument makes a clicking sound along with a meter reading that alerts the technician. The clicking increases as the technician moves closer to the source of radiation and decreases as the technician moves away from the source (Figure 4.5).

Figure 4.5 A Geiger Counter Detects Radioactivity from Exposed Individuals.
A worker uses a Geiger counter to check individuals for contamination after the 2011 disaster at the Fukushima nuclear plant in Japan.

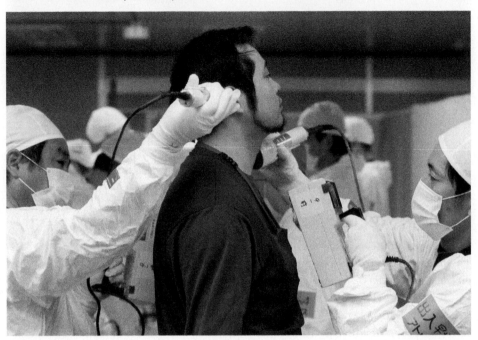

Scientists are interested in measurements of both the amount of radiation emitted by a radioactive source and the amount of radiation absorbed by an individual. For this reason, they use several units to quantify overall exposure.

Units of Radiation

When a laboratory receives a radioactive sample, technicians measure the *activity* of the sample using the **curie (Ci)**. This unit indicates *the number of nuclei that decay per unit of time*. One curie equals 3.7×10^{10} nuclei disintegrations/second, which corresponds to the decay rate of one gram of the element radium. Another unit that is used to measure radioactivity is the **becquerel (Bq)**, which is defined as one disintegration per second (Table 4.2).

Curies and becquerels are useful for quantifying radioactive emission. Units of **absorbed dose** are more appropriate for quantifying and describing the amount of radiation an individual absorbs as the result of exposure. An absorbed dose measurement indicates the energy of radiation absorbed per mass of tissue. The **rad (D)** and the **gray (Gy)** are common units of absorbed dose (see Table 4.3).

The absorbed dose is useful information but does not take into consideration the penetrating power of the different types of radioactivity. The **effective dose** takes into account penetrating power with the amount of radiation absorbed to provide a measurement that more clearly indicates the effect a dose of radiation will have on the cells

Table 4.2 Units Used to Measure Radiation.

Type of Measurement	Common Unit	SI Unit	Relationship
Activity	Curie (Ci)	Becquerel (Bq)	$1\,Ci = 3.7 \times 10^{10}\,Bq$
Absorbed Dose	Rod (D) Gray (Gy)	Gray (Gy)	$1\,Gy = 100\,D$
Effective Dose	Rem	Sievert (Sv)	$1\,Sv = 100\,rem$

Figure 4.6 Technician Testing Nuclear Medicine Dosing Equipment.
Medical officials must regularly check dosing equipment to avoid mistakes when giving patients dosages of radio-pharmaceuticals.

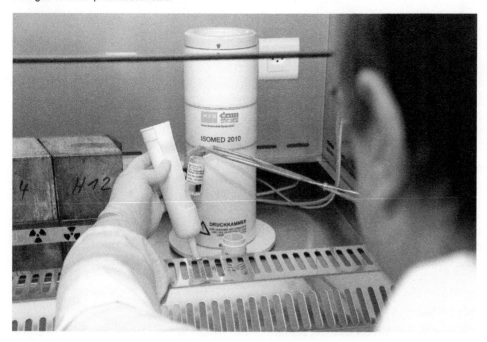

of the body (Figure 4.6). Effective dose is the absorbed dose multiplied by a radiation-weighting factor (W_R). The factor varies for the different types of radiation described in Section 4.2. For example, an alpha particle has a radiation-weighing factor of 20. In contrast, both beta and gamma radiation have a radiation-weighing factor of 1.

$$\text{Effective dose} = \text{absorbed dose} \times W_R$$

When the unit of absorbed dose is the *gray*, the unit of the effective dose is the **sievert (Sv)**. The **rem** incorporates the weighting factor to indicate an effective dosage (see Table 4.2). One rem—of any type of radiation (alpha, beta, or gamma)—produces an equivalent amount of tissue damage.

Predict answers and see step-by-step solutions: **Learn 4.2:** Radiation Dosage in the Pearson eText.

Apply what you have just learned: **Practice 4.9** in the Pearson eText.

Explore how Chemistry and Biology connect: **BioConnect 4.1:** Biological Effects of Radiation in the Pearson eText.

Quiz yourself on the content of this section: **Check 4.3** in the Pearson eText.

4.4 Half-Life

The rate of decay of specific radioactive nuclei varies greatly from one isotope to another. Some nuclei decay only slightly over thousands of years, while others decay completely within a fraction of a second. Therefore, it is useful to have a common measurement that allows us to compare radioisotopes by decay rate.

Figure 4.14 Decay of Fluorine-18 over Three Half-Lives.

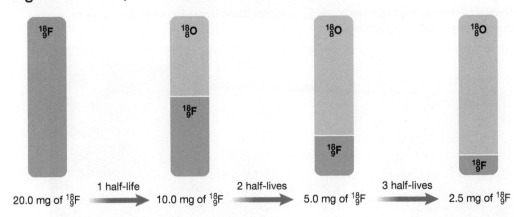

The **half-life** of a radioisotope is the time it takes one-half of a sample of that radioisotope to decay. For example, ^{18}F (fluorine-18) has a half-life of 110 minutes. When ^{18}F decays, it produces ^{18}O (oxygen-18) and a positron particle.

$$^{18}_{9}\text{F} \rightarrow ^{18}_{8}\text{O} + ^{0}_{+1}\beta$$

Suppose we have a 20.0-mg sample of $^{18}_{9}$F. After 110 minutes (one half-life), half of the original sample decays and 10.0 mg of $^{18}_{9}$F remains. After 220 minutes (two half-lives), 5.00 mg of ^{18}F remains. After three half-lives (330 minutes), only 2.50 mg of the original ^{18}F is left (Figure 4.14).

Ranges of Half-Lives

A variety of naturally occurring radioisotopes have long half-lives (Table 4.3). These radioisotopes decay over thousands or even millions of years, disintegrating slowly and releasing small amounts of radiation. Synthetic radioisotopes often decay rapidly. In general, synthetic radioisotopes are characterized by short half-lives. From a medical dosage standpoint, using radioisotopes that have a short half-life helps to avoid unintended side effects from excess radiation. A therapeutic synthetic radioisotope given to a patient in a medical treatment is essentially gone within a few days or in some cases a few hours due to its short half-life. Learn more about half-life calculations in VisibleChem Video 4.2.

Table 4.3 Radioisotope Half-lives.

Isotope	Name	Decay Process	Half-life
$^{238}_{92}$U	uranium-238	alpha	4.5×10^9 yr
$^{14}_{6}$C	carbon-14	beta	5730 yr
$^{137}_{55}$Cs	cesium-137	beta	30.2 yr
$^{153}_{64}$Gd	gadolinium-153	gamma	8 months
$^{234}_{90}$Th	thorium-234	beta	24.1 days
$^{223}_{90}$Ra	radium-223	alpha	11 days
$^{222}_{86}$Rn	radon-222	alpha	3.8 days
$^{39}_{66}$Y	yttrium-90	beta	2.7 days
$^{212}_{82}$Pb	lead-212	beta	10.4 hours
$^{258}_{106}$Sg	seaborgium-258	alpha	0.0029 s

Watch this concept come to life: **VisibleChem Video 4.2:** Half-Life Calculations and **VisibleChem Video 4.3:** Carbon Dating in the Pearson eText.

Apply what you have just learned: **Practice 4.10** in the Pearson eText.

Quiz yourself on the content of this section: **Check 4.4** in the Pearson eText.

4.5 Radioisotopes in Medicine

Nuclear medicine is a medical specialty that uses a variety of radioisotopes, sometimes called **radiopharmaceuticals**, to treat or diagnose disease (Figure 4.15). Radiopharmaceuticals are introduced into a patient's body by injection, swallowing, or inhalation. The amount of radiopharmaceuticals is typically very small and administered to a specific location in the body. The radioactive part of the radiopharmaceutical emits radiation that can be detected, which is also helpful in diagnosis.

Diagnosis

Physicians use radiopharmaceuticals to determine whether the heart can pump blood adequately, if the brain is receiving an adequate blood supply, and if brain cells are functioning normally. Nuclear medicine can also be employed to explore the functionality of the kidneys, determine whether the stomach is emptying properly, quantify blood volume or lung function, and determine bone density. Other radiopharmaceuticals help find cancers, identify sites of seizures, and even assess the damage to the heart after a heart attack.

Treatment

Radiation emitted by radioisotopes can be used to attack rapidly dividing tumor cells. Common cancer treatment plans involve placing radiopharmaceuticals internally at the site of a tumor within the body. One example of this approach involves radioactive

Figure 4.15 Examples of Radiopharmaceutical Applications in Nuclear Medicine.

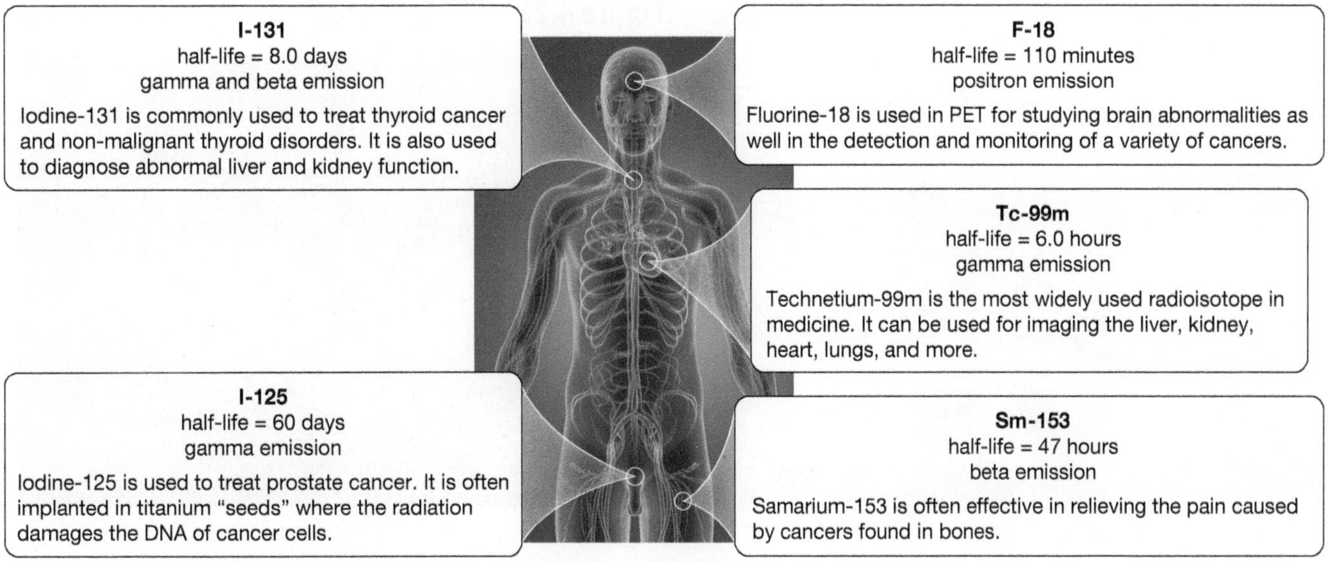

I-131
half-life = 8.0 days
gamma and beta emission

Iodine-131 is commonly used to treat thyroid cancer and non-malignant thyroid disorders. It is also used to diagnose abnormal liver and kidney function.

F-18
half-life = 110 minutes
positron emission

Fluorine-18 is used in PET for studying brain abnormalities as well in the detection and monitoring of a variety of cancers.

Tc-99m
half-life = 6.0 hours
gamma emission

Technetium-99m is the most widely used radioisotope in medicine. It can be used for imaging the liver, kidney, heart, lungs, and more.

I-125
half-life = 60 days
gamma emission

Iodine-125 is used to treat prostate cancer. It is often implanted in titanium "seeds" where the radiation damages the DNA of cancer cells.

Sm-153
half-life = 47 hours
beta emission

Samarium-153 is often effective in relieving the pain caused by cancers found in bones.

"seeds" or wires that are implanted close to a tumor. Health care workers use iodine-125 seeds to treat prostate cancer and iridium-192 wires to battle some breast cancers. Another approach involves attaching or incorporating radioisotopes in molecules that are designed to target cancer cells specifically. This is a method for imaging, monitoring, and treating tumors.

BioConnect 4.2 (contains Figures 4.16–4.19) provides a specific example of this type of nuclear medicine, which is called positron emission tomography (PET).

 Explore how Chemistry and Biology connect: **BioConnect 4.2:** Monitoring Disease with Radioisotopes in the Pearson eText.

Medical Diagnosis Without Radioactivity

There are a number of different methods for imaging and diagnosing disease. Not all of them use radioactivity. X-rays, CT scans and MRIs, for example, all produce images of internal body parts and do not involve nuclear reactions.

X-rays are high-energy radiation that image bone and internal organs. In clinics and hospitals, x-rays are generated within sophisticated instruments and precisely directed to areas of interest on a patient. As the x-ray beam passes through the body, it is absorbed to varying degrees depending on the density of the material it encounters. Detectors record these differences and generate contrast images that health care professionals interpret to diagnose disease. X-rays are a form of radiation but are lower in energy and produced in a different way than gamma rays. Even though x-rays are not produced in nuclear reactions, they can still cause harm to tissue and must be limited in use.

Computed tomography (CT) scans also use x-rays to produce high-resolution images of internal organs. CT scanners provide three-dimensional views of the body's organs (Figures 4.20–4.22). They are commonly used to diagnose bleeding and tumors in the brain and abdomen.

Magnetic resonance imaging (MRI) utilizes low-energy radio waves, not produced by nuclear reactions, to view internal organs. MRIs are most effective for visualizing soft tissue.

Figure 4.20 A Patient Receiving a CT Scan to Diagnose her Condition.

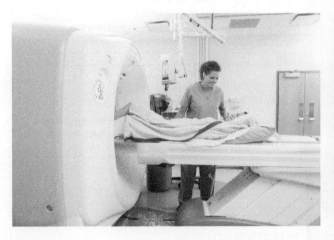

Figure 4.21 Cross-Sectional CT Image of a Patient's Abdomen.

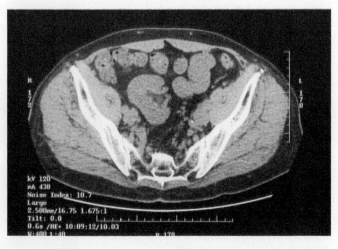

Figure 4.22 A CT Scanner uses an X-ray Source to Produce Cross-Sectional Images of a Patient.

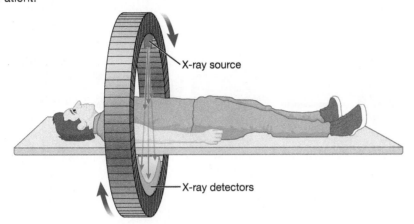

X-ray source

X-ray detectors

Quiz yourself on the content of this section: **Check 4.5** in the Pearson eText.

4.6 Nuclear Fission and Fusion

The first sections of this chapter are about radioactive decay, but decay is not the only kind of nuclear reaction that occurs. Another type of nuclear reaction involves particles that bombard atoms. This bombardment can form new isotopes in a process called **transmutation**. Under very specific conditions, other types of nuclear events occur in conjunction with transmutation. Several heavy isotopes, for example, can undergo a splitting process called **fission**. In contrast, some light nuclei join together in a process called **fusion**. Fission and fusion were discovered in the late 1930s. With their discovery, humans became aware of the huge amounts of energy associated with nuclear reactions.

Fission

The nuclear reaction that occurs when uranium-235 is bombarded with neutrons is an example of nuclear fission (Figure 4.23). During fission, the original uranium isotope splits into two lighter isotopes (Kr-91 and Ba-142) and releases three neutrons. Several other fission products are possible for this reaction, but this is one of the more common examples of the fission of U-235.

Chain Reactions and Nuclear Power Plants

The fission reaction illustrated in Figure 4.23 begins when one neutron bombards the uranium isotope. The resulting nucleus is unstable and splits into the two lighter isotopes. This fission reaction also releases a large amount of energy and three additional neutrons. These high-energy neutrons bombard other uranium-235 nuclei resulting in a chain reaction (Figure 4.24). A **chain reaction** involves the rapid increase in the number of neutrons. These neutrons continue to initiate the fission process. To sustain this nuclear chain reaction, a sufficient amount of U-235 must be present. This amount is the **critical mass**. When a critical mass is available, the chain reaction continues, and an atomic explosion occurs.

Nuclear fission can be initiated in a more controlled fashion with less than critical mass of U-235 present. The energy this controlled fission produces is used to produce electricity. Nuclear power plants use a controlled fission process, which takes place in traditional uranium nuclear reactors, to produce energy around the world (Figures 4.25 and 4.26).

Figure 4.23 Fission of Uranium-235.

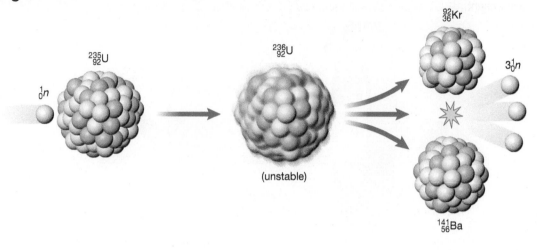

Figure 4.24 Chain Reaction of Uranium-235.

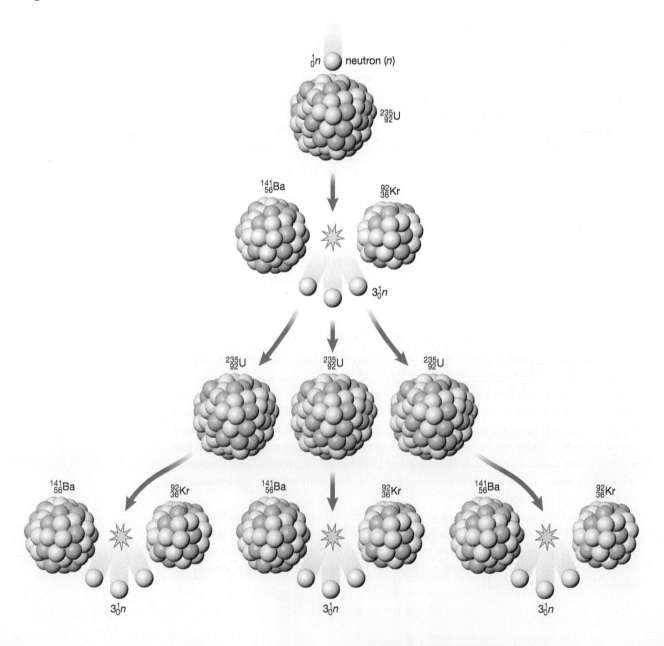

Figure 4.25 World Distribution of Energy Production.

Nuclear energy power plants are used to generate around 10% of the world's electricity.

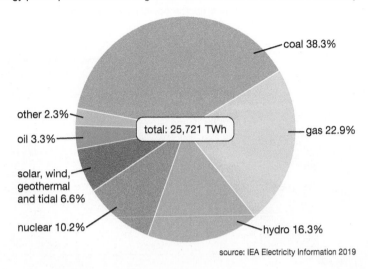

source: IEA Electricity Information 2019

Figure 4.26 Nuclear Energy Generation by Country in 2019.

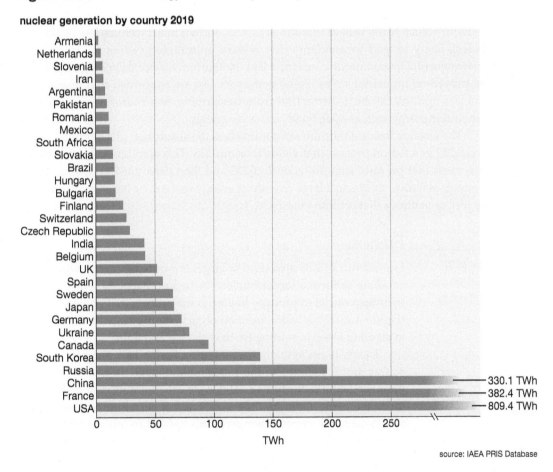

source: IAEA PRIS Database

Thorium as an Alternative

In recent years, thorium-232 reactors have gained attention from a number of scientists and countries around the world. This is because thorium reactors have several desirable features compared to traditional uranium nuclear reactors (Figure 4.27). Thorium is a naturally occurring radioactive element and is four times more abundant than uranium

Figure 4.27 The CANDU Reactors at China's Qinshan Site.

This plant can run on thorium and on uranium recovered from other reactors. Thorium reactors are under development as alternatives to traditional nuclear power plants that use uranium-235.

in Earth's crust. Many believe thorium is a more efficient fuel, produces less waste, and is less likely to lead to accidents that release unintended radioactivity into the environment. Opponents are concerned that the thorium reactor technology has yet to be proved on industrial scales. Some detractors also are concerned that researching nuclear options can be a distraction from developing non-radioactive sources of renewable energy such as solar, wind, and wave energy.

The reaction inside a thorium reactor involves the absorption of a neutron by thorium-232 in a fission process that yields thorium-233. This is followed by two decay processes that produce first protactinium-233 and then uranium-233. Uranium-233 undergoes fission, releasing a large amount of energy that can be harnessed and used, as well as neutrons that continue the cycle.

Fusion

Figure 4.28 Fusion of Hydrogen Nuclei to Produce Helium.

This fusion reaction produces a large amount of energy.

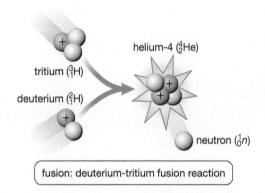

tritium ($^3_1$H)

deuterium ($^2_1$H)

helium-4 ($^4_2$He)

neutron ($^1_0$n)

fusion: deuterium-tritium fusion reaction

Lighter nuclei can also release large amounts of energy when they combine to form a larger nucleus in fusion reactions. The fusion of hydrogen nuclei to produce helium is the process that powers the sun (Figure 4.28). This fusion reaction occurs continuously in the sun (and in all other stars) providing Earth with heat and light.

Scientists are actively investigating fusion as a potential energy source, but it remains in the experimental stage. In one of the most promising efforts, thirty-five nations are collaborating on a fusion reactor called ITER (Latin for "the way") in southern France. One important issue is the extreme temperatures needed to initiate and sustain nuclear fusion. Temperatures as high as 100,000,000 °C are required. The difficulty with achieving these extreme reaction conditions has thus far prevented fusion reactors from becoming a viable method for producing energy for human use.

Quiz yourself on the content of this section: **Check 4.6** in the Pearson eText.

Chapter Summary

4.1 Radioactivity

Learning Objective: Define radioactivity and represent radioisotopes with correct atomic symbols.

Nuclear radiations involve atomic nuclei undergoing transformations. These transformations can result in alpha particles, beta particles, positrons, or gamma rays being emitted from the decaying nuclei. Each form of radioactivity has unique characteristics. The changes within the decaying nuclei are reflected in changes in the atomic number (A) and/or mass number (Z) of the element emitting nuclear radiation. Too much radiation can be harmful to DNA and cause health problems, but appropriate amounts of radiation are used to detect and treat a wide range of health problems in hospital settings.

Key Terms

radiation
radioactive
radioactivity
radioisotope

4.2 Nuclear Reactions

Learning Objective: Identify the types of radioactivity and common nuclear reactions using nuclear equations.

During nuclear reactions, radiation is emitted in the form of alpha particles, beta particles, positrons, and/or gamma rays. In a nuclear equation, the sum of both the mass numbers (A) and the atomic numbers (Z) must be equal on both sides of a nuclear equation (Table 4.1).

VisibleChem Video 4.1: Nuclear Reactions

Key Terms

alpha emission	gamma emission	positron
alpha particle	gamma ray	positron emission
beta emission	nuclear equation	radioactive decay
beta particle	nuclear reaction	

4.3 Detecting and Measuring Radioactivity

Learning Objective: Describe how scientists detect and measure radiation and recognize the common units used in nuclear chemistry.

Radiation can be detected and measured using a variety of scientific instruments, including the Geiger counter. Scientists and heathcare professionals quantify the amount of radiation emitted (activity) by a radioactive source, the amount of radiation absorbed (the absorbed dose), and the biological damage (effective dose) using several standard units of measure (Table 4.2). We can use unit conversions to calculate and express these different forms of quantified radiation.

BioConnect 4.1: Biological Effects of Radiation

Key Terms

absorbed dose	Geiger counter	radon
becquerel (Bq)	gray (Gy)	rem
curie (Ci)	rad (D)	sievert (Sv)
effective dose	radiation sickness	

4.4 Half-life

Learning Objective: Calculate the amount of radioisotope remaining after one or more half-life.

The half-life of a radioisotope is the time required for one-half of the radioactive atoms in a sample to decay (Figure 4.14). The rate of decay, and thus the half-life, of different radioisotopes varies from fractions of a second to billions of years. Half-life is used to determine dosage amounts when radioisotopes are used in medicine and to date carbon-containing objects.

VisibleChem Video 4.2: Half-Life Calculations

VisibleChem Video 4.3: Carbon Dating

Key Term

half-life

4.5 Radioisotopes in Medicine

Learning Objective: Explain how nuclear chemistry is used in medicine.

Nuclear medicine uses targeted and appropriate dosing of alpha, beta, positron, and gamma radiation for the diagnosis and treatment of a broad range of medical conditions (Figure 4.15). Each year, tens of millions of patients around the world receive diagnostic tracer amounts or therapeutic doses of radiopharmaceuticals.

BioConnect 4.2: Monitoring Disease with Radioisotopes

Key Terms

computed tomography (CT)	positron emission tomography (PET)	radiopharmaceutical
magnetic resonance imaging (MRI)	(from BioConnect 4.2)	x-ray

4.6 Nuclear Fission & Fusion

Learning Objective: Describe nuclear fission and fusion.

Nuclear fusion combines small lighter elements into larger heavier elements. Nuclear fission splits large heavy elements into smaller ones. Both processes release tremendous amounts of energy. Nuclear power plants currently utilize nuclear fission to produce electricity for the growing energy demands of the human population. The heat and light that our planet receives from the sun comes from nuclear fusion.

Key Terms

chain reaction	fission	transmutation
critical mass	fusion	

The **End-of-Chapter Problems** are located in the back of the book in Appendix A.

 End-of-Chapter Quiz   Have you mastered the content of this chapter? Try the **End-of-Chapter Quiz** in the Pearson eText.

1. Which statement about radiation and radioactivity is correct?
   a) Radiation only comes from nuclear weapons or radiation leaks from nuclear power plants.
   b) Radiation can be a helpful tool in healthcare.
   c) Radioactivity is characterized by the emission of clusters of atoms from a nucleus.
   d) Radioactivity was discovered by Albert Einstein.

2. How many protons (p) and neutrons (n) does the technetium isotope, $^{99}_{43}\text{Tc}$ contain?
   a) 99 protons, 43 neutrons
   b) 43 protons, 56 neutrons
   c) 56 protons, 99 neutrons
   d) 56 protons, 43 neutrons

3. How many neutrons (n) and electrons (e) are in a neutral atom of the chlorine-37 isotope?
   a) 37 neutrons, 37 electrons
   b) 20 neutrons, 37 electrons
   c) 37 neutrons, 17 electrons
   d) 20 neutrons, 17 electrons

4. Which is a product of alpha radiation?
   a) $_2^4$He
   b) $_{-1}^0$e
   c) $_0^0\gamma$
   d) $_{+1}^0$e

5. Beta radiation produces_____.
   a) positrons
   b) bozons
   c) electrons
   d) microwaves

6. Which statement is true about beta emission of the $_{15}^{32}$P isotope?
   a) Photons are released and the resulting nucleus is $_{16}^{32}$S.
   b) Electrons are released and the resulting nucleus has an atomic number of 15 (phosphorous).
   c) Electrons are released and the resulting nucleus is $_{16}^{33}$P.
   d) Electrons are released and the resulting nucleus is $_{16}^{32}$S.

7. Gamma ray emission from naturally occurring radioactive isotopes can take place with either alpha or beta decay. Fill in the missing products for the reaction that occurs when cobalt-60 undergoes beta decay and emits gamma rays.

   $$_{27}^{60}\text{Co} \rightarrow {_{28}^{60}}\text{Ni} + ? + ?$$

   a) $_{+1}^0$e + $_2^4$He
   b) $_{-1}^0$e + $_0^0\gamma$
   c) $_2^4$He + $_0^0\gamma$
   d) $_{+1}^0$e + $_0^0\gamma$

8. The ^{40}K isotope is the largest source of natural radioactivity in humans and animals. Although it can decay through positron emission, most atoms of potassium-40 undergo beta decay. Fill in the missing product for the nuclear equation for the beta emission of potassium-40.

   $$_{19}^{40}\text{K} \rightarrow ? + {_{-1}^0}\text{e}$$

   a) $_{20}^{40}$K
   b) $_{20}^{40}$Ar
   c) $_{20}^{40}$Ca
   d) $_{19}^{39}$Ca

9. Which type of emission has a negative charge?
   a) alpha particles
   b) beta particles
   c) gamma rays
   d) positrons

10. Which of the following is *not* a scientific abbreviation for a unit in nuclear chemistry?
    a) Se
    b) Bq
    c) Gy
    d) rem

11. Jobs that involve working with radiation require careful monitoring of exposure to help prevent increased risk of:
    a) arthritis
    b) bone fractures
    c) cancer
    d) hearing loss

12. A patient receiving external beam radiation treatment for his prostate cancer is given a dose of 76 Gray (Gy). What is his dose in rad if the radiation is in the form of gamma rays? (1 Gy = 100 rad)
    a) 7600 rad
    b) 1/7600 rad
    c) 0.76 rad
    d) 7600 Gy

13. A breast cancer patient receives 16 equal doses of radiation treatment during a five-week period. If the total dose for the entire treatment plan was 55 Gy, what dose (in Gy) did the patient receive on each visit?
    a) 0.29 Gy/visit
    b) 3.4 Gy/visit
    c) 3.2 Gy/visit
    d) 11 Gy/visit

14. Which describes a half-life in nuclear chemistry?
    a) the time required for a cancer tumor to shrink by one half
    b) the amount of a radioactive material that causes half the people exposed to get cancer
    c) the amount of time required for one-half of a radioactive sample to decay
    d) the time required for half the population to exceed maximum radiation exposure levels

15. The Uranium-235 isotope is used in nuclear reactors and has a half-life of 7.038×10^8 years. If you live 100 years, approximately how much of a radioactive sample of uranium-235 will have decayed in your lifetime?
    a) nearly one half
    b) about three fourths
    c) about one eighth
    d) only an extremely small fraction

16. Which of the following radioactive isotopes does not have a well-recognized and useful medical application?

a) iodine-123

b) technetium-99m

c) aluminum-27

d) fluorine-18

17. Uranium-235 is the only naturally occurring isotope to undergo nuclear fission when bombarded with a stream of neutrons. Select the missing isotope needed to complete the fission reaction.

$$^{235}_{92}U + ^{1}_{0}n \rightarrow 2^{1}_{0}n + ^{97}_{40}Zr + ?$$

a) $^{97}_{40}Zr$

b) $^{136}_{52}Te$

c) $^{137}_{52}Te$

d) $^{52}_{137}Te$

18. What is a *similarity* between nuclear fusion and nuclear fission?

a) Both nuclear fusion and fission start with the same isotopes.

b) Both nuclear fusion and fission release tremendous amounts of energy.

c) Both nuclear fusion and fission involve atomic nuclei coming together to form a heavier element.

d) Nuclear fusion and fission start with different materials but produce the same product isotopes.

19. What is a *difference* between nuclear fusion and nuclear fission?

a) Nuclear fusion involves light elements coming together to form heavier isotopes, while nuclear fission involves the fragmentation of nuclei into lighter isotopes.

b) Nuclear fission only occurs in the sun, and nuclear fusion can only occur on Earth.

c) Nuclear fusion releases energy, while nuclear fission only consumes energy.

d) Nuclear fusion occurs when large elements combine to form lighter elements, and nuclear fission occurs with a wide range of elements such as fluorine, cobalt, sodium, and uranium.

Unit 1
Bringing It All Together

How Can We Use Atoms and Nuclear Chemistry to Find and Treat Disease?

CHEMISTRY APPLICATION We opened Unit 1 with a look at how scientists are using our understanding of the atom to help find and treat disease. We learned about the potentially devastating disease, hyperinsulinism **(HI; Figure U1.5)**. HI is treatable, but healthcare providers must be able to determine whether the disease is diffuse (spread throughout the pancreas) or focal (found in a specific region of the pancreas).

Thankfully, a strong understanding of the structure of the atom and nuclear chemistry has led to a variety of better diagnostic and treatment options. The molecule, Fluorodopa F18, can be used to visualize the location of the disease, allowing surgeons to remove the disease-causing region in focal disease (Figure U1.6).

Recall from BioConnect 4.2, that positron emission tomography (PET) is the imaging technique that can be used to visualize the location of disease. In this case, Fluorodopa F-18 is injected into the patient, absorbed by the target tissue, and then the scanner detects particles released (positrons) in a nuclear decay process.

$$^{18}_{9}\text{F} \rightarrow ^{18}_{8}\text{O} + ^{0}_{+1}\beta$$
$$\text{positron}$$

Figure U1.5 Hyperinsulinism is Life-Threatening for Infants.

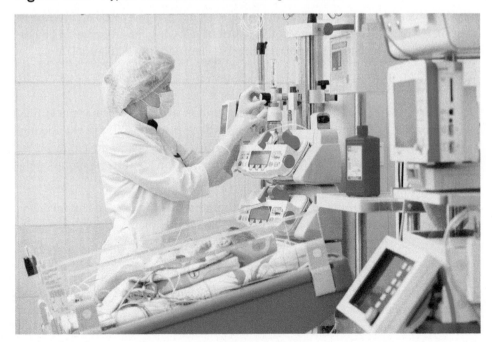

Figure U1.6 The Radiopharmaceutical Fluorodopa F18.

This compound is used to visualize the pancreas. The F-18 isotope in the compound releases positrons so that diseased tissue can be seen.

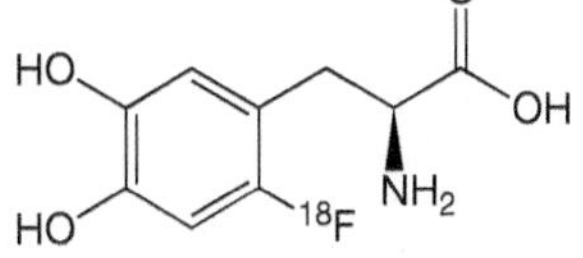

Figure U1.7 A PET Scan of the Brain.

Warmer colors indicate greater uptake of Fluorodopa F-18.

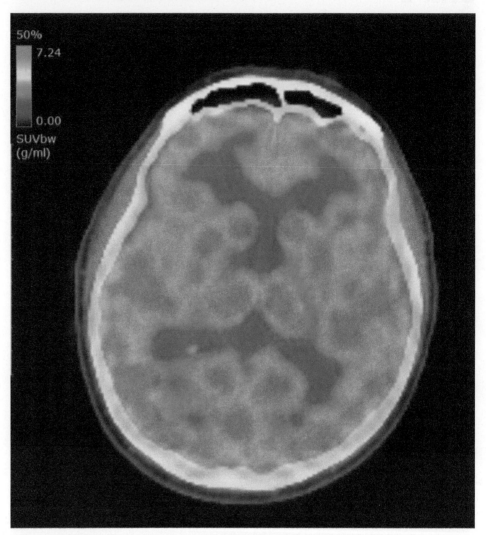

The radioisotope fluorine-18 is converted to an oxygen-18 isotope and releases a positron ($_{+1}^{0}\beta$). The scanner detects the positrons allowing for an image to be produced revealing which tissues absorbed the most Fluorodopa F-18 (Figure U1.7).

Questions to Think About

1. Based on what you learned in this unit, look at the radiopharmaceutical Fluorodopa F-18 (Figure U1.6) and consider these questions: (i) can you identify the five elements that make up this molecule? (ii) can you name the family on the periodic table that fluorine (F) belongs to? (iii) can you identify the group on the periodic table that carbon belongs to?

2. Based on your learning in this unit, is it common for the dosage of a medicine given to a patient to depend on the patient's weight? Explain.

3. How many electrons, protons, and neutrons does the isotope fluorine-18 contain? How many valence electrons are found in a fluorine (F) atom?

4. Describe the nuclear process that occurs when the Fluorodopa F-18 molecule is used in combination with PET to obtain an image of the pancreas. Can you identify the type of radioactivity that is released? When F-18 decays, what new isotope forms?

Figure U1.8 Structure of a Typical Scientific Paper.

Abstract	Provides a short summary of the entire paper.
Introduction	Summarizes what's known about the issue or problem and introduces the research question.
Methods	A detailed description of how the researchers did their work.
Results	Data from the study presented in tables, graphs, and other figures.
Discussion	Explains the significance of the results and connects it to the other studies.

Exploring Scientific Literature

To learn about potential treatment and diagnostics like Fluorodopa F18, healthcare providers must often look to the primary literature. Primary literature refers to scientific papers written by scientists for other scientists in their fields. Thus, these papers are often very specific and technical. Unfortunately, they are also the most current and detailed sources of information. Learning how to navigate a scientific paper more easily can help you access the most current information and perhaps provide important, even life-saving, information for a friend, family member, or patient.

Scientific papers usually follow a very rigid structure (Figure U1.8). Understanding this structure can help you find the information you need and avoid some of the more complex parts of the paper.

The abstract is often the most useful part of a paper as it provides a short summary of the entire paper. In the remaining sections, the authors will provide more background about their topic (Introduction), provide detailed descriptions of how they did their work (Methods), present their data (Results), and explain the significance of their findings (Discussion).

A Closer Look at the Data

A French study published in the scientific journal, the *European Journal of Nuclear Medicine and Molecular Imaging,* (Ribeiro *et al,* 2007) reports on the efforts of a research team to determine whether or not Fluorodopa F18 was effective at distinguishing focal and diffuse forms of HI. A portion of the abstract from this paper is shown below.

Methods: Forty-nine children were studied with [^{18}F]fluoro-L-DOPA. A thoracoabdominal scan was acquired 45–65 min after the injection of 4.2 ± 1.0 MBq/kg of [^{18}F]fluoro-L-DOPA. Additionally, 12 of the 49 children were submitted to pancreatic venous catheterisation for blood samples (PVS) and 31 were also investigated using MRI.

Results: We identified abnormal focal pancreatic uptake of [^{18}F]fluoro-L-DOPA in 15 children, whereas diffuse radiotracer uptake was observed in the pancreatic area in the other 34 patients. In children studied with both PET and PVS, the results were concordant in 11/12 cases. All patients with focal radiotracer uptake and nine of the patients with diffuse pancreatic radiotracer accumulation, unresponsive to medical treatment, were submitted to surgery. In 21 of these 24 patients, the histopathological results confirmed the PET findings. In focal forms, selective surgery was followed by clinical remission without carbohydrate intolerance.

Conclusion: These data demonstrate that PET with [^{18}F]fluoro-L-DOPA is an accurate non-invasive technique allowing differential diagnosis between focal and diffuse forms of HI.

Questions to Think About

Read the abstract and use it to answer the following questions:

1. In your own words, summarize the researchers' approach. How did they answer their question about whether or not Fluorodopa F18 was an effective diagnostic?

2. What did these researchers discover? Were there results true for all the patients they examined? If not, what other types of factors might help explain their results?

3. Can you think of any potential limitations to the study they conducted? How might you resolve these limitations?

References

Ribeiro, MJ., Boddaert, N., Bellanné-Chantelot, C. *et al.* The added value of [^{18}F]fluoro-L-DOPA PET in the diagnosis of hyperinsulinism of infancy: a retrospective study involving 49 children. *Eur J Nucl Med Mol Imaging* **34**, 2120–2128 (2007). https://doi.org/10.1007/s00259-007-0498-y

Unit 2
Introduction
Ionic and Covalent Bonding Models

Chapter 5: Ionic Compounds
Chapter 6: Covalent Compounds
Chapter 7: Molecular Polarity and Intermolecular Forces

Recent approaches to targeting cancer cells include using special chemical linkers to attach chemotherapy drugs to antibodies, allowing them to specifically target cancer cells while minimizing the impact on healthy cells nearby. Researchers can use similar techniques to help visualize cancer cells.

Figure U2.1 Antibodies can be Engineered to Bind to Cancer Cells, Delivering Drugs Directly to the Cancer.

Unit 2: Introduction
Targeting Cancer: Why is Chemical Bonding Important in Medicine?

 To learn more about how to turn cancer against itself, watch **Video U2.1** in the Pearson eText.

Unit 2 opens with a compelling illustration of how scientists are using a creative approach to more effectively treat cancer while minimizing the collateral damage caused by many conventional cancer treatments (Figure U2.2). This new approach requires a deep understanding of the fundamental chemistry we'll explore in this three-chapter unit on chemical bonding. In this unit, we learn about two important types of chemical bonding, and the forces that attract molecules to each other. These topics relate directly to a wide range of chemical and physical behaviors of every-day materials such as water and cooking oil, as well as the biological processes operating within each of our cells. We will see that the specific type of chemical bonding, the three-dimensional shape of molecules, and the forces that exist between molecules, all help explain our natural world as well as many modern medical treatments.

In Chapter 5, we'll learn that some atoms *transfer electrons* between each other to become electrically charged, and that oppositely charged atoms (or groups of atoms) are then strongly attracted to each other. In Chapter 6, we examine how and when atoms become bonded together to form large and small molecules through the process of *sharing* their electrons with each other. We also learn in Chapter 6 how to predict the

Figure U2.2 Patient Receiving Chemotherapy Drugs.

Conventional cancer treatments target all rapidly dividing cells in the body, causing an array of side effects such as nausea, hair loss, and fatigue.

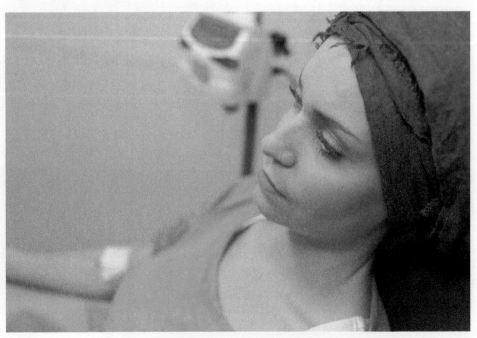

shape of molecules. In Chapter 7 we expand upon the topics in Chapter 5 and 6 to learn that electrons are often not shared equally between atoms, and how this unequal sharing leads to electron rich and electron poor regions on molecules. We also learn about the attractive forces that exist between multiple intact molecules, and how these forces between molecules play critical roles in our natural world, biological processes, and medical treatments such as cancer diagnosis and treatment. At the end of this unit, we will conclude with a detailed look at how scientists are using their understanding of chemical bonding and the attractive forces between molecules to develop modern methods to treat breast cancer.

Unit 2 Chemistry Application: Targeting Cancer

You probably know someone who has battled cancer; it's the second leading cause of death in the U.S. The term cancer is used to describe many different diseases in which abnormal cells divide uncontrollably and are able to invade other tissues (Figure U2.3). Thus, most conventional chemotherapy drugs target rapidly dividing cells. Unfortunately for the patient, this includes the blood-forming cells of the bone marrow, hair follicles, and the cells lining the mouth and digestive tract. Patients on these drugs often experience severely compromised immune systems, hair loss, nausea, and fatigue as both healthy and cancerous cells succumb to the drugs.

In many ways, this approach of killing any rapidly dividing cell is quite primitive; it simply relies on killing the cancer faster than you kill the patient. For at least a hundred years, scientists have been dreaming of tools that would selectively target cancer cells, and spare the patients' healthy cells—a so-called "magic bullet".

Today that dream is becoming a reality. Scientists are taking advantage of the specificity of **antibodies** to turn them into homing devices that deliver deadly doses of powerful drugs directly to cancer cells. Antibodies are sticky proteins produced by our immune system. These proteins recognize and bind to *specific*, foreign molecules called **antigens** (Figure U2.4). This binding of the antibody to the foreign antigen helps

Figure U2.3 Diagnosing Cancer.

Pathologists examine tissue samples from patients to look for evidence of uncontrolled cell division.

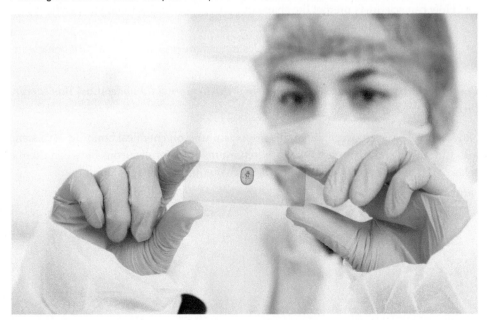

Figure U2.4 Antibodies.

The immune system produces sticky proteins called antibodies that bind to specific molecules called antigens. Antibodies bind to foreign antigens on foreign viruses or bacteria, for example, targeting them for destruction and helping us recover from an infection.

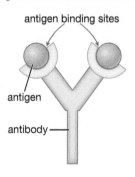

Figure U2.5 Conjugated Antibodies.

Antibodies can be used to deliver toxic drugs directly to cancer cells, minimizing some of the common side effects of conventional chemotherapy.

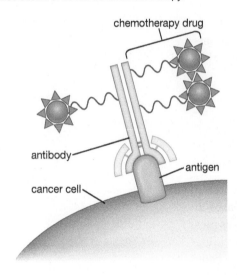

chemotherapy drug

antibody

cancer cell

antigen

us launch an immune response, targeting any cells or viruses containing the foreign antigens for destruction.

Fortunately, many types of cancerous cells display abnormal proteins or antigens on their surface. Thus, antibodies can be produced in the lab to bind specifically to the surface of cancer cells while ignoring their healthy neighbors. These so-called "naked antibodies" are often enough to slow the progression of a cancer by allowing the patient's own body to launch a more effective immune response against the cancerous cells. But they're even more powerful when coupled with toxic drugs.

Early efforts to employ carefully targeted antibodies to deliver toxic payloads to cancer cells involved attaching existing chemotherapy drugs to specific antibodies, creating a **conjugated antibody** (Figure U2.5). These conjugated antibodies would circulate in a patient's system until they found a matching antigen, the cancer cell. Researchers quickly realized, however, that conventional drugs weren't nearly toxic enough to kill off a cancer as the antibodies delivered them at a much lower concentration than had been used in traditional chemotherapy. They would need to attach much more toxic compounds. And treating a patient with an even more toxic compound would require great confidence in their ability to deliver the drug to the correct cells.

The first "armed" or conjugated antibody (Mylotarg) was approved by the FDA to treat a bone marrow cancer, acute myeloid leukemia, in 2000. By 2010, however, the drug was voluntarily removed from the market. Its toxic payload was "falling off" the antibody, and patients were dying. This approach was promising, but only if chemists could ensure that the bond between the antibody and its toxic payload was secure. By 2017, the drug had been approved again with a modified dosing protocol, illustrating the many challenges associated with bringing a new drug to market.

Questions to Think About

What chemistry do we need to know to understand this cancer therapy? Here are some questions to consider as you move through this unit:

- What types of bonds hold molecules, like a chemotherapy drug and its antibody, together?
- What forces allow an antibody to "stick" to its target antigen?
- How can scientists predict the shape of molecules in order to target specific types of cells or receptors in the body?
- What other characteristics of molecules determine how a chemical will behave in the body?

What chemistry would you like to know in order to more fully understand this cancer therapy?

Now that we have an overview of this important unit on chemical bonding, let's step into Chapter 5 and explore how and when atoms transfer electrons between themselves to create electrically charged particles that your life depends upon.

Chapter 5
Ionic Compounds

Salt deposits on the shore of Laguna Salada de Torrevieja in Spain. Algae growing in the salty water produce the stunning pink color.

 ## Chapter Outline

Learning Objectives

5.1 Define and describe ionic bonding.

5.2 Determine the charge on ions using the periodic table and the octet rule.

5.3 Write formulas for ionic compounds.

5.4 Write the name of ionic compounds from a given formula, and provide the formula when given the name of an ionic compound.

5.5 Recognize the common polyatomic ions and write the name and formula of compounds with polyatomic ions.

Introduction

Chemical bonds are responsible for the formation of the millions of different compounds and molecules that carry out a wide range of different functions in nature. The concept of bonding lies at the very core of chemistry. An understanding of chemical bonding can help us understand what coral reefs are made of, and what is in the multivitamins many of us choose to take (Figure 5.1). As we learn more about bonding, we also learn what *ions* are and why they're so important in IV solutions.

5.1 Introduction to Bonding

The overwhelming majority of elements combine with other elements to form compounds. Recall from Section 1.2, that a compound is composed of two or more different elements. Compounds range in size from quite small to very large. In fact, any number, from two to hundreds or even thousands, of atoms can join together to produce a wide range of chemical compounds. Table salt, for example, is a simple compound in which sodium and chlorine bond together in a repetitive pattern (Figure 5.2).

Valence electrons, which we discussed in Chapter 3, are the electrons that play a role in compound formation. Atoms join together in two general ways:

1. *Valence electrons can transfer from the atoms of one element to the atoms of another element to form* **ionic compounds**.

2. *Valence electrons can be shared between two atoms or among atoms of different elements to form* **covalent compounds**.

These two processes form **chemical bonds**, *which are the forces that hold atoms of elements together in a compound*. Depending on which atoms are involved, different types of chemical bonds form under different circumstances (Figure 5.3). For example, when a metal and a nonmetal bond together, one or more electrons transfers from the metal to the nonmetal. This process produces **ions**, which are *charged atoms* that are attracted to one another.

The result of this electron transfer and ion formation process is an **ionic bond**. Ionic bonds *result from an electrostatic attraction between oppositely charged ions*. Sodium chloride (NaCl), or table salt, is an example of an ionic compound that contains ionic bonds.

Figure 5.1 Ionic Bonds in our Lives.

A) The foundation of the great diversity of life associated with coral reefs is the ability of the reef-forming organisms to produce calcium carbonate, a type of compound we discuss in this chapter. **B)** Multivitamins contain an array of compounds that play important roles in maintaining proper cell function. **C)** The correct mixture of chemicals at the correct concentration is an essential component of IV treatments.

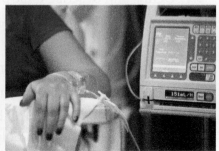

A   B   C

Figure 5.2 Table Salt is a compound.

The salt people sprinkle on food is a compound that forms when a sodium atom and a chlorine atom bond to each other.

Figure 5.3 Ionic and Covalent Bonding Models.

A transfer of valence electrons results in an ionic bond. Sharing of valence electrons produces a covalent bond.

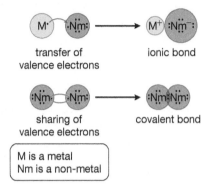

M is a metal
Nm is a non-metal

In contrast, when a nonmetal or a metalloid bonds with another nonmetal, they share electrons. This *electron sharing process produces* **covalent bonds**. The vast majority of compounds on Earth contain covalent bonds, including most of the chemical compounds that make up the human body. Differentiating between ionic and covalent compounds and understanding where we find each type of compound in nature is one of our tasks throughout the next few chapters. We discuss ionic bonding in this chapter and move on to covalent bonding in Chapter 6.

Quiz yourself on the content of this section: **Check 5.1** in the Pearson eText.

5.2 Ions

Now that we know that most compounds in nature are either ionic or covalent, let's take a closer look at how ionic bonds form from oppositely charged ions. An ion *is an electrically charged particle that forms when electrons are gained or lost by an atom.* There are two types of ions (Figure 5.4), which we define here:

cation: When a neutral atom *loses* one or more electrons, the result is a positively charged ion called a cation. A cation that we encounter often in this chapter is the sodium ion (Na^+), which has a positive one ($+1$) charge.

anion: When a neutral atom *gains* one or more electrons, the result is a negatively charged ion called an anion. The chloride ion (Cl^-) is an anion with a negative one (-1) charge.

So, which elements gain electrons to become anions, and which lose electrons to become cations? *In general, metals tend to lose electrons to become positively charged cations, and nonmetals tend to gain electrons to become negatively charged anions.*

The periodic table is a very useful tool for determining whether an element forms a cation or an anion upon ionization. Notice that sodium (Na) is located on the far left-hand side of the periodic table in the metal region (Figure 5.5). As we saw in the previous example, sodium forms a cation with a +1 charge. Chlorine, on the other hand, is found in the nonmetal region of the periodic table and forms an anion with a charge of -1.

Figure 5.4 Cation and Anion Formation.

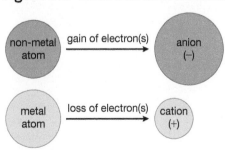

Figure 5.5 Periodic Table of the Elements Illustrating the Location of Metals and Nonmetals.

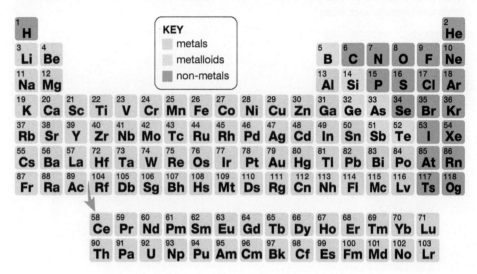

Take a moment to explore the periodic table and notice which elements gain electrons and which lose electrons in the ionization process.

Gaining and Losing Electrons to Form Ions

Let's explore specific examples of elements that lose electrons to form cations, and elements that gain electrons to form anions. As we can see in Figure 5.6, an electrically neutral (uncharged) sodium atom contains eleven protons and eleven electrons. When sodium forms an ion, the outer valence electron is lost, which results in an ion that has eleven protons and ten electrons. This ionization process results in a positively charged cation (Na^+).

Chlorine is an example of an element that gains one electron to form an anion. An uncharged chlorine atom contains seventeen protons and seventeen electrons. After the atom gains one electron, the chloride anion (Figure 5.7) forms. The additional electron causes the atom to become a negatively charged ion (Cl^-) with a total electron count of eighteen.

Figure 5.6 Ionization of a Sodium Atom.

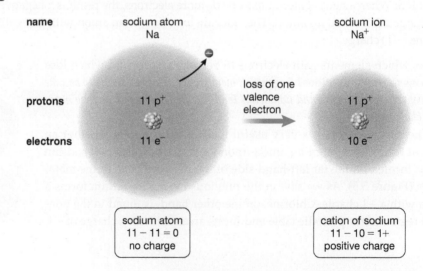

Figure 5.7 Ionization of a Chlorine Atom.

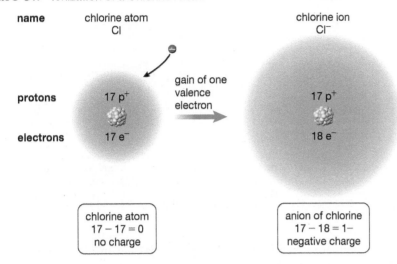

name chlorine atom Cl   chlorine ion Cl⁻

gain of one valence electron

protons 17 p⁺   17 p⁺

electrons 17 e⁻   18 e⁻

chlorine atom
17 − 17 = 0
no charge

anion of chlorine
17 − 18 = 1−
negative charge

Predict answers and see step-by-step solutions: **Learn 5.1:** Determining the Number of Protons and Electrons from Ion Symbols in the Pearson eText.

Apply what you have just learned: **Practice 5.1** in the Pearson eText.

Ionic Charges and the Periodic Table

Metal atoms lose electrons and nonmetal atoms gain electrons, but what determines how many electrons are gained or lost by each specific element? The **octet rule** states that the main group elements gain and lose enough electrons to fill the outer shell of the atom. A full electron shell for most element atoms has *eight electrons*. This is very useful for making predictions about the charge on an ion.

Octet Rule
Atoms tend to gain, lose, or share one or more valence electrons in order to have eight electrons in their outermost shell. In doing so, atoms obtain the same number of electrons in their outermost shell as the nearest noble gas.

Atoms form ions to obtain an octet of electrons. For main group elements, we use the periodic table to predict the number of electrons a given atom will lose or gain when it forms an ion. Recall from *Section 3.4*, that we can determine the number of valence electrons of the main group elements from the element's location on the periodic table (which is the same as its group number). We use this same strategy to determine the charge on ions for each element. A key feature of the periodic table is that elements in the same group have the same number of electrons in their outermost shell. *As a result, elements in the same group on the periodic table form ions of the same charge.*

Consider the group 1A, 2A, and 3A metals listed in Table 5.1. In general, metals react in nature to lose one or more electrons to form positively charged cations. The metals in group 1A (Li, Na, K, Rb, and Cs) tend to lose one electron to form ions with a +1 charge. Metals in group 2A (Be, Mg, Ca, Sr, and Ba) lose two electrons to form ions with a +2 charge. Group 3A metals (Al, Ga, In, and Tl) lose three electrons to form ions with a +3 charge. However, of these group 3A metals, only aluminum (Al^{3+}) forms ionic compounds. The other metals in group 3A tend to form compounds with covalent bonds.

Table 5.1 Examples of Monatomic Ions and Their Nearest Noble Gases.

noble gases			Metals lose valence electrons			Nonmetals gain valence electrons				noble gases
		1A (1)	2A (2)	3A (13)	5A (15)	6A (16)	7A (17)		
He	←	Li^+							
Ne	←	Na^+	Mg^{2+}	Al^{3+}	N^{3-}	O^{2-}	F^-	→	Ne
Ar	←	K^+	Ca^{2+}		P^{3-}	S^{2-}	Cl^-	→	Ar
Kr	←	Rb^+	Sr^{2+}				Br^-	→	Kr
Xe	←	Cs^+	Ba^{2+}				I^-	→	Xe

Despite the exceptions in group 3, the overall pattern is clear. In all three groups, metals lose electrons to form ions with the same number of electrons as the nearest noble gas.

Nonmetals tend to form negatively charged anions by gaining one or more electron. As shown in Table 5.1, group 7A elements (F, Cl, Br, and I) gain one electron to have the same number of electrons as the nearest noble gas and therefore form -1 ions. Oxygen and sulfur (group 6A) gain two electrons giving these ions a -2 charge. Group 5A elements gain three electrons to form a -3 charge. Thanks to this pattern of how the main group elements ionize, the periodic table is a great tool for determining ionic charges. We refer to this pattern of ionization throughout this chapter and beyond.

Metals with Variable Charges

Many of the transition metals as well as several main group metals form more than one cation, making it difficult to utilize the periodic table to predict charges for these metals. For example, iron exists as a Fe^{2+} ion in some compounds and as Fe^{3+} in other compounds. Lead (Pb) forms both a $+2$ cation and a $+4$ cation. Figure 5.8 provides examples of common metal cations. Notice the metals that have more than one ion. Refer to Figure 5.8 when determining charges for the metals that are difficult to predict using the periodic table.

Figure 5.8 Ionic Charges of Common Metals Ions.

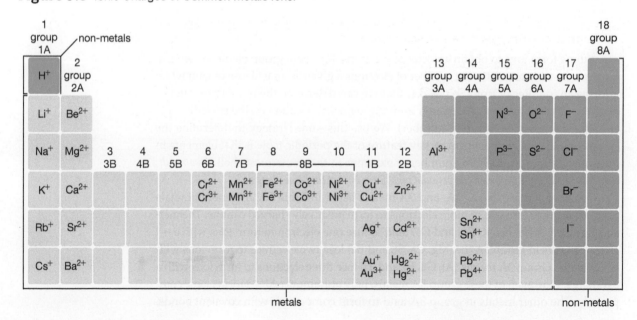

Forming Ions Using Electron Configurations

Let's explore the octet rule in more detail by analyzing how ions form using electron configurations, a concept we learned about in Section 3.5. Sodium (Na), for example, contains eleven protons and eleven electrons as a neutral atom. It has the electron configuration shown here with one valence electron in the 3s subshell. When sodium forms an ion, the 3s electron is lost, resulting in an ion that has eleven protons and ten electrons. This ionization process results in a positively charged cation (Na^+) that has the same electron configuration as the nearest noble gas (which is neon (Ne) in this case). Notice that the nearest noble gas is often in the row above the metal ion.

> The electron in the 3s subshell is lost to form an ion that has eight electrons (an octet) in the outer shell.

$$Na: 1s^2 2s^2 2p^6 3s^1 \longrightarrow Na^+: \underbrace{1s^2 2s^2 2p^6}_{\text{[Ne] (\textit{nearest noble gas})}}$$

We can further explain ion formation using electron configurations. Chlorine, for example, has an unfilled outer third subshell containing seven electrons as shown here. Gaining one electron allows chlorine to satisfy the octet rule and obtain the same electron configuration as the nearest noble gas (argon (Ar) in this case). The electron configuration for the chloride anion is the same as argon and there are eight electrons in the outer shell. Click on VisibleChem Video 5.1 to explore more examples of how atoms transfer electrons to form ions.

> An electron is gained in the 3p subshell to form an ion that has an octet.

$$Cl: 1s^2 2s^2 2p^6 3s^2 3p^5 \longrightarrow Cl^-: \underbrace{1s^2 2s^2 2p^6 3s^2 3p^6}_{\text{[Ar] (\textit{nearest noble gas})}}$$

Watch this concept come to life: **VisibleChem Video 5.1:** Formation of Ions in the Pearson eText.

Predict answers and see step-by-step solutions: **Learn 5.2:** Representing Ions in the Pearson eText.

Apply what you have just learned: **Practice 5.2** in the Pearson eText.

Predict answers and see step-by-step solutions: **Learn 5.3:** using the Periodic Table to Determine Ionic Charges in the Pearson eText.

Apply what you have just learned: **Practice 5.3–5.4** in the Pearson eText.

Explore how Chemistry and Biology connect: **BioConnect 5.1:** Ions in the Body in the Pearson eText.

Quiz yourself on the content of this section: **Check 5.2** in the Pearson eText.

5.3 Ionic Compounds

Now that we have discussed how ions form, let's turn our attention to how ionic bonding occurs to form stable ionic compounds, and how we can predict the formula of an ionic compound using the periodic table. Recall from Section 5.1 that *ionic bonds form between two oppositely charged ions that have a strong electrostatic attraction.* These attractive forces hold ions together in a specific, predictable ratio to form

Figure 5.13 Table Salt (Sodium Chloride).

Sodium and chloride ions bond together to form the ionic compound sodium chloride (NaCl). Zooming into the atomic level of the NaCl compound reveals the ordered structure that consists of alternating positive sodium ions and negative chloride ions called a crystal lattice.

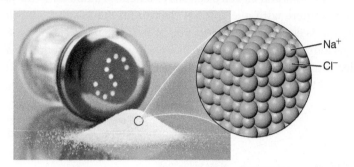

ionic compounds. Ionic compounds are solids at room temperature and usually form crystals with a very ordered structure called a **crystal lattice** (Figure 5.13). This crystalline structure leads to a variety of properties that we explore in detail at the end of this section. Before we do that, let's take a closer look at how ionic compounds form.

Formation of Ionic Compounds from Elements

Ionic compounds form in chemical reactions that generate heat. One example of this is the formation of the ionic compound sodium chloride (NaCl) from sodium metal and chlorine gas (Figure 5.14).

Sodium is a soft grey metal that reacts with chlorine gas when the two elements are in close proximity to one another. First, ions (Na$^+$ and Cl$^-$) form through an electron transfer process. Then the compound (NaCl) forms. Take a look at Video 5.1 to view the chemical process that occurs as sodium chloride forms from the elements sodium and chlorine.

Video 5.1: Formation of Sodium Chloride.

Figure 5.14 Formation of Sodium Chloride from Elements.

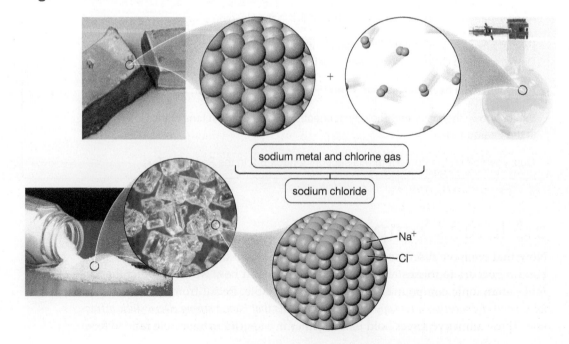

Figure 5.15 Ionic Compound Formation.

A) Sodium and chlorine undergo ionization to form ions. **B)** The oppositely charged ions are attracted to one another to form ionic bonds, which ultimately leads to ionic compound formation.

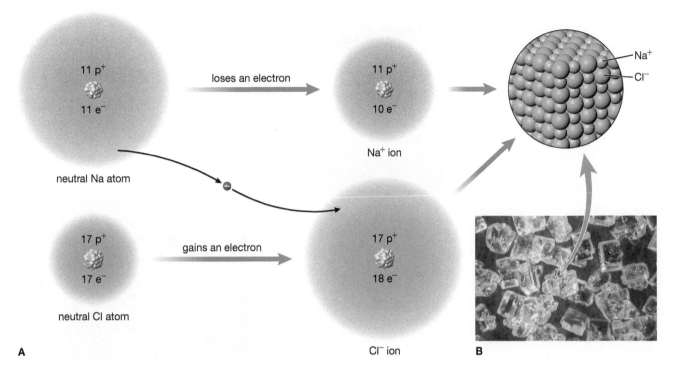

A Cl^- ion   B

A closer look at the formation of sodium chloride (NaCl) is provided in Figure 5.15. Notice how the electron lost from sodium is transferred from the metal to the non-metal to form ions. In this case, sodium loses an electron to form a sodium ion (Na^+), and chlorine gains the same electron to form the chloride ion (Cl^-). Once the oppositely charged ions are formed, a strong attraction occurs between the ions to form an ionic bond. In this case, only one of each of the ions is needed in the formula (NaCl) to achieve an overall neutral charge on the compound. Notice that the cation (Na^+) is always written first followed by the anion (Cl^-). Most of the sodium chloride we consume as table salt is either extracted from Earth or harvested by evaporating sea salt in salt ponds (Figure 5.16).

Predicting Chemical Formulas for Ionic Compounds

Now that we have seen how ionic compounds form from positive and negative ions, let's consider how to predict the chemical formula for ionic compounds. Keep in mind that the sum of all the ionic charges in a compound must be zero, which means that the positive and negative charges must ultimately be equal. The ionic compound calcium oxide (CaO) provides a good example to get us started with this task (Figure 5.17A). The calcium ion in this compound has a +2 charge (Ca^{2+}) and the oxygen a −2 charge (O^{2-}). Notice that when charges are added, we end up with zero ($+2 + -2 = 0$). Although the individual ions in the compound each have a charge, the overall compound is electrically neutral. The ionic charges are not shown in the formula for the compound.

Calcium chloride provides another example (Figure 5.17B). In this case, the charges are not equal, and we include subscripts to indicate the number of each ion needed to balance charge. Two chloride ions are needed to balance each calcium

Figure 5.16 Harvesting Sea Salt.

The mounds contain a mixture of ionic compounds (salts). Sodium chloride makes up a significant percentage of the salt found in the mounds.

Figure 5.17 Chemical Formulas of Ionic Compounds.

A) Calcium oxide, commonly called quicklime, is used in steel production. A single calcium ion balances the charge of the oxygen ion. **B)** Calcium chloride is one of the primary ingredients in deicers used on winter roads. Two chloride ions balance the charge of the calcium ion.

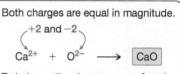

Both charges are equal in magnitude.

+2 and −2

$$Ca^{2+} + O^{2-} \longrightarrow \boxed{CaO}$$

To balance the charges, one of each ion is needed.

A

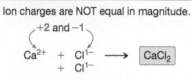

Ion charges are NOT equal in magnitude.

+2 and −1

$$Ca^{2+} + \begin{matrix} Cl^{1-} \\ + \ Cl^{1-} \end{matrix} \longrightarrow \boxed{CaCl_2}$$

To balance the charges, 2 Cl⁻ anions are needed for each Ca^{2+}.

B

ion. When the charges are added up, again, we end up with zero $(+2 + 2(-1) = 0)$. The compound is electrically neutral. Explore VisibleChem Video 5.2 to view more examples.

 Watch this concept come to life: **VisibleChem Video 5.2:** Formation of Ionic Compounds in the Pearson eText.

Predict answers and see step-by-step solutions: **Learn 5.4:** Writing Formulas for Ionic Compounds from Ions in the Pearson eText.

Apply what you have just learned: **Practice 5.5** in the Pearson eText.

Properties of Ionic Compounds

Ionic compounds have a crystal lattice structure that consists of alternating positive and negative ions with a strong attractive force holding the ions together. Because of this structure, most ionic compounds share the following properties:

High Melting Point: The **melting point** is the temperature at which a substance changes from solid to liquid. Because of the strong electrostatic attractions between ions in ionic compounds high temperatures are necessary to provide enough energy to melt these compounds. For example, solid sodium chloride (NaCl) melts at 801 °C (Figure 5.18).

High Conductivity: Conductivity is a substance's ability to transmit electricity. Although ionic compounds are composed of ions with electric charges

Figure 5.18 Molten Salt Concentrated Solar Plant.

Arrays of mirrors direct light to a massive tower containing salts like sodium chloride. The molten salt can be used to boil water, producing steam that generates electricity. Molten salt can be stored in insulated tanks on the ground allowing electricity to be produced later, even if the sun is not shining.

(positively-charged cations and negatively-charged anions), they are generally unable to conduct electricity in the solid state. This is because the charged ions in ionic solids are not able to move, and moving electrons are necessary for electricity to be conducted. However, if an ionic solid is melted at high temperature and changes to the liquid state, its ions become mobile and can conduct electricity.

High Solubility: Solubility is a substance's capacity to be dissolved, especially in water. When ionic compounds dissolve in water, the ions within the crystal lattice become surrounded by water molecules and flow freely with the liquid water and conduct electricity (Figure 5.19). This is a very important point, because we all need ions dissolved in water for our cells to function properly. As we discuss in later chapters, if the concentration of ions in our bodies is not maintained within a certain range, we can become very sick.

Quiz yourself on the content of this section: **Check 5.3** in the Pearson eText.

Figure 5.19 Sodium Ions and Chloride Ions Surrounded by Water Molecules.

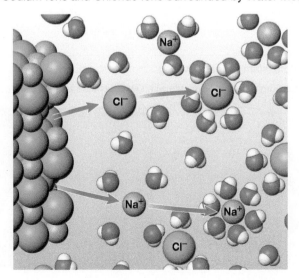

5.4 Naming Ionic Compounds

Naming systems provide a common language for chemical compounds and allow scientists and medical professionals to communicate with one another. For example, intravenous fluids (IV) administered to patients in hospitals often contain a range of ions and compounds such as potassium ions (K^+) or sodium chloride (Figure 5.20). For scientists and medical professionals to communicate effectively, a systematic naming system is critical.

In this section, we focus on naming ionic **binary compounds**, which are *compounds composed of two elements or two ions*. All ionic compound names provide the cation name first, followed by the anion name. We will learn to name ions individually and then put the names of the cation and anion together to create the name of the complete ionic formula.

Naming Ions

To name cations of main group metals, we use the name of the element.

Ca^{2+} calcium

Na^+ sodium

Mg^{2+} magnesium

To name transition metal ions that have more than one possible cation (see Figure 5.8), we indicate the charge on the ion using a Roman numeral in parentheses.

Iron is an example of a transition metal that has two possible cations, Fe^{2+} and Fe^{3+}. The names of the iron cations include a Roman numeral that corresponds to the charge on the ion.

Fe^{2+} iron(II)

Fe^{3+} iron(III)

Metal cations play a significant role in human health. One way they are consumed is through fruits and vegetables (Figure 5.21).

Calcium ion—Ca^{2+}: Adults need 1000 mg/day

Iron(II) ion—Fe^{2+}: Women and teenage girls need at least 15 mg/day, men can get by on 10 mg/day.

To name simple anions, we use the name of the element, but change the ending to *–ide*.

Cl^- chlor**ide**

Br^- brom**ide**

O^{2-} ox**ide**

Figure 5.20 Potassium Chloride IV Bag.

Potassium chloride is administered to patients with low potassium levels.

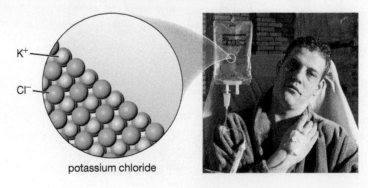

potassium chloride

Figure 5.21 Fruits and Vegetables Contain Numerous Ions that are Important for Human Health.

Plants absorb ions from the soil. Most of the minerals in the human diet come directly from plants, such as fruits and vegetables, or indirectly from animal sources. Minerals may also be present in drinking water, but this depends on the location of the water source. Calcium and iron are two examples of important ions that humans must ingest by consuming healthy foods.

Apply what you have just learned: **Practice 5.6 and 5.7** in the Pearson eText.

Naming Ionic Compounds that Include Cations from Main Group Elements

Now that we know how to name cations and anions, let's put these ideas together to name ionic compounds, several of which are found in multivitamins (Figure 5.22).

To name these compounds, place the cation first followed by the anion. If the metal forms one specific cation, do not use a Roman numeral in the name. For example, naming the ionic compound KI involves naming the main group cation (*potassium*) then naming the anion and adding an *–ide* ending (*iodide*). Look closely at how we name the compounds-*potassium iodide and magnesium oxide.*

K^+	I^-	KI
potassium	iodide	potassium iodide

Mg^{2+}	O^{2-}	MgO
magnesium	oxide	magnesium oxide

Naming Ionic Compounds that include Metals with Variable Charge

To name ionic compounds that contain a metal with a variable charge, there is an additional step to consider. In this case, we must indicate the charge using a Roman numeral, so the first step is to determine what the charge is on the metal. To do this, we use

Figure 5.22 Multivitamins.

Multivitamin pills often contain a variety of ionic compounds.

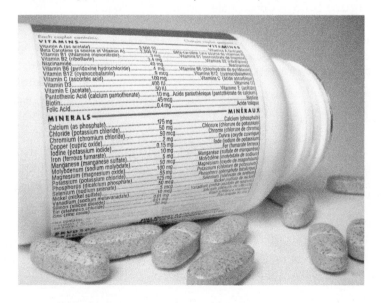

the known charge on the anion to figure out the charge on the metal. For example, when given the chemical formula $CrCl_2$, we can use the known charge on a chloride ion (Cl^-) to figure out the charge on chromium (Cr). Since there are two chloride anions, each of which has a -1 charge, the chromium cation must have a $+2$ charge to make the overall charge of the compound zero.

$$CrCl_2$$
$$Cr^{2+} \qquad 2Cl^- = -2$$

Once we know the charge on the cation, we add a Roman numeral to the name to indicate the $+2$ charge:

Cr^{2+} chromium(**II**)

Cl^- chlor*ide*

We write the name of the compound by listing the cation followed by the anion.

chromium(II) chloride

Predict answers and see step-by-step solutions: **Learn 5.5:** Writing the Name of Ionic Compounds in the Pearson eText.

Apply what you have just learned: **Practice 5.8** in the Pearson eText.

Predict answers and see step-by-step solutions: **Learn 5.6:** Naming Ionic Compounds with Cations that have Variable Charges in the Pearson eText.

Apply what you have just learned: **Practice 5.9 and 5.10** in the Pearson eText.

Writing Formulas for Ionic Compounds

It is also helpful to produce the chemical formula when given the name of an ionic compound. We take the following steps to carry out this task:

1. *Determine the charges on both the cation and anion*

2. *Use the charges to determine which subscripts are needed to balance charges*

3. *Write the formula with the metal (cation) first, followed by the nonmetal (anion)*

For example, magnesium chloride is an ionic compound that can be administered by IV to treat a dangerous condition during pregnancy called eclampsia (Figure 5.23).

To determine the chemical formula from the compound name, *magnesium chloride*, begin by determining the charges on both the cation and anion. Magnesium is a group 2A metal that forms a cation with a $+2$ charge. Chlorine is a group 7A element that gains one electron to form the Cl^- anion during ionic bonding. To balance the overall charge on the compound, use the charge on the cation to determine the number of anions needed.

Figure 5.23 A Concentrated Magnesium Chloride Solution.

This solution may be diluted and used to treat eclampsia, severe asthma, and included in an IV solution to treat a patient with low magnesium levels.

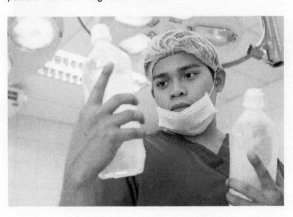

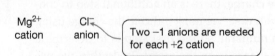

Mg^{2+} cation Cl^- anion   Two -1 anions are needed for each $+2$ cation

The last step is to write the formula using subscripts to show the number of ions needed to form a compound with zero overall charge. Write the cation first, followed by the anion. In this case, the formula is: $MgCl_2$.

Predict answers and see step-by-step solutions: **Learn 5.7:** Determining the Chemical Formula of an Ionic Compound from its Name in the Pearson eText.

Apply what you have just learned: **Practice 5.11** in the Pearson eText.

Quiz yourself on the content of this section: **Check 5.4** in the Pearson eText.

5.5 Polyatomic Ions

In addition to the single atom ions that we've been discussing in this chapter, *it is possible for a group of covalently bound atoms to have an overall ionic charge.* These charged groups of atoms are **polyatomic ions**. Many common polyatomic ions contain a non-metal bonded to oxygen atoms. For example, sulfur and oxygen combine to form the polyatomic sulfate ion (SO_4^{2-}). Similarly, nitrogen and oxygen combine to form the polyatomic nitrate ion (NO_3^-). Table 5.3 lists common polyatomic ions. Notice that the table only contains two ions that are positively charged, the hydronium ion (H_3O^+) and the ammonium ion (NH_4^+). These are the only two positively charged polyatomic ions we discuss in this chapter.

The names of the most common polyatomic ions typically contain the suffix *–ate* such as sulfate, nitrate, and carbonate. Becoming familiar with the *–ate suffix* will help to recognize when a compound contains a polyatomic ion. The *-ite* ending is present when there is more than one way of combining oxygen with another nonmetal and two different ions form. For example, there are two polyatomic ions that form from nitrogen and oxygen: nitrate (NO_3^-) and nitrite (NO_2^-). To begin learning the polyatomic ions, it is useful to become familiar with the ions that are in bold in Table 5.3.

Ionic Compounds that Include Polyatomic Ions

The atoms in a polyatomic ion are held together with covalent bonds (which involve the sharing of electrons), which we discuss further in Chapter 6. Here we focus on how polyatomic ions combine with other oppositely charged ions to form ionic

Table 5.3 Common Polyatomic Ions.

Nonmetal	Formula	Name
Carbon	**CO_3^{2-}**	**Carbonate**
	HCO_3^-	Hydrogen carbonate or bicarbonate
	$CH_3CO_2^-$	Acetate
	CN^-	Cyanide
Nitrogen	**NO_3^-**	**Nitrate**
	NO_2^-	Nitrite
Oxygen	**OH^-**	**Hydroxide**
Phosphorus	**PO_4^{3-}**	**Phosphate**
	HPO_4^{2-}	Hydrogen phosphate
	$H_2PO_4^-$	Dihydrogen phosphate
Sulfur	**SO_4^{2-}**	**Sulfate**
	HSO_4^-	Hydrogen sulfate or bisulfate
	SO_3^{2-}	Sulfite
	HSO_3^-	Hydrogen sulfite or bisulfite

Figure 5.24 Coral Reefs are Composed of Calcium Carbonate.

A) The Great Barrier Reef of Australia is the world's largest coral reef. **B)** Corals are animals that produce skeletons made of calcium carbonate. **C)** Calcium carbonate forms when a positively charged calcium ion bonds to a negatively charged carbonate ion.

polyatomic carbonate ion (CO_3^{2-})

calcium ion (Ca^{2+})

calcium carbonate ($CaCO_3$)

A   B   C

compounds. Consider the bonding of a calcium ion (Ca^{2+}) with the carbonate ion (CO_3^{2-}) to produce calcium carbonate. Calcium carbonate is an ionic compound that is found throughout nature. Calcium carbonate is important in coral reefs and the protective shells of numerous marine creatures (Figure 5.24).

$$Ca^{2+} + CO_3^{2-} \rightarrow CaCO_3$$

To write chemical formulas that contain polyatomic ions, we follow a similar process as we used in Section 5.3. Polyatomic ions typically have negative charges and take the place of the nonmetal ions we saw in the formula examples in Section 5.3. As before, we include subscripts to achieve charge balance. Formulas must represent electrically neutral compounds. For the calcium carbonate example, the metal ion has a +2 charge, and the polyatomic ion has a −2 charge. In this case, we don't need subscripts. We write the formula by writing the cation first followed by the polyatomic ion. Table 5.4 lists some other examples of ionic compounds that contain polyatomic ions and are important in the healthcare industry.

Table 5.4 Ionic Compounds that Contain Polyatomic Ions.

Metal Ion	Polyatomic Ion	Ionic Compound	Medical Application
Ba^{2+}	SO_4^{2-}	$BaSO_4$	X-rays
Fe^{2+}	SO_4^{2-}	$FeSO_4$	Treatment for iron deficiency
Li^+	CO_3^{2-}	Li_2CO_3	Treatment for bipolar disorder
Na^+	HCO_3^-	$NaHCO_3$	Antacid

 Predict answers and see step-by-step solutions: **Learn 5.8:** Providing the Chemical Formula of an Ionic Compound that Includes a Polyatomic Ion in the Pearson eText.

Apply what you have just learned: **Practice 5.12** in the Pearson eText.

Naming Ionic Compounds with Polyatomic Ions

Naming compounds that include polyatomic ions is similar to naming ionic compounds. As we discussed in Section 5.4, we write the name of the positive ion first, followed by the name of the anion, which in these compounds is a polyatomic ion. It is a good idea to consult Table 5.3 to find the charge and name of the polyatomic ions.

Figure 5.25 Fertilizer Dispensed on Crops.

Farmers around the world apply approximately 200 million tons of fertilizer each year.

Most of the ingredients in fertilizer (Figure 5.25) are ionic compounds that contain polyatomic ions (Table 5.5). Consider the compound KNO_3, which is one of the most common ingredients in fertilizer. To name this compound, we use the element name for K (potassium) and then we recognize that the nitrate ion (NO_3^-) is present. Once we have the names of both ions, we put the names together, with the cation first (potassium nitrate).

$$K^+ \quad NO_3^- \quad KNO_3$$
potassium   nitrate   potassium nitrate

If an ionic compound requires more than one polyatomic ion to obtain charge balance, we include parentheses around the whole polyatomic ion formula along with a subscript. For example, iron(III) nitrate requires three nitrate ions to counterbalance the +3 charge on iron.

$$Fe^{3+} \quad NO_3^- \times 3 \quad Fe(NO_3)_3$$
Iron(III)   nitrate   iron(III) nitrate

In this case, we place the polyatomic nitrate ion in parentheses and include the subscript 3. Table 5.5 lists several examples of the names of ionic compounds that contain polyatomic ions.

Table 5.5 Major Ingredients of Fertilizer.

Many ionic compounds contain polyatomic ions including the major ingredients of fertilizer.

	Metal Ion	Polyatomic Ion	Compound & Name
a.	K^+ potassium	NO_3^- nitrate	KNO_3 **potassium nitrate**
b.	K^+ potassium	SO_4^{2-} sulfate	K_2SO_4 **potassium sulfate**
c.	NH_4^+ ammonium	NO_3^- nitrate	$(NH_4)_3NO_3$ **ammonium nitrate**
d.	NH_4^+ ammonium	SO_4^{2-} nitrate	$(NH_4)_2SO_4$ **ammonium sulfate**
e.	NH_4^+ ammonium	PO_4^{3-} phosphate	$(NH_4)_3PO_4$ **ammonium phosphate**

Apply what you have just learned: **Practice 5.13** in the Pearson eText.

Explore how Chemistry and Biology connect: **BioConnect 5.2:** Polyatomic Ions and the Environment in the Pearson eText.

Quiz yourself on the content of this section: **Check 5.5** in the Pearson eText.

Chapter Summary

5.1 Introduction to Bonding

Learning Objective: Define and describe ionic bonding.

Chemical bonds hold atoms together, forming the millions of different compounds and molecules. Ionic bonding involves the *transfer* of electrons between elements to form electrically charged ions. Oppositely charged ions are strongly attracted to each other and bond together to form an overall electrically neutral ionic compound. Ionic bonding, the topic of this chapter, typically occurs between a metal and a nonmetal, or between a metal and a polyatomic ion. Covalent bonding, the topic of Chapter 6, involves the *sharing* of electrons between atoms of different elements to form covalent compounds. Covalent bonding typically occurs between two nonmetals, or between a nonmetal and a metalloid.

Key Terms

chemical bond	covalent compound	ionic bond
covalent bond	ion	ionic compound

5.2 Ions

Learning Objective: Determine the charge on ions using the periodic table and the octet rule.

The octet rule states that atoms generally gain, lose, or share the number of electrons needed so that they end up with eight valence electrons in their outer shell. Ions form when a neutral atom either gains or accepts electrons. Cations are positively (+) charged ions that form when a neutral atom (generally a metal) *loses* one or more electrons. Anions are negatively (−) charged ions that form when a neutral atom (generally a nonmetal) *gains* one or more electrons. The periodic table is a very useful tool for determining whether an element forms a cation or an anion and the charge of that ion. Transition metals form cations, but the charge of the cations is less predictable in terms of the number of electrons that will be lost in the ionization process. Many of the transition metals form two or more different positive ions.

VisibleChem Video 5.1: Formation of Ions

BioConnect 5.1: Ions in the Body

Key Terms

anion
cation
octet rule

5.3 Ionic Compounds

Learning Objective: Write formulas for ionic compounds.

Ionic bonding occurs as a result of the attraction between oppositely charged ions. Chemical formulas of ionic compounds require that the sum of all ionic charges in a compound equal zero. Ions pack together in tightly held three-dimensional arrays in ionic compounds with alternating positive and negatively charged ions to create a crystal lattice. Because of the solid crystal lattice structures of ionic compounds, they have high melting points due to strong attractive forces among the tightly packed ions.

VisibleChem Video 5.2: Formation of Ionic Compounds

Video 5.1: Formation of Sodium Chloride

Key Terms

conductivity
crystal lattice
melting point
solubility

5.4 Naming Ionic Compounds

Learning Objective: Write the name of ionic compounds from a given formula, and provide the formula when given the name of an ionic compound.

To name cations of metals, we use the name of the element from which they are formed. If the cation is a transition metal, we add a Roman numeral indicating charge after the element name. For example, the potassium cation is K^+, and the cobalt(II) transition metal cation is Co^{2+}. To name anions of nonmetals, we write the name of the element, and replace the ending with *-ide*. For example, the chloride anion is Cl^-, and the sulfide anion is S^{2-}. To name ionic compounds, we list the cation first, followed by the negatively charged anion with a space between the two names. For example, LiBr is *lithium bromide* and $CaCl_2$ is *calcium chloride*.

Key Term

binary compound

5.5 Polyatomic Ions

Learning Objective: Recognize the common polyatomic ions and write the name and formula of compounds with polyatomic ions.

Polyatomic ions contain two or more covalently bonded atoms that collectively carry an overall charge. The names of a number of common polyatomic ions contain the suffix *-ate*, such as phosphate, sulfate, nitrate, and carbonate.

Knowing the names, formulas, and charges of several common polyatomic ions is useful because these ions play many roles in biology, medicine, and the environment.

BioConnect 5.2: Polyatomic Ions and the Environment

Key Term

polyatomic ion

 # End-of-Chapter Quiz

Have you mastered the content of this chapter? Try the **End-of-Chapter Quiz** in the Pearson eText.

1. What occurs when two atoms react and a positively charged ion forms?
a) Electrons are shared between two or more atoms in this process.
b) Electrons transfer to the atom that forms the positively charged ion.
c) Protons transfer to the atom that forms the positively charged ion.
d) Electrons transfer from the atom that forms the positively charged ion.

2. Which statement is true about chemical bonding?
a) Protons are shared or transferred between atoms during bonding.
b) Electrons are shared or transferred between atoms during bonding.
c) Only elements with even numbers of electrons bond to elements with odd numbers of protons.
d) Atoms only bond with other atoms containing different numbers of electrons.

3. What is the total number of electrons and the charge on the ion that forms when magnesium loses two electrons?
   a) 12 total electrons, Mg^{2+}
   b) 12 total electrons, Mg^{+}
   c) 10 total electrons, Mg^{2+}
   d) 11 total electrons, Mg^{+}

4. Which of the following elements forms ions of different charges?
   a) bromine
   b) potassium
   c) beryllium
   d) nickel

5. What is the charge on the cobalt ion in the ionic compound $CoCl_3$?
   a) 8+
   b) 3+
   c) 3−
   d) 2−

6. How many protons and electrons are in the O^{2-} ion?
   a) 8 protons, 8 electrons
   b) 8 protons, 6 electrons
   c) 6 protons, 8 electrons
   d) 8 protons, 10 electrons

7. What is the formula for the ionic compound formed by calcium and iodine?
   a) Ca_2I_3
   b) CI_2
   c) CaI_2
   d) CaI

8. Manganese(II) sulfide is an ionic compound found in the mineral Alabandite. What is the correct formula for this compound?
   a) MnS
   b) Mg_2Su
   c) M_2S
   d) Mg_2S

9. What is the formula for the ionic compound that cesium and oxygen form?
   a) CsO
   b) CsO_2
   c) Cs_2O
   d) CsO_3

10. What is the correct name for the ionic compound SrO?
    a) strontium oxygen
    b) stranium oxide
    c) strontium(I) oxygen
    d) strontium oxide

11. The ionic compound CoO is used in blue colored glazes and enamels in the ceramics industry. What is the correct name for this ionic compound?
    a) cobalt oxygen
    b) calcium oxide
    c) cobalt(II) oxide
    d) cobalt(I) oxide

12. What is the correct name for the ionic compound RbI?
    a) rubidium iodine
    b) rubidium iodide
    c) rubidium mono-oxygen
    d) rubidium(I) iodide

13. Ammonium sulfate is used in the agricultural industry as a fertilizer. What is the correct formula for ammonium sulfate?
    a) $(NH_4)_2 SO$
    b) NH_3SO_4
    c) $(NH_4)_2 SO_4$
    d) $(NH_3)_3 SO_3$

14. What is the correct name for $Cu(NO_3)_2$?
    a) currium dinitrate
    b) copper (II) nitrate
    c) copper dinitrate
    d) copper nitrate

15. The ionic compound NaF is added to drinking water and dental treatments to strengthen teeth and make them more resistant to cavities. What is the correct name for NaF?
    a) sodium (I) fluoride
    b) sodium fluorine
    c) natrium monofluoride
    d) sodium fluoride

Chapter 6
Covalent Compounds

Covalent bonds link together the atoms in our DNA, providing the chemical basis for who we are.

⌄ Chapter Outline

Learning Objectives

6.1 Define and describe covalent bonding.

6.2 Compare and contrast covalent and ionic compounds.

6.3 Draw covalent compounds using Lewis structures.

6.4 Predict the shapes of covalent compounds using VSEPR theory.

6.5 Write the name of a binary covalent compound from a given formula and provide the formula when given the name of a covalent compound.

6.6 Recognize a variety of ways to represent covalent compounds.

Introduction

What types of forces attach chemotherapy drugs to the antibodies that deliver them (Figure 6.1)? How can DNA be successfully recovered from a human that's been dead for over 5000 years (Figure 6.2)? How can scientists design drugs to effectively target a specific virus or other pathogen? In Chapter 5, we examined the characteristics of ionic bonding, we now turn to the other major bonding model, covalent bonding. From the simplest covalently bonded molecule, hydrogen gas (H_2), to the greenhouse gas methane (CH_4), to the glucose molecule ($C_6H_{12}O_6$) that helps support life, many of the compounds that affect our daily lives are covalent. These important molecules form when atoms share electrons. In this chapter, we explore the nature of the covalent bond and covalently bonded molecules.

Figure 6.1 Antibodies Approaching Cell Receptors.

In this artist's image, antibodies approach the surface of a cancer cell. Covalent bonds attach powerful drugs to antibodies allowing targeted delivery to cancer cells.

Figure 6.2 Otzi the Iceman Mummy.

This mummified body, discovered on the border between Austria and Italy in the Alps in 1991, is estimated to be 5300 years old. Strong covalent bonds connect the atoms that make up DNA, the molecule that transfers genetic information between generations, allowing scientists to recover and analyze DNA from ancient samples.

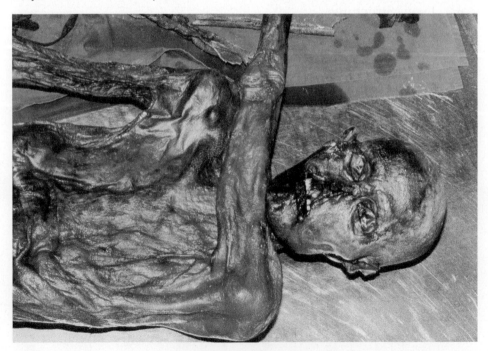

6.1 Introduction to Covalent Bonding

In 1916, chemist Gilbert Newton Lewis published a famous article *"The Atom and the Molecule."* In the article, Lewis proposed that a chemical bond is a pair of electrons shared by two atoms. The theory Lewis put forward provides a powerful and easy-to-use tool to draw and predict molecular structure. Molecular structure is very important because it ultimately governs molecular function (Figure 6.3). We revisit Lewis's work in Section 6.3 when we learn how to draw molecules using *Lewis structures*. In this section, we begin with a discussion of the nature of covalent bonds.

As we saw in Section 5.1, covalent bonding *involves the sharing of electrons between two atoms*. In ionic bonding, in contrast, ions form when one or more electrons transfer from one atom to another. So, how does this sharing of electrons happen, and why do covalent bonds form?

How Atoms Share Electrons to Form Covalent Bonds

A covalent bond forms between two atoms because the nucleus of an atom is positively charged, and the electrons around the nucleus are negatively charged.

As a specific example, consider a situation when two hydrogen atoms, which are the smallest atoms on the periodic table, approach each other and bond to form the simplest covalently bonded molecule possible, H_2. When the two atoms approach each other (Figure 6.4), the positively charged nucleus of each atom becomes close

---

Figure 6.3 Gilbert Newton Lewis in His Lab.

Lewis originally drew atoms as cubes, with each point representing possible electron positions. This idea was eventually incorporated into Lewis structures.

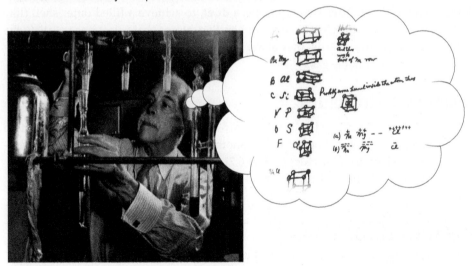

Figure 6.4 A Balancing Act.

Attractive and repulsive forces lead to the formation of covalent bond between two atoms.

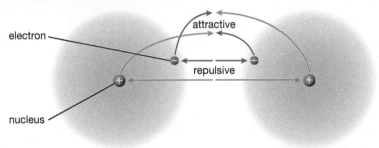

enough to feel an electrical attraction to the negatively charged electron in the electron cloud of the other atom. This attraction pulls the two atoms closer together. At the same time that the attractive forces are at work, the positively charged nuclei of the two atoms begin to repel each other. The result is a balancing act between opposite charges attracting and like charges repelling, which ultimately determines the strength and length of a covalent bond.

Representing Covalent Bonds and Electrons in Molecules

A hydrogen atom has one valence electron. A hydrogen molecule (H_2) consists of two hydrogen atoms that share a pair of valence electrons to create a covalent bond. We represent the bonding valence electron pair with a *line* or *two dots* (Figure 6.5). This symbolism is very common and something you will encounter throughout your studies of chemistry.

The bond between hydrogen and fluorine in the hydrogen fluoride molecule (HF) is also a covalent bond (Figure 6.6). Hydrogen has one valence electron and fluorine has seven. Each atom shares one valence electron to form a single two-electron covalent bond that we represent with a line. The fluorine atom contains three additional pairs of electrons that are not shared with hydrogen. We refer to these pairs of unshared electrons as **nonbonded electron pairs** or **lone pairs**. We represent each lone pair of electrons with a pair of dots.

In both covalently bonded molecules (H_2 and HF), the electron sharing process provides a stable arrangement, since the shared electrons provide each atom with the number of electrons as the nearest noble gas. Fluorine requires eight total electrons, which is the same number found in the nearest noble gas, neon. Hydrogen (H), on the other hand, only requires two electrons, a **duet**, to achieve a filled outer shell (like helium its nearest noble gas). In covalent bonding, atoms share electrons to satisfy the octet rule, or in other words, they share electrons to have the same number of electrons as the nearest noble gas.

Diatomic Molecules

The hydrogen molecule (H_2) is a **diatomic molecule** because it contains just two atoms that are covalently bonded to one another. There are seven elements that naturally occur as diatomic molecules (Figure 6.7). The air we breathe is composed primarily of two diatomic molecules, oxygen (O_2) and nitrogen (N_2; Figure 6.8).

Figure 6.5 Covalent Bonds Represented with Both Dots and Lines as Illustrated on the Hydrogen Molecule (H_2).

Figure 6.6 Bonding Electrons and Nonbonding Electrons Are Shown on the Hydrogen Fluoride Molecule (HF).

Hydrogen only needs a total of *two* electrons to be stable. Fluorine follows the octet rule and must share electrons to obtain eight total electrons.

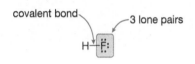

Figure 6.7 Diatomic Molecules.

Seven elements exist in their natural state as diatomic molecules.

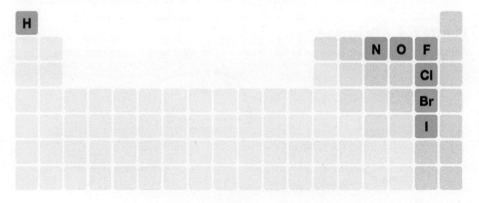

Figure 6.8 Diatomic Molecules in Air.

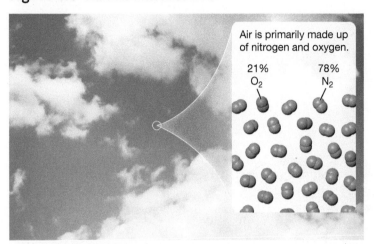

Air is primarily made up of nitrogen and oxygen.

21%
O_2

78%
N_2

Figure 6.9 Double and Triple Bonds.

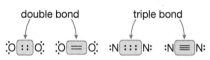

double bond   triple bond

In addition to single covalent bonds, multiple covalent bonds are possible. Oxygen (O_2), for example, must form a **double bond**, or share two pairs of electrons to satisfy the octet rule. Nitrogen (N_2) forms a **triple bond**, which is made up of three shared pairs of electrons. We symbolize multiple bonds using additional lines to represent shared pairs of electrons (Figure 6.9).

Apply what you have just learned: **Practice 6.1** in the Pearson eText.

Quiz yourself on the content of this section: **Check 6.1** in the Pearson eText.

6.2 Covalent Bonding and the Periodic Table

How do we know if two atoms will form an ionic bond or form a covalent bond? Covalent bonds form when two nonmetals combine, or when a bond forms between a nonmetal and a metalloid. Nonmetals do not easily lose electrons, especially to other nonmetal atoms, and therefore nonmetals rely on sharing electrons to form chemical bonds. When we determine whether a compound contains ionic or covalent bonds, the first thing to consider is whether metals or nonmetals are present in the compound. This is information that we can retrieve from the periodic table (Figure 6.10).

The following are two important guidelines to remember about ionic and covalent bonds:

- An ionic bond forms between a metal and nonmetal.
- A covalent bond forms between two nonmetals or between a nonmetal and a metalloid.

Examples of Covalent Compounds

The covalent compounds, methane (CH_4), ammonia (NH_3), and water (H_2O) are examples that feature nonmetals covalently bonding to satisfy the octet rule. Methane (CH_4), the main component in natural gas, is a covalent compound. In methane

Figure 6.10 Nonmetal & Metalloid Region of Periodic Table.

Nonmetals bond with other nonmetals by sharing electrons to form covalent bonds.

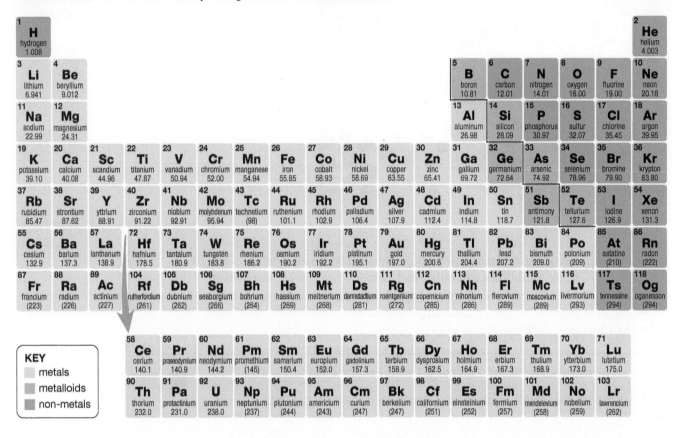

(Figure 6.11a), carbon is the **central atom**. The central atom in a molecule or poly-atomic ion is bonded to more than one other atom. Carbon, oxygen, and nitrogen are examples of elements that often serve as central atoms because they form more than one covalent bond when present in a molecule. Carbon has four valence electrons, each of which is available for bond formation. In methane, carbon shares each one of its four valence electrons with a hydrogen atom, and the hydrogen atoms each share one valence electron with the central carbon atom. The final methane structure contains *eight shared electrons* for carbon and *two shared electrons* for each hydrogen atom. Methane is a stable compound that satisfies the octet rule.

In ammonia (NH_3), nitrogen is the central atom. In this covalent compound, nitrogen has five valence electrons and therefore forms three covalent bonds and has one lone pair and achieves an octet (Figure 6.11b). Water (H_2O) has a central oxygen atom that has six valence electrons. In this molecule oxygen must share two electrons, forming two covalent bonds, to have the same number of elctrons as the nearest noble gas (Figure 6.11c). A water molecule also has two lone pairs on the oxygen central atom.

In all of these molecules, hydrogen forms a single convalent bond with another atom to achieve a duet.

Using the Periodic Table to Predict the Number of Covalent Bonds

The three molecules we just explored (CH_4, NH_3, and H_2O) illustrate a pattern of covalent bond formation that mirrors the organization of the periodic table. *An*

Figure 6.11 Three Examples of Covalent Compounds.

A) Methane (CH_4) burns in stovetop burners to provide heat. In methane, carbon forms four covalent bonds with four hydrogen atoms. **B)** Ammonia (NH_3) can be stored in compression tanks until needed to produce a variety of cleaning products. In ammonia, nitrogen forms three covalent bonds with three hydrogen atoms. **C)** In the water molecule, oxygen forms two covalent bonds with hydrogen to satisfy the octet rule.

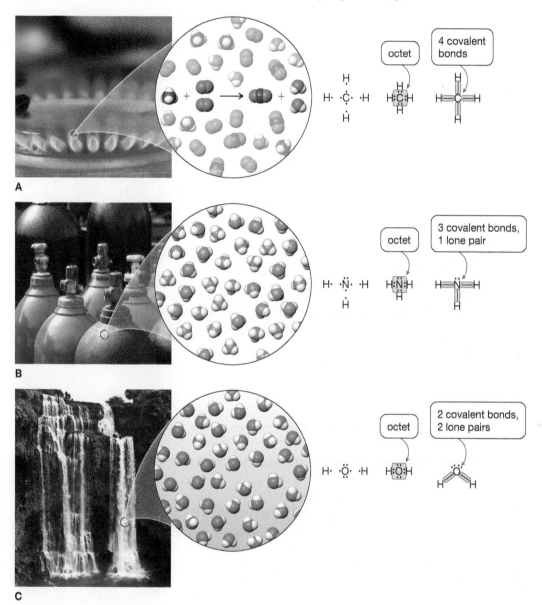

element's position in the periodic table (specifically its group number) indicates the number of covalent bonds it will form. For example, notice that many of the nonmetals and metalloids (Figure 6.12) form a specific number of covalent bonds with other atoms in an effort to obtain the same number of electrons as the nearest noble gas. For example, carbon (C) is four elements to the left of the noble gases and to form stable compounds, it must share four electrons to form four covalent bonds with other atoms. Nitrogen (N) is three positions over and typically forms three bonds. Oxygen (O) is two elements over from the noble gases and must form two bonds to satisfy the octet rule.

In the upcoming sections of this chapter, we will see how this pattern of bonding is useful for drawing and predicting the shapes of covalent compounds.

Figure 6.12 Bonding Patterns in Nonmetals.

This partial periodic table illustrates the typical bonding patterns for the nonmetals.

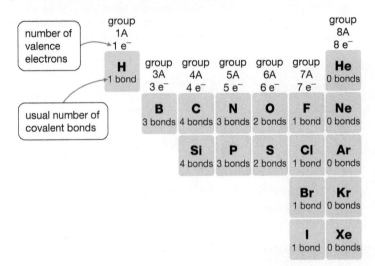

Apply what you have just learned: **Practice 6.2 and 6.3** in the Pearson eText.

Quiz yourself on the content of this section: **Check 6.2** in the Pearson eText.

6.3 Lewis Structures

The chemical formula of a compound, such as CO_2, provides the ratio of atoms in the compound, but it does not indicate how the atoms are connected, nor does it show the electrons. **Lewis structures**, in contrast, do provide this level of detail (Figure 6.13).

Figure 6.13 Carbon Dioxide.

A) We can represent the greenhouse gas, carbon dioxide, with either its chemical formula, or its Lewis structure. The Lewis structure provides additional information about the arrangement of atoms and electrons in the molecule. **B)** The U.S. emitted 6,577 million metric tons of CO_2 in 2019 (EPA).

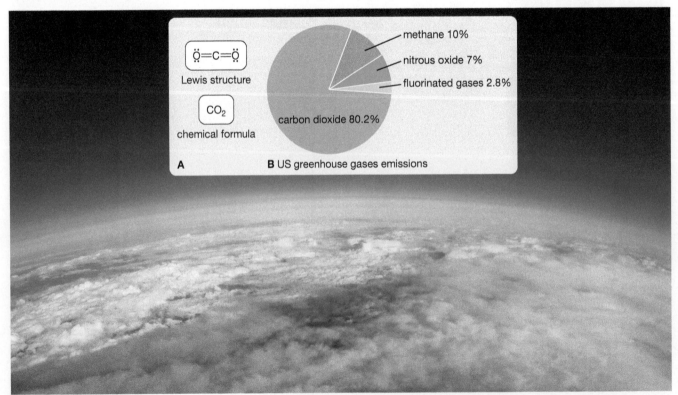

Lewis structures are a way of representing atoms or molecules by showing electrons as dots surrounding an element symbol. They illustrate the connection between atoms in a molecule, as well as the specific arrangement of electrons in a covalent compound, including both the bonding electrons and nonbonding electrons. In this section, you learn to draw Lewis structures. Becoming familiar with these structures can expand your understanding of how molecules are put together.

There are four general steps for drawing Lewis structures (Figure 6.14).

1. Determine the total number of valence electrons on each structure and use only those electrons to form bonds.

2. Identify the central atom, which is typically the element that has the fewest atoms in the chemical formula.

3. Connect atoms by placing valence electrons so that every atom has an octet of electrons, except hydrogen, which should have a duet. *Remember to count shared electrons for both covalently bonded atoms involved.*

4. Use multiple bonds if necessary.

These rules provide a general approach for drawing covalent compounds. You can get a closer look at specific examples in VisibleChem Videos 6.1–6.3. Learns 6.1–6.3 illustrate the step-by-step procedure for drawing Lewis structures.

Watch this concept come to life:
VisibleChem Video 6.1: Drawing the Lewis Structure of Methane, **VisibleChem Video 6.2:** Drawing the Lewis Structure of Water, and **VisibleChem Video 6.3:** Drawing the Lewis Structure of Carbon Tetrachloride.

Predict answers and see step-by-step solutions: **Learn 6.1:** Drawing Lewis Structures of Covalent Compounds in the Pearson eText.

Apply what you have just learned: **Practice 6.4 and 6.5** in the Pearson eText.

Figure 6.14 Steps for Drawing Lewis Structures.

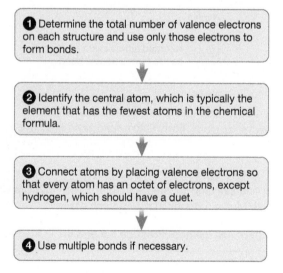

1. Determine the total number of valence electrons on each structure and use only those electrons to form bonds.

2. Identify the central atom, which is typically the element that has the fewest atoms in the chemical formula.

3. Connect atoms by placing valence electrons so that every atom has an octet of electrons, except hydrogen, which should have a duet.

4. Use multiple bonds if necessary.

Drawing Lewis Structures Using Multiple Bonds

In its liquid form, nitrogen (N_2) is very cold (approximately -200 °C) and freezes any living tissue it touches. Health professionals use liquid nitrogen to treat a variety of skin conditions (Figure 6.15). This small molecule has an interesting Lewis structure that contains a triple bond, *one with three shared pairs of electrons.*

The N_2 molecule has ten valence electrons. If we draw N_2's Lewis structure and we place only a single bond between the nitrogen atoms, each nitrogen atom is short of an octet of electrons (Figure 6.16). To solve this situation, we convert nonbonding pairs of electrons to multiple bonds. By sharing two additional electron pairs so that the molecule has a triple bond, we give each nitrogen atom an octet.

Continue to Learn 6.2 to explore the steps for drawing Lewis structures for molecules that require multiple bonds.

Figure 6.15 Liquid Nitrogen (N_2) is Used to Treat Skin Growths.

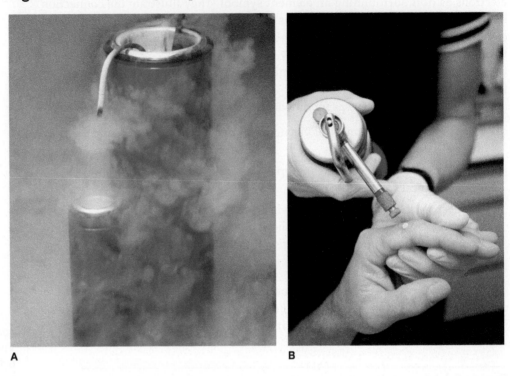

A   B

Figure 6.16 Lewis Structure for N_2 Requires a Triple Bond.

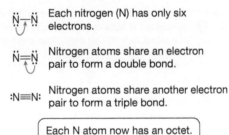

N̈—N̈   Each nitrogen (N) has only six electrons.

N̈=N̈   Nitrogen atoms share an electron pair to form a double bond.

:N≡N: Nitrogen atoms share another electron pair to form a triple bond.

Each N atom now has an octet.

Predict answers and see step-by-step solutions: **Learn 6.2:** Drawing Lewis Structures for Molecules with Multiple Bonds in the Pearson eText.

Apply what you have just learned: **Practice 6.6 and 6.7** in the Pearson eText.

Drawing Lewis Structures for Molecules with More than One Central Atom

In larger molecules, the number of central atoms increases, and their Lewis structures become more complicated. The good news is that the steps for drawing Lewis structures for larger molecules remain the same. For example, ethanol, commonly known as drinking alcohol, but also used as a biofuel additive, has the chemical formula C_2H_6O (Figure 6.17).

In this molecule there are three central atoms, the two carbon atoms and the oxygen atom. The two carbons atoms are bonded to each other, the oxygen atom is bonded to the middle carbon atom, and hydrogen atoms are attached to each of the three central atoms. Notice that each central atom shares electrons to obtain an octet of electrons. Oxygen generally forms two bonds and has two unpaired electrons. This is true for the oxygen atom in the ethanol molecule.

Figure 6.17 Ethanol has Three Central Atoms.

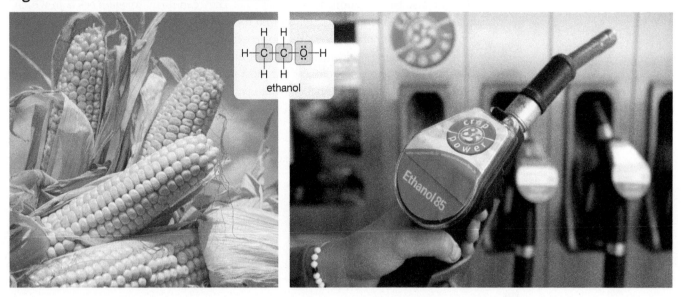

Larger molecules can also contain double and triple bonds. Formic acid (CH_2O_2), secreted by ants for attack and defense purposes, has two central atoms and contains a double bond.

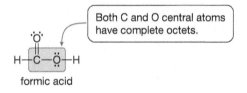

Both C and O central atoms have complete octets.

formic acid

Click on Learn 6.3 to step through the process for drawing Lewis structures for molecules with more than one central atom. After you complete Learn 6.3, explore BioConnect 6.1 (contains Figures 6.18–6.22) to learn about four classes of **biomolecules**, large molecules with multiple central atoms that are important in nature. Even the atoms in very large biomolecules share electrons to follow the octet rule.

Predict answers and see step-by-step solutions: **Learn 6.3:** Drawing Lewis Structures for Molecules with More Than One Central Atom in the Pearson eText.

Apply what you have just learned: **Practice 6.8 and 6.9** in the Pearson eText.

Explore how Chemistry and Biology connect: **BioConnect 6.1:** Life is Made of Large Molecules in the Pearson eText.

Exceptions to the Octet Rule

The most common molecules are generally composed of atoms that follow the octet rule. However, there can be exceptions to any rule and there are some elements that do not obey the octet rule. We have already seen that hydrogen is an exception to the octet rule, accommodating only two electrons when bonding. What are some other exceptions?

Boron, in group 3A of the periodic table, is also an exception to the octet rule. The group 3A elements do not have enough valence electrons to achieve octets, and form stable compounds that have only six shared electrons.

Compounds that form from elements in the third row and beyond on the periodic table can also be exceptions to the octet rule. They can form *expanded octets* in which there are *more* than eight electrons around the central atom. Sulfur and phosphorus are the two most common elements that form expanded octets.

Although these molecules are interesting, they are not as common as the molecules that follow the octet rule. For the most part, we will focus on the common molecules that are relevant to medicine, the body, and the environment.

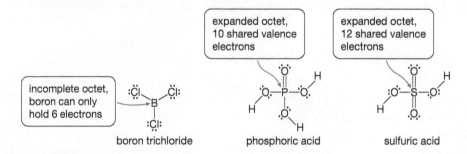

boron trichloride   phosphoric acid   sulfuric acid

 Quiz yourself on the content of this section: **Check 6.3** in the Pearson eText.

6.4 Predicting Shapes of Molecules

Molecular structure and shape play a critical role in how molecules function. One example of this structure-function relationship is the *aquaporin* protein molecule, which is a selective water channel (Figure 6.23).

In cell membranes, aquaporins serve as channels that allow water to pass in and out of the cell. These proteins are widely distributed in all types of life–from bacteria to plants and animals. There are several different aquaporins in the human body.

Figure 6.23 Aquaporin Molecule in a Cell Membrane.

The unique shape of water molecules allows them to pass through aquaporin protein channels. If too much water is allowed to pass from the blood to the brain, pressure may build up, a condition known as a cerebral edema. Aquaporin protein channels help regulate the flow of water to prevent this condition.

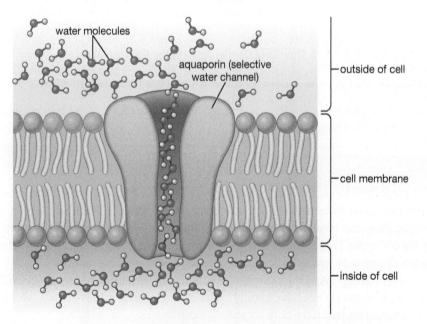

Some diseases are connected to the impaired function of these channels. Aquaporins in the brain, for example, may permit or allow excess water to move from the blood into the tissues of the brain. If excess water builds up inside the skull producing pressure, the pressure can damage the delicate tissues of the brain.

The numerous atoms in the large *aquaporin* protein molecules form an intricate and specific structure. This structure allows water, but not other molecules, to cross the membrane. The molecular shape of both the protein and the water molecules passing through the protein is critical to the specific and crucial role *aquaporin* protein molecules play.

How do we know what the shape of a molecule is? To begin exploring the answer to this question, consider the Lewis structure of a water molecule.

$$H-\ddot{O}-H$$

The structure effectively shows how the atoms are connected but it does not indicate the shape of the molecule in three dimensions. As written, the molecule looks linear, but what other shape might a water molecule adopt in three dimensions?

Counting Electron Groups to Predict Shapes of Molecules

In this section of the chapter, we consider the **valence shell electron pair repulsion (VSEPR) theory**. While the name VSEPR sounds complex, this helpful theory is based upon the intuitive idea that negatively charged electron pairs repel each other. As we learn about VSEPR, it important to keep in mind that electrons are negatively charged and that "like" charges repel each other. This is true whether the electrons are engaged in bonding or not.

To make predictions about shape around a central atom, (such as the oxygen atom in a water molecule), the first thing we consider is the number of **electron groups** on a central atom. Electron groups are the electrons—both nonbonding and bonding—on a central atom. An electron group is made up of valence electrons found either as lone pairs or in bonds. The electrons that make up a single or a multiple bond are counted as one electron group.

In general, there are three possible arrangements of electron groups on a central atom. Each arrangement has specific bond angles (Figure 6.24). The number of electron groups ultimately determines the arrangement of the atoms and therefore a given molecule's particular shape. A molecule made up of a central atom with two electron-groups is **linear** with a bond angle of 180°. A molecule with three groups around a central atom is **trigonal planar** (with 120° angles), and one with four groups is **tetrahedral** (with 109.5° angles). We refer to these arrangements as the molecular geometry of molecules.

Explore VisibleChem Video 6.4 and 6.5 to learn how to use VSEPR theory to predict the shape and bond angles of a variety of small molecules.

180°

120°

109.5°

linear   trigonal planar   tetrahedral

Figure 6.24 Molecular Shape.

Three common molecular shapes are shown using three-dimensional rotatable models.

Watch this concept come to life: **VisibleChem Video 6.4:** Shapes of Molecules and **VisibleChem Video 6.5:** Using VSEPR Theory to Predict the Shapes of Molecules in the Pearson eText.

Using VSEPR theory to Predict Molecular Shapes

As we discussed in VisibleChem Videos 6.4 and 6.5, in order to predict the shape of a molecule, we use Table 6.1 that summarizes the most common molecular shapes and we follow these three steps (Figure 6.25).

Complete Learn 6.4 and the following practice exercises to continue your investigation of how to use VSEPR theory to predict molecular shape.

Table 6.1 Summary of Molecular Geometry.

Number of bonds	Number of lone pairs	Total number of electron groups	Molecular geometry	Example	Approximate bond angle
2	0	2	linear	O=C=O	180°
3	0	3	trigonal planar	H⋯C=O (H)	120°
2	1		bent	O=S:	~120°
4	0	4	tetrahedral	H⋯C(H)(H)H	109.5°
3	1		trigonal pyramidal	H⋯N(H)H	~109.5°
2	2		bent	H⋯O⋯H	~109.5°

Figure 6.25 Steps for Using VSEPR Theory to Predict Shapes of Molecules

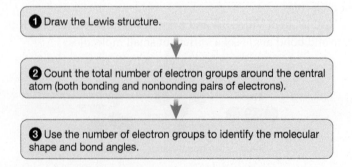

❶ Draw the Lewis structure.

❷ Count the total number of electron groups around the central atom (both bonding and nonbonding pairs of electrons).

❸ Use the number of electron groups to identify the molecular shape and bond angles.

Predict answers and see step-by-step solutions: **Learn 6.4:** Using VSEPR to Predict the Shape of Small Molecules in the Pearson eText.

Apply what you have just learned: **Practice 6.10–6.12** in the Pearson eText.

The Shapes of Molecules with More Than One Central Atom

We can also use VSEPR theory to determine the three-dimensional shape of larger molecules. To do this, we focus on one central atom at a time. Consider, for example, the molecule acetaldehyde (Figure 6.26). When we apply VSEPR theory to the carbon on the left (in the CH_3 group), we can determine that this part of the molecule is tetrahedral. In contrast, the part of the molecule that includes the carbon on the right ($O=C-H$) is trigonal planar.

Similarly, we can apply VSEPR theory to the molecule ethylene (Figure 6.27). In this molecule, the shape around each central carbon atom is trigonal planar with bond angles of approximately $120°$. Most molecules, especially all the large biomolecules that play important roles in the human body, have more than one central atom.

Click on BioConnect 6.2 (contains Figures 6.28–6.29) to discover how molecular shape plays a significant role in how biological processes are triggered.

Figure 6.26 Molecular Shape of the Acetaldehyde Molecule.

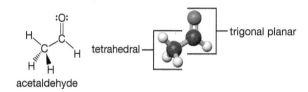

Figure 6.27 Molecular Shape of the Ethylene Molecule.

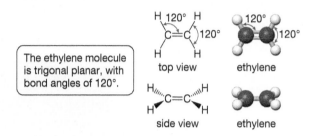

The ethylene molecule is trigonal planar, with bond angles of 120°.

Explore how Chemistry and Biology connect: **BioConnect 6.2:** Biological Impacts of Molecular Shape in the Pearson eText.

Quiz yourself on the content of this section: **Check 6.4** in the Pearson eText.

6.5 Naming Covalent Compounds

In order to communicate effectively, scientists have developed a systematic way to name covalent compounds. To name a binary molecular compound, we follow two steps (Figure 6.30).

STEP 1: Name the first nonmetal in the formula using the element name and name the second nonmetal using its element name with the *–ide* ending.

STEP 2: Use a prefix to indicate the number of atoms of each element in the formula (Table 6.2).

Figure 6.30 Steps for Naming Covalent Compounds.

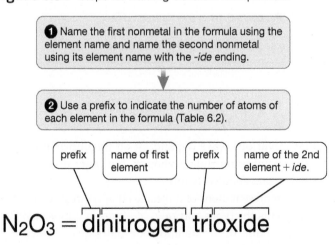

Table 6.2 Numerical Prefixes Used in Chemical Names.

Number	Prefix
1	mono-
2	di-
3	tri-
4	tetra-
5	penta-
6	hexa-
7	hepta-
8	octa-
9	nona-
10	deca-

For example, the molecule N_2O_3 is *dinitrogen **trioxide*** because it has two nitrogen atoms and three oxygen atoms.

If there is only one atom of the first element in the formula, the prefix *mono-* is typically omitted. The name of the molecule SO_2, for example, is *sulfur **dioxide*** because it has one sulfur atom and two oxygen atoms (Figure 6.31). Notice that the *mono-* prefix is left off sulfur, the first element in the molecule. We name the compound CO similarly: *carbon monoxide*. Again, we omit the prefix *mono-* from the first element.

Click on Learn 6.5 to use these rules to name two covalent compounds. Then proceed to Learn 6.6 to learn how to convert chemical names to chemical formulas.

Figure 6.31 Sulfur Dioxide is Released into the Atmosphere when Fossil Fuels are Burned.

Prefixes communicate important information about the composition of molecules. From its name, we know the pollutant, sulfur dioxide, for example, is composed of one sulfur atom and two oxygen atoms (SO_2). Sulfur dioxide is released as fossil fuels are burned. SO_2 is associated with a wide range of respiratory problems and contributes to acid rain.

Predict answers and see step-by-step solutions: **Learn 6.5:** Naming Binary Covalent Compounds in the Pearson eText.

Apply what you have just learned: **Practice 6.13** in the Pearson eText.

Predict answers and see step-by-step solutions: **Learn 6.6:** Writing the Chemical Formula from the Name of a Covalent Compound in the Pearson eText.

Apply what you have just learned: **Practice 6.14** in the Pearson eText.

Quiz yourself on the content of this section: **Check 6.5** in the Pearson eText.

6.6 Representing Molecules

Chemists represent molecules in various ways depending on the information they want to convey. Sometimes the chemical formula is enough, but other times a three-dimensional visual showing molecular shape is helpful.

Table 6.3 summarizes several representations of molecules that chemists commonly use. The chemical formula represents the types and ratio of atoms in a molecule. The Lewis structure shows the connection of atoms and lone pairs in a molecule. A

Table 6.3 Representing Molecules

Chemical formula	Lewis structure	Ball and stick	Space filling
Methane = CH_4	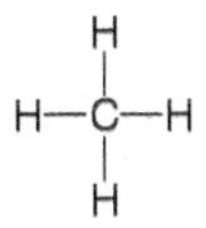 H—C—H (with H above and below)	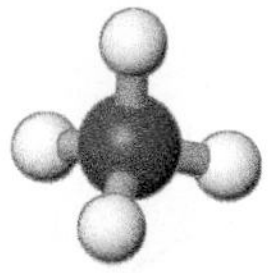	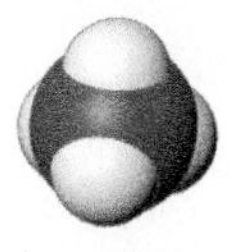
Water = H_2O	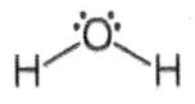 H—O—H (with lone pairs on O)	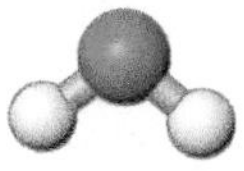	
Ammonia = NH_3	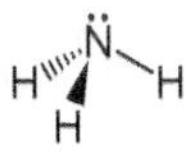 H—N—H (with H below and lone pair)	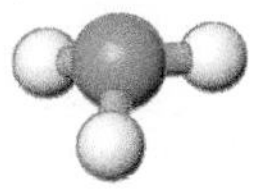	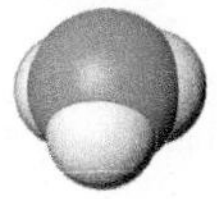

ball-and-stick model shows the atoms, bonds, and the three-dimensional (3D) shape of a molecule. A **space-filling model** illustrates the space occupied by the atoms and bonds.

Skeletal Structures

In addition to structures that reveal the connections between atoms and molecular shape, chemists also use a shorthand method to simplify large molecules. This shorthand method involves omitting both carbon and hydrogen atoms from structures to make them faster and more convenient to draw. This result of this style of representation is a **skeletal structure**.

Instead of including the symbol for each carbon and hydrogen atom in the molecule, in a skeletal structure, we represent the carbon atoms at the end of each bond or intersection of two bonds. Looking at this structure, we can predict the location and number of the hydrogen atoms by knowing that carbon requires four bonds to be stable. The butane and cyclohexane molecules provide examples of how to interpret skeletal structures (Figure 6.32 and Figure 6.33). This notation is widely used in science disciplines.

> Apply what you have just learned: **Practice 6.15 and 6.16** in the Pearson eText.

Molecular Structure of Drug Molecules

As we have discussed in this chapter, covalent bonds hold molecules and compounds together. Covalent bonding is responsible for the bonding among the atoms that make up most drugs, medicines, and other biologically important molecules. Some of the most commonly prescribed covalently bonded drugs in the U.S. include antibiotics to fight bacterial infections, as well as molecules that help control pain and blood pressure (Figure 6.34).

Figure 6.32 Lewis Structure and Skeletal Structure of Butane (C_4H_{10}).

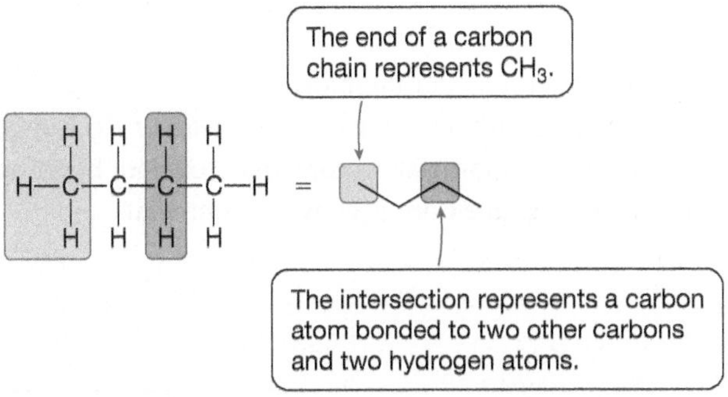

The end of a carbon chain represents CH_3.

The intersection represents a carbon atom bonded to two other carbons and two hydrogen atoms.

Figure 6.33 Lewis Structure and Skeletal Structure of Cyclohexane (C_6H_{12}).

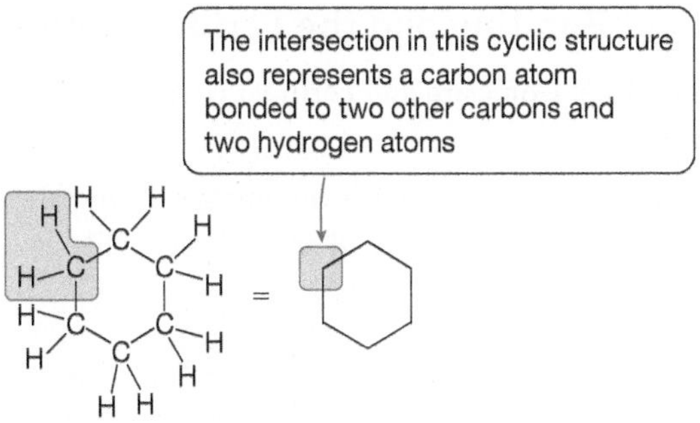

The intersection in this cyclic structure also represents a carbon atom bonded to two other carbons and two hydrogen atoms

Figure 6.34 Common Drug Molecules.

Drug	Molecular structure
ibuprofen used to treat pain	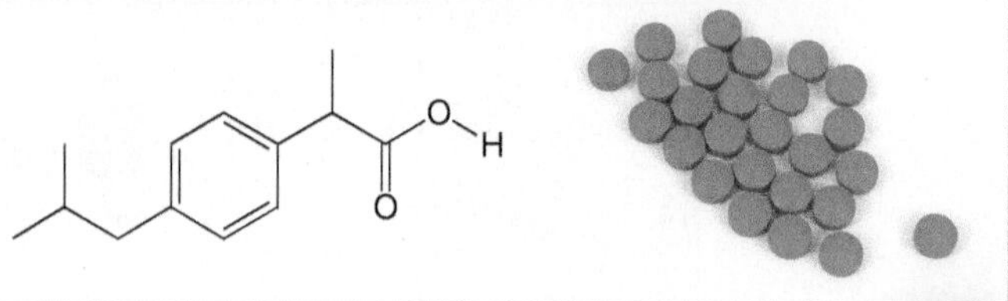
lisinopril used to treat hypertension and congestive heart failure	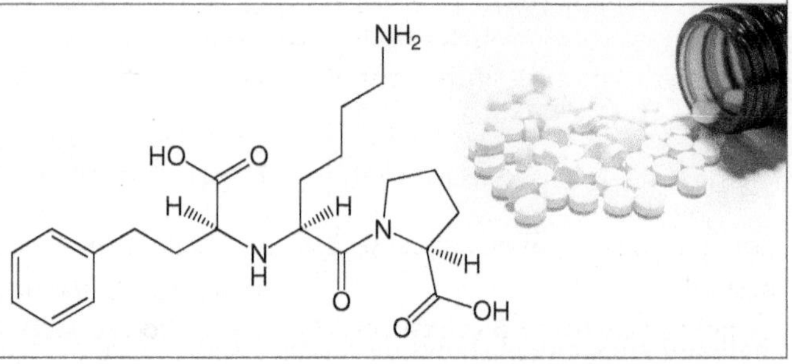

Apply what you have just learned: **Practice 6.17 and 6.18** in the Pearson eText.

Video 6.2: Dasatinib Leukemia Drug Action.

Quiz yourself on the content of this section: **Check 6.6** in the Pearson eText.

As you continue learning chemistry, keep in mind that there are often important connections between molecular structure and molecular function. The structure of a molecule can give chemists clues and allow them to make predictions about how a molecule functions. These clues can help them design new molecules to carry out specific desired functions (Video 6.2). Fighting diseases and solving some of our biggest environmental problems require that we focus on the relationship between the structure of molecules and how molecules function.

Chapter Summary

6.1   Introduction to Covalent Compounds

Learning Objective: **Define and describe covalent bonding.**

Covalent bonding connects atoms through the sharing of electrons. By sharing electrons, multiple atoms join to form millions of different molecules—many of which have biological and environmental importance.

Key Terms

diatomic molecule	duet	nonbonded electron pair
double bond	lone pair	triple bond

6.2   Covalent Bonding and the Periodic Table

Learning Objective: **Compare and contrast covalent and ionic compounds.**

Atoms in the periodic table are metals, nonmetals, or metalloids. Nonmetals do not easily lose electrons, especially to other nonmetal atoms, and therefore bond by sharing electrons. Ionic bonding involves the direct transfer of electron(s) from a metal and a nonmetal. In constrast. covalent bonding involves the sharing of electrons between nonmetals.

Key Term

central atom

6.3 Lewis Structures

Learning Objective: Draw covalent compounds using Lewis structures.

Lewis structures help us understand the bonding and shape of molecules in nature. In a Lewis structure, a line connecting two atoms represents a covalent bond that forms when two atoms each share one electron with each other. A pair of dots (:) indicates a pair of nonbonding electrons on a Lewis structure. Only the outermost valence electrons are shown in Lewis structures. Nonmetals generally react to end up with eight electrons according to the octet rule. These eight electrons can be a combination of covalently shared electrons and nonbonding electron pairs.

VisibleChem Video 6.1: Drawing the Lewis Structure of Methane

VisibleChem Video 6.2: Drawing the Lewis Structure of Water

VisibleChem Video 6.3: Drawing the Lewis Structure of Carbon Tetrachloride

BioConnect 6.1: Life is Made of Large Molecules

Key Terms

amino acid (from BioConnect 6.1)
biomolecule
carbohydrate (from BioConnect 6.1)
deoxyribonucleic acid (DNA) (from BioConnect 6.1)

glucose (from BioConnect 6.1)
Lewis structures (from BioConnect 6.1)
lipid (from BioConnect 6.1)
nucleic acid (from BioConnect 6.1)

proteins (from BioConnect 6.1)
saturated fat (from BioConnect 6.1)
starch (from BioConnect 6.1)
unsaturated fat (from BioConnect 6.1)

6.4 Predicting the Shapes of Molecules

Learning Objective: Predict the shapes of covalent compounds using VSEPR theory.

We apply valence shell electron pair repulsion (VSEPR) theory to draw and predict the shape of covalently bonded molecules. The specific shape of a molecule depends on the number of bonded groups and nonbonding lone pairs surrounding the central atom. The most common geometries are: two groups around a central atom (linear with bond angles of 180° *between groups*), three groups (trigonal planar with bond angle(s) of 120° *between groups*), and four groups (tetrahedral with bond angle(s) of 109.5° *between groups*).

VisibleChem Video 6.4: Shapes of Molecules

VisibleChem Video 6.5: Using VSEPR Theory to Predict the Shapes of Molecules

BioConnect 6.2: Biological Impacts of Molecular Shape

Key Terms

antibodies (from BioConnect 6.2)
antigens (from BioConnect 6.2)
electron group

linear
signaling molecule (from BioConnect 6.2)
tetrahedral

trigonal planar
valence shell electron pair repulsion (VSEPR) theory

6.5 Naming Covalent Compounds

Learning Objective: Write the name of a binary covalent compound from a given formula and provide the formula when given the name of a covalent compound.

When naming a binary molecule containing two nonmetals, we use the mono-, di-, tri-, etc. prefixes to indicate the number of atoms of each element in the formula. We use the -ide ending for the second element.

6.6 Representing Molecules

Learning Objective: Recognize a variety of ways to represent covalent compounds.

There are many ways to represent molecules including ball-and-stick models, space-filling models, and skeletal structures. Covalent bonding holds together the atoms that make up drugs, medicines, and other biologically important molecules. The wide range of effective drugs and medicines currently available in modern medicine feature covalently bonded molecules.

Video 6.2: Dasatinib Leukemia Drug Action

Key Terms

ball-and-stick model
skeletal structure
space-filling model

 End-of-Chapter Quiz Have you mastered the content of this chapter? Try the **End-of-Chapter Quiz** in the Pearson eText.

1. Covalent bonds form when atoms _____ electrons.
 a) transfer
 b) share
 c) cancel
 d) a, b, and c

2. What is the shape around the indicated carbon atom in the given structure?

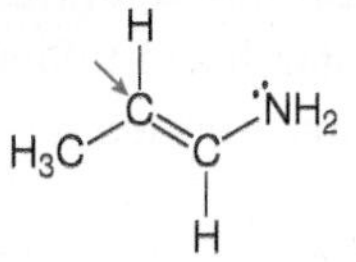

 a) linear
 b) bent
 c) trigonal planar
 d) tetrahedral

3. What are the bond angles in a tetrahedral bonding geometry?
 a) 180°
 b) 120.4°
 c) 109.5°
 d) 90°
 e) 60°

4. What is the correct chemical formula for "laughing gas" dinitrogen monoxide?
 a) NO_2
 b) N_2O_2
 c) NO
 d) N_2O

5. Estimate the bond angles around the indicated carbon atom in the given structure.

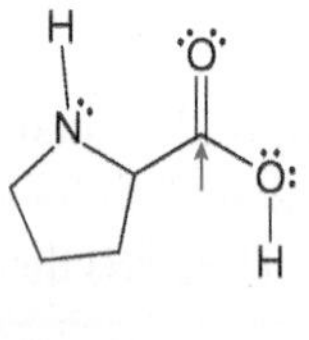

 a) 90°
 b) 109.5°
 c) 120°
 d) 180°

6. Which element can have more than eight valence electrons around it when present in a covalent compound?
 a) C
 b) B
 c) N
 d) P

7. According to valence shell electron pair repulsion (VSEPR) theory, which determines the shape around a given atom in a molecule?
 a) a bonded atom
 b) a lone pair of electrons
 c) a photon
 d) both a and b
 e) None of these answers are correct.

8. Which Lewis structure is *correctly* drawn?
 a) 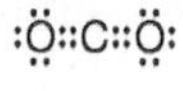 :Ö::C::Ö:
 b) H:N:H H
 c) H::Ö: H
 d) 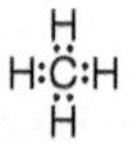 H H:C:H H

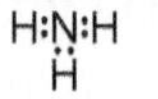

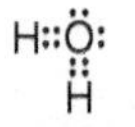

9. How many bonding groups around a central atom result in a tetrahedral structure?
 a) 1
 b) 2
 c) 3
 d) 4

10. Which Lewis structure is *not* correct?
 a) 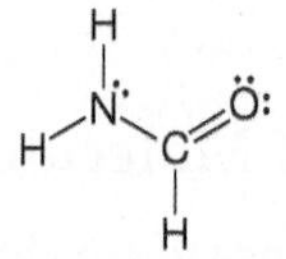
 b) 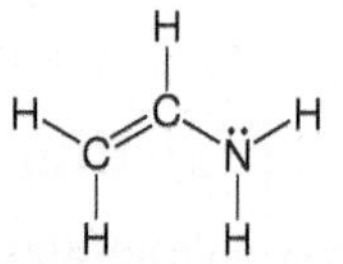
 c) 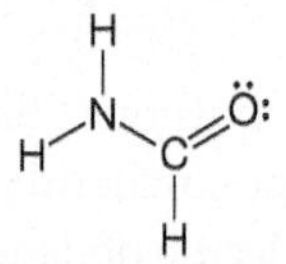
 d)

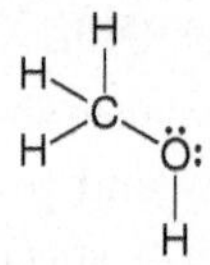

11. Cysteine is an amino acid found in proteins. Which central atom(s) have trigonal pyramidal geometry around them in the given cysteine structure?

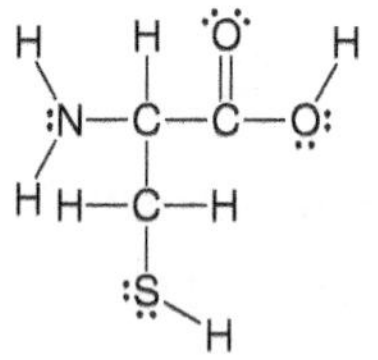

 a) N
 b) S
 c) C
 d) O

12. Modern medicines and biomolecules are generally: _____ (choose any/all that apply)
 a) composed of several metal atoms connected in different patterns.
 b) have different geometries around different atoms.
 c) made up of ions with different shapes and numbers of electrons.
 d) composed of many covalently bonded atoms such as carbon, nitrogen, oxygen, and hydrogen.

Chapter 7
Molecular Polarity and Intermolecular Forces

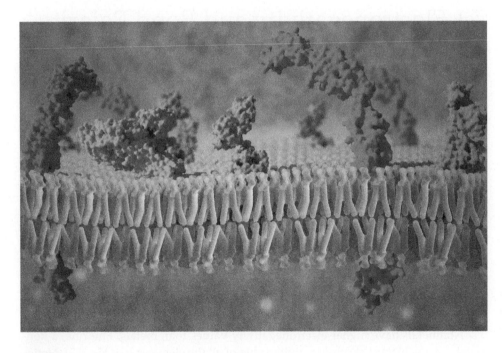

The delicate cell membrane, just two molecules thick, defines and protects all the cells in our bodies.

 ## Chapter Outline

Learning Objectives

7.1 Determine the polarity of a chemical bond using electronegativity values of atoms.

7.2 Predict whether a molecule is polar or nonpolar.

7.3 Identify polar and nonpolar regions of large molecules.

7.4 Recognize and describe the types of intermolecular forces.

Introduction

How do antibodies bind to specific molecules on a cell surface (Figure 7.1a)? Why don't oil and water mix (Figure 7.1b)? What makes honey feel sticky (Figure 7.1c)? In this chapter, we explore the fundamental reasons why some molecules are attracted to each other, while others are not. As you continue to learn about and understand chemical bonding, you will learn more about how the type of atoms, type of bonds, and the three-dimensional arrangement of atoms play an essential role in the behavior of the molecules on our planet. The distribution of electrons across individual bonds, and across entire molecules, plays a critical role in determining the structure and function of molecules in our natural world.

7.1 Electronegativity and Bond Polarity

In Chapters 5 and 6 we focused on two cases of bonding: ionic bonds and covalent bonds. These bonds are formed by *either* complete transfer of elections (ionic), or complete electron sharing (covalent). In most compounds, however, the bonds that form are somewhere in between these two extremes. In fact, the bonds in the majority of compounds are considered to be **polar covalent**, which means there is an uneven sharing of electrons between the atoms in the bond. To better understand this idea, let's explore the concept of electronegativity.

Electronegativity

In order to predict what type of bond forms between two atoms, we need to know the electronegativity of the atoms engaged in bonding. **Electronegativity (EN)** is the relative ability of a bonded atom to attract shared electrons. The famous chemist Linus Pauling (1901–1994) developed a scale of relative electronegativity values that range from 0.0–4.0 (Figure 7.2). The atom with a higher electronegativity value has a greater attraction for the shared electrons in a bond. This scale allows us to make predictions about the extent to which electrons are shared in a covalent bond.

Nonmetals have higher electronegativity values than metals. Fluorine, a non-metal, has the highest electronegativity value of all the elements (see Fig. 7.2). Notice that fluorine is located on the upper right corner of the periodic table surrounded by some of the other elements with high electronegativity values. In contrast, the left side

Figure 7.1 Impact of Polarity and Intermolecular Forces.

A) The polarity of molecules and intermolecular forces can help explain the properties of substances such as antibodies that carry toxic drugs to cancer cells **B)** These forces can also help environmental scientists think about how to most effectively clean up oil spills and **C)** even explain everyday phenomena like the stickiness of honey.

A   B   C

Figure 7.2 Electronegativity of the Elements.

Linus Pauling developed a scale from 0.0–4.0 of relative electronegativity values for the elements. Electronegativity values tend to increase from left to right and from bottom to top of the periodic table. Atoms with higher electronegativity values have a stronger attraction to the shared electrons in a bond.

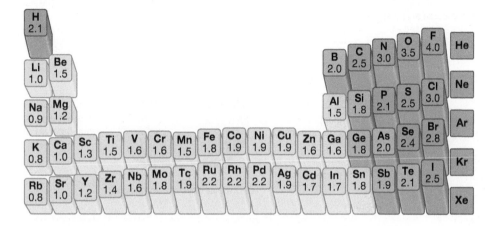

of the periodic table contains metals with low electronegativity values, especially metals located in the lower left. The transition metals also have relatively low electronegativity values in comparison to nonmetals.

The noble gases are not assigned electronegativity values. This is because the noble gases do not tend to engage in bonding because they have a full outer shell of electrons (see Section 5.2 for a review of the octet rule).

We summarize electronegativity trends with the following statement:

> *In general, electronegativity increases from left to right and from bottom to top of the periodic table.*

Click on Learn 7.1 to compare electronegativity values of elements across the periodic table.

Predict answers and see step-by-step solutions: **Learn 7.1:** Comparing Electronegativity Values for Elements Across the Periodic Table in the Pearson eText.

Apply what you have just learned: **Practice 7.1** in the Pearson eText.

Polar and Nonpolar Covalent Bonds

Now that we have introduced electronegativity, let's move on to predicting whether a bond is polar or nonpolar. **Polarity** is the result of an unequal distribution of electron density, which produces positive and negative regions in a bond. The electrons in a polar bond are more attracted toward the more electronegative atom. This makes that atom partially negatively charged. We indicate this partial negative charge with the lower case Greek letter delta combined with a negative sign (δ^-). On the other end of a polar bond is the atom with a lower electronegativity value. This atom has a partial positive charge due to the reduced electron density around the less electronegative atom. We indicate this partial positive charge with a delta symbol and a positive sign (δ^+).

Figure 7.3 Representing Polar Covalent Bonds.

A) We represent polarity in a number of ways. Partial charge symbols (δ) with a positive or negative sign indicate charge for each end of a polar molecule. An electrostatic potential map uses color to show electron distribution over a molecule. In this color map, red indicates areas of partial negative charge and blue represents partial positive charge. A dipole arrow points towards the negative end of a molecule. **B)** There is no difference in electronegativity between the two chlorine atoms in the Cl_2 molecule and therefore this molecule is nonpolar.

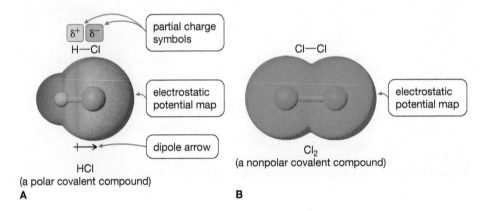

HCl
(a polar covalent compound)

A

Cl_2
(a nonpolar covalent compound)

B

As an example, let's consider the bond between hydrogen (H) and chlorine (Cl) in Figure 7.3. Notice that chlorine has a partial negative charge due to the higher electronegativity value, and hydrogen takes on a partial positive charge in this bonding situation. Bonds between hydrogen and chlorine are *polar covalent*. Hydrogen is electron-rich in this bond and chlorine is electron-poor as the **electrostatic potential map** illustrates with color in Figure 7.3a. We therefore say that the HCl bond has a **dipole**, *which is a separation of negative and positive charge.*

In contrast, the two chlorine atoms (Cl—Cl) in Figure 7.3b do not have a difference in electronegativity. These two chlorine atoms, therefore, form a **nonpolar covalent** bond.

In addition to representing bond polarity with partial charge symbols (δ^-, δ^+), we also can use a **dipole arrow** to show the separation of charges that occurs in a polar bond. The dipole arrow indicates a polar bond by starting at the positive charge and pointing towards the negative charge (See Fig 7.3).

A Continuum of Bonding Types

Our ability to predict the behavior of molecules is greatly improved if we understand that rather than extreme categories of bond types, there is a spectrum or continuum of options (Figure 7.4). The difference in electronegativity (sometimes abbreviated ΔEN) of the atoms participating in the covalent bond determines the bond type. In general,

Figure 7.4 The Continuum of Bond Types.

Rather than discrete categories of ionic and covalent, most bonds fall on a spectrum between the two. Bond polarity is determined by the relative electronegativity of the atoms involved.

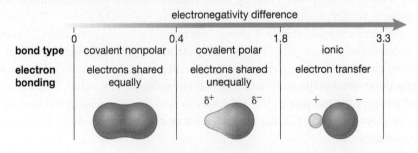

an electronegativity difference between atoms of 0.0–0.4 indicates that the electrons are shared almost equally, resulting in a nonpolar bond. A carbon-carbon bond, for example, is nonpolar because there is no difference between the electronegativity values of the two bonded atoms.

As the electronegativity difference increases, so does the polarity of the bond. A carbon-oxygen bond is more polar than a nitrogen-oxygen bond due to the larger electronegativity difference between the atoms involved (Figure 7.5). Both of these bonds are polar covalent because the electronegativity difference falls between 0.5–1.8. Larger differences in electronegativity, EN differences that are 1.8 or greater, result in ionic bonds. Recall that in ionic bonds, electrons are transferred from one atom to the other instead of being shared as they are in covalent bonds. Explore Learn 7.2 to learn how to use EN difference to predict bond type.

Figure 7.5 Carbon Forms Polar Bonds with Both Nitrogen and Oxygen.

The carbon-oxygen bond is more polar than the carbon-nitrogen bond due to the greater difference in electronegativity.

less polar

$\delta^+ \downarrow \delta^-$
C—N

more polar

$\delta^+ \downarrow \delta^-$
C—O

electronegativity difference: $3.0 - 2.5 = 0.5$	electronegativity difference: $3.5 - 2.5 = 1.0$

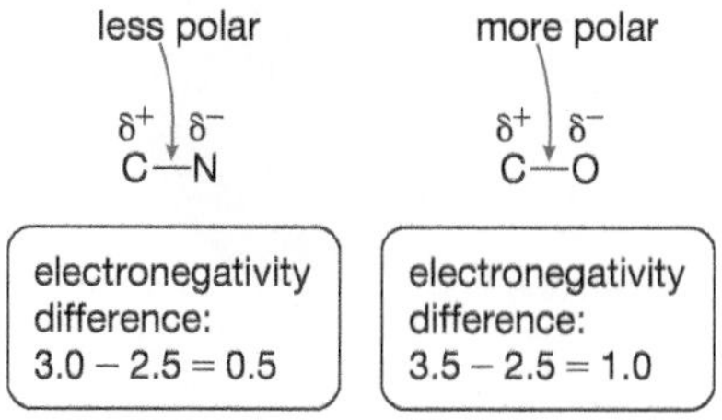

Predict answers and see step-by-step solutions: **Learn 7.2:** Predicting Bond Type and Assigning Partial Charges in the Pearson eText.

Apply what you have just learned: **Practice 7.2 and 7.3** in the Pearson eText.

Quiz yourself on the content of this section: **Check 7.1** in the Pearson eText.

7.2 Polarity of Molecules

When we can determine the polarity of molecules, we can predict how molecules interact with other molecules. This is particularly significant when exploring biological systems. Most biological processes rely on attractions between molecules. These attractions are determined by a molecule's polarity. This idea is even more interesting when we consider that some molecules can have both polar regions and nonpolar regions. In other words, some larger molecules are both polar and nonpolar at the same time. We discuss this idea further in Section 7.3. Before we do that, let's explore molecular polarity in more detail.

Recall from Section 7.1 that a covalent bond is polar when it involves atoms that have different electronegativity values. This is due to an unequal sharing of electrons. Hydrogen fluoride (HF) is an example of a molecule with only one bond. This makes it relatively straightforward to predict the polarity of the bond and the overall molecular polarity. The bond between hydrogen and fluorine is polar because the difference in electronegativity is $4.0 - 2.1 = 1.9$. Therefore, the molecule is polar too (Figure 7.6). What if there are more than two atoms in a molecule? How do we predict whether a molecule is polar or nonpolar as molecules get larger?

The polarity of the bonds in a molecule is one of the primary factors to consider when determining polarity of molecules with more than two atoms. The other factor we need to consider is the shape of the molecule and whether or not bond dipoles cancel each other. As we will see in this section, the presence of polar bonds does not always lead to a polar molecule. To determine whether a molecule is polar, we must investigate the overall charge distribution across the molecule. *If there is an uneven distribution of charge across the molecule, then the molecule is polar. On the other hand, if polar bonds are present, but the charge is evenly distributed across the molecule, then the molecule is nonpolar.*

Figure 7.6 Electrostatic Potential Map of Hydrogen Fluoride (HF).

This diagram illustrates the charge distributions across a molecule. The red end represents the partial negative end of the molecule where the fluorine is located, and the blue end represents the partial positive end where the hydrogen atom is located.

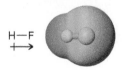

H—F
⟼

Determining molecular polarity:

Are the bonds polar or nonpolar?
How does the shape of the molecule affect charge distribution?

Figure 7.7 The Nonpolar Methane Molecule (CH_4).

The methane molecule has only nonpolar bonds and therefore is a nonpolar molecule.

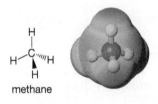

methane

Nonpolar Molecules

Nonpolar molecules either have only nonpolar bonds, or they contain polar bonds where the bond dipoles cancel each other. The methane molecule (CH_4) is a good example of the first situation. In CH_4 all the bonds are nonpolar and therefore the molecule is nonpolar (Figure 7.7). Recall that the difference in electronegativity between carbon and hydrogen is too small for CH_4 to be considered a polar bond (The difference in electronegativity between C and H is $2.5 - 2.1 = 0.4$.) The electrostatic potential map of methane in Figure 7.7 illustrates the symmetric distribution of charge across the methane molecule.

Carbon tetrachloride (CCl_4), on the other hand, contains slightly polar bonds (EN difference $2.5 - 2.0 = 0.5$), but due to the tetrahedral shape of the molecule (Figure 7.8), the dipoles cancel out. This leads to symmetrical charge distribution across the molecule, so carbon tetrachloride is nonpolar overall. Carbon tetrachloride is an example of the second type of nonpolar molecule in which bond dipoles cancel each other. We explore this idea in more depth in VisibleChem Video 7.1.

Figure 7.8 The Nonpolar Carbon Tetrachloride Molecule (CCl_4).

This molecule has a symmetrical charge distribution across the molecule and therefore is nonpolar.

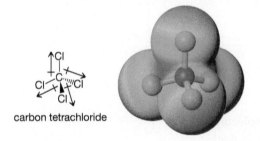

carbon tetrachloride

Polar Molecules

In contrast to nonpolar molecules, polar molecules have asymmetrical charge distribution. Therefore, polar molecules have a positive end and a negative end. We represent the uneven charge with partial charge symbols or a dipole arrow. Dipoles do not cancel out in polar molecules. This may be due to the shape of the molecule or because there may be different atoms around the central atom. For example, ammonia (NH_3) is a polar molecule that has polar bonds with dipoles that do not cancel out (Figure 7.9).

Chloromethane (CH_3Cl) is another example of a polar molecule (Figure 7.10). The presence of different atoms around a central atom usually results in uneven charge distribution and leads to a polar molecule. Explore additional examples of how to predict whether a molecule is polar or nonpolar in VisibleChem Video 7.1 and Learn 7.3.

Figure 7.9 The Polar Ammonia Molecule (NH_3).

The ammonia molecule has three dipoles that do not cancel out. The electron density map illustrates the electron rich partially negative region with the color red on the end where the nitrogen atom is located.

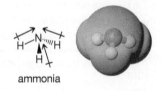

ammonia

Figure 7.10 The Polar Chloromethane Molecule (CH_3Cl).

This molecule has one bond dipole on the C—Cl bond that does not cancel out. The electron density map shows the electron-rich partially negative region with the color red on the end where the fluorine atom is located.

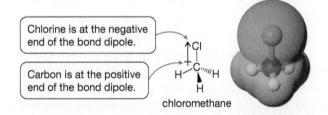

Chlorine is at the negative end of the bond dipole.

Carbon is at the positive end of the bond dipole.

chloromethane

Watch this concept come to life: **VisibleChem Video 7.1:** Exploring the Polarity of Molecules in the Pearson eText.

Predict answers and see step-by-step solutions: **Learn 7.3:** Predicting Whether a Small Molecule is Polar or Nonpolar in the Pearson eText.

Apply what you have just learned: **Practice 7.4** in the Pearson eText.

Quiz yourself on the content of this section: **Check 7.2** in the Pearson eText.

7.3 Polarity of Large Molecules

So far in this chapter, we've considered only small molecules that can readily be identified as either polar or nonpolar. Many molecules, however, have more complex structures that can contain nonpolar, polar, and even ionic groups within a single molecule. A number of biomolecules fall into this category and have regions of differing polarity that greatly affect how they interact with other molecules. The molecule that is largely responsible for the structure of the cell membrane (Figure 7.11) is an example of this. We investigate this molecule along with the structure of the cell membrane in more detail in BioConnect 7.1.

Biomolecules tend to consist of a carbon backbone with a variety of groups attached to the backbone. This structure may feature polar and nonpolar regions and a unique three-dimensional shape that directly affects the molecule's biological function. In this section, we discuss how to identify polar and nonpolar regions of larger molecules. As you continue your studies in chemistry, biology, and medicine, the identification process will become more and more intuitive.

Figure 7.11 Cell Membranes.

All cells, including these cancer cells, are surrounded by a protective membrane. Cell membranes are composed of large molecules that have one polar end and one nonpolar end.

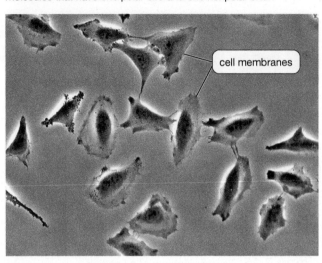

cell membranes

Hydrocarbons

Hydrocarbons are organic compounds that contain only hydrogen and carbon. We study this group of molecules in more detail in Chapter 13. Here, we focus on charge distribution in hydrocarbon molecules. The electronegativity difference between hydrogen and carbon is 0.4, which means that all of the carbon-hydrogen bonds in a hydrocarbon are nonpolar. The characteristically symmetrical shape of hydrocarbons also contributes to relatively equal charge distribution. Both of these factors (bond polarity and molecular shape) are responsible for the nonpolar nature of hydrocarbons. Octane (C_8H_{18}) is a small hydrocarbon that has eight carbon atoms and eighteen hydrogen atoms (Figure 7.12). It is an overall nonpolar molecule because only carbon and hydrogen are present.

Figure 7.12 The Structure of a Typical Hydrocarbon.

Gasoline, a mixture of hydrocarbons, includes octane (C_8H_{18}). As both carbon-carbon bonds and carbon-hydrogen bonds are nonpolar, the octane molecule is nonpolar.

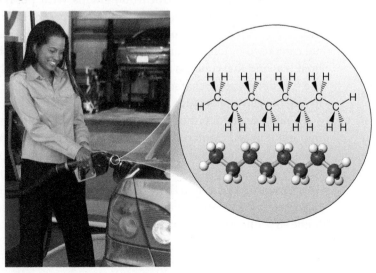

Figure 7.13 The Structure of the Alcohol, Ethanol (C_2H_5OH).

Ethanol, the alcohol people drink and manufacturers add to fuels, is a short two-carbon hydrocarbon chain with an added hydroxyl group (—OH). The presence of the electronegative oxygen atom makes ethanol a polar molecule.

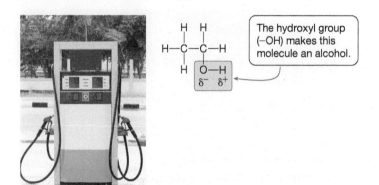

The hydroxyl group (—OH) makes this molecule an alcohol.

Figure 7.14 The Polar and Nonpolar Regions of the Alcohol Pentanol.

Some alcohols have both polar and nonpolar regions.

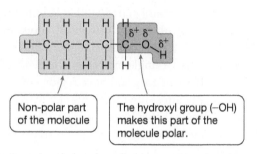

Non-polar part of the molecule

The hydroxyl group (—OH) makes this part of the molecule polar.

Figure 7.15 Representations of a Lecithin Molecule.

A lecithin molecule is composed of two nonpolar hydrocarbon chains or tails and a polar head. Cell membranes contain lecithin molecules.

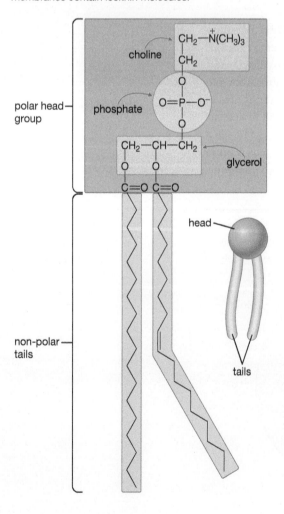

Alcohols

A hydrocarbon chain in which a hydrogen atom has been replaced with a **hydroxyl group** (—OH) is an **alcohol** (Figure 7.13). What do you think the oxygen atom in the hydroxyl group does to the polarity of the molecule? The carbon-oxygen bond is polar, and therefore adds a polar group to the molecule. The —OH group has a large effect on molecular polarity when the hydrocarbon chain is small, but as the hydrocarbon chain gets larger, the overall molecule becomes less polar.

A single alcohol molecule can include regions that are polar and regions that are nonpolar. This is especially true as molecules become larger and larger. The pentanol alcohol molecule in Figure 7.14 is an example of this. There are five carbon atoms on one end of this molecule and an —OH group on the other end. The hydrocarbon region of this molecule is nonpolar while the —OH group is polar.

Phospholipids

Now that we have a basic understanding of polar bonds, small polar molecules, and hydrocarbon chains with polar groups attached, we can begin to understand the properties of large bio-molecules, such as **phospholipids**. Recall from Chapter 6 that lipids are composed of long chains of carbon and hydrogen. A phospho-lipid is a lipid that contains a phosphate group. **A phosphate group** is a functional group characterized by a phosphorus atom bonded to four oxygen atoms (three single bonds and one double bond).

Consider the lecithin molecule—a phospholipid molecule important in cell membrane formation. The lecithin phospholipid molecule has a nonpolar covalent region, composed of two hydro-carbon chains or "tails" and a polar "head" region (Figure 7.15). This structure is crucial to the way the cell membrane functions. In BioConnect 7.1 (contains Figures 7.16–7.18) we explore cell membrane structure and function further.

Explore how Chemistry and Biology connect: **BioConnect 7.1:** Understanding Membrane Structure in the Pearson eText.

Predict answers and see step-by-step solutions: **Learn 7.4:** Identifying Polar and Nonpolar Regions of Large Molecules in the Pearson eText.

Apply what you have just learned: **Practice 7.5** in the Pearson eText.

Quiz yourself on the content of this section: **Check 7.3** in the Pearson eText.

7.4 Intermolecular Forces

Determining whether a molecule is polar or not is the first step in understanding how a molecule interacts with other molecules. The vast majority of biological processes involve attractions between molecules that result from interactions between oppositely charged ends of polar molecules, or even weak interactions between nonpolar molecules. We refer to the attractions between molecules as **intermolecular forces**. These forces between molecules are relatively weak compared to chemical bonds between atoms within molecules because these forces typically involve smaller charges that are farther apart. This difference is illustrated in Figure 7.19. The intermolecular force is represented with the dotted line in the figure. Bonding forces, such as covalent and ionic bonds, that act within molecules are relatively strong because they involve larger charges that are closer together. So, what are these attractive forces *between* molecules?

There are three major types of intermolecular forces: *London dispersion forces, dipole-dipole forces, and hydrogen bonds.* In this section, we discuss each type in more detail. The goal is for you to develop your ability to identify when specific intermolecular forces are present.

Figure 7.19 Intermolecular Force Between Hydrogen Chloride Molecules.

Intermolecular forces are attractions *between* molecules. These forces are weaker than the attractions *within* molecules that create bonds. The intermolecular force between two hydrogen chloride molecules is illustrated with a dotted line.

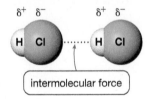

London Dispersion Forces

All molecules, regardless of structure, experience *London dispersion forces* (also called Van der Waals forces). **London dispersion forces** are temporary attractive forces that result when the electrons in two adjacent atoms occupy positions that make the atoms form temporary dipoles. A hydrogen molecule (H_2) provides an example of how this works (Figure 7.20). Electrons in a covalent H_2 molecule are in constant motion, but at any given time a temporary dipole can develop. This temporary dipole can induce

Figure 7.20 London Dispersion Forces Between Hydrogen Molecules.

A) Hydrogen is a nonpolar covalent molecule **B)** A temporary dipole can develop on H_2, which induces a dipole on a second molecule. A temporary weak attraction forms between the two molecules.

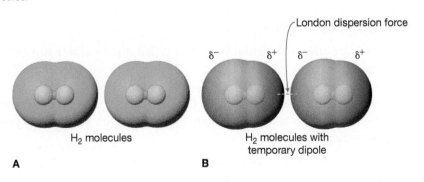

Figure 7.21 London Dispersion Forces Between Nonpolar Hydrocarbon Molecules.

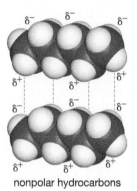

nonpolar hydrocarbons

Figure 7.22 London dispersion Forces Help Geckos Stick to a Variety of Surfaces.

another temporary dipole in a nearby H_2 molecule. A weak attraction—the London dispersion force—forms between these two covalent molecules. Although these forces are quite weak, they allow for attractions to occur between nonpolar covalent compounds. All covalent compounds can engage in London dispersion forces. However, these are the only intermolecular forces nonpolar molecules exhibit.

As we discussed in the Section 7.3, hydrocarbons are composed of only carbon and hydrogen atoms and therefore are nonpolar covalent molecules. These molecules are attracted to one another through weak London dispersion forces. Pentane molecules (C_5H_{12}), for example, exhibit London dispersion forces between molecules (Figure 7.21). The hydrocarbon regions of larger biomolecules also exhibit London dispersion forces. Nonpolar regions of biomolecules, such as the hydrocarbon chains in phospholipids that make up cell membranes, and the hydrocarbon backbones of other large biological molecules, such as proteins, are attracted to one another through weak London dispersion forces.

While individual London dispersion forces are quite weak, they can collectively be powerful. Geckos, for example, are small lizards found in warm climates around the world that adhere easily to vertical surfaces and can even hang from the ceiling with a single foot (Figure 7.22). Scientists believe geckos use London dispersion forces to adhere to a variety of surfaces.

Dipole-Dipole Forces

Figure 7.23 Dipole-Dipole Forces Between Oppositely Charged Ends of Polar Molecules.

dipole-dipole

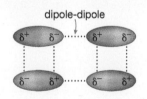

Polar molecules are affected by attractive forces called **dipole-dipole forces**, which form when the partially negative end of one molecule is attracted to the partially positive end of another molecule (Figure 7.23). The forces experienced by hydrogen chloride (HCl) molecules provide an example (Figure 7.24). Notice that the partially negative end of one molecule forms a dipole-dipole force with the partially positive end of another molecule.

Figure 7.24 Dipole-Dipole Force Between Hydrogen Chloride Molecules.

The partially negative chlorine atom of one molecule is attracted to the partially positive hydrogen atom of another molecule.

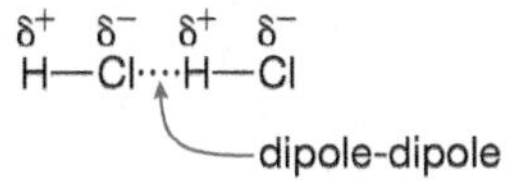

$$\overset{\delta^+}{H}-\overset{\delta^-}{Cl}\cdots\overset{\delta^+}{H}-\overset{\delta^-}{Cl}$$

dipole-dipole

Figure 7.25 Hydrogen Bonding Between Water Molecules (H_2O).

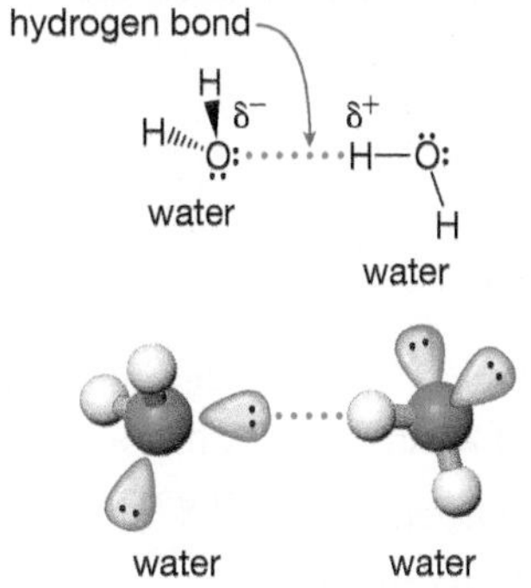

hydrogen bond

water

water

Figure 7.26 Hydrogen Bonding Between Ammonia Molecules (NH_3).

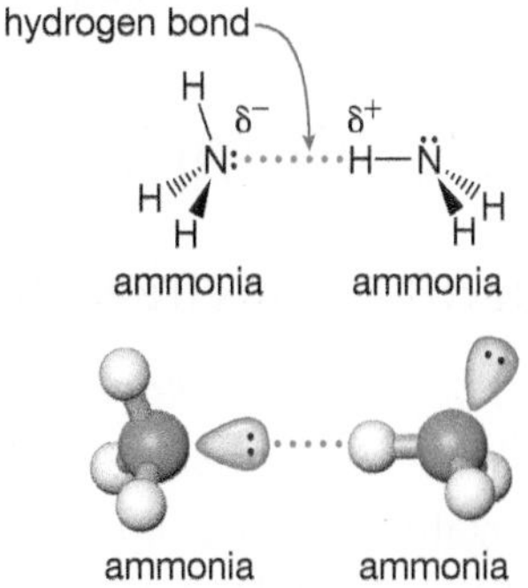

hydrogen bond

ammonia   ammonia

ammonia   ammonia

Hydrogen Bonds

Some polar molecules experience a special type of dipole-dipole force called a *hydrogen bond*. Hydrogen bonds are an especially strong intermolecular force. A **hydrogen bond** forms between a hydrogen atom (H) that is covalently bonded to an oxygen, nitrogen, or fluorine of one molecule and an oxygen, nitrogen or fluorine atom of a second molecule. These forces are especially significant because of the role they play in the structure of large biomolecules such as deoxyribonucleic acid (DNA) and proteins. We take a closer look at these in BioConnect 7.2 (contains Figures 7.27–7.31).

Water molecules provide a common example of hydrogen bonding. Take a look at how the attractions between water molecules in Figure 7.25 fits the hydrogen bond definition. The hydrogen atoms in water are covalently bonded to an oxygen atom and form hydrogen bonds to the oxygen of another water molecule. Ammonia molecules also form hydrogen bonds. In this case, a hydrogen atom that is covalently bonded to nitrogen in one ammonia molecule forms a hydrogen bond with the nitrogen of another ammonia molecule (Figure 7.26). Hydrogen bonds are quite strong compared to the other intermolecular forces. They play a significant role in how the molecules that form these strong attractions behave.

Explore all three categories of intermolecular forces in VisibleChem Video 7.2 and Learn 7.5.

Watch this concept come to life: **VisibleChem Video 7.2:** Forces Between Molecules in the Pearson eText.

Predict answers and see step-by-step solutions: **Learn 7.5:** Identifying Intermolecular Forces in the Pearson eText.

Apply what you have just learned: **Practice 7.6 and 7.7** in the Pearson eText.

Explore how Chemistry and Biology connect: **BioConnect 7.2:** Intermolecular Forces in Biomolecules in the Pearson eText.

Quiz yourself on the content of this section: **Check 7.4** in the Pearson eText.

Chapter Summary

7.1 Electronegativity & Bond Polarity

Learning Objective: Determine the polarity of a chemical bond using electronegativity values of atoms.

Electronegativity is the ability of a bonded atom to attract electrons in toward it. The relative electronegativity of all elements is ranked on a scale from 0.0–4.0. In general, electronegativity increases from left to right and from bottom to top of the periodic table. Bond polarity increases as the difference in electronegativity between two bonded elements increases. Nonpolar bonds are characterized by differences of electronegativity between 0.0–0.4 because the electrons are shared almost equally. Polar bonds are generally characterized by electronegativity difference between 0.5–1.8. When the difference in electronegativity is greater than 1.8, electrons are so unequally shared that electrons are transferred from one element to the other, forming ionic bonds.

Key Terms

covalent bond	electron density map	polar covalent
dipole	electronegativity (EN)	polarity
dipole arrow	nonpolar covalent	

7.2 Molecular Polarity

Learning Objective: Predict whether a molecule is polar or nonpolar.

Polar molecules contain polar bonds that have an uneven charge distribution across the molecule and a symmetrical geometry that does not allow the bond dipoles to cancel each other out. Water (H_2O) is a common polar molecule that contains polar covalent bonds. The geometry of a water molecule does not allow the bond dipoles to cancel each other, so the water molecule overall is polar. Carbon dioxide (CO_2) is also a molecule that contains polar bonds. However, in contrast to water, the symmetry of the CO_2 molecule allows bond dipoles to cancel each other, so carbon dioxide is nonpolar.

VisibleChem Video 7.1: Exploring the Polarity of Molecules

7.3 Polarity of Large Molecules

Learning Objective: Identify polar and nonpolar regions of large molecules.

Large molecules often have both polar and nonpolar regions. Hydrocarbons are organic compounds that contain only hydrogen and carbon and are therefore nonpolar due to the small difference in electronegativity between carbon and hydrogen. Most large biologically important molecules contain a hydrocarbon backbone, with one or more polar groups added to the backbone structure to give the molecule a specific structure, function, or properties.

BioConnect 7.1: Understanding Membrane Structure

Key Terms

alcohol	hydrophobic (from BioConnect 7.1)	phosphate group
hydrocarbon	hydroxyl group (—OH)	phospholipid bilayer
hydrophilic (from BioConnect 7.1)	phospholipid	(from BioConnect 7.1)

7.4 Intermolecular Forces

Learning Objective: Recognize and describe the types of intermolecular forces.

Intermolecular forces are the attractive forces between neighboring molecules (or between different regions of large molecules). Nonpolar molecules are attracted to each other by London dispersion forces. London dispersion forces result from temporary changes in electron distribution in a molecule, which gives rise to temporary dipoles in neighboring molecules that are weakly attracted to one another. Dipole-dipole forces result when the partially negative end of one

molecule is attracted to the partially positive end of another nearby molecule. Some polar molecules experience a special type of dipole-dipole force called a hydrogen bond. This intermolecular force is especially strong, and forms between a hydrogen atom (H) that is covalently bonded to an oxygen, nitrogen, or fluorine of one molecule and an oxygen, nitrogen, or fluorine atom of a second molecule.

VisibleChem Video 7.2: Forces Between Molecules

BioConnect 7.2: Intermolecular Forces in Biomolecules

Key Terms

coronaviruses (from BioConnect 7.2)

dipole-dipole force

hydrogen bond

intermolecular forces

London dispersion force

 End-of-Chapter Quiz

Have you mastered the content of this chapter? Try the **End-of-Chapter Quiz** in the Pearson eText.

1. Which statement about polar bonds is true?
 a) Polar bonds only form between a metal and a nonmetal.
 b) Polar bonds result from a 0.0–0.4 difference in electronegativity between two bonded atoms.
 c) Polar bonds always result in nonpolar molecules.
 d) Polar bonds result from a 0.5–1.9 difference in electronegativity between two bonded atoms.

2. Which molecule can form a hydrogen bond with another of the same molecule?

3. Which is the most polar bond?
 a) Si—Cl   **b)** B—H
 c) N—Br   **d)** C—F

4. Which molecule is nonpolar?

5. Without doing any calculations, predict which vitamin is the most polar in the group? (Hint: You do not need to subtract electronegativity values to determine bond polarity for the bonds in these molecules. Instead, look

the molecules over and identify polar bonds that you already recognize.)

vitamin A

vitamin D

vitamin C

 a) vitamin A
 b) vitamin D
 c) vitamin C
 d) It is not possible to predict which vitamin is most polar with the given information.

6. Which molecule is polar?

a)

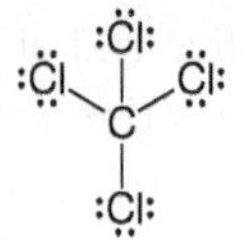

b) 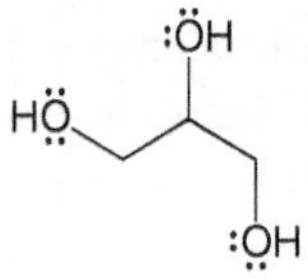 :ÖH
HÖ
:ÖH

c) 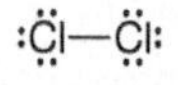 :C̈l—C̈l:

d) 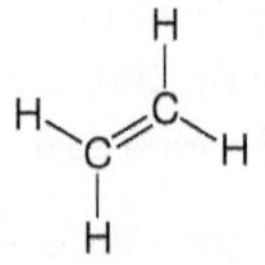
H
H—C
 ‖
H—C
H

7. Which type(s) of intermolecular forces does a molecule of octanol (shown here) experience with another molecule of octanol?

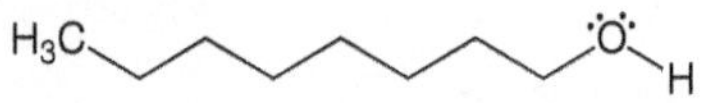

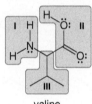

a) London dispersion forces only

b) dipole-dipole forces and hydrogen bonding only

c) hydrogen bonding only

d) London dispersion forces, hydrogen bonding, and dipole-dipole forces

8. The structure of the amino acid Valine is given. Which region(s) of this essential amino acid are polar?

valine

a) Region III is the only polar region.

b) Regions I and II are the only polar regions.

c) Regions I, II, and III are all polar.

d) Region II is the only polar region.

9. Which is the *least* polar covalent bond?

a) S—S

b) S—O

c) P—S

d) P—O

10. Which molecule(s) are *polar*?

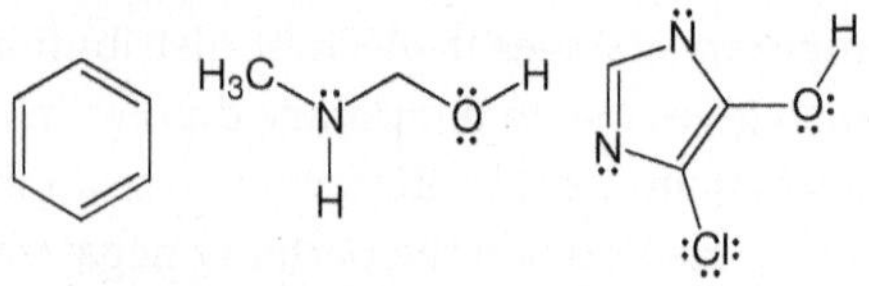

I   II   III

a) Molecules II and III are polar.

b) Only molecule I is polar.

c) Only molecule II is polar.

d) Only molecule III is polar.

11. What is the strongest intermolecular force between molecules of adrenaline (epinephrine) and molecules of water?

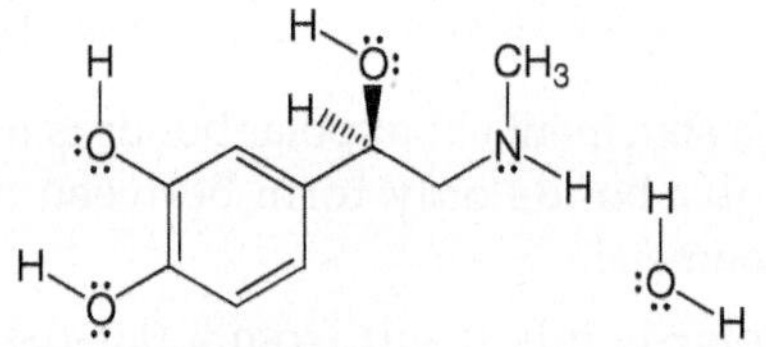

adrenaline   water

a) hydrogen bonding

b) dipole-dipole

c) London dispersion forces

d) London dispersion and neutron forces

Unit 2
Bringing It All Together

Why Is Chemical Bonding Important in Medicine?

CHEMISTRY APPLICATION We opened Unit 2 with a look at how scientists are using chemistry to develop innovative new strategies to treat an array of diseases, including cancer. Now let's circle back to our unit theme of how the fundamental chemistry in this unit relates directly to important biomedical research and applications such as the development of new cancer treatments. In May of 2021, the FDA approved the 100th antibody-based drug, a list that includes many antibody-drug conjugates. The development of special linkers that covalently attach the toxins to the targeted antibodies has been critical to the success of these treatments (Figure U2.6).

One of the best-known therapies is TDM-1 (ado-trastuzumab), approved for the treatment of specific, advanced, breast cancers. Approximately 20% of breast cancers are known as HER2-positive. HER2 (human epidermal growth factor receptor 2) is a protein found in small amounts on the surface of some cells. In a HER2-positive breast cancer, however, the cells have large numbers of these receptors that can stimulate the growth of the cancer cells. This type of breast cancer is more common in younger women, and tends to be more aggressive than other forms (Figure U2.7). The risk of recurrence is also much greater for HER2-positive cancers.

Figure U2.6 Conjugated Antibodies.

Conventional cancer treatments target all rapidly dividing cells in the body, causing an array of side effects such as nausea, hair loss, and fatigue. Conjugated antibodies, in contrast, can deliver toxic drugs specifically to cancer cells.

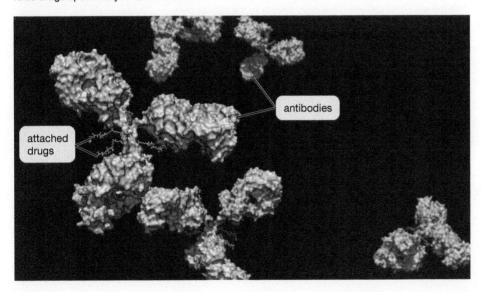

Figure U2.7 Screening Mammography.

Mammograms use X-rays to detect early breast cancer. While HER2-positive breast cancers are typically much more aggressive, the survival rate with early detection is high.

This conjugated antibody, TDM-1, was a welcome addition to the treatments available to women battling these aggressive, HER2-positive tumors. TDM-1 uses a special linker to covalently attach the toxin DM1 to an antibody specific to the HER2 receptor on the cell surface (Figure U2.8). This creates the so-called "magic bullet" that delivers the drug precisely to the cancer cells, sparing most of the body's healthy cells. This approach significantly increases the survival time and decreases the side effects experienced by patients.

Figure U2.8 TDM-1.

TDM-1- contains an antibody specific to the HER2 receptor on many breast cancer cells. A chemical linker covalently attaches the DMI toxin to the antibody, delivering the drug directly to the cancer cells.

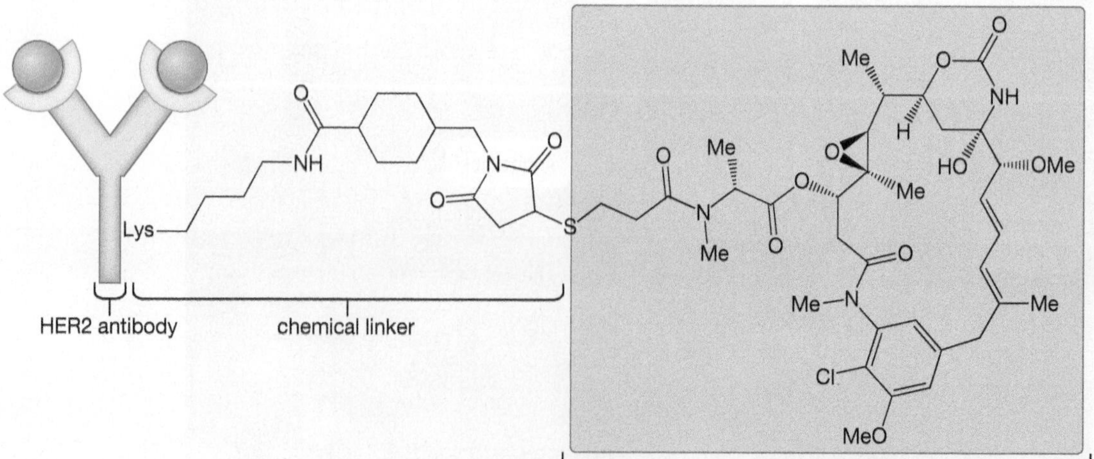

Questions to Think About

1. Based on what you learned in this unit, look at the DM1 molecule (Fig. U2.8) and consider these questions: (i) is the DM1 molecule held together with ionic or covalent bonds? (ii) can you identify any polar regions on the DM1 molecule? (iii) can you find any non-polar regions on the DM1 molecule?

2. Draw the DM1 molecule on a separate sheet of paper and show all the carbons and hydrogen atoms that are not shown. Why do chemists use shorthand "line bond" notation for molecules that contain carbon and hydrogen?

3. Find the N-H group connected to the antibody and complete the Lewis structure of this group by adding a lone pair of electrons. What is the shape of this part of the molecule where N is the central atom?

4. What type of intermolecular forces do you think the DM1 molecule forms with the water in a patient's blood?

5. Do you think the DM1 molecule is larger, smaller, or about the same size as the antibody it is linked to? Explain.

A Closer Look at the Data

TDM-1 was approved by the FDA in 2013 based on the results of an extensive clinical trial comparing the effectiveness of TDM-1 with the standard treatment at the time for HER2+ breast cancer. The results of the trial were published in the scientific journal, *The New England Journal of Medicine*, (Verma *et al*, 2012). Figure U2.9 is taken from this paper. Recall from Chapter 1 that primary papers like these are written by scientists for other specialists in their field. Thus, you should expect the text and figures to be complex and include some jargon that you might not be familiar with. Thankfully the complexity gets easier to sift through as you continue to practice interpreting scientific papers and data.

Figure U2.9 Progression-Free Survival of TDM-1 Treated Patients.

Median progression-free survival was 3.2 months longer in the T-DMI group than the lapatinib-capecitabine group.

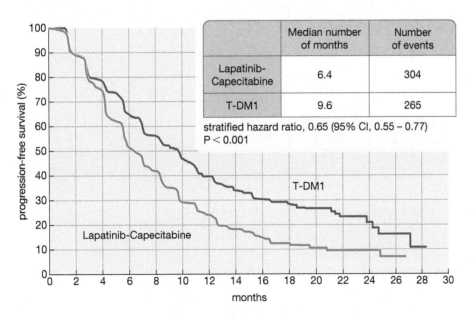

	Median number of months	Number of events
Lapatinib-Capecitabine	6.4	304
T-DM1	9.6	265

stratified hazard ratio, 0.65 (95% CI, 0.55 – 0.77)
$P < 0.001$

Questions to Think About

Examine Figure U2.8 and answer the following questions:

1. When trying to interpret a graph, it's always a good idea to make sure you clearly understand each axis. In your own words, explain what each axis represents in this graph.

2. This study was done in patients with aggressive, recurring HER2-positive breast cancers. What difference did the treatment with this conjugated antibody, TDM-1, make for this cohort of patients?

3. What did the developers of TDM-1 have to understand about the structure of both their drug as well as the HER2 receptor in order to develop a therapeutic approach like this?

We opened Unit 2 with a look at how scientists are using chemistry to develop powerful, targeted approaches to treat an array of diseases, including cancer. With this biomedical application in mind, we then learned about the importance of ionic bonding that results from the direct transfer of electrons from one atom to another. In Chapter 6, we examined another type of chemical bonding that occurs when atoms share electrons. The sharing of electrons to form covalent bonds is how most of the biologically important molecules of life are held together. We also saw how molecules adopt different shapes, and often have an unequal distribution of electrons across them which leads to electron rich and electron poor regions within the same molecule. In Chapter 7, we applied our understanding of chemical bonding to discover how multiple molecules are attracted to one another—an effect you can physically feel as the "stickiness" on your fingers when you have honey or jelly on them.

Unit 3
Introduction
Chemical Reactions and Energy

Chapter 8: Chemical Reactions
Chapter 9: Energy, Rate, and Equilibrium

In 2003 the scientific community was rocked by a study that altered the color and disease susceptibility of mice by simply feeding their mothers additional nutrients during pregnancy (Figure U3.1). The leaner, healthier offspring did not have any mutations to their DNA. The additional nutrients had simply turned off a specific gene. This discovery raised many important questions. Was DNA no longer destiny? How could adding tiny molecules containing carbon and hydrogen to the mouse DNA have such a profound impact on its health? And could similar molecules be affecting our own health?

Figure U3.1 Agouti Mice.
A) Agouti mice have a gene that gives them a yellow coat and makes them susceptible to cancer and diabetes. The gene has been turned off by environmental factors in the brown mouse (right).
B) The dramatic difference between the two mice is due not to changes in their DNA but rather a change in the mother's nutrition.

A

B

Unit 3: Introduction
How Can Tiny Labels on Our DNA Profoundly Affect Our Health?

To learn more about the implications of how attaching small molecules to our DNA can dramatically influence our characteristics and health, and even be passed to our offspring, watch **Video U3.1** in the Pearson eText.

Unit 3 opens with a provocative look at how a simple change in the labels on our DNA can dramatically alter our characteristics. The discovery of the Agouti mouse (see Fig. U3.1) helped launch the study of **epigenetics.** The field focuses on how heritable traits can be associated not with changes to the sequence of our DNA but rather with other chemical modifications to the molecule. Understanding these modifications has led to dramatic changes in how we detect and treat an array of diseases (Figure U3.2).

In this unit, we will learn more about chemical reactions, including the reactions that can so profoundly change how we use, and pass on, our DNA. We'll explore the concept of energy and how understanding energy can help us predict when chemical reactions will occur. This knowledge will help us better understand the numerous new diagnostic and treatment approaches that utilize epigenetics.

Figure U3.2 Epigenetics and Health.

A) In 2016 the Food and Drug Administration (FDA) approved the first blood-based test to detect colorectal cancer. The test screens for epigenetic changes common in colorectal cancer cells and provides a much less invasive diagnostic tool than a colonoscopy. **B)** Epigenetics offers new approaches to treating Alzheimer's disease, a degenerative brain disease that affects an estimated five million Americans. **C)** Research suggests that a father's exposure to environmental chemicals, particularly a group of chemicals called phthalates, may affect the epigenetic labels on his sperm.

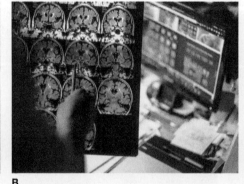

A   B   C

Unit 3 Chemistry Application: How Do Chemical Labels on Our DNA Impact Our Health?

Scientists have long believed that the order of the bases (A, T, C, and G) in our DNA makes each of us unique and that it's this unique sequence we pass on to our children (Figure U3.3). Epigenetics, however, has added a new layer of complexity to our understanding of inheritance and disease. We now know that a variety of environmental factors can influence how you attach small chemical labels known as methyl groups (CH_3) on the C's in our DNA. These methyl groups can influence which genes we use and when. And evidence suggests we can pass the patterns we acquire during our lives on to our children.

In this unit, we'll explore chemical reactions in general and follow-up on the reaction that attaches these methyl groups to our DNA.

Figure U3.3 DNA.

DNA is found in every one of our cells. The sequence of A's, T's, C's, and G's in our DNA makes each of us unique and is passed on to our children. Environmental factors, however, can trigger the addition of methyl groups (CH_3) on the C's. This can influence which genes we use and cause disease. These environmentally induced patterns can also be passed to our offspring.

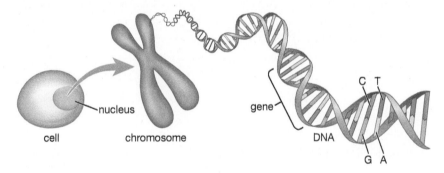

Questions to Think About

What chemistry do we need to know to understand the chemical reactions that drive epigenetics? Here are some questions to consider as you move through this unit:

- How do chemical reactions rearrange atoms in molecules?
- What determines whether or not a reaction will occur?
- How can we regulate which reactions occur in our bodies?

What chemistry would you like to know in order to more fully understand epigenetics?

Now that we have an overview of this unit, let's step into Chapter 8 and learn more about chemical reactions!

Chapter 8
Chemical Reactions

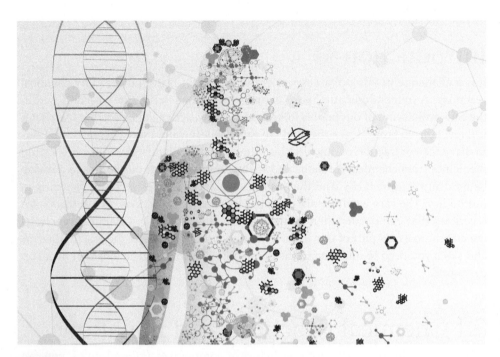

Chemical reactions with our DNA can have profound impacts on our health.

 Chapter Outline

- **8.1** Chemical Reactions and Equations
- **8.2** Types of Reactions
- **8.3** Oxidation-Reduction Reactions
- **8.4** The Mole
- **8.5** Molar Mass and Mole Calculations
- **8.6** Calculations in Chemical Reactions
- **8.7** Limiting Reactant

Learning Objectives

- **8.1** Use chemical equations and coefficients to represent and balance chemical reactions.
- **8.2** Identify combination, decomposition, replacement, and combustion chemical reactions.
- **8.3** Analyze the outcomes of oxidation-reduction reactions.

8.4 Use Avogadro's number to calculate moles and particles.

8.5 Determine the molar mass of a substance.

8.6 Calculate the amount of one substance in a reaction when given the amount of another substance in the reaction.

8.7 Determine the limiting reactant and percent yield of a chemical reaction.

Introduction

It is a challenge to think of an aspect of our lives that is not powered by chemical reactions. A tremendous number of chemical reactions occur every second within the cells and tissues of our bodies to keep us healthy, active, and alert. We use chemical reactions to break down the food we eat for energy and more chemical reactions to drive the contraction of our muscles (Figure 8.1A). Scientists produce life-saving medicines from chemical reactions and study the reactions in our bodies to develop better drugs (Figure 8.1B). And the reactions we depend on are not just occurring in our bodies. The cars we drive are powered by chemical reactions, as are the explosive fires that can occur when vehicles crash (Figure 8.1C). Chemical reactions are critical to every part of our lives. In this chapter, we explore the essential terms and skills you need to understand the diverse set of chemical reactions that make up our world.

8.1 Chemical Reactions and Equations

Now that you have a grasp on the structure of compounds and molecules, you can learn more about how compounds and molecules undergo chemical changes to produce new substances. Recall that a chemical change involves the conversion of substances into one or more new substances that have different chemical formulas and properties. A **chemical reaction** is the process that takes place when a chemical change is occurring. In chemical reactions, bonds break, elements rearrange and new bonds form to produce new substances. Consider the common chemical reaction between hydrogen (H_2) and oxygen (O_2). In this chemical reaction, the bonds in both the H_2 and O_2 molecules break and new bonds form to produce H_2O. Many chemical reactions, including the reaction between H_2 and O_2, release energy as

---

Figure 8.1 Chemical Reactions in our Daily Lives.

A) The energy and nutrients we get from our food provide the energy we need to drive the chemical reactions that keep us alive.
B) Life-saving medicines are produced by chemical reactions. **C)** A car powered by combustion reactions catches fire.

A   B   C

they occur. The energy released from this reaction can power vehicles (Figure 8.2) that are quieter, more efficient, and produce only water vapor in their exhaust.

Indicators of Chemical Reactions

Chemical reactions often involve a visible change that provides clues to what happened in the reaction. A chemical change sometimes involves a color change or the release of a gas in the form of bubbles. In other cases, a solid forms from two liquids or heat is produced so that a flask containing the reaction feels warm to the touch. Watch what happens when lead(II) nitrate and potassium iodide react (Video 8.1).

Indicators of chemical reactions can be seen in nature as well. When the leaves on trees change colors, several chemical reactions are occurring over time (Figure 8.3). The molecule that is responsible for the green color in leaves (chlorophyll) undergoes chemical reactions forming molecules that exhibit a range of other colors. All of these reactions involve the breaking of bonds and the formation of new bonds to produce new compounds.

Chemical Equations

The reaction between natural gas, methane (CH_4), and oxygen (O_2) is a reaction we rely on every day to cook our food, heat our homes, and power our devices. The detailed diagram in Figure 8.4 can help you visualize this reaction. While this kind of visualization is very useful, chemists more commonly use symbols to more efficiently communicate about chemical reaction and the processes that are too small to see.

A **chemical equation** is an expression that uses chemical formulas and other symbols to represent a reaction (Figure 8.4). The **reactants**—the starting substances—are on the left side of the equation. The **products**—the new substances—are on the right side of the equation. When there is more than one reactant or product, (+) signs separate them. A **reaction arrow** separates the reactants from the products and points toward the products to indicate the direction of the chemical reaction. In many

Figure 8.2 Hydrogen Fuel Cell Bus.

The chemical reaction between H_2 and O_2 to produce water (H_2O) provides the energy to power alternative fuel vehicles.

Video 8.1:

A Yellow Solid Forms when Potassium Iodide and Lead(II) Nitrate React

Figure 8.3 Fall Colors.

Chemical reactions break down the green compounds in leaves revealing fall colors.

Figure 8.4 Molecular Level Visualization of a Chemical Reaction.

The reaction between CH_4 and O_2 produces CO_2 and H_2O. This reaction occurs when natural gas is ignited in the presence of oxygen from the air and gaseous carbon dioxide and water vapor are released. The chemical equation for this reaction is shown in the inset.

oxygen (O_2)

water (H_2O)

methane (CH_4)

carbon dioxide (CO_2)

reactants   reaction arrow   products

$$CH_4(g) + 2O_2(g) \longrightarrow CO_2(g) + 2H_2O(g)$$

reactions, each formula includes an abbreviation that indicates the physical state of each substance: *solid (s), liquid (l), gas (g), or aqueous (aq)*. A substance in the **aqueous** state is dissolved in water.

 Apply what you have just learned: **Practice 8.1** in the Pearson eText.

Balancing Chemical Equations

The whole numbers in front of the molecular formulas in a chemical equation are **coefficients**. Chemists place coefficients in front of each formula to produce a **balanced equation**, which is an equation that has an equal number of atoms of each element on both sides. When a chemical reaction occurs, the atoms of each element in the reaction are rearranged but not created or destroyed. The chemical equation must represent this and therefore must have the same number of atoms of each element on both sides of the equation.

Recall that methane (CH_4), and oxygen (O_2) react to produce carbon dioxide (CO_2) and water (H_2O) (Figure 8.5). To balance the equation, identify and count the number of atoms of each element on both sides of the equation. The coefficient in front of each formula indicates how many molecules or atoms of that substance are present. When there is no coefficient in front of the formula, you can assume that there is one molecule. In the equation in Figure 8.5, there is one carbon atom, four hydrogen atoms, and four oxygen atoms on each side. The equation is balanced.

Figure 8.5 A Balanced Chemical Equation.

This illustration represents the chemical reaction between CH_4 and O_2 using space-filling models and a chemical equation. The coefficients in front of each molecule in the equation balance the chemical equation. There must be an equal number of all atoms on each side of the equation.

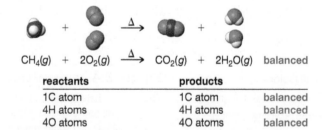

reactants	products	
1C atom	1C atom	balanced
4H atoms	4H atoms	balanced
4O atoms	4O atoms	balanced

When you encounter an unbalanced chemical equation, you can use coefficients and a trial and error process to balance the equation. Note that you can only use coefficients to balance a chemical equation. Do not adjust subscripts on the reactants and products to change the number of atoms in an equation. In VisibleChem Video 8.1 you explore this process and practice balancing several unbalanced chemical equations in the practice problems.

 Watch this concept come to life: **VisibleChem Video 8.1:** Writing and Balancing Chemical Equations and **VisibleChem Video 8.2:** Balancing Chemical Equations in the Pearson eText.

Apply what you have just learned: **Practice 8.2–8.4** in the Pearson eText.

Quiz yourself on the content of this section: **Check 8.1** in the Pearson eText.

8.2 Types of Reactions

Many different types of chemical reactions occur in nature and in the laboratory. For this reason, chemists classify reactions into four types: *combination, decomposition, replacement,* and *combustion*. Some reactions do not fit into just one of these categories, but the classification system is useful to help communicate the general type of chemical change occurring in a reaction.

Combination Reactions

Combination reactions are reactions between two or more elements or compounds to form one product. If the reactants are A and B, a combination reaction produces AB as the product.

The reaction of magnesium and oxygen to form magnesium oxide is an example of a combination reaction (Figure 8.6).

$$2Mg(s) + O_2(g) \rightarrow 2MgO(s)$$

Figure 8.6 A Combination Reaction in Fireworks.

Magnesium metal combines with oxygen in the air to produce magnesium oxide. Magnesium gives off a very bright white when it burns. Firework manufacturers use it to produce white sparks and improve brilliance.

| 2Mg(s) | + | O₂(g) | ⟶ | 2MgO(s) |
| magnesium | | oxygen | | magnesium oxide |

The formation of proteins from amino acids is also an example of a combination reaction that occurs in the human body (Figure 8.7).

Figure 8.7 Formation of a Protein from Amino Acids is a Combination Reaction.

The insulin protein, for example, is a chain of 51 amino acids that are all linked together in combination reactions.

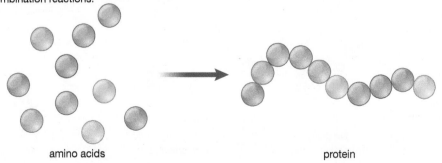

amino acids   protein

Figure 8.8 Molecular Level View of a Decomposition Reaction.

Hydrogen peroxide (H_2O_2) decomposes to produce water (H_2O) and the oxygen (O_2) bubbling in this wound. Hydrogen peroxide is a strong disinfectant that kills many types of bacteria. Most professionals, however, now recommend against using H_2O_2 to disinfect wounds as it can damage cells and slow the healing process.

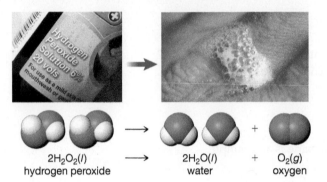

$2H_2O_2(l)$ $\longrightarrow$ $2H_2O(l)$ + $O_2(g)$
hydrogen peroxide   water   oxygen

Decomposition Reactions

In a **decomposition reaction**, a single reactant splits into two or more products. The decomposition reaction of AB, a generic reactant, produces A and B as products.

$$\boxed{A\ B} \longrightarrow \boxed{A} + \boxed{B}$$

You can purchase hydrogen peroxide (H_2O_2), for example, at the drug store as a three percent solution. This means the bottle contains ninety-seven percent water and three percent hydrogen peroxide. When you use it as an antiseptic and apply it to a wound, the solution foams and bubbles (Figure 8.8). This occurs because of a decomposition reaction. Hydrogen peroxide (H_2O_2) is decomposing to produce water (H_2O) and oxygen gas (O_2). The bubbles you see are pure O_2 gas.

Single Replacement Reactions

In a replacement reaction, elements in a compound are replaced with other elements. A **single replacement reaction** involves one element replacing another element in a compound. In this example, a generic element, A, replaces element B to form a compound with C.

$$\boxed{A} + \boxed{B\ C} \longrightarrow \boxed{A\ C} + \boxed{B}$$
single replacement

In the reaction of zinc with hydrochloric acid (HCl), for example, zinc replaces a hydrogen atom to produce zinc chloride (Figure 8.9).

$$Zn(s) + 2HCl(aq) \rightarrow ZnCl_2(aq) + H_2(g)$$

A single replacement reaction allows bacteria to produce new cell walls as they grow and reproduce. The antibiotic fosfomycin stops this reaction, so healthcare providers prescribe it to treat bacterial infections (Figure 8.10).

Figure 8.9 Molecular Level View of a Single Replacement Reaction.

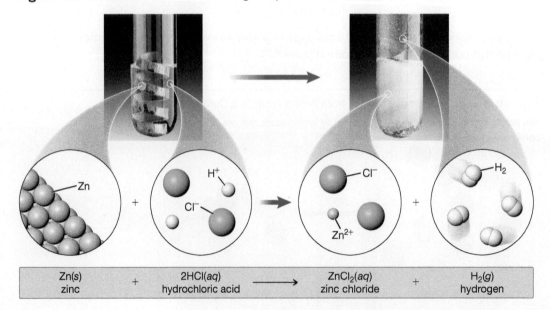

| $Zn(s)$ | + | $2HCl(aq)$ | $\longrightarrow$ | $ZnCl_2(aq)$ | + | $H_2(g)$ |
| zinc | | hydrochloric acid | | zinc chloride | | hydrogen |

Figure 8.10 Bacteria use a Single Replacement Reaction to Produce their Cell Walls.

A phosphate group replaces a sugar nucleotide as bacteria build their cell walls. Antibiotics that block this reaction can help treat bacterial infections by destroying the cell walls of the bacteria.

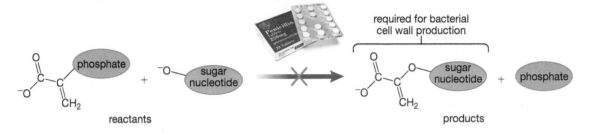

Double Replacement Reactions

A **double replacement reaction** involves two elements that switch places. In this example, the generic element, B, switches places with element D.

$$A\,B + C\,D \longrightarrow A\,D + C\,B$$

double replacement

In the double replacement reaction of sodium sulfate with barium chloride, barium ions switch places with sodium ions to form barium sulfate and sodium chloride (Figure 8.11). The charges on the ions determine the chemical formula of each product.

Figure 8.11 Molecular Level View of a Double Replacement Reaction.

Barium and sodium switch places in this reaction, producing barium sulfate and sodium chloride from sodium sulfate and barium chloride.

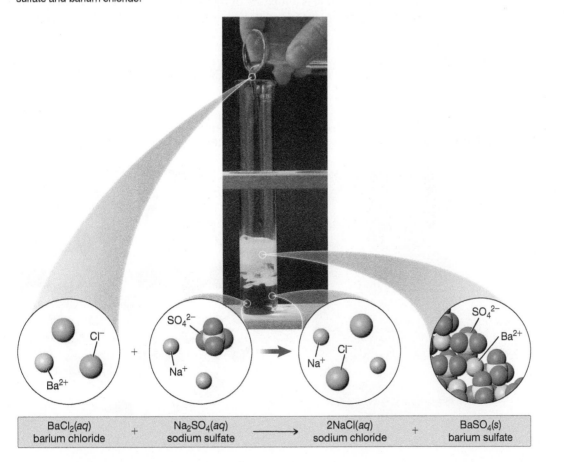

For example, the sodium ion (Na^+) has a charge of +1 and the chloride ion (Cl^-) has a charge of −1, so the neutral compound is NaCl. The same is true for barium and sulfate, the barium ion (Ba^{2+}) has a +2 charge and the sulfate ion (SO_4^{2-}) has a charge of −2, so the neutral compound is $BaSO_4$.

$$Na_2SO_4(aq) + BaCl_2(aq) \rightarrow BaSO_4(s) + 2NaCl(aq)$$

Combustion Reactions

In a **combustion reaction**, a hydrocarbon burns in oxygen (O_2) to produce carbon dioxide (CO_2), water (H_2O), and heat. The reaction of the hydrocarbon methane (CH_4) with oxygen (O_2) discussed in Section 8.1 is an example of a combustion reaction. Recall that methane reacts with oxygen to produce carbon dioxide and water vapor.

$$CH_4(g) + 2O_2(g) \rightarrow CO_2(g) + 2H_2O(g)$$
methane

Another combustion reaction is the reaction of propane gas (C_3H_8) with oxygen to produce carbon dioxide and water vapor. Propane is the fuel source in gas barbecues and other portable heating devices (Figure 8.12).

$$C_3H_8(g) + 5O_2(g) \rightarrow 3CO_2(g) + 4H_2O(g)$$
propane

The burning of gasoline in combustion engine automobiles is another common combustion reaction. Gasoline is a mixture of hydrocarbons that burns to release carbon dioxide and water vapor. One of the main hydrocarbons found in gasoline is octane (C_8H_{18}).

$$2C_8H_{18}(g) + 25O_2(g) \rightarrow 16CO_2(g) + 18H_2O(g)$$
octane

Figure 8.12 A Molecular Level Visualization of Propane Gas, C_3H_8.

These four reaction categories (*combination, decomposition, replacement,* and *combustion*) provide a way for chemists to generalize how chemical reactions proceed (Table 8.1). Given the large number of possible chemical reactions in the world, establishing a way to categorize reactions provides a convenient way to discuss and describe them. In fact, thousands of chemical reactions occur in the human body, many of which follow the patterns of the four types of reactions discussed in this section. After completing Practice 8.5 in the Pearson eText, click on BioConnect 8.1 (contains Figures 8.13–819) to learn about two chemical reactions that are responsible for controlling the way our DNA behaves.

Table 8.1 Summary of the Types of Reactions.

Types of reactions	
Combination reactions are characterized by two or more elements or compounds forming one product.	A + B ⟶ A B
Decomposition reactions are characterized by a single reactant splitting into two or more products.	A B ⟶ A + B
Single replacement reactions are characterized by a single element replacing another element in a compound.	A + B C ⟶ A C + B
Double replacement reactions are characterized by two elements switching places to form new products.	A B + C D ⟶ A D + C B

Apply what you have just learned: **Practice 8.5** in the Pearson eText.

Explore how Chemistry and Biology connect: **BioConnect 8.1:** Chemical Reactions Help Regulate DNA in the Pearson eText.

Quiz yourself on the content of this section: **Check 8.2** in the Pearson eText.

8.3 Oxidation-Reduction Reactions

In the previous section, you learned about four types of chemical reactions. This entire section is dedicated to an additional type of chemical reaction. We single out **oxidation-reduction reactions** or **redox reactions** because they are common in our everyday lives, in biological systems, and in energy production.

Redox reactions involve the transfer of electrons from one substance to another. **Oxidation** is the loss of electrons and **reduction** is the gain of electrons (Figure 8.20). These two processes occur together in an oxidation-reduction chemical reaction.

One common oxidation-reduction reaction is the rusting of iron metal (Fe), which involves the oxidation of iron by oxygen in air (O_2) to form iron(III) oxide (Fe_2O_3).

$$4Fe(s) + 3O_2(g) \rightarrow 2Fe_2O_3(s)$$

oxidized   reduced   rust

Figure 8.20 Oxidation-Reduction Reactions.

A) Oxidation is the loss of electrons. Reduction is the gain of electrons. **B)** Many students use the memory trick "Leo the lion says ger" to help them remember these two important terms.

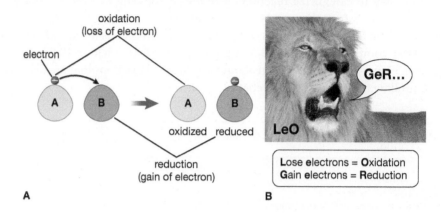

In this reaction, iron (Fe) undergoes oxidation. It loses electrons to become Fe^{3+}. The electrons are gained by oxygen and it becomes O^{2-}. Oxygen, therefore, undergoes reduction. The iron and oxygen ions combine to form the product iron(III) oxide, which is the orange red solid commonly called rust (Figure 8.21).

Gaining and Losing Electrons in Redox Reactions

Knowing some general trends can help you to identify oxidation-reduction reactions. *Metals tend to lose electrons to form positive ions, whereas nonmetals gain electrons to form negative ions.* For example, sodium metal (Na) readily loses electrons—is oxidized—to

Figure 8.21 Rust is the Result of an Oxidation-Reduction Reaction.

Iron metal loses electrons (is oxidized) while oxygen gains electrons (is reduced). As a result, iron(III) oxide, which we call rust, forms.

Figure 8.22 Sodium Chloride Forms in a Redox Reaction.

The metal, sodium, loses an electron and is oxidized. The nonmetal, chlorine, gains an electron and is reduced.

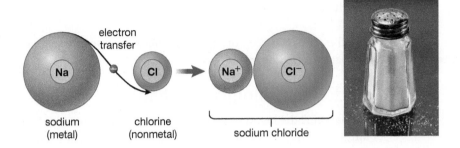

electron transfer

sodium (metal) chlorine (nonmetal) sodium chloride

form the cation Na^+. Similarly, iron metal (Fe) oxidizes to become Fe^{3+} by losing three electrons.

$$Na \rightarrow Na^+ + e^-$$
$$Fe \rightarrow Fe^{3+} + 3e^-$$

Oxidation
Electrons are lost

The nonmetal, Cl_2, on the other hand, readily gains electrons in a reduction process to become $2Cl^-$. Oxygen (O_2), another nonmetal, gains four electrons—is reduced to become $2O^{2-}$.

$$Cl_2 + 2e^- \rightarrow 2Cl^-$$
$$O_2 + 4e^- \rightarrow 2O^{2-}$$

Reduction
Electrons are gained

The formation of table salt (NaCl) illustrates how oxidation and reduction take place at the same time in a redox reaction (Figure 8.22). Sodium loses an electron in an oxidation process and Cl_2 gains electrons in a reduction process. The overall oxidation-reduction equation is:

oxidized

$$2Na(s) + Cl_2(g) \longrightarrow 2NaCl(s)$$

reduced

Batteries and Redox

Battery technology is based on oxidation-reduction reactions. When electrons are lost by an element in an oxidation reaction, their loss generates electricity to power electronic devices. The electrons are generated at the negative end of the battery and move towards the positive end.

An artificial pacemaker is a small battery-operated device that helps the heart beat in regular rhythm. The pacemaker provides a small electric stimulation when it detects that the heart is beating too slow. Surgeons place the pacemaker under the skin near the collarbone and connect it to the heart with wires (Figure 8.23). Pacemakers contain a small, long-lasting battery that uses lithium-ion redox chemistry to power the life-saving device.

Figure 8.23 Scan of Human Chest Cavity Showing Pacemaker and Wire.

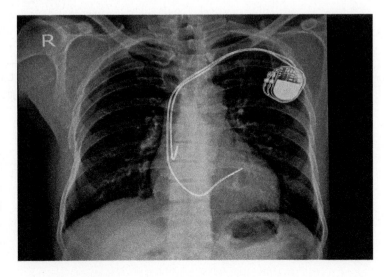

The redox reaction in a pacemaker involves the oxidation of lithium metal (Li) to the lithium ion (Li^+) and the reduction of iodine (I_2) to the iodide ion (I^-).

Apply what you have just learned: **Practice 8.6** in the Pearson eText.

$$\text{Oxidation:} \quad 2Li \rightarrow 2Li^+ + 2e^- \quad (\textbf{loss of } e^-)$$
$$\text{Reduction:} \quad I_2 + 2e^- \rightarrow 2I^- \quad (\textbf{gain of } e^-)$$

The electron generated by the oxidation of lithium moves to the positive side of the battery where the reduction of iodine takes place.

Redox in Biological Systems

Oxidation is the loss of electrons. In addition, it also can involve the addition of oxygen or the loss of hydrogen. In a similar way, reduction is the gain of electrons, but it also can be the loss of oxygen or the gain of hydrogen (Figure 8.24). These alternate definitions of oxidation and reduction are common ways to describe redox reactions in biological systems (Table 8.2).

The liver, for example, contains a family of enzymes called cytochrome 450 oxidases. These enzymes play a crucial role in eliminating a variety of toxins and drugs from the body. The enzymes often work by adding an oxygen to (oxidizing) a toxin (Figure 8.25). The addition of oxygen creates a more soluble compound that can be more easily excreted in urine. After completing Practice 8.7 in the Pearson eText, read BioConnect 8.2 (contains Figures 8.26–8.31) to learn how redox reactions power our bodies.

Table 8.2 Summary of the Characteristics of Oxidation Reduction Reactions.

	Always involves	May involve
Oxidation	loss of electrons	addition of oxygen
		loss of hydrogen
Reduction	gain of electrons	loss of oxygen
		gain of hydrogen

Figure 8.24 NAD^+ is Reduced to NADH.

NADH is an electron shuttle that transports electrons around our cells. When we digest our food, for example, NAD^+ picks up electrons from the food molecules and uses them to make energy in the form of ATP.

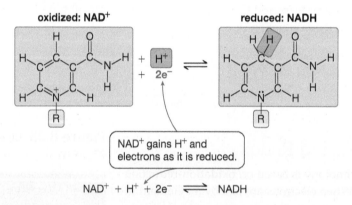

Figure 8.25 Enzymes in the Liver Transfer Oxygen to Toxins.

Enzymes oxidize toxins, and the additional oxygen makes the toxin a more soluble compound that is more easily excreted in urine.

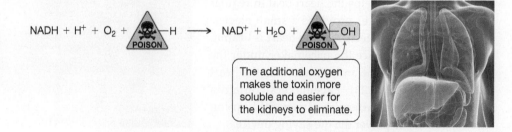

Apply what you have just learned: **Practice 8.7** in the Pearson eText.

Explore how Chemistry and Biology connect: **BioConnect 8.2:** Redox Reactions Power Our Bodies in the Pearson eText.

Quiz yourself on the content of this section: **Check 8.3** in the Pearson eText.

8.4 The Mole

Up to this point we have discussed atoms and molecules as single entities, one at a time. While this works well when exploring the structure and properties of individual atoms and molecules, it does present a problem when working with substances in a laboratory. Recall from Section 3.1 that atoms and molecules are so small that you cannot see them under the most powerful light microscopes. In a laboratory setting, it is more convenient to talk about and work with much larger quantities of atoms and molecules. For this reason, chemists refer to a quantity called the **mole** (abbreviated to **mol**).

A mole is a specific quantity, similar to a dozen (12), a case (24), or a ream (500). It is not very convenient to purchase individual eggs at the store; buying eggs twelve at a time is generally more practical. The primary difference between a mole and a dozen is that a mole is a much larger quantity. A dozen is 12 items. A mole is 6.02×10^{23} items. This large amount is a convenient scale to use when working with atoms, molecules, or ions.

The value 6.02×10^{23} is **Avogadro's number**, named for the Italian scientist Amedeo Avogadro (1776–1856) who first proposed the mole concept in the 1800s. One mole always contains Avogadro's number of particles.

1 mole O atoms $= 6.02 \times 10^{23}$ O atoms

1 mole of CO_2 molecules $= 6.02 \times 10^{23}$ CO_2 molecules

1 mole of Na^+ ions $= 6.02 \times 10^{23}$ Na^+ ions

Click on Video 8.2 to explore the concept of the *mole* and to gain a better conception of the massive size of Avogadro's number.

Video 8.2:
Mole Concept.

Moles to Molecules

Chemists are comfortable working with quantities of substances in units of moles, but sometimes they want to know the actual number of molecules. It is also possible that they know the number of molecules and they want to know the mole quantity as well. In both cases, a conversion between moles and number of molecules is possible.

One mole is always Avogadro's number (6.02×10^{23}) of particles (atoms, molecules, or ions). You can use Avogadro's number as a conversion factor to carry out these calculations. You can write this conversion factor, like all conversion factors, in two ways:

$$\frac{1 \text{ mol}}{6.02 \times 10^{23} \text{ atoms}} \quad \text{or} \quad \frac{6.02 \times 10^{23} \text{ atoms}}{1 \text{ mol}}$$

For example, imagine you have a large number of carbon atoms, such as 1.83×10^{22} atoms. Converting this large number of atoms to moles provides a more convenient and reasonable number. Recall that you can apply dimensional analysis (Section 2.3) to this problem and use the conversion factors so that units cancel. To accomplish this, you begin with the original quantity and multiply by a conversion factor in a way that leaves the desired units in your answer.

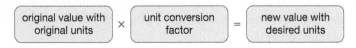

In this case, your carbon atoms are the original value, Avogadro's number is the conversion factor, and you are seeking moles of carbon atoms. You set up the problem like this:

$$\boxed{\begin{array}{c}\text{atoms}\\\text{of A}\end{array}} \xrightarrow[\text{conversion factor}]{6.02 \times 10^{23}} \boxed{\begin{array}{c}\text{moles}\\\text{of A}\end{array}}$$

$$\left[\frac{1.83 \times 10^{24} \ \text{carbon atoms}}{1}\right]\left[\frac{1 \ \text{mol carbon}}{6.02 \times 10^{23} \ \text{carbon atoms}}\right] = 3.04 \ \text{mol carbon}$$

Click on Learn 8.1 to see another example of how to convert a given mole amount to number of molecules.

Predict answers and see step-by-step solutions: **Learn 8.1:** Converting Between Molecules and Moles in the Pearson eText.

Apply what you have just learned: **Practice 8.8 and 8.9** in the Pearson eText.

Quiz yourself on the content of this section: **Check 8.4** in the Pearson eText.

8.5 Molar Mass and Mole Calculations

In addition to calculating the number of molecules in a sample from moles, chemists also perform calculations that determine the molecules present in a sample from the mass. Single atoms and molecules are much too small to count or weigh individually, but you can use a balance to weigh a sample to determine the sample's mass in grams (g). Once you measure and know the gram amount, you can convert to moles and if necessary, convert all the way to the number of molecules. This provides a way to "count by weighing."

Molar Mass of Elements

Figure 8.32 The Element Carbon has an Atomic Mass of 12.01 amu and a Molar Mass of 12.01 g/mol.

Figure 8.33 One Mole of Sulfur (S) and of Iron (Fe).

S
32.07 g

Fe
55.85 g

Chemists work with large numbers of atoms and molecules in the laboratory. A mass value called the molar mass is a useful tool for working with large numbers. **Molar mass** is the mass of one mole of any substance reported in grams per mole (g/mol). To gain a better understanding of the molar mass value, let's briefly review the range of common mass values in chemistry. Recall from Section 3.2 that the atomic mass value is the weighted average of the mass of an element. Atomic mass values are listed on the periodic table along with the chemical symbols of the elements. The atomic mass value is the mass of one individual atom of the element and is recorded in atomic mass units (amu). For example, carbon has an atomic mass of 12.01 amu, so the mass of one atom of carbon (on average) is 12.01 amu (Figure 8.32).

One mole of carbon atoms (6.02×10^{23} atoms) has a mass of 12.01 grams. This is the molar mass of carbon. Notice that the molar mass of carbon has the same numeric value as the atomic mass of one individual atom of carbon:

One atom of carbon on average has a mass of 12.01 amu.

One mole of carbon atoms has a molar mass of 12.01 g/mol.

For this reason, you can use the periodic table to obtain the molar mass of elements. For example, one mole of sulfur (S) weighs 32.07 g and one mole of iron (Fe) weighs 55.85 g (Figure 8.33).

Molar Mass of Compounds

You determine the **formula mass** by adding up the individual atomic mass values for each element found in a molecule or compound. For example, the formula mass of water (H_2O) is the sum of the mass values for two atoms of hydrogen and one atom of oxygen:

Formula Mass of H_2O

atomic mass of 1 oxygen atom =		16.00 amu
atomic mass of 2 hydrogen atoms =	2(1.01) =	2.02 amu
formula mass of H_2O =		18.02 amu

You can also use the term **molecular mass** in place of formula mass for covalent compounds such as water (Figure 8.34). Since the formula mass of water is 18.02 amu, its molar mass is 18.02 g/mol. One mole of water weighs 18.02 grams. This applies to all compounds and molecules. The formula mass of a compound is the compound's molar mass with units of grams per mole (g/mol).

You can see one mole of two different compounds in Figure 8.35. Notice that the mass of a substance per mole varies depending on the size of the compound. One mole of sucrose ($C_{12}H_{22}O_{11}$), for example, fills a beaker and weighs 342.34 grams. One mole of NaCl, on the other hand, does not fill the beaker and only weighs 58.44 grams.

Figure 8.34 The Formula Mass of Water (H_2O).

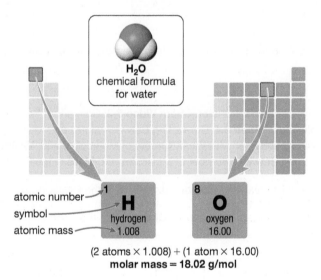

Figure 8.35 One Mole of a Variety of Compounds

Click on Learn 8.2 to see how to calculate the molar mass of the pain reliever ibuprofen.

Predict answers and see step-by-step solutions: **Learn 8.2:** Calculating Molar Mass in the Pearson eText.

Apply what you have just learned: **Practice 8.10** in the Pearson eText.

Mass-to-Mole Conversions

Molar mass is a useful conversion factor for converting between grams and moles, a calculation that chemists perform regularly in the lab. This is particularly true for chemists who are working to design and make new drugs.

Let's begin with a straightforward example of using a molar mass as a conversion factor between grams and moles. You can write the molar mass of NaCl (58.44 g/mol) as a conversion factor in two different ways.

$$\frac{58.44 \text{ g NaCl}}{1 \text{ mol NaCl}} \quad \text{or} \quad \frac{1 \text{ mol NaCl}}{58.44 \text{ g NaCl}}$$

You can use these conversion factors to determine the number of moles of NaCl in a given mass amount or to determine the mass in grams in a given number of moles. The key to a successful conversion sequence is to make sure units cancel out.

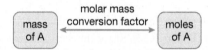

Because you know the number of particles in a mole, using this process you can also convert the mass in grams to the number of molecules or atoms. In this case you use both the molar mass and Avogadro's number (6.02×10^{23}) to perform a two-step calculation. This process—converting from grams to moles to molecules—is shown in this diagram of a conversion sequence pathway. Again, you can follow these steps in the reverse as well. It just depends on what information is given in the initial problem.

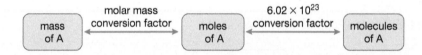

Explore VisibleChem Videos 8.3–8.6 to learn more about how to perform these calculations.

Watch this concept come to life: **VisibleChem Video 8.3:** Converting Between Mass and Moles, **VisibleChem Video 8.4:** Converting Between Moles and Mass, **VisibleChem Video 8.5:** Converting Between Mass and Number of Molecules, and **VisibleChem Video 8.6:** Converting Between Number of Molecules and Mass in the Pearson eText.

Apply what you have just learned: **Practice 8.11–8.13** in the Pearson eText.

Quiz yourself on the content of this section: **Check 8.5** in the Pearson eText.

8.6 Calculations in Chemical Reactions

Scientists use chemical reactions to synthesize the materials and drugs that people depend on every day (Figure 8.36). For example, the antibacterial medicine amoxicillin, classified by the World Health Organization as an "Essential Medicine," is one of the most prescribed drugs to combat bacterial infections.

In order to correctly prepare a drug such as amoxicillin, chemists perform calculations to determine the appropriate amounts of materials to start with and the maximum amount of product that they can produce from these starting materials. In the case of amoxicillin, chemists combine two reactants (HPGME and APA) to produce the product (Figure 8.37). Before carrying out this reaction in the lab, a chemist determines how much of each substance to weigh out and how much product they can make from the reactants. They perform these calculations by first balancing the chemical equation to obtain the correct ratios of each molecule in the reaction.

Figure 8.36 Production of Medicine.

Figure 8.37 The Chemical Synthesis of the Antibacterial Drug Amoxicillin.

This reaction involves combining the appropriate amounts of two building block reactants (HPGME and APA). A new chemical bond (shown in red) forms that joins the two building blocks to create the product of the reaction.

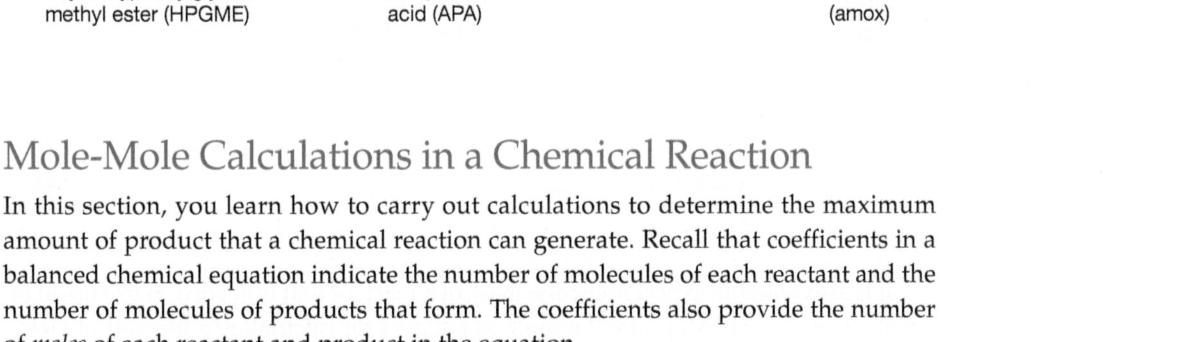

4-hydroxyphenylglycine methyl ester (HPGME)

6-aminopenicianic acid (APA)

amoxicillin (amox)

Mole-Mole Calculations in a Chemical Reaction

In this section, you learn how to carry out calculations to determine the maximum amount of product that a chemical reaction can generate. Recall that coefficients in a balanced chemical equation indicate the number of molecules of each reactant and the number of molecules of products that form. The coefficients also provide the number of *moles* of each reactant and product in the equation.

$$1N_2(g) \quad + \quad 1O_2(g) \quad \rightarrow \quad 2NO(g)$$

one molecule N_2 one molecule N_2 two molecules NO
one mole N_2 one mole N_2 two moles NO

The coefficients from a balanced equation provide a **mole ratio**, the ratio of number of moles of reactants that combine and the relative number of moles of product formed.

mole ratios: $\dfrac{1 \text{ mol } N_2}{1 \text{ mol } O_2}$ $\dfrac{1 \text{ mol } N_2}{2 \text{ mol NO}}$ $\dfrac{1 \text{ mol } O_2}{2 \text{ mol NO}}$

In this example, for every one mole of N_2 that is used up, two moles of NO are produced. The mole ratio provides a way to calculate the amount of product that can be formed from a given amount of reactant. It also provides a way to determine the amount of the other reactant (O_2) needed to use up all of the N_2 that is present at the beginning of the reaction. In this case, for every one mole of N_2 that reacts, one mole of O_2 is needed.

You can use mole ratios as conversion factors to determine the moles of product when given the moles of reactant as illustrated in this conversion pathway. When calculating, be sure to include the mole ratio step using the coefficients in the balanced equation (even if the ratio is 1:1). This helps you cancel units across the calculation and gives you confidence in the units of your answer. Learn 8.3 illustrates this process.

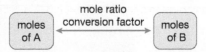

 Predict answers and see step-by-step solutions: **Learn 8.3:** Calculating Moles using Mole Ratios in the Pearson eText.

Apply what you have just learned: **Practice 8.14** in the Pearson eText.

Converting Mass of Reactant to Mass of Product

Perhaps the most common calculation performed by chemists when working in the laboratory is determining the maximum product mass from a given mass of reactant. This calculation allows chemists to determine the amount of material in grams that they can expect to produce.

This maximum calculated value is called the **theoretical yield**. The steps in the pathway to calculate a theoretical yield are shown here. You convert the mass in grams of reactant to moles of reactant using the molar mass conversion factor in Step 1. In Step 2, you convert moles of reactant to moles of product using the mole ratio conversion factor from the balanced chemical equation. In the final step (Step 3), you use the molar mass of the product to convert moles of product to the mass in grams.

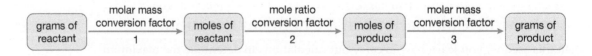

It is also possible to determine the mass of a reactant that is needed to use up all of the first reactant. The steps are the same as outlined for calculating a theoretical yield, but the second and third steps involve the second reactant, not the product as shown in this pathway:

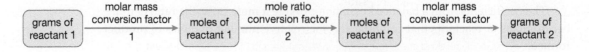

Click on Learn 8.4 to convert grams of reactant to grams of product.

Predict answers and see step-by-step solutions: **Learn 8.4:** Converting Grams of Reactant to Grams of Product in the Pearson eText.

Apply what you have just learned: Practice **8.15 and 8.16** in the Pearson eText.

Click on Learn 8.5 to convert grams of one reactant to grams of another reactant.

Predict answers and see step-by-step solutions: **Learn 8.5:** Converting Grams of One Reactant to Grams of Another Reactant in the Pearson eText.

Apply what you have just learned: **Practice 8.17 and 8.18** in the Pearson eText.

Quiz yourself on the content of this section: **Check 8.6** in the Pearson eText.

8.7 Limiting Reactant

Up to this point you have used chemical calculations to determine maximum product amounts produced when you are given the amount of one of the reactants. In this case, you assume that there is excess amount of a second or even third reactant. In many other cases, however, the amount of more than one of the reactants is known. How can you determine the mass of products if you're given the mass amounts of more than one reactant? To carry out this type of calculation, you must determine which reactant will be used up first. This reactant is called the **limiting reactant**.

Let's consider the idea of a limiting reactant by exploring a non-chemistry example first. To make a ham sandwich, you need two slices of bread, one piece of ham, and one leaf of lettuce to make each sandwich (Figure 8.38).

If you started with six slices of bread, and two slices of ham and three leaves of lettuce, you can make only two sandwiches. All of the ham is used up after making two sandwiches. In other words, the amount of ham limits your ability to make more sandwiches. In this situation, the ham is the *limiting reactant*. The bread and lettuce are present in excess and some of each is left over.

In a chemical reaction, one of the reactants generally limits the amount of product produced. When you know the amount of more than one reactant, the first step to determine the amount of product is to figure out which reactant is the limiting reactant. Once you know the limiting reactant, you can determine the product amounts from the limiting reactant amount. Because the other reactants are in excess, you can ignore them when carrying out the calculation. Learn 8.6 and 8.7 illustrate how to use a chemical equation and reactant amounts to determine the limiting reactant and calculate the amount of product that forms.

Figure 8.38 The Limiting Reactant Concept.

In this example the ham runs out first and is therefore the limiting reactant. The limiting reactant determines how much product (ham sandwiches) we can make. In this case, we can make two sandwiches.

Reactants   **Products**

Predict answers and see step-by-step solutions: **Learn 8.6:** Determining the Limiting Reactant and Calculating the Amount of Product that Forms in the Pearson eText.

Apply what you have just learned: **Practice 8.19** in the Pearson eText.

Predict answers and see step-by-step solutions: **Learn 8.7:** Determining the Limiting Reactant and Calculating the Mass of Product that Forms in the Pearson eText.

Apply what you have just learned: **Practice 8.20** in the Pearson eText.

Percent Yield

Recall that the theoretical yield is the maximum mass of product that can be produced from a specific amount of reactant (see Learn 8.4 and Learn 8.7). The amount of product produced from a real chemical reaction in a laboratory is always less than the maximum amount. During an actual reaction in a laboratory, there is often loss due to human error and the production of unwanted side products. The end result is that the mass of desired product is less than the maximum possible. The amount of product obtained in the real reaction is referred to as **actual yield.**

Chemists generally report the results of a chemical reaction using a **percent yield**, which they calculate using both the actual yield and the theoretical yield.

$$\text{percent yield} = \frac{\text{actual yield}}{\text{theoretical yield}} \times 100\%$$

For example, a pharmaceutical chemist working to prepare amoxicillin in a laboratory recovers 4.37 kg of pure product from a reaction. Her theoretical yield calculations indicate the maximum amount she could have recovered from her starting reactant amounts was 4.75 kg. Her percent yield is therefore 92.0%.

$$\text{percent yield} = \frac{4.37 \ \cancel{\text{kg}}}{4.75 \ \cancel{\text{kg}}} \times 100 = 92.0\% \text{ yield}$$

Apply what you have just learned: **Practice 8.21 and 8.22** in the Pearson eText.

Quiz yourself on the content of this section: **Check 8.7** in the Pearson eText.

Chapter Summary

8.1 Chemical Reactions and Equations

Learning Objective: Use chemical equations and coefficients to represent and balance chemical reactions.

Chemical reactions convert reactants into products. Balanced chemical equations represent reactions. To balance a chemical equation, place coefficients in front of reactants and products so that the number of atoms of each element is the same on both sides of the equation (Figure 8.5).

Video 8.1: A Yellow Solid Forms when Lead(II) Nitrate and Potassium Iodide React

VisibleChem Video 8.1: Writing and Balancing Chemical Equations

VisibleChem Video 8.2: Balancing Chemical Equations

Key Terms

aqueous	chemical reaction	reactant
balanced equation	coefficient	reaction arrow
chemical equation	product	

8.2 Types of Reactions

Learning Objective: Identify combination, decomposition, replacement, and combustion chemical reactions.

There are several types of common chemical reactions including combination, decomposition, single replacement, double replacement, and combustion reactions. Combination reactions involve a reaction between two or more elements or compounds to form one product. Decomposition reactions occur when a single reactant splits into two or more products. A single replacement reaction occurs when one element switches places with another element in a compound. A double replacement reaction involves two elements that switch places (Table 8.1).

BioConnect 8.1: Chemical Reactions Help Regulate DNA

Key Terms

acetyl group (CH_3CO) (from
    BioConnect 8.1)
combination reaction
combustion reaction
decomposition reaction

acetylation
    (from BioConnect 8.1)
DNA methylation
    (from BioConnect 8.1)
double replacement reaction
epigenetics (from BioConnect 8.1)

gene (from BioConnect 8.1)
gene regulation
    (from BioConnect 8.1)
methyl group (CH_3)
    (from BioConnect 8.1)
single replacement reaction

8.3 Oxidation-Reduction Reactions

Learning Objective: Analyze the outcomes of oxidation-reduction reactions.

Oxidation-reduction reactions (redox reactions) are a common class of reactions. Redox reactions involve the transfer of electrons. Oxidation is the loss of electrons and reduction is the gain of electrons. These two processes occur together in an oxidation-reduction chemical reaction (Figure 8.20). The reactions in batteries, the rusting of iron, and the biological processes that produce energy for our bodies are redox reactions.

BioConnect 8.2: Redox Reactions Power Our Bodies

Key Terms

cellular respiration
    (from BioConnect 8.2)

electron transport chains
    (from BioConnect 8.2)
mitochondria (from BioConnect 8.2)

oxidation
oxidation-reduction (redox) reaction
reduction

8.4 The Mole

Learning Objective: Use Avogadro's number to calculate moles and particles.

The mole (mol) provides a convenient way to quantify large quantities of very small particles such as atoms, molecules, and ions. There are 6.02×10^{23} particles in one mole, a number referred to as Avogadro's number. You can use Avogadro's number as a conversion factor to convert a quantity expressed in moles to the number of molecules present in a sample.

Video 8.2: Mole Concept

Key Terms

Avogadro's number (6.02×10^{23})
mole (mol)

8.5 Molar Mass and Mole Calculations

Learning Objective: Determine the molar mass of a substance.

Molar mass is the mass of one mole of any substance in grams per mole (g/mol). The molar mass of an atom is the atomic mass of that atom expressed in units of grams per mol (g/mol). The molar mass of substances, such as polyatomic ions, compounds, and molecules, is the sum of the atomic masses of the atoms in that substance. Conversion factors allow us to convert between grams, moles, and number of particles in a given sample.

VisibleChem Video 8.3: Converting Between Mass and Moles

VisibleChem Video 8.4: Converting Between Moles and Mass

VisibleChem Video 8.5: Converting Between Mass and Number of Molecules

VisibleChem Video 8.6: Converting Between Number of Molecules and Mass

Key Terms

formula mass
molar mass
molecular mass

8.6 Calculations in Chemical Reactions

Learning Objective: Calculate the amount of one substance in a reaction when given the amount of another substance in the reaction.

In order to synthesize the materials and drugs that people depend on every day, scientists use a series of calculations to determine the appropriate amounts of materials to start with and the maximum amount of product possible from these starting materials. You can perform similar calculations by first balancing a chemical equation to obtain the correct mole ratios of each molecule in the reaction. You can use mole ratios as conversion factors to determine the moles of product when given the moles of reactant. You can calculate theoretical yield (maximum product mass) by converting the mass of a reactant to the mass of the product possible.

Key Terms

mole ratio
theoretical yield

8.7 Limiting Reactant

Learning Objective: Determine the limiting reactant and percent yield of a chemical reaction.

A chemical reaction that involves two or more substances, often uses up one of the materials before the other(s). The material that is used up first is the limiting reactant. When the limiting reactant has been completely used, the reaction stops, even though some of the other starting material(s) may still be present. Limiting reactant calculations allow scientists to determine the maximum amount of product that can be produced when the amount of more than one reactant is known. Chemists generally report the results of a chemical reaction using a percent yield, which is calculated using both the actual yield and the theoretical yield.

Key Terms

actual yield
limiting reactant
percent yield

End-of-Chapter Quiz

Have you mastered the content of this chapter? Try the **End-of-Chapter Quiz** in the Pearson eText.

1. Which statement about the balanced reaction is correct?

$$4NH_3(g) + 5O_2(g) \rightarrow 4NO(g) + 6H_2O(l)$$

a) The products of the reaction are $NO(g)$ and $NH_3(g)$.

b) The reactants in this reaction are $NH_3(g)$ and $H_2O(l)$.

c) The products of the reaction are $H_2O(l)$ and $NO(g)$.

d) The reactants in this reaction are $O_2(g)$ and $H_2O(l)$.

2. Supply the missing coefficients to balance this chemical equation.

$$\_\_CH_3NH_2(g) + 9O_2(g) \rightarrow$$
$$\_\_CO_2(g) + 2N_2(g) + 10H_2O(g)$$

    a) 2, 4   b) 4, 2   c) 2, 2   d) 4, 4

3. Supply the missing coefficients to balance this chemical equation.

$$4KNO_3(s) \rightarrow \_\_K_2O(g) + 5O_2(g) + \_\_N_2(g)$$

a) 2, 3   b) 2, 2   c) 1, 3   d) 3, 2

4. Consider this general reaction and classify its reaction type.

$$ABC_3 \rightarrow AC + BC_2$$

a) combination
b) decomposition
c) single replacement
d) double replacement

5. Which reaction shows a reduction occurring?

a) $Fe \rightarrow Fe^{3+} + 3e^-$
b) $Ni^{2+} + 2e^- \rightarrow Ni$
c) $Li \rightarrow Li^+ + 1e^-$
d) $Ca^{2+} \rightarrow Ca^{2+}$

6. Which statement accurately describes this reaction?

$$Co \rightarrow Co^{2+} + 2e^-$$

a) Calcium is oxidized by the loss of two electrons resulting in the formation of the calcium ion with a charge of 2+.
b) Cobalt is reduced to form the cobalt ion with a charge of 2+ and the release of two electrons.
c) Cobalt is oxidized by the loss of two electrons resulting in the formation of the cobalt ion with a charge of 2+.
d) Cobalt is oxidized by the gain of two electrons to form the cobalt ion with a charge of 2+.

7. If a handful of sand from the beach contains 3.76×10^{23} silicon atoms, how many moles of silicon atoms does it contain?

a) 0.625 mol silicon atoms
b) 1.60 mol silicon atoms
c) 2.26×10^{47} mol silicon atoms
d) 1.60×10^{23} mol silicon atoms

8. If a deep breath of air in your lungs contains 4.70×10^{-2} moles of oxygen molecules, how many molecules of oxygen does it contain?

a) 4.70
b) 3.53×10^{-23} molecules oxygen
c) 1.28×10^{25} molecules oxygen
d) 2.83×10^{22} molecules oxygen

9. Histamine ($C_5H_9N_3$) is a molecule involved in a number of biological processes including inflammation and allergic reactions. Use the atomic masses provided to calculate the molar mass of histamine

and express your answer carrying two digits to the right of the decimal place. Atomic masses: nitrogen 14.01, hydrogen 1.01, and carbon 12.01.

a) 102.08 g/mol
b) 111.17 g/mol
c) 69.14 g/mol
d) 4.08×10^{13} kg

10. The drug fentanyl is a very powerful synthetic opioid that is 50 to 100 times more potent than morphine. Because of its high potency, fentanyl drug overdoses are on the rise across the U.S. If a drug user who overdosed was found to have injected 5.25 mg of fentanyl (5.25×10^{-3} g), how many moles of fentanyl did the person inject? The molecular formula of fentanyl is $C_{22}H_{28}N_2O$.

a) 0.75 mg/mL
b) 1.77 mol fentanyl
c) 1.56×10^{-5} mol fentanyl
d) 0.57 mol fentanyl

11. Formaldehyde (CH_2O) is a naturally occurring molecule and a building block in a variety of materials. It is also toxic at elevated levels and the US National Toxicology Program has listed formaldehyde as a known human carcinogen (indicating that it may cause cancer). How many molecules are contained in 2.25 grams of formaldehyde? The molar mass of formaldehyde is 30.03 grams/mole.

a) 1.35×10^{24} molecules formaldehyde
b) 4.51×10^{22} molecules formaldehyde
c) 7.49×10^{-2} molecules formaldehyde
d) 8.03×10^{24} mL molecules formaldehyde

12. Manufacturers produce billions of kilograms of calcium oxide (CaO), also known as quick lime, annually for steelmaking and other processes. CaO can react with carbon dioxide (CO_2) in the air to form calcium carbonate ($CaCO_3$), a substance found in limestone and the shells of marine organisms. According to the reaction shown here, how many

grams of $CaCO_3$ can form when 78.5 g CaO react with CO_2 in the air?

$$CaO(s) + CO_2(g) \rightarrow CaCO_3(s)$$

a) 1.40×10^2 g $CaCo_3$

b) 7.86×10^3 g $CaCO_3$

c) 1.40 g $CaCO_3$

d) 71.5 g $CaCO_3$

13. Hydrofluoric acid (HF) is used in the semiconductor industry as an etching and cleaning agent for silicon wafers (which are composed mainly of SiO_2). Use this reaction to calculate the number of grams $SiO_2(s)$ that can react with 2.50×10^{-5} grams HF on the surface of a silicon chip.

$$SiO_2(s) + 4HF(aq) \rightarrow SiF_4(g) + 2H_2O(l)$$

a) 7.51×10^{-5} g SiO_2

b) 3.76×10^{-4} g SiO_2

c) 0.301 g SiO_2

d) 1.20×10^7 g SiO_2

14. In a research project, a scientist combines 3.25 g of ammonium oxalate $(NH_4)_2C_2O_4$ with an excess amount of calcium chloride, and recovers 2.85 g of calcium oxalate (CaC_2O_4). What is the percent yield in this experiment? The molar mass of ammonium oxalate $(NH_4)_2C_2O_4$ is 124.10 g/mol and the molar mass of CaC_2O_4 is 128.097 g/mol.

$$CaCl_2(aq) + (NH_4)_2C_2O_4(aq) \rightarrow$$
$$CaC_2O_4(s) + 2NH_4Cl(aq)$$

a) 118%

b) 0.851%

c) 87.7%

d) 85.1%

15. When 6.25 mol of NH_3 are mixed with 5.31 mol of O_2, what is the limiting reactant in the reaction?

$$4NH_3(g) + 3O_2(g) \rightarrow 2N_2(g) + 6H_2O(g)$$

a) N_2 is the limiting reactant.

b) NH_3 is the limiting reactant.

c) O_2 is the limiting reactant.

d) H_2O is the limiting reactant.

16. Copper (II) phosphate is naturally occurring copper salt found in the mineral libethenite. Use the balanced reaction to calculate the mass of $Cu_3(PO_4)_2(s)$ that is produced when 18.20 g Na_3PO_4 react with 16.75 g $CuCl_2$. Possibly useful molar masses include: $Na_3PO_4 = 163.94$ g/mol, $CuCl_2 = 134.45$ g/mol, and $Cu_3(PO_4)_2 = 380.58$ g/mol.

$$2Na_3PO_4(aq) + 3CuCl_2(aq) \rightarrow$$
$$Cu_3(PO_4)_2(s) + 6NaCl(aq)$$

a) 15.80 g $Cu_3(PO_4)_2$

b) 21.13 g $Cu_3(PO_4)_2$

c) 47.41 g $Cu_3(PO_4)_2$

d) 142.2 g $Cu_3(PO_4)_2$

Chapter 9
Energy, Rate, and Equilibrium

Energy is the capacity to do work. Wind turbines can generate electricity to power homes and vehicles

Chapter Outline

Learning Objectives

9.1 Define energy and convert between energy units.

9.2 Describe how energy is absorbed or released in a chemical reaction and classify chemical reactions as endothermic or exothermic.

9.3 Represent the energy of chemical reactions using energy diagrams.

9.4 Predict the effect of concentration, temperature, and catalysts on the rate of reactions.

9.5 Describe the fundamental features of dynamic chemical equilibrium, write the expression for the equilibrium constant, and predict the direction a reaction at equilibrium will shift when disturbed.

9.6 Calculate equilibrium constants for reactions at equilibrium when given equilibrium concentrations of the reactants and products.

Introduction

What does the word "energy" *really* mean? Why do we use the word to describe so many different things in everyday life? For example, electrical energy allows us to turn on the lights in a room, the energy involved in a car crash causes severe damage, and a parent describes an excited child as having "lots of energy" (Figure 9.1). We also often refer to the energies our bodies get every day from the food we eat. Around a campfire, we can feel the heat energy released, see the light energy produced by the flame, and even hear sound energy as the wood cracks and pops. But where does all of this energy come from? In this chapter, we explore some important concepts about energy. We learn how the bonds broken and formed in reactions, the balance between reactants and products, and even the rate of reactions all relate to the energy in the chemical reactions of everyday life.

9.1 Energy

When people study chemistry, problem solve, eat, walk, or go for a run, they are using energy. **Energy** is the capacity to do work. In science, we categorize energy as either kinetic or potential energy. **Kinetic energy** is energy in motion, while **potential energy** is stored energy. A person standing on a cliff has stored potential energy due to position or location; once the person launches off the cliff into the water below, that potential energy is converted to kinetic energy, the energy of motion (Figure 9.2). Similarly, water at the top of a waterfall has potential energy due to its position. As the water tumbles over the edge, its potential energy converts to kinetic energy.

Both food and fossil fuels, such as gasoline, contain potential energy in the chemical bonds of the molecules in these substances. When we digest food or burn fuel to power an automobile, the potential energy converts to kinetic energy. We use that kinetic energy to move and carry out our daily tasks (Figure 9.3). These examples show how energy converts from one form to another.

These examples also illustrate the **law of conservation of energy**. The law of conservation of energy states that the total energy in the universe does not change because energy cannot be created or destroyed. Energy converts from one form to another but

Figure 9.1 Common Forms of Energy.

Consider **A)** a fire burning, **B)** young children running, and **C)** a car crash. All of these common experiences involve energy.

A   B   C

Figure 9.2 Kinetic and Potential Energy.

Both the person on the top of the cliff and the water above the falls have potential energy. As they fall, the potential energy is converted to kinetic energy.

Figure 9.3 Digestion Converts Potential Energy in the Chemical Bonds in Food into Kinetic Energy.

the total amount in the universe is constant. We explore this law in the next section and discuss how chemical bonds release the potential energy they store during chemical reactions in the form of heat energy that we can use to do work.

Units of Energy

We commonly use two different units to measure and quantify energy: the calorie and the joule. The **calorie (cal)** is the amount of energy needed to raise the temperature of one gram of water one degree celsius. The **joule (J)** is related to the calorie; **1 cal = 4.184 J.** Both the calorie and the joule are small amounts of energy. For this reason, we often use kilocalorie (kcal) and kilojoules (kJ) when referring to the energy associated with chemical reactions.

$$1 \text{ kcal} = 1000 \text{ cal}$$
$$1 \text{ kJ} = 1000 \text{ J}$$
$$1 \text{ kcal} = 4.184 \text{ kJ}$$
$$1 \text{ cal} = 4.184 \text{ J}$$

In a nutrition context, one **Calorie** (with an uppercase C) is the same as one kilocalorie. The Calorie amounts you see on food labels report the number of kilocalories.

Figure 9.4 Generating Energy.

Humans are continuously developing creative ways to harness different forms of energy. **A)** The energy stored in the chemical bonds of the food they eat allows farmers in Africa to use a step pump for watering their crops. **B)** Pedaling provides the energy for the clothes-washing machine developed by this young woman (Remya Jose). **C)** Small solar arrays provide power to houses, **D)** allowing these children to do homework after dark.

A   B   C   D

In common usage, people refer to the "calories" in food when they are actually talking about kilocalories. We discuss food Calories in more detail in BioConnect 9.1 (contains Figures 9.5–9.7).

$$1 \text{ kcal} = 1 \text{ Calorie}$$

To put this in perspective, when a person sits for one hour, she consumes around 420 kJ. If that same person walks for one hour, her body consumes 800 kJ. Many electrical applications measure energy using the watt (W). One watt is equal to 1 joule/sec. A typical household solar panel system can produce 1 kWh (1,000 watts) per 250-watt panel in just four hours of full sun each day (Figure 9.4). That's enough energy to power ten common LED household light bulbs for over six hours.

Explore how Chemistry and Biology connect: **BioConnect 9.1:** The Energy in Our Food in the Pearson eText.

Apply what you have just learned: **Practice 19.1 and 9.2** in the Pearson eText.

Quiz yourself on the content of this section: **Check 9.1** in the Pearson eText.

9.2 Energy Changes in Reactions

A chemical reaction involves bonds breaking in the reactants and new bonds forming to produce products. Breaking a bond consumes energy. In contrast, forming a bond releases energy. For example, when methane (CH_4) reacts with oxygen (O_2) in a combustion reaction to produce carbon dioxide (CO_2) and water (H_2O), energy is required to break the carbon-hydrogen bonds and the oxygen-oxygen bonds. The stronger the bond, the more energy it takes to break it. When the new carbon-oxygen bonds and hydrogen-oxygen bonds form to produce products, however, energy is released (Figure 9.8).

$$CH_4(g) + 2O_2(g) \rightarrow CO_2(g) + 2H_2O(g)$$

Chemists can quantify the energy required to break specific bonds. The energy it takes to break a bond is its **bond energy**. Table 9.1 lists some common bond energies. Each bond energy in the table is the amount of energy needed to break each of these bonds. It is also the amount of energy given off when the same bond forms in a chemical reaction. For example, 410 kJ of energy are needed to break one mole of C—H bonds and 499 kJ to break one mole of O=O bonds. Conversely when one mole of C—H bonds form 410 kJ is released and when one mole of O=O bonds form 499 kJ is released. Notice that bond energy values vary depending on which atoms make up the specific bonds.

Table 9.1 Common Bond Energies.

Bond	Bond Energies (kJ/mol)
H—H	436
H—C	410
H—O	460
C—O	350
C—N	300
O=O	499

Figure 9.8 Breaking Bonds Requires Energy While Forming Bonds Releases Energy.

Burning natural gas converts methane and oxygen into carbon dioxide and water, releasing energy in the form of heat.

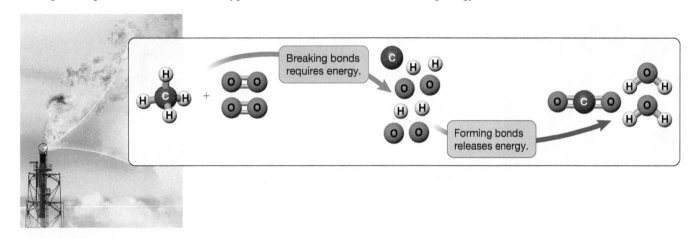

Apply what you have just learned: **Practice 9.3 and 9.4** in the Pearson eText.

Energy Involved in Chemical Reactions

In some cases, energy is absorbed when a chemical reaction occurs and in other cases excess energy is released, generally in the form of heat. We can determine the overall energy of a given chemical reaction by considering all the bonds that break and all the bonds that form during the reaction.

Chemists refer to the energy that a reaction either absorbs or releases to the surroundings as the **heat of reaction**. The heat of reaction is also the **enthalpy change** for the given reaction. We symbolize the enthalpy change with a ΔH. The heat of reaction has a $(+)$ or $(-)$ sign depending on whether the reaction absorbs or releases heat (Figure 9.9).

When heat is absorbed in an overall reaction, the reaction is **endothermic** and the ΔH value is positive $(+)$. This means that in that reaction, more energy is required to break the bonds than is released in forming bonds. In contrast, when a reaction releases heat to the surroundings, the reaction is **exothermic** and the ΔH is negative $(-)$. In this case, more heat is released upon new bond formation than is needed to break bonds.

$$\text{endothermic} = +\Delta H \ (\text{energy is absorbed})$$
$$\text{exothermic} = -\Delta H \ (\text{energy is released})$$

Figure 9.9 Exothermic and Endothermic Reactions.

Exothermic reactions release energy as heat and have a negative ΔH. Endothermic reactions absorb energy and have a positive ΔH.

endothermic reaction ($+\Delta H$) energy absorbed by surroundings

heat

exothermic reaction ($-\Delta H$) energy released to the surroundings

heat

Apply what you have just learned: **Practice 9.5** in the Pearson eText.

Figure 9.10 Cold Packs Use Endothermic Reactions to Cool Injured Joints or Muscles.

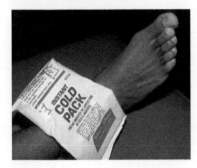

Endothermic Reactions

Endothermic reactions absorb heat from the surroundings. We can often tell if an endothermic reaction happens if we observe a reduction in temperature. An instant cold pack uses an endothermic process to lower the temperature of the pack. People use cold packs such as these to treat injuries when ice is not available (Figure 9.10). These packs generally have two compartments. One contains water and the other contains a chemical substance, usually ammonium nitrate. When the pack is squeezed, ammonium nitrate dissolves in water and the following solution process (dissolving) occurs.

$$NH_4NO_3(s) \rightarrow NH_4^+(aq) + NO_3^-(aq)$$
$$\Delta H = +26 \text{ kJ}$$
$$\textbf{(endothermic)}$$

Dissolving ammonium nitrate in water involves energy. Note that the enthalpy value for the dissolving process is positive, indicating an endothermic reaction. Energy from the surroundings is absorbed causing the surroundings, or the cold pack, to cool down.

Plants produce most of the food we eat through the process of **photosynthesis**. During photosynthesis, plants use sunlight and CO_2 in the air and water to create oxygen and sugars (Figure 9.11). Photosynthesis is crucial to all life on Earth. Animals breathe the oxygen and consume the sugars that plants produce (and/or other animals that consume plants). Photosynthesis is also an endothermic reaction that uses energy from the sun.

$$6CO_2(g) + 6H_2O(l) \rightarrow C_6H_{12}O_6(aq) + 6O_2(g)$$
$$\Delta H = +2836.8 \text{ kJ}$$
$$\textbf{(endothermic)}$$

Figure 9.11 Photosynthesis Produces our Food Using Endothermic Reactions Requiring Energy from the Sun.

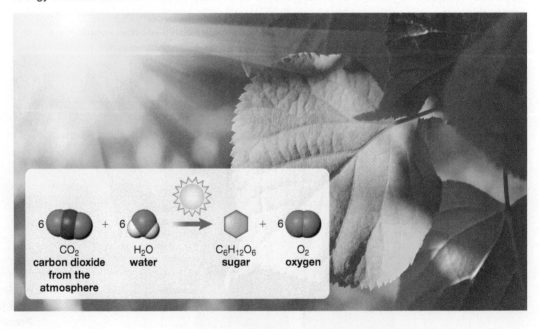

Exothermic Reactions

Some exothermic reactions release only small amounts of energy, but other reactions release a great deal of energy and are highly exothermic. The combustion of natural gas (also called methane, CH_4), that we explored in the beginning of this section is a highly exothermic chemical reaction. In this reaction, methane gas reacts with two moles of oxygen to produce one mole of carbon dioxide (CO_2) and two moles of water (H_2O). The exothermic reaction has a ΔH value of -802 kJ:

$$CH_4(g) + 2O_2(g) \rightarrow CO_2(g) + 2H_2O(g)$$
$$\Delta H = -802 \text{ kJ}$$
$$\textbf{(exothermic)}$$

The bonds in CH_4 and O_2 break and the bonds in the products form. The reaction releases energy in the form of heat and is therefore exothermic (Figure 9.12).

Recall from BioConnect 8.2 the redox reaction that helps power our cells in mitochondria when our bodies break down sugars and other food molecules (Figure 9.13).

Figure 9.12 "Fire Mountain".

There is a place on the Absheron Peninsula near Baku, the capital of Azerbaijan, where a natural gas fire burns continuously. This reaction releases heat to the surroundings and is highly exothermic.

Figure 9.13 Exothermic Reactions Power our Bodies.

We break down sugars and other molecules in our mitochondria to produce the energy our bodies need.

Figure 9.14 Jamaican Sprinter Usain Bolt Won Eight Olympic Gold Medals.

Bolt's legendary sprints, like our own everyday activities, are fueled by large amounts of ATP, which his body uses to power the contraction of his muscles. His cells also need ATP to build the proteins that make up his muscles.

This redox reaction, too, is an exothermic reaction. Our bodies use the energy produced in this reaction in many ways.

$$C_6H_{12}O_6(s) + 6O_2(g) \rightarrow 6CO_2(g) + 6H_2O(l)$$
$$\Delta H = -686 \text{ kJ}$$
(exothermic)

ATP in Our Bodies

Many of the reactions in our bodies are exothermic reactions. The heat released from these reactions helps us maintain a constant body temperature.

One of the most common exothermic reactions in the body involves **adenosine triphosphate (ATP)**. ATP is often called the energy currency of the cell. We digest food both to obtain necessary building blocks and to collect chemical energy in the form of ATP. The ATP from our food powers a wide array of functions including muscle contraction, transport and signaling between cells, and the endothermic reactions we use to build complex molecules such as DNA and proteins (Figure 9.14). Our bodies consume an extraordinary amount of ATP each day–up to our own body weight. This is possible because we continually "drain" and "recharge" the same pool of ATP molecules.

The ATP in our bodies functions much like rechargeable batteries. In its "charged" or high-energy state, the ATP molecule has three phosphate groups attached to it (Figure 9.15). This "charged" ATP reacts with water to produce a free phosphate group and the lower-energy "drained" adenosine diphosphate (ADP) molecule. This reaction releases energy. Our bodies use the energy that the reaction releases to do work in the cell. Our bodies then "recharge" the low-energy ADP with energy from our food.

Figure 9.15 ATP Consists of Three Phosphate Groups, Ribose, and Adenine.

ATP releases energy as it loses a phosphate group becoming ADP.

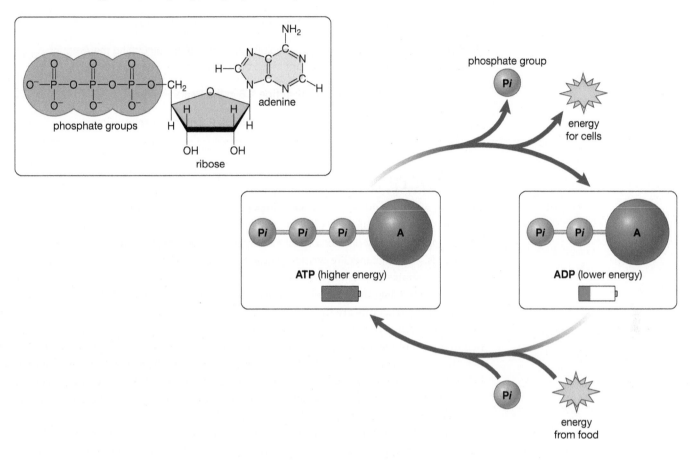

Apply what you have just learned: **Practice 9.6** in the Pearson eText.

Calculations Using Enthalpy of Reactions

When we know the heat of reaction (ΔH), we can determine the amount of heat produced from a given amount of reactants or products. The coefficients in the equation along with the enthalpy change provide conversion factors to solve a variety of problems.

For example, the combustion of one mole of methane releases 802 kJ. This amount of heat is specific to this balanced chemical reaction. The following equation releases 802 kJ for every two moles of water it produces:

$$CH_4(g) + 2O_2(g) \rightarrow CO_2(g) + 2H_2O(g) \qquad \Delta H = -802 \text{ kJ}$$

Learn 9.1 illustrates how we can use the enthalpy change of a balanced reaction as a conversion factor to determine the amount of energy (in the form of heat) released when a specific amount of reactants are consumed. Learn 9.2 illustrates how to solve a similar problem. In this second example, we determine the amount of energy (in the form of heat) released when a specific amount of products form.

Predict answers and see step-by-step solutions: **Learn 9.1:** Calculating the Amount of Heat Generated by a Reaction from Mass of Reactant in the Pearson eText.

Apply what you have just learned: **Practice 9.7** in the Pearson eText.

Predict answers and see step-by-step solutions: **Learn 9.2:** Calculating the Amount of Heat Generated by a Reaction from Mass of Product in the Pearson eText.

Apply what you have just learned: **Practice 9.8** in the Pearson eText.

Quiz yourself on the content of this section: **Check 9.2** in the Pearson eText.

9.3 Energy Diagrams and Activation Energy

Chemists often use unique representations or symbols to communicate about concepts or ideas. An **energy diagram** illustrates the energy in a chemical reaction (Figure 9.16) by plotting the energy on the vertical axis, and the progress of the reaction on the horizontal axis. The reactants are written on the left side and the products on the right side. A curve illustrates how energy changes over time. The position of the reactants and the products on the diagram indicates whether the reaction is endothermic or exothermic.

When the reactants are higher in energy than the products, the reaction is overall exothermic. An exothermic reaction releases energy to the surroundings and has a negative heat of reaction (ΔH). When the reactants are lower in energy than the products, the reaction is endothermic. An endothermic reaction absorbs energy overall and has a positive heat of reaction (ΔH). The vertical distance between the reactants and products on the diagram represents the quantity of ΔH. The greater the distance between the reactants and products, the greater the ΔH.

In order for a reaction to occur, reactant particles need to collide and interact. These collisions among molecules do not always result in the formation of products. Sometimes reactant particles rebound from a collision unchanged. This is the result of an ineffective collision. To undergo an effective collision, the particles must collide with a sufficient amount of energy and with a specific orientation. As an effective collision occurs, the reactant bonds are partially broken and the new product bonds are partially formed. This high energy state is called the **transition state**. On an energy diagram the transition state is located at the top of the "hill" as illustrated in Figure 9.16.

Figure 9.16 Energy Diagrams Illustrate the Energy Changes that Occur as a Reaction Proceeds.

A) The reactants in an exothermic reaction are higher on the diagram than the products. **B)** The products in an endothermic reaction are higher on the diagram than the reactants. Activation energy, which is the minimum amount of energy the chemical reaction needs to proceed, is represented by the "hill" on each diagram. Recall that the heat of reaction (ΔH) is the difference in energy between reactants and products.

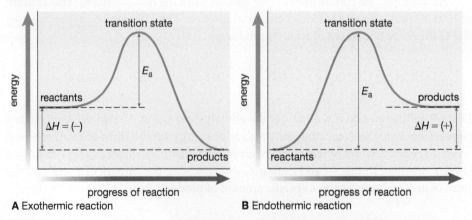

Activation energy (E_a) is the minimum kinetic energy that colliding reactant particles must possess in order for their collisions to result in a chemical reaction (Figure 9.16). Every chemical reaction has a unique activation energy and this energy value is represented on an energy diagram as the "hill". (Figure 9.16). The vertical distance from reactants to the top of the hill represents the magnitude of the activation energy. The higher the hill, the greater the activation energy.

In VisibleChem Videos 9.1 and 9.2 you further explore energy diagrams, particle collisions, and activation energy.

Watch this concept come to life: **VisibleChem Video 9.1:** Energy Diagrams and Activation Energy and **VisibleChem Video 9.2:** Molecular Collisions that Lead to Products in the Pearson eText.

Apply what you have just learned: **Practice 9.9** in the Pearson eText.

Quiz yourself on the content of this section: **Check 9.3** in the Pearson eText.

9.4 Reaction Rates

All living organisms regulate the rate of the chemical reactions in their bodies. The rate of a chemical reaction is how fast the reaction occurs. Bats, for example, have very high metabolic rates. (The word *metabolic* refers to the chemical processes that occur within a living organism in order to maintain life.) The reactions in their bodies occur very fast and therefore consume a lot of energy. But many bat species aren't able to find enough food in winter to maintain their high energy needs. For this reason, these bats hibernate, dramatically reducing their metabolic rate by dropping their body temperature (Figure 9.17). In hibernation, a bat may reduce its energy needs by up to 98%. This is an example of how the **reaction rate**—the speed of a chemical reaction—is important in biological systems. Chemical reactions proceed at a wide range of speeds.

A chemical reaction with a fast rate converts a large fraction of the reactants into products in a short period of time (Figure 9.18). In the first reaction in Figure 9.18, the

---

Figure 9.17 Many Bats Hibernate, Lowering Their Body Temperature to Lower Their Metabolic Rate.

Figure 9.18 The Rate of a Chemical Reaction.

Reactions with a fast rate convert reactants to products very quickly. Reactions with slow rates require more time to produce products.

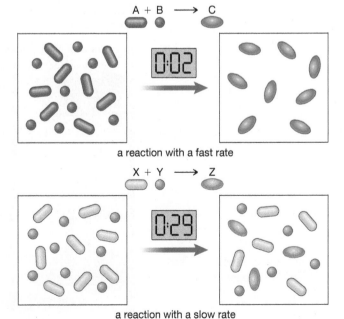

a reaction with a fast rate

a reaction with a slow rate

reactants (A and B) are all converted to the product (C) in approximately 2 seconds. This is a relatively fast rate compared to the second reaction, which still contains mostly reactants (X and Y) at the 29-second point. Chemical reactions that proceed at a slow rate require more time to produce products. We express the rate of a reaction as the change in concentration of reactants or products over the change in time.

$$\text{Rate of reaction} = \frac{\text{change in concentration of reactant or product}}{\text{change in time}}$$

Reactant Concentration and Temperature Affect Reaction Rate

Recall from VisibleChem Video 9.1 that chemical reactions occur when particles collide. The rate of a chemical reaction depends on the number and effectiveness of the collisions among particles. When the concentration of reactants increases, more collisions occur, and the rate of reaction increases.

> Increasing the concentration of reactants increases the rate of reaction.

In the beginning of this section, we discussed bats that hibernate to slow the chemical reactions involved with their metabolism. The rate of these same chemical reactions increases as the bats come out of hibernation and warm up. We store food in our refrigerators for a similar reason—by placing the food in a colder environment, we slow down the chemical reactions that cause food to spoil (Figure 9.19).

The rates of chemical reactions are, in general, highly sensitive to temperature changes. For every 10 °C increase in temperature, the rate of chemical reactions in the human body double or even triple. This is due to the increase in the number of collisions between reactant particles that occur as temperature increases. It can also be explained in terms of the increased kinetic energy in the reactants as the temperature goes up. At higher temperatures, there is more kinetic energy in the reactants and more particles have sufficient energy to break bonds and proceed to products.

> Increasing the temperature of reactants increases the rate of reaction.

Figure 9.19 Refrigerators Cool Food, Slowing the Chemical Reactions that Cause Food to Spoil.

Apply what you have just learned: **Practice 9.10** in the Pearson eText.

Figure 9.20 Catalysts Speed the Rate of Reaction by Lowering the Activation Energy.

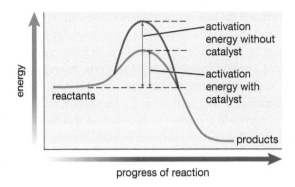

Catalysts Affect Reaction Rate

Like increasing reactant concentration and temperature, adding a **catalyst** to a chemical reaction also increases the rate. A catalyst works by providing an alternative pathway from reactants to products that has lower activation energy (Figure 9.20). With a lower "energy hill to climb," the reaction is able to proceed more quickly. Catalysts increase the rate of chemical reactions but are not consumed and can therefore be used again and again. For this reason, we often write the catalyst above the arrow in a chemical equation.

A common example of a catalyst can be found in the exhaust system of a car inside the catalytic converter (Figure 9.21). In this case the catalyst is platinum, rubidium, or palladium on the surface of the converter. These catalysts help to accelerate the reaction that converts exhaust pollutants, such as hydrocarbons, nitrogen oxide (NO) and carbon monoxide (CO), into less harmful substances. Without a functioning catalytic converter, these pollutants are released into the atmosphere and create smog.

In our bodies, protein catalysts called **enzymes** lower the activation energy of chemical reactions. Understanding the structure and function of enzymes allows chemists to better predict the chemical reactions that happen in our bodies as well as design better drugs and screen for genetic disorders. Explore BioConnect 9.2 (contains Figures 9.22–9.25) to learn more about these critical catalysts.

Figure 9.21 Catalytic Converters.

Metal catalysts in catalytic converters speed up the reactions that convert air pollutants such as nitrogen oxide (NO) and carbon monoxide (CO) into less harmful molecules such as water and carbon dioxide.

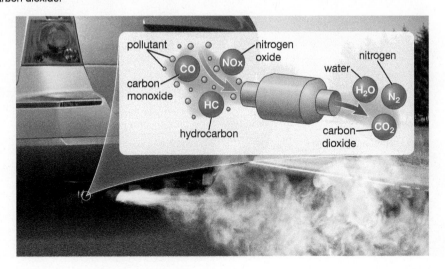

Explore how Chemistry and Biology connect: **BioConnect: 9.2** Enzymes are Biological Catalysts in the Pearson eText.

Quiz yourself on the content of this section: **Check 9.4** in the Pearson eText.

9.5 Equilibrium

In Section 9.3 we examined the *rate* of chemical reactions. In this section we explore the *extent* and *direction* of chemical reactions. First, however, let's consider the idea that chemical reactions can be reversible. Up until now in this chapter, we have explored chemical reactions that proceed from reactants to products and go all the way to completion. Sometimes, however, chemical reactions can be **reversible**. For a reaction to be reversible, the reaction must form products in the forward direction and it must also re-form reactants and progress in the reverse direction. A double arrow indicates that a chemical reaction is reversible and can proceed in both directions.

Forward Reaction

A + B $\rightleftharpoons$ AB

Reverse Reaction

This reversible equation illustrates that the reactants A and B proceed to the right to form the product AB. Once AB is present in a sufficient amount, the reaction proceeds in the reverse direction to re-form A and B. When the rate of the forward reaction is equal to the rate of the reverse reaction, the reaction is in a state of **dynamic equilibrium**. When a reaction is at dynamic equilibrium, the amount of reactants and products do not change, but the reaction continues to proceed in both directions at the same speed. This is similar to what happens as people both leave and enter the city of San Francisco over the Golden Gate Bridge (Figure 9.26).

Reversible Chemical Reactions

Consider the reversible reaction in which two molecules of the brown gas NO_2 (nitrogen dioxide) combine to form the clear gas N_2O_4 (dinitrogen tetroxide; Figure 9.27). The rate of the forward reaction is fast at first, but the forward reaction rate decreases as the concentration of reactants decreases. The rate of the reverse reaction is slow at first, but the reverse reaction rate speeds up as more product forms. When the rate of the forward reaction is equal to the rate of the reverse reaction, the amounts of products and reactants do not change, and the system is in a state of dynamic equilibrium.

Figure 9.26 Traffic Equilibrium on the Golden Gate Bridge in San Francisco.

Dynamic equilibrium can be understood by thinking about a time of day when two-way traffic is crossing a bridge at about the same rate in both directions. The population of people on each side of the bridge may be different, but with equal numbers of cars coming and going into and out of the city, the population of people on each side of the bridge remains the same.

Figure 9.27 Dynamic Equilibrium.

A reaction reaches dynamic equilibrium when the concentrations of the reactants and products no longer change. The molecular level figures illustrate the progression of the reaction between NO_2 molecules to produce N_2O_4. The concentrations of the reactants and products change rapidly initially but then stop changing when the reaction reaches equilibrium. At equilibrium, both the forward and reverse reactions are occurring at the same rate. The graph illustrates this same progression—the reactants decrease over time and the products increase until the reaction reaches equilibrium

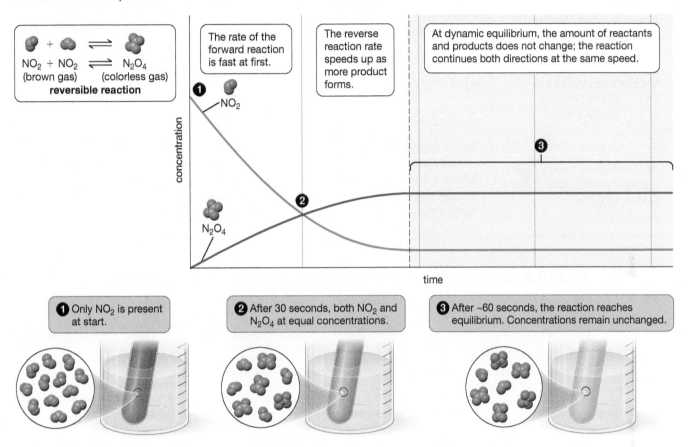

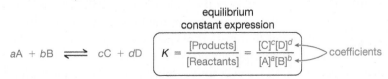

At equilibrium we describe the process as *dynamic* because the forward and reverse reactions do not stop, but continue on at the same rate. It is important to also note that at equilibrium the reaction continues to occur in both directions, but because the rates of both the forward and reverse reactions are equal, the concentrations remain unchanged. However, this does not mean that at equilibrium the concentrations of the reactants are equal to the concentrations of products. In fact, chemical reactions at equilibrium rarely have equal reactant and product concentrations.

Equilibrium Constant

We just discussed that at equilibrium the concentration of reactants and products are no longer changing. We can use these equilibrium concentrations to set up a relationship between reactants and products. This relationship is the **equilibrium constant, K**. Consider the general chemical equation shown here. In this equation, A and B are reactants, C and D are products and a, b, c and d are the respective coefficients. The equilibrium constant (K) for this reaction is the ratio of the concentration of products (C and D) to the concentration of reactants (A and B) at equilibrium. In the equation, we raise each concentration term to the power that corresponds to its coefficient in the balanced chemical equation.

$$aA + bB \rightleftharpoons cC + dD \qquad K = \frac{[\text{Products}]}{[\text{Reactants}]} = \frac{[C]^c[D]^d}{[A]^a[B]^b}$$

equilibrium constant expression

coefficients

Watch this concept come to life:
Video 9.3: If Molecules were People, **VisibleChem Video 9.3:** The Significance of the Equilibrium Constant, and **VisibleChem Video 9.4:** Le Chatelier's Principle in the Pearson eText.

Apply what you have just learned: **Practice 9.11–9.14** in the Pearson eText.

The brackets ([ ]) around each reactant and product in the **equilibrium constant expression**, indicate the concentration in number of moles in a given volume. In this case, it is in units of moles per liter (mol/L). Only substances whose concentrations change appear in an equilibrium expression. Solids (indicated with an *s*) and liquids (indicated with a *l*) have constant concentrations and do not appear in the equilibrium expression.

In VisibleChem Videos 9.3–9.5, we explore in more detail the concept of equilibrium, the equilibrium constant (K), and what the value of the equilibrium constant tells us about a reversible reaction that has reached equilibrium. VisibleChem Video 9.5 also introduces **Le Chatelier's Principle**, a rule that explains how changes affect a reaction at equilibrium. Le Chatelier's Principle allows us to make predictions about what happens when a stress is added to a reaction in equilibrium.

Le Chatelier's Principle Summary

As we just discussed in VisibleChem Video 9.5, Le Chatelier's principle states that a chemical reaction in equilibrium responds to a stress by minimizing the disturbance. When a stress or disturbance is applied to a reaction at equilibrium, the rate of the forward and reverse reactions change to offset the stress and regain equilibrium. Table 9.2 is a summary of how a chemical reaction at equilibrium shifts when changes in concentration, temperature, and pressure occur.

Table 9.2 The Effects of Concentration, Temperature, and Pressure Changes on Equilibrium.

Concentration A concentration change for reactants or products shifts equilibrium.	Temperature A temperature change shifts equilibrium, effecting endothermic and exothermic reactions differently.	Pressure A pressure change shifts equilibrium only when gases are present.
Increase concentration of reactants shifts right ⟶ A + B ⇌ **C + D**	**Increase temperature – Endothermic** shifts right ⟶ heat + A + B ⇌ **C + D**	**Increase pressure** Reaction will shift towards side with fewer moles of gas.
Increase concentration of products shifts left ⟵ **A + B** ⇌ C + D	**Increase temperature – Exothermic** shifts left ⟵ **A + B** ⇌ C + D + heat	shifts right ⟶ A(*g*) + 2B(*g*) ⇌ **C(*g*) + D(*g*)**
Decrease concentration of reactants shifts left ⟵ **A + B** ⇌ C + D	**Decrease temperature – Endothermic** shifts left ⟵ heat + **A + B** ⇌ C + D	**Decrease pressure** Reaction will shift towards side with more moles of gas.
Decrease concentration of products shifts right ⟶ A + B ⇌ **C + D**	**Decrease temperature – Exothermic** shifts right ⟶ A + B ⇌ **C + D** + heat	shifts left ⟵ **A(*g*) + 2B(*g*)** ⇌ C(*g*) + D(*g*)

Manipulating the Equilibrium State

Le Chatelier's principle has very practical applications. Chemists use their knowledge of Le Chatelier's principle to drive a variety of reactions. For example, they may want to favor a product in a reaction for drug production or a specific industrial process. Biological reactions are also influenced by changes in temperature, pressure, and the concentration of reactants and products. Le Chatelier's principle can help scientists and healthcare providers design therapies to improve health outcomes.

For example, a very important protein in the blood (hemoglobin) binds oxygen in the lungs and releases oxygen all over the body (Figure 9.28). Patients with emphysema, a chronic breakdown of the air sacs in the lungs, have difficulty absorbing enough oxygen in their lungs to transport oxygen to their muscles and other tissues. These patients are often given supplemental oxygen (Figure 9.29). Increasing the concentration of oxygen, a reactant, drives the equilibrium reaction in their lungs towards

Figure 9.28 Oxygen is Delivered to the Body by Hemoglobin.

Hemoglobin binds to oxygen in the lungs and releases it in muscles and other low-oxygen tissues. The binding and release of oxygen is a reversible reaction driven by changes in the concentration of oxygen.

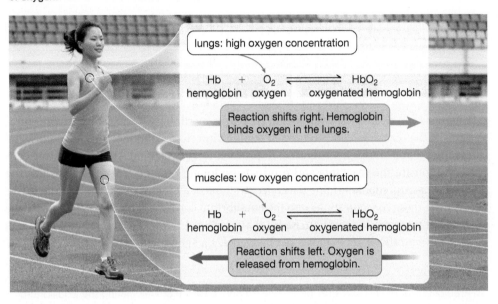

Figure 9.29 Lungs of an Emphysema Patient.

The walls of the air sacs (alveoli) of the lungs are damaged in a patient with emphysema. This limits the amount of oxygen that can be captured by the lungs and transported to the body via the blood. Many patients with emphysema are treated with supplemental oxygen. This increase in the oxygen concentration in the lungs drives the reaction towards the product, helping deliver oxygen.

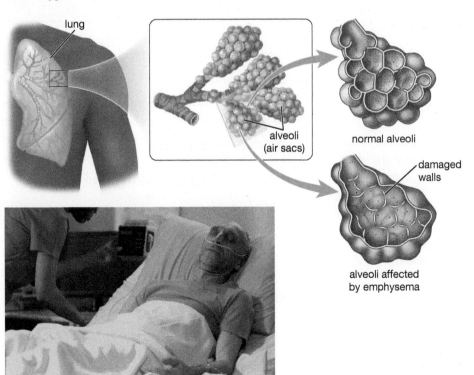

the product, which is hemoglobin-bound oxygen (Figure 9.28). This hemoglobin-bound oxygen travels through the body in the patient's blood, delivering much-needed oxygen to muscles.

 Quiz yourself on the content of this section: **Check 9.5** in the Pearson eText.

9.6 Calculating Equilibrium Constants

Chemists can determine equilibrium constants by directly measuring the concentrations of the reactants and products at equilibrium. To accomplish this, they allow the reaction that is under investigation to proceed to equilibrium. At that point, the concentrations of the reactants and products no longer change. They then analyze the reaction mixture to determine the concentrations of all the reactants and products. We can plug these concentrations into the equilibrium constant expression to calculate the constant for a specific reaction. Recall that brackets [ ] indicate concentrations. In this case concentrations are in moles per liter (mol/L), symbolized as M.

 Predict answers and see step-by-step solutions: **Learn 9.3:** Calculating the Equilibrium Constant in the Pearson eText.

Apply what you have just learned: **Practice 9.15 and 9.16** in the Pearson eText.

Quiz yourself on the content of this section: **Check 9.6** in the Pearson eText.

Chapter Summary

9.1 Energy

Learning Objective: Define energy and convert between energy units.

Energy is the capacity to do work. The law of conservation of energy states that the total energy in the universe does not change and that energy is neither created nor destroyed. Energy can, however, be converted from one form to another and unit conversions allow us to track these changes. Energy in motion is kinetic energy. Stored energy is potential energy.

BioConnect 9.1: The Energy in Our Food

Key Terms

basal metabolic rate (BMR)
   (from BioConnect 9.1)
Calorie (Cal)
calorie (cal)

energy
joule (J)
kinetic energy
law of conservation of energy

metabolism (from BioConnect 9.1)
potential energy

Key Equations

1 kcal = 1000 cal
1 kJ = 1000 J

1 kcal = 4.184 kJ
1 cal = 4.184 J

1 kcal = 1 Calorie

9.2 Energy Changes in Reactions

Learning Objective: Describe how energy is absorbed or released in a chemical reaction and classify chemical reactions as either endothermic or exothermic.

Chemical reactions involve bonds breaking in reactants, and new bonds forming to produce products. Breaking bonds requires energy, forming bonds releases energy (Figure 9.8). Different bonds have different strengths (bond energies; Table 9.1). The enthalpy change (ΔH) of a reaction is the difference between the energy needed to break bonds in the reactants, and the energy released from the bonds formation in the products. If the sign of ΔH for a reaction is positive ($+$), energy is absorbed and the chemical reaction is endothermic. If the sign of ΔH for a reaction is negative ($-$), energy is released and the chemical reaction is exothermic (Figure 9.9). Energy diagrams and enthalpy calculations allow us to better understand chemical reactions.

Key Terms

adenosine triphosphate (ATP)
bond energy
endothermic

enthalpy change (ΔH)
exothermic

heat of reaction
photosynthesis

9.3 Energy Diagrams and Activation Energy

Learning Objective: Represent the energy of chemical reactions using energy diagrams.

An energy diagram illustrates the energy involved in a chemical reaction as it progresses. If the reactants are higher in energy than the products, the reaction is overall exothermic. An exothermic reaction releases energy to the surroundings. If the reactants are lower in energy than the products, the reaction is endothermic. An endothermic reaction absorbs energy from the surroundings. The vertical distance between the reactants and products on the diagram represents the quantity of ΔH. The greater the distance between the reactants and products, the greater the numeric values of ΔH. Activation energy (E_a) is the minimum energy that colliding reactant particles must possess in order for their collision to result in a chemical reaction (Figure 9.16).

VisibleChem Video 9.1: Energy Diagrams and Activation Energy

VisibleChem Video 9.2: Molecular Collisions that Lead to Products

Key Terms

activation energy (E_a)
energy diagram
transition state

9.4 Reaction Rates

Learning Objective: Predict the effect of concentration, temperature, and catalysts on the rate of reactions.

Chemical reactions operate at a wide range of rates. The rate of a reaction is the change in concentration of reactant or product over time (Figure 9.18). Because reactants must effectively collide with each other in order to react, increasing the concentration of reactants increases the rate of reaction. Increasing the temperature of reactants also increases the rate of reaction because the reactants are able to collide more frequently and with more energy during each collision. A catalyst is a substance that increases the rate of a chemical reaction by lowering the energy of activation for the reaction. Catalysts are not consumed by the reaction (Figure 9.20).

BioConnect 9.2: Enzymes are Biological Catalysts

Key Terms

catalyst
enzymes
reaction rate
signaling molecule (from BioConnect 9.2)

9.5 Equilibrium

Learning Objective: Describe the fundamental features of dynamic chemical equilibrium, write the expression for the equilibrium constant, and predict the direction a reaction at equilibrium will shift when disturbed.

Many chemical reactions are reversible; this is indicated by a double direction reaction arrow ($\rightleftharpoons$). When the rate of the forward reaction is equal to the rate of the reverse reaction, the concentrations of all reactants and products do not change, and the system is in dynamic equilibrium (Figure 9.27). The equilibrium constant (K) is a way to quantify the concentrations of reactants and products at equilibrium, and also gives us a sense of how much the reaction proceeds in the forward direction. A large numeric K value indicates that products are favored in the reaction equilibrium. A small K value indicates that reactants are favored at equilibrium. Intermediate values of K indicate that a significant amount of both products and reactions exist at equilibrium.

Video 9.3: If Molecules were People

VisibleChem Video 9.3: The Significance of the Equilibrium Constant

VisibleChem Video 9.4: Le Chatelier's Principle

Key Terms

dynamic equilibrium
equilibrium constant, K
equilibrium constant expression
reversible
Le Chatelier's principle

Key Equations

equilibrium
constant expression

$$aA + bB \rightleftharpoons cC + dD \qquad K = \frac{[\text{Products}]}{[\text{Reactants}]} = \frac{[C]^c[D]^d}{[A]^a[B]^b} \longleftarrow \text{coefficients}$$

9.6 Calculating Equilibrium Constants

Learning Objective: Calculate equilibrium constants for reactions at equilibrium when given equilibrium concentrations of the reactants and products.

Chemists directly measure the concentrations of the reactants and products at equilibrium. We can calculate equilibrium constants using those concentrations. The molar concentrations of all reactants and products once they are measured are plugged into the equilibrium constant (K) expression.

 End-of-Chapter Quiz · Have you mastered the content of this chapter? Try the **End-of-Chapter Quiz** in the Pearson eText.

1. Complete the sentence. A book sitting high on a book-shelf has _____ energy and the energy in a bowl of rice is _____.
   a) kinetic, potential
   b) potential, potential
   c) potential, kinetic
   d) kinetic, kinetic

2. Small solar panels can generate electricity to power energy efficient LED lights. This technology allows students in areas where traditional electricity does not reach to study at night and get a better education. If a 5-watt energy-efficient LED light bulb working for 2 hours uses 36 kJ of energy from the solar panel, how many kcal is this?
   a) 151 kcal   b) 0.116
   c) 8.6 kcal   d) 8.6×10^3 kcal

3. A patient receives 2.5 L of an IV solution over the course of a day in hospital. Among other information printed on the label of the IV solution is the following: "Glucose 5% Intravenous Infusion BP: 50.0 g/l. Each ml contains 50 mg glucose. Approximately 210 kcal/L." How many kJ of energy are in the 2.5 L of glucose IV solution the patient receives?

a) 1.3×10^2 kcal b) 1.1×10^5 kcal

c) 6.3×10^3 kcal d) 2.2×10^3 kcal

4. After studying for an exam, you go for a long walk and stop at a fast-food restaurant and eat a cheeseburger, French fries, and a large cola drink. While eating, you add up the total food Calories (1 Cal = 1 kcal) in your meal by looking at the Calorie chart posted on the restaurant wall. If your meal contained 1250 Calories and you expended 820 kJ/h walking to the restaurant and you will continue walking at the same pace after your meal, how many hours do you need to walk in order to use up the Calories you ate in the meal?

a) 2.7 h b) 2.5×10^5 h

c) 1.5 h d) 6.4 h

5. After jogging with friends, your smart watch indicates that you ran for 35.5 min while expending 2350 kJ per hour (kJ/h) during the jog. How many food Calories (kcal) did you burn during your jog?

a) 2.0×10^4 kcal (food Calories)

b) 332 kcal (food Calories)

c) 2.3×10^5 kcal (food Calories)

d) 2.0×10^4 kcal (food Calories)

6. How many kJ of heat are produced when 58.5 g CH_4 are used to cook a meal for a family?

$$CH_4(g) + 2O_2(g) \rightarrow CO_2(g) + 2H_2O(g) \quad \Delta H = -802 \text{ kj}$$

a) 2.93×10^3 kJ

b) 4.69×10^4 kJ

c) 1.28×10^{25} molecules oxygen

d) 4.55×10^{22} molecules oxygen

7. When an electric current is passed through water (H_2O), water molecules can be split into hydrogen gas (H_2) and oxygen gas (O_2) in a process known as electrolysis. Running an electrical current of 1.23 V through water causes the atoms in water to separate and recombine as gaseous hydrogen (H_2) and oxygen (O_2). This process has been used to generate oxygen gas for astronauts to breathe on the international space station. How many kJ are required to produce 95.0 g O_2?

$$2H_2O(g) \rightarrow 2H_2(g) + O_2(g) \quad \Delta H = 484 \text{ kJ}$$

a) 2.87×10^3 kJ b) 1.44×10^3 kJ

c) 69.14 kJ d) 4.60×10^4 kJ

8. In a chemical reaction, the _____ is the energy difference between reactants and products.

a) product energy

b) activation energy

c) reactant energy

d) heat of reaction (enthalpy, ΔH)

9. Refrigerators and freezers help perishable foods last longer by_____.

a) reducing the activation energy

b) decreasing the rate of reactions

c) increasing the levels of biomolecules

d) increasing the levels of gamma rays

10. What effect does decreasing the activation energy of a reaction have on the rate of reaction?

a) The reaction rate slows down if activation energy is decreased.

b) The reaction rate is unchanged if the activation energy is decreased because the ΔH enthalpy value is unchanged.

c) We cannot predict the effect of decreasing the activation energy on the reaction rate because the product energy level remains the same in either case.

d) The reaction rate speeds up if the activation energy is decreased.

11. A chemical reaction has reached dynamic equilibrium when _____.

a) all of the starting reactant material has been converted into product

b) the concentrations of reactants and products are equal

c) the rate of the forward and reverse reactions are the same

d) all of the product decays completely back to reactants

12. What is the correct form of the equilibrium expression for this reaction?

$$2A_2 + 4B \rightleftharpoons A_2B_2 + 2AB$$

a) $K = \dfrac{[A_2B_2]2[AB]}{2[A_2]4[B]}$

b) $K = \dfrac{[A_2B_2][AB]}{[A_2][B]}$

c) $K = \dfrac{[A_2]^2[B]^4}{[A_2B_2][AB]^2}$

d) $K = \dfrac{[A_2B_2][AB]^2}{[A_2]^2[B]^4}$

13. Which of the equilibrium constant (K) values is for a reaction that strongly favors reactants?
a) $K = 0.0095$
b) $K = 0.021$
c) $K = 1.1 \times 10^{-6}$
d) $K = 1.0 \times 10^{4}$

14. Which of these changes shifts the equilibrium of the given reaction to favor reactants?

$$2N_2O(g) + 3O_2(g) \rightleftharpoons 4NO_2(g) + heat$$

a) adding more N_2O and removing heat
b) adding more O_2 and heat
c) adding more NO_2 and heat
d) removing heat and adding more O_2

15. What is the effect of increasing the pressure on the system under equilibrium for the given reaction?

$$2CO(g) + O_2(g) \rightleftharpoons 2CO_2(g)$$

a) no change to the system
b) an increase in the amount of reactants CO and O_2
c) a decrease in the amount of product CO_2
d) an increase in the amount of product CO_2

16. Phosgene gas ($COCl_2$) is a toxic gas that also happens to be a very useful building block molecule for making pharmaceutical drugs and other consumer products. An equilibrium mixture contains the following concentrations: $COCl_2 = 3.7 \times 10^{-1}$, $CO = 1.2 \times 10^{-2}$, and $Cl_2 = 2.5 \times 10^{-2}$. What is the equilibrium constant for the reaction under these conditions?

$$CO(g) + Cl_2(g) \rightleftharpoons COCl_2(g)$$

a) 8.1×10^{-4}
b) 1.2
c) 4.1×10^{-1}
d) 1.2×10^{3}

17. Butyric acid ($HC_4H_7O_2$) is a product of fermentation of fiber in the colon by certain types of intestinal bacteria. Butyric acid helps people maintain a healthy intestinal lining, can reduce symptoms of inflammatory bowel disease, and may even lower the risk of colon cancer. If the equilibrium concentration of $HC_4H_7O_2$ in the intestine is 0.13, and the equilibrium concentration of $C_4H_7O_2^-$ is 1.4×10^{-3}, what is the concentration of the H^+ ion produced by the given reaction? The equilibrium constant (K) for butyric acid is 1.5×10^{-5}.

$$HC_4H_7O_2(aq) \rightleftharpoons H^+(aq) + C_4H_7O_2^-(aq)$$

a) 6.2×10^{6}
b) 1.4×10^{-3}
c) 1.6×10^{-7}
d) 1.5×10^{-5}

Unit 3
Bringing It All Together

How Do Chemical Labels on Our DNA Impact Our Health?

CHEMISTRY APPLICATION We opened Unit 3 with a look at some of the ways epigenetics is changing our understanding of inheritance and disease. In BioConnect 8.1 we explored DNA methylation and noted that methylation generally turns genes off (Figure U3.4). With our deeper understanding of chemical reactions and energy, we can now take a closer look at the mechanism behind this gene silencing.

Figure U3.4 DNA Methylation Turns Genes Off.

The methyl groups (red) added to the DNA (black) cause the DNA to condense, blocking access to any genes in the condensed area.

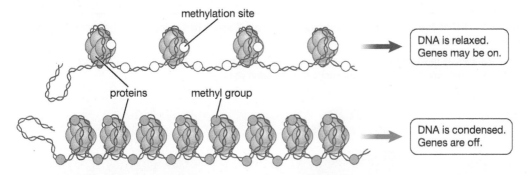

The additional methyl groups added to the DNA recruit a group of enzymes called histone deacetylases (HDACs). These enzymes, like all catalysts, help lower the activation energy of the reaction that removes acetyl groups from the proteins our DNA is wrapped around. This process causes the DNA to condense, turning any genes in the area off.

The removal of the acetyl groups is a reversible reaction. Another group of enzymes called histone acetyl transferases (HATs) catalyze the reverse reaction, adding acetyl groups and helping turn genes on (Figure U3.5). Understanding the factors that affect this equilibrium can allow us to target a wide range of diseases.

Understanding the reversible nature of these acetylation reactions has led to some fascinating insights on many common diseases, including Alzheimer's disease. Alzheimer's disease affects an estimated five million Americans. Individuals with the disease gradually lose their ability to think clearly and remember recent events (Figure U3.6). While progress has been made in identifying genetic and environmental factors that contribute to Alzheimer's disease, there are still few effective treatments and no cure for this devastating disease. Researchers have discovered, however, that the level of histone acetylation is much lower in the brains of patients who've died with advanced Alzheimer's. In other words, Alzheimer's patients appear to have more regions of their DNA silenced than similarly aged individuals without dementia symptoms.

Figure U3.5 Methylated DNA Attracts Histone Deacetylase Enzymes.

Removing the acetyl groups causes the DNA to condense, silencing genes.

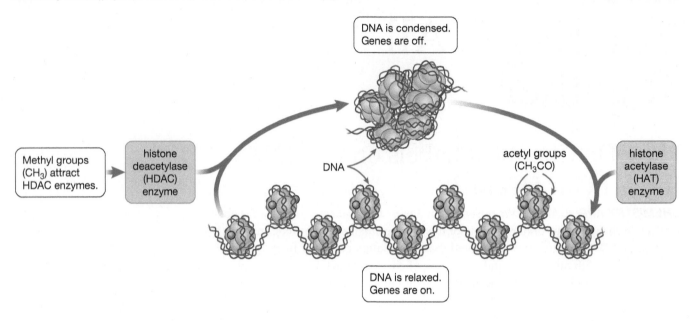

Figure U3.6 A) Advanced Alzheimer's Disease Causes a Dramatic Loss of Brain Tissue. **B)** Caring for Alzheimer's Patients can be Stressful and Isolating for Family Members.

Caring for family members with Alzheimer's disease has both psychological and financial impacts. An estimated 16 million Americans provide over 17 billion unpaid hours of caregiving for family and friends with Alzheimer's disease each year.

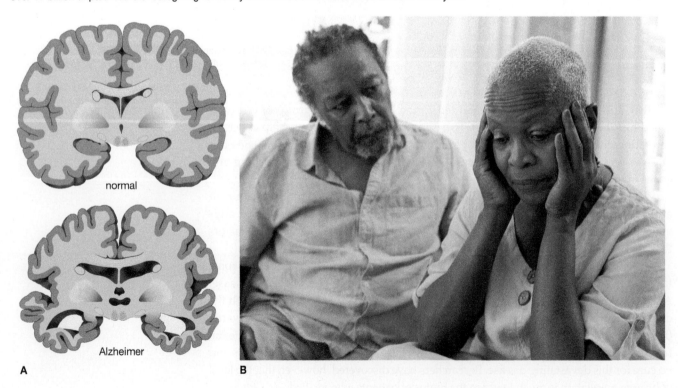

The discovery of changes in the epigenetics of Alzheimer's patients has launched a search for drugs that can inhibit the histone deacetylase enzymes that normally remove acetyl groups, silencing regions of DNA. Researchers hope that by slowing the chemical reaction that removes the acetyl groups they may be able to slow or even reverse the damage caused by Alzheimer's disease.

Questions to Think About

1. Recall the various types of reactions we studied in this unit. What type of reaction is the methylation of DNA? How do you know?

2. The reactions that add and remove methyl groups from DNA are catalyzed by enzymes. What do enzymes do? How do they speed up reactions?

3. What would an energy diagram look like for the exothermic DNA methylation reaction? How would an enzyme change the energy diagram?

4. What other factors might contribute to speeding up this methylation reaction?

A Closer Look at the Data

Several genes are known to affect an individual's risk of developing Alzheimer's disease. But researchers have long suspected that epigenetics may also play a role. A 2021 study published in the scientific journal, *Genome Medicine*, investigated patterns of DNA methylation by examining blood samples from thousands of individuals (Walker *et al.*, 2021). Figure U3.7 shows the level of methylation in both high-risk and low-risk individuals at two specific locations in their DNA.

Figure U3.7 Level of Methylation in High-risk and Low-risk Individuals at Two Specific Locations in Their DNA.

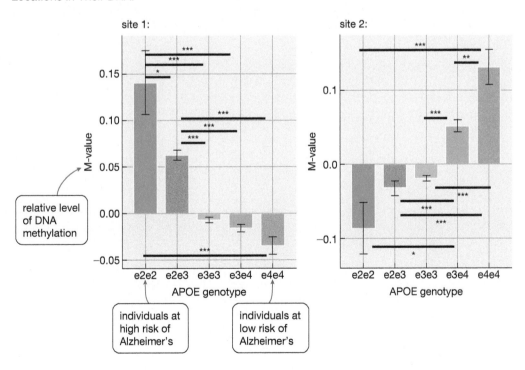

Questions to Think About

Examine Figure U3.7 and use it to answer the following questions:

1. Part A shows the relative amount of DNA methylation at one specific location in the DNA. How does the methylation pattern compare between high-risk and low-risk individuals?

2. Part B shows the relative amount of DNA methylation at a second, different location in the DNA. How does the methylation pattern compare between high-risk and low-risk individuals? Is this pattern consistent with what was found at site 1?

3. Recall the methylating DNA attracts the enzyme, histone deacetylase (see Fig. U3.5). Would you expect a gene located at site 1 to be off or on? Explain. What about a gene at site 2?

We opened Unit 3 with a look at how small chemical reactions on the surface of our DNA can have dramatic impacts on our health. We've explored the types of chemical reactions and some of the energy principles that guide them. Our understanding of the role of enzyme catalysts can help us predict the impact of therapeutic enzyme inhibitors. New discoveries from our continued efforts to understand the chemical reactions driving epigenetics may lead to exciting new options to diagnose and treat a wide range of diseases.

Unit 4

Introduction

Gases, Solutions, Acids, and Bases

Chapter 10: Gases and Phase Changes

Chapter 11: Solutions

Chapter 12: Acids and Bases

The COVID-19 pandemic unleashed an enormous demand for ventilators and other medical supplies as millions of people around the world found themselves struggling to get enough oxygen into their lungs. These life-saving ventilators provide patients with an array of medical conditions a better chance of survival.

Figure U4.1 A Patient on a Ventilator.

Some COVID-19 patients require a ventilator to deliver enough oxygen into their damaged lungs.

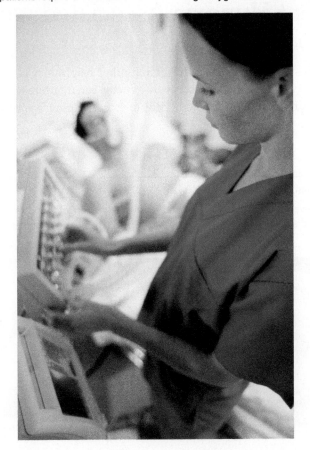

Unit 4: Introduction
How Can Healthcare Providers Help Their COVID-19 Patients Get Enough Oxygen?

 To learn more about how this essential tool—the ventilator—helps patients with severe COVID-19 and an array of other life-threatening conditions, watch **Video U4.1** in the Pearson eText.

Unit 4 opens with a closer look at the role of ventilators and other medical interventions in maintaining lung function. Lungs perform several critical tasks including obtaining oxygen, in the form of O_2, from the environment and eliminating excess carbon dioxide (CO_2) from our bodies. Healthcare providers monitor oxygen levels in their patients in order to quickly detect and respond to low oxygen levels (Figure U4.2).

In this unit, we will learn more about the behavior of gases, how and why solutions form, and what makes a substance an acid or a base. Combined, this knowledge will help us better understand the challenge of regulating O_2 and other gases in a variety of environments, including our own lungs.

Unit 4 Chemistry Application: How Can Chemistry Help Us Understand the Silent Hypoxia Associated with COVID-19?

Many patients suffering from COVID-19 and other respiratory diseases experience *hypoxia*—low oxygen in their tissues. Severe hypoxia can interfere with the function of the heart, brain, and other organs. People experiencing hypoxia often report

Figure U4.2 Maintaining Adequate Oxygen Levels.

A) A device called a pulse oximeter can measure oxygen levels in the blood. **B)** Healthcare providers have an array of options to help increase oxygen levels including hand-held bags to inflate the lungs and **C)** oxygen masks to increase the concentration of oxygen entering the lungs.

A   B   C

Figure U4.3 Hypoxia.

Hypoxic individuals have too little oxygen in their tissues and typically experience a range of symptoms.

headaches, a shortness of breath, coughing, and a rapid heart rate (Figure U4.3). In other words, hypoxic individuals are usually uncomfortable and recognize that something's not right.

Some COVID-19 patients, however, experience *silent hypoxia*. In silent hypoxia, patients' oxygen levels are alarmingly low and yet they experience few, if any, of the typical symptoms. A healthy individual should have a blood oxygen saturation level of 95% or higher. COVID-19 patients suffering from silent hypoxia, in contrast, often have life-threatening blood oxygen saturation levels of 50-80%. The causes of silent hypoxia in COVID-19 patients are poorly understood, but most certainly involve a change in how the body responds to changes in levels of oxygen and carbon dioxide in the blood.

In this unit, we'll explore the behavior of O_2, CO_2, and other gases. We will also continue to investigate how gases and other substances dissolve in water to make a solution, and in some cases, how a substance contributes to the acidity of these solutions. Understanding these fundamental chemical processes will help us more deeply understand the puzzling phenomenon of silent hypoxia.

Questions to Think About

What chemistry do we need to know to understand the challenges of delivering oxygen (O_2) and removing carbon dioxide (CO_2) in the lungs? Here are some questions to consider as you move through this unit:

- Why does oxygen gas (O_2) dissolve in blood?
- What other gases are found in our blood?
- What mechanisms do we have to help increase the concentration of O_2 in our blood?
- How do the gas laws explain how our lungs work?
- What happens to blood when dissolved CO_2 concentrations get too high?
- What mechanisms do we have to help reduce the impact of excess CO_2 in our blood?

What chemistry would you like to know in order to more fully understand this problem?

Now that we have an overview of this unit, let's step into Chapter 10 and learn more about the behavior of O_2, CO_2, and other gases!

Chapter 10
Gases and Phase Change

The chemical and physical properties of gases explain much about our world: from how oxygen moves into and around our bodies to a hot air balloon's seemingly effortless rise.

⌄ Chapter Outline

Learning Objectives

10.1 Apply the kinetic molecular theory to describe properties of gases.

10.2 Use the gas laws to describe and calculate the relationship between volume, temperature, and pressure of a gas sample.

10.3 Apply Avogadro's law to describe the relationship between amount of gas and volume.

10.4 Apply the ideal gas law to determine P, V, T, or n of gases when given three of the four variables.

10.5 Use Dalton's law to determine total and partial pressures of gas mixtures.

10.6 Describe the relationship between the strength of intermolecular forces and phase changes including boiling/melting points of substances.

10.7 Calculate energy quantities needed to undergo phase changes using heat of vaporization and heat of fusion values.

Introduction

An astronaut in space, a patient in the hospital, and a scuba diver all rely on gases to survive difficult situations (Figure 10.1). Outer space is extremely cold, and in outer space, there is no atmospheric pressure or oxygen. A space suit provides regulated pressure, temperature, and air so an astronaut is able to work outside of the spacecraft. Supplemental oxygen helps patients with reduced lung function deliver adequate amounts of oxygen to their tissues. The pressurized air tanks carried by scuba divers allow them to breathe underwater. In this chapter, we explore these examples in more detail and become familiar with the world of gases all around us. We also explore how the temperature, pressure, volume, and amounts of gases are all interconnected through a few straightforward mathematical relationships. Understanding these relationships allows us to make predictions and solve problems about the behavior of gases. A discussion of phase changes between the states of matter–such as how a liquid changes to a gas and how a solid changes to a liquid–completes this chapter. This discussion provides atomic level explanations of events that occur in our everyday lives.

Figure 10.1 Understanding the Behavior of Gases is Critical to Survival.

A) An astronaut's space suit provides regulated temperature, pressure, and air and creates an environment similar to that found back home on Earth's surface. **B)** A patient in the hospital receives supplemental oxygen through a breathing mask that provides much-needed life support. **C)** A scuba diver can function for extended periods of time underwater by breathing pressurized air from scuba tanks.

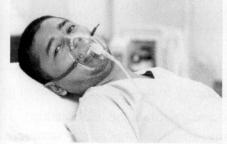

A   B   C

10.1 Properties of Gases

The gases in air that we discuss in the chapter introduction all behave differently in chemical reactions, yet many of the properties of these different gases are the same. The **kinetic molecular theory** provides a model to explain gas behavior. This theory describes a gas as a collection of particles in constant motion that collide with one another and the walls of their container. Understanding this behavior requires that we zoom down to the atomic level. Imagine, for example, what it is going on inside a balloon filled with helium (He) where the atoms are moving rapidly in all directions (Figure 10.2).

Kinetic molecular theory, which explains the behavior of gases, is based on the following assumptions:

1. A gas consists of small particles (atoms or molecules) that are in constant rapid motion.

2. A single gas particle moves in a straight line until it collides with another particle or the wall of the container. These collisions cause gas particles to travel in new directions.

3. The size of a gas particle is extremely small compared to the space between gas particles.

4. The attractive forces between gas particles are so small that they do not need to be considered.

5. The kinetic energy of a gas particle increases with increasing temperature.

The rapid motion of gas particles explains how gases fill their container quickly and how multiple gases rapidly mix. You can quickly detect an opened bottle of perfume on one side of a room, for example, on the other side of the room as the gas particles from the perfume bottle move and collide with one another to ultimately spread throughout the room. Increasing the temperature of a gas speeds up this process. As temperature increases, gas particles move at faster average speeds (Figure 10.3).

Figure 10.2 Gas Particles Fill Balloons.

Gas particles are in rapid motion, colliding with other particles and the walls of the container. When considering this artist's representation of gas particles, remember that individual particles are small—a single helium balloon can easily hold more than 4×10^{23} helium atoms.

Figure 10.3 Gas Particles in Motion.

Gas particles are in rapid motion, traveling in straight lines until they collide with other gas particles or the wall of the container. Increasing the temperature increases the energy of the particles and the number of collisions.

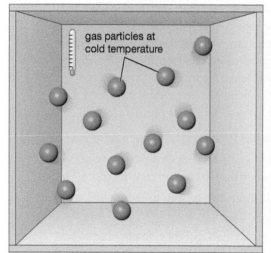
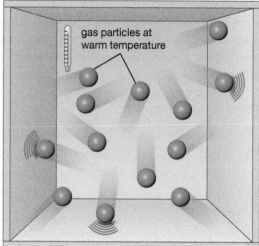

Pressure

When gas particles hit the walls of a container, they exert pressure. **Pressure** (P) is the force (F) exerted on a surface per unit area (A) (Figure 10.4).

$$\text{pressure (P)} = \frac{\text{force (F)}}{\text{area (A)}}$$

Like a ball hitting a wall, gas particles exert force by colliding with the walls of their container. Each gas particle is extremely small, yet the forces of many particles quickly add up, resulting in pressure.

Gas particles in the air, which are mostly oxygen (O_2) and nitrogen (N_2), exert a pressure on the surface of Earth called **atmospheric pressure** (Figure 10.5). The more gas particles the greater the pressure exerted. At higher altitudes there are fewer gas particles than at sea level and therefore atmospheric pressure is lower. At lower altitudes, where there are more gas particles, the pressure is higher.

Figure 10.4 Pressure is the Result of Gas Particles Colliding with the Walls of Their Container.

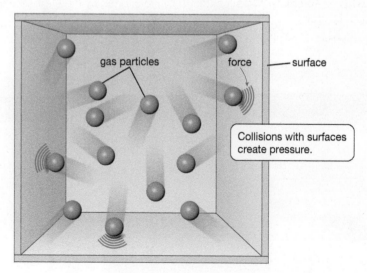

Figure 10.5 Atmospheric Pressure is Greater at Sea Level and Decreases with Altitude.

In this diagram, the darker the arrow, the more particles per unit area and the higher the atmospheric pressure.

Mt. Fairweather
(elevation 15,325 ft.)
$P = 0.6$ atm

sea level:
$P = 1.0$ atm

Units of Pressure

One common unit of pressure is the **millimeter of mercury (mmHg)**, which was established when the **barometer** was invented. A millimeter of mercury is the same as a **torr**. A barometer is a glass tube submerged in a pool of mercury. Atmospheric pressure on the liquid's surface forces the liquid mercury up the tube (Figure 10.6). We measure the amount of pressure by reading the height of the column of mercury in the tube. Atmospheric pressure at sea level is 760 mmHg. Meteorologists use barometers

Figure 10.6 A Barometer Measures the Pressure Exerted by the Atmosphere on a Pool of Liquid Mercury.

Atmospheric pressure is 760 mm Hg (1 atm).

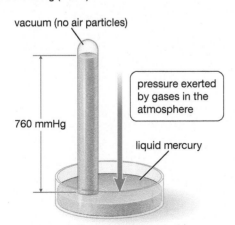

vacuum (no air particles)

pressure exerted
by gases in the
atmosphere

760 mmHg

liquid mercury

Figure 10.7 Barometer Gauge.

to make predictions about specific weather conditions. High pressure indicates clear weather, while low pressure indicates stormy weather. Barometer gauges may indicate these conditions (Figure 10.7).

There are several other commonly used units of pressure. An **atmosphere (atm)** is a unit of pressure; 1 atm = 760 mm Hg. The **pascal (Pa)** is a much smaller unit of pressure; 1 atm = 101,325 Pa. People in the United States use **pounds per square inch (psi)** for measuring pressure in bike tires and other inflatable items; 1 atm = 14.7 psi. A **bar** is used in weather reports and is almost equivalent to an atmosphere (1 atm = 1.01325 bar).

$$
\begin{aligned}
1 \text{ atm} &= 760 \text{ mmHg} \\
&= 760 \text{ torr} \\
&= 101{,}325 \text{ pa} \\
&= 14.7 \text{ psi} \\
&= 1.01325 \text{ bar}
\end{aligned}
$$

To convert between units of pressure, use these unit equivalencies as conversion factors as illustrated in Learn 10.1.

Predict answers and see step-by-step solutions: **Learn 10.1:** Converting Between Pressure Units in the Pearson eText.

Apply what you have just learned: **Practice 10.1** in the Pearson eText.

Gases in Earth's Atmosphere

The composition of the atmosphere has always been of considerable interest. It is important to us as it relates to weather, breathing, and the health of our oceans (Figure 10.8). It was not until the early 1800s that scientists recognized that the atmosphere is a mixture of gases in different percentages (Table 10.1). At this time, scientists identified oxygen (O_2), nitrogen (N_2) and argon (Ar) as the three major components of the atmosphere.

By the 1920s scientists had access to better instruments and were able to determine that there are many other gases present in the atmosphere in addition to oxygen,

Figure 10.8 Earth's Atmosphere is Composed of a Variety of Gases that Interface with the Surface of the Oceans.

Table 10.1 Percentage of Gases in Earth's Atmosphere.

Gas	Percent
nitrogen (N_2)	78%
oxygen (O_2)	21%
argon (Ar)	0.93%
carbon dioxide (CO_2)	0.042%
water vapor (H_2O)	0–4%
methane (CH_4)	trace
sulfur dioxide (SO_2)	trace
nitrous oxide (N_2O)	trace
nitrogen oxides (NO, NO_2)	trace
Ozone (O_3)	trace
Neon (Ne), Helium (He), Krypton (Kr)	trace

nitrogen, and argon. Most of these other gases, however, are present in trace (very small) amounts. Today, scientists monitor the composition of the atmosphere on a regular basis. Some atmospheric gases (such as O_2 and N_2) stay constant in terms of their percentage, but other gases vary in amounts over time and can impact major global processes such as weather patterns and ocean currents.

Carbon Dioxide in Earth's Atmosphere

While oxygen and nitrogen are essential for life on Earth, they have little impact on weather and long-term climate trends. It is other gases, although present in only small amounts, that influence climate. In particular, it is the **greenhouse gases**—such as carbon dioxide (CO_2), methane (CH_4), and nitrous oxide (N_2O)—that absorb heat emitted by Earth and warm the atmosphere, a process known as the **greenhouse effect**. Click on Video 10.1 to explore the greenhouse effect.

Video 10.1:
Greenhouse Effect.

Without greenhouse gases, the surface of Earth would be approximately 30 degrees Celsius cooler. The greenhouse effect and greenhouse gases are essential for maintaining a livable temperature. However, current increases in greenhouse gases in the atmosphere are causing **global warming** (a long-term gradual heating of Earth's atmosphere) and **climate change** to occur. These greenhouse gases are also contributing to acidification of the world's oceans.

Carbon dioxide (CO_2) is present naturally in Earth's atmosphere, but it is also the primary greenhouse gas produced by human activity. The majority of human-generated emissions of CO_2 into the atmosphere result from our combustion of fossil fuels for energy and transportation. The concentration of CO_2 in the atmosphere has increased dramatically over the past 60 years (Figure 10.9).

Quiz yourself on the content of this section: **Check 10.1** in the Pearson eText.

Figure 10.9 Carbon Dioxide Concentration from 1958–Present.

The concentration of CO_2 in Earth's atmosphere has been measured at the Mauna Loa Observatory since 1958. The concentration has dramatically increased since the first measurement was taken.

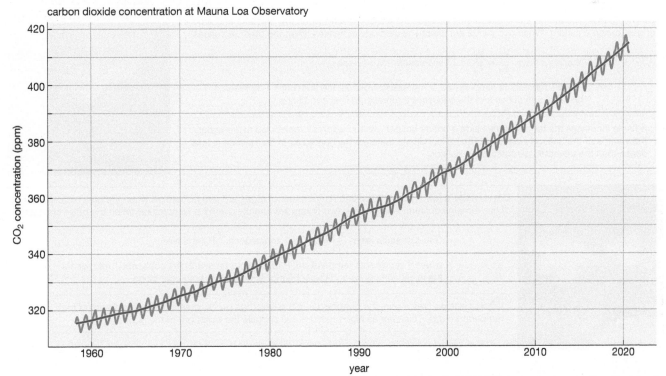

data: Dr. Pieter Tans, NOAA/ESRL (www.esrl.noaa.gov/gmd/ccgg/trends/) and Dr. Ralph Keeling, Scripps Institution of Oceanography (scrippsco2.ucsd.edu/), accessed 2020-10-31

10.2 Gas Laws

The **gas laws** explain the relationship between the pressure (P), volume (V), temperature (T) and the number of moles (n) in a gas sample. The three gas laws are **Boyle's law**, **Charles's law**, and **Gay-Lussac's law**. These laws predict the behavior of a gas sample as conditions change. Explore the relationships between these variables in Figure 10.10.

The Combined Gas Law

We can express all three gas laws (Boyle's, Charles's, and Gay-Lussac's law) in the **combined gas law**. The combined gas law relates pressure, volume, and temperature in a single equation. Using the combined gas law, we can solve problems that involve changes in conditions (initial to final) as long as the amount of gas in a sample does not change.

$$\frac{P_1 V_1}{T_1} = \frac{P_2 V_2}{T_2} \quad \text{combined gas law}$$

Figure 10.10 Three Gas Laws Explain the Relationship Between the Pressure, Volume, and Temperature of a Gas Sample.

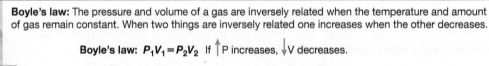

Boyle's law: The pressure and volume of a gas are inversely related when the temperature and amount of gas remain constant. When two things are inversely related one increases when the other decreases.

Boyle's law: $P_1 V_1 = P_2 V_2$ If ↑P increases, ↓V decreases.

where P represents pressure, V represents volume, the subscript 1 represents the initial conditions and the subscript 2 represents final conditions.

As a SCUBA diver descends, pressure increases, decreasing the volume of air in his mask (Boyle's Law). Divers who neglect to add air to their masks can rupture the blood vessels in their eyes.

Charles's law: The temperature and volume of a gas are directly related when the pressure and amount of gas remain constant. When two things are directly related one increases when the other increases.

Charles's law: $\frac{V_1}{T_1} = \frac{V_2}{T_2}$ If ↑T increases, ↑V increases.

where T represents temperature, V represents volume, the subscript 1 represents the initial conditions and the subscript 2 represents final conditions.

A flame increases the temperature inside a hot air balloon. As the warm air molecules move faster, the volume of the balloon increases. The balloon floats because the heated air in the balloon is less dense than the unheated air outside the balloon.

Gay-Lussac's law: The pressure and temperature of a gas are directly related when the volume and amount of gas remain constant. Again, when two things are directly related one increases when the other increases.

Gay-Lussac's law: $\frac{P_1}{T_1} = \frac{P_2}{T_2}$ If ↑T increases, ↑P increases.

where T represents temperature, P represents pressure, the subscript 1 represents the initial conditions and the subscript 2 represents final conditions.

When a person fires a gun, the gunpowder in the cartridge burns, creating a large amount of high temperature gas. This creates high pressure that propels the bullet out of the gun.

If we know five of the six terms in the combined gas law, we can rearrange the equation to calculate the unknown term. The combined gas law equation is therefore useful for quantifying how a change in two conditions impacts the third condition. For example, we can quantify how a change in temperature and pressure impacts final volume (V_2). Meteorologists perform this type of calculation regularly when working with weather balloons (Figure 10.11). As a weather balloon rises, both its pressure and temperature change. It is useful to determine how these changes impact the volume of the balloon.

If any of the three conditions—pressure, volume, and temperature—is constant, that term drops out of the equation leaving behind one of the other three gas laws (Boyle's, Charles's, or Gay-Lussac's law; See Figure 10.10).

$$\text{Since } \frac{P_1 V_1}{T_1} = \frac{P_2 V_2}{T_2}$$

At constant T: $P_1 V_1 = P_2 V_2$ (T cancels out on both sides, which leaves Boyle's law.)

At constant P: $\dfrac{V_1}{T_1} = \dfrac{V_2}{T_2}$ (P cancels out on both sides which leaves Charles's law.)

At constant V: $\dfrac{P_1}{T_1} = \dfrac{P_2}{T_2}$ (V cancels out on both sides witch leaves Gay-Lussac's law.)

When we perform calculations with the combined gas law equation, we must convert given temperature values to the Kelvin scale. Select VisibleChem Video 10.1 and BioConnect 10.1 (contains Figures 10.12–10.16) in the Pearson eText to explore how to perform calculations using the combined gas law as well as the individual gas laws.

Figure 10.11 Weather Balloon. Weather balloons collect data about Earth's atmosphere, such as temperature, pressure, and humidity. These helium-filled balloons can float as high as 40,000 m. Weather agencies release approximately 800 official weather balloons two times a day around the globe.

Watch this concept come to life: **VisibleChem Video 10.1:** Gas Laws in the Pearson eText.

Apply what you have just learned: **Practice 10.2–10.4** in the Pearson eText.

Explore how Chemistry and Biology connect: **BioConnect: 10.1** Gas Laws Predict Lung Function in the Pearson eText.

Quiz yourself on the content of this section: **Check 10.2** in the Pearson eText.

10.3 Avogadro's Law

In the gas laws we discussed in Sections 10.2 and 10.3, the amount of gas, or moles of gas (n), remained constant. **Avogadro's Law** is another gas law that provides a relationship between the volume of a gas and the number of moles of gas (n). This law states that the volume of a gas is directly related to the number of moles of gas when the pressure and temperature remain constant (Figure 10.17). In other words, as the number of moles of gas increases, the volume also increases. Avogadro's law applies regardless of the identity of the gas.

Figure 10.17 Avogadro's Law Explains the Relationship Between the Volume and moles of gas (*n*).

Avogadro's law: The volume and number of moles of gas are directly related when the pressure and temperature remain constant. When two things are directly related, one increases when the other increases.

Avogadro's law: $\dfrac{V_1}{n_1} = \dfrac{V_2}{n_2}$ If $\uparrow$ n increases, $\uparrow$ V increases.

where V represents volume, n represents number of moles, the subscript 1 represents the initial conditions and the subscript 2 represents final conditions.

When a person blows up a balloon, the number of gas particles inside the balloon increases and at the same time, the volume of the balloon increases. This is similar to what happens in our lungs, when we take a big deep breath.

E Apply what you have just learned: **Practice 10.5** in the Pearson eText.

STP and Molar Volume

Any two gases that contain the same number of moles of gas at the same temperature and pressure have equal volumes. This is an important concept that Avogadro's Law helps us understand. Gas particles are so small and generally free from attractive forces between particles. Because of this, the identity of the gas particles does not impact the volume of a gas sample. For this reason, we can compare the molar amount of any two gases by comparing their volumes at the same temperature and pressure. It doesn't matter which type of gas they are. For example, 0.5 moles of argon (Ar) gas and 0.5 moles of helium (He) gas at the same temperature and pressure occupy the same volume. Similarly, they occupy the same volume as 0.5 moles of oxygen (O_2) gas or 0.5 moles of carbon dioxide (CO_2) gas

Scientists established a **standard temperature and pressure (STP)** to make it convenient to compare gas samples. STP conditions are set at 1 atm and 273 K (0 °C).

STP Conditions: Pressure $=$ 1 atm (760 mmHg)
Temperature $=$ 273 K (0 °C)

Under STP conditions, one mole of any gas occupies 22.4 L (Figure 10.18). This volume (22.4 L) is the **molar volume** of all gases at STP.

Figure 10.18 Molar Volume.

One mole of any gas at STP has a volume of 22.4 L.

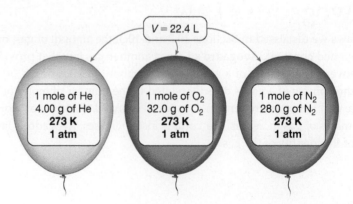

Notice that despite the different masses of the gases in Figure 10.18, the volumes of the balloons are the same for all three gases. This is because the same amount (one mole) of gas particles is present in each balloon.

Molar Volume: At STP, 1 mole of any gas has a volume of 22.4 L

Under STP conditions, the molar volume serves as a conversion factor between moles of gas and volume as demonstrated in Learn 10.2.

Predict answers and see step-by-step solutions: **Learn 10.2:** Using Avogadro's Law to Determine Amounts of Gas at STP in the Pearson eText.

Apply what you have just learned: **Practice 10.6** in the Pearson eText.

Quiz yourself on the content of this section: **Check 10.3** in the Pearson eText.

10.4 The Ideal Gas Law

The **ideal gas law** combines all of the relationships that we have discussed so far into one law that addresses all four properties of gases—pressure (P), volume (V), temperature (T), and number of moles (n). The ideal gas law includes an **ideal gas constant (R)**, which is equal to the product of pressure and volume divided by the product of moles and temperature.

$$\frac{PV}{nT} = R \quad (R \text{ is the ideal gas constant})$$

The value of the ideal gas constant is the same for all gases and has the value:

$$R = 0.0821 \frac{L \cdot atm}{mol \cdot K}$$

The ideal gas equation is more commonly written as:

$$PV = nRT$$

We can use the ideal gas equation to determine the value of one of the four variables when given the other three. The ideal gas equation provides a close approximation of the behavior of most gases under typical conditions. Maintaining the pressure on a space station, for example, requires that all four components of the ideal gas equation are considered and monitored at all times (Figure 10.19).

We report the gas constant in the following units:

pressure (P): atmospheres (atm)
volume (V): liters (L)
temperature (T): kelvins (K)
moles (n): moles (mol)

When solving problems with the ideal gas law, all units must agree with those in the gas constant (R) to ensure proper unit cancellation. Select VisibleChem Video 10.2 to explore how to use the ideal gas law to solve problems.

Figure 10.19 Pressure and the Ideal Gas Equation in Space.

There is no air pressure in space, but a space station must be maintained at a pressure close to that of sea level on Earth (1.0 atm) for the astronauts' comfort and survival. This is achieved by considering the variables in the ideal gas equation–temperature, volume of the space station, and the number of moles of gas. To achieve the desired pressure in the space station, the temperature is maintained at a constant level while gas is pumped into the station. If gas leaks out of the station into space, more gas must be released into the station from storage tanks. Exiting the station for a spacewalk requires a spacesuit that prevents dramatic changes in pressure as astronauts enter and leave from the station. A space suit's design maintains pressure and temperature and provides a gas exchange system for breathing.

 Watch this concept come to life: **Video 10.2:** Problem Solving Using the Ideal Gas Law in the Pearson eText.

Apply what you have just learned: **Practice 10.7 and 10.8** in the Pearson eText.

Quiz yourself on the content of this section: **Check 10.4** in the Pearson eText.

10.5 Dalton's Law of Partial Pressures

Gas samples are often not pure; they are mixtures of gases. Dry air, for example, is a mixture of nitrogen, oxygen, argon, carbon dioxide and a few other gases in trace amounts (see Table 10.1). Mixtures of gases behave similarly to a pure gas. For this reason, the ideal gas law applies to mixtures of gases in the same way it applies to pure gases. Recall from Section 10.1 that gas particles are very far apart and therefore behave independently. As a result, each component of a gas mixture exerts a **partial pressure** (P_n), the pressure that is equal to the pressure it would exert by itself. In an air sample from the atmosphere, for example, Nitrogen (N_2) exerts a partial pressure that is 78% of the total pressure. Oxygen (O_2) exerts a partial pressure that is 21% of the total pressure.

With this phenomenon in mind in the early 1800s, chemist John Dalton proposed that in a mixture of gases, the total pressure is the sum of the partial pressures of individual gases. This relationship if referred to as **Dalton's Law**:

$$P_{Total} = P_1 + P_2 + P_3 + \cdots$$

where P_{total} is the total pressure and $P_1, P_2, P_3 \cdots$ are the partial pressures of each of the components of the mixture.

In other words, when two tanks of pure gas are combined to form a gas mixture, the total pressure of the mixture is equal to the sum of the pressures in the individual tanks (Figure 10.20). In this example, a tank of helium at 2.0 atm combines with a tank of argon at 4.0 atm to produce a gas mixture that has a pressure of 6.0 atm.

We can use Dalton's Law to determine partial pressure of gases in a mixture if we know the total pressure and percent composition of the mixture. Explore Learn 10.3 to see how to complete this type of a calculation. BioConnect 10.2 (contains Figures 10.21–10.25) discusses how the low partial pressure of oxygen atop Mt. Everest affects climbers, and how climbers combat it.

Figure 10.20 Dalton's Law.

The total pressure of a mixture of gases is equal to the sum of the partial pressures of each gas present in the mixture.

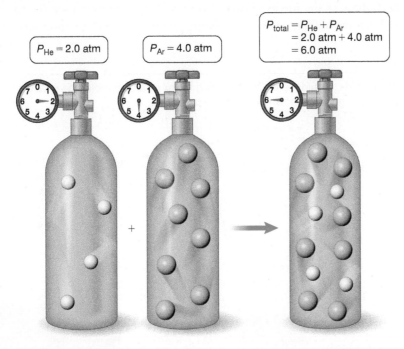

$P_{He} = 2.0$ atm

$P_{Ar} = 4.0$ atm

$$P_{total} = P_{He} + P_{Ar}$$
$$= 2.0 \text{ atm} + 4.0 \text{ atm}$$
$$= 6.0 \text{ atm}$$

+

Predict answers and see step-by-step solutions: **Learn 10.3:** Using Dalton's Law to Determine Partial Pressures in the Pearson eText.

Apply what you have just learned: **Practice 10.9 and 10.10** in the Pearson eText.

Explore how Chemistry and Biology connect: **BioConnect: 10.2** Breathing at Altitude in the Pearson eText.

Quiz yourself on the content of this section: **Check 10.5** in the Pearson eText.

10.6 Phase Changes

To complete our exploration of gases, we now consider how gases are related to the other phases of matter (liquids and solids). In particular, we explore **phase changes**, also known as *state changes*. Phase changes involve the transformation of one phase of matter, or state of matter, into another (Figure 10.26). **Vaporization**, the process by which a substance changes from the liquid phase to the gaseous phase, is one example of a phase change. The transition from a gas back to a liquid, which is **condensation**, is the opposite of vaporization. The phase changes between the liquid and solid phase are **melting**, the conversion of a solid into a liquid, and **freezing**, the conversion of a liquid to a solid.

The phase changes between gas and solid are less common in our everyday life. **Sublimation** is the transition from solid to gas and **deposition** is the transition from gas to solid. Carbon dioxide is an example of a substance that undergoes sublimation at room temperature and pressure (Figure 10.27). Dry ice is the common term for the solid state of carbon dioxide. Dry ice, as you can see in the photograph, visibly sublimates directly from a solid to a gas.

Boiling Point, Melting Point, and Intermolecular Forces

When a liquid is heated, the particles in the liquid move faster. At a temperature called the **boiling point (bp)**, the particles of the liquid have sufficient energy to overcome the attractive forces between liquid particles. At this point, the liquid undergoes a phase change to the gaseous phase (Figure 10.28).

Similarly, the **melting point (mp)** is the temperature at which a solid changes to the liquid phase as the forces between solid particles are overcome (Figure 10.29). Table 10.2 lists the boiling points and melting points of several common substances.

Figure 10.26 Phase Changes Between Solids, Liquids, and Gases. Using water as an example, the phase changes between solid and liquid and between liquid and gas are shown on the molecular level.

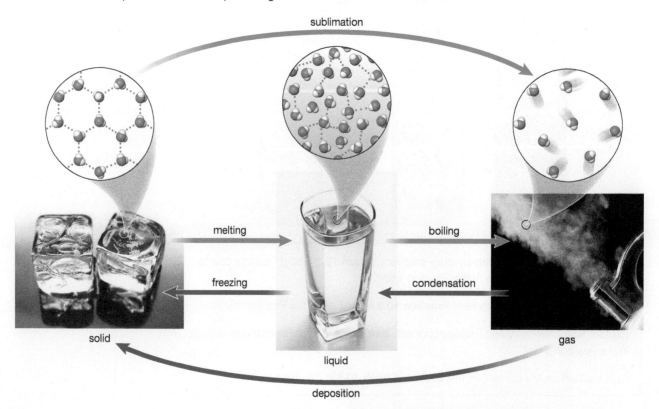

sublimation

melting

freezing

boiling

condensation

solid

liquid

gas

deposition

Figure 10.27 Dry Ice (Solid Carbon Dioxide) Undergoes Sublimation.

Sublimation is a phase change from a solid to a gas.

Table 10.2 Boiling Points and Melting Points of Common Substances.

Substance	Boiling Point (°C)	Melting Point (°C)
water (H_2O)	100.0	0.0
ethanol (C_2H_6O)	78.5	−117
butane (C_4H_{10})	−0.5	−138
propane (C_3H_8)	−42	−188
ammonia (NH_3)	−33	−78

Figure 10.28 Liquid Water Molecules Converting to the Gaseous Phase at the Boiling Point for Water.

Intermolecular forces between liquid water molecules are overcome to convert the liquid to a gas when it boils. In the inset drawing, the particles within the bubble are in the gaseous state. The bubbles are surrounded by particles still in the liquid state.

Why are the boiling points and melting points so different for each substance? Recall from VisibleChem 7.2 the types of intermolecular forces that exist among molecules: dipole-dipole forces, hydrogen bonds, and dispersion forces. It is these forces, acting between individual molecules, that determine boiling points and melting points. The stronger these forces are, the more energy that is needed to overcome them and undergo a phase change. For a substance to vaporize, for example, the intermolecular forces must be broken in order for the substance to change from the liquid to the gaseous phase. VisibleChem Videos 10.3 and 10.4 explore this relationship in more detail.

Figure 10.29 Solid Water Molecules Converting to the Liquid Phase at the Melting Point for Water.
Intermolecular forces between solid water molecules are overcome to convert the solid to a liquid during melting.

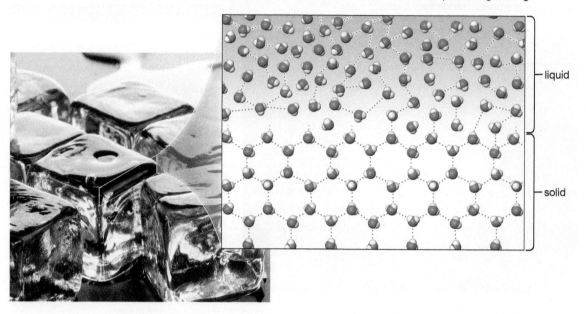

liquid

solid

 Watch this concept come to life: **VisibleChem Video 10.2:** Intermolecular Forces and
the Relationship to Boiling and Melting Points and **VisibleChem Video 10.3:** Predicting
Relative Boiling Points in the Pearson eText.

Apply what you have just learned: **Practice 10.11** in the Pearson eText.

Quiz yourself on the content of this section: **Check 10.6** in the Pearson eText.

10.7 Energy and Phase Changes

In order for a liquid to convert to a gas (vaporization), an input of energy must overcome the intermolecular forces among molecules in the substance (Figure 10.30).
Recall from Chapter 9 that an endothermic process absorbs energy. As an input of
energy is required, vaporization is therefore **endothermic**. The amount of energy
required to completely vaporize one gram of substance once it reaches its boiling point
is that substance's **heat of vaporization**. The process that is the reverse of vaporization
is condensation, the phase change from a gas to a liquid. Condensation is an exothermic process. Condensation releases energy as the gas particles slow down and enter
the liquid phase. The amount of energy released during exothermic condensation
equals the amount of energy absorbed during endothermic vaporization.

Figure 10.30 Vaporization is an Endothermic Process while Condensation is an
Exothermic Process.

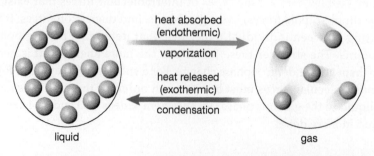

heat absorbed
(endothermic)

vaporization

heat released
(exothermic)

condensation

liquid

gas

Figure 10.31 Melting is an Endothermic Process while Freezing is an Exothermic Process.

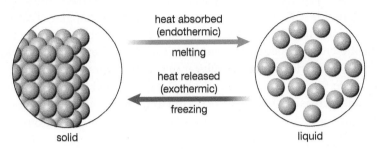

Melting is also an endothermic process; energy is required for the phase change from a solid to a liquid (Figure 10.31). Freezing releases energy when the liquid particles slow down and become more organized in the solid phase. Therefore, freezing is an exothermic process. The amount of energy required to melt one gram of substance at its melting point is the substance's **heat of fusion**.

We report both the heat of vaporization and the heat of fusion in units of joules per gram (J/g) or calorie/gram (cal/g). Table 10.3 lists the heats of vaporization and heats of fusion for several common substances. Notice how substances with strong intermolecular forces (such as H_2O) have higher heat of vaporization values than substances with weaker intermolecular forces (such as butane). We can use these energy values to determine how much energy is absorbed or released when a particular amount of a substance undergoes a phase change. We demonstrate these calculations in Learn 10.4 and Learn 10.5.

Table 10.3 Heats of Fusion and Heats of Vaporization of Common Substances.

Substance	Heat of Fusion cal/g (J/g)	Heat of Vaporization cal/g (J/g)
water (H_2O)	79.7 (333)	540 (2260)
ethanol (C_2H_6O)	26.1 (109)	200 (837)
butane (C_4H_{10})	19.2 (80.3)	92.5 (387)
ammonia (NH_3)	84.0 (351)	327 (1370)

Predict answers and see step-by-step solutions: **Learn 10.4:** Using Heat of Vaporization to Determine Energy Amounts in the Pearson eText.

Apply what you have just learned: **Practice 10.12** in the Pearson eText.

Predict answers and see step-by-step solutions: **Learn 10.5:** Using Heat of Fusion to Determine Energy Amounts in the Pearson eText.

Apply what you have just learned: **Practice 10.13** in the Pearson eText.

Heating Curves

We can summarize the behavior of gases and phase changes using **heating curves** that represent the energy involved when substances undergo changes of state. Different substances have different heating curves. The heating curve for water is shown in Figure 10.32. In heating curves, temperature is on the vertical y axis and heat added is on the horizontal x axis.

The heating curve for water in Figure 10.32 begins with the solid phase of water at 25°C. As the solid water, or ice, is heated (1), the temperature rises until it reaches 0°C. At this point, heat is still added, but the temperature is not changing. This is indicated by a horizontal line (2). The line does not climb because the heat added at this point is providing the energy needed to overcome the forces between solid particles to undergo melting, not to change the substance's temperature. Only after all the water molecules are in the liquid state, does the heat that is added increase the temperature again (3). This increase in temperature occurs until the boiling point, which is 100°C for water. Again, the horizontal line indicates that a change in phase from liquid to gas is occurring (4). The phase is changing but the temperature remains constant, and the temperature line does not climb. The additional heat provides the energy needed to overcome the intermolecular forces between liquid water molecules. The added heat does not change the substance's temperature. Only after all the molecules are in the gaseous state, the temperature rises again as more heat is added (5).

Figure 10.32 Heating Curve for H_2O.

Heating curves illustrate how temperature increases and phase changes occur as heat is added to a substance.

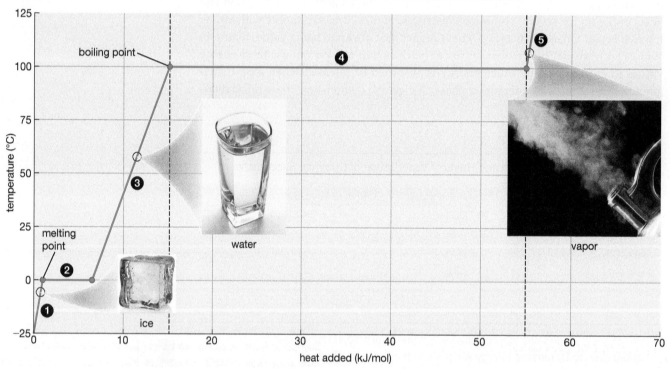

Quiz yourself on the content of this section: **Check 10.7** in the Pearson eText.

Chapter Summary

10.1 Properties of Gases

Learning Objective: Use the kinetic molecular theory to describe properties of gases.

The kinetic molecular theory of gases describes gas behavior. Gases consist of rapidly moving particles with large amounts of space between them relative to their particle size (Figure 10.3). Collisions between gas particles and against container walls create pressure, which is defined as force per unit area ($P = F/A$). The attractive forces between gas molecules are so small that they do not need to be considered, and the kinetic energy of a gas particle increases with increasing temperature. Common units of pressure include atmospheres (atm), millimeters of mercury (mmHg), torr, Pascals (Pa), and pounds per square inch (psi). Conversion factors allow convenient conversion among these units of pressure.

Video 10.1: Greenhouse Effect

Key Terms

atmosphere (atm)
atmospheric pressure
bar
barometer
climate change

global warming
greenhouse effect
greenhouse gas
kinetic molecular theory
millimeter of mercury (mmHg)

pascal (Pa)
pounds per square inch (psi)
pressure (P)
torr

Key Equations and Constants

$$
\begin{aligned}
1\ \text{atm} &= 760\ \text{mmHg} \\
&= 760\ \text{torr} \\
&= 101{,}325\ \text{Pa} \\
&= 14.7\ \text{psi} \\
&= 1.01325\ \text{bar}
\end{aligned}
$$

10.2 Gas Laws

Learning Objective: Use the gas laws to describe and calculate the relationship between volume, temperature, and pressure of a gas sample.

The gas laws are based on the kinetic molecular theory of gases and provide a set of relationships between volume (V), temperature (T), and pressure (P) of a gas sample (Figure 10.10). Boyle's Law states that the pressure and volume of a gas are inversely related when the temperature and amount of gas remain constant: V is proportional to $1/P$. Charles's Law states that the temperature and volume of a gas are directly related when the pressure and amount of gas remain constant: V is proportional to T. Gay-Lussac's Law states that the pressure and temperature of a gas are directly related when the volume and amount of gas remain constant: P is proportional to T. All three gas laws are combined in the combined gas law. We use the combined gas law to solve problems that involve a change in conditions as long as the amount of gas in the sample does not change. If any of these variables—*pressure, temperature, or volume*—remains constant in a given situation, then that variable cancels out and the equation becomes further simplified.

VisibleChem Video 10.1: Gas Laws

BioConnect 10.1: Gas Laws Predict Lung Function

Key Terms

Boyle's Law
Charles's Law

combined gas law
gas laws

Gay-Lussac's Law

Key Equations and Constants

$$P_1V_1 = P_2V_2$$

$$\frac{V_1}{T_1} = \frac{V_2}{T_2}$$

$$\frac{P_1}{T_1} = \frac{P_2}{T_2}$$

$$\frac{P_1V_1}{T_1} = \frac{P_2V_2}{T_2}$$

10.3 Avogadro's Law

Learning Objective: Apply Avogadro's law to describe the relationship between amount of gas and volume.

Avogadro's Law states that the volume of a gas is directly related to the number of moles of gas when the pressure and temperature remain constant: V is proportional to n (Figure 10.17). As the number of moles of gas increases, the volume also increases regardless of the identity of the gas. Avogadro's Law and the other gas laws often incorporate standard temperature and pressure (STP). The conditions of STP are 273 K (0°C) and 1 atm pressure. Under STP conditions, one mole of any gas occupies 22.4 L, the molar volume.

Key Terms

Avogadro's Law
molar volume
Standard Temperature and Pressure (STP)

Key Equations and Constants

$$\frac{V_1}{n_1} = \frac{V_2}{n_2}$$

10.4 The Ideal Gas Law

Learning Objective: Apply the ideal gas law to determine P, V, T, or n of a gas when given three of the four variables.

The ideal gas law includes all four properties of gases—pressure (P), volume (V), temperature (T) and number of moles (n) and is commonly written as $PV = nRT$.

The ideal gas law also includes the ideal gas constant (R), which has the value:

$$R = 0.0821 \frac{L \cdot atm}{mol \cdot K}$$

We can use the ideal gas law to determine the value of one of the four variables when given the other three. Problem solving using the ideal gas equation provides a close approximation of the behavior of most gases under typical conditions.

Video 10.2: Problem Solving Using the Ideal Gas Law

Key Terms

ideal gas Law
ideal gas constant (R)

Key Equations and Constants

$PV = nRT$

$$R = 0.0821 \frac{L \cdot atm}{mol \cdot K}$$

10.5 Dalton's Law of Partial Pressures

Learning Objective: Use Dalton's law to determine total and partial pressures of gas mixtures.

Many gas samples in everyday life are mixtures containing more than one type of gas. Fortunately, gas mixtures behave similarly to pure gas samples, so the ideal gas law also applies to mixtures. Dalton's Law states that the total pressure is the sum of the partial pressures of individual gases. We can use percentages of individual gas components within a gas mixture to calculate partial pressures of component gases by multiplying the corresponding percent of a given component by the total pressure of the mixture.

Key Terms

Dalton's Law
partial pressure (P_n)

Key Equations and Constants

$$P_{Total} = P_1 + P_2 + P_3 + \cdots$$

10.6 Phase Changes

Learning Objective: Describe the relationship between the strength of intermolecular forces and phase changes including boiling/melting points of substances.

The transformation of one phase of matter into another is a phase change. Melting and freezing are phase changes between the liquid and solid phase and are opposite processes. Vaporization and condensation are phase changes between the liquid and gas phase and are opposite processes. Sublimation is the direct transition from solid to gas, and deposition is the transition from gas to solid. The boiling point (bp) of a liquid is the temperature at which the particles of the liquid have sufficient energy to overcome the attractive intermolecular forces between liquid particles and undergo a phase change into the gaseous phase. The melting point (mp) of a solid is the temperature at which the forces between solid particles are overcome and a solid is converted to the liquid phase. The strength of the intermolecular forces between molecules in the liquid phase as well as the molecular weight of the molecules being considered are major factors that impact the boiling point of a liquid.

VisibleChem Video 10.2: Intermolecular Forces and the Relationship to Boiling and Melting Points

VisibleChem Video 10.3: Predicting Relative Boiling Points

Key Terms

boiling point (bp)	freezing	phase changes
condensation	melting	sublimation
deposition	melting point (mp)	vaporization

10.7 Energy and Phase Changes

Learning Objective: Calculate energy quantities needed to undergo phase changes using heat of vaporization and heat of fusion values.

Vaporization requires the input of energy (endothermic) to overcome the intermolecular forces between the molecules in the liquid. The amount of energy required to vaporize one gram of substance once it reaches its boiling point is the heat of vaporization. Condensation is the reverse of vaporization. It is an exothermic process that releases energy as the gas particles slow down and enter the liquid phase (Figure 10.30). Melting is also an endothermic process. Freezing releases energy when the liquid particles slow down and become more organized in the solid phase making freezing an exothermic process (Figure 10.31). The amount of energy required to melt one gram of a solid substance at its melting point is heat of fusion. Calculations involving the heats of fusion and heats of vaporization allow for the quantification of energy amounts involved with phase changes. Phase changes and the energy involved can be represented on a heating curve (Figure 10.32). Heating curves represent the temperature on the y axis (vertical) and heat added on the x axis (horizontal). The phase changes are represented by the horizontal (flat) portions of the diagram.

Key Terms

endothermic
heat of fusion
heat of vaporization
heating curve

 End-of-Chapter Quiz
Have you mastered the content of this chapter? Try the **End-of-Chapter Quiz** in the Pearson eText.

1. A car tire has an air pressure of 2.21×10^5 Pa. What is the tire pressure in units of pounds per square inch (psi)?
a) 3.21×10^{-4} psi
b) 6.74 psi
c) 32.1 psi
d) 3.29×10^{11} psi

2. Weather reports sometimes express atmospheric pressure in units of "bars" (bar) or millibar (mbar), where 1 bar = 0.9869 atm. While watching the news, you hear the weather forecaster predict an atmospheric pressure of 1020 mbar. What is this pressure expressed in units of pounds per square inch (psi)? Possibly useful information: 1 atm = 760 mmHg, 1000 mbar = 1 bar, 1 atm = 14.7 psi and 1 atm = 101,325 Pa.
a) 1.48×10^4 psi
b) 15.2 psi
c) 14.2 psi
d) 14.8 psi

3. If the volume of a gas in a closed container is doubled and the temperature is held constant, what happens to the pressure of the gas in the container?
a) The pressure also doubles.
b) The pressure is multiplied by the new volume.
c) The pressure decreases by one half.
d) The pressure is divided by the temperature.

4. A friend in chemistry class says that if the temperature of a gas sample is decreased from 40°C to 20°C at constant pressure, then its volume also decreases by half. Do you agree?
a) Yes, Charles's Law states that the temperature and volume of a gas are directly related when the pressure and amount of gas remain constant. So, if the temperature is decreased by half from 40°C to 20°C at constant pressure then the volume should also decrease by half.
b) No, Boyle's Law states that the pressure and volume of a gas are inversely related, so if the

temperature is decreased by half from 40°C to 20°C, then the volume should double.
c) Yes, the pressure and temperature of a gas are directly related when the volume and amount of gas remain constant.
d) No, it is true that temperature and volume are directly proportional, but the temperatures used in gas law equations must be expressed in kelvins.

5. A gas has a volume of 2.75 L at 1.25 atm and 18°C. At what temperature on the Kelvin scale does it have a volume of 4.25 L at 625 mmHg?
a) 18.3 K
b) 296 K
c) 2.25×10^5 K
d) 3.38×10^{-3} K

6. The compressed-air tank carried by a scuba diver has a volume of 6.75 L and a pressure of 115 atm at 22°C. What would the volume of air in the tank be if it were released and allowed to expand at the more typical pressure of 1.00 atm and a slightly warmer temperature of 28°C?
a) 792 L
b) 988 L
c) 5.99×10^{-2} L
d) 761 L

7. How many moles of ammonia gas (NH_3) are in a 5.25 L container of ammonia at STP?
a) 4.27 mol
b) 118 mol
c) 0.234 mol
d) 4.27 mol

8. An 8.25 L sample of oxygen gas containing 1.15 mol is added to another oxygen gas sample containing 1.25 mol. The container is allowed to expand with unchanged temperature and pressure. What is the new volume of the combined gas samples?
a) 8.97 L
b) 3.95 L
c) 7.58×10^{-2} L
d) 17.2 L

9. If a 17.5-g sample of CO_2 has a volume of 475 mL at 315 K, what is its pressure in atmospheres?
    a) 2.17×10^{-2} atm
    b) 21.7 atm
    c) 953 atm
    d) 217 atm

10. Much of the energy humans get from the foods we eat comes from the breakdown of the molecule **glucose** ($C_6H_{12}O_6$). Glucose metabolism is exothermic and yields the energy-rich compound **adenosine triphosphate (ATP)** that fuels a wide range of cellular reactions in our bodies. The basic chemical equation for the breakdown of glucose is the given **oxidation reaction**. Calculate the volume of carbon dioxide (CO_2) gas produced at normal body temperature (37°C) and 0.987 atm when 35.5 g of glucose is consumed.

$$C_6H_{12}O_6(aq) + 6O_2(g) \rightarrow 6CO_2(g) + 6H_2O(l) + heat$$

    a) 915 L
    b) 0.606 L
    c) 5.08 L
    d) 5.08×10^{-3} L

11. Natural gas is used in many homes for heating and cooking. The main ingredient in natural gas is methane (CH_4). Natural gas leaks can be a safety concern due to risk of an explosion so delivery lines must be monitored. If a gas company detects a pipeline leak that has released a volume of 86.5 L, how many moles of CH_4 were released? Assume the gas is 100% methane (CH_4), the atmospheric pressure is 725 mmHg, and the temperature is 11°C at the time of the leak.
    a) 3.54 mol
    b) 2.69×10^3 mol
    c) 91.4 mol
    d) 0.283 mol

12. A mixture of gases contains nitrogen (N_2), oxygen (O_2), and carbon dioxide (CO_2). If the pressure of the nitrogen gas is 415 torr, the pressure of the oxygen gas is 125 torr, and the total pressure in the container is 735 torr, what is the partial pressure of the carbon dioxide in atm?
    a) 195 atm
    b) 1.48×10^5 atm
    c) 1.68 atm
    d) 0.257 atm

13. The point at which molecules in the liquid phase have enough kinetic energy to overcome the attractive intermolecular forces between molecules is the

    _____.
    a) freezing point
    b) melting point
    c) boiling point
    d) hydrogen bonding point

14. What is the primary reason that water (H_2O) has a much higher boiling point than methane (CH_4), even though the two molecules have similar molar masses? The bp of $H_2O = 100$°C and the bp of $CH_4 = -161.5$°C.
    a) Water is non-polar and has stronger intermolecular forces than methane, which is polar and experiences hydrogen bonds.
    b) Water is polar and experiences hydrogen bonding, while methane is nonpolar and only experiences weak dispersion forces.
    c) Water (H_2O) is polar and does not experience hydrogen bonding as strongly as methane (CH_4) because water only has two hydrogen atoms and methane has four hydrogen atoms.
    d) Water has a lower freezing point than methane, so it has a higher boiling point than methane.

15. You enjoy a cold drink with 18.7 g ice in it on a warm day. How many kilojoules (kJ) of energy are needed to melt the ice?
    a) 6.23×10^3 kJ
    b) 6.23 kJ
    c) 5.62×10^{-5} kJ
    d) 6.23×10^6 kJ

16. Which segment of the given heating curve represents the phase change from solid to liquid.

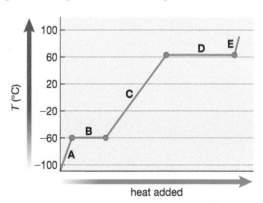

    a) segment A
    b) segment B
    c) segment C
    d) segment D

17. Which segment(s) of the given heating curve represent(s) the phase change from liquid to gas.

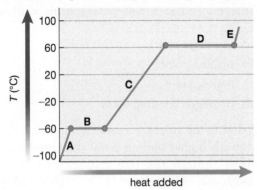

a) segment B

b) segments B and D

c) segment C

d) segment D

18. Which segment(s) of the given heating curve represent(s) the heating of the liquid from the melting point temperature to the boiling point temperature.

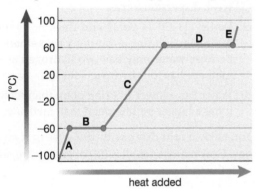

a) segment A

b) segments A and C

c) segment C

d) segment E

19. Consider the given heating curve and select the best explanation for why there are flat segments in the curve, where the temperature does not change, even though heat is continuously added to the system.

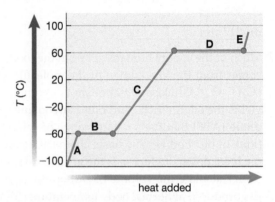

a) The flat segments represent delay times where nothing happens for a few minutes in the heating process.

b) The flat segments represent the warming of the solid, the warming of the liquid, and the warming of the gas so temperature does not change during these steps.

c) The flat segments represent places where no heat is absorbed so the temperature remains constant.

d) During the flat segments, added heat is used by the substance to undergo phase changes.

Chapter 11
Solutions

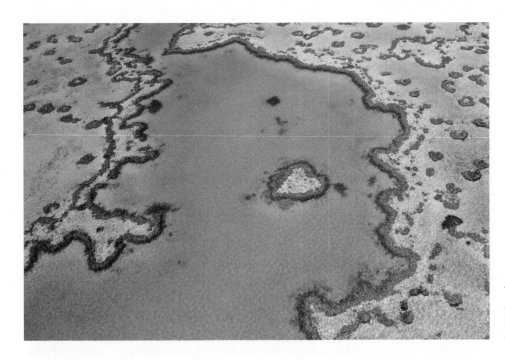

The seawater in the oceans is a complex solution that sustains both marine life as well as Earth's atmosphere and climate.

 ## Chapter Outline

Learning Objectives

11.1 Describe the effects of intermolecular forces on the properties of liquids.

11.2 Explain how solutions form based on the structure of the solute and solvent components.

11.3 Predict the solubility of a substance based on the polarity of molecules.

11.4 Predict the solubility of specific solutes in specific solvents based on the effects of temperature and pressure.

11.5 Calculate the concentration of solutions and use solution concentrations as a conversion factor.

11.6 Determine the effect of dissolved particles on the boiling point and freezing point of solutions.

11.7 Describe the process of osmosis and how osmosis functions in the cell and is related to dialysis.

Introduction

Water is vital to life on Earth. Earth is often called "the blue planet" because seventy percent of Earth's surface is covered in water (Figure 11.1). In gaseous form, water exists as water vapor in the air that helps regulate Earth's temperature and weather patterns. In liquid form, water is present in rivers and lakes that support freshwater ecosystems, in icecaps and glaciers that help control sea levels, and below the surface as soil moisture and groundwater. Our bodies are over 60 percent water. Water allows blood to carry nutrients to cells and regulates body temperature. With all of the water on Earth, it might surprise you that only about one percent of the Earth's water is drinkable. Access to clean drinking water is a global health issue for much of the world's population.

Most of the water on Earth exists in *solution* form—containing a variety of dissolved substances. We define and explain solutions in detail in Section 11.2. In the rest of this chapter, we explore the properties of pure liquids, and of solutions that contain dissolved gases, liquids, or solids. Understanding solutions can help us predict what sorts of compounds dissolve in water, and how those compounds act once they enter our bodies. After learning about liquids and solutions, you will have a better understanding of your own body, and how life on Earth is an interconnected set of water-based ecosystems.

Figure 11.1 Water is the liquid of life on Earth.

A) Sometimes called the blue planet, over 70 percent of Earth's surface is covered with water solutions containing dissolved solids, liquids, and gases. **B)** Blood is a complex, water-based solution. **C)** Millions of people lack access to clean drinking water.

A   B   C

11.1 Liquids

Liquid molecules are much closer together than gas molecules. The closer proximity of liquid molecules to each other presents the opportunity for them to interact with one another through intermolecular forces (see Section 7.4). Many of the properties of liquids depend on the strength and nature of these forces. Just as liquids differ from gases, they also differ from solids. Unlike molecules in a solid, liquid molecules can move freely and do not have a definite shape. As liquid molecules rapidly move, they often escape from the surface of the liquid and become gaseous (Figure 11.2). In an open container, liquid molecules become gaseous, and leave the container in a process called evaporation.

The process of evaporation is similar to that of vaporization (see Chapter 10). However, evaporation occurs when liquid molecules escape into the gaseous state at temperatures *lower than the boiling point*. Recall that vaporization occurs when liquid molecules escape into the gaseous state *at the boiling point of the liquid.*

You may have witnessed an example of evaporation in the street after a rainy day as a puddle slowly disappears (Figure 11.3). The liquid water molecules that make up the puddle escape from the surface of the puddle. Recall from VisibleChem Video 10.2 that molecules in liquids that have strong intermolecular forces, such as the strong hydrogen bonds between water molecules, need more energy to escape to the gaseous state than molecules in liquids with weak intermolecular forces.

Figure 11.2 Water Molecules Escape from the Liquid State to the Gaseous State in an Open Container.

The liquid state contains molecules that interact with one another through intermolecular forces. These forces play a role in how liquids behave. Hydrogen bonds are overcome as liquid water molecules enter the gaseous state.

Figure 11.3 Evaporation of Rain Puddles.

Over time, liquid water molecules overcome hydrogen bonds to become gas molecules and the puddle this child is enjoying will dry up.

Figure 11.4 Evaporation of Liquid Water Molecules in a Closed Container.

A) Water molecules begin to escape from the liquid state to become gas molecules. **B)** As water molecules build up in the gas state, some re-enter the liquid state. **C)** When the number of molecules leaving the liquid state is equal to the number of gas molecules joining the liquid state, the system is at equilibrium.

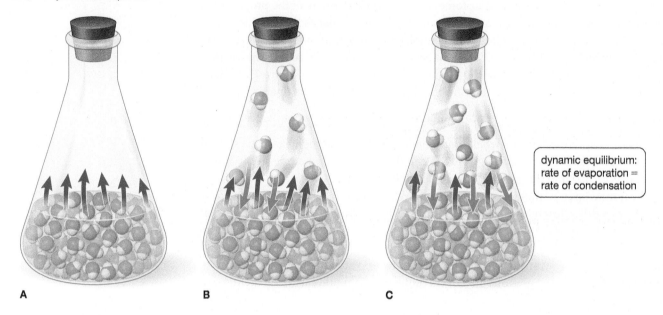

dynamic equilibrium:
rate of evaporation =
rate of condensation

A   B   C

Vapor Pressure

A liquid in a closed container presents a different situation than liquids in open containers because the gaseous molecules cannot escape from the container (Figure 11.4). Instead, in a *closed* container some of the gas molecules join the liquid state again. Over time, the number of molecules escaping the liquid state equals the number of gas molecules rejoining the liquid state. At this point the system is at equilibrium. **Vapor pressure** is the pressure the gas molecules exert when at equilibrium with a liquid in a closed container.

The vapor pressure of a liquid depends on the temperature and the strength of intermolecular forces. Liquids with stronger intermolecular forces have lower vapor pressures because the molecules are strongly attracted to each other. This makes it difficult for molecules to escape into the gas phase. Fewer gas molecules exert less pressure. Liquids with weaker intermolecular forces have higher vapor pressures because the molecules are only weakly attracted to each other. This makes it easier for molecules to escape into the gas phase. More gas molecules exert more pressure.

Water, for example, has stronger intermolecular forces than the liquid acetone. Water therefore has a lower vapor pressure than acetone. Acetone is commonly found in nail polish remover and paint thinner (Figure 11.5). Opening a bottle of nail polish remover often releases a vapor with a strong odor. The relatively low vapor pressure of acetone is responsible for the amount of gaseous acetone inside the bottle.

Vapor pressure of a liquid also depends on temperature. At a higher temperature, more molecules have enough energy to escape from the liquid, and more gas molecules exert more pressure. At a lower temperature, fewer molecules have sufficient energy to escape from the liquid, and fewer gas molecules exert less pressure.

Figure 11.5 Nail Polish Remover Often Contains Acetone.

The weak intermolecular forces in liquid acetone allow acetone molecules to readily escape into the gaseous phase. We quickly smell the gaseous acetone when a bottle of nail polish remover is opened.

Apply what you have just learned: **Practice 11.1** in the Pearson eText.

Viscosity

Many properties of liquids can be explained by considering strength of intermolecular forces. One such property is **viscosity**, which is the measure of a liquid's resistance to flow. Gasoline is composed of small nonpolar molecules with only weak intermolecular forces, and it has a relatively low viscosity (Figure 11.6). The molecules in honey, in contrast, are composed of larger polar molecules with relatively strong intermolecular forces. As a result, honey has a high viscosity (Figure 11.7).

Apply what you have just learned: **Practice 11.2** in the Pearson eText.

Intermolecular Forces and the Ability to Dissolve Substances

Intermolecular forces play an important role in a liquid's ability to dissolve different substances. Water, for example, dissolves many polar and ionic substances. This is why it is the primary substance that transports compounds in our bodies and on Earth. It is the highly polar nature of water that gives it this ability. **Ion-dipole** interactions allow water molecules to dissolve ionic compounds such as sodium chloride (NaCl). In the example in Figure 11.8, the partially positive side of water (hydrogen side) forms an ion-dipole with the negative ion (Cl^-), while the partially negative side of water (oxygen side) forms an ion-dipole with the positive ion (Na^+). We discuss the formation of this kind of mixture and water's ability to dissolve other types of substances in more detail in the next section.

Water and Life

When comparing properties of liquids, water is unique. Water has a low molar mass (18.02 g/mol) yet is a liquid at room temperature with a relatively high boiling point (100°C). No other substance has this unique combination of qualities and falls into this category. These properties are due to the highly polar nature of water, and the

Figure 11.6 Gasoline.

Many of the liquid molecules in gasoline have weak intermolecular forces and therefore gasoline has low viscosity compared to honey.

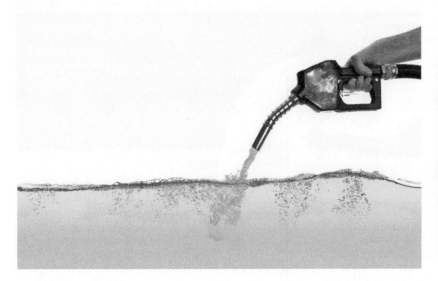

Figure 11.7 Honey.

Honey is composed of a variety of large polar molecules with relatively strong intermolecular forces and therefore has high viscosity.

Figure 11.8 Water Dissolves Ionic Compounds through Ion-Dipole Interactions.
Negatively charged ions (in this case Cl⁻) form ion-dipoles with the partially positive side of water molecules.
Positively charged ions (in this case Na⁺) form ion-dipoles with the partially negative side of water molecules.

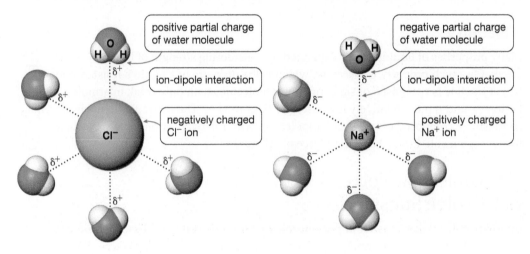

ability of the water molecule to form hydrogen bonds with four other water molecules. The strong intermolecular forces between water molecules are associated with water's high boiling point, low vapor pressure, high viscosity, and its ability to dissolve a wide variety of substances.

Life as we know it would not exist without water (Figure 11.9). Water is the most common and essential liquid on Earth. The majority of our body is composed of water. Water flows through our blood, carrying oxygen and nutrients to cells and eliminating waste through sweat, urine, and other fluids. Without water, the

Figure 11.9 Functions of Water in the Human Body.
Water supports all the major systems in the body. While we can survive weeks without food, humans can survive just days without water.

Figure 11.10 Finding Fresh Water to Drink.

average human cannot survive for more than a few days. Unfortunately, clean drinking water is scarce for many people around the globe (Figure 11.10). In fact, the United Nations notes that roughly half of all humans already live in water-scarce areas at least one month a year.

Quiz yourself on the content of this section: **Check 11.1** in the Pearson eText.

11.2 Solutions

A **solution** is a homogeneous mixture of two or more substances. The substance present in the least amount in the solution is the **solute**, and the substance present in the majority is the **solvent**.

There are many different types of solutions. A solution can be composed of a solid and a liquid, but it can also be composed of a gas in a liquid, a liquid in a liquid, and other combinations (Table 11.1).

Seawater is a solution in which the solvent is water, and the major solute is the solid sodium chloride (NaCl). Seawater also contains many other ionic compounds (see Chapter 5) and, like all bodies of water, contains **dissolved gases**. Oxygen (O_2)

Table 11.1 Solution Types.

Solutions can form from solutes and solvents that are in solid, liquid, or gas form. The solution that forms is in the same state as the solvent. Seawater, for example, contains mostly solids dissolved to make a solution, but the state of the solution is liquid because liquid water is the solvent. There are other possibilities for combining solute and solvent phases that are not included in the table.

Solution Phase	Solute Phase	Solvent Phase	Example
Gaseous solution	Gas	Gas	Air (mainly oxygen and nitrogen)
Liquid solution	Gas	Liquid	Club soda (CO_2 and water)
	Liquid	Liquid	Vodka (ethanol and water)
	Solid	Liquid	Seawater (salt and water)
Solid solution	Solid	Solid	Brass (copper and zinc) and other alloys

Figure 11.11 Liquid/Gas Solutions.

Rivers, lakes, and oceans all contain dissolved gases, including carbon dioxide and oxygen. Fish depend on adequate levels of dissolved oxygen. When levels of dissolved oxygen fall, dead zones may occur.

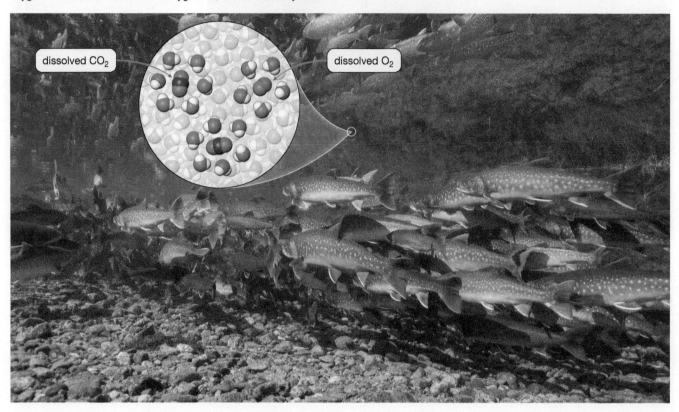

dissolved CO_2 dissolved O_2

and carbon dioxide (CO_2) are two atmospheric gases that enter oceans, lakes, and rivers, and form a liquid/gas solution (Figure 11.11).

In an **aqueous solution**, water is the solvent. Aqueous solutions are very common in nature due to the abundance of water on Earth and because water is a very effective solvent as we discussed in Section 11.1. We spend most of this chapter exploring aqueous solutions.

Formation of Solutions

Solutions form when a solute disperses in a solvent and a uniform mixture of chemical components results. The nature of the attractions between solute and solvent determines whether a solution forms or not. If these attractions, or intermolecular forces, are similar in nature and strength, then a solution forms. Another way to view this is to consider the polarities of the solute and solvent. Polar solvents, such as water, tend to dissolve polar and ionic solutes. Nonpolar solvents, in a similar manner, tend to dissolve or mix with nonpolar solutes (Table 11.2).

Chemists use the phrase "*like dissolves like*" to refer to the idea that similar types of forces, or similar polarities between solute and solvent, lead to solution formation. Chemists also say that a solute is **soluble** in a solvent, if a solution forms when the two are mixed. When two substances have opposite polarity (i.e., a polar solvent and a nonpolar solute) a solution does not form. The term **insoluble** describes that a solute does not dissolve in a solvent.

Although water is perhaps the most common polar solvent on Earth, there are a variety of other solvents that we commonly use in a laboratory setting (Table 11.2). Some of these solvents are polar and some are nonpolar. Scientists select an appropriate solvent based on the solution they need.

Table 11.2 Some Common Polar and Nonpolar Solvents.

Polar solvents, such as water, acetone, and methanol, dissolve polar and ionic substances. Nonpolar solvents, such as carbon tetrachloride, toluene, and hexane, dissolve nonpolar substances.

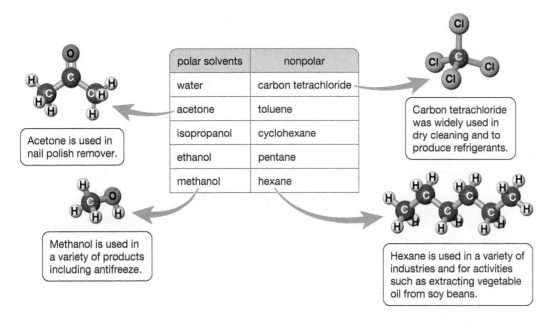

polar solvents	nonpolar
water	carbon tetrachloride
acetone	toluene
isopropanol	cyclohexane
ethanol	pentane
methanol	hexane

Acetone is used in nail polish remover.

Carbon tetrachloride was widely used in dry cleaning and to produce refrigerants.

Methanol is used in a variety of products including antifreeze.

Hexane is used in a variety of industries and for activities such as extracting vegetable oil from soy beans.

Electrolytes and Nonelectrolytes

A solute that dissolves in water to form ions and conduct electricity is an **electrolyte**. When **nonelectrolytes** dissolve in water, they do not separate into ions and therefore do not conduct electricity. We can detect the presence of ions that conduct electricity in a solution by connecting a light bulb to two electrodes and a battery (Figure 11.12).

Figure 11.12 Electrolyte and Nonelectrolyte.

Table salt (NaCl) is an electrolyte that dissociates into sodium ions (Na^+) and chloride ions (Cl^-). Sugar ($C_{12}H_{22}O_{11}$) is a molecular compound that does not form ions when dissolved ion water. Sugar is therefore a nonelectrolyte.

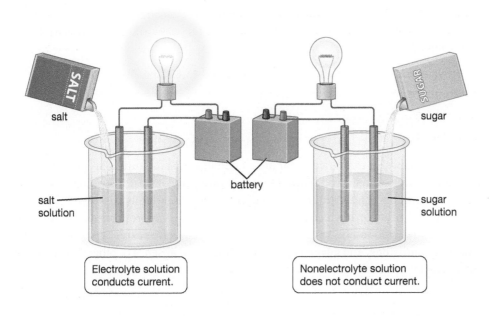

Electrolyte solution conducts current.

Nonelectrolyte solution does not conduct current.

The light bulb lights up when the ions in the solution conduct electricity. If no ions are present, the light bulb will not light up.

Sodium chloride or table salt (NaCl) is an electrolyte that ionizes into Na^+ cations and Cl^- anions in water. We write this in the form of an equation as shown here:

$$NaCl(s) \rightarrow Na^+(aq) + Cl^-(aq)$$

The ions present in a sodium chloride solution conduct electricity lighting the bulb in the apparatus. Like NaCl, many ionic compounds completely **dissociate**—break apart into ions, when placed in water and are strong electrolytes (Table 11.3).

Table 11.3 Strong Electrolytes, Weak Electrolytes, and Nonelectrolytes.

Many ionic compounds are strong electrolytes. In contrast, molecular compounds are either weak electrolytes or nonelectrolytes.

Type of Solute	Dissociates	Types of Particles in Solution	Conducts Electricity?	Examples
Strong electrolyte	Completely	Ions only	Yes	Ionic compounds such as NaCl, KBr, $MgCl_2$, $NaNO_3$, NaOH, KOH, HCl, HBr, HI, HNO_3, $HClO_4$, H_2SO_4
Weak electrolyte	Partially	Mostly molecules and a few ions	Weakly	HF, H_2O, NH_3, CH_3COOH (acetic acid)
Nonelectrolyte	None	Molecules only	No	Carbon compounds such as CH_3OH (methanol), C_2H_5OH (ethanol), $C_{12}H_{22}O_{11}$ (sucrose), CH_4N_2O (urea)

In contrast, a sugar solution does not light up a light bulb. Sucrose molecules $(C_{12}H_{22}O_{11})$ are nonelectrolytes. Sucrose dissolves in water but does not dissociate into ions. Many polar molecules are either weak electrolytes or nonelectrolytes (see Table 11.3). Weak electrolytes only partially dissociate.

Click on VisibleChem Videos 11.1–11.3 to continue investigating how aqueous solutions form on the atomic level.

Watch this concept come to life: **VisibleChem Video 11.1:** Ionic Compounds Dissociate into Ions in Water, **VisibleChem Video 11.2:** Compounds that Are Soluble in Water, and **VisibleChem Video 11.3:** Nonpolar Compounds and Nonpolar Solvents in the Pearson eText.

Apply what you have just learned: **Practice 11.3 and 11.4** in the Pearson eText.

Colloids, Emulsions, and Suspensions

The solutions we've examined so far are all homogenous mixtures; the solutions have the same composition throughout. Many mixtures, in contrast to homogenous mixtures, contain particles that are suspended but not completely dissolved. The size, identity, and number of suspended particles all affect the properties of these more complex mixtures. In Figure 11.13, we introduce and define three types of mixtures: **colloids**, **emulsions**, and **suspensions**. The presence or absence of other dissolved solutes also determine their characteristics.

Figure 11.13 Colloids, Emulsions, and Suspensions.

Often one or more different types of suspended particles are found within solutions containing multiple dissolved solutes. Colloids, emulsions, and suspensions are more complex in their makeup and properties than pure solutions that contain only completely dissolved solutes.

colloid	emulsion	suspension
A **colloid** is a mixture containing insoluble particles that are larger than atoms or typical small molecules but too small to be visible without the aid of a microscope (generally in the range of 1 nm to 1000 nm). Particles in a colloidal mixture do not easily settle out or float to the top over short periods of time.	An **emulsion** is a type of colloid that contains small droplets of one liquid dispersed in another that form a mixture of two or more insoluble liquids. Although the insoluble liquids can mix temporarily, they tend to settle into different layers over time.	A **suspension** is similar to a colloid, but because the particles in a suspension are larger than those in either a colloid or an emulsion, they more readily settle to the bottom of a container.
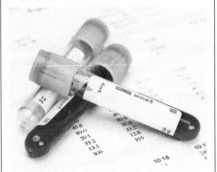		
Blood is often considered a colloid as the cells do not separate from the fluid (plasma) unless we place the sample in an instrument call a centrifuge that spins the sample, pulling the heavier cells to the bottom of the tube.	Oil and vinegar salad dressing is a common emulsion. The small droplets of fat in whole milk create an emulsion as well.	Muddy water is a suspension. The silt and sand readily settle out.

Quiz yourself on the content of this section: **Check 11.2** in the Pearson eText.

11.3 Solutions in the Human Body and the Environment

Complex solutions surround us both in our bodies (in blood), and in our environment (in rivers, soils, and oceans). These solutions often contain specific solutes. And additional substances also dissolve in these solutions when exposure or ingestion occurs. Whether or not a substance will stay in our bodies after we are exposed to it depends on the polarity of the substance. This is also true for substances that are put into the environment. The polarity of the substance's molecules determines where the molecules end up. Using the concept of "like dissolves like," we can predict and understand the solubility of molecules surprisingly well.

Vitamins are substances our bodies need in very small amounts to function normally. Some of the vitamins our bodies need are vitamin A, the B vitamins, vitamin C, vitamin D, vitamin E, and vitamin K. We can obtain most of the vitamins we need by eating a balanced diet that includes fresh vegetables and fruit. However, many people also choose to take vitamin supplements (Figure 11.14A).

We can predict the solubility of most vitamins by examining their molecular structure (Figure 11.14B and 11.14C). As a general rule, **water-soluble** vitamins (such as vitamins B and C) contain one or more polar groups for every five or fewer nonpolar carbon atoms. In contrast, **fat-soluble** vitamins (such as vitamins A, D, E, and K) have

Figure 11.14 Vitamins.

A) In a 2019 study by the Council for Responsible Nutrition, 77% of adults in the U.S. reported taking dietary supplements. Most large studies of dietary supplements like these have failed to demonstrate a significant benefit. **B)** Vitamin C is polar and dissolves in polar solvents, such as water. **C)** Vitamin A has far fewer polar groups and is nonpolar and therefore dissolves in nonpolar solvents, such as fats.

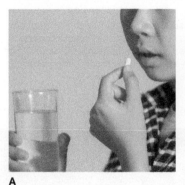
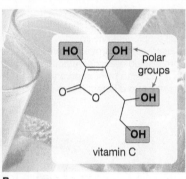
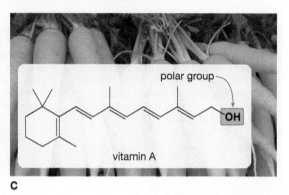

A   B   C

fewer polar groups and larger nonpolar hydrocarbon regions. Our bodies process the molecules in these two different broad solubility classes in different ways.

Water-soluble, mostly polar, vitamins are easily absorbed in the small intestines where plenty of water is present. These mostly polar molecules are also easily excreted in our urine. Water-soluble vitamins are generally not stored in the body. For this reason, we need to consume them regularly.

In contrast, vitamins with a molecular structure that is mostly nonpolar are best absorbed when we eat them with oils or fats. These vitamins are stored in our livers and the fat-storing tissue in our bodies. Nonpolar fat molecules mix well with nonpolar vitamins. This ability of humans and other animals to store nonpolar vitamins in our livers and fatty tissues means that toxic levels can accumulate if we consume nonpolar vitamins in excess. For example, excess vitamin A, can slow growth in children and cause dizziness and blurred vision. It is also associated with birth defects.

Solubility of Toxins in the Environment

Industrialization introduced many new substances that were both useful to society and harmful to the environment, humans, and wildlife. A class of these substances has recently been identified as persistent, *bioaccumulative*, and toxic chemicals. Chemicals in this category are referred to as **persistent bioaccumulative toxic substances (PBTs)**. Bioaccumulative substances accumulate in tissues because animals take them in faster than we can excrete them or break them down. The list of molecules that have been classified as PBTs is quite long and contains a number of pesticides and toxins released in engine exhaust (Figure 11.15).

Figure 11.15 Molecular Structure of Some Environmental Toxins.

Toxins have a range of chemical structures that impact solubility and biological activity.

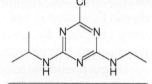

benzo(a)pyrene: found in automobile exhaust, wood and cigarette smoke, and charbroiled food; binds to DNA and causes cancer

hexachlorobenzene: widely used to kill fungi on plant seeds; now banned; causes cancer

atrazine: used to kill weeds; common contaminant in drinking water; may disrupt reproductive systems

Figure 11.16 Bioaccumulation Leads to Biomagnification.

Fat-soluble toxins can accumulate in the tissues of small organisms. As large numbers of these smaller organisms are ingested, the toxins are transferred to larger animals. Their concentrations become magnified in predators such as orca whales.

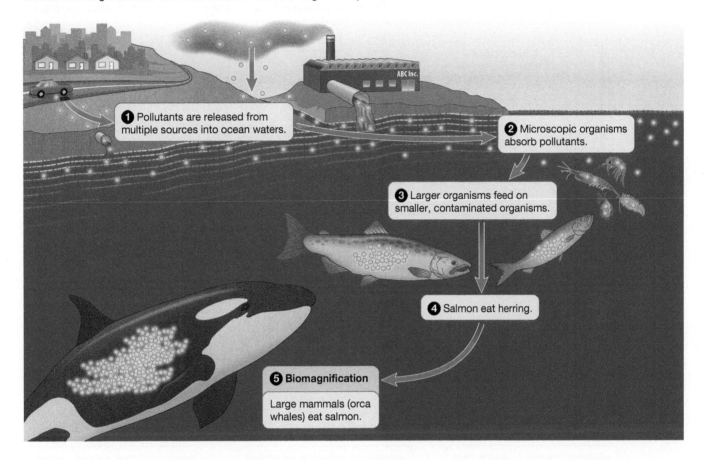

1 Pollutants are released from multiple sources into ocean waters.

2 Microscopic organisms absorb pollutants.

3 Larger organisms feed on smaller, contaminated organisms.

4 Salmon eat herring.

5 Biomagnification

Large mammals (orca whales) eat salmon.

Most PBTs are nonpolar or only slightly polar molecules. This means that they are fat-soluble and more likely to accumulate in the fatty tissues of humans and animals. When larger animals (including humans) eat smaller animals, the *biomagnification* of toxins can cause serious health and reproductive problems (Figure 11.16). It is important to note that not *all* toxins are nonpolar and fat-soluble. Recall from BioConnect 2.2 that the pesticide atrazine has relatively high water solubility, which is why it can pollute drinking water.

Solubility of Drugs

Developing effective medicines depends, in large part, on the relative solubility of drugs in different body fluids and tissues. Medications that can be taken orally instead of injected are preferable. Oral medicines are less expensive to administer and have higher rates of patient compliance (patients are more likely to take them). In order to be effective, oral medications must be soluble enough to dissolve in the stomach or small intestine and able to pass through cells into the bloodstream.

The common pain reliever ibuprofen, for example, is a fairly nonpolar molecule. Because it is nonpolar, it has low solubility in the stomach. Many formulations help overcome this obstacle by packaging ibuprofen as a salt or dissolved in a less polar solvent inside a capsule (Figure 11.17).

As we discuss in later chapters, the solubility, chemical stability, and specific three-dimensional structure of a molecule dictate its *bioavailability* and overall function (Figure 11.18). Researchers in the pharmaceutical industry focus on these attributes

Figure 11.17 Ibuprofen.

Ibuprofen, like all oral drugs, must dissolve in the aqueous solution of the stomach and small intestine and then move across cell membranes to enter the blood. In this graph, the concentration of ibuprofen in the blood (vertical axis) starts at zero but increases rapidly over time (horizontal axis), as the molecule moves from the stomach and intestine into the blood. Ibuprofen is eventually removed from the blood by the liver, so its concentration drops over time.

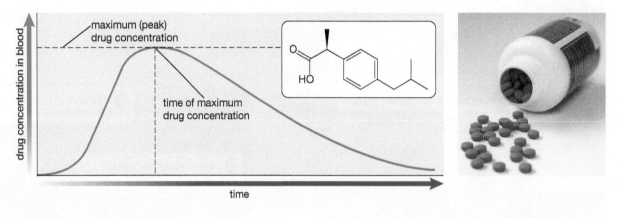

Figure 11.18 Molecular Structure of Common Drugs.

You can see the polar groups that make these drugs soluble in water in the structure of these three common drug molecules.

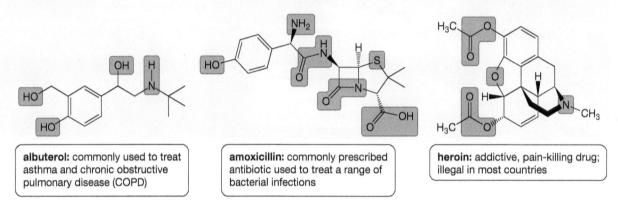

albuterol: commonly used to treat asthma and chronic obstructive pulmonary disease (COPD)

amoxicillin: commonly prescribed antibiotic used to treat a range of bacterial infections

heroin: addictive, pain-killing drug; illegal in most countries

during the development of drug molecules in an effort to provide safe and effective medicines. These researchers also must be knowledgeable of the contents of all the complex solutions found in the human body. Click on BioConnect 11.1 (contains Figures 11.19–11.23) to explore body solutions in more detail.

 Explore how Chemistry and Biology connect: **BioConnect: 11.1** Solutions in Our Bodies in the Pearson eText.

Apply what you have just learned: **Practice 11.5 and 11.6** in the Pearson eText.

Quiz yourself on the content of this section: **Check 11.3** in the Pearson eText.

11.4 Factors Affecting Solubility

The **solubility** of a substance is the amount of solute that dissolves in a given amount of solvent at a specific temperature and pressure. We usually report solubility in grams of solute per 100 mL of solution (g/100 mL). If a solution contains less than the maximum amount of solute that can be dissolved, the solution is **unsaturated** (Figure 11.24).

Figure 11.24 Unsaturated and Saturated Solutions.

A solution is unsaturated if it contains less than the maximum amount of solute possible. A saturated solution contains the maximum amount of solute with some undissolved solute present. In a saturated solution, particles are dissolving at the same rate they are recrystallizing.

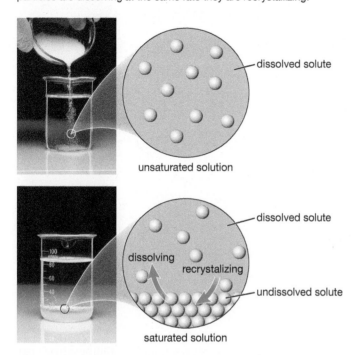

unsaturated solution

dissolved solute

dissolving
recrystalizing

dissolved solute

undissolved solute

saturated solution

Figure 11.25 Kidney Stone.

Kidney stones can be very painful. Smaller stones (<5 mm) often pass spontaneously but others require ultrasound or surgery.

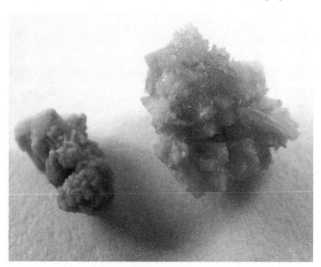

A solution that contains the maximum amount of solute that can be dissolved in it is **saturated**. If we add additional solute to a saturated solution, the additional substance remains undissolved. At the point of saturation, solute particles are dissolving at the same rate that solute particles are **recrystallizing** and forming back into solids).

$$\text{Solute + solvent} \xrightleftharpoons[\text{Solute recrystallizes}]{\text{Solute dissolves}} \text{Saturated solution}$$

Kidney stones develop when compounds in the body are present in excess amounts that cannot be dissolved in the urine (Figure 11.25). In this case, urine becomes saturated with salts, such as calcium phosphate, that begin to form tiny crystals inside the kidney. Over time, these crystals can bind together to form larger "stones." Insufficient fluid intake, which causes dehydration, is one of the causes of kidney stones.

The Effect of Temperature on the Solubility of Solids

The polarity of the solute and solvent (Section 11.2), temperature, and pressure affect the solubility of a substance. The impact of temperature on solubility affects only the solubility of solids in liquids and the solubility of gases in liquids. The solubility of solids in water, in general, increases when temperature increases. You may have noticed, for example, that more sugar dissolves when you add sugar to a hot cup of tea than when you add sugar to a cold cup of tea (Figure 11.26). Ionic compounds also follow this trend. The solubility of most ionic compounds in water increases with increasing temperature (Figure 11.27).

Figure 11.26 Sugar Dissolving in a Hot Cup of Tea.

Solubility of solids generally increases as the temperature increases.

Figure 11.27 Solubility of Ionic Compounds at Different Temperatures.

Solubility of ionic compounds generally increases with increasing temperature as shown here on the graph of solubility vs. temperature. All of the salts on this graph show an upward solubility trend with the exception of Na_2SO_4, which decreases in solubility as temperature increases.

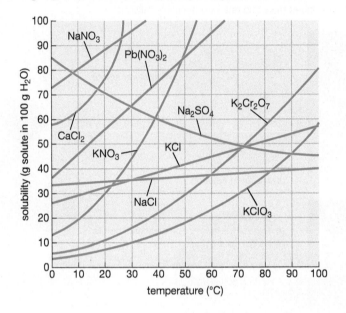

Solids that are more soluble at high temperatures than low temperatures can form a **supersaturated** solution. A supersaturated solution contains even more solute than a saturated solution. We can form supersaturated solutions by dissolving solute at high temperatures, which allows more solute to dissolve. As the solution cools, solubility decreases and the solute precipitates out of the solution as a solid. You can see this happening to the supersaturated solution of sodium acetate in Figure 11.28. In some cases, however, as the solution cools, it remains supersaturated for an extended period of time. These solutions are unstable and quickly form a solid precipitate if the solution is disturbed. Beautiful crystals can form when supersaturated solutions at elevated temperatures are cooled and then disturbed.

The Effect of Temperature on the Solubility of Gases

The solubility of gases decreases with increasing temperature. As temperature increases, the dissolved gas molecules move more rapidly and can more easily escape from the solution into the gas state. This lowers solubility.

The decreasing solubility of gases, particularly oxygen, can have dramatic effects on fish who depend on the oxygen that is dissolved in bodies of water. Most cold-water fish need at least 8 mg/L of dissolved oxygen. Levels of dissolved oxygen decrease by about 1 mg/L for each 10 °C increase in water temperature. Scientists measure dissolved oxygen in bodies of water using a portable probe (Figure 11.29). An increase in water temperature, especially when coupled with nutrient enrichment (see BioConnect 5.2) can trigger massive fish kills (Figure 11.30).

The Effect of Pressure on Solubility

Pressure has almost no effect on solubility of solids or liquids, but it has a strong effect on the solubility of gases. As pressure increases, the solubility of a gas also increases. As pressure decreases, the solubility of a gas decreases. We have all experienced this

Figure 11.28 Supersaturated Solution of Sodium Acetate.

A seed crystal provides the disturbance needed for a supersaturated solution to produce solid crystals.

Seed crystal

supersaturated solution of sodium acetate

solid sodium acetate forming

Figure 11.29 A Dissolved Oxygen Probe Measures Oxygen Levels in Bodies of Water.

Figure 11.30 Fish Kill.

Low levels of dissolved oxygen can rapidly kill fish.

Figure 11.31 Effect of Pressure on Solubility of Carbon Dioxide in Soda.

When a can of soda is sealed, the carbon dioxide is under pressure. Opening the container lowers the pressure, which decreases the solubility of carbon dioxide gas. Bubbles form and gas escapes into the air.

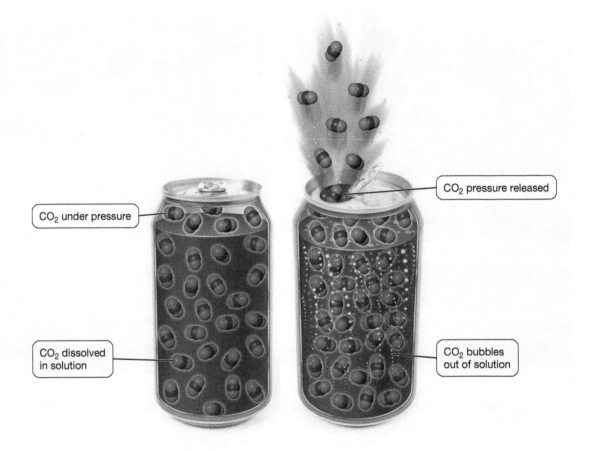

CO$_2$ under pressure

CO$_2$ dissolved in solution

CO$_2$ pressure released

CO$_2$ bubbles out of solution

effect when opening a can of soda. When soda is processed, the manufacturer adds carbon dioxide gas before sealing the container (Figure 11.31).

The additional CO$_2$ gas above the liquid in the can increases the pressure. This increase in pressure also increases the solubility of carbon dioxide in the liquid. When we pop open the container, we reduce the pressure. The solubility of carbon dioxide decreases and the gas escapes from the liquid. *Henry's law* describes the effect of pressure on gas solubility:

> **Henry's law:** *the solubility of a gas in a liquid is directly proportional to the partial pressure of the gas over the liquid.*

In other words, if the partial pressure of a gas above a liquid doubles, solubility doubles and if the partial pressure of a gas is decreased by one third, solubility decreases by one third.

We see Henry's law at work in Earth's oceans. As the partial pressure of greenhouse gas carbon dioxide continues to increase in the atmosphere above oceans (Figure 11.32), the solubility of carbon dioxide in the ocean also increases. Carbon dioxide dissolving in the oceans is the leading cause of increasing ocean acidification. After working Practice 11.7, click on BioConnect 11.2 (contains Figures 11.33–11.37) to learn about how dissolved carbon dioxide plays an important role in the health of organisms that live in the oceans.

Figure 11.32 An increase in Carbon Dioxide in the Atmosphere Leads to Increased Solubility of Carbon Dioxide in the Ocean.

Carbon dioxide from the atmosphere dissolves in the ocean as described by Henry's law.

Increasing the concentration of carbon dioxide in the atmosphere increases the solubility of carbon dioxide in the ocean.

Apply what you have just learned: **Practice 11.7** in the Pearson eText.

Explore how Chemistry and Biology connect: **BioConnect: 11.2** CO_2 in Our Oceans in the Pearson eText.

Quiz yourself on the content of this section: **Check 11.4** in the Pearson eText.

11.5 Solution Concentrations and Dilution

Scientists and healthcare workers regularly quantify **concentration**, which is the amount of solute dissolved in a given amount of solution at a given temperature and pressure. Epinephrine, for example, is a medication used to treat a number of conditions including cardiac arrest (Figure 11.39). Pharmaceutical companies distribute this medication in solution form. The bottle's label lists the solution concentration of epinephrine. When a patient needs the medication urgently, medical staff must quickly interpret the concentration and convert it to a dosage amount that can be administered in the appropriate amount. We measure and report solution concentrations using several different units. For people working in healthcare environments, converting between units can be a necessary skill, particularly when determining dosage amounts.

In this section, we explore several common units of concentration. We focus on *percent (%; both mass/volume* and *volume/volume percent)* and *molarity (M)*, which is the number of moles in a given amount of solution. Recall from Chapter 2 (Section 2.5), that we already explored parts per million and parts per billion as the units we use to report the concentration of toxins in water, soil, and air.

Figure 11.39 Epinephrine Concentration Is Listed on Bottles.

Healthcare workers must interpret the units of concentration on the bottles of medication given to patients to ensure proper dosage.

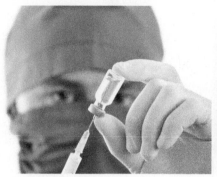
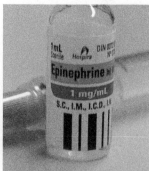

Figure 11.40 Sodium Chloride Solution.

The percent (0.9%) listed on the label is a mass/volume percent concentration.

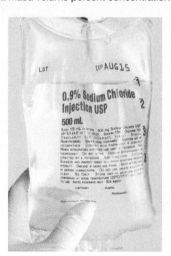

Percent Concentration

Expressing solution concentrations in terms of a percent is common practice. If the solute is a solid, for example, the most common percent concentration is **mass/volume percent (m/v%)**. Mass/volume percent is the grams of solid solute dissolved in 100 mL of solution. To calculate m/v%, we divide the grams of solute by the volume of solution and multiply by 100%.

$$\text{mass/volume percent (m/v\%)} = \frac{\text{grams of solute}}{\text{milliliters of solution}} \times 100\%$$

For example, health care workers use 0.9% sodium chloride irrigation solution to wash wounds in a hospital setting (Figure 11.40). This solution contains 0.9 grams of NaCl for every 100 mL of solution.

$$\text{m/v\%} = \frac{0.9 \text{ g NaCl}}{100 \text{ mL solution}} \times 100\% = 0.9\%$$

Apply what you have just learned: **Practice 11.8** in the Pearson eText.

Figure 11.41 Rubbing Alcohol.

The percent listed on the bottle (70%) is a volume/volume percent concentration.

Volume/Volume Percent Concentration

When the solute is a liquid instead of a solid, we report the concentration using **volume/volume percent (v/v%)**. Volume/volume percent is the milliliters of liquid solute dissolved in 100 mL of solution. To calculate this, we divide the mL of solute by the milliliters solution and multiply by 100%.

$$\text{volume/volume percent (v/v\%)} = \frac{\text{volume of solute}}{\text{volume of solution}} \times 100\%$$

Rubbing alcohol from the drug store is generally a 70% solution containing 70 mL of isopropyl alcohol and 100 mL of solution (Figure 11.41).

$$\text{v/v\%} = \frac{70 \text{ mL isopropyl alcohol}}{100 \text{ mL solution}} \times 100\% = 70\%$$

Apply what you have just learned: **Practice 11.9** in the Pearson eText.

Figure 11.42 Workers Harvest Sea Salt for Cooking from a Salt Pan Along the Tainan coast in Taiwan.

Molarity

In chemistry and biochemistry laboratories, **molarity (M)** is a common way to report solution concentrations. Molarity is the moles of solute per liter of solution.

$$\text{molarity } (M) = \frac{\text{moles of solute}}{\text{liters of solution}} = \frac{\text{mol}}{\text{L}}$$

For example, the world's oceans contain approximately 0.5 M NaCl, which means that each liter of ocean water contains approximately 0.5 moles of NaCl, or about 29.2 grams dissolved NaCl.

$$\text{molarity } (M) = \frac{0.5 \text{ mol NaCl}}{1 \text{ L solution}} = 0.5 \ M \text{ NaCl}$$

When sea water evaporates, it leaves behind dissolved salt, which people harvest and sell worldwide as sea salt for cooking (Figure 11.42).

Molarity is the number of moles solute per liter of solution (mol/L), but the concentrations of many important biological and medical substances are measured at much lower concentrations due to potency. It is quite common to express concentrations of substances using the following metric prefixes:

millimolar	1 mM	$= 1 \times 10^{-3} \ M$
micromolar	1 μM	$= 1 \times 10^{-6} \ M$
nanomolar	1 nM	$= 1 \times 10^{-9} \ M$
picomolar	1 pM	$= 1 \times 10^{-12} \ M$

Apply what you have just learned: **Practice 11.10** in the Pearson eText.

Dilution

Scientists store many solutions in high concentrations, called **stock solutions**, which they then *dilute* to make other solutions at lower concentrations. **Dilution** is the addition of solvent to lower the concentration of a solution (Figure 11.43).

Over-the-counter medications are sometimes available as concentrated solutions that you must dilute to a less concentrated solution before taking the recommended dose. Similarly, in your home, you may need to dilute surface cleaner if it is sold in a

Figure 11.43 Concentrated Solutions are Diluted to Prepare Less Concentrated Solutions.

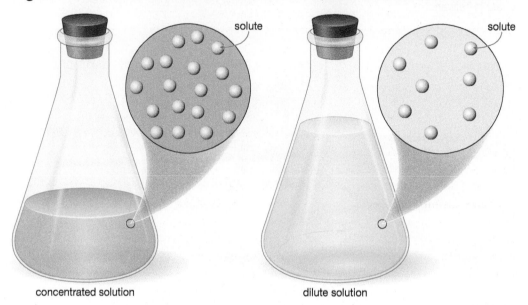

concentrated solution   dilute solution

concentrated form before using it for cleaning. In both of these examples the dilution process involves placing a specified amount of the concentrated solution in a container and adding a specific amount of solvent (usually water) to achieve the desired new diluted concentration.

To complete the calculations needed to carry out a dilution to a lower concentration from a stock solution it is useful to keep in mind that you are changing the amount of solvent not the amount of solute. The solute amount does not change during the dilution process. In fact, **the moles of solute in the concentrated solution are equal to the moles of solute in the diluted solution.** We can apply this idea to complete dilution calculations as we do in the following example:

$$\text{moles solute} = \text{molarity} \times \text{volume} = \left[\frac{\text{mol}}{\cancel{L}}\right]\left[\frac{\cancel{L}}{1}\right] = \text{mol} \quad \text{therefore,}$$

$$M_1V_1 = M_2V_2$$

In this equation, M_1 and V_1 are the initial values (original solution) and M_2 and V_2 are the final values (dilute solution). We can revise this and write it more broadly to include concentrations (C) other than molarity as:

$$C_1V_1 = C_2V_2$$

In this case, C_1 and V_1 are the initial values (original solution) and C_2 and V_2 are the final values (dilute solution).

Click on VisibleChem Videos 11.4–11.6 to explore calculations for working with solutions and dilutions.

Watch this concept come to life: **VisibleChem Video 11.4:** Reporting Solution Concentration as Percent, **VisibleChem Video 11.5:** Reporting Solution Concentration as Molarity (*M*), and **VisibleChem Video 11.6:** Solution Dilution Calculations in the Pearson eText.

Apply what you have just learned: **Practice 11.11–11.13** in the Pearson eText.

Quiz yourself on the content of this section: **Check 11.5** in the Pearson eText.

11.6 Colligative Properties

Adding a solute to a solvent to prepare a solution changes several physical properties of the solvent. These physical properties, which are **colligative properties**, depend only on the concentration of solute particles in the solution. In this section, we explore two colligative properties: *boiling point elevation* and *freezing point depression*.

The effect of solute particles on the boiling point and freezing point of a solution depends on whether the solute is volatile or nonvolatile. A **volatile** solute readily escapes the solution into the vapor phase. A **nonvolatile** solute does not readily escape into the vapor phase. A nonvolatile solute, therefore, has a larger impact on the colligative properties of solutions than a volatile solute.

Consider a solution composed of a solvent and a nonvolatile solute (Figure 11.44). The pure solvent has a specific vapor pressure before we add a solute. When we add a nonvolatile solute, the rate of vaporization of solvent molecules slows. This is because the solute particles take up space at the solution's surface, and this reduces the number of solvent molecules that can escape into the vapor phase. Equilibrium is reestablished in the closed container with fewer gas molecules above the solution compared to the pure solvent. As a result, the vapor pressure above the solution is lower than the vapor pressure above the pure solvent.

Boiling Point Elevation

How does the lower vapor pressure of the solution impact the boiling point of the solution? If a solution has a lower vapor pressure, the solution must be raised to a higher temperature in order to boil. The boiling point for a solution (made up of a solvent and a nonvolatile solute) is therefore higher than the boiling point for the pure solvent (Figure 11.45). This relatively higher boiling point for the solution compared to the pure solvent is a colligative property referred to as **boiling point elevation**.

> **A solvent that contains a nonvolatile solute has a higher boiling point than the pure solvent.**

Figure 11.44 A Solution Has a Lower Vapor Pressure than a Pure Solvent.

The presence of a solute slows the rate of vaporization and ultimately lowers the vapor pressure.

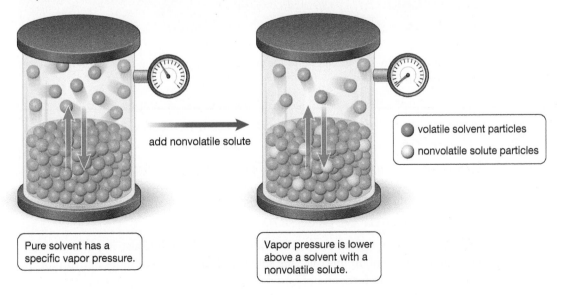

add nonvolatile solute

- ● volatile solvent particles
- ○ nonvolatile solute particles

Pure solvent has a specific vapor pressure.

Vapor pressure is lower above a solvent with a nonvolatile solute.

The magnitude of boiling point elevation depends on the number of solute particles present. When water is the solvent, one mole of a nonvolatile solute raises the boiling temperature of one kilogram of water by 0.51 °C. For example, if we add one mole of sucrose to one kilogram of water (boiling point of 100 °C) the boiling temperature of the solution rises to 100.51 °C.

> The boiling point of pure water (100 °C) *increases* by 0.51 °C for every 1.0 mole of nonvolatile solute dissolved per kilogram of water.

Because ionic compounds dissociate into ions when dissolved, the total number of ions in the solution is needed to determine the boiling point. For example, NaCl dissociates into two particles in solution (Na^+ and Cl^-). This means that for every mole of NaCl there are two moles of particles in solution. For this reason, the addition of one mole of NaCl raises the boiling temperature of 1 kg of water by 2 × 0.51 °C (1.02 °C) to 101.02 °C.

Figure 11.45 Ethylene Glycol ($C_2H_6O_2$) is the Main ingredient in Coolant and Serves to Elevate the Boiling Point of Water to Prevent Overheating in Cars.

Coolant and antifreeze are the same solution. This solution raises the boiling point of water in the radiator to prevent the water from boiling when temperatures rise, and it lowers the freezing point to prevent freezing. Freezing point depression is discussed in the next section.

Click on Learn 11.1 to calculate the new boiling point of a solution with known solute concentration.

 Predict answers and see step-by-step solutions: **Learn 11.1:** Boiling Point Elevation in the Pearson eText.

Apply what you have just learned: **Practice 11.14** in the Pearson eText.

Freezing Point Depression

Just as boiling point increases when a solute is present, a solute also impacts the freezing point of a solvent. In this case, the solute molecules make it more difficult for the solvent molecules to form an ordered solid. For this reason, lower temperatures are required to freeze a solution than to freeze a pure solvent. This colligative property is **freezing point depression**.

> A solvent that contains a nonvolatile solute has a lower freezing point than the pure solvent.

Using the same examples as before, one mole of sucrose lowers the freezing point of one kilogram of water (freezing point of 0.0 °C) to −1.86 °C. This value is specific for water. The freezing points of different solvents decrease by different amounts.

> The freezing point of pure water (0.0 °C) *decreases* by 1.86 °C for every 1.0 mole of any nonvolatile solute dissolved per kilogram of water.

Since soluble ionic compounds break apart into ions when dissolved, one mole of NaCl contributes two particles (Na⁺ and Cl⁻) for each one mole of compound. Dissolving one mole of NaCl lowers the freezing point by 3.72 °C (or 2 × 1.86 °C) to −3.72 °C. Ionic compounds dissociate into ions, which have a bigger impact on the lowering of the freezing point. This is in contrast to molecular compounds, such as sucrose, that do not dissociate.

Several types of frogs utilize freezing point depression to survive winter (Figure 11.46). The formation of ice crystals in cells is usually lethal to animals. Some frogs, however, can dramatically increase the concentration of glucose in their cells. This lowers the freezing point of the solutions in their cells and prevents their cells from freezing. Since the cells are not damaged by the freezing temperatures, they are able to recover their function when temperatures rise again. Many scientists hope that understanding the frog's technique will eventually allow them to freeze, store, and revive human organs, reducing the logistical complexities of organ transplants.

Figure 11.46 A Hibernating Frog.

Several species of frogs survive freezing temperatures by increasing the concentration of glucose or other solutes in their cells. Notice that although the water running into this frog's den is frozen, the frog has survived.

Predict answers and see step-by-step solutions: **Learn 11.2:** Freezing Point Depression in the Pearson eText.

Apply what you have just learned: **Practice 11.15** in the Pearson eText.

Quiz yourself on the content of this section: **Check 11.6** in the Pearson eText.

11.7 Osmosis and Dialysis

As we've discussed throughout this chapter, water-based solutions are essential to supporting life. In our bodies, most of these solutions are separated from one another by *cell membranes*. Cell membranes separate the interior of the cell from the outside environment. They are **semipermeable** barriers, allowing some substances to cross while blocking the movement of others.

Diffusion is the spontaneous movement of molecules or particles from areas of higher concentration to areas of lower concentration. Water diffuses across membranes through **osmosis**, the process by which molecules of a solvent pass through a semipermeable membrane from a less concentrated solution into a more concentrated solution. Most solutes, in contrast to water, cannot cross membranes. The concentration of solutes drives the direction water diffuses. During osmosis, water molecules move through a semipermeable membrane from the solution with the lowest concentration of solute into the solution with the highest concentration of solute (Video 11.7).

Watch this concept come to life: **Video 11.1:** Water Diffuses Across a Membrane Toward the Hypertonic Solution in the Pearson eText.

We can demonstrate osmosis using the apparatus in Video 11.7. The apparatus is a U-shaped tube that is divided in half with a semipermeable membrane in the middle. Initially, pure water is on one side of the membrane and a solution is on the other. The semipermeable membrane allows water to freely diffuse in both directions but blocks the solute from crossing. Because the solution on the right has a higher concentration of solute than the water on the left, water initially flows towards the solution. This causes a rise in the solution volume on the right, and a fall in water volume on the left. The transfer of solvent molecules continues until equilibrium is attained. At equilibrium, water molecules move in both directions at equal rates.

Osmotic pressure is the pressure needed to prevent osmosis. It is the minimum pressure that would have to be applied to a solution to prevent the inward flow of the pure solvent across a semipermeable membrane. Similar to the colligative properties explored in Section 11.6, osmotic pressure depends on the concentration of solute particles in the solution. The greater the solute concentration, the higher the osmotic pressure. In other words, when more particles of solute are present, more external pressure is needed to counter the effects of osmosis.

When we compare two solutions to understand which way water will move across a membrane, we only need to consider the total solute concentration, regardless of what the solute is. Two solutions with the same solute concentration are **isotonic**. A solution with a higher concentration of solute is **hypertonic**, while a solution with lower solute concentration is **hypotonic**. Water diffuses across a membrane towards the hypertonic solution (see Video 11.7).

Osmosis in Cells

Osmosis is vital for living cells. All living cells contain a water-based solution and are bathed in other water-based solutions. Human *red blood cells (RBCs)*, for example, maintain a constant volume because they are isotonic to our blood (Figure 11.47). Recall that this means that RBCs have the same solute concentration as our blood. RBCs placed in a hypotonic solution quickly burst like over-inflated balloons. RBCs in a hypertonic solution shrivel as they lose volume (Figure 11.48). Our kidneys maintain a narrow range of total dissolved solutes in the blood, helping ensure the healthy isotonic environment our RBCs need.

Figure 11.47 A Red Blood Cell (RBC) in an Isotonic Solution.

Water diffuses in and out of the RBC at equal rates as the total solute concentration is the same inside and outside the cell.

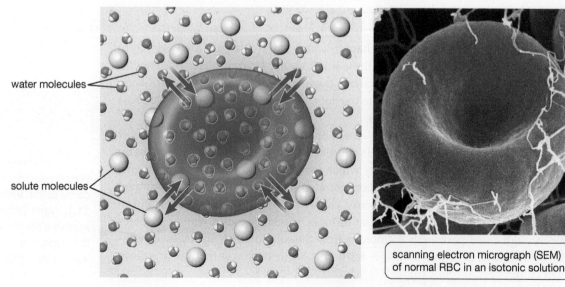

water molecules

solute molecules

scanning electron micrograph (SEM) of normal RBC in an isotonic solution

Figure 11.48 Red Blood Cells (RBCs) in Hypotonic, Isotonic, and Hypertonic Solutions.

Water diffuses towards the hypertonic solution. RBCs in hypotonic solutions burst due to this influx of water. RBCs in hypertonic solutions shrivel as water leaves the cells.

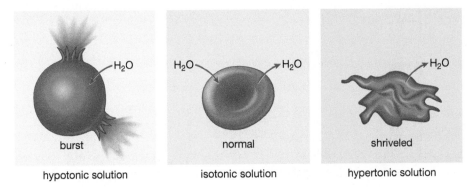

Plant cells, in contrast, are almost always in hypotonic solutions. When you water your houseplants, for example, the water you pour over them has far fewer solutes than the solution inside the plant cells. The water is hypotonic compared to the solution. Fortunately, plant cells in hypotonic solutions don't rupture like animal cells. A thick cell wall outside their membrane creates pressure inside the cells. This pressure drives the hypotonic water out as fast as diffusion drives it in. Pressurized (*turgid*) cells help plants maintain their structure (Figure 11.49).

Reverse Osmosis

In osmosis, solvent molecules flow across a semipermeable membrane towards a hypertonic (more concentrated) solution. In **reverse osmosis**, pressure drives water across a semipermeable membrane towards a hypotonic (less concentrated) solution (Figure 11.50). The process requires energy to produce the pressure but is frequently used to purify water in places where drinking water is scarce.

In 2015, San Diego County opened the Carlsbad desalination plant. In doing so, Carlsbad joined other coastal cities, such as Dubai, that have long produced their drinking water from salt water (Figure 11.51). The plant uses reverse osmosis to remove salt from seawater, and produce drinking water. The Carlsbad plant was the largest ever built in the Western hemisphere and cost $1 billion to build. It can produce 50 million gallons of drinking water a day.

Figure 11.49 Plant Cells Function Best in a Hypotonic Environment.

The plant cell wall protects the cell from bursting and creates pressure. Plants that have cells that are not turgid wilt.

Figure 11.50 Reverse Osmosis Uses Pressure to Force Water Across a Semipermeable Membrane Towards a Hypotonic Solution.

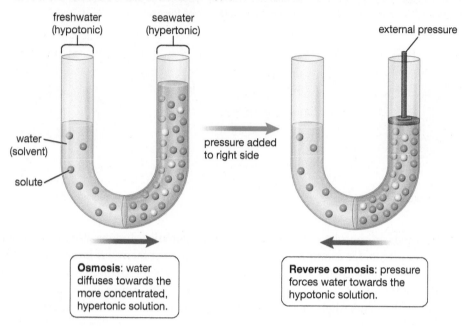

Figure 11.51 A Desalination Plant in Dubai.

Figure 11.52 A Patient Undergoes Kidney Dialysis.

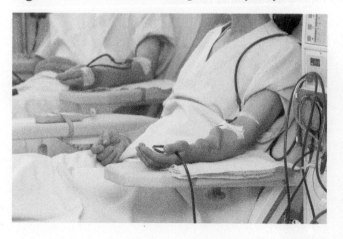

Advocates of the plant argue that it creates a drought-proof source of drinking water in drought-prone California. Opponents argue that the water is expensive to generate, uses too much energy to produce, and creates high-salt waste that can damage marine ecosystems.

Dialysis

The kidneys play an important role in our bodies, filtering waste solutes out of our blood for excretion in urine (see Fig. 11.21). When the kidneys stop functioning, waste products accumulate, and quickly become life threatening.

Dialysis is the process of using a semipermeable membrane to separate suspended colloidal particles from dissolved ions or molecules. Chemists often use dialysis in the lab to purify substances. And healthcare workers also use dialysis to purify blood for patients with kidney failure.

Patients with kidney issues typically undergo dialysis treatment three times a week (Figure 11.52). During treatment, healthcare providers connect patients to a machine that acts as an artificial kidney. The machine pumps the patient's blood through a series of tubes of permeable membranes. Waste products move through the membranes from the blood into an isotonic solution, the *dialysate*. The purified blood then returns to the patient (Figure 11.53).

Figure 11.53 Dialysis Machine.

Dialysis machines use semipermeable membranes to remove waste products from a patient's blood into an isotonic solution, the dialysate, before returning it to the body.

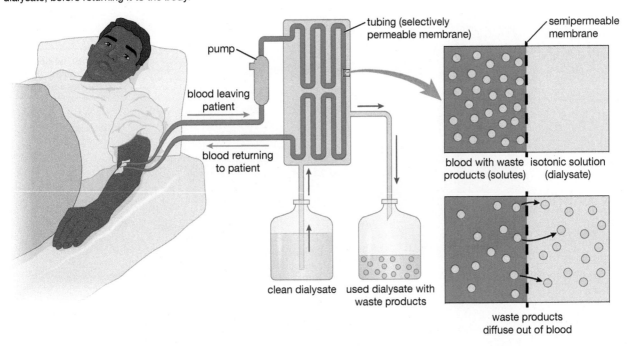

Solubility and the Blood-Brain Barrier

The brain also uses a semipermeable membrane to control what can enter and leave this delicate organ. This semipermeable membrane is the *blood–brain barrier (BBB)*. The BBB is made of a thin layer of cells tightly connected to one another (Figure 11.54). It protects our brains by preventing most toxins and bacteria from crossing into the brain from the bloodstream.

The BBB separates the circulating blood from the brain. It stops toxins and bacteria but allows water, specific gases, and fat-soluble molecules to enter by diffusion. Other molecules that are crucial to brain function, such as glucose and amino acids, also are able to cross the BBB membrane. A variety of medical conditions such as multiple sclerosis (MS), bacterial meningitis, Alzheimer's disease, AIDS, and brain trauma negatively affect the BBB.

A major challenge for the development and delivery of pharmaceutical drugs to the central nervous system for the treatment of numerous conditions is that the blood–brain barrier prevents the uptake of most pharmaceutical drugs. The majority of successful drugs are small or medium sized fat-soluble molecules that are able to cross the BBB by diffusion through the membrane. Predicting which molecules will and will not pass across the blood brain barrier is difficult and involves many factors. However, a general guideline is that molecules that have a molar mass of less than 400 g/mol, and form less than eight hydrogen bonds have a reasonable chance of crossing the blood brain barrier.

Figure 11.54 The Blood Brain Barrier (BBB).

The BBB is a special layer of cells that forms a semipermeable barrier that allows small molecules to diffuse into the brain while blocking the uptake of larger molecules.

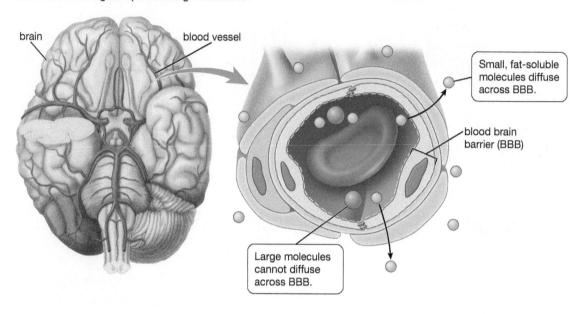

Quiz yourself on the content of this section: **Check 11.7** in the Pearson eText.

Chapter Summary

11.1 Liquids

Learning Objective: Describe the effects of intermolecular forces on the properties of liquids.

In the liquid state, molecules are much closer to each other than molecules in the gaseous state and are attracted to each other through intermolecular forces. These forces must be overcome for a liquid to convert to the gaseous state through evaporation (Figure 11.4). The pressure exerted by a vapor in equilibrium with its liquid form is vapor pressure. As the strength of intermolecular forces increases, vapor pressure decreases. Viscosity is a measure of a liquid's resistance to flow and increases as the strength of intermolecular forces increases. Intermolecular forces are also involved in a liquid's ability to dissolve substances. Water can interact with ionic compounds, for example, through ion-dipole forces (Figure 11.8). Water is the most common and essential liquid on Earth mostly due to its ability to form hydrogen bonds.

Key Terms

Ion-dipole
vapor pressure
viscosity

11.2   Solutions

Learning Objective: Explain how solutions form based on the structure of the solute and solvent components.

A solution is a homogeneous mixture of two or more substances. The substance present in the least amount in the solution is the solute, and the substance present in the majority is the solvent. A solution can be a solid dissolved in a liquid, a liquid dissolved in a liquid, or a gas dissolved in a liquid. In an aqueous solution, water is the solvent. The polarity of the water molecule allows it to readily dissolve polar substances (through dipole-dipole forces and hydrogen bonding) as well as ionic substances (through ion-dipole forces). Water therefore forms a broad range of solutions that support life on Earth. Colloids are mixtures, such as milk or blood, that are made up of larger particles evenly dispersed and not heavy enough to settle out.

VisibleChem Video 11.1: Ionic Compounds Dissociate into Ions in Water

VisibleChem Video 11.2: Compounds that Are Soluble in Water

VisibleChem Video 11.3: Nonpolar Compounds and Nonpolar Solvents

Key Terms

aqueous solution	emulsions	solute
colloids	insoluble	solution
dissociate	nonelectrolyte	solvent
dissolved gases	soluble	suspensions
electrolyte		

11.3   Solubility in the Human Body and the Environment

Learning Objective: Predict the solubility of a substance based on the polarity of molecules.

The concept "like dissolves like" allows us to make predictions about the solubility of molecules. As a general rule, water-soluble compounds contain one or more polar groups for every five or fewer nonpolar carbon atoms. In contrast, fat-soluble compounds tend to have fewer polar groups and larger nonpolar hydrocarbon regions. Whether a molecule, such as a vitamin, toxin, or drug, is primarily water-soluble or primarily fat-soluble plays a critical role in determining the physical location and biological activity of the molecule in our bodies and the environment. Toxins that are especially persistent, bioaccumulative, and toxic (PBTs) can have strong, negative effects in the environment and food chain (Figure 11.16). The solubility, chemical stability, and specific three-dimensional structure of a molecule dictate its bioavailability and overall function. Researchers focus on these attributes during the development of drug molecules in an effort to provide safe and effective medicines.

BioConnect 11.1: Solutions in our Bodies

Key Terms

fat-soluble
persistent bioaccumulative toxic substance (PBTs)
water-soluble

11.4   Factors Affecting Solubility

Learning Objective: Predict the solubility of specific solutes in specific solvents based on the effects of temperature and pressure.

The solubility of a substance is the amount of solute that dissolves in a given amount of solvent at a given temperature and pressure. If a solution has less than the maximum amount of solute dissolved, the solution is unsaturated. A solution that has the maximum amount of solute dissolved is saturated (Figure 11.24). If additional solute is added to a saturated solution, the additional substance remains undissolved. A supersaturated solution contains more solute than a saturated solution and can sometimes be formed by dissolving a solute at high temperatures allowing more solute to dissolve and cooling slowly. Solids are generally more soluble in a liquid solvent at high temperatures than low temperatures. In contrast, the solubility of gases decreases with increasing temperature. As temperature increases in a solution containing a dissolved gas, the gas molecules move more rapidly and more easily escape from the solution into the gas state, lowering solubility. Pressure has almost no effect on solubility of solids or liquids but has a strong effect on the solubility of gases. As pressure increases, the solubility of a gas increases (Figure 11.31). As pressure decreases, the solubility of a gas decreases. Henry's law states that the solubility of a gas in a liquid is directly proportional to the partial pressure of the gas over the liquid.

BioConnect 11.2: CO_2 in Our Oceans

Key Terms

Henry's law   saturated   supersaturated
recrystallizing   solubility   unsaturated

11.5 Solution Concentrations and Dilution

Learning Objective: Calculate the concentration of solutions and use solution concentrations as a conversion factor.

The concentration of a solution is the amount of solute dissolved in a certain amount of solution. Mass/volume percent (m/v%), Volume/volume percent (m/v%), molarity (*M*; mol/L), parts per million (ppm), and parts per billion (ppb) are all common ways to express concentrations as ratios of a certain amount of solute in a given amount of material such as a solvent. When a solution is diluted, the moles of solute in the concentrated solution are equal to the moles of solute in the diluted solution (Figure 11.43). The dilution process increases the volume of solvent, so the concentration of the sample decreases. We use the expression $M_1V_1 = M_2V_2$ for dilution calculations involving molarity. We use the general expression $C_1V_1 = C_2V_2$ more broadly for dilution calculations.

VisibleChem Video 11.4: Reporting Solution Concentration as a Percent

VisibleChem Video 11.5: Reporting Solution Concentration as Molarity (*M*)

VisibleChem Video 11.6: Solution Dilution Calculations

Key Terms

concentration   mass/volume percent (m/v%)   stock solutions
dilution   molarity (M)   volume/volume percent (v/v%)

Key Equations and Constants

$$\text{Volume/volume percent (v/v\%)} = \frac{\text{volume of solute}}{\text{volume of solution}} \times 100\%$$

$$\text{Mass/volume percent (m/v\%)} = \frac{\text{grams of solute}}{\text{milliliters of solution}} \times 100\%$$

$$\text{Molarity } (M) = \frac{\text{moles of solute}}{\text{liters of solution}} = \frac{\text{mol}}{\text{L}}$$

$$M_1V_1 = M_2V_2$$
$$C_1V_1 = C_2V_2$$

11.6 Colligative Properties

Learning Objective: Determine the effect of dissolved particles on the boiling point and freezing point of solutions.

Adding a solute to a solvent to prepare a solution changes several physical properties of the solvent. These colligative properties depend only on the concentration of solute particles in the solution. A solvent that contains a nonvolatile solute has a higher boiling point than the pure solvent. This is boiling point elevation. A solvent that contains a nonvolatile solute has a lower freezing point than the pure solvent. This is freezing point depression. Ionic substances separate into their component ions when dissolved in water to make aqueous solutions. The total number of moles of solute particles must be considered when calculating boiling point elevation or freezing point depression.

For example, one mole of NaCl (*s*) separates into two moles of aqueous ions when dissolved in water (one mole of Na$^+$ ions and one mole of Cl$^-$ ions).

Key Terms

boiling point elevation	freezing point depression	volatile
colligative properties	nonvolatile	

11.7 Osmosis and Dialysis

Learning Objective: Describe the process of osmosis and how osmosis functions in the cell and is related to dialysis.

Osmosis is the process by which water passes through a semipermeable membrane (such as a cell membrane) into a solution of higher solute concentration in order to equalize the solute concentrations on both sides of the membrane. The driving force (liquid pressure) associated with osmosis is dependent on solute concentration and temperature. The pressure that must be applied to a solution to prevent osmosis from occurring is the osmotic pressure. Two solutions with the same solute concentration are isotonic. A solution with a higher concentration of solute is hypertonic. A solution with lower solute concentration is

hypotonic. Water always diffuses across a membrane towards the hypertonic solution. The cells of living organisms are constantly regulating the amount of water relative to dissolved solutes in order to remain healthy. Reverse osmosis is a process used to produce fresh drinking water from salty water that utilizes physical pressure to reverse the natural flow of water in osmosis. Dialysis is the separation of suspended colloidal particles from dissolved ions or molecules using a semipermeable membrane. Dialysis is used to purify blood for patients with kidney failure, or in the laboratory to purify substances.

Video 11.1: Water Diffuses Across a Membrane Towards the Hypertonic Solution

Key Terms

dialysis	hypotonic	osmotic pressure
diffusion	isotonic	reverse osmosis
hypertonic	osmosis	semipermeable

 End-of-Chapter Quiz   Have you mastered the content of this chapter? Try the **End-of-Chapter Quiz** in the Pearson eText.

1. Which statement best defines vapor pressure?
   a) the standard pressure and temperature (STP) of a molar volume of pure gas
   b) the Dalton partial pressure value at 1.0 atmospheric of any normal gas
   c) the ratio of total pressure to the total volume of 1.0 mole of gas at the normal boiling point
   d) the pressure exerted above a liquid at equilibrium by gas molecules in a closed container

2. What intermolecular force is involved when ionic compounds (such as NaCl) in water dissolve to form a solution?
   a) dipole-dipole forces
   b) dipole-induced dipole forces
   c) hydrogen bonds
   d) ion-dipole forces

3. If a given liquid has a low vapor pressure relative to other liquids composed of molecules of similar size, what does that imply about the strength of the intermolecular forces in the low vapor pressure liquid?
   a) The intermolecular forces in the low vapor pressure liquid are relatively strong.
   b) The intermolecular forces in the low vapor pressure liquid are inversely related to the volume of the container.
   c) The intermolecular forces in the low vapor pressure liquid are relatively weak.
   d) The intermolecular forces in the low vapor pressure liquid are not different in strength because vapor pressure is not dependent on the strength of intermolecular forces.

4. Which is the best definition of the *solute* in a homogeneous solution?
   a) the substance that is the most polar
   b) the substance present in the least amount
   c) the substance with the highest vapor pressure
   d) the substance present in the majority

5. What type of solutes dissolve best in polar solvents?
   a) polar and ionic solutes
   b) nonpolar and viscous solutes
   c) immiscible and nonvolatile solutes
   d) high molecular weight and high vapor pressure solutes

6. Methamphetamine (also known as "meth") is a highly addictive stimulant drug that users snort, smoke, or inject. Unfortunately, meth, alcohol, and most drugs can pass to babies through breast milk, causing developmental disorders, addiction, and a range of negative health issues for children. Which numbered shaded region(s) of the methamphetamine molecule contribute(s) to fat-solubility?

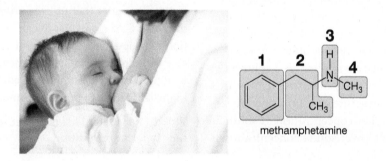

methamphetamine

   a) regions 2, 3, and 4 only
   b) region 3 only
   c) regions 1, 2, and 4
   d) region 1 only

7. The blood–brain barrier (BBB) is a semipermeable membrane that selectively regulates the entry of substances into the brain from the blood in order to protect the brain. By separating the circulating blood from the brain, the BBB allows water and specific gases, and fat-soluble molecules to enter by diffusion, and at the same time selectively transports other molecules that are crucial to brain function. As a result, the BBB presents a major challenge for the delivery of pharmaceutical drugs because it blocks the entrance of most pharmaceutical drugs. The THC molecule (active ingredient in marijuana) is a fat-soluble drug. As the liver processes THC in the body, a —COOH (carboxylic acid) group is added to the THC molecule. How does the solubility of THC compare to THC—COOH in the urine? Both molecules are shown here.

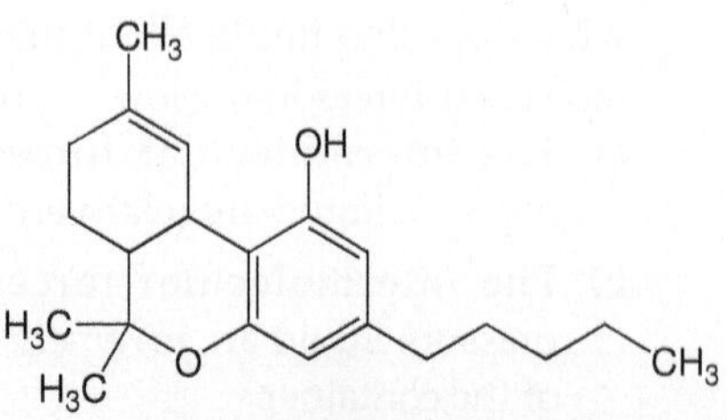

THC molecule

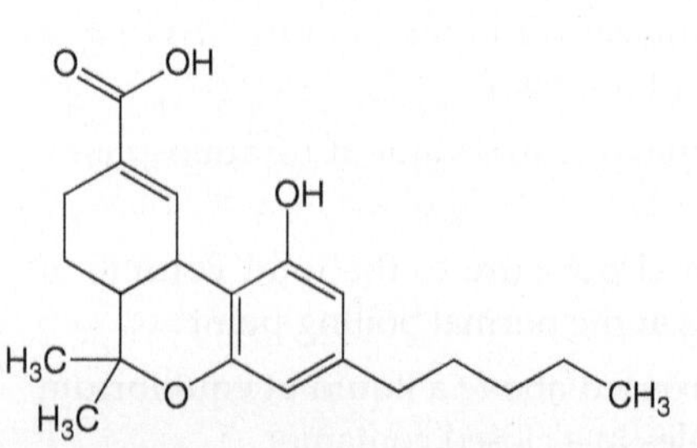

THC-COOH molecule

   a) The THC—COOH molecule is less soluble in urine than THC.
   b) The THC—COOH molecule has the same solubility in urine as THC.
   c) The THC—COOH molecule is more soluble in urine than THC.
   d) Solubility of the THC—COOH molecule in urine cannot be compared to THC because they are two different molecules.

8. Each molecule shown here has biological importance. Dopamine is a neurotransmitter, sucrose is table sugar, and testosterone is a hormone. Using your knowledge of polarity, the concept of like-dissolves-like, and the relative ratio of polar regions compared to nonpolar regions within each molecule, rank the relative water solubility of these three molecules from least soluble to most soluble.

dopamine   sucrose   testosterone

a) Dopamine is least soluble, sucrose is intermediate, and testosterone is the most soluble.

b) Sucrose is least soluble, testosterone is intermediate, and dopamine is the most soluble.

c) Testosterone is least soluble, sucrose is intermediate, and dopamine is the most soluble.

d) Testosterone is least soluble, dopamine is intermediate, and sucrose is the most soluble.

---

9. Which action increases the solubility of a typical salt in water?
a) decreasing the amount of water
b) increasing the temperature of the water
c) decreasing the temperature of the water
d) increasing the amount of salt

10. Many large fish live in cold water. Which of the following is a possible explanation for this preference?
a) Cold water has a larger molar mass than warm water has, which helps the larger fish survive.
b) Cold water dissolves more solid solutes than warm water does, which helps the larger fish survive.
c) Cold water mixes better with other liquids than warm water does, which helps the larger fish survive.
d) Cold water contains more dissolved oxygen than warm water and larger fish may require a greater amount of oxygen than smaller fish.

11. What happens to the mass/volume percent composition (m/v%) of an aqueous solution containing a nonvolatile solute if some of the water is boiled away?
a) The mass percent composition of the solution remains unchanged since mass/volume percent (m/v%) = grams solute/milliliters of solution × 100%.
b) The mass percent composition of the solution decreases since mass/volume percent (m/v%) = grams solute/milliliters of solution × 100%.
c) The mass percent composition of the solution cannot be predicted unless values are given to use in the calculation: mass/volume percent (m/v%) = grams solute/milliliters of solution × 100%.
d) The mass percent composition of the solution increases since mass/volume percent (m/v%) = grams solute/milliliters of solution × 100%.

12. A solution is prepared by dissolving 25.0 grams glucose in enough water to produce 525 mL of solution. What is the mass/volume % concentration of glucose in the solution?
a) 21.0% (m/v%)
b) 47.6% (m/v%)
c) 4.76×10^{-2}% (m/v%)
d) 4.76% (m/v%)

13. The drug Tegretol (also known as carbamazepine) helps patients manage schizophrenia and epileptic seizures. The drug is available in liquid form at a concentration of 100 mg/5 mL. What is this concentration expressed as a mass/volume %?
a) 2% (m/v%)
b) 20% (m/v%)
c) 5% (m/v%)
d) 2000% (m/v%)

14. Hydrogen peroxide (H_2O_2) is a disinfectant that is effective against a broad-range of viruses, bacteria, and yeasts. Solutions of hydrogen peroxide often come in bottles containing 3% (v/v%) H_2O_2 in water. How many milliliters of hydrogen peroxide are in 25 mL of a 3.0% (v/v%) solution? Express your answer with two significant figures.
a) 75 mL
b) 0.75 mL
c) 8.3 mL
d) 12 mL

15. Diazepam (Valium) is a drug that produces a calming effect. It is used to treat anxiety disorders, alcohol withdrawal symptoms, and muscle spasms. A nurse is asked to measure out 75.0 mg (7.50×10^{-2} g) of diazepam on a laboratory scale and dissolve it in enough IV saline solution to prepare 25.0 ml of a diazepam solution for a patient. What is the molarity of the drug solution that the nurse is asked to prepare? The molar mass of diazepam is 284.7 g/mol. Express your answer in scientific notation with three significant figures.

a) $1.05 \times 10^{-2} \ M$

b) $3.00 \times 10^3 \ M$

c) $8.54 \times 10^2 \ M$

d) $1.05 \times 10^1 \ M$

16. What happens to the molarity of a solution if you increase the amount of solute?

a) The molarity of the solution decreases because the moles of solute per liter of solution decreases.

b) The molarity of the solution increases because the moles of solute per liter of solution increases.

c) The molarity of the solution is unchanged because molarity is the ratio of the moles of solute per liter of solution.

d) The impact on the molarity of the solution cannot be predicted without being given the values to calculate the molarity.

17. Vancomycin is a commonly prescribed antibiotic used to treat a range of bacterial infections. For serious infections, vancomycin is often delivered through an IV bag to patients in the hospital. How many milliliters of a 50. mg/mL stock solution of vancomycin does a nurse need to add to an IV bag in order to prepare 250 mL of an 8.0 mg/mL vancomycin IV solution for her patient? Express your answer with two significant figures.

a) $2.5 \times 10^{-2} \ mL$

b) $1.6 \times 10^2 \ mL$

c) 40. mL

d) $1.0 \times 10^5 \ mL$

18. What is the boiling point of a solution prepared from 2.3 mol of KCl in 1.00 kg of water? Note that when dissolved in water, KCl separates into K^+ ions and Cl^- ions. Express your answer to the nearest tenth of a degree Celsius.

a) 97.7 °C

b) 102.3 °C

c) 101.2 °C

d) 2.3 °C

19. Select the correct statement about the freezing point of blood compared to the freezing point of drinking water.

a) The freezing point of blood is higher than the freezing point of drinking water because drinking water is more pure.

b) The freezing point of blood is lower than the freezing point of drinking water because the molar mass of blood is lower than the molar mass of water.

c) The freezing point of blood is lower than the freezing point of drinking water because blood contains a higher concentration of dissolved substances than drinking water.

d) The freezing point of blood is higher than the freezing point of drinking water because blood contains a higher concentration of dissolved substances in it than drinking water.

20. Why does the solution used for a patient undergoing kidney dialysis treatment contain isotonic NaCl, KCl, and glucose instead of just pure water?

a) Pure water is more easily contaminated by bacteria and viruses than a solution of NaCl, KCl, and glucose.

b) The solution of NaCl, KCl, and glucose boils at a lower temperature than pure water, which helps the patient stay warm during the procedure.

c) The solution of NaCl, KCl, and glucose is hypotonic, so it keeps the blood hypertonic during the procedure.

d) The solution of NaCl, KCl, and glucose is isotonic so that it does not create blood solute imbalances that can stress the blood cells, tissues, or other organs in the body.

Chapter 12
Acids and Bases

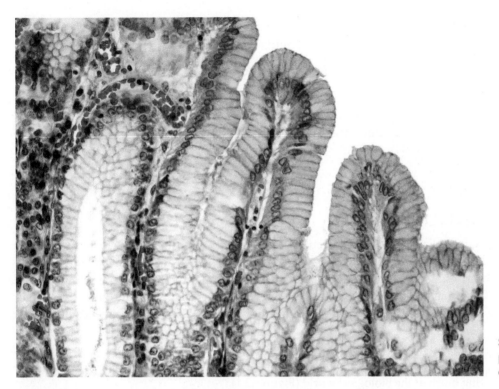

Specialized cells in the stomach produce strong acids to digest our food.

Chapter Outline

Learning Objectives

12.1 Identify and define acids, bases, and conjugate acid-base pairs.

12.2 Explain the difference between strong and weak acids and bases.

12.3 Write the acid dissociation constant expression (K_a) and relate it to acid strength.

12.4 Use the water dissociation constant (K_w) and ion concentrations to determine if a solution is acidic, basic, or neutral.

12.5 Calculate pH to report the acidity or basicity of a solution from 0–14.

12.6 Write balanced equations for neutralization reactions and recognize reactions of acids with bicarbonate and carbonate.

12.7 Calculate the molarity of an acid or base solution from titration measurements.

12.8 Explain the role of the weak acid and conjugate base in a buffer and calculate the buffer's pH.

Introduction

Life on Earth involves molecules, ions, and other substances interacting with each other every second of every day in an impressive range of chemical and physical processes. As we discussed in Chapter 11, water plays a vital role in providing a fluid environment to support these movements and interactions within aqueous solutions. Water also reacts with itself and other substances to form two of the most important ions in nature: H^+ and OH^- ions. These ions play a significant role in acid-base chemistry. In this chapter, we discuss what acids and bases are. We then examine how acids, bases, and water interact within aqueous solutions and govern the chemistry underlying much of the biological world (Figure 12.1).

Figure 12.1 Acids and Bases in Our Water-Based World.

A) Hydrochloric acid in our stomach helps us digest the food we eat but can cause indigestion. Many people treat indigestion with antacids.
B) A healthcare worker administers lactic acid in the form of lactate in an IV solution to help patients maintain blood glucose levels.
C) Bases and fats are the key ingredients in common hand soaps.

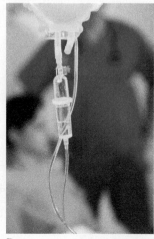

A　　　　　　　　　　B　　　　　　　　　　C

12.1 Defining Acids and Bases

The first scientists to define **acids** described them simply as substances that produce hydrogen ions (H^+) when dissolved in water. For example, when the compound HCl is dissolved in water, H^+ and Cl^- ions form in the solution. Therefore, HCl is an acid (Figure 12.2). A hydrogen ion (H^+) is a hydrogen atom that has lost its one electron, which leaves it with just one proton. For this reason, we often refer to a hydrogen ion as a proton.

Hydrogen ions are highly reactive. A hydrogen ion rapidly binds to water to form the **hydronium ion (H_3O^+)**.

$$H\text{—}\overset{..}{\underset{H}{O}}: \;+\; H^+ \;\longrightarrow\; \left[H\text{—}\overset{..}{\underset{H}{O}}\text{—}H \right]^+$$

| water | hydrogen ion | hydronium ion |

We use the general formula HA to refer to any acid. We can use either H^+ or H_3O^+ to represent the product that forms when any acid dissolves in water. The two equations we show here both represent the ionization (the dissociation into ions) of an acid in water. The equations are interchangeable. Notice that when we use H^+ in the equation, we omit water. When we use H_3O^+, on the other hand, we include water on the reactant side of the equation.

$$HA(aq) \;\rightarrow\; H^+(aq) \;+\; A^-(aq)$$

acid   hydrogen ion

When water is directly specified, the equation becomes:

$$HA(aq) + H_2O(l) \;\rightarrow\; H_3O^+(aq) + A^-(aq)$$

acid   water   hydronium ion

Acids

Acids have a sour taste and are very reactive compounds. Acids are common in nature. Figure 12.3 illustrates three common acids that impact humans on a daily basis. Notice that each acid produces H^+ in aqueous solution.

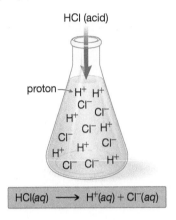

Figure 12.2 Hydrochloric Acid. HCl, an acid, produces hydrogen ions (H^+) when dissolved in water.

$$HCl(aq) \;\longrightarrow\; H^+(aq) + Cl^-(aq)$$

Figure 12.3 Three Common Acids in Everyday Life.

hydrochloric acid
Hydrochloric acid (HCl) is a corrosive substance that has many applications in industry, is found in numerous household cleaning products, and plays an important role in the digestion in our stomachs. HCl, like many other strong acids, can dissolve metals and mineral deposits.

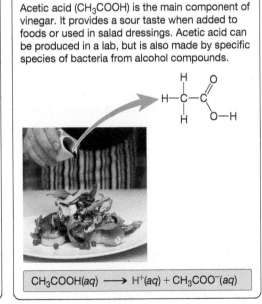

$$HCl(aq) \;\longrightarrow\; H^+(aq) + Cl^-(aq)$$

acetic acid
Acetic acid (CH_3COOH) is the main component of vinegar. It provides a sour taste when added to foods or used in salad dressings. Acetic acid can be produced in a lab, but is also made by specific species of bacteria from alcohol compounds.

$$CH_3COOH(aq) \;\longrightarrow\; H^+(aq) + CH_3COO^-(aq)$$

citric acid
Citric acid ($C_6H_8O_7$) is found naturally in citrus fruits such as oranges, lemons, and limes. Citric acid can be isolated from these fruits or produced in a laboratory. This weak acid is used as an additive to beverages, other food products, and in household cleaners.

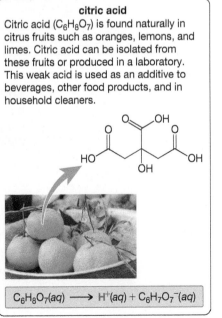

$$C_6H_8O_7(aq) \;\longrightarrow\; H^+(aq) + C_6H_7O_7^-(aq)$$

Bases

Bases are compounds that form a metal ion and **hydroxide ion (OH⁻)** when dissolved in water (Figure 12.4). Most bases form from group 1A and group 2A metals (LiOH, NaOH, KOH, and $Ca(OH)_2$). These hydroxide bases have many uses; they have a bitter taste and can be slippery to the touch (Figure 12.5).

Brønsted-Lowry Definition of Acids and Bases

In the 1920s, chemists Johannes Brønsted and Thomas Lowry refined the definition of acids and bases. According to the Brønsted-Lowry definition, an acid is a substance that donates a proton (H^+), and a base is a substance that accepts a proton (H^+).

> **Brønsted-Lowry acid: donates H^+**
>
> **Brønsted-Lowry base: accepts H^+**

This definition focuses on the transfer of H^+ ions in a chemical reaction between an acid and a base. For example, when the acid HCl dissolves in water, it donates a proton. The proton is transferred from HCl to H_2O (Figure 12.6). Water is the Brønsted-Lowry base in this reaction because water accepts a proton to produce hydronium ions (H_3O^+).

This reaction is one of the many chemical reactions that occurs in our stomach. Stomach acid is a digestive fluid composed of HCl and other compounds that aid in digestion.

Figure 12.4 Sodium Hydroxide in Water.

A base produces OH⁻ in an aqueous solution.

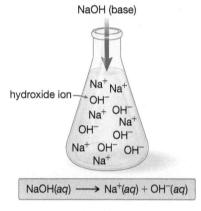

$$NaOH(aq) \longrightarrow Na^+(aq) + OH^-(aq)$$

Figure 12.5 Two Common Bases in Everyday Life.

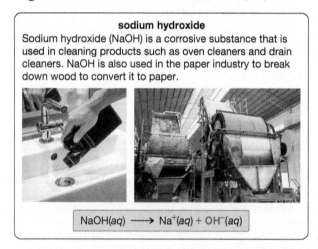

sodium hydroxide
Sodium hydroxide (NaOH) is a corrosive substance that is used in cleaning products such as oven cleaners and drain cleaners. NaOH is also used in the paper industry to break down wood to convert it to paper.

$$NaOH(aq) \longrightarrow Na^+(aq) + OH^-(aq)$$

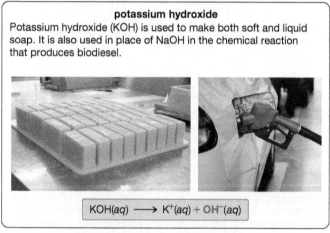

potassium hydroxide
Potassium hydroxide (KOH) is used to make both soft and liquid soap. It is also used in place of NaOH in the chemical reaction that produces biodiesel.

$$KOH(aq) \longrightarrow K^+(aq) + OH^-(aq)$$

Figure 12.6 The Brønsted-Lowry Acid, Hydrogen Chloride.

Brønsted-Lowry acids donate protons. HCl is a Brønsted-Lowry acid found in our stomach that aids in digestion of proteins. Hydrogen chloride accepts a proton from water forming Cl⁻ and hydronium (H_3O^+) ions.

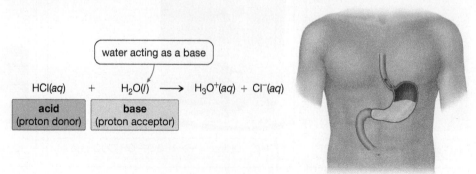

water acting as a base

$$HCl(aq) + H_2O(l) \longrightarrow H_3O^+(aq) + Cl^-(aq)$$

acid (proton donor) base (proton acceptor)

Figure 12.7 The Brønsted-Lowry Base, Ammonia.

Brønsted-Lowry bases accept protons. Ammonia (NH_3) is a Brønsted-Lowry base that farmers use as a fertilizer. They directly apply ammonia to fields using a large tank pulled behind a tractor. A chemical reaction occurs as NH_3 reacts with the water in moist soil. Ammonia accepts a proton donated by the water molecule, forming NH_4^+ and hydroxide (OH^-) ions.

A Brønsted-Lowry base is a proton acceptor. According to the Brønsted-Lowry definition, the base category includes compounds such as ammonia (NH_3). In water, ammonia (NH_3) accepts a proton from H_2O, producing ammonium (NH_4^+) and hydroxide (OH^-) as products (Figure 12.7). In this case, water functions as the Brønsted-Lowry acid by donating an H^+.

Notice that when water is in the presence of an acid, it acts as a base. In the presence of a base, however, water acts as an acid. A molecule that can act as both an acid and a base is **amphoteric**.

Apply what you have just learned: **Practice 12.1** in the Pearson eText.

Conjugate Acid-Base Pairs

When a base accepts a proton from an acid, it becomes the **conjugate acid** of the original base (Figure 12.8). The only difference between a base and its conjugate acid is one proton.

Figure 12.8 Conjugate Acid-Base Pairs.

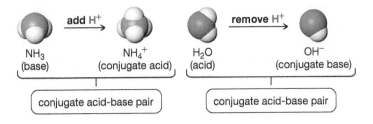

Notice that when a base accepts a proton, the charge increases by one in the positive direction. For example, NH_3 the base, becomes the conjugate acid NH_4^+. Similarly, when the acid in the reaction donates a proton, it becomes the **conjugate base** of the original acid. When an acid donates a proton, the charge increases by one in the negative direction. For example, H_2O, the acid, becomes the conjugate base OH^-. An acid and its conjugate base and a base and its conjugate acid are **conjugate acid-base pairs**.

We represent this pairing using an equation. In this reaction, ammonia (NH_3) and the ammonium ion (NH_4^+) are a conjugate acid-base pair, and water and hydroxide ion (OH^-) are a conjugate acid-base pair. In both cases, the two components of the pair differ by one hydrogen atom.

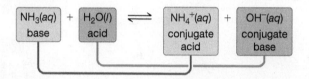

Another example is the reaction of sulfuric acid (H_2SO_4) with water. In this case, sulfuric acid donates a proton and the conjugate base that forms is HSO_4^-. Water, in this reaction, is the base. It pairs with the hydronium ion (H_3O^+) as the conjugate acid.

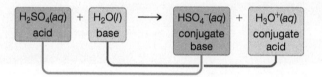

Notice that after a neutral compound loses a proton, it has a -1 charge. In the example we just discussed, H_2SO_4, converts to HSO_4^-. Similarly, after a neutral compound gains a proton, it has a $+1$ charge. The conversion of the neutral water molecule (H_2O) to its conjugate acid, the positive hydronium ion H_3O^+, illustrates how the gain of a proton results in a positively charged ion.

Apply what you have just learned: **Practice 12.2 and 12.3** in the Pearson eText.

Predict answers and see step-by-step solutions: **Learn 12.1:** Identifying Conjugate Acid-Base Pairs in the Pearson eText.

Apply what you have just learned: **Practice 12.4** in the Pearson eText.

The Carboxylic Acid Group

Many acids in nature contain a **carboxylic acid group** (—**COOH**), which is composed of one carbon atom, two oxygen atoms, and a hydrogen atom (Figure 12.9). This collection of atoms is found in small biological molecules such as acetic acid and in large biomolecules such as fatty acids and proteins. Figure 12.9 illustrates the structure of a carboxylic acid group as well as two examples of acids that contain this group.

Figure 12.9 The Carboxylic Acid Group.

Acetic acid and lactic acid are two common carboxylic acid containing molecules.

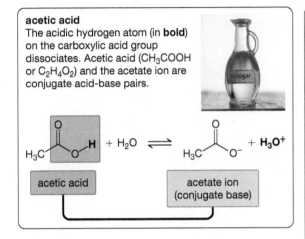

the carboxylic acid group
The carbon atom in this group is bonded to two oxygen atoms, one with a double bond and the other with a single bond. The oxygen with the single bond to carbon is also bonded to a hydrogen atom. It is the hydrogen atom that is acidic and is therefore released as an H⁺ in aqueous solution.

acetic acid
The acidic hydrogen atom (in **bold**) on the carboxylic acid group dissociates. Acetic acid (CH_3COOH or $C_2H_4O_2$) and the acetate ion are conjugate acid-base pairs.

acetic acid → acetate ion (conjugate base)

lactic acid
In water, the acidic hydrogen atom (in **bold**) on the carboxylic acid group of lactic acid also dissociates. Lactic acid and the lactate ion are conjugate acid-base pairs.

lactic acid → lactate ion (conjugate base)

Lactic acid is perhaps best known as the purported cause of the burn and soreness felt in our muscles after vigorous exercise. Recent research, however, suggests that lactate may actually provide critical fuel for working muscles. And the soreness we experience is probably due to inflammation and damage to the muscle fibers during intense exercise rather than a "lactic acid burn."

If you enjoy a cup of yogurt after a good workout, you've also got lactic acid to thank. Bacteria produce lactic acid from the sugar in milk. The proteins in the milk denature in the acid, contributing to the creamy texture of yogurt.

Apply what you have just learned: **Practice 12.5** in the Pearson eText.

Quiz yourself on the content of this section: **Check 12.1** in the Pearson eText.

12.2 Acid and Base Strength

There are clear differences among acids. This is especially true when we compare acid compounds by their strength. Battery acid, for example, can cause serious damage to human skin, whereas vinegar is not generally harmful. The same is true for bases—there are both strong and weak bases. Strong bases are also known to cause serious damage to human health upon exposure.

What determines how strong or weak an acid or base is? We classify acids and bases as strong or weak based on the extent to which they break apart into ions in water or dissociate. When a strong acid dissolves in water, 100% of the acid dissociates. A single forward arrow represents the dissociation of a strong acid in water.

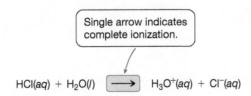

Single arrow indicates complete ionization.

$HCl(aq) + H_2O(l) \longrightarrow H_3O^+(aq) + Cl^-(aq)$

Table 12.1 Strong and Weak Acids and their Conjugate Bases.

Only six acids are strong. All other acids are weak. The stronger the acid, the weaker the conjugate base. The weaker the acid, the stronger the conjugate base.

Acid		Conjugate base
strong acids		
hydroiodic acid	HI	I^-
hydrobromic acid	HBr	Br^-
perchloric acid	$HClO_4$	ClO_4^-
hydrochloric acid	HCl	Cl^-
sulfuric acid	H_2SO_4	HSO_4^-
nitric acid	HNO_3	NO_3^-
hydronium ion	H_3O^+	H_2O
weak acids		
phosphoric acid	H_3PO_4	$H_2PO_4^-$
hydrofluoric acid	HF	F^-
acetic acid	CH_3COOH	CH_3COO^-
carbonic acid	H_2CO_3	HCO_3^-
ammonium ion	NH_4^+	NH_3
hydrocyanic acid	HCN	CN^-
water	H_2O	OH^-

increasing acid strength (left arrow, upward)

increasing base strength (right arrow, downward)

When a strong acid dissociates, a weak conjugate base forms (Table 12.1). This is because a strong acid readily donates a proton, forming a conjugate base that has only a slight attraction for H^+. Because of this conjugate base's weak attraction, it is a weak base.

A weak acid, in contrast to a strong acid, only ionizes (dissociates into ions) slightly in water. It forms only a small amount of H_3O^+ ions. The reaction of a weak acid, such as HF, in water creates a solution mixture that proceeds towards equilibrium but favors the reactants. A double arrow indicates a reversible process, and in this case, favors the reactants–the substances that have not ionized. When a weak acid dissociates, a strong conjugate base forms (See Table 12.1).

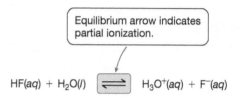

Equilibrium arrow indicates partial ionization.

$$HF(aq) + H_2O(l) \rightleftharpoons H_3O^+(aq) + F^-(aq)$$

Base Strength

Many people associate acids with the potential for burns but may overlook the reactivity of bases (Figure 12.10).

Like strong acids, strong bases ionize completely in water, whereas weak bases (like weak acids) only slightly ionize (see Table 12.2). Metal hydroxides, such as NaOH, are strong bases. They completely dissociate to produce metal ions (Na^+) and hydroxide ions (OH^-). A single arrow indicates this reaction only proceeds in the forward direction.

$$NaOH(aq) \rightarrow Na^+(aq) + OH^-(aq)$$

Figure 12.10 A Train Derails Spilling a Strong Base.

In 2016 a train carrying the strong base, sodium hydroxide, derailed in Washington D.C. Manufacturers use sodium hydroxide to produce a variety of products including paper and detergents. After the crash, a tanker car carrying 15,500 gallons of the base began leaking. Emergency responders (inset) must quickly assess the hazards of a chemical leak in order to protect both the responders and the public.

Weak bases react with water in a reversible reaction that produces an equilibrium mixture of reactants and products. At equilibrium, a solution containing a weak base consists of mainly the base compound that has not dissociated into ions. Weak bases are therefore weak electrolytes that are poor proton acceptors.

$$NH_3(aq) + H_2O(l) \rightleftharpoons NH_4^+(aq) + OH^-(aq)$$

Ammonia (NH_3), for example, is a weak base that ionizes to produce some OH^-, but mostly remains intact as NH_3.

To continue exploring acid and base strength select VisibleChem Videos 12.1 and 12.2.

Table 12.2 Select Strong and Weak Bases.

Strong Bases: completely dissociate to produce OH⁻	
lithium hydroxide	LiOH
sodium hydroxide	NaOH
potassium hydroxide	KOH
calcium hydroxide	$Ca(OH)_2$
strontium hydroxide	$Sr(OH)_2$
barium hydroxide	$Ba(OH)_2$
Weak Bases: only partially react with water to produce OH⁻	
ammonia	NH_3
methylamine	CH_3NH_2

Watch this concept come to life: **VisibleChem Video 12.1:** Strong vs. Weak Acids and Bases and **VisibleChem Video 12.2:** Predicting the Direction of Equilibrium using Acid and Base Strength in the Pearson eText.

Apply what you have just learned: **Practice 12.6 and 12.7** in the Pearson eText.

Diprotic Acids

Some acids, called **diprotic acids**, have two H^+ ions to donate. The two H^+ ions dissociate from a diprotic acid individually, one at a time. Sulfuric acid (H_2SO_4), for example, is a diprotic acid with two H^+ ions to donate. Phosphoric acid (H_3PO_4) is a **triprotic acid** because it has three H^+ ions to donate.

Carbonic acid (H_2CO_3) is a weak diprotic acid. It donates the first H^+ to water to produce the hydronium ion (H_3O^+) and the bicarbonate ion (HCO_3^-). The bicarbonate ion (HCO_3^-) is also a weak acid. Thus, a second dissociation takes place to produce another hydronium ion and the carbonate ion (CO_3^{2-}; Figure 12.11).

$$H_2CO_3(aq) + H_2O(l) \rightarrow HCO_3^-(aq) + H_3O^+(aq)$$
carbonic   bicarbonate
acid   ion

$$HCO_3^-(aq) + H_2O(l) \rightarrow CO_3^{2-}(aq) + H_3O^+(aq)$$
bicarbonate   carbonate
ion   ion

Because carbonic acid is a weak diprotic acid to begin with, when it dissolves in water, a complex equilibrium mixture forms that contains all the compounds and ions shown in Figure 12.11.

This is the chemistry at work when CO_2 gas from the atmosphere dissolves in ocean water. As more and more CO_2 is released into the atmosphere, more carbonic acid forms in the ocean—leading to increased ocean acidification (Figure 12.12). Recall

Figure 12.11 Carbonic Acid, Bicarbonate Ion, and Carbonate Ion.

Carbonic acid is a diprotic acid that can donate two hydrogen ions.

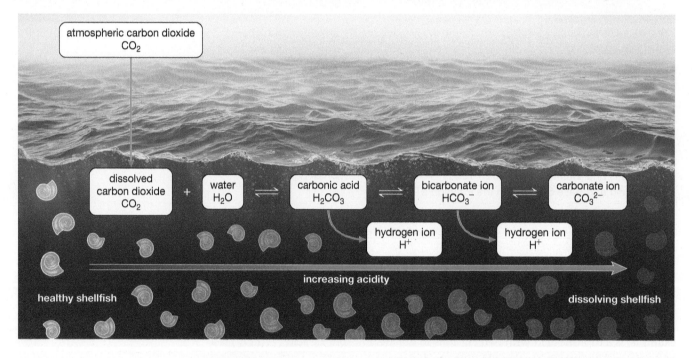

H_2CO_3
carbonic acid

HCO_3^-
bicarbonate ion

CO_3^{2-}
carbonate ion

Figure 12.12 The Chemistry of Ocean Acidification.

A reaction takes place between carbon dioxide and water to produce the diprotic acid, carbonic acid, which then dissociates to produce a complex mixture of ions (HCO_3^-, CO_3^{2-}, and H^+). As CO_2 increases in the atmosphere above the ocean the amount of carbon dioxide that dissolves in the oceans increases and shifts the equilibrium towards a more acidic solution. The increasing acidity can dissolve the shells of marine organisms.

from BioConnect 11.2 that the ocean is a delicate ecosystem that is home to a vast array of marine species. Many of these species are adversely impacted by the increased levels of acid in the ocean.

 Apply what you have just learned: **Practice 12.8** in the Pearson eText.

Quiz yourself on the content of this section: **Check 12.2** in the Pearson eText.

12.3 Acid Dissociation Constants

Strong acids completely ionize in water, and therefore we use a single arrow in these reactions, and do not consider equilibrium. The reactions of weak acids in water, however, do reach equilibrium because only a fraction of the weak acid molecules at any given time have dissociated into ions. For this reason, each weak acid has equilibrium constant, K. Recall from Chapter 9 that the equilibrium constant expression is the ratio of the concentration of the products to the concentration of the reactants. (Recall also

Figure 12.13 Acid Dissociation Constants Guide Treatment After Exposure.
Hydrofluoric acid (HF) is found in a variety of commercial products including rust remover. This patient has tissue damage from exposure to a rust removal product containing 10% HF. Both the acidic protons and the reactive fluoride ions released as the acid dissociates damage tissues.

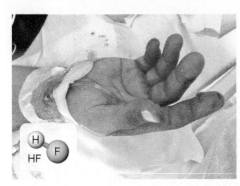

that the square brackets represent concentration.) In the case of a weak acid the equilibrium constant is the **acid dissociation constant, K_a**.

We quantify K_a by first writing out the acid dissociation constant expression for a weak acid (represented by HA). The acid dissociation constant expression is the concentration of the products divided by the concentration of the weak acid. Recall from Section 9.4 that water is a pure liquid with constant concentration. For this reason, we omit water from the expression.

$$HA(aq) + H_2O(l) \rightarrow H_3O^+(aq) + A^-(aq)$$
weak acid

$$K_a = \frac{[H_3O^+][A^-]}{[HA]}$$
acid dissociation constant expression

Acid dissociation constants (K_a) are often included in resources for emergency medical personnel and poison control centers. The K_a values provide a quick measure of an acid's strength and help healthcare workers determine the best treatment (Figure 12.13).

Calculating and Comparing Acid Dissociation Constants

Each weak acid dissociates to a different extent and K_a values differ from acid to acid. The stronger the acid, the higher the concentration of products and the larger the value of K_a (See Table 12.3).

For example, the K_a value for formic acid ($HCHO_2$), an acid that can be found in ant and bee venom, is 1.8×10^{-4} (Figure 12.14). Notice that this number is quite a bit less than 1, indicating that the reactants are heavily favored. In other words, there is more reactant, formic acid, present at equilibrium than the ions on the product side.

$$HCHO_2(aq) + H_2O(l) \rightleftharpoons H_3O^+(aq) + CHO_2^-(aq)$$
reactants favored
$$K_a \ll 1$$
$$K_a = \frac{[H_3O^+][CHO_2^-]}{[HCHO_2]} = 1.8 \times 10^{-4}$$

Table 12.3 K_a Values for Selected Weak Acids.

Acid		K_a
phosphoric acid	H_3PO_4	7.5×10^{-3}
nitrous acid	HNO_2	4.5×10^{-4}
hydrofluoric acid	HF	3.5×10^{-4}
formic acid	$HCHO_2$	1.8×10^{-4}
acetic acid	CH_3COOH	1.8×10^{-5}
carbonic acid	H_2CO_3	4.3×10^{-7}
hydrosulfuric acid	H_2S	9.1×10^{-8}
dihydrogen phosphate ion	$H_2PO_4^-$	6.2×10^{-8}
hydrocyanic acid	HCN	4.9×10^{-10}
bicarbonate ion	HCO_3^-	5.6×10^{-11}
hydrogen phosphate	HPO_4^{2-}	2.2×10^{-13}

increasing acid strength

Figure 12.14 Some Species of Ants Produce Formic Acid.

Formic acid is in ant and bee venom, as well as the fine hairs of stinging nettles. When stings occur, the insects inject the venom containing the formic acid into the victim, causing a burning sensation.

HCHO₂
formic acid

Predict answers and see step-by-step solutions: **Learn 12.2:** Writing an Acid Dissociation Constant (K_a) Expression in the Pearson eText.

Apply what you have just learned: **Practice 12.9** in the Pearson eText.

Predict answers and see step-by-step solutions: **Learn 12.3:** Using K_a Values to Determine Relative Acid Strength in the Pearson eText.

Apply what you have just learned: **Practice 12.10** in the Pearson eText.

Quiz yourself on the content of this section: **Check 12.3** in the Pearson eText.

12.4 Pure Water Ionization

Recall that water can act as either a Brønsted-Lowry acid or a Brønsted-Lowry base. In pure water, two molecules of water undergo a reaction in which an H⁺ transfers from one water molecule to another. This forward reaction involves one molecule of water acting as a base, and the other water molecule acting as an acid. The forward reaction produces H_3O^+ and OH^-. The reverse reaction also occurs to re-form two water molecules. The equilibrium process for this reaction heavily favors the reactants (H_2O) producing only very small amounts of product (H_3O^+ and OH^-). In other words, pure water dissociates only a very small amount. We represent this reaction with the equation shown in Figure 12.15. The double arrow indicates that equilibrium is ultimately established.

The equilibrium constant expression for the ionization of water reaction is the ratio of the concentration of the products to the concentration of the reactants. The specific equilibrium constant for this reaction is the **water dissociation constant**, K_w.

Figure 12.15 Ionization of Water.

Water can act as both an acid and a base. The reactants, H_2O, are heavily favored in equilibrium.

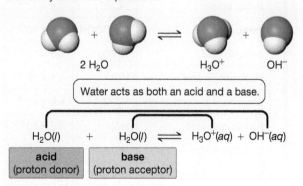

$$2\,H_2O \rightleftharpoons H_3O^+ + OH^-$$

Water acts as both an acid and a base.

$$H_2O(l) + H_2O(l) \rightleftharpoons H_3O^+(aq) + OH^-(aq)$$

| **acid** (proton donor) | **base** (proton acceptor) | |

Notice that we exclude water from the expression, because it is a pure liquid. This leaves only the ions on the product side in the expression for K_w.

$$K_w = [H_3O^+][OH^-]$$

Neutral, Acidic, or Basic?

Measuring the $[H_3O^+]$ and $[OH^-]$ of solutions is necessary in many fields including medicine, winemaking, and agriculture. To determine these concentrations, we need the equilibrium constant for the ionization of water (K_w). For example, a physician may assess the $[H_3O^+]$ and $[OH^-]$ of a patient's urine to determine the likelihood of a patient developing kidney stones and whether or not certain medications are impacting acid levels in the body (Figure 12.16).

For pure water, chemists have determined that $[H_3O^+]$ and $[OH^-]$ are 1.0×10^{-7} M at 25 °C. We can use this value to calculate K_w at this same temperature by plugging it into the expression.

$$K_w = [H_3O^+][OH^-] = [1.0 \times 10^{-7}][1.0 \times 10^{-7}] = 1.0 \times 10^{-14} \text{ at } 25\,°C$$

All aqueous solutions contain H_3O^+ and OH^-. When the concentrations of these two ions are equal, the solution is considered **neutral**. This is the case for pure water. In pure water, $[H_3O^+] = [OH^-] = 1.0 \times 10^{-7}$ M. If we add acid to the water, however, $[H_3O^+]$ increases and $[OH^-]$ decreases and the solution is acidic. If we add base to water, $[OH^-]$ increases and $[H_3O^+]$ decreases and the solution is basic.

neutral solution:	$[H_3O^+] = [OH^-] = 1.0 \times 10^{-7}$ M
acidic solution:	$[H_3O^+] > [OH^-]$ and $[H_3O^+] > 1.0 \times 10^{-7}$ M
basic solution:	$[OH^-] > [H_3O^+]$ and $[OH^-] > 1.0 \times 10^{-7}$ M

In other words, if the $[OH^-]$ is greater than $[H_3O^+]$ and the $[OH^-]$ is greater than 1.0×10^{-7}, the solution is basic. Alternatively, if $[H_3O^+]$ is greater than $[OH^-]$ and the $[H_3O^+]$ is greater than 1.0×10^{-7}, the solution is acidic.

Calculating $[H_3O^+]$ and $[OH^-]$

The value of K_w is used for all aqueous solutions (not just pure water), and remains constant (1.0×10^{-14}) at 25 °C. We can use this constant to determine $[H_3O^+]$, and $[OH^-]$ of different acid and base solutions. If we add acid to pure water, for example, we disturb the ionization of water reaction by increasing the amount of H_3O^+ in the solution. If we know the new concentration of $[H_3O^+]$ and the value of K_w, we can determine the $[OH^-]$. More generally, if we know the concentration of either ion, H_3O^+ or OH^-, we can determine the concentration of the other by rearranging the expression for K_w.

$$K_w = [H_3O^+][OH^-]$$

$$[OH^-] = \frac{K_w}{[H_3O^+]} \quad \text{or} \quad [H_3O^+] = \frac{K_w}{[OH^-]}$$

Click on Learn 12.4 to explore how to use K_w to determine either $[H_3O^+]$ or $[OH^-]$.

Figure 12.16 Urine Acidity Testing.

Medical professionals routinely test urine for excess acid. Increased $[H_3O^+]$ is an indicator of health problems including the development of kidney stones.

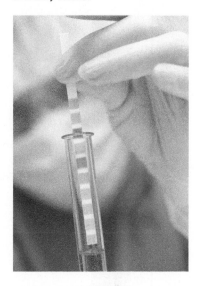

Predict answers and see step-by-step solutions: **Learn 12.4:** Using K_w to Calculate $[H_3O^+]$ and $[OH^-]$ in the Pearson eText.

Apply what you have just learned: **Practice 12.11 and 12.12** in the Pearson eText.

Quiz yourself on the content of this section: **Check 12.4** in the Pearson eText.

Figure 12.17 pH Scale.

The pH scale ranges from 0–14. Solutions with pH values below 7.0 are acidic, pH values equal to 7.0 are neutral, and pH values above 7.0 are alkaline.

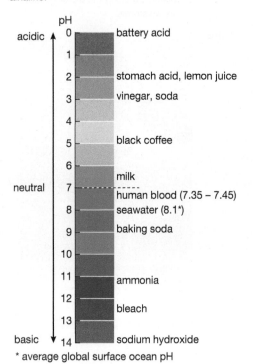

* average global surface ocean pH

12.5 pH

In Section 12.4 we discussed how to determine $[H_3O^+]$ and $[OH^-]$ using K_w. The concentration values are generally very small numbers. In order to measure and report these concentrations in a more convenient way, scientists developed the pH scale. The pH scale ranges from 0–14 (Figure 12.17). **pH** is the negative logarithm (log) of the $[H_3O^+]$. It is more convenient to refer to a number between 0–14 to describe the acidity of a solution than to report the small concentration values for $[H_3O^+]$.

$$pH = -\log[H_3O^+]$$

The $[H_3O^+]$ for lemon juice, for example, is 5.0×10^{-3} M. Using the pH scale, this translates to a pH value of 2.30:

$$pH = -\log[5.0 \times 10^{-3}] = 2.30$$

We use the pH scale to report if a solution is acidic, basic, or neutral based on the values we introduced in Section 12.4:

Acidic Solution:	$pH < 7$	$[H_3O^+] > 1.0 \times 10^{-7}$ M
Neutral Solution:	$pH = 7$	$[H_3O^+] = 1.0 \times 10^{-7}$ M
Basic Solution:	$pH > 7$	$[H_3O^+] < 1.0 \times 10^{-7}$ M

Notice that the higher the $[H_3O^+]$, the lower the pH and the lower the $[H_3O^+]$, the higher the pH. Explore VisibleChem Videos 12.3 and 12.4 to learn more about the pH scale, how to use your calculator to determine pH from $[H_3O^+]$, and how scientists measure pH in the laboratory and in the ocean.

 Watch this concept come to life: **VisibleChem Video 12.3:** Calculating pH and H_3O^+ Concentration and **VisibleChem Video 12.4:** Small Changes in pH Indicate Large Changes in H_3O^+ Concentration in the Pearson eText.

Apply what you have just learned: **Practice 12.13–12.15** in the Pearson eText.

Quiz yourself on the content of this section: **Check 12.5** in the Pearson eText.

12.6 Acid-Base Reactions

The acid-base reactions we have explored so far in this chapter involve water as one of the reactants. The two **acid-base reactions** that we discuss in this section involve acids reacting with hydroxide (OH^-), and acids reacting with carbonate (CO_3^{2-}), and bicarbonate (HCO_3^-). These two categories of acid-base reactions are common both in the laboratory and in nature.

When we combine an acid with a strong base, an acid reacts with hydroxide (OH^-). The base provides the OH^-, which undergoes a reaction with the H^+ ion donated by the acid. In these **neutralization** reactions, strong or weak acids react with a strong base to produce water and a salt (Figure 12.18). The reaction of HCl with NaOH is a neutralization reaction. Water and an ionic compound–which we refer to as a **salt**–are the products. In this reaction, the salt is NaCl.

$$HCl(aq) + NaOH(aq) \longrightarrow H_2O(l) + NaCl(aq)$$
$$\text{acid} \qquad \text{base} \qquad \qquad \text{water} \qquad \text{salt}$$

The acid and base are shown in the following version of the same reaction as ionized. This illustrates how the H^+ donated from the acid combines with the OH^- from the base to form water.

$$H^+(aq) + Cl^-(aq) + Na^+(aq) + OH^-(aq) \rightarrow H_2O(l) + Na^+(aq) + Cl^-(aq)$$

The salt forms from the sodium ion (Na^+) and chloride ion (Cl^-) that remain in solution. The H^+ ions and OH^- form water. The Na^+ and Cl^- ions are **spectator ions**, which do not take part in the reaction. We can remove the salt ions from the reaction equation, in order to more clearly see the reaction that takes place to form water.

$$H^+(aq) + OH^-(aq) \rightarrow H_2O(l)$$

Click on Learn 12.5 to see how to write and balance neutralization reactions.

Predict answers and see step-by-step solutions: **Learn 12.5:** Balancing Neutralization Reactions in the Pearson eText.

Apply what you have just learned: **Practice 12.16** in the Pearson eText.

Figure 12.18 Antacids.

People take antacids to neutralize excess stomach acid (HCl). Some of these commercial antacids contain both $Mg(OH)_2$ and $Al(OH)_3$ as the active ingredients, which react with HCl in the stomach.

$Al(OH)_3(s) + 3HCl \rightarrow$
$\qquad\qquad 3H_2O(l) + AlCl_3(aq)$
$Mg(OH)_2(s) + 2HCl \rightarrow$
$\qquad\qquad 2H_2O(l) + MgCl_2(aq)$

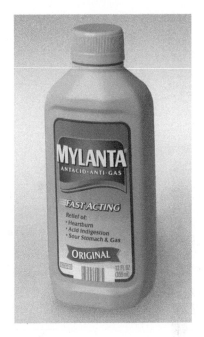

Diprotic Acid Neutralization Reactions

When diprotic acids undergo neutralization reactions with OH^-, the balanced reaction requires two moles of base for every one mole of acid. We can examine this 2:1 ratio in the neutralization reaction between the diprotic acid H_2SO_4 and KOH. For every one mole of H_2SO_4, two moles of KOH are needed to neutralize the acid. We indicate this with the coefficient 2 in front of KOH.

$$H_2SO_4(aq) + 2KOH(aq) \rightarrow 2H_2O(l) + K_2SO_4(aq)$$

Writing an equation that shows the acid, base, and salt in their ionized form provides a clear view of the 2:1 ratio. Each mole of acid produces two moles of H^+ ions. Given that there are two moles of KOH from the balanced equation, two moles of hydroxide are present as well.

$$2H^+(aq) + SO_4{}^{2-}(aq) + 2K^+(aq) + 2OH^-(aq) \rightarrow 2H_2O(l) + 2K^+(aq) + SO_4{}^{2-}(aq)$$

Removing the salt ions (K^+ and $SO_4{}^{2-}$) leaves us with the following net equation:

$$H^+(aq) + OH^-(aq) \rightarrow H_2O(l)$$

A similar neutralization reaction occurs when sulfuric acid (H_2SO_4) forms in the upper atmosphere and falls to Earth as **acid rain** and reacts with metal hydroxides in the soil. The neutralizing effect of this reaction is useful for limiting acid rain damage, yet when compounds such as $Al(OH)_3$ are present in the soil, another problem arises. The neutralization reaction produces salt ions, and water as expected, and in this case, the

Figure 12.19 Impacts of Acid Rain on Forests.

Acid rain can react with metal hydroxides in soils to release metals. These reactions can produce toxic metal ions, damaging or even killing plants including these trees in Grayson Highlands State Park, Virginia.

metal ion (Al^{3+}) is also produced upon neutralization. Once Al^{3+} is in solution it can enter the root system of trees and plants causing damage and even death (Figure 12.19).

$$3H_2SO_4(aq) + \mathbf{2Al(OH)_3}(aq) \rightarrow 6H_2O(l) + \mathbf{Al_2(SO_4)_3}(aq)$$

acid rain   metal hydroxides in soil

$$6H^+(aq) + 3SO_4{}^{2-}(aq) + \mathbf{2Al^{3+}}(aq) + 6OH^-(aq) \rightarrow 6H_2O(l) + \mathbf{2Al^{3+}}(aq) + 3SO_4{}^{2-}(aq)$$

damaging to trees and plants

 Apply what you have just learned: **Practice 12.7** in the Pearson eText.

Reactions of Carbonate and Bicarbonate with Acids

Figure 12.20 A Geologist Tests Rocks for the Presence of Carbonates to Help Identify a Rock.

Acid-base reactions between an acid and a carbonate ion ($CO_3{}^{2-}$) or an acid and a bicarbonate ion ($HCO_3{}^-$) produce carbon dioxide gas, water, and a salt. The reaction of hydrochloric acid (HCl) with sodium carbonate (Na_2CO_3) and the reaction of hydrochloric acid (HCl) with sodium bicarbonate ($NaHCO_3$) are both examples of this type of reaction.

$$2HCl(aq) + Na_2CO_3(aq) \rightarrow CO_2(g) + H_2O(l) + 2NaCl(aq)$$
$$HCl(aq) + NaHCO_3(aq) \rightarrow CO_2(g) + H_2O(l) + NaCl(aq)$$

These reactions involve the intermediate production of carbon acid (H_2CO_3), which quickly converts to carbon dioxide and water. In the following equation, we have removed the salt ions (Na^+ and Cl^-) so we can focus on the H^+ transfer and the subsequent reaction that produces CO_2 and water.

$$H^+(aq) + HCO_3{}^-(aq) \rightarrow H_2CO_3(aq) \rightarrow CO_2(g) + H_2O(l)$$

Field geologists take advantage of this quick reaction to help identify rocks. Most carry a bottle of hydrochloric acid (HCl) solution with them while working in the field. To determine a rock sample's identity, they place a few drops on the sample. If the sample is limestone, which contains calcium carbonate ($CaCO_3$), the HCl will fizz rapidly on contact as CO_2 is produced (Figure 12.20).

Explore BioConnect 12.1 (contains Figures 12.21–12.27) to see how a similar reaction between stomach acid (HCl) and sodium bicarbonate (NaHCO$_3$) takes place, as well as details about stomach anatomy and illnesses related to stomach acid problems.

Explore how Chemistry and Biology connect: **BioConnect: 12.1** Acids in Our Stomachs in the Pearson eText.

Quiz yourself on the content of this section: **Check 12.6** in the Pearson eText.

12.7 Titration

Titration is a laboratory method we can use to determine the concentration of an acid or base solution. To perform a titration, we neutralize a solution with unknown concentration with a known amount of another solution. For example, if we need to determine the molarity of a solution of HCl, we perform a titration using a strong base, such as NaOH, with a known concentration. The neutralization reaction between HCl and NaOH provides a way to quantify the amount of acid present in the solution.

$$\text{HCl}(aq) + \text{NaOH}(aq) \rightarrow \text{H}_2\text{O}(l) + \text{NaCl}(aq)$$

<table>
<tr><td>unknown
molarity</td><td>known
molarity</td></tr>
</table>

A **burette** is a piece of laboratory glassware that allows us to add a solution of known molarity in small quantities to a solution of unknown molarity. The titration procedure also requires an **indicator**, which is a compound that instantly turns color when the pH of a solution goes from acidic to basic or vice versa. **Phenolphthalein** is a common indicator. It is colorless in an acidic solution and turns bright pink in a basic solution. When we use phenolphthalein as the indicator, we know that neutralization has occurred when the solution turns pink. This change of color occurs at the **endpoint**—the point at which the moles of added base are equal to the moles of H$^+$ present. From the measured amount of acid, and the measured amount of base utilized in the titration, we can determine the concentration of the acid solution.

Explore VisibleChem Video 12.5 to see how a titration is used in a laboratory setting. Learn 12.6 provides insight into how to carry out the calculations that accompany a titration procedure.

Watch this concept come to life: **VisibleChem Video 12.5:** Titration of HCl with NaOH in the Pearson eText.

Predict answers and see step-by-step solutions: **Learn 12.6:** Determining Acid Molarity from a Titration in the Pearson eText.

Apply what you have just learned: **Practice 12.18 and 12.19** in the Pearson eText.

Quiz yourself on the content of this section: **Check 12.7** in the Pearson eText.

12.8 Buffers

Drastic changes in pH occur when we add acid or base to pure water. If we add acid or base to a **buffer** solution, in contrast, the pH changes very little. Figure 12.28 illustrates how the pH of pure water changes from 7.0 to 4.0 when we add a small amount of acid, and from 7.0 to 10.5 when we add a small amount of base. These are dramatic shifts compared to the impact on the pH of the buffer solution. When we add acid to

Figure 12.28 The Effect of Buffer on pH Changes.

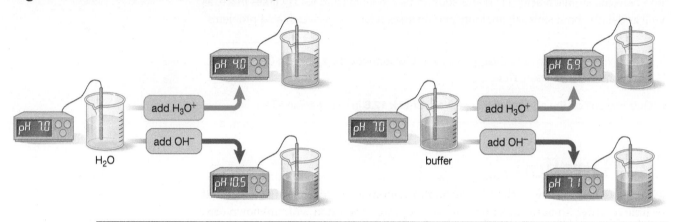

Figure 12.29 Preparing a Buffer Composed of Acetate and Sodium Acetate.

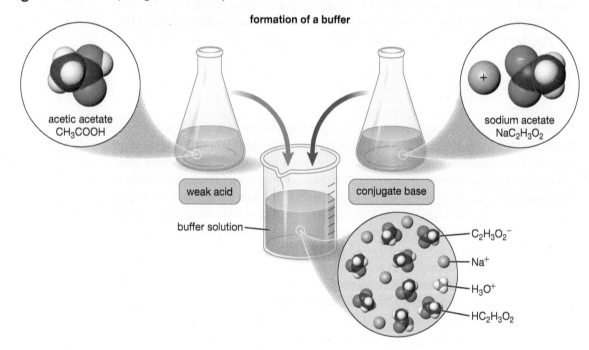

the buffer in this example, the pH only drops 0.1 on the pH scale and when we add base to the buffer solution, the pH only increases 0.1.

Buffer solutions are essential in biological systems because most biochemical reactions require a pH that remains within a narrow range. Human blood, for example, contains several buffers that maintain blood pH between 7.35–7.45. If the pH drops below or above this range, illness or even death occurs.

Most buffers are composed of approximately equal amounts of a weak acid and the salt of the weak acid's conjugate base. One example of a buffer solution is acetic acid ($HC_2H_3O_2$) combined with its salt, sodium acetate ($NaC_2H_3O_2$), in equal amounts (Figure 12.29). A buffer solution maintains the pH of a solution by neutralizing small amounts of added acid or base. Chemists often prepare buffers and use them in a laboratory setting to keep the pH of chemical reactions consistent. Buffers are also common in the human body, soil, and large natural bodies of water.

How Does a Buffer Maintain pH?

How is a buffer able to absorb acid or base with very little change in pH? If we take a closer look at the previous example of a buffer solution composed of a weak acid and its conjugate base ($HC_2H_3O_2$ and $NaC_2H_3O_2$) in equal amounts, we can see the reactions that buffer the solution. Acetic acid is a weak acid that dissociates to produce a very small amount of its conjugate base, $C_2H_3O_2^-$. Adding more of this ion in the form of a salt compound creates a solution that includes both the weak acid and the conjugate base in approximately equal amounts.

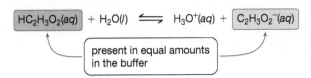

$$HC_2H_3O_2(aq) + H_2O(l) \rightleftharpoons H_3O^+(aq) + C_2H_3O_2^-(aq)$$

present in equal amounts in the buffer

When we add a small amount of acid (H_3O^+) to this buffer solution, it reacts with the conjugate base ($C_2H_3O_2^-$) and shifts the equilibrium towards reactants. This results in a slight decrease in the amount of $C_2H_3O_2^-$ and a slight increase in the amount of $HC_2H_3O_2$. However, the pH is relatively unchanged. You can view this process in VisibleChem Video 12.6.

When we add a small amount of base (OH^-) to the same buffer, it reacts with acetic acid ($HC_2H_3O_2$), which shifts the equilibrium towards products. This results in a slight decrease in $HC_2H_3O_2$ and a slight increase in $C_2H_3O_2^-$. But again, the pH is unchanged or only slightly increased.

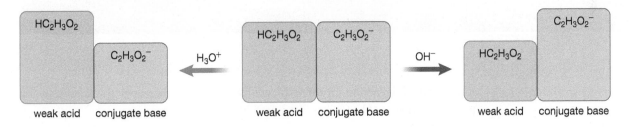

Watch this concept come to life: **VisibleChem Video 12.6:** How a Buffer Maintains pH in the Pearson eText.

Apply what you have just learned: **Practice 12.20 and 12.21** in the Pearson eText.

Calculating pH of a Buffer

We use the K_a expression and K_a value to calculate the pH of a buffer solution both before, and after acids, or bases are added to the buffer. Table 12.4 lists some common buffers and their associated K_a values. The carbonic acid (H_2CO_3)/bicarbonate (HCO_3^-) buffer, for example, helps buffer the pH of our blood. It has a K_a constant equal to 4.3×10^{-7} (Figure 12.30). We discuss this in more detail in BioConnect 12.2.

Table 12.4 Common Buffers.

Buffer	Weak Acid	Conjugate Base	K_a
acetic acid/acetate	CH_3COOH	CH_3COO^-	1.8×10^{-5}
carbonic acid/bicarbonate	H_2CO_3	HCO_3^-	4.3×10^{-7}
bicarbonate/carbonate	HCO_3^-	CO_3^{2-}	5.6×10^{-11}
dihydrogen phosphate/hydrogen phosphate	$H_2PO_4^-$	HPO_4^{2-}	6.2×10^{-8}
hydrogen phosphate/phosphate	HPO_4^-	PO_4^{3-}	2.2×10^{-13}

Figure 12.30 Carbonic Acid/Bicarbonate Buffer in Blood.

Blood pH must remain between 7.35 and 7.45. The carbonic acid/bicarbonate buffer helps maintain this critical range.

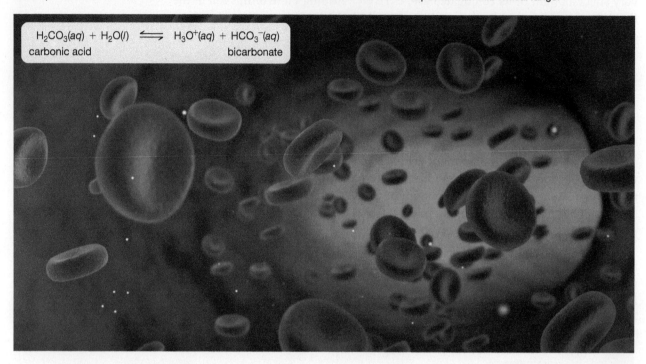

$$H_2CO_3(aq) + H_2O(l) \rightleftharpoons H_3O^+(aq) + HCO_3^-(aq)$$

carbonic acid   bicarbonate

We write the reaction for the weak acid in water and rearrange the K_a expression equation to solve for $[H_3O^+]$ as illustrated here.

$$H_2CO_3(aq) + H_2O(l) \rightleftharpoons H_3O^+(aq) + HCO_3^-(aq)$$

$$K_a = \frac{[H_3O^+][HCO_3^-]}{[H_2CO_3]}$$

Rearranging the expression to solve for $[H_3O^+]$:

$$[H_3O^+] = K_a \times \frac{[H_2CO_3]}{[HCO_3^-]}$$

Then we can plug the concentrations of the weak acid and its conjugate base and the K_a value into the rearranged K_a expression. Once we know the $[H_3O^+]$, we use the pH equation to obtain the pH.

$$pH = -\log[H_3O^+]$$

Learn 12.7 includes all the steps for solving for the pH of a buffer.

Predict answers and see step-by-step solutions: **Learn 12.7:** Calculating the pH of a Buffer in the Pearson eText.

Apply what you have just learned: **Practice 12.22** in the Pearson eText.

Figure 12.31 A Helicopter Releases Calcium Carbonate into an Acidic Lake to Increase the pH and Buffering Capacity of the Water.

Natural Buffers

Buffer systems maintain pH in a narrow range to prevent stressful or even deadly conditions. Oceans and lakes, for example, contain several natural buffers including the bicarbonate/carbonate buffer system.

$$HCO_3^-(aq) + H_2O(l) \rightleftharpoons H_3O^+(aq) + CO_3^{2-}(aq)$$

The limestone rock ($CaCO_3$) that surrounds many lakes naturally provides a buffer when it releases CO_3^{2-} into the water. These lake waters can buffer additional acidic and basic compounds that end up in the lake. When acid rain falls, for example, the additional acid reacts with CO_3^{2-}, minimizing the impact of the acid rain. In cases where lakes do not have limestone nearby, lake water can become over acidic putting the animals and plants that live in the lake in danger. Humans attempt to address this problem by adding large amounts of conjugate base in the form of a salt compound, such as calcium carbonate ($CaCO_3$), to the lake (Figure 12.31).

Like lakes, body fluids also contain buffer compounds. If the pH in blood, for example, changes significantly, it can have a major impact on human health. Blood contains buffers that maintain a consistent pH, even though we ingest acids and bases in the foods we eat. Without these buffers in our blood, significant illnesses can occur. **Respiratory acidosis**, for example, is a life-threatening condition that occurs when blood pH becomes too low because acid amounts exceed the capacity of the buffers in the human body. Select BioConnect 12.2 (contains Figures 12.32–12.36) to explore this condition in more detail.

Explore how Chemistry and Biology connect: **BioConnect: 12.2** Buffers in Our Blood in the Pearson eText.

Quiz yourself on the content of this section: **Check 12.8** in the Pearson eText.

Chapter Summary

12.1   Defining Acids and Bases

Learning Objective: Identify and define acids, bases, and conjugate acid-base pairs.

Acids are proton (H^+) donors (Figure 12.2). Bases are proton (H^+) acceptors (Figure 12.4). Conjugate acid-base pairs lie on opposite sides of a chemical reaction arrow and differ by a proton. The acid donates a proton and becomes the conjugate base of the acid. Similarly, the base accepts a proton and becomes the conjugate acid of the base. A common acid-base conjugate pair is NH_3 and NH_4^+. When a

neutral compound loses a proton, it is left with a -1 charge. For example, when electrically neutral sulfuric acid (H_2SO_4) loses a proton, it becomes the negatively charged ion HSO_4^-. When a neutral compound gains a proton, it takes on a $+1$ charge. When electrically neutral water (H_2O) gains a proton, it becomes the positively charged hydronium ion H_3O^+. The carboxylic acid group (CO_2H) is common in biological molecules.

Key Terms

acid	Brønsted-Lowry base: accepts H^+	conjugate base
amphoteric	carboxylic acid group (—COOH)	hydronium ion (H_3O^+)
base	conjugate acid	hydroxide ion (OH^-)
Brønsted-Lowry acid: donates H^+	conjugate acid-base pair	

12.2   Strengths of Acids and Bases

Learning Objective: Explain the difference between strong and weak acids and bases.

We classify acids and bases as strong or weak based on the extent to which they dissociate (break apart into ions) in water. When a strong acid, such as HCl, dissolves in water, 100 percent of the acid dissociates into H^+ and Cl^- ions. When a strong base, such as NaOH, dissolves in water, 100 percent of the base dissociates into Na^+ and OH^- ions. A single forward arrow represents the dissociation of a strong acid or a strong base in water. When strong acids (such as HCl) dissociate, a weak conjugate base (Cl^-) forms, and vice versa. A weak acid, on the other hand, only ionizes slightly in water, forming only a small amount of H_3O^+ ions. The reaction of a weak acid, such as acetic acid

(CH_3CO_2H) in water creates a solution mixture that proceeds towards equilibrium but favors the reactants. In this type of reaction, a double arrow indicates a reversible process that favors the reactants (the substances that have not ionized). Similarly, weak bases only slightly ionize. The position of the equilibrium depends on the strength of the acids and bases on both sides. Diprotic acids (such as H_2SO_4) have two H^+ ions to donate. Triprotic acids (such as H_3PO_4) have three protons to donate.

VisibleChem Video 12.1: Strong vs. Weak Acids and Bases

VisibleChem Video 12.2: Predicting the Direction of Equilibrium Using Acid and Base Strength

Key Terms

diprotic acid
triprotic acid

12.3   Acid Dissociation Constants

Learning Objective: Write the acid dissociation constant expression (K_a) and relate it to acid strength.

Weak acids do not dissociate completely in water. At any given time, only a fraction of the weak acid molecules are

dissociated into ions. We use the equilibrium constant (K_a) to express the relative ratio of dissociated vs. non-dissociated acid in solution. The equilibrium constant expression is the ratio of the concentration of the products to the concentration of the reactants. For a general weak acid (HA) in water, we write the reaction as: $HA(aq) + H_2O(l) \rightleftharpoons H_3O^+(aq) + A^-(aq)$. The acid dissociation constant expression for this reaction is $K_a = [H_3O^+][A^-]/[HA]$. The larger the value of K_a, the stronger the acid, and the greater the fraction of acid molecules that have dissociated into ions. The smaller the K_a value, the weaker the acid is, and the smaller the fraction of molecules that have dissociated into ions (Table 12.3).

Key Term

acid dissociation constant (K_a)

Key Equation

$$K_a = \frac{[H_3O^+][A^-]}{[HA]}$$

12.4 Water Ionization

Learning Objective: Use the water dissociation constant (K_w) and ion concentrations to determine if a solution is acidic, basic, or neutral.

Water is an amphoteric substance; it can act as both a Brønsted-Lowry acid and a Brønsted-Lowry base. Two molecules of water can react with each other in an equilibrium reaction to form an H_3O^+ ion and an OH^- ion. The equilibrium constant expression for this reaction is the water dissociation constant (K_w), written as $K_w = [H_3O^+][OH^-]$. For pure water, $K_w = [H_3O^+][OH^-] = [1.0 \times 10^{-7}]$ $[1.0 \times 10^{-7}] = 1.0 \times 10^{-14}$ at 25 °C. When $[H_3O^+]$ and $[OH^-]$ are equal in a solution, the solution is neutral. If we add acid to water, there is an increase in $[H_3O^+]$ and a decrease in $[OH^-]$, which results in an acidic solution. When we add a base to water, there is an increase in $[OH^-]$ and a decrease in $[H_3O^+]$, producing a basic solution. $[H_3O^+] = [OH^-] = 1.0 \times 10^{-7}$ M. Acidic Solution: $[H_3O^+] > [OH^-]$ and $[H_3O^+] > 1.0 \times 10^{-7}$ M. Basic Solution: $[OH^-] > [H_3O^+]$ and $[OH^-] > 1.0 \times 10^{-7}$ M.

Key Terms

water dissociation constant (K_w)
neutral

Key Equations

$$K_w = [H_3O^+][OH^-] = [1.0 \times 10^{-7}][1.0 \times 10^{-7}] = 1.0 \times 10^{-14} \text{ at 25 °C}$$

$$[OH^-] = \frac{K_w}{[H_3O^+]} \quad \text{or} \quad [H_3O^+] = \frac{K_w}{[OH^-]}$$

12.5 pH

Learning Objective: Calculate pH to report the acidity and basicity of a solution from 0–14.

We use the logarithmic pH scale to express the concentration of hydronium ion (H_3O^+) because it allows us to express a wide range of concentrations within a range of 0–14 (Figure 12.17). Being able to measure or calculate pH is important for many fields of science and medicine. Mathematically, $pH = -\log_{10}[H_3O^+]$, where the hydronium ion concentration is expressed in terms of molarity (M = mol solute/L solution). Acidic solutions have pH values less than 7, neutral solutions have pH = 7, and basic solutions have pH values greater than 7. It is important to realize that the negative sign in the pH equation means that the higher the $[H_3O^+]$, the lower the pH, and the lower the $[H_3O^+]$, the higher the pH.

VisibleChem Video 12.3: Calculating pH and $[H_3O^+]$

VisibleChem Video 12.4: Small Changes in pH Indicate Large Changes in $[H_3O^+]$

Key Term

pH

Key Equation

$pH = -\log[H_3O^+]$

12.6 Acid-Base Reactions

Learning Objective: Write balanced equations for neutralization reactions and recognize reactions of acids with bicarbonate and carbonate.

Acids and bases can react to neutralize each other. For example, hydrochloric acid (HCl) reacts with sodium hydroxide (NaOH) to form a salt (NaCl) and water in aqueous solution. The reaction involves H^+ combining with OH^- to form the product of the reaction, water (H_2O). The dissolved Na^+ and Cl^- spectator ions remain unchanged in the reaction and are simply ions in solution before and after the neutralization reaction. One mole of NaOH can react with one mole of HCl to form one mole of water (H_2O) that contains one mole of Na^+ ions and one

mole of Cl^- ions. In contrast, the diprotic acid H_2SO_4 can react with two moles of a base (such as NaOH) because it has two moles of protons for every one mole of H_2SO_4. Likewise, one mole of the triprotic acid H_3PO_4 can react with three moles of a base (such as NaOH) because H_3PO_4 has three protons. Similarly, one mole of sodium carbonate Na_2CO_3 can react with two moles of an acid because it can accept two moles of H^+ ions to form H_2CO_3. Carbonic acid (H_2CO_3) is an especially important acid because it is in equilibrium with its breakdown products carbon dioxide (CO_2) and water (H_2O), which has implications for global CO_2 levels and ocean acidification.

BioConnect 12.1: Acids in Our Stomachs

Key Terms

acid rain	neutralization	salt
acid-base reaction	spectator ion	

12.7 Titration

Learning Objective: Calculate the molarity of an acid or base solution from titration measurements.

In the laboratory, chemists use neutralization reactions in the titration process to determine the unknown concentration of an acid or base solution. Using a solution of known concentration in a measuring device (such as a burette containing NaOH), we can determine the unknown concentration of an acid solution (such as HCl). A pH indicator provides a visual cue when the neutralization reaction is

complete, and all the acid has reacted with the added base. At this point, the unknown number of moles of acid present in the acidic solution exactly equals the number of moles of base added from the burette. Knowing the volume and concentration of base that neutralizes the acid, we can calculate the number of moles of acid and the molarity of acid in the unknown sample.

VisibleChem Video 12.5: Titration of HCl with NaOH

Key Terms

burette	indicator	titration
endpoint	phenolphthalein	

12.8 Buffers

Learning Objective: Explain the role of the weak acid and conjugate base in a buffer and calculate its pH.

A buffer is an equilibrium mixture of a weak acid-base conjugate pair dissolved in water in approximately equal concentrations. Because both a weak acid and a weak base

are present in solution, minimal changes in pH occur when small amounts of either a strong base or strong acid are added (Figure 12.28). We calculate the pH of a buffer by solving for $[H_3O^+]$ in the K_a expression for the weak acid and then using the equation, $pH = -\log[H_3O^+]$. Buffers are very common in both the laboratory and in biological systems where they prevent large variations in pH that can stress cells, organisms, and ecosystems.

VisibleChem Video 12.6: How a Buffer Maintains pH

BioConnect 12.2: Buffers in the Blood

Key Terms

buffer
respiratory acidosis

 End-of-Chapter Quiz

Have you mastered the content of this chapter? Try the **End-of-Chapter Quiz** in the Pearson eText.

1. When HCl dissolves in water, it is a source of _____. When NaOH dissolves in water it is a source of _____ .
   a) hydroxide ions; hydrogen ions
   b) H^+ ions that are basic; OH^- ions that are acidic
   c) H^+ ions that are acidic; OH^- ions that are basic
   d) Cl^- ions that are strongly acidic; Na^+ ions that are strongly basic

2. Iron (II) sulfate is commonly used in mineral supplements for humans, animals, and soil for agricultural purposes. In which reaction is the sulfate ion (SO_4^{2-}) acting as a base to form its conjugate acid?
   a) $HSO_4^-(aq) + H_2O(l) \rightleftharpoons H_2SO_4(aq) + OH^-(aq)$
   b) $SO_4^{2-}(aq) + H_2O(l) \rightleftharpoons HSO_4^-(aq) + H_3O^+(aq)$
   c) $SO_4^{2-}(aq) + 2OH^-(aq) \rightleftharpoons HSO_4^-(aq) + H_2O(l)$
   d) $SO_4^{2-}(aq) + H_2O(l) \rightleftharpoons HSO_4^-(aq) + OH^-(aq)$

3. Propionic acid ($CH_3CH_2CO_2H$) is a molecule with a carboxylic acid group. Propionic acid's conjugate base, which we refer to as the propionate ion, is involved in the metabolism of oils and fats in your body. Which of the following reactions represents a propionic acid reacting to produce its conjugate base?
   a)

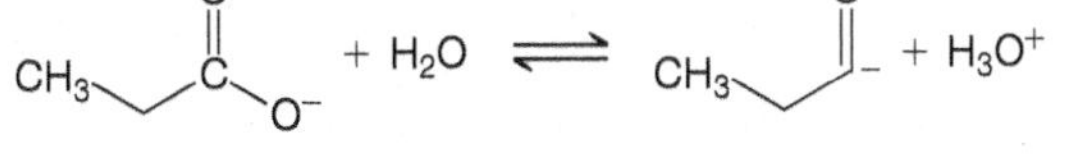

   CH₃—C(=O)—O⁻ + H₂O ⇌ CH₃—C(=O)—H + H₃O⁺

   b)

   CH₃—CH₂—C(=O)—O—H + H₂O ⇌ CH₃—CH₂—C(=O)—O⁻ + H₃O⁺

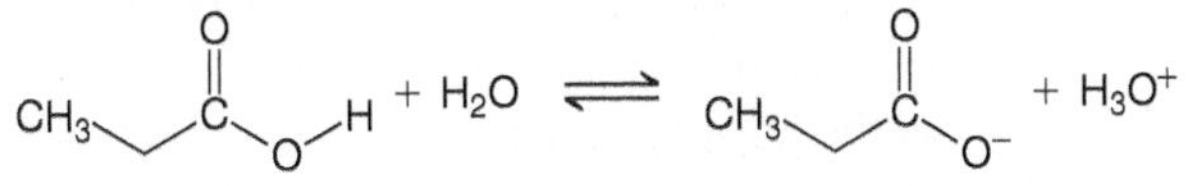

   c)

   CH₃—CH₂—C(=O)—O—H + H₂O ⇌ CH₃—CH₂—C(=O)—O⁺(H)—H + OH⁻

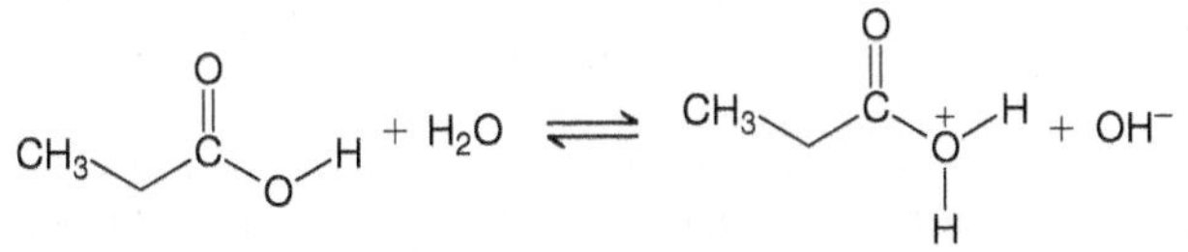

   d)

   CH₃—CH₂—C(=O)—O—H + H₂O ⇌ CH₃—CH₂—C(=O)—O⁻ + OH⁻

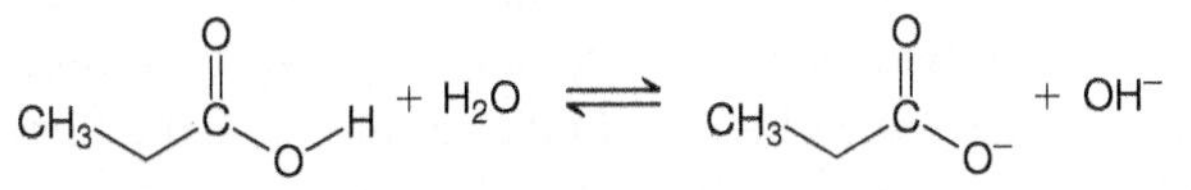

4. Phosphoric acid (H_3PO_4) and boric acid (H_3BO_3) are both triprotic acids used in the production of circuit boards for the global electronics industry. Employees of circuit board manufacturing facilities work with these acids routinely, and accidents occasionally cause acid burns. Paramedics and hospital staff need to know the relative strength of acids that patients have been exposed to in order to provide the appropriate treatment. Two acid burn patients arrive in your hospital needing treatment. One has been exposed to phosphoric acid and the other to boric acid. Which patient has been burned by the stronger acid? The K_a of $H_3PO_4 = 7.5 \times 10^{-3}$ and the K_a of $H_3BO_3 = 7.3 \times 10^{-10}$.
   a) The patient burned by H_3BO_3 has been exposed to the stronger acid since the K_a of boric acid is larger than the K_a of phosphoric acid.
   b) The patient burned by H_3BO_3 has been exposed to the stronger acid since the K_a of boric acid is smaller than the K_a of phosphoric acid.
   c) The patient burned by H_3PO_4 has been exposed to the stronger acid since the K_a of phosphoric acid is larger than the K_a of boric acid.
   d) The patient burned by H_3PO_4 has been exposed to the stronger acid since the K_a of phosphoric acid is smaller than the K_a of boric acid.

5. Given that weak acid-base equilibrium reactions involve an acid and a base on both the reactant side and on the product side, complete the statement: "The direction of the weak acid-base equilibrium favors the formation of the _____ acid and the _____ base."
   a) weaker, weaker   b) weaker, stronger
   c) stronger, weaker   d) stronger, stronger

6. Which acid ionizes to the greatest extent in water?
   a) HCN (hydrocyanic acid)
   b) H_3PO_4 (phosphoric acid)
   c) H_2SO_4 (sulfuric acid)
   d) HBr (hydrobromic acid)

7. Which statement correctly describes the importance of acid dissociation constants (K_a)?
   a) Determining K_a is especially important for strong acid equilibrium situations.
   b) K_a values help us understand the relative strengths of weak acids.
   c) K_a is always a number much less than one for strong acids.
   d) Expressions for K_a always include the concentration of water because these reactions describe acids dissociating in water.

8. Pyruvic acid (CH_3COCO_2H) is a weak acid containing the carboxylic acid group discussed in Section 12.1. The pyruvate ion ($CH_3COCO_2^-$) is the conjugate base of pyruvic acid and is a key intermediate in cellular metabolism. Within cells, both the acid and its conjugate base are in equilibrium according to the K_a expression for pyruvic acid. Select the correct K_a expression for the dissociation equilibrium of pyruvic acid.

pyruvic acid
(CH_3COCO_2H)

pyruvate ion
(CH_3COCO_2)

   a) $K_a = \dfrac{[H_3O^+][CH_3COCO_2H]}{[CH_3COCO_2^-]}$

   b) $K_a = \dfrac{[H_3O^+][CH_3COCO_2^-]}{[CH_3COCO_2H][H_2O]}$

   c) $K_a = \dfrac{[CH_3COCO_2^-]}{[CH_3COCO_2H]}$

   d) $K_a = \dfrac{[H_3O^+][CH_3COCO_2^-]}{[CH_3COCO_2H]}$

9. We can use the K_w expression to determine either the $[H_3O^+]$ or $[OH^-]$ in a given problem, when one of these concentration terms can be measured, or is given. Which value in the K_w expression is always known?
   a) the value of the salt concentration
   b) the value of the hydroxide ion concentration, $[OH^-]$
   c) the value of the hydronium ion concentration, $[H_3O^+]$
   d) the value of K_w

10. The production and recycling of paper products is a multi-billion-dollar global industry. Sodium hydroxide (NaOH) is used in certain paper processing steps. An environmental health and safety officer checks a processing solution in a paper mill and finds the hydroxide ion concentration in a NaOH processing solution is 3.5×10^{-5} M. What is the concentration of hydronium ion in the solution?
   a) $[H_3O^+] = 1.0 \times 10^{-14}$ M
   b) $[H_3O^+] = 2.9 \times 10^{-10}$ M
   c) $[H_3O^+] = 3.5 \times 10^9$ M
   d) $[H_3O^+] = 2.9 \times 10^{10}$ M

11. Both a conceptual understanding and a quantitative understanding of pH are important. Patients often ask nurses and other health care professionals are often asked for explanations about blood and urine tests that include pH values. Which statement is true about pH?
   a) The lower the pH, the more acidic the sample is.
   b) The lower the pH, the lower the acidity of the sample.
   c) The higher the pH, the more acidic the sample is.
   d) The higher the pH, the less basic the sample is.

12. A student is studying with a friend for a nursing school and allied health entrance exam such as the National League for Nursing Pre-Admission Exam (NLN PAX-RN/PN) and is asked which statement about pH is correct?
   a) A difference of one pH unit corresponds to a difference of $1 M [H_3O^+]$.
   b) The lower the pH, the lower the concentration of hydronium ion, $[H_3O^+]$.
   c) A difference of one pH unit corresponds to a difference of 10 times higher or lower in acidity.
   d) The higher the pH, the lower the concentration of hydroxide ions, $[OH^-]$.

13. Which statement could be true about the results of a patient's blood test?
   a) A higher-than-normal blood pH could indicate that the patient's blood is more acidic than a sample in the normal range.
   b) A lower-than-normal blood pH could indicate that the patient's blood is more basic than a sample in the normal range.
   c) A higher-than-normal blood pH could indicate that the patient's blood is more basic than a sample in the normal range.
   d) A lower-than-normal blood pH could indicate that the patient's blood is less acidic than a sample in the normal range.

14. Bile is a complex mixture produced in the liver and secreted into the gallbladder where the body concentrates it and uses it to help digest fats and also neutralize hydrochloric acid that passes from the stomach into the small intestine. A sample of bile from a sick patient is tested and found to have a $[H_3O^+] = 4.1 \times 10^{-9}$.

What is the pH of the bile sample? Is the bile sample acidic, basic, or neutral?

a) pH = 9.61; basic

b) pH = 8.39; basic

c) pH = -8.39; basic

d) pH = 8.39; acidic

15. A person with metabolic alkalosis has an elevated blood pH that is above the normal range of 7.35–7.45. This elevation occurs from the loss of H^+ from the body and/or an increased bicarbonate (HCO_3^-) level. The condition can result from a variety of causes including improper kidney function, alcohol abuse, and excessive vomiting. To help reduce the blood pH to the normal range, one treatment involves intravenous (IV) injection of ammonium chloride (NH_4Cl), a weak acid. Select the correctly balanced acid-base reaction between the weak acid ammonium chloride and the bicarbonate ion acting as a weak base (in the form of the potassium bicarbonate salt $KHCO_3$) to produce ammonia (NH_3), carbonic acid (H_2CO_3), and potassium chloride (KCl) in the blood of a patient undergoing treatment for metabolic alkalosis.

a) $NH_3Cl + KH_2CO_3 \rightleftharpoons NH_3 + H_2CO_3 + KCl$

b) $NH_4Cl + KHCO_3 \rightleftharpoons NH_3 + H_2CO_3 + KCl$

c) $NH_4Cl + KHCO_3 \rightleftharpoons NH_5 + CO_3^{2-} + KCl$

d) $NH_4Cl + 2KHCO_3 \rightleftharpoons NH_3 + H_2CO_3 + 2KCl$

16. Barium hydroxide ($Ba(OH)_2$) is used in water purification processes and in the production of lubricants and oil additives. Phosphoric acid (H_3PO_4) has a number of uses in the food and fertilizer industries and is also used for rust removal. Select the correct balanced equation and the correct overall equation for the formation of water for the reaction that occurs when phosphoric acid (H_3PO_4) is completely neutralized by barium hydroxide ($Ba(OH)_2$).

a) $H_3PO_4(aq) + 3Ba(OH)_2(aq) \rightarrow 6H_2O(l) + Ba_3(PO_4)_2(aq)$

$6H^+(aq) + 6OH^-(aq) \rightarrow 6H_2O(l)$

b) $2H_3PO_4(aq) + 3Ba(OH)_2(aq) \rightarrow 6H_2O(l) + Ba_3(PO_4)_2(aq)$

$3H^+(aq) + 3OH^-(aq) \rightarrow 6H_2O(l)$

c) $2H_3PO_4(aq) + 3Ba(OH)_2(aq) \rightarrow 6H_2O(l) + Ba_3(PO_4)_2(aq)$

$6H^+(aq) + 6OH^-(aq) \rightarrow 6H_2O(l)$

d) $2H_3PO_4(aq) + 3Ba(OH)_2(aq) \rightarrow 6H_2O(l) + Ba(PO_4)(aq)$

$3H^+(aq) + 2OH^-(aq) \rightarrow 3H_2O(l)$

17. The main ingredient in vinegar is acetic acid (CH_3CO_2H). A food scientist tests a 45.5-mL vinegar sample in a titration and determines that 52.2 mL of 0.195-M NaOH is required to completely neutralize the acetic acid in the vinegar. What is the concentration of acetic acid in the vinegar sample?

$$CH_3CO_2H(aq) + NaOH(aq) \rightarrow H_2O(l) + Na^+CH_3CO_2^-(aq)$$

a) The $[CH_3CO_2H]$ in the vinegar is 0.224 M.

b) The $[CH_3CO_2H]$ in the vinegar is 10.2 M.

c) The $[CH_3CO_2H]$ in the vinegar is 224 M.

d) The $[CH_3CO_2H]$ in the vinegar is 2.24 × 10^{-4} M.

18. Which statement is true about the end point of a titration involving hydrochloric acid and sodium hydroxide?

a) The K_a of H^+ from the acid is equal to the volume of OH^- from the base.

b) The moles of H^+ from the acid are equal to the pH of OH^- from the base.

c) The moles of H^+ from the acid are equal to the moles of OH^- from the base.

d) The concentration of H^+ from the acid is equal to the moles of OH^- from the base.

19. You perform a titration in chemistry lab with your lab partner and find that 15.5 mL of a 0.275-M HCl solution is required to completely neutralize a 37.5-mL test sample of NaOH. What is the molarity of the NaOH test solution?

$$HCl(aq) + NaOH(aq) \rightarrow H_2O(l) + NaCl(aq)$$

a) 97.7 °C

b) [NaOH] = 0.114 M

c) [NaOH] = 1.14 × 10^{-4} M

d) [NaOH] = 4.26 M

20. Which of these pairs combine to make a good buffer?
   a) equal concentrations of $HC_2H_3O_2$ (acetic acid) and NaOH (sodium hydroxide)
   b) equal concentrations of $NaHCO_3$ (sodium bicarbonate) and NaOH (sodium hydroxide)
   c) equal concentrations of HCl (Hydrochloric acid) and HCN (hydrocyanic acid)
   d) equal concentrations of $HC_2H_3O_2$ (acetic acid) and $C_2H_3O_2^-Na^+$ (sodium acetate)

21. What is the pH of a phosphate buffer made from 0.50-M H_2PO_4 and 0.40-M HPO_4^{2}? The K_a for H_2PO_4 is 6.2×10^{-8}. Express your answer in standard decimal form with three significant figures. *Hint*: Buffers do not always include exactly equal concentrations of the weak acid and its conjugate base. Solve this problem using the method you learned in the chapter and substitute in the slightly different concentrations during the numeric calculations.

$$H_2PO_4^-(aq) + H_2O(l) \leftrightharpoons HPO_4^{2-}(aq) + H_3O^+(aq)$$

   a) pH = 7.11   b) pH = 7.30
   c) pH = 8.89   d) pH = −7.11

Unit 4

Bringing It All Together

How Can Chemistry Help Us Understand the Silent Hypoxia Associated with COVID-19?

CHEMISTRY APPLICATION We opened Unit 4 with a look at the challenge of using ventilators and other strategies to maintain lung function in patients (Figure U4.4). Our study of gas behavior and the gas laws in Chapter 10 allowed us to more deeply understand this challenge. We've explored how CO_2 can dissolve in the oceans and in our blood (Chapter 11) as well as the impact this additional CO_2 can have on the pH of these solutions (Chapter 12). We can now think more deeply about both the treatment of hypoxic patients as well as some of the potential underlying causes of silent hypoxia by applying what we know about the behavior of gases when breathing, the factors that determine their solubility in aqueous solutions such as blood, and the buffering system present in our blood that mitigates the impact of excess acid.

Figure U4.4 Monitoring a Patient on a Ventilator.

Figure U4.5 Lung Structure and Function.

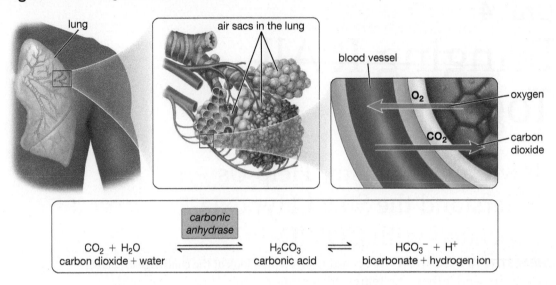

Under normal conditions, we breathe by creating lower pressure in our lungs, which draws in oxygen-rich air. Exhaling used air clears carbon dioxide-rich air from our lungs. This exchange of gases is essential for maintaining pH in our blood and for optimizing cognitive function—as we know, our brains need oxygen to function.

These gases enter our system by exiting the lungs and dissolving in the blood. Oxygen gas (O_2) diffuses from the lungs to the blood and is carried to the tissues. Carbon dioxide gas (CO_2), on the other hand, is produced in the tissues and then carried back to the lungs as both a dissolved gas and as the bicarbonate ion (HCO_3^-). Once it reaches the lungs, bicarbonate is converted back to CO_2 gas and exhaled (Figure U4.5).

When the lungs are not functioning well, oxygen saturation drops, and excess CO_2 can build up in the blood. Increased CO_2 concentration in the blood can cause *respiratory acidosis,* a condition in which excess carbon dioxide in the blood is converted to carbonic acid decreasing blood pH below normal levels. This drop in pH typically triggers an increase in breathing rate, helping to restore adequate oxygen and remove the excess CO_2. COVID-19 patients with silent hypoxia, however, do not experience this increased breathing rate or any of the discomfort normally associated with hypoxia.

Scientists are not completely sure why COVID-19 patients don't respond to the drop in blood pH. It is possible that the virus that causes COVID-19 may impact the brain, interfering with the typical response to hypoxia. Other scientists note that while many other respiratory diseases cause the air sacs in the lungs to fill with fluid, the air sacs in patients with serious COVID-19 collapse. This difference in the structure of the lungs may allow CO_2 to diffuse out of the lung normally, but prevent sufficient oxygen from diffusing in. Other scientists suspect that changes in how blood flows through the lungs may help explain the low oxygen levels seen in many COVID-19 patients.

Regardless of its ultimate cause, silent hypoxia is strongly correlated with low survival rates for COVID-19 patients. Thus, detecting and minimizing these precipitous drops in oxygen levels are essential to ensuring the best possible outcomes for COVID-19 patients.

Questions to Think About

1. Examine Figure U4.5. Which direction does the equilibrium shift when excess CO_2 is present? Does this shift increase or decrease the pH of the blood?

2. How does the carbonic acid/bicarbonate buffer in blood prevent excess acid from decreasing pH? What substance does excess H^+ react with to remove it from blood?

3. The kidneys can increase the amount of H^+ released in the urine. They also have a bicarbonate reserve that can be released into the blood. How would each of these actions affect the pH of the blood?

4. Moderately low blood oxygen levels may be treated with supplemental oxygen administered through a tube or mask. What effect would supplemental oxygen have on the partial pressure of oxygen in the lungs?

A Closer Look at the Data

To better understand the role of hypoxia in the outcome of COVID-19 patients, a group of researchers in Peru conducted a *retrospective* study in late 2020 (Mejía *et al.*, 2020). In a retrospective study, researchers look at existing data to better understand events that have taken place in the past. In this case, the researchers looked back at the medical records of 369 COVID-19 patients admitted to their hospital early in the pandemic.

The researchers used the data to construct a *survivorship curve* (Figure U4.6). A survivorship curve graphically represents the proportion of individuals still alive over a specific time range. In this study, the researchers divided the COVID-19 patients into four groups based on their level of oxygen saturation (SaO_2) when they were admitted to the hospital. (Recall that a normal oxygen saturation level is >95%.)

Figure U4.6 Survivorship Curve for COVID-19 Patients Groups by Oxygen Saturation Category at Admission.

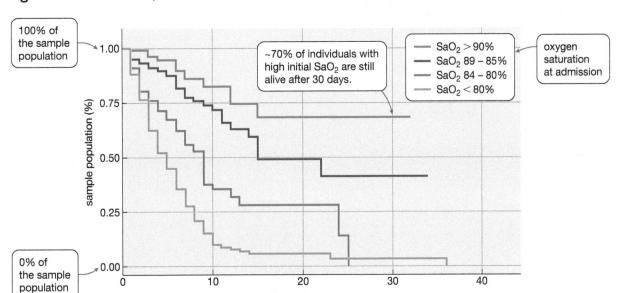

Questions to Think About

Examine the survivorship curve and use it to answer the following questions:

1. When trying to interpret a graph, it's always a good idea to make sure you clearly understand each axis. In your own words, explain what each axis represents in this graph.

2. How do individuals with higher oxygen saturation levels at admission (>90%) fare compared to those with the lowest oxygen saturation levels at admission (<80%)?

3. Why might this finding be useful in planning the response to COVID-19 outbreaks, particularly in areas where healthcare resources may be limited?

Reference

Paper is open access. Mejía F, Medina C, Cornejo E, Morello E, Vásquez S, Alave J, et al. (2020) Oxygen saturation as a predictor of mortality in hospitalized adult patients with COVID-19 in a public hospital in Lima, Peru. PLoS ONE 15(12): e0244171. https://doi.org/10.1371/journal.pone.0244171

Unit 5

Introduction
Exploring Organic Molecules—Alcohols, Ethers, and Thiols

Chapter 13: Introduction to Organic Molecules
Chapter 14: Alcohols, Ethers, Thiols, and Chiral Molecules

In 2014, the deadly disease tuberculosis (TB) passed an ominous milestone to become the world's leading cause of death from infectious disease, a position it held until the SARS-CoV-2 virus caused the COVID-19 pandemic. The World Health Organization estimates that 10 million people fall ill with TB each year, and 1.5 million of them die.

Globally, the WHO estimates that about one-quarter of the world's population carries TB bacteria, although a much smaller percentage of these people will develop the disease. Even in the U.S., authorities believe that millions of people are infected with dormant tuberculosis and roughly 10,000 people develop active TB each year. These statistics are alarming, but even more alarming is the recent rise in multidrug-resistant TB (MDR TB) and extensively drug-resistant TB (XDR TB; Figure U5.1).

Figure U5.1 Treating Tuberculosis.

Over half a million people a year are diagnosed with drug-resistant TB. Successful treatment of these strains of TB requires treatment with at least five anti-TB drugs for at least 20 months. The duration and expense of treatment is a substantial burden, particularly in countries with fewer healthcare resources.

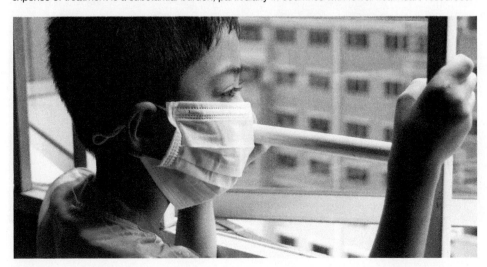

Treating these new super bugs and stopping their spread will require coordinated efforts from healthcare providers and careful attention to the chemistry involved in designing new drugs.

Unit 5: Introduction
How Can We Combat the Looming Crisis of Drug-Resistant Tuberculosis?

 To learn more about the biology and history of tuberculosis, watch **Video U5.1** in the Pearson eText.

Unit 5 opens with an overview of the biology and history of tuberculosis, one of the world's most lethal infectious diseases. Tuberculosis is an airborne disease caused by the bacterium, *Mycobacterium tuberculosis*. TB most often affects the lungs and can be spread from person to person through airborne droplets from sneezes and coughs (Figure U5.2). Infected individuals often experience symptoms that include bad

Figure U5.2 Tuberculosis Most Often Affects the Lungs.
People can get infected with the TB bacterium when they inhale droplets from a cough or sneeze of an infected person.

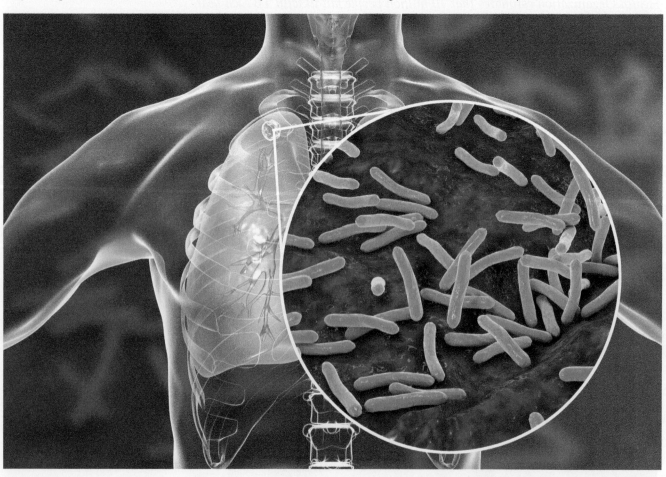

Figure U5.3 Incomplete Treatment of a Bacterial Infection Drives the Development of Drug Resistance.

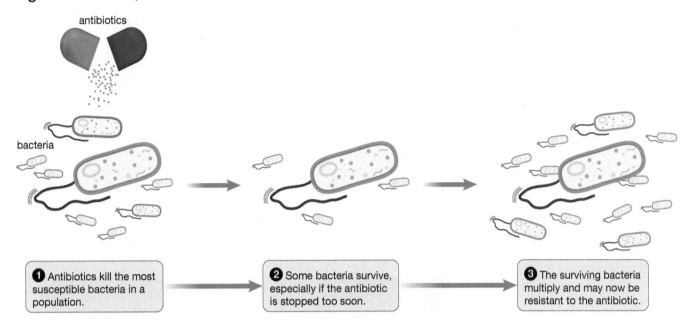

① Antibiotics kill the most susceptible bacteria in a population.

② Some bacteria survive, especially if the antibiotic is stopped too soon.

③ The surviving bacteria multiply and may now be resistant to the antibiotic.

coughs, weight loss, fever, and night sweats. When left untreated, TB kills about 45% of those infected. For patients who also have HIV, that number increases to nearly 100%.

In 2017 the U.S. Centers for Disease Control (CDC) issued an alarming report warning of an explosive rise in the number of tuberculosis infections that are resistant to antibiotics. Antibiotic resistance develops when healthcare practitioners don't correctly diagnose and treat a TB infection, or when patients are unable or unwilling to complete the treatment, which can take six to nine months (Figure U5.3). The CDC estimates that by 2040 30% of TB cases in Russia, for example, will be drug resistant. In this era of rapid, affordable travel, the emergence of drug resistant, potentially untreatable strains of TB anywhere is a global crisis.

Unfortunately, even when TB is not drug-resistant, patients typically need six months of consistent treatment to eradicate the bacteria that cause TB. In this unit, we will learn more about molecules like the tuberculosis drug, ethambutol (Figure U5.4). Ethambutol is one of the World Health Organization's Essential Medicines and is often included in the first set of drugs a TB patient is prescribed.

Ethambutol is an organic compound composed mostly of carbon and hydrogen that also contains oxygen and nitrogen atoms. We explore the structure, properties, and reactions of a variety of organic compounds in Chapters 13 and 14. We also investigate how the three-dimensional shape of organic compounds plays an important role in how they react in the human body. Even small differences in three-dimensional structure of ethambutol, for example, have a large impact on its ability to function effectively as an anti-TB drug.

Figure U5.4 Ethambutol.

Ethambutol, in combination with several other drugs, is part of the standard course of treatment for tuberculosis.

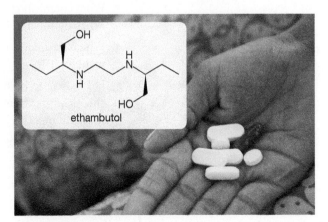

ethambutol

Unit 5 Chemistry Application: How Can We Use Chemistry to Combat Drug-Resistant TB?

The increase in both MDR-TB and XDR-TB is alarming. Resistant strains of TB require longer, more expensive treatment and are much more likely to be fatal (Figure U5.5). Combatting this ominous problem requires multiple approaches, including understanding the mechanisms that allow the TB bacteria to survive the drugs. This information can help researchers both design better drugs as well as identify molecules that may help restore the ability of our existing drugs to attack the disease.

Figure U5.5   Monitoring the Treatment of MDR-TB.

X-rays can be used to monitor a TB patient's response to treatment. The white, threadlike structures on this x-ray indicate the presence of TB in both this patient's lungs.

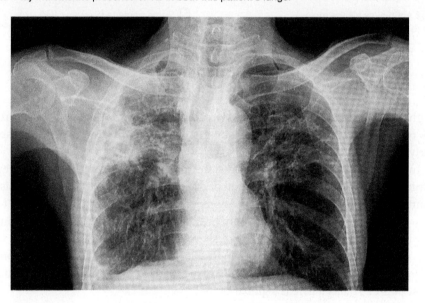

 ## Questions to Think About

What chemistry do we need to know to understand the challenges combatting drug-resistant TB? Here are some questions to consider as you move through Unit 5:

- What chemical characteristics of ethambutol and other TB drugs might help the drugs dissolve in the blood stream to fight the TB infection?
- Which structural features of the ethambutol molecule make it an effective treatment for TB?
- For a drug to be highly effective, do you think it should be extremely reactive chemically, extremely stable and non-reactive, or have a balance between these two extremes?
- What three-dimensional structural elements are important for a drug to be effective against TB?

What chemistry would you like to know in order to more fully understand this problem?

Now that we have an overview of this unit, let's step into Chapter 13 and learn more about the general characteristics of organic molecules like ethambutol and other TB drugs.

Chapter 13
Introduction to Organic Molecules

Organic molecules come in an enormous variety of sizes and shapes due to the variety of ways carbon atoms can be joined together.

Chapter Outline

Learning Objectives

13.1 Recognize the fundamental structural features of organic compounds and use appropriate representations to draw molecules.

13.2 Identify and draw the first ten acyclic simple alkanes (C_1–C_{10}) and the first four cycloalkanes (C_3–C_6).

13.3 Recognize branching in alkanes and draw structural isomers for branched alkanes and haloalkanes.

13.4 Identify alkenes and alkynes and draw *cis-trans* isomers of alkenes.

13.5 Identify and draw aromatic compounds.

13.6 Use the IUPAC system for naming organic compounds to convert from structure to name and from name to structure for simple alkanes, alkenes, alkynes, and benzene compounds.

Introduction

Organic chemistry is the study of carbon-based compounds. An entire branch of chemistry is dedicated to the study of molecules with carbon backbones, which may seem surprising at first. But once you witness the amazing diversity of the carbon-based molecules that are common in organic and biochemistry, you will come to recognize and appreciate the complexity and beauty of this branch of chemistry. From the food we eat and the reactions that run our cells to the drugs we take when we are sick, every second of our lives involves the molecules that are the subject of organic chemistry. Carbon-based organic molecules (Figure 13.1) are the building blocks in our bodies and just about everything that surrounds us.

Figure 13.1 Organic Chemistry.

Organic chemistry is all around us. **A)** Many life-saving drugs are organic molecules. **B)** The food we eat supplies the organic compounds our bodies need. **C)** Even the plastics we depend on to provide proper medical care are organic compounds.

A

B

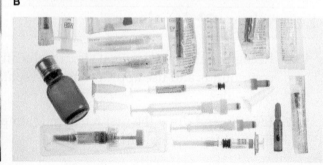

C

13.1 Organic Compounds

The term "organic" is used in several ways in our everyday language. For example, you hear it used generally to refer to environmentally friendly farming practices, or consumer products that are more natural than others. In chemistry, in contrast, we use the term organic very specifically to describe covalent compounds containing the element carbon. Carbon atoms have the unique ability to form multiple covalent bonds with each other and other atoms, making carbon the key element in a diverse array of covalent compounds. **Organic compounds** are composed mostly of carbon and hydrogen but may also include oxygen, nitrogen, sulfur, phosphorus, chlorine, and other elements.

Biomolecules, including large molecules such as proteins, carbohydrates, lipids, and DNA, are organic compounds (see BioConnect 6.1). Compounds that do not contain carbon and hydrogen are **inorganic compounds**. Sodium chloride (NaCl) is an ionic inorganic compound (Figure 13.2).

Apply what you have just learned: **Practice 13.1** in the Pearson eText.

Covalent Bonds in Carbon Compounds

In Chapter 6, you used Lewis structures to represent the structure of covalent compounds. In this chapter you continue to use Lewis structures for organic compounds, but you also will learn about other representations that show three-dimensional shape and provide a shorthand method for drawing large molecules. For example, methane (CH_4), the main component of natural gas, is a simple organic compound. Recall that

Figure 13.2 Organic and Inorganic Compounds.

Organic molecules such as the fats found in olive oil are composed primarily of carbon, hydrogen, and oxygen. Inorganic compounds, such as table salt (NaCl), do not contain carbon and hydrogen.

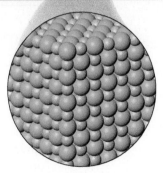

Figure 13.3 Carbon Forms Single, Double, and Triple Bonds.

When four atoms bond to carbon in an organic molecule a single bond forms between the two carbons. We represent a single bond as two electrons or as a line. When three atoms bond to a carbon atom a double bond forms between the two carbons (represented with two electron pairs or two lines). When just two atoms bond to a carbon atom a triple bond forms between the two carbons (represented with three electron pairs or as three lines).

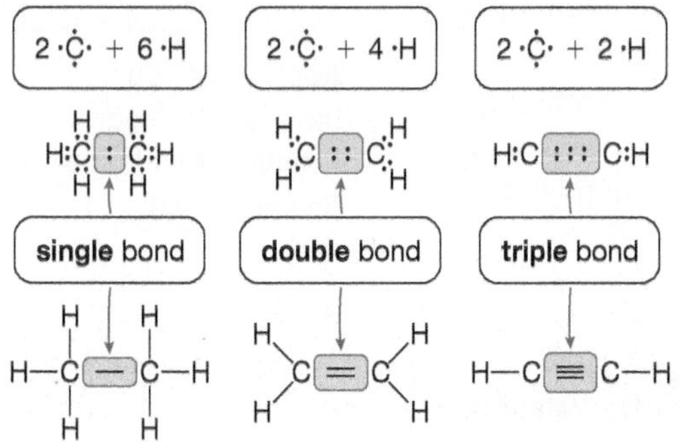

Figure 13.4 Carbon Compounds can Be Both Chains and Rings.

Carbon atoms link together in a variety of ways including straight chains, branched chains, and rings.

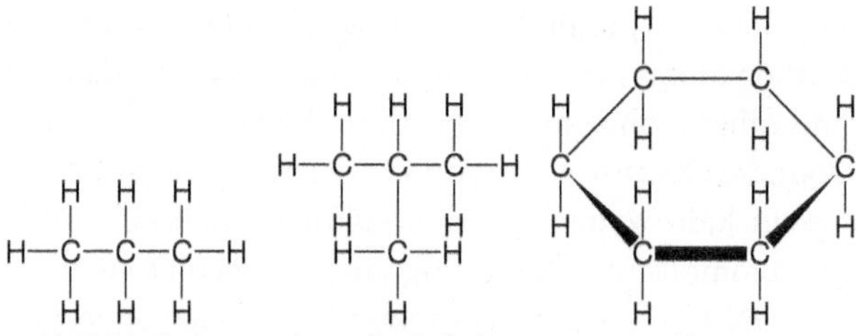

straight chain   branched chain   ring

carbon is a Group 4A element on the periodic table and it has four valence electrons available for bonding. Hydrogen is a Group 1A element with one valence electron. As you can see here, the Lewis structure for methane has four single bonds each containing two shared electrons from carbon and hydrogen. Carbon always forms four covalent bonds and hydrogen forms one covalent bond.

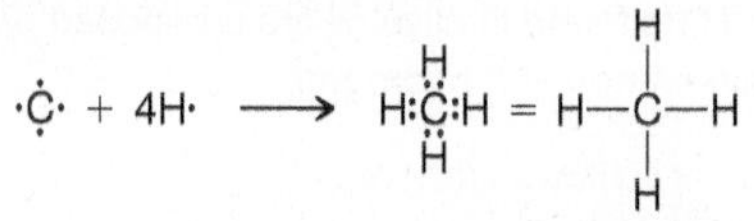

methane

Carbon can form single, double, and triple bonds (Figure 13.3). Carbon is a Group 4A element with four valence electrons that always forms four covalent bonds. These four bonds can be: four single bonds; one double bond and two single bonds; or one triple bond and one single bond.

Organic compounds are composed of carbon backbone chains (both straight chains and branched chains), and rings (Figure 13.4). We discuss the length of the chain, and the types of rings in more detail in the upcoming sections of this chapter and future chapters.

 Apply what you have just learned: **Practice 13.2** in the Pearson eText.

Shapes of Organic Molecules

Molecular structure and shape, which we discussed in Section 6.4, play a critical role in how molecules function. (Revisit BioConnect 6.2 to review the discussion of the biological impacts of molecular shape.)

Recall that you can predict the shape of organic molecules using VSEPR theory (Section 6.4). When carbon is bonded to two other atoms, as it is, for example, in the ethyne molecule, the molecular shape is linear and has a bond angle of 180° (Figure 13.5). Three atoms around carbon produce a trigonal planar shape with 120° bond angles. Four atoms around carbon produce a tetrahedral shape with 109.5° bond angles. Recall that when there is more than one central atom in a molecule, you apply VSEPR theory to each central atom individually.

Figure 13.5 The Number of Bonds Between Carbons Changes the Shape of the Molecule and Its Chemical Properties.

Carbon forms single, double, or triple bonds with other carbons. Different bond types produce different bond angles and affect the chemical structure and properties of substances.

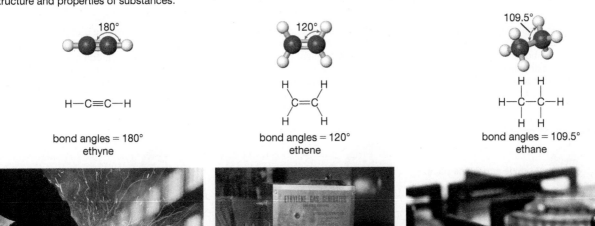

H—C≡C—H

bond angles = 180°
ethyne

bond angles = 120°
ethene

bond angles = 109.5°
ethane

Ethyne (also known as acetylene) produces a high-temperature flame useful for welding and cutting metal.

Ethene (also known as ethylene) is a naturally occurring plant hormone that is a gas at room temperature. Fruit production operations use it to ripen stored fruit.

Ethane is second most abundant compound in natural gas (after methane). Natural gas is used in many parts of the world to heat homes and cook food.

Apply what you have just learned: **Practice 13.3** in the Pearson eText.

Representing Organic Molecules

Chemists use a variety of representations of molecules to convey information about the structure and shape of organic compounds (Figure 13.6). Sometimes the chemical formula conveys enough information while other times a three-dimensional (3D) model showing molecular shape is more useful.

For organic compounds we generally use one of three models to show three-dimensional molecular shape. A space-filling model illustrates the space occupied by the atoms and bonds. A ball-and-stick model shows the atoms, bonds, and the three-dimensional shape of a molecule.

Wedge-dash drawings show three-dimensional shapes using lines for bonds in the plane of the paper, wedges for bonds that extend out from the page and dashes for bonds that extend back behind the page. Learn 13.1 demonstrates how to draw a wedge-dash drawing to represent three-dimensional structures of organic molecules.

Figure 13.6 Three-Dimensional Representations of Methane.

A) space-filling model, **B)** ball-and-stick model, **C)** wedge-dash model.

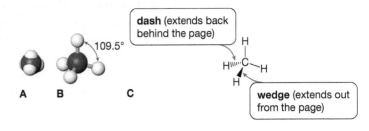

dash (extends back behind the page)

wedge (extends out from the page)

Predict answers and see step-by-step solutions: **Learn 13.1:** Drawing Wedge-Dash Structures of Molecules in the Pearson eText.

Apply what you have just learned: **Practice 13.4** in the Pearson eText.

Figure 13.7 Common Bonding Patterns for Heteroatoms in Organic Molecules.

Each heteroatom forms a specific number of bonds and has a specific number of lone pairs of electrons. The number of lone pairs allows you to predict the number of bonds each heteroatom forms in an organic molecule.

Oxygen in organic compounds
Oxygen is a heteroatom that often bonds to carbon through both a single bond and a double bond. Oxygen generally forms two covalent bonds, has two lone pairs of electrons, and when bonded to a carbon with a single bond has a bent shape with an approximate bond angle of 109.5°.

 2 bonds and 2 lone pairs

Nitrogen in organic compounds
Nitrogen is a heteroatom that generally forms three covalent bonds to other atoms, has one lone pair of electrons, and adopts a trigonal pyramidal shape with an approximate bond angle of 109.5°.

 3 bonds and 1 lone pair

Fluorine in organic compounds
Fluorine, and other halogens, form one single bond to carbon atoms in organic compounds and have three lone pairs of electrons.

 1 bond and 3 lone pairs

Tuberculosis (TB) is a disease caused by *Mycobacterium tuberculosis* (*M. tuberculosis*) bacteria. Ethambutol is one of the drugs used to treat TB, discussed in the Unit 5 Introduction. Ethambutol, an organic molecule, has carbon and hydrogen atoms as you would expect in an organic compound and also includes oxygen and nitrogen heteroatoms.

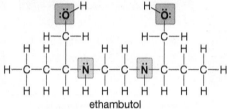

ethambutol

Heteroatoms in Organic Compounds

Apply what you have just learned: **Practice 13.5** in the Pearson eText.

In addition to hydrogen, other non-metal elements, such as oxygen, nitrogen, phosphorus, sulfur, and the halogens covalently bond to the carbon backbone of organic molecules to compose the millions of different organic molecules on Earth. **Heteroatoms** are the atoms in an organic compound that are not carbon and hydrogen (Figure 13.7).

Condensed Structures

Most organic compounds are quite large. Their size presents a challenge when we want to represent molecular structure. For this reason, chemists have developed a variety of shorthand strategies to represent organic molecules. **Condensed structures**, for example, provide all the atoms in a molecule but do not generally show bonds unless there is branching in the carbon backbone or heteroatoms are present. More specifically, a condensed structure shows the hydrogen atoms attached to each carbon as groups of atoms, such as $-CH_3$. A condensed structure does not illustrate bonds between carbon atoms, and between carbon and hydrogen. The condensed structure for propane (C_3H_8) is shown here as an example.

$$C_3H_8 \qquad CH_3CH_2CH_3 \qquad \text{(Lewis structure of propane)}$$

molecular formula   condensed structure   Lewis structure

least expanded ⟶ most expanded

Note that the molecular formula indicates the number of each atom present in the compound and the Lewis structure shows the arrangement of all the atoms in the compound. The condensed structure is in between the two in terms of detail.

In a condensed structure the atoms are written from left to right mirroring the Lewis structure (Figure 13.8). For example, in the condensed structure in Figure 13.8,

Figure 13.8 Condensed Structures.

Condensed structures represent the Lewis structure of organic molecules. To create a condensed structure, begin with the carbon on the left, representing each carbon and indicating the groups attached to it.

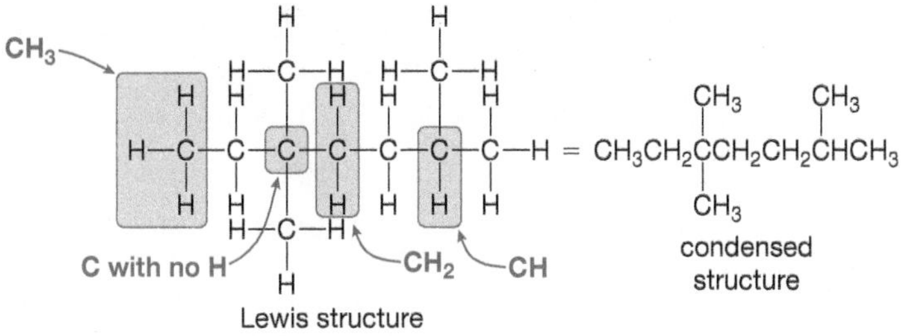

the carbon atom that is bonded to three hydrogen atoms in the condensed structure is written as CH_3; the carbon attached to two hydrogen atoms is written as CH_2; and the carbon atoms that are bonded to one hydrogen atom are written as CH.

> Predict answers and see step-by-step solutions: **Learn 13.2:** Drawing Condensed Structures in the Pearson eText.
>
> Apply what you have just learned: **Practice 13.6** in the Pearson eText.

Skeletal Structures

Another shorthand approach to representing organic molecules involves **skeletal structures.** This method omits both carbon and hydrogen atoms from the structure to make drawing faster and less tedious. Instead of writing the symbol for each carbon and hydrogen atom in the molecule, we represent the carbon atoms as the end of each bond, or as the intersection of two bonds. The bonds between carbon atoms are lines, and the angles of the bonds indicate molecular shape. This angle drawing, which is sometimes referred to as "ziz-zag" drawing, illustrates the tetrahedral shape of each carbon. You can predict the location and number of hydrogen atoms on a skeletal structure by remembering that carbon requires four bonds. A pentane molecule, shown here, has five carbon atoms connected by four bonds. You omit the hydrogen atoms, which are shown in the Lewis structure, in the skeletal structure.

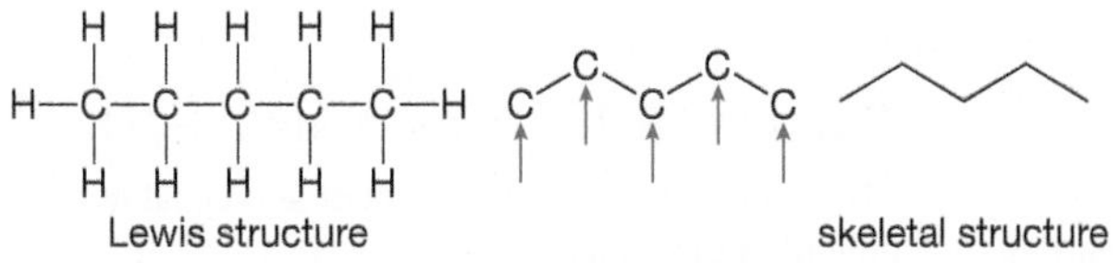

Lewis structure

skeletal structure

Skeletal structures for rings are geometric shapes with carbon atoms at the corners. See the example shown here for cyclopentane. You can again predict where the hydrogen atoms are by knowing that carbon is most stable with four bonds. Each carbon in cyclopentane is bonded to two hydrogen atoms.

Lewis structure

skeletal structure

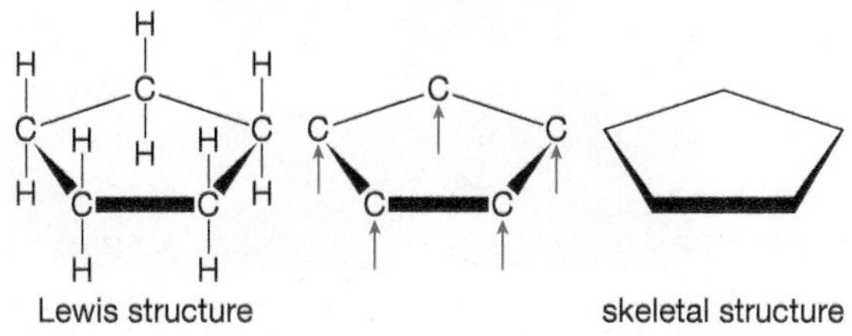

When using skeletal structures to show organic molecules that contain heteroatoms, such as oxygen and nitrogen, you include the heteroatoms along with their bonds. You also include any hydrogen atoms that are attached to heteroatoms on the structure. Consider the Lewis structure and skeletal structure of the amino acid serine shown here.

Lewis structure   skeletal structure

Predict answers and see step-by-step solutions: **Learn 13.3:** Interpreting Skeletal Structures in the Pearson eText.

Apply what you have just learned: **Practice 13.7** in the Pearson eText.

Quiz yourself on the content of this section: **Check 13.1** in the Pearson eText.

13.2 Alkanes and Cycloalkanes

Hydrocarbons are organic compounds that only contain the elements carbon and hydrogen. In the next three sections, we introduce four different types of hydrocarbons. The first type are the **alkanes**, which are hydrocarbons that have only C—C single bonds and C—H single bonds. Alkanes are sometimes described as **saturated** because each carbon is bonded to the maximum number of hydrogen atoms.

Acyclic alkanes are alkanes that can be either straight-chains or branched chains, but do not contain cyclic (ring) structures. Propane is a straight-chain acyclic alkane with three carbon atoms arranged in a chain and eight hydrogen atoms bonded to the carbon atoms (Figure 13.9).

Stearic acid is a more complex molecule that has an acyclic alkane "tail" but also contains two oxygen atoms. Because it includes oxygen, stearic acid is not a hydrocarbon molecule even though it includes a hydrocarbon tail. Stearic acid is found in animal fat. Many biomolecules contain alkane tails that are often represented using the skeletal "zig-zag" structure (Figure 13.10).

Figure 13.9 Propane.

This acyclic alkane has three carbon atoms and functions as a fuel that can be easily transported in tanks to power gas grills and stoves. Notice that each carbon atom in the propane molecule has four bonds. (Remember, carbon can only form four bonds.)

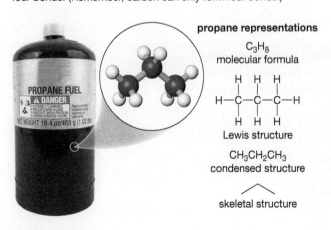

propane representations

C_3H_8
molecular formula

Lewis structure

$CH_3CH_2CH_3$
condensed structure

skeletal structure

Figure 13.10 Stearic Acid ($C_{18}H_{36}O_2$).

This molecule is a component of animal fat and features a long hydrocarbon chain.

Cycloalkanes are alkanes that contain carbon atoms arranged in one or more rings. Cyclohexane, shown here, is a simple cycloalkane with six carbon atoms bonded to one another to form a hexagon shape. We explore the other simple cycloalkanes with between three and six carbon atoms later in this section. In addition to the simple cycloalkanes, multiple rings of various sizes are found throughout nature and often form the backbone of complex large molecules, such as the hormone testosterone. Notice that there are both five- and six- carbon rings in the testosterone molecule shown here with cyclohexane.

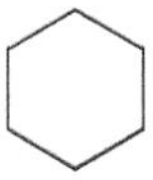

cyclohexane 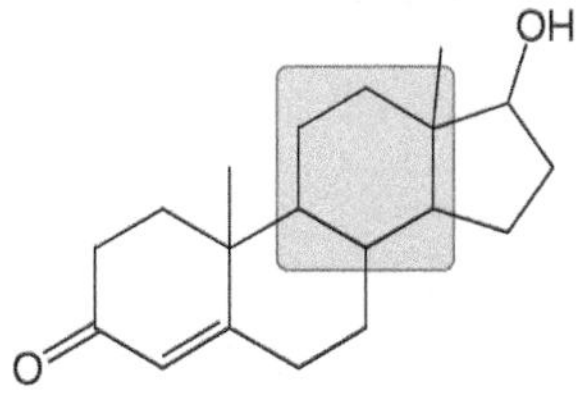   testosterone

Straight-Chain Alkanes

Table 13.1 lists the straight-chain alkanes that have between one and ten carbon atoms. Methane (CH_4) is the simplest of the alkanes with only one carbon atom. Ethane (C_2H_6) contains two carbon atoms. Propane (C_3H_8) contains three carbon atoms, and so on. Prefixes indicate chain length, and the –*ane* ending indicates the molecule is an alkane. The general formula for acyclic alkanes (no rings) is C_nH_{2n+2}, where "*n*" is the number of carbon atoms. Butane, for example, has four carbon atoms ($n = 4$), and ten hydrogen atoms ($2n + 2 = 10$). Since each carbon in an alkane has four atoms attached, each carbon is tetrahedral with 109.5° bond angles.

> Apply what you
> have just learned:
> **Practice 13.8** in the
> Pearson eText.

Cycloalkanes

In addition to chains, carbon also forms saturated rings called cycloalkanes. We form the name of simple cycloalkanes by adding the prefix *cyclo-* to the acyclic alkane names. The prefix *cyclo-* indicates that the molecule has a ring (cyclic) structure present. The simplest cycloalkane is cyclopropane, which contains three carbon atoms linked together in a ring. The propane part of the name indicates that the cyclopropane molecule has three carbons. The general formula for a cycloalkane is C_nH_{2n}. Notice that each cycloalkane has two fewer hydrogen atoms than the corresponding acyclic alkane.

Table 13.1 Names and Structures of the First Ten Straight-Chain Alkanes.

Number of carbon atoms	Prefix	Name of alkane	Molecular formula	Condensed structure	Skeletal structure
1	meth	methane	CH_4	CH_4	
2	eth	ethane	C_2H_6	CH_3CH_3	
3	prop	propane	C_3H_8	$CH_3CH_2CH_3$	
4	but	butane	C_4H_{10}	$CH_3CH_2CH_2CH_3$	
5	pent	pentane	C_5H_{12}	$CH_3CH_2CH_2CH_2CH_3$	
6	hex	hexane	C_6H_{14}	$CH_3CH_2CH_2CH_2CH_2CH_3$	
7	hept	heptane	C_7H_{16}	$CH_3CH_2CH_2CH_2CH_2CH_2CH_3$	
8	oct	octane	C_8H_{18}	$CH_3CH_2CH_2CH_2CH_2CH_2CH_2CH_3$	
9	non	nonane	C_9H_{20}	$CH_3CH_2CH_2CH_2CH_2CH_2CH_2CH_2CH_3$	
10	dec	decane	$C_{10}H_{22}$	$CH_3CH_2CH_2CH_2CH_2CH_2CH_2CH_2CH_2CH_3$	

Table 13.2 Names and Structures of Common Cycloalkanes.

Name	cyclopropane	cyclobutane	cyclopentane	cyclohexane
Molecular formula	C_3H_6	C_4H_8	C_5H_{10}	C_6H_{12}
Ball-and-stick model				
Skeletal structure	△	□	⬠	⬡

Apply what you have just learned: **Practice 13.9** in the Pearson eText.

While rings of any size are possible, rings that contain between three to six carbon atoms are very common in nature. For this reason, we list only these simple cycloalkanes in Table 13.2. Skeletal structures are particularly useful for representing rings. Cyclopropane takes the shape of a triangle, cyclobutane a square, cyclopentane a pentagon, and cyclohexane a hexagon.

Properties of Alkanes

Alkanes play many useful roles in our everyday lives, particularly as a source of energy. The small alkanes (methane, ethane, propane, butane) are gases at room temperature and we use them as fuel in a variety of heating and cooking devices. Natural gas (methane; CH_4), for example, powers furnaces, gas cooktops, and water heaters. Alkanes with five to eight carbon atoms are liquids at room temperature and are the main components in gasoline, which powers combustion engine automobiles (Figure 13.11). Alkanes

Figure 13.11 Refining Crude Oil.

Crude oil contains a diverse array of hydrocarbons. The refining process employs heat to separate the molecules based on their chemical properties. The smaller molecules have fewer carbons, lower boiling points, and burn easily. Larger molecules have higher boiling points and do not burn as easily.

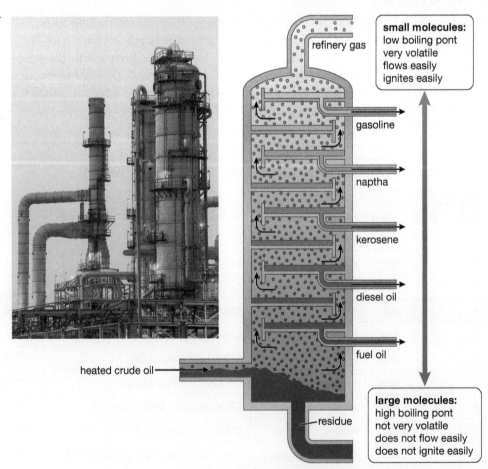

small molecules:
low boiling pont
very volatile
flows easily
ignites easily

refinery gas

gasoline

naptha

kerosene

diesel oil

fuel oil

heated crude oil

residue

large molecules:
high boiling pont
not very volatile
does not flow easily
does not ignite easily

Figure 13.12 The 2010 Deepwater Horizon Fire.

On April 20, 2010, on the off-shore drilling rig Deepwater Horizon, a geyser of drilling mud, methane gas, and water erupted and quickly exploded. A massive fire burned as the flammable mix of hydrocarbons erupted from the well.

Figure 13.13 A Floating Oil Slick After the Deepwater Horizon Spill in 2010.

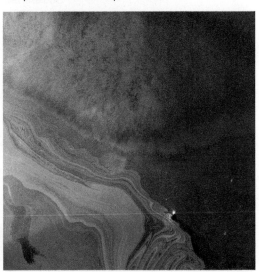

with nine to seventeen carbon atoms are also liquids at room temperature. They are the primary components in the other less common fuels such as kerosene, diesel, and jet fuels. Motor oil is a complex mixture of alkanes of all sizes.

Alkanes contain only nonpolar C—C and C—H bonds, so they are nonpolar molecules that are insoluble in water. Recall from Section 11.2 that "like-dissolves-like." Because water is polar and alkanes are nonpolar, water and alkanes do not mix. Alkanes have densities ranging from 0.62 g/mL on the low end to 0.79 g/mL on the high end. Notice that alkanes are less dense than water, which has a density of 1.00 g/mL.

These two properties of alkanes—their insolubility in water and their density—can lead to dramatic environmental impacts when crude oil spills into the ocean (Figure 13.12). When oil enters a body of water, it does not mix with water. Instead it forms a layer on the surface of the water that can spread out across a large region (Figure 13.13).

Reactions of Alkanes

Since alkanes are nonpolar without functional groups present, they are not considered generally reactive. However, alkanes readily react with oxygen in combustion reactions to produce carbon dioxide, water, and release energy. Methane, for example, undergoes combustion to release energy that we harness to cook our food and heat our homes (Figure 13.14).

$$CH_4(g) + 2O_2(g) \rightarrow CO_2(g) + 2H_2O(g) + \text{energy}$$
methane

The use of natural gas, or methane, as a fuel source is rapidly growing in popularity as it becomes more readily available. The use of natural gas, however, is complicated, because methane is a gas at room temperature and therefore is difficult to contain. The potential for gas leaks is a big safety concern, as leaks can lead to dangerous explosions. The presence of unreacted natural gas in the atmosphere is also a concern because methane is a particularly potent greenhouse gas that contributes to the greenhouse effect and climate change. Increasing dependence on natural gas for fuel could lead to more leaks, and more unwanted greenhouse gases in the atmosphere.

Figure 13.14 Combustion of Methane in a Cooktop.

Figure 13.15 Biodiesel Contains Methyl Stearate.

Biodiesel releases fewer toxic substances into the atmosphere when combusted compared to gasoline.

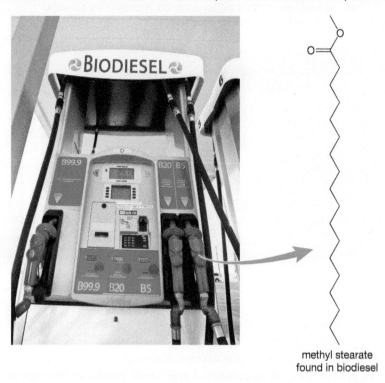

methyl stearate
found in biodiesel

Another common alkane and a key component of gasoline, octane undergoes a combustion reaction in gas-powered automobiles.

$$2C_8H_{18}(g) + 25O_2(g) \rightarrow 16CO_2(g) + 18H_2O(g) + \text{energy}$$
octane

Unfortunately, combustion of gasoline results in undesired side products. Scientists are actively searching for alternatives to fossil fuels, such as octane, that come from oil deposits deep in the ground. Biofuels have been in development for many years and, while not the answer to all the concerns surrounding combustion engine fuels, they tend to burn cleaner, releasing less carbon soot into the atmosphere. One example of a biofuel molecule is methyl stearate, which like octane can undergo combustion to produce energy and fuel vehicles (Figure 13.15). Notice that the methyl stearate molecule has a long alkane chain, but also contains two oxygen atoms on one end of the molecule.

 Quiz yourself on the content of this section: **Check 13.2** in the Pearson eText.

13.3 Branched Alkanes and Haloalkanes

In addition to simple straight-chain alkanes, there are also alkane molecules that have carbon chains that branch off of the central backbone of carbon atoms. These alkanes are **branched alkanes**. For example, a molecule with four carbon atoms can exist as a straight chain of carbon atoms or instead, one of its carbon atoms can be attached to the middle carbon in the chain, creating a branch (Figure 13.16). The latter molecule is a branched alkane. While these two molecules have the same chemical formula, they are two different molecules with different names and different properties. A branch is often referred to as a **substituent**, which is an atom or group of atoms that replaces a hydrogen atom on a carbon backbone chain.

One common branched alkane is polyethylene, the world's most abundant plastic. Manufacturers produce over 80 million tons of polyethylene each year. Polyethylene can adopt a straight-chain or a branched-chain structure. Chemists control whether branching will occur by adjusting the manufacturing process. The branches alter the characteristics of the plastic. The structure of both the straight-chain and branched-chain polyethylene molecules contains extremely long hydrocarbon chains, only part of which are shown in each structure in Figure 13.17. VisibleChem Video 13.6 describes how these plastic molecules are made.

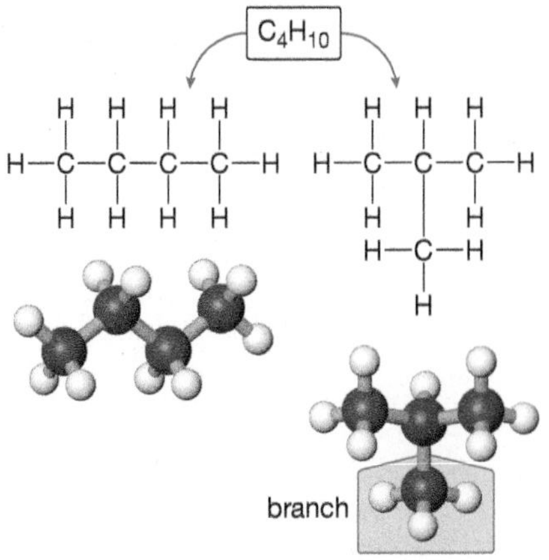

Haloalkanes

Alkanes that contain one or more atoms of the halogen family (F, Cl, Br, or I) are **haloalkanes.** Isoflurane is a haloalkane with several halogen atoms

Figure 13.16 Branching in C_4H_{10}.

C_4H_{10} can exist as a straight-chain alkane or as a branched alkane.

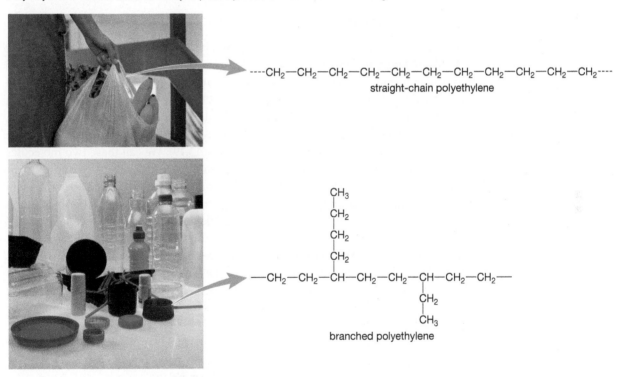

branch

Figure 13.17 The Structure of Polyethylene.

Polyethylene is used to make a variety of plastic products. It can be either a straight chain or a branched alkane.

$$----CH_2—CH_2—CH_2—CH_2—CH_2—CH_2—CH_2—CH_2—CH_2—CH_2—CH_2----$$
straight-chain polyethylene

branched polyethylene

Figure 13.18 Isoflurane Is a Haloalkane Commonly Used As a General Anesthetic.

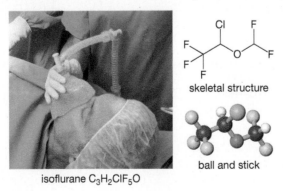

skeletal structure

ball and stick

isoflurane $C_3H_2ClF_5O$

bonded to the carbon atoms in the molecule (Figure 13.18). Isoflurane is a general anesthetic on the World Health Organization's Model List of Essential Medicines. In the isoflurane molecule, there are several halogen atoms in the hydrocarbon chain including three fluorine atoms on one carbon, two fluorine atoms on another carbon, and a single chlorine atom on yet another carbon atom. Notice that the skeletal structure omits the carbon atoms and hydrogen atoms as expected, but the halogens and other heteroatoms are indicated.

Chloropentane is a simple haloalkane. It has one chlorine substituent (shown in green) bonded to one of the carbon atoms in the chain. The halogen atom in haloalkane molecules forms one bond to carbon and has three lone pairs of electrons. Small haloalkanes, such as chloropentane, are often used in the laboratory as building blocks to make larger more complex molecules.

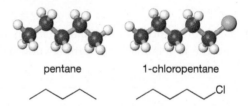

pentane   1-chloropentane

Structural Isomers

The arrangement of atoms in a molecule of any type is not provided in the molecular formula. In fact, there are often several different ways to arrange the atoms for a single molecular formula. Butane (C_4H_{10}), for example, is a four-carbon straight-chain alkane with the carbon atoms in one continuous chain. As we saw earlier in this section (Figure 13.16), another possible arrangement of atoms for this same molecular formula involves linking the carbon atoms in a different way—with a branch composed of one carbon atom, and three hydrogen atoms (Figure 13.19). We call these two molecules **structural isomers**, compounds that have the same molecular formula but different arrangement of atoms. Structural isomers are possible for all types of molecules; we will explore this concept further in the next several chapters. Each structural isomer has its own unique name. You will learn how to name alkanes at the end of this chapter.

Figure 13.20 shows the structural isomers for the haloalkane with the formula C_3H_7Cl. In this case, the chlorine atom is on one end of the chain of carbon atoms in one of the isomers, and on the carbon atom in the center on the other isomer. Note that placing a chlorine atom on the other end of the chain results in a molecule that is the same as the first molecule. For this reason, there are only two structural isomers for the formula C_3H_7Cl.

Figure 13.19 Structural Isomers for C_4H_{10}.

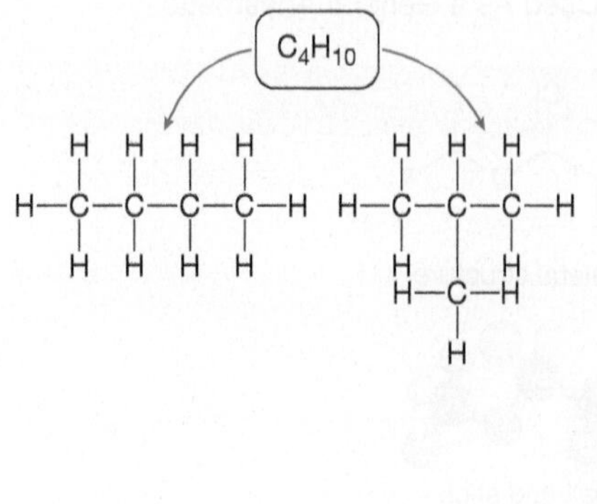

Figure 13.20 Structural Isomers for C_3H_7Cl.

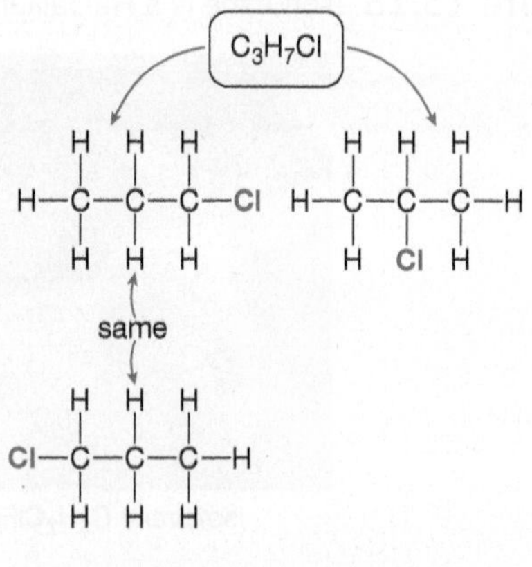

Figure 13.21 Two Essential Amino Acids that Are Structural Isomers.

Leucine and isoleucine are amino acids that are structural isomers. Essential amino acids must be consumed in the food we eat. Both animal and plant protein are good sources of essential amino acids.

The amino acids, leucine and isoleucine, are biologically important structural isomers (Figure 13.21). Notice that the CH_3 group is attached to the third carbon in the chain in one structure, and to the second carbon in the chain in the other structure. Amino acids are the building blocks of proteins, and these structurally similar, but functionally different, amino acids are both necessary for proper cellular function and health. Both leucine and isoleucine are essential amino acids, which means that our body cannot produce them, and we must obtain these compounds from the food we eat.

Gaining a good understanding of the bonding patterns in the alkanes and how we represent organic compounds sets the stage for much of the information in the chapters to come. Explore VisibleChem Videos 13.1–13.3 to expand your knowledge of the structure of this important class of hydrocarbons.

> Watch this concept come to life: **VisibleChem Video 13.1:** Rotation Around Carbon-Carbon Single Bonds, **VisibleChem Video 13.2:** Drawing Structural Isomers, and **VisibleChem Video 13.3:** Interpreting Skeletal Structures of Large Organic Molecules in the Pearson eText.
>
> Apply what you have just learned: **Practice 13.10–13.12** in the Pearson eText.
>
> Quiz yourself on the content of this section: **Check 13.3** in the Pearson eText.

13.4 Alkenes and Alkynes

Now that we've explored the alkanes, a saturated family of hydrocarbons, we turn our attention to two families of hydrocarbons that contain carbon-carbon multiple bonds. Recall that saturated hydrocarbons are so-called because each carbon is bonded to the maximum number of hydrogen atoms. **Alkenes** are compounds that contain carbon-carbon double bonds. **Alkynes** contain carbon-carbon triple bonds. Because alkenes and alkynes have double and triple bonds respectively, they are unsaturated hydrocarbons.

The double and triple bonds in alkenes and alkynes are considered **functional groups**. A functional group is an atom or group of atoms that is reactive. Functional groups are the locations on molecules where chemical reactions take place. You will learn about many functional groups in this part of the text, and we explore some of the reactions in which functional groups take part later in this section.

And just as cycloalkanes are cyclic structures containing only carbon-carbon single bonds. Cycloalkenes are cyclic structures that contain at least one carbon-carbon double bond. Cycloalkynes are cyclic structures that contain at least one carbon-carbon triple bond.

Alkenes and alkynes are common molecules in nature. Vitamins, drug molecules, and natural antifungal compounds are just a few of the common compounds with double and triple bonds (Figure 13.22).

Figure 13.22 Alkenes and Alkynes in Our World.

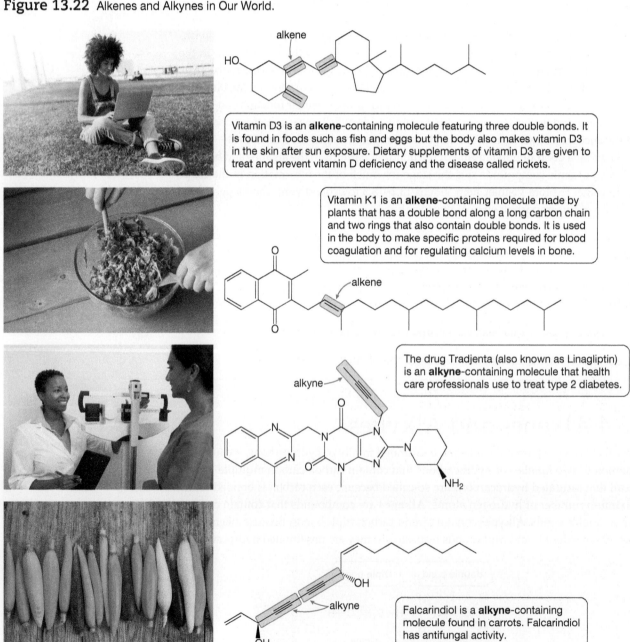

Vitamin D3 is an **alkene**-containing molecule featuring three double bonds. It is found in foods such as fish and eggs but the body also makes vitamin D3 in the skin after sun exposure. Dietary supplements of vitamin D3 are given to treat and prevent vitamin D deficiency and the disease called rickets.

Vitamin K1 is an **alkene**-containing molecule made by plants that has a double bond along a long carbon chain and two rings that also contain double bonds. It is used in the body to make specific proteins required for blood coagulation and for regulating calcium levels in bone.

The drug Tradjenta (also known as Linagliptin) is an **alkyne**-containing molecule that health care professionals use to treat type 2 diabetes.

Falcarindiol is a **alkyne**-containing molecule found in carrots. Falcarindiol has antifungal activity.

Figure 13.23 Ethene.

Ethene, also called ethylene, is an alkane with two carbon atoms joined by a double bond. Each carbon atom has two additional hydrogen atoms. Ethene is a plant hormone often used to ripen fruit such as bananas that are picked and shipped while green.

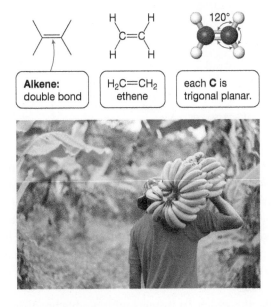

| Alkene: double bond | $H_2C=CH_2$ ethene | each **C** is trigonal planar. |

Figure 13.24 Ethyne.

Ethyne, also called acetylene, is an alkyne with a carbon-carbon triple bond. Each carbon has just one hydrogen atom. The combustion of ethyne is used in welding to melt metals.

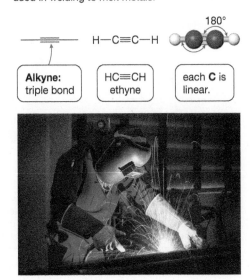

| Alkyne: triple bond | $HC\equiv CH$ ethyne | each **C** is linear. |

Simple Alkenes and Alkynes

The general formula for alkenes is C_nH_{2n}. Notice that an alkene has two fewer hydrogen atoms than an alkane (which you will recall have the general formula C_nH_{2n+2}). In the simplest alkene–ethene (C_2H_4)—a double bond connects two carbon atoms, and each carbon atom is bonded to two hydrogen atoms. The corresponding alkane–ethane (C_2H_6)—has two additional hydrogen atoms. The shape at each carbon linked to the double bond in an alkene is trigonal planar with 120° bond angles. Ethene, also commonly referred to as ethylene, is a plant hormone that plays a critical role in promoting the ripening of fruit (Figure 13.23).

Ethyne (C_2H_2), also known as acetylene, is the simplest member of the alkyne family (Figure 13.24). The ethyne molecule has a carbon-carbon triple bond and each carbon atom is bonded to just one hydrogen atom. The general formula for alkynes is C_nH_{2n-2}. Each carbon is bonded to two atoms, so each carbon has a linear shape with 180° bond angles. Acetylene is commonly used in welding where it undergoes combustion with oxygen to produce very high temperatures.

Table 13.3 provides a comparison of alkanes, alkenes, and alkynes.

Table 13.3 Comparison of the Simple Alkanes, Alkenes, and Alkynes

Alkane	Alkene	Alkyne
CH_3-CH_3 ethane	$H_2C=CH_2$ ethene (ethylene)	$HC\equiv CH$ ethyne (acetylene)
$CH_3-CH_2-CH_3$ propane	$H_3C-CH=CH_2$ propene	$H_3C-C\equiv CH$ propyne

Apply what you have just learned: **Practice 13.13 and 13.14** in the Pearson eText.

Cis-Trans Isomers

Like alkanes, both alkenes and alkynes have structural isomers. For example, there are three alkene structural isomers with the molecular formula C_4H_8.

$$CH_2=CHCH_2CH_3 \quad CH_3CH=CHCH_3 \quad CH_2=\overset{\overset{\displaystyle CH_3}{|}}{C}CH_3$$

Figure 13.25 *Cis* and *Trans* Isomers.

Rotation around a carbon double bond is restricted, which results in *cis-trans* isomers. The *trans* isomer for this molecule has the CH_3 groups on opposite sides of the double bond, whereas the *cis* isomer has the two CH_3 groups on the same side.

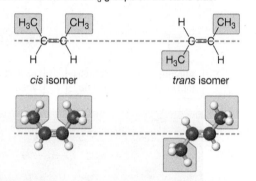

cis isomer   *trans* isomer

This view shows the similar groups (in boxes) on the same side of the line through the double bond.

This view shows the similar groups (in boxes) on the opposite side of the line through the double bond.

Figure 13.26 *Cis-Trans* Isomers Often Have Unique Biological Properties.

The drug Tecfidera only contains the *trans* isomer of this molecule, which is used in the treatment of multiple sclerosis (MS). The *cis* isomer is not effective in treating MS.

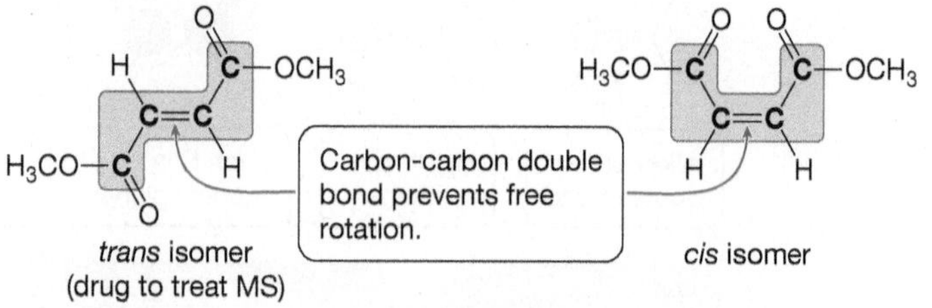

trans isomer
(drug to treat MS)

Carbon-carbon double bond prevents free rotation.

cis isomer

In addition to structural isomers, alkenes have another possible type of isomer that alkynes don't have. While carbon-carbon single bonds freely rotate, as you learned in Visi-bleChem Video 13.1, the carbon-carbon double bonds in alkenes cannot freely rotate. In contrast to C—C bonds, C=C bonds lock groups into fixed positions. *Groups on one side of the double bond cannot rotate to the other side in alkene molecules.* For this reason, alkenes form ***cis-trans* isomers** (Figure 13.25).

For C_4H_8 for example, the structural isomers with double bonds in between the second and third carbon are *cis-trans* isomers. There are two ways the atoms around the double bond can arrange themselves. The two CH_3 groups can be on the same side of the double bond or on opposite sides. These two structures represent different compounds; one is the *cis* isomer the other is the *trans* isomer. A ***cis* isomer** occurs when substituent groups are on the same side of the double bond. A ***trans* isomer** occurs when substituent groups are on the opposite side of the double bond.

Often the *cis* and *trans* isomers of the same molecule behave very differently, and chemists take this into account when they design drugs. The drug Tecfidera, for example, is used to treat patients with relapsing multiple sclerosis (MS). Only the *trans* isomer has the desired medicinal effect (Figure 13.26).

Reactions of Alkenes

Organic molecules undergo specific characteristic chemical reactions depending on which functional group is present. Alkenes, for example, undergo **addition reactions.** As shown here, addition reactions add new groups (X and Y) to the double bond of an alkene converting the double bond to a single bond and adding the new groups to the molecule. Table 13.4 is a summary of alkene addition reactions.

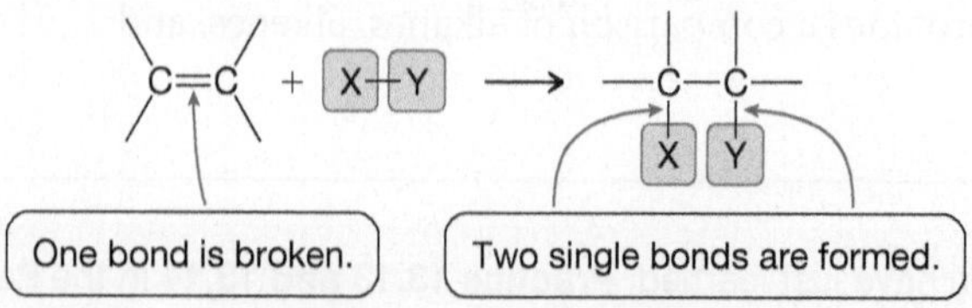

$$C=C + X-Y \longrightarrow -C-C-$$
$$X \quad Y$$

One bond is broken.   Two single bonds are formed.

When hydrogen (H_2) adds to an alkene the addition reaction is called **hydrogenation** and produces an alkane. When halogens, such as Cl_2 and Br_2, add to alkenes, the addition reaction is called **halogenation.** Halogenation reactions produce **dihalides,** which are molecules with two halogens present in the molecule. Hydrogen halides, such as HCl and HBr, undergo addition reactions called **hydrohalogenation** reactions to produce haloalkanes. **Hydration** reactions involve the addition of water to an alkene.

Alkene polymerization reactions are another type of addition reaction. Polymers are large molecules made up of repeating units called monomers. There are many different types of polymers and monomers. Our focus in this section is on polymers that

Table 13.4 Summary Table of Alkene Addition Reactions.

Hydrogenation	**Hydrogenation** is the addition of hydrogen (H_2) to an alkene. 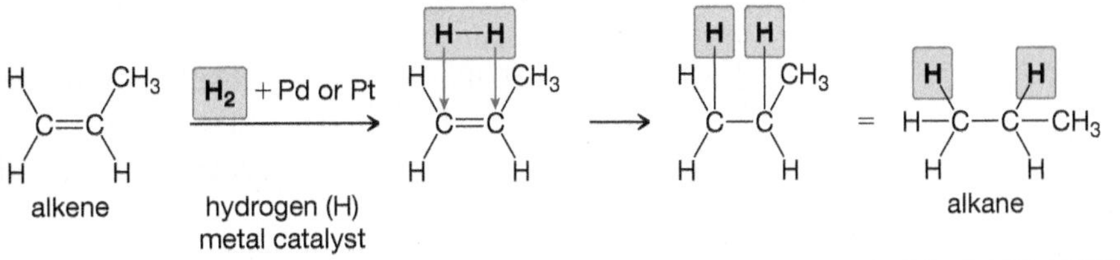
Halogenation	**Halogenation** is the addition of halogen (X_2; where $X = Br$ or Cl) to an alkene. 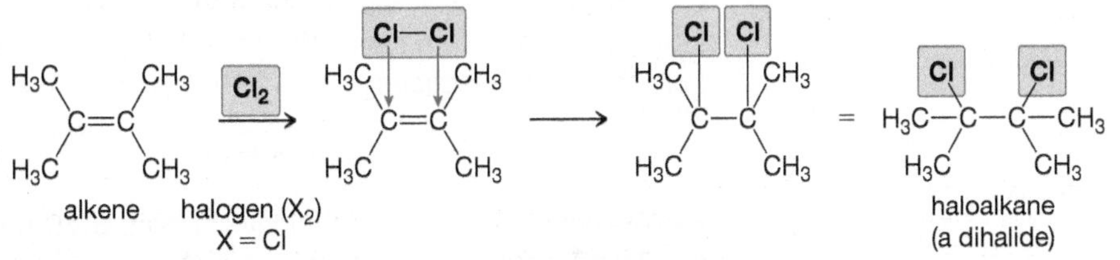
Polymerization	**Polymerization** is the joining together of alkene monomers to make polymers. 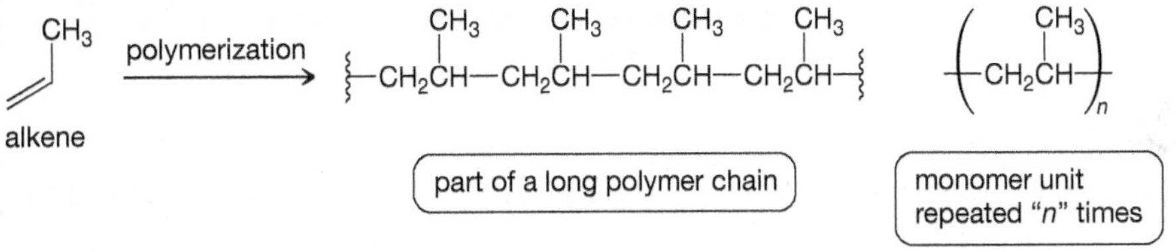 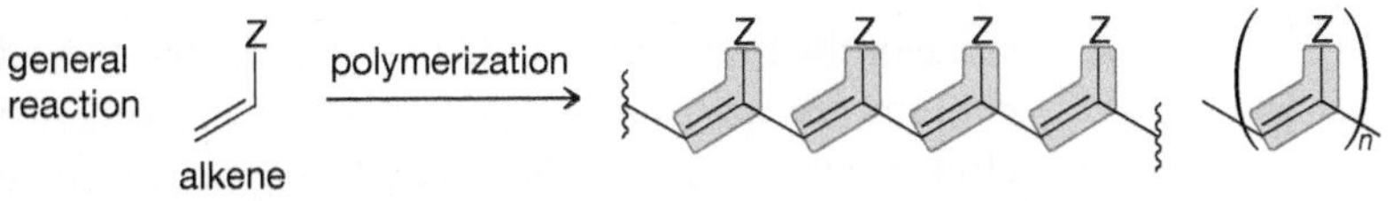
Hydrohalogenation	**Hydrohalogenation** is the addition of HX (where $X = Cl$ or Br) to an alkene. 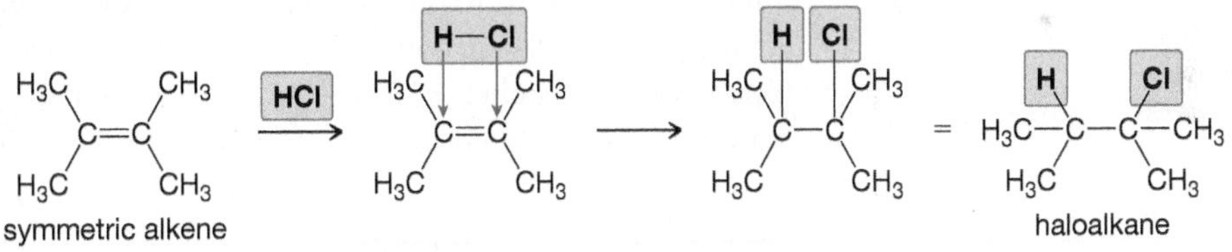 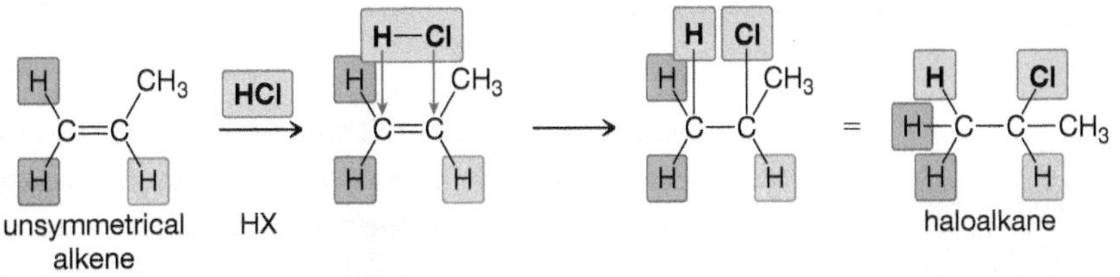
Hydration	**Hydration** is the addition of water (H_2O) to an alkene. 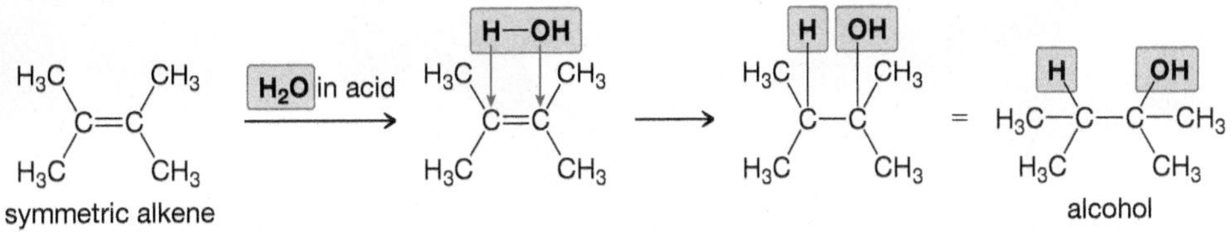 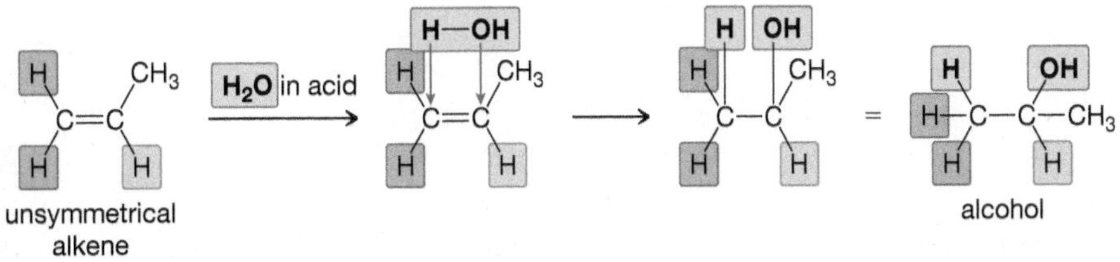

are produced from alkenes. Polymerization reactions produce polymers through reactions that link monomers together in long chains. Alkenes undergo polymerization reactions to produce a variety of polymers, some of which function as plastic materials that are used in a wide variety of products and other synthetic materials. For a summary of these reaction types, view Table 13.4. Explore VisibleChem Videos 13.4–13.6 to learn more about alkenes and the details of addition reactions including how to predict their products. Then explore BioConnect 13.1 (contains Figures 13.27–13.34) to investigate the significance the structure of alkenes plays in heart disease.

Watch this concept come to life: **VisibleChem Video 13.4:** Recognizing and Drawing *Cis* and *Trans* Isomers, **VisibleChem Video 13.5:** Predicting Products of Alkene Halogenation Addition Reactions, and **VisibleChem Video 13.6:** Understanding Polymerization Reactions of Alkenes in the Pearson eText.

Apply what you have just learned: **Practice 13.15–13.18** in the Pearson eText.

Explore how Chemistry and Biology connect: **BioConnect: 13.1** Fats in Our Diets in the Pearson eText.

Quiz yourself on the content of this section: **Check 13.4** in the Pearson eText.

13.5 Aromatic Compounds

The family of hydrocarbons you learn about in this section are called aromatic because some of the first compounds of this type discovered had pleasant aromas. **Aromatic compounds** are hydrocarbons that feature ring structures with an arrangement of electrons that produces increased stability. This increased stability lowers the reactivity of the aromatic compounds. Numerous molecules contain aromatic rings including molecules found in nature as well as molecules used in the manufacturing of a wide array of products. If you cook, you probably use several common aromatic compounds in the kitchen to flavor your food, such as cinnamaldehyde from cinnamon, vanillin from vanilla beans, and thymol from thyme leaves (Figure 13.35).

Figure 13.35 Examples of Aromatic Compounds.

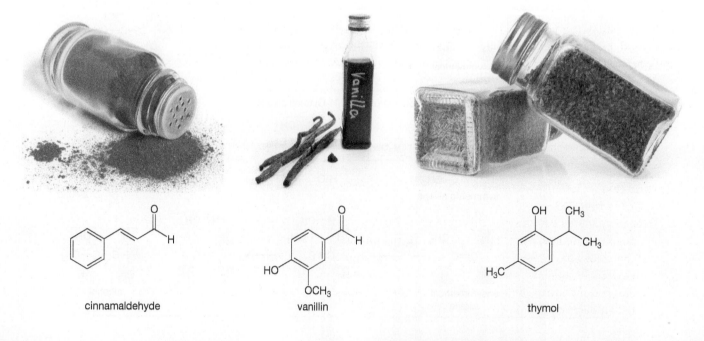

cinnamaldehyde

vanillin

thymol

Benzene Rings

A large number of compounds in the aromatic family contain **benzene** rings. Benzene is a colorless liquid with a sweet odor that is found in crude oil and gasoline. It is primarily used in the laboratory as a building block for a vast array of other substances. Benzene was once used as an industrial solvent, but its use as a solvent decreased after it was linked to leukemia and other cancers.

Benzene is a six-carbon ring with one hydrogen atom attached to each carbon and is often represented with three alternating double bonds inside the ring (Figure 13.36).

While benzene is drawn showing three double bonds, benzene is not considered an alkene, despite the "ene" ending of its name. In benzene rings, all the carbon atoms in the ring share the electrons from the double bonds equally. This characteristic of benzene rings creates a stable structure. Their stable structure means that aromatic molecules such as benzene have different chemical reactivity than alkenes. For example, aromatic compounds do not undergo the addition reactions that characterize alkenes.

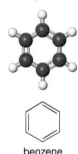

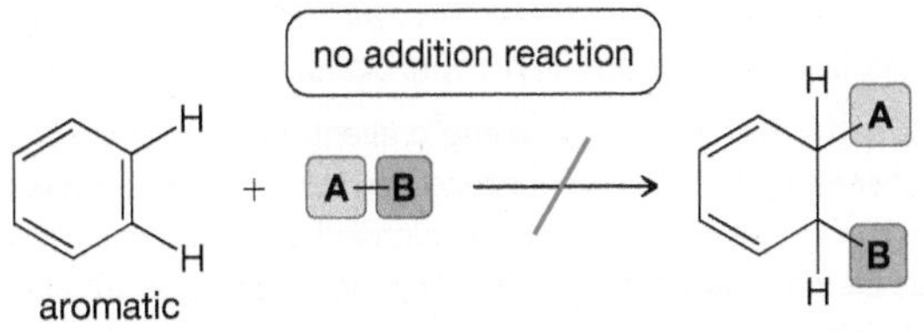

Figure 13.36 Benzene is a Six-Carbon Ring with Alternating Double and Single Bonds.

benzene

This unique feature of benzene rings requires a new representation, one that illustrates the sharing of six electrons with six carbon atoms. To show this, chemists draw two rings, shift the double bonds over by one bond in the second ring, and place a double-headed arrow between the two ring structures (Figure 13.37). Alternatively, we can represent benzene with a single six-sided ring with a circle inside as you see on the right in Figure 13.37. The circle inside the ring represents the three double bonds distributed across all six-carbon atoms. You will encounter both representations in Figure 13.37 in your study of chemistry.

Figure 13.37 Benzene is a Six-Carbon Ring with Alternating Double and Single Bonds.

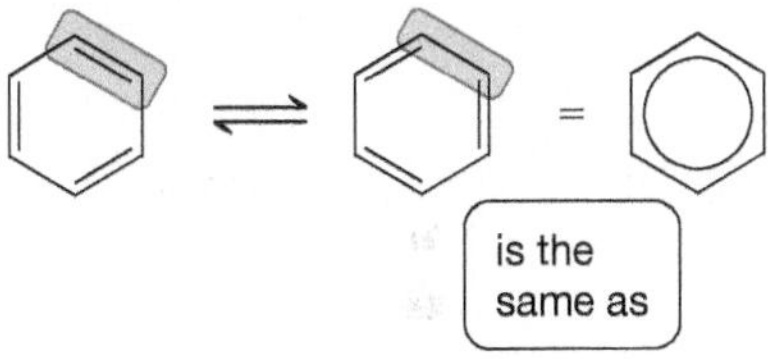

is the same as

Substituted Aromatic Compounds

Many molecules, both natural and synthetic, contain aromatic benzene rings. Most of the time these rings have a variety of substituents present. (Recall that a branch called a substituent is an atom or group of atoms that replaces a hydrogen atom on a carbon backbone chain.) Aromatic compounds do not undergo addition reactions like alkenes do. Instead, they undergo substitution reactions. In **substitution reactions**, an H atom on the aromatic ring is replaced by a substituent, preserving the aromatic ring.

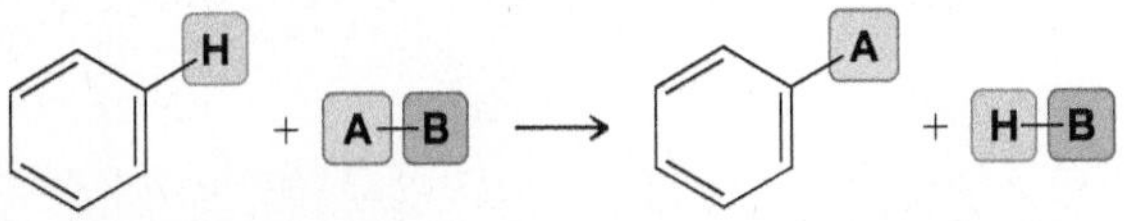

Aromatic hydrocarbon molecules that include substituents are called **substituted aromatic compounds** or **substituted benzenes**. Figure 13.38 shows a benzene ring that contains from 1–3 —OH groups as examples, however there are many possible substituents found on benzene rings (i.e. —NH$_2$, Cl, Br).

Monosubstituted benzenes have one substituent attached to the ring and **disubstituted benzenes** have two substituents attached (see Figure 13.38). Benzene rings with three or more substituents are **polysubstituted benzenes.**

Several common drugs and biologically important molecules are composed of substituted aromatic compounds (Figure 13.39).

Figure 13.38 Substituted Benzenes.

Benzene no substituents	**Mono**substituted benzene ring	**Di**substituted benzene ring	**Tri**substituted benzene ring
a building block molecule	used in the plastics industry	used to make pharmaceutical drugs and pesticides	intermediate in the biodegradation of many aromatic compounds

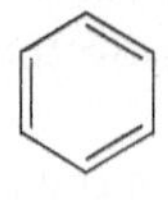

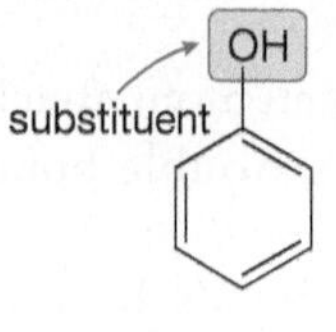

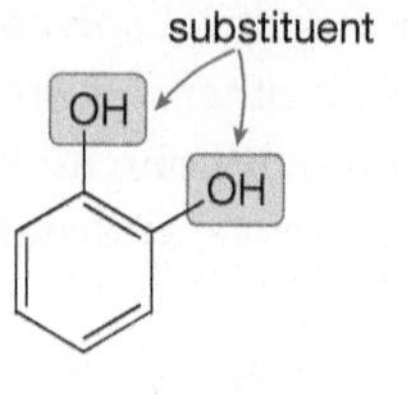

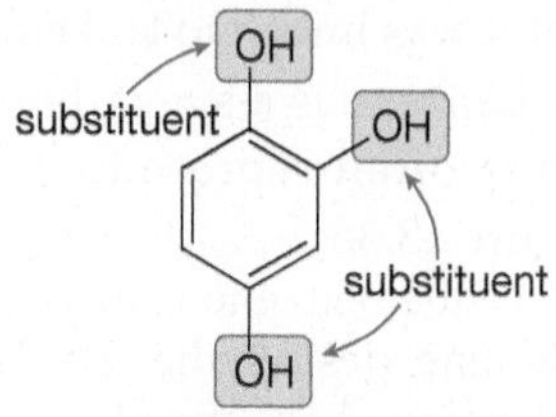

Figure 13.39 Substituted Aromatic Hydrocarbons.

A) Salmeterol is a drug used in the maintenance and prevention of asthma symptoms and chronic obstructive pulmonary disease (COPD). One benzene ring in this molecule has three substituents (boxed in the structure). **B)** Dopamine is a chemical released by nerve cells to send signals to other nerve cells. Dopamine is also a polysubstituted benzene ring with three substituents (boxed in the structure) bonded to the ring.

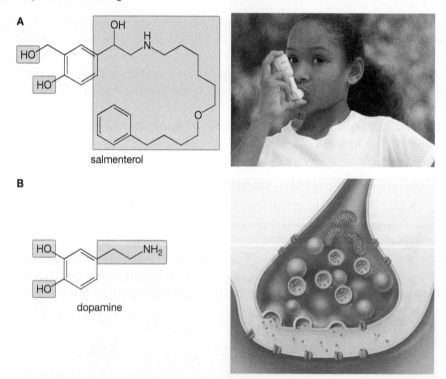

salmenterol

dopamine

Polycyclic Aromatic Hydrocarbons (PAHs)

Some aromatic compounds which contain multiple benzenes are called **polycyclic aromatic hydrocarbons (PAHs).** Naphthalene is a PAH that has two benzene rings joined together. Anthracene and phenanthrene are PAHs that each contain three joined benzene rings, and pyrene is a PAH with four joined benzene rings (Figure 13.40). Select BioConnect 13.2 (contains Figures 13.41–13.49) to explore additional PAH compounds and the impact they have on human health.

Figure 13.40 Polycyclic Aromatic Hydrocarbons (PAHs).

Naphthalene is a PAH molecule containing two benzene rings. Anthracene and phenanthrene each have three benzene rings. Pyrene has four benzene rings. These compounds are produced during incomplete combustion of oil products and released into the atmosphere where they can impact human health.

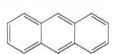

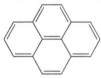

naphthalene
(2 benzene rings)

anthracene
(3 benzene rings)

phenanthrene
(3 benzene rings)

pyrene
(4 benzene rings)

Apply what you have just learned: **Practice 13.19** in the Pearson eText.

Explore how Chemistry and Biology connect: **BioConnect: 13.2** PAHs in Our Bodies in the Pearson eText.

Quiz yourself on the content of this section: **Check 13.5** in the Pearson eText.

13.6 Naming Organic Compounds

Chemists follow specific rules when naming compounds. This process of devising or choosing names for things is **nomenclature**. The International Union of Pure and Applied Chemistry (IUPAC) establishes the rules for the nomenclature of organic compounds. The rules ensure that each compound has an unambiguous and unique name, allowing chemists from all over the world to communicate with each other. Explore Videos 13.1–31.4 to learn how to name the compounds discussed in this chapter. You can also review the rules for naming compounds in the nomenclature appendix.

Video 13.1: Introduction to Nomenclature, **Video 13.2**: Nomenclature: Alkanes and Cycloalkanes, **Video 13.3**: Nomenclature: Alkenes and Alkynes, and **Video 13.4:** Nomenclature: Benzene Compounds in the Pearson eText.

Quiz yourself on the content of this section: **Check 13.6** in the Pearson eText.

Chapter Summary

13.1 Organic Compounds

Learning Objective: Recognize the fundamental structural features of organic compounds and use appropriate representations to draw molecules.

Organic compounds are composed mostly of carbon and hydrogen but can include other elements. Carbon atoms generally form bonds with four other atoms, creating a diverse array of organic structures with carbon backbones including straight chains, branched chains, and rings. You can predict the shapes of organic molecules using VSEPR theory. Chemists use a variety of representations to show the structure of organic molecules including space-filling models, ball-and-stick models, wedge-dash drawings, and skeletal structures. Condensed structures can also be used to show just the atoms in a molecule, including heteroatoms.

Key Terms

condensed structure	organic chemistry	skeletal structure
heteroatom	organic compound	wedge-dash
inorganic compound		

13.2 Alkanes and Cycloalkanes

Learning Objective: Identify and draw the first ten acyclic simple alkanes (C_1–C_{10}) and the first four cycloalkanes (C_3–C_6).

Alkanes are hydrocarbons with only C—C and C—H single bonds. They can be acyclic (straight or branching chains) or cycloalkanes (rings). Alkanes are all nonpolar and don't mix well with water. They do, however, combine with oxygen in combustion reactions to heat our homes, cook our food, and power combustion engines.

Key Terms

acyclic alkane	cycloalkane	saturated
alkane	hydrocarbon	

13.3 Branched Alkanes and Haloalkanes

Learning Objective: Recognize branching in alkanes and draw structural isomers for branched alkanes and haloalkanes.

Branched alkanes, such as polyethylene, are also hydrocarbons with only C—C and C—H single bonds. Some of these branching molecules can also contain one or more halogen atoms; these molecules are haloalkanes. Branching alkanes form structural isomers in which two or more different arrangements of atoms have the same molecular formula.

VisibleChem Video 13.1: Rotation Around Carbon-Carbon Single Bonds

VisibleChem Video 13.2: Drawing Structural Isomers

VisibleChem Video 13.3: Interpreting Skeletal Structures of Large Organic Molecules

Key Terms

branched alkane
haloalkane
structural isomer
substituent

13.4 Alkenes and Alkynes

Learning Objective: Identify alkenes and alkynes and draw *cis-trans* isomers of alkenes.

Alkenes are hydrocarbons that contain carbon-carbon double bonds. Alkynes contain carbon-carbon triple bonds. The general structural formula for alkenes is C_nH_{2n}. The general structural formula for alkynes is C_nH_{2n-2}. The double bond in alkenes prevents free rotation around the double bond, creating the possibility of *cis* and *trans* isomers. *Cis* isomers occur when substituent groups are on the same side of the double bond. *Trans* isomers have substituent groups on opposite sides of the double bond.

VisibleChem Video 13.4: Recognizing and Drawing *Cis* and *Trans* Isomers

VisibleChem Video 13.5: Predicting Products of Alkene Halogenation Addition Reactions

VisibleChem Video 13.6: Understanding Polymerization Reactions of Alkenes

BioConnect 13.1: Fats in our Diets

Key Terms

addition reactions
alkene
alkyne
cis isomer
cis-trans isomer
cholesterol (from BioConnect 13.1)
dihalides

functional group
halogenation
high-density lipoproteins (HDL) (from BioConnect 13.1)
hydration
hydrogenated fat (from BioConnect 13.1)
hydrogenation

hydrohalogenation
low-density lipoproteins (LDL) (from BioConnect 13.1)
saturated fat (from BioConnect 13.1)
trans fat (from BioConnect 13.1)
trans isomer
unsaturated fat (from BioConnect 13.1)

13.5 Aromatic Compounds

Learning Objective: Identify and draw aromatic compounds.

Aromatic compounds are unsaturated hydrocarbons that have cyclic structures with multiple double bonds present. Benzene, for example, is a six-carbon ring with one hydrogen atom attached to each carbon and three alternating double bonds. Benzene rings are found in a large number of molecules, some of which have substituted benzene rings, or fused benzene rings. Fused benzene rings are characteristic of a family of molecules called polycyclic aromatic hydrocarbons (PAHs), many of which cause cancer in humans.

BioConnect 13.2: PAHs in Our Bodies

Key Terms

apoptosis (from BioConnect 13.2)
aromatic compound
benzene
carcinogen (from BioConnect 13.2)
disubstituted benzene

monosubstituted benzene
polycyclic aromatic hydrocarbons (PAHs)
polysubstituted benzene
substituted aromatic compound (substituted benzene)

substitution reaction
tumor-suppressor gene (from BioConnect 13.2)

13.6 Naming Organic Compounds

Learning Objective: Use the IUPAC system for naming organic compounds to convert from structure to name and from name to structure for simple alkanes, alkenes, alkynes, and benzene compounds.

The International Union of Pure and Applied Chemistry has a specific set of rules to ensure that each organic compound has a unique and unambiguous chemical name. These rules allow scientists to communicate effectively about specific molecules.

Video 13.1: Introduction to Nomenclature

Video 13.2: Nomenclature: Alkanes and Cycloalkanes

Video 13.3: Nomenclature: Alkenes and Alkynes

Video 13.4: Nomenclature: Benzene Compounds

Key Term

Nomenclature

End-of-Chapter Quiz Have you mastered the content of this chapter? Try the **End-of-Chapter Quiz** in the Pearson eText.

1. Carbon has _____ valence electrons and can form a maximum of _____ single bonds.
   a) eight; four
   b) four; four
   c) eight; two
   d) four; eight

2. The molecule 2-propanol (commonly called rubbing alcohol) is used to disinfect the skin around the site of an injection. Which is the correct expanded Lewis structure of the 2-propanol molecule $CH_3CHOHCH_3$?

a)

H—C—C—O—C—H

b)

H—C—C—H—O—H—C—H

c)

H—C—C—C—H

d)

H—C—C—C—H

3. Amino acids are the building blocks of proteins. Valine is one of the essential amino acids; it must be obtained from the food we eat because our bodies cannot make it. Select the correctly drawn condensed structure for the valine molecule. Its expanded Lewis structure is given.

a)
$H_2N—C—C—OH$
     $C—CH_3$
     CH_3

b)
     CH_3
$H_2N—CH—C—OH$
     CH_3

c)
$H_2N—CH—C—OH$
$H_3C—CH$ NH_2
     CH_3

d)
$H_2N—CH—C—OH$
     $CH—CH_3$
     CH_3

4. Methadone is a medication used to treat people who have become addicted to heroin or narcotic pain medicines. Methadone reduces cravings and withdrawal symptoms. Consider the given skeletal structure of the methadone molecule, and select the correct statement about the number of hydrogen atoms bonded to each carbon indicated in the structure.

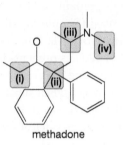

methadone

a) There are two hydrogen atoms bonded to carbon (i), four hydrogen atoms bonded to carbon (ii), one hydrogen atom bonded to carbon (iii), and three hydrogen atoms bonded to carbon (iv).

b) There are two hydrogen atoms bonded to carbon (i), no hydrogen atoms bonded to carbon (ii), two hydrogen atoms bonded to carbon (iii), and three hydrogen atoms bonded to carbon (iv).

c) There are no hydrogen atoms bonded to carbon (i), four hydrogen atoms bonded to carbon (ii), one hydrogen atom bonded to carbon (iii), and three hydrogen atoms bonded to carbon (iv).

d) There are two hydrogen atoms bonded to carbon (i), no hydrogen atoms bonded to carbon (ii), one hydrogen atom bonded to carbon (iii) and three hydrogen atoms bonded to carbon (iv)

5. Valproic acid is a drug used to treat epilepsy, bipolar disorder, and migraine headaches. Select the correctly drawn skeletal structure for valproic acid. Its Lewis structure is given.

valproic acid

a)

b)

c)

d)

6. Select the condensed structure and the skeletal structure that match.

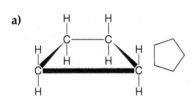

a)  CH₃CH₂CH₂CH₂CH₂CH₂CH₃

b)  CH₃CH₂CH₂CH₂CH₂CH₃

c)  CH₃CH₂CH₂CH₂CH₂CH₂CH₃

d)  CH₃CH₂CCH₂CH₂CH₃

7. In which cycloalkane pair does the skeletal structure match the Lewis structure?

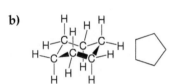

a)

b)

c)

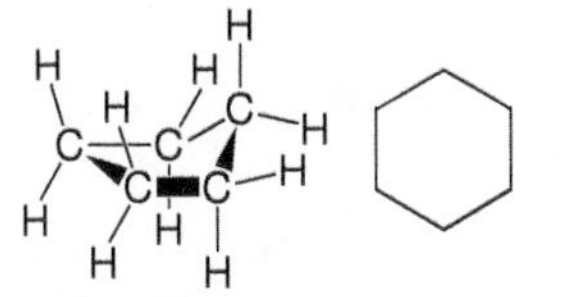

d)

8. Which statement about the general properties of alkanes is most correct?
a) Alkanes are generally more dense than water, and are non-polar.
b) Alkanes are generally less dense than water, and are non-polar.
c) Alkanes are generally more dense than water, and have about the same polarity as water.
d) Alkanes are generally less dense than water, and have about the same polarity as water.

9. In which cycloalkane pair does the skeletal structure match the molecular formula?

a) 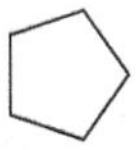 C_5H_{12}

b)  C_3H_9

c) C_6H_6

d) 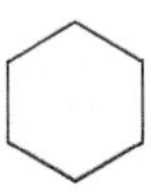 C_6H_{12}

10. The molecule pregabalin is used in the treatment of pain caused by nerve damage due to spinal cord injury, diabetes, shingles, and fibromyalgia. Examine the given Lewis structure of pregabalin and select the skeletal structure of a structural isomer of pregabalin.

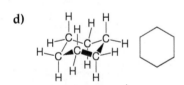

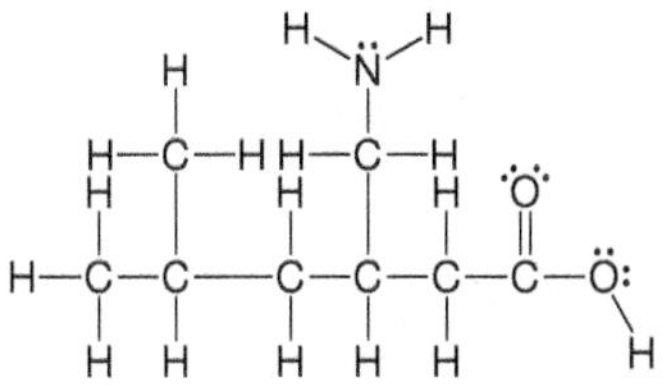

pregabalin

a)

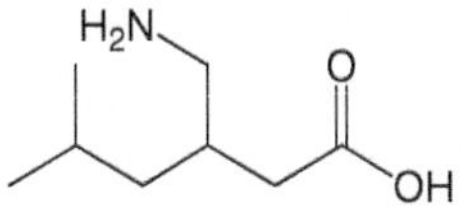

b)

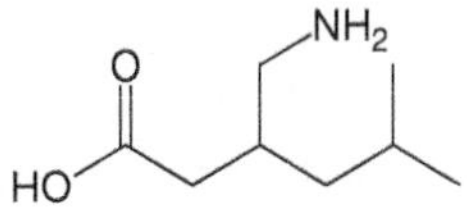

c)

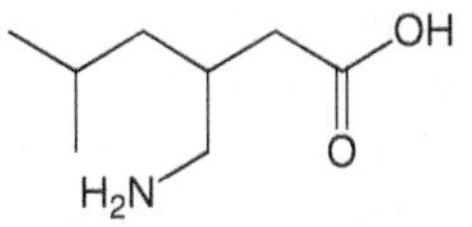

d)

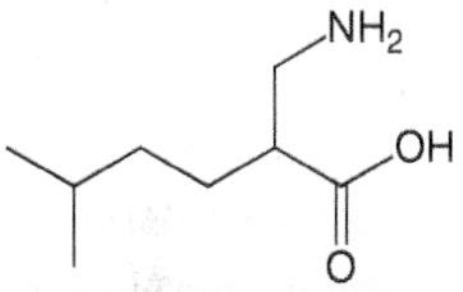

11. Malaria is a mosquito-borne infectious disease that affects millions of people worldwide each year, resulting in hundreds of thousands of deaths. The drug chloroquine prevents and treats malaria, and is on the World Health Organization's List of Essential Medicines. The structure of chloroquine is given. Which of the answer options is a structural isomer of chloroquine? Remember that rotation can occur around single carbon bonds.

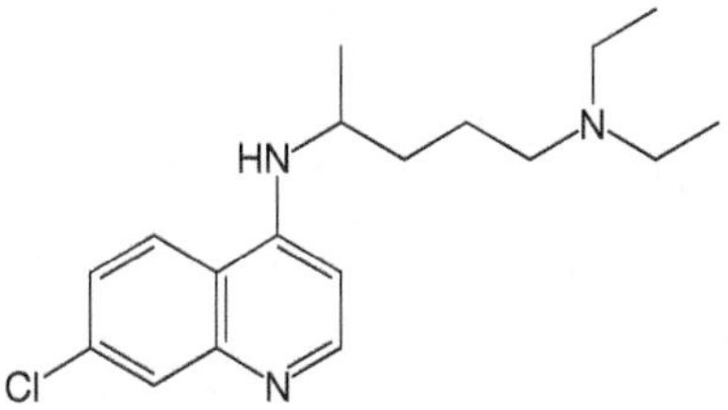

chloroquine

a)

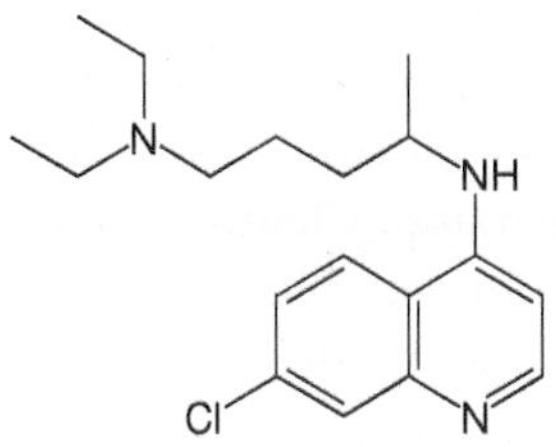

b)

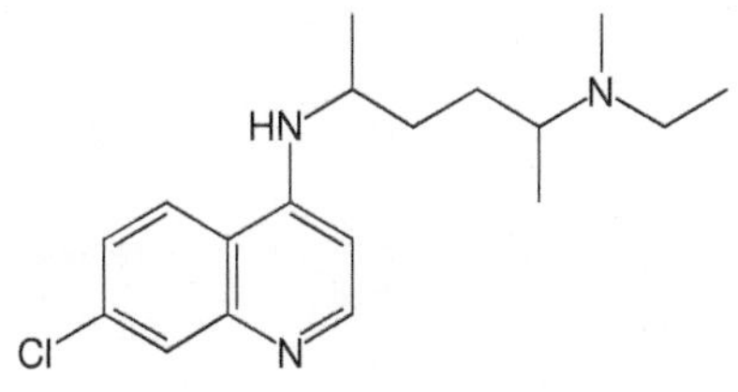

c)

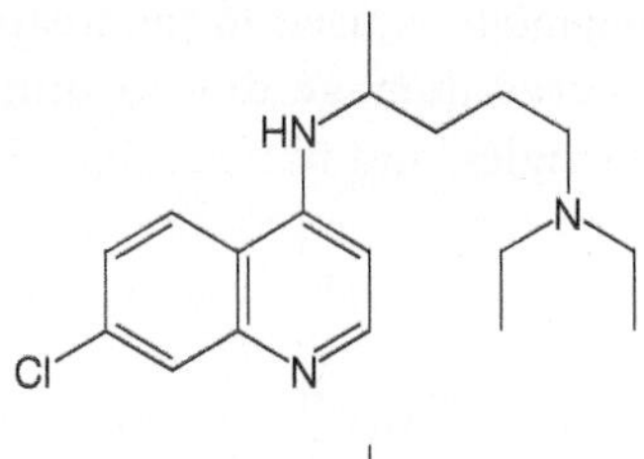

d)

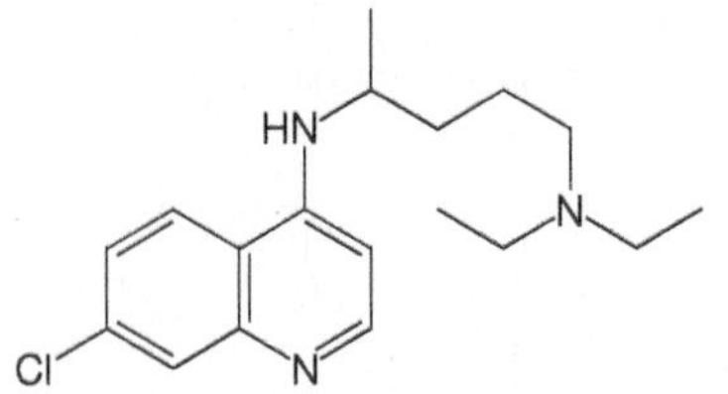

12. Sucralose is an artificial sweetener and sugar substitute that is found in a number of low-calorie food and beverage products. It is also consumed by people with diabetes because it can help them regulate their insulin levels. Sucralose is made by replacing select groups on sucrose (table sugar) molecules with chlorine atoms. This process makes sucralose more difficult for the body to break down than sucrose. Study the given skeletal structure of sucralose and select the correct molecular formula for sucralose.

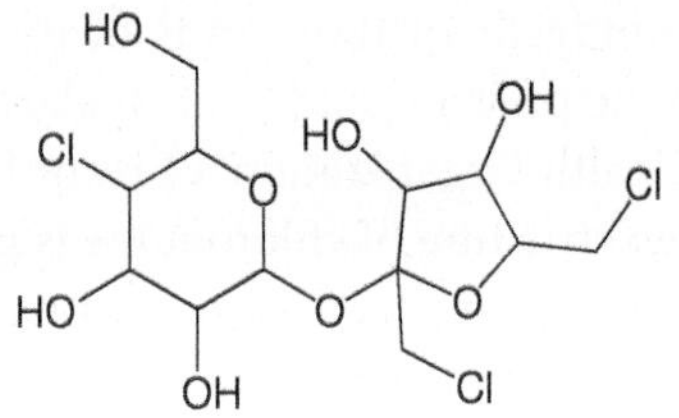

sucralose

a) $C_{12}H_{11}Cl_3O_8$

b) $C_{14}H_{11}Cl_3O_6$

c) $C_{12}H_{19}Cl_3O_8$

d) $C_{12}H_{19}Cl_2O_8$

13. Cicutoxin is a poisonous molecule found in a group of plants native to swamps and wet habitats in North America and parts of Europe. These poisonous plants are sometimes mistaken for edible roots such as wild carrot, ginseng, or parsnip. Cicutoxin disrupts the central nervous system and may result in death if sufficient quantities are ingested. Which statement about the cicutoxin molecule (shown here) is correct?

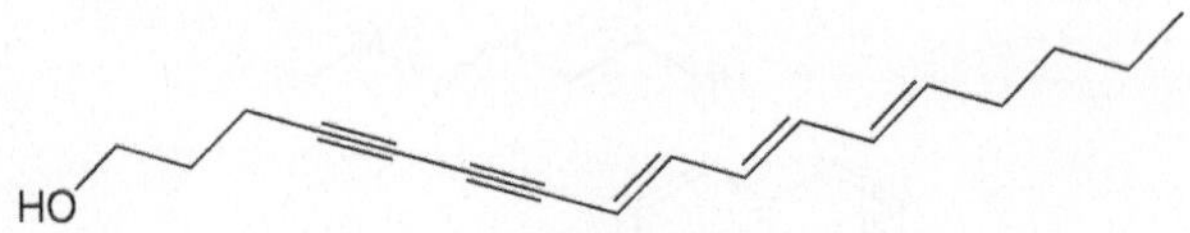

cicutoxin

a) The cicutoxin molecule contains three *cis* alkene functional groups and one alkyne functional group.

b) The cicutoxin molecule contains three *trans* alkene functional groups and two alkyne functional groups.

c) The cicutoxin molecule contains three *cis* alkene functional groups and two alkyne functional groups.

d) The cicutoxin molecule contains five *trans* alkene functional groups.

14. The molecule nepetalactone is a natural product in the plant catnip (*Nepeta cataria*) that attracts cats. What is the product of the reaction when nepetalactone undergoes a catalytic hydrogenation reaction?

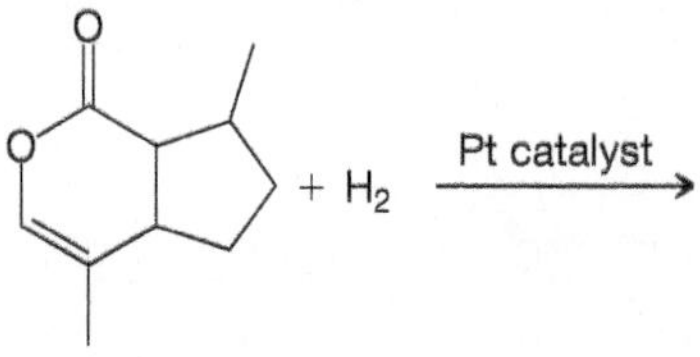

nepetalactone

a)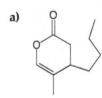

b)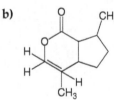

c)

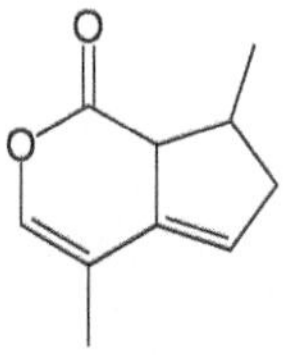

d)

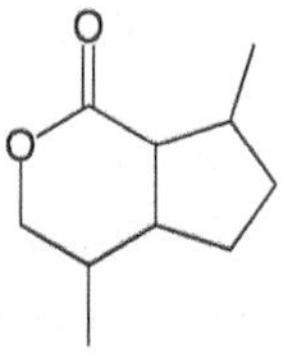

15. What is the product of the given reaction?

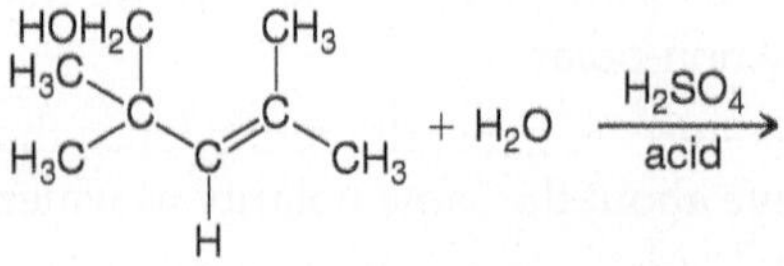

a)

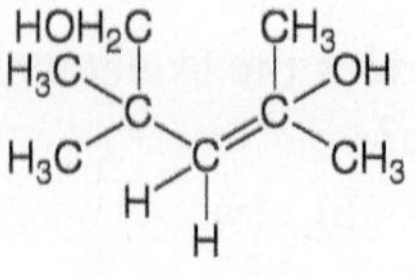

b)

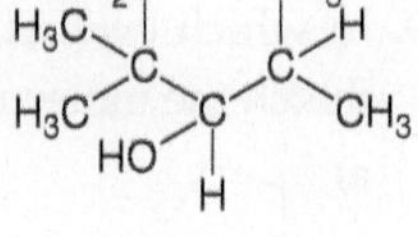

c)

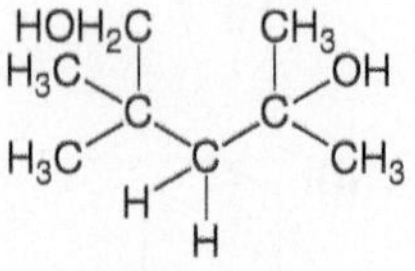

d)

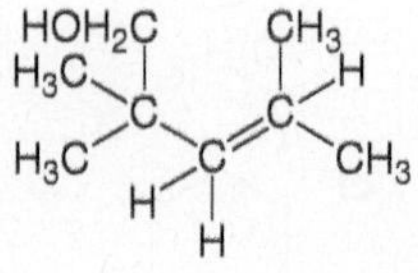

16. The molecule dexmedetomidine (also known as the drug Precedex) is an aromatic ring-containing compound that is used as a sedative and to treat anxiety. Examine the given skeletal structure of dexmedetomidine and select the Lewis structure that correctly represents this molecule.

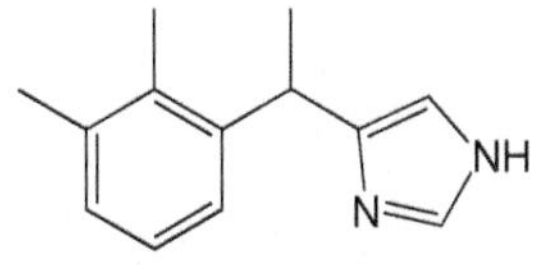

dexmedetomidine

a)

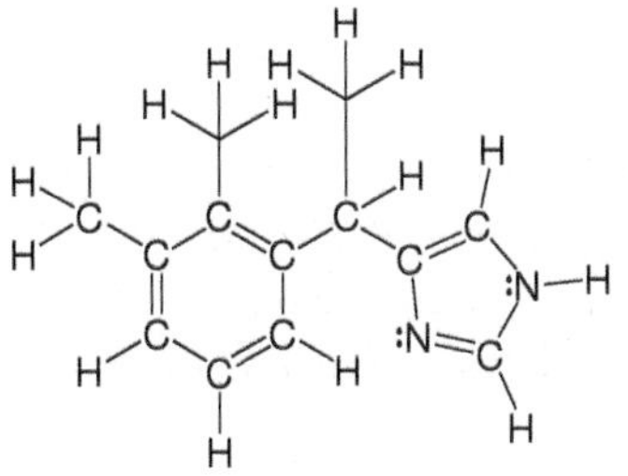

b)

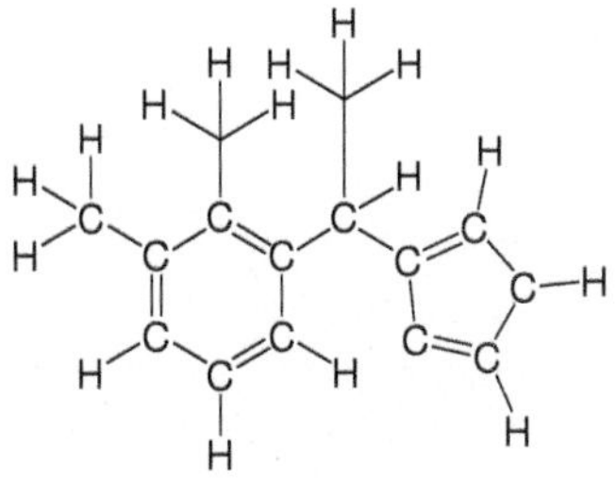

c)

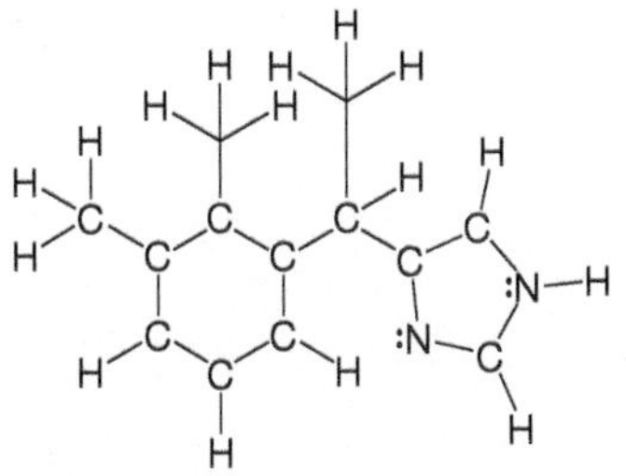

d)

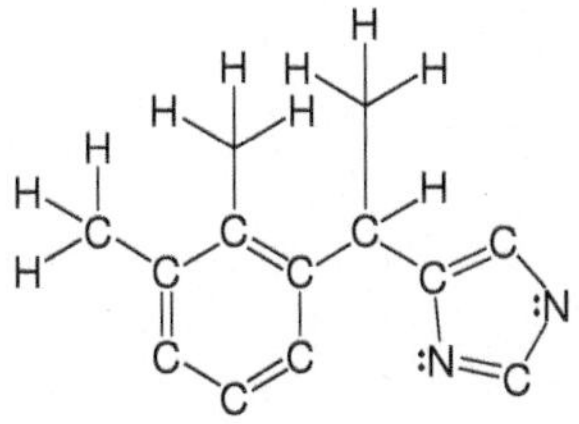

17. The molecule methylphenidate (also known as Ritalin) is an aromatic ring-containing drug that is commonly used to treat attention deficit hyperactivity disorder (ADHD). Examine the given Lewis structure of methylphenidate and determine which skeletal structure correctly represents this molecule.

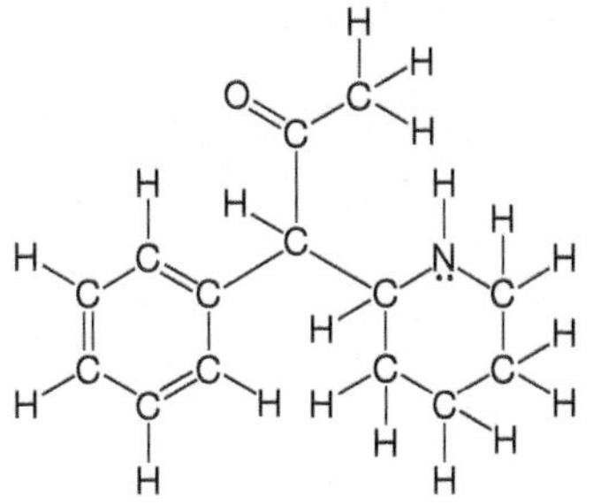

methylphenidate

a) 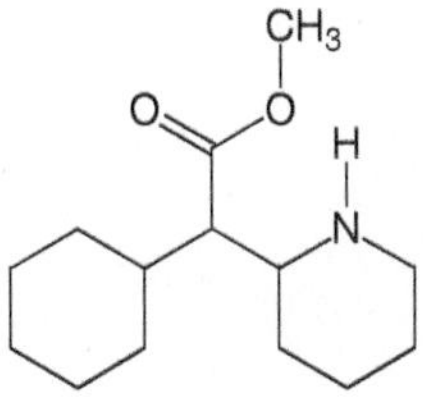 CH_3

b)

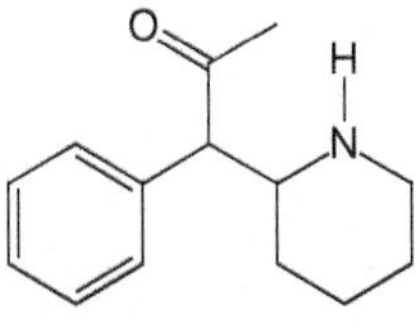

c) CH_3

d) 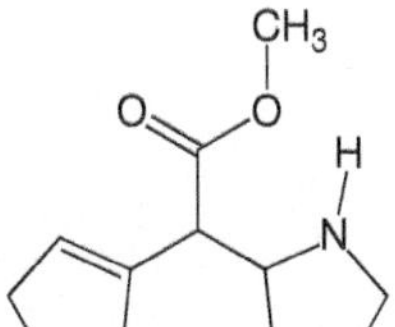 CH_3

18. Which molecule is *not* a polycyclic aromatic hydrocarbon (PAH)?

a) 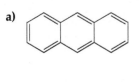   **b)** 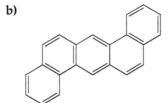   **c)** 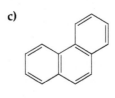   **d)**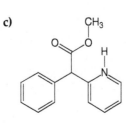

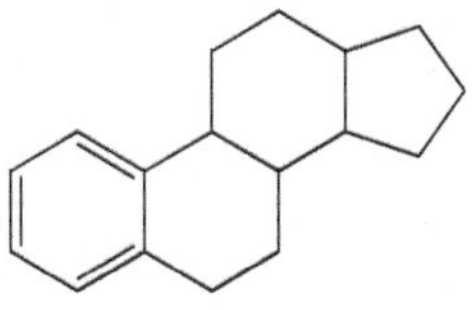

19. Select the correct IUPAC name for this molecule.

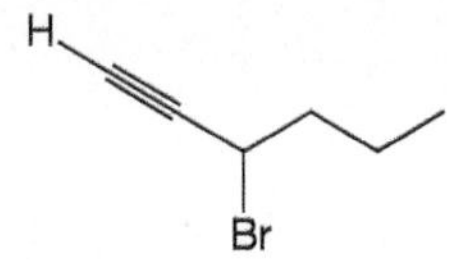

a) 3-bromo-1-hexyne
b) 4-bromo-5-hexyne
c) 3-bromo-1-hexene
d) 3-bromo-2-hexyne

20. Select the correct IUPAC name for this molecule.

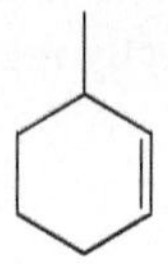

a) 3-methylcyclohexane
b) 1-methyl-2-cyclohexene
c) 3-methylcyclohexene
d) 3-methylcyclohexyne

Chapter 14
Alcohols, Ethers, Thiols, and Chiral Molecules

The enzyme alcohol dehydrogenase breaks down ethanol in the liver and lining of the stomach.

Chapter Outline

Learning Objectives

14.1 Analyze the structural and physical properties of alcohols.

14.2 Analyze the structural and physical properties of ethers.

14.3 Analyze the structural and physical properties of sulfur functional groups (thiols, thioethers).

14.4 Determine the products of the reactions of alcohols and thiols (dehydration of alcohols, and oxidation of thiols).

14.5 Distinguish between chiral and achiral molecules.

14.6 Name alcohols, ethers, and thiols according to the IUPAC system.

Introduction

Our world is largely composed of organic compounds–covalent compounds containing the element carbon. Given the vast array of organic compounds, how can we begin to predict their properties? One approach is to focus on the properties of **functional groups**. *Alcohols*, *ethers*, and *thiols* are three groups of organic compounds. Each of these groups contains a specific functional group. Learning to recognize these functional groups helps us predict the properties of a wide range of different molecules, many of which are part of our daily lives (Figure 14.1). We explore these three functional groups of organic molecules throughout this chapter. We also investigate how the three-dimensional shapes of molecules play a significant role in how molecules react in the body. For that reason, molecular shape is a guiding principle for chemists who design new drugs.

14.1 Alcohols

Recall from Chapter 13 that organic compounds contain carbon-carbon (C—C) and carbon-hydrogen (C—H) bonds. They also contain heteroatoms (atoms in an organic compound that are not carbon and hydrogen). Heteroatoms are sometimes found as part of functional groups, an atom or group of atoms with characteristic chemical and physical properties. Functional groups may contain a heteroatom, a multiple bond, or sometimes both. Generally, the functional group in an organic compound determines the molecule's shape, properties, and the type of reactions it undergoes. In other words, if functional groups are part of a molecule, they determine the primary interactions with other molecules and the typical chemical reactions that a molecule participates in.

Chemists abbreviate the hydrogen and carbon part of an organic molecule in order to highlight the functional group. A capital letter **R** represents the carbon backbone of an organic molecule.

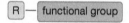

Figure 14.1 Alcohols, Ethers, and Thiols in our Lives.

Recognizing functional groups helps us predict the properties of organic molecules. **A)** Alcohols are commonly used in disinfectants. **B)** Ethers have a long history in anesthesia. **C)** Thiols produce the aroma of roasted coffee.

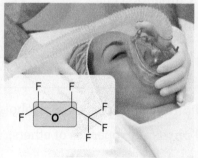

A   B   C

Figure 14.2 Three Alcohols.

A) Methanol (CH_3OH) is a one-carbon alcohol molecule used in many industrial processes and found in household cleaners such as window cleaner. It is a very toxic substance and if ingested in only small amounts can lead to blindness and even death. **B)** Ethanol (CH_3CH_2OH) is the alcohol in alcoholic beverages. It forms when carbohydrates in fruits or grains ferment. **C)** Isopropyl alcohol (C_3H_8O) is a common component of antiseptics, disinfectants, and detergents.

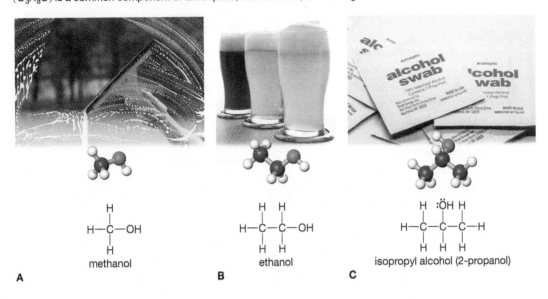

methanol   ethanol   isopropyl alcohol (2-propanol)

A   **B**   **C**

Alcohols are organic molecules that contain a hydroxyl functional group (OH) (Figure 14.2). The hydroxyl group determines the properties of this class of molecules as well as the chemical reactions that alcohols are involved in. The general structure of alcohols includes an R for the rest of the molecule (the carbon backbone) and highlights the OH functional group as shown here. Methanol (CH_3OH) is a small, short-chain alcohol molecule that has a CH_3 carbon backbone (R) bonded to the hydroxyl functional group (OH).

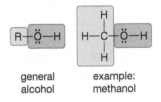

general   example:
alcohol   methanol

Structure of Alcohols

All alcohols contain a hydroxyl group bonded to a tetrahedral carbon atom. The hydroxyl oxygen atom is also bonded to one hydrogen atom and has two lone pairs of electrons. This arrangement of bonds and electron pairs leads to a bent shape with a C—O—H bond angle around 109.5°.

lone pairs of
electrons

H_3C—Ö:

H

bent   109.5°

Oxygen is more electronegative than carbon and hydrogen and therefore the C—O bond and O—H bond in a hydroxyl group are both polar bonds. These polar bonds combined with the bent shape contribute to the overall polarity of the alcohol functional group. In this representation of the hydroxyl group, the dipole arrows (see Chapter 7) indicate bond polarity. When we add the arrows, they result in an overall dipole in the direction of the oxygen atom.

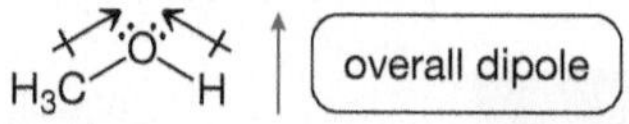

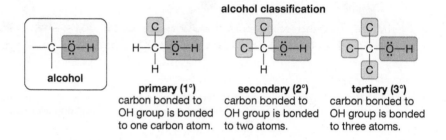

overall dipole

We classify alcohols as **primary (1°)**, **secondary (2°)**, or **tertiary (3°)** depending on the number of carbon atoms bonded to the carbon with the OH group. In primary alcohols, this carbon is bonded to one other carbon. In secondary alcohols, this carbon is bonded to two carbons, and in tertiary alcohols, this carbon is bonded to three carbons. In Learn 14.1 you classify the vitamin D molecule as a 1°, 2°, or 3° alcohol.

alcohol classification

alcohol

primary (1°)
carbon bonded to OH group is bonded to one carbon atom.

secondary (2°)
carbon bonded to OH group is bonded to two atoms.

tertiary (3°)
carbon bonded to OH group is bonded to three atoms.

Predict answers and see step-by-step solutions: **Learn 14.1:** Classifying Alcohols as 1°, 2°, or 3° in the Pearson eText.

Apply what you have just learned: **Practice 14.1 and 14.2** in the Pearson eText.

Hydrogen Bonding in Alcohols

The polarity of alcohol molecules plays a significant role in their properties. The oxygen in the hydroxyl functional group has a partial negative charge and the hydrogen atom has a partial positive charge. Because of these partial charges and the polarity of the hydroxyl group, alcohols form strong intermolecular forces between molecules. Just as they do in water, hydrogen bonds, the most prominent intermolecular forces between alcohol molecules, play a key role in how alcohol molecules interact with other molecules.

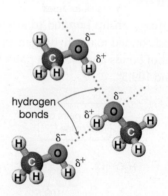

hydrogen bonds

As a result of hydrogen bonding, alcohols have higher than expected boiling points. The strong hydrogen bonds between alcohol molecules make it more difficult for liquid alcohol molecules to escape to the vapor phase (see VisibleChem Video 10.3).

For this reason, when compared to the corresponding hydrocarbons of similar mass, for example, alcohol boiling points are much higher.

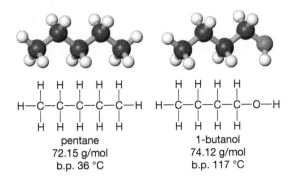

pentane
72.15 g/mol
b.p. 36 °C

1-butanol
74.12 g/mol
b.p. 117 °C

> Apply what you have just learned: **Practice 14.3 and 14.4** in the Pearson eText.

Solubility of Alcohols in Water

We can predict the solubility of alcohols in water using the rule like-dissolves-like. Similar to water, alcohols have a polar hydroxyl group (OH) that is capable of hydrogen bonding. More specifically, in alcohols, the atoms in the OH functional group form hydrogen bonds with both the H atom and the O atom in water. For this reason, alcohols are soluble in water, but only if the nonpolar hydrocarbon part of the molecule is not too large. As the length of the carbon chain increases, the polar OH group becomes an ever-smaller part of the molecule, and as a result, solubility decreases.

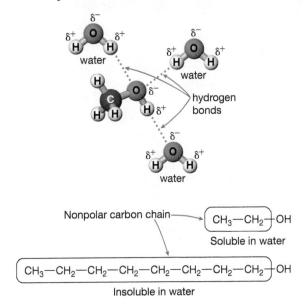

Nonpolar carbon chain

CH_3—CH_2—OH
Soluble in water

CH_3—CH_2—CH_2—CH_2—CH_2—CH_2—CH_2—CH_2—OH
Insoluble in water

> **Small alcohols (fewer than five carbon atoms) are soluble in water. Larger alcohols (five or more carbon atoms) are <u>in</u>soluble in water.**

In some cases, a molecule has more than one hydroxyl group. Ethylene glycol is an example of a molecule with two hydroxyl groups. The glycerin molecule has three hydroxyl groups. These additional hydroxyl groups increase alcohol solubility in water.

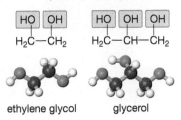

HO   OH
H_2C—CH_2

HO   OH   OH
H_2C—CH—CH_2

ethylene glycol   glycerol

> Apply what you have just learned: **Practice 14.5** in the Pearson eText.

Alcohols in Nature and Medicine

Hydroxyl groups are common in molecules throughout nature, and in many molecules we use medicinally (Figure 14.3–5). Many of these hydroxyl-containing molecules are much larger than the simple alcohols discussed earlier in this section and may contain other functional groups in addition to the hydroxyl group. Chemists typically classify these larger molecules into different groups, and do not always refer to them as alcohols. Glucose, for example, contains five hydroxyl groups, and is classified as a carbohydrate, a family of biomolecules we explore in Chapter 16.

One familiar molecule is the alcohol humans often consume in beverages: ethanol. Explore BioConnect 14.1 (contains Figures 14.6–14.11) to learn more about how our bodies process ethanol, and the more dangerous alcohol, methanol.

Figure 14.3 Serine is an Amino Acid that Contains a Primary Alcohol Group.

Amino acids are the building blocks of proteins that run cellular processes and are required in our diet. The amino acid serine contains a primary alcohol group. Insulin helps regulate blood sugar levels and is a protein made of two chains of amino acids including serine. The shape of the folded insulin protein is essential to its function.

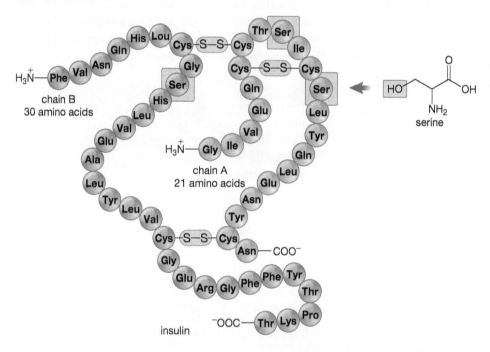

Figure 14.4 Glucose is a Carbohydrate that Contains Primary and Secondary Alcohol Groups.

Glucose contains a primary alcohol group and four secondary alcohol groups. Better known as blood sugar, glucose (represented with blue circles) provides energy for your body each day. Excess glucose in the blood, however, causes damage to nerves, blood vessels, and organs.

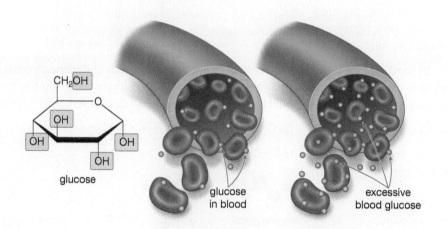

Figure 14.5 Imodium is a Drug that Contains a Tertiary Alcohol Group.

The drug loperamide (Imodium) contains a tertiary alcohol group. It is an anti-diarrheal medication on the World Health Organization's Essential Medicines list. Diarrhea usually results from a gastrointestinal infection caused by a variety of bacterial, viral, and parasitic organisms. These can be spread through contaminated food or drinking water, but also from person-to-person contact. Loss of fluids and electrolytes can be serious and even life-threatening if not corrected.

loperamide (Imodium)

Explore how Chemistry and Biology connect: **BioConnect: 14.1** Alcohols in Our Bodies in the Pearson eText.

Quiz yourself on the content of this section: **Check 14.1** in the Pearson eText.

14.2 Ethers

Ethers are organic compounds that feature a functional group that is an oxygen atom bonded to two carbon groups. Some ethers contain identical carbon groups (R) on each side of the oxygen, but most ethers have different carbon groups (R and R') on each side of the oxygen. We therefore typically refer to an ether group as R—O—R or R—O—R'. Diethyl ether, a common solvent used in the laboratory, has the same R group (—CH_2CH_3) on both sides. The ether anisole, on the other hand, has a —CH_3 group on one side of the oxygen atom and a benzene ring on the other side. You can see the structure of both here.

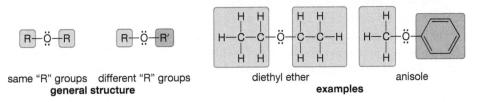

same "R" groups   different "R" groups
general structure

diethyl ether   anisole
examples

The oxygen atom in every ether molecule functional group is bonded to two carbon atoms and has two lone pairs of electrons. This arrangement of bonds and electron pairs results in a bent shape with a C—O—C bond angle around 109.5° so ether groups contain an oxygen atom bonded to a tetrahedral carbon atom on each side. Like in alcohols, the polar C—O bonds combined with the bent shape contribute to the overall polarity of the ether functional group.

In some cases, the oxygen atom of the ether functional group is contained in a ring. A general term for this type of group is a **heterocycle.** When an ether molecule contains a heterocycle, we call this group (the oxygen atom contained in a ring) a **cyclic ether**. The heteroatom in a cyclic ether is oxygen, but nitrogen and sulfur also form similar rings. Heterocycles are common in nature.

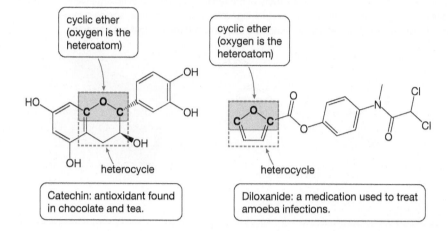

cyclic ether (oxygen is the heteroatom)
heterocycle
Catechin: antioxidant found in chocolate and tea.
cyclic ether (oxygen is the heteroatom)
heterocycle
Diloxanide: a medication used to treat amoeba infections.

Apply what you have just learned: **Practice 14.6** in the Pearson eText.

Properties of Ethers

In contrast to alcohols, ether molecules do not include a hydrogen atom bonded to an oxygen atom, therefore ethers do not form intermolecular hydrogen bonds with each other.

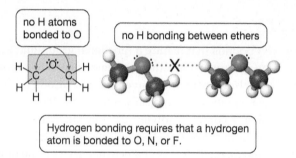

no H atoms bonded to O
no H bonding between ethers
Hydrogen bonding requires that a hydrogen atom is bonded to O, N, or F.

Because ethers are not capable of hydrogen bonding, they have weaker intermolecular forces than alcohols. Ethers are polar, however, so they have stronger dipole-dipole intermolecular forces than the corresponding alkanes that we discussed in Chapter 13. A comparison of boiling points illustrates this trend. Ethers have higher boiling points than alkanes of similar mass, but lower boiling points than alcohols of similar mass.

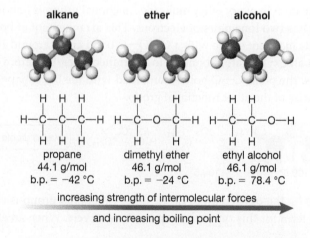

alkane
ether
alcohol
propane
44.1 g/mol
b.p. = −42 °C
dimethyl ether
46.1 g/mol
b.p. = −24 °C
ethyl alcohol
46.1 g/mol
b.p. = 78.4 °C
increasing strength of intermolecular forces
and increasing boiling point

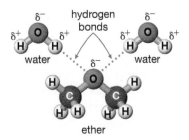

While ether molecules do not form hydrogen bonds with each other, they do form hydrogen bonds with water. Water has a hydrogen atom bonded to oxygen that can form a hydrogen bond with the oxygen on ethers. Small ethers are therefore soluble in water, and large ethers are insoluble in water. As the length of the carbon chain increases, the polar ether group becomes a smaller part of the molecule, and solubility decreases.

Apply what you have just learned: **Practice 14.7 and 14.8** in the Pearson eText.

Ethers in Nature and Medicine

Ether functional groups are in a variety of molecules including vitamins, and many drug molecules that treat a range of medical conditions and diseases. The ether functional group is stable chemically, which is especially helpful for drug molecules that may be shipped around the world and stored over extended periods of time. The slight polarity of the ether group increases solubility in blood (which is largely water). This allows drug molecules to travel easily through the body. Both of these useful properties are in part responsible for the widespread use of ethers in medicines and everyday life. Two examples are provided in Figure 14.12.

Figure 14.12 Ethers Molecules Found in Nature and Medicine.

Vitamin E is a cyclic ether-containing molecule found in food sources such as wheat germ, almonds, peanuts, and olives. Vitamin E deficiency can cause neurological problems and anemia. Amlodipine is an ether-containing drug on the World Health Organization's Essential Medicines List. It is used to treat high blood pressure and coronary heart disease.

vitamin E

amlodipine

Quiz yourself on the content of this section: **Check 14.2** in the Pearson eText.

14.3 Functional Groups Containing Sulfur

Recall that alcohols contain a hydroxyl functional group (OH). Thiols have a similar structure to alcohols except the functional group contains a sulfur atom bonded to a hydrogen atom (SH). **Thiol** groups have the general formula of R—S—H. Similar to the oxygen atom in the OH functional groups of alcohols, the sulfur atom is bonded to one tetrahedral carbon atom and one hydrogen atom and has two lone pairs of electrons. The thiol group is therefore bent with a C—S—H bond angle around 109.5°.

Methanethiol and cysteine both have a thiol functional group. Methanethiol is a natural substance found in animals and plants. Cysteine is the only amino acid with a thiol group.

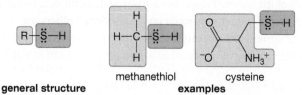

general structure   methanethiol   cysteine
examples

Sulfur is also present in **thioethers**, a class of organic molecules that are similar in structure and properties to ethers. The sulfur atom in thioethers is bonded to two carbon groups with a bent shape and 109.5° C—S—C bond angle. Dimethyl sulfide is a thioether found in marine algae and is also produced by cooking vegetables such as corn and cabbage. Methionine is the only thioether-containing amino acid.

same "R" groups   different "R" groups   dimethyl sulfide   methionine
general thioether   **examples**

Dithiols and cyclic thioethers are two additional types of organic molecules that contain sulfur. Dithiols contain two thiol groups. Dimercaptosuccinic acid (DMSA) is a dithiol used to treat lead, mercury, and arsenic-poisoning. Cyclic thioethers contain a thioether in a ring. Biotin is a cyclic thioether and is a water-soluble B-vitamin (vitamin B_7). Biotin is necessary for cell growth, the metabolism of fats, and other cellular processes.

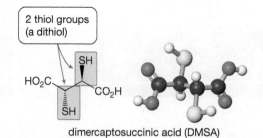

dimercaptosuccinic acid (DMSA)

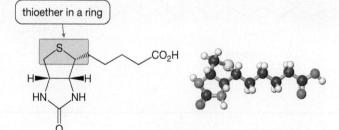

biotin
cyclic thioether

Apply what you have just learned: **Practice 14.9 and 14.10** in the Pearson eText.

Properties of Thiols

Thiols are not capable of hydrogen bonding, and therefore have weaker intermolecular forces compared to alcohols with the same mass and shape. Thiols therefore have lower melting and boiling points than alcohols.

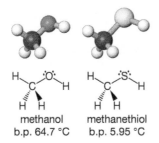

methanol
b.p. 64.7 °C

methanethiol
b.p. 5.95 °C

Thiols are best known for their strong odor. The foul-smelling spray skunks use as a defense mechanism, for example, contains a variety of thiol molecules (Figure 14.13a). Figures 14.13b and 14.13c illustrate other thiols that have strong odors.

Figure 14.13 Thiols with Strong Odors.

A) Skunk spray contains several thiols. **B)** *tert*-Butylthiol is added to natural gas tanks as a way to detect gas leaks and help prevent dangerous explosions. **C)** Thiols are responsible for the distinctive smell of coffee, as well as some of its subtle flavors.

A

B

C

Apply what you have just learned: **Practice 14.11–14.14** in the Pearson eText.

Thiols and Thioethers in Nature and Medicine

Like the other functional groups discussed thus far in this chapter, thiols and thio-ethers are found naturally in plants, in our bodies, and in drug molecules used to treat a range of diseases (Figure 14.14).

Figure 14.14 Thiols and Thioethers in Food and Medicine.

Glutathione is a thiol containing antioxidant that is important in a number of cellular processes in the human body. Your body produces most of the glutathione it needs, but foods such as asparagus, avocado, spinach, broccoli, and others are also good sources of glutathione. Meropenem is a thioether-containing broad-spectrum antibiotic used to treat a wide variety of infections. It is on the World Health Organization's Essential Medicines List.

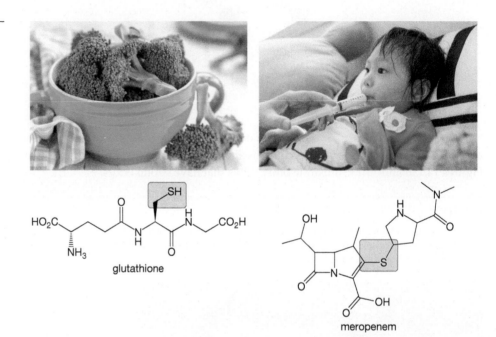

glutathione

meropenem

 Quiz yourself on the content of this section: **Check 14.3** in the Pearson eText.

14.4 Reactions of Alcohols and Thiols

The reactions of alcohols and thiols play a significant role in how the human body functions. For example, BioConnect 14.1 describes a thiol reaction that is involved in intestinal problems that can affect travelers.

The hydroxyl group in alcohols acts as a reactive center in two types of reactions: **dehydration reactions** and **oxidation reactions**. Dehydration reactions involve the loss of water from alcohol molecules and produce alkenes. A dehydration reaction often produces more than one alkene molecule. However only one of the alkenes is considered to be the major product. **Zaitsev's Rule** provides a method for predicting both major and minor alkene products for dehydration reactions. The major product is the alkene that has the more-substituted double bond. In other words, the alkene in which more carbon atoms are bonded to the carbons that are a part of the double bond is the major product. The major product depends on which side of the alcohol group the neighboring hydrogen is removed. An example of how Zaitsev's rule is used is presented in VisibleChem Video 14.1.

Oxidation reactions of alcohols involve the replacement of C—H bonds with C—O bonds producing a **carbonyl group (C=O).** The carbonyl group is part of several functional groups such as aldehydes, ketones, and carboxylic acids. These three functional groups are found in the products of alcohol oxidation reactions.

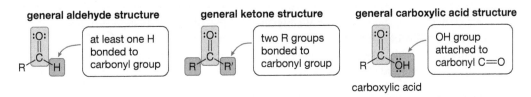

general aldehyde structure | **general ketone structure** | **general carboxylic acid structure**

at least one H bonded to carbonyl group

two R groups bonded to carbonyl group

OH group attached to carbonyl C=O

carboxylic acid

You will encounter these functional groups in future chapters, however a brief introduction in this section is useful as you explore reactions of alcohols. An aldehyde group is composed of a carbonyl group found at the end of a carbon chain in which the carbonyl carbon is bonded to at least one H atom. In a ketone, the carbonyl carbon is bonded to two carbon groups (R and R′) and no H atoms. A carboxylic acid is a functional group with a hydroxyl group (OH) bonded to a carbonyl carbon.

Recall from Section 8.3 that oxidation involves the loss of elections, the addition of oxygen, or the loss of hydrogen. Because hydrogen atoms are lost in this reaction, it is an oxidation reaction. Chemists often use the symbol [O] to indicate an oxidation reaction especially when organic and biomolecules are involved.

Oxidation reactions of thiols produce **disulfides,** compounds that contain a sulfur-sulfur bond. Two hydrogen atoms are lost in the formation of disulfides from thiols and therefore this reaction is also referred to as an oxidation reaction. The reverse reaction, reduction of disulfides to thiols, also occurs. In this reduction reaction, hydrogen is gained. Chemists use the symbol [R] to indicate a reduction reaction.

Table 14.1 provides a summary of these three reaction types. Explore VisibleChem Videos 14.1–14.3 to learn more about the details of these reactions including how to predict their products. Then select BioConnect 14.2 (contains Figures 14.15–14.21) to explore the significance of disulfide bonds in biological systems.

Table 14.1 Summary of Alcohol and Thiol Reactions.

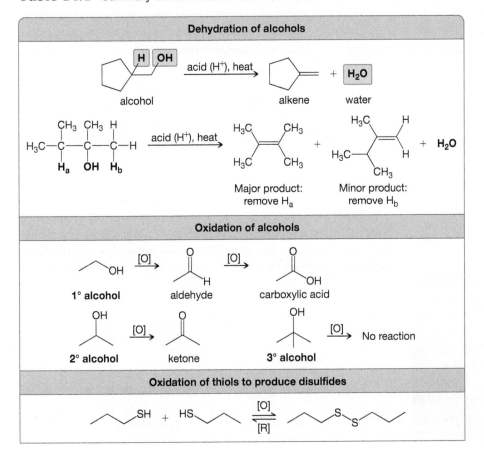

Watch this concept come to life: **VisibleChem Video 14.1:** Dehydration Reactions of Alcohols, **VisibleChem Video 14.2:** Oxidation Reactions of Alcohols, and **VisibleChem Video 14.3:** Oxidation Reactions of Thiols to Produce Disulfides in the Pearson eText.

Apply what you have just learned: **Practice 14.15–14.7** in the Pearson eText.

Explore how Chemistry and Biology connect: **BioConnect: 14.2** Disulfide Bonds in Proteins in the Pearson eText.

Quiz yourself on the content of this section: **Check 14.4** in the Pearson eText.

14.5 Three-Dimensional Shape: Chiral Molecules

Tuberculosis (TB) is one of the deadliest global diseases, and as you learned in the Unit 5 Introduction, there has been a recent surge in multidrug-resistant TB (MDR TB). An antibiotic drug treats infection by killing bacteria. However multidrug-resistant bacteria survive the treatment and reproduce, passing on their resistance genes. As antibiotics become less and less useful for treating resistant TB, new drugs are needed (Figure 14.22).

The design of new antibiotic drugs must take into account the three-dimensional arrangement of atoms. As you will discover in this section, there is generally one way that atoms can be arranged in three dimensions to elicit the desired medicinal response in the body. In fighting TB, the desired response is to function as an antibiotic, even for multidrug-resistant bacteria. In this section, we investigate a new way to think about the three-dimensional shape of molecules, and how three-dimensionality of drug molecules plays a large role in the effectiveness of a specific treatment.

Recall from Chapter 13 that **structural isomers** have the same chemical formula but differ in how the atoms in the molecule are connected. For example, two structural isomers with the chemical formula C_4H_{10} are shown here.

Figure 14.22 Antibiotic Drugs for Treating Tuberculosis (TB).

Healthcare providers generally prescribe a combination of drugs to treat TB. Reports of multiple-drug resistant TB have increased, prompting scientists to escalate the effort to design new more effective drugs.

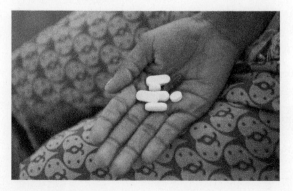

Structural isomers are also possible across different functional groups. Ethanol, for example, is an alcohol that has the same chemical formula as dimethyl ether. These two molecules are structural isomers, yet ethanol has a hydroxyl group and dimethyl ether has an oxygen atom bonded to two carbon atoms.

Chirality

Some isomers have the same chemical formula and have the same atom connectivity—yet differ in the way that the atoms are arranged in space. These isomers are **stereoisomers;** they differ only in the three-dimensional arrangement of atoms. A specific group of stereoisomers is the result of the arrangement of groups around tetrahedral carbon atoms. To identify stereoisomers of carbon compounds chemists, consider **mirror images** of molecules. This may sound strange at first, but an evaluation of a molecule's mirror image provides a useful approach to assessing whether molecules are stereoisomers or not.

Take a look at both your hands. Left and right hands are mirror images of each other, but they are not identical. If you attempt to line up your two hands one on top of another, you will notice that it is not possible. Your hands are **nonsuperimposable** (Figure 14.23a).

A molecule or object that is nonsuperimposable on its mirror image is **chiral.** We also refer to stereoisomers that cannot be superimposed as **enantiomers.** A molecule or object that is **superimposable** on its mirror image, on the other hand, is **achiral.** A flask is an example of an achiral object that is superimposable with its mirror image (Figure 14.23b).

Explore Visible Chem 14.2 to learn more about how chirality applies to carbon molecules and how to identify **chiral carbon centers** within large molecules.

Figure 14.23 Chiral and Achiral Objects.

a) Left and right hands are mirror images, cannot be superimposed, and are chiral objects. **b)** A flask is superimposable with its mirror image and is therefore achiral.

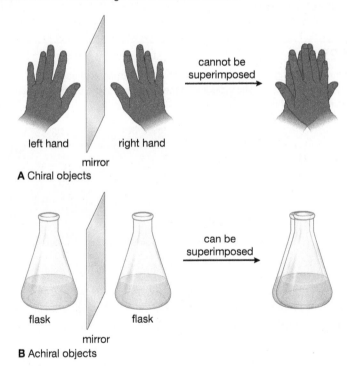

Watch this concept come to life: **VisibleChem Video 14.4:** Chirality of Objects and **VisibleChem Video 14.5:** Chiral Compounds in the Pearson eText.

Apply what you have just learned: **Practice 14.18 and 14.19** in the Pearson eText.

Figure 14.24 Enzymes Bind Specific Enantiomers.

The protein targets of drugs recognize just one enantiomer.

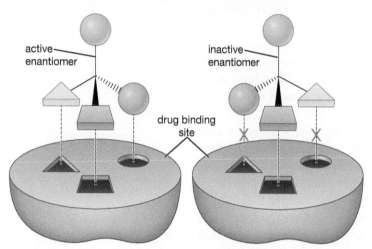

Bioactivity of Chiral Molecules

Many biological compounds have chiral carbon centers, including some carbohydrates, proteins, and even DNA. The three-dimensional structure of these molecules has a direct impact on how they function in the body. We explore these biomolecules and their stereochemistry in more detail in the chapters to come.

Like biomolecules, drug molecules are often chiral. Each molecule in a pair of chiral molecules can interact with the body in a different way. For example, one enantiomer of a drug may have a desired medicinal effect, whereas the other enantiomer does not. This occurs because a drug molecule, such as the one shown in Figure 14.24, may have three groups that can interact with the specific binding sites of the receptor. The enantiomer, in contrast, can never be arranged such that all three groups bind to the binding site. For this reason, the inactive enantiomer does not fit in the same receptor, and does not initiate the same response.

Linezolid is a chiral drug that provides an example of this—one enantiomer has the desired response in the body, and the other does not (Figure 14.25). Linezolid is an antibiotic used to treat a number of infections including methicillin-resistant *Staphylococcus aureus* (MRSA). MRSA is resistant to many commonly used antibiotics. The active enantiomer of linezolid has potent antibiotic activity whereas the inactive enantiomer lacks these properties.

Figure 14.25

The enantiomers of Linezolid are non-superimposable mirror images of each other. Only one enantiomer functions as an antibiotic including in the treatment of the *Staphylococcus aureus* (MRSA, shown in the upper right corner).

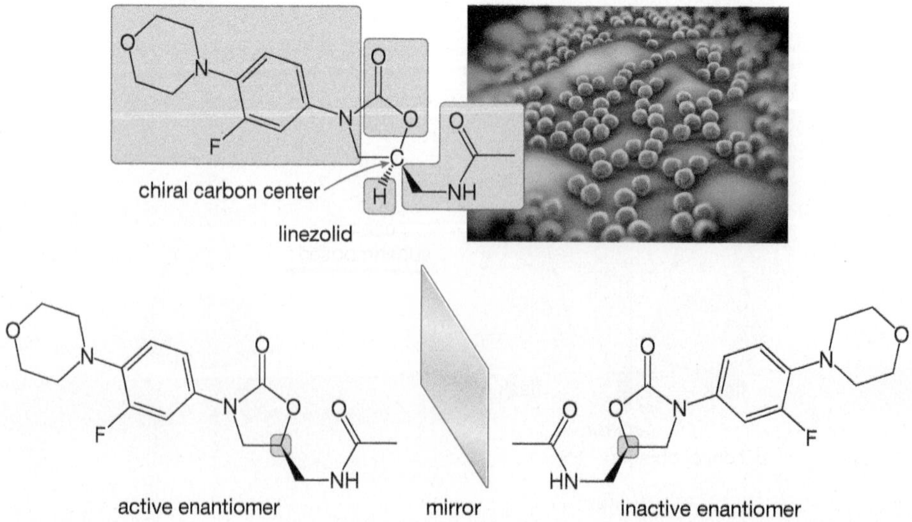

chiral carbon center

linezolid

active enantiomer   mirror   inactive enantiomer

Chiral Drugs

Ketamine is a chiral drug that is used in anesthesia and for intensive care sedation (Figure 14.26). The drug is administered as a mixture of the two enantiomers when used in this way. Ketamine is also currently under investigation for use as an

Figure 14.26 Enantiomers of Ketamine.

A mixture containing both enantiomers of ketamine is used as a sedative. Neither enantiomer is harmful, but the active enantiomer has recently demonstrated antidepressant activity.

chiral carbon center

ketamine

active enantiomer   mirror   inactive enantiomer

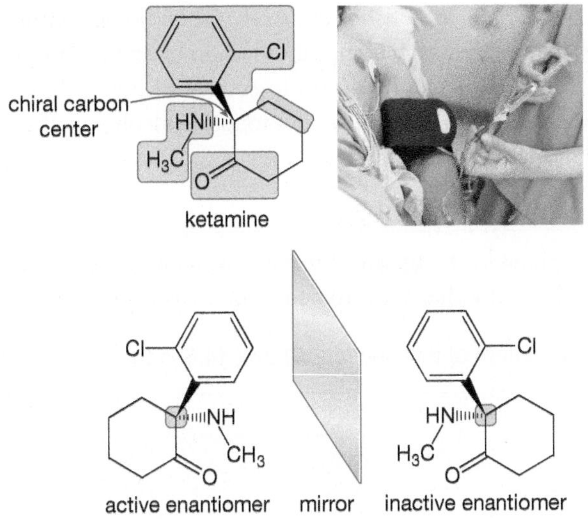

antidepressant. In a recent study, one enantiomer of this drug molecule demonstrated superior antidepressant activity over the other enantiomer.

In some cases, an inactive enantiomer has a negative effect on the body. Ethambutol is a chiral drug used to treat tuberculosis (TB) that illustrates this situation. There are two chiral carbon centers in the ethambutol molecule, which complicates matters, but the two stereoisomers shown in Figure 14.27 are nonsuperimposable mirror images, or enantiomers. Each has very different biological activity. The active enantiomer is used as a drug to treat tuberculosis (TB), and the other enantiomer causes blindness. In this case, it is essential to separate the two enantiomers before administering it to patients.

Figure 14.27 Enantiomers of the Tuberculosis Drug, Ethambutol.

One enantiomer is effective at treating tuberculosis. The other, however, causes blindness and is not effective against TB.

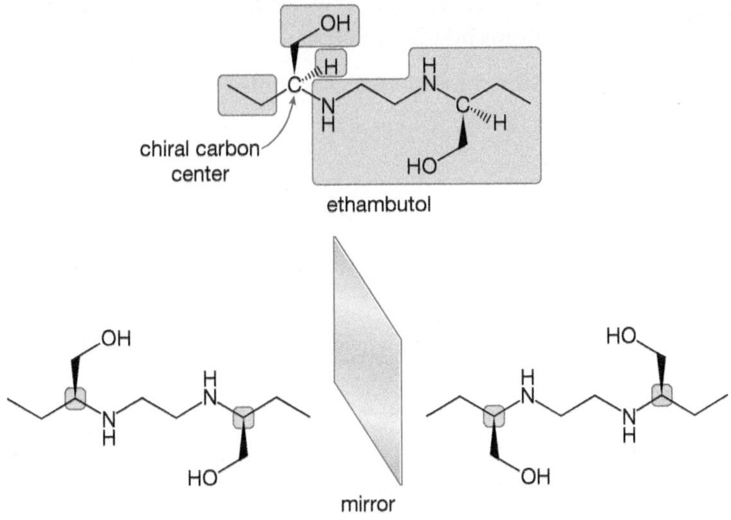

chiral carbon center

ethambutol

mirror

Quiz yourself on the content of this section: **Check 14.5** in the Pearson eText.

14.6 Naming Alcohols, Ethers, and Thiols

Chemists follow specific rules when naming compounds. This process of devising or choosing names for things is nomenclature. The International Union of Pure and Applied Chemistry (IUPAC) establishes the rules for the nomenclature of organic compounds. The rules ensure that each compound has an unambiguous and unique name, allowing chemists from all over the world to communicate with each other. Explore Nomenclature Videos 14.6–14.8 to learn how to name alcohols, ethers and thiols. You can also review the rules for naming compounds in the nomenclature appendix.

Watch this concept come to life: **Video 14.2:** Nomenclature: Alcohols, **Video 14.3** Nomenclature: Ethers, and **Video 14.4** Nomenclature: Thiols in the Pearson eText.

Quiz yourself on the content of this section: **Check 14.6** in the Pearson eText.

Chapter Summary

14.1 Alcohols

Learning Objective: Analyze the structural and physical properties of alcohols.

Alcohols are organic molecules that each contain a hydroxyl functional group (OH) attached to a carbon atom in the general form R—O—H. The hydroxyl oxygen atom is bonded to one hydrogen atom, and has two lone pairs of electrons, resulting in a bent shape around the oxygen atom with a C—O—H bond angle around 109.5°. The alcohol group is polar, and allows hydrogen bonds to form with alcohols of the same type, water, other alcohols, and other molecules capable of hydrogen bonding. Hydrogen bonds are a strong intermolecular force that give alcohols relatively high boiling points compared to other non-hydrogen bonding molecules of similar mass. Hydrogen bonding also allows alcohols containing five or fewer carbon atoms to dissolve in water. Alcohols are primary (1°), secondary (2°), or tertiary (3°), depending on the number of carbon atoms bonded to the carbon with the OH group.

BioConnect 14.1: Alcohols in our Bodies

Key Terms

alcohols
functional group
primary alcohol
secondary alcohol
tertiary alcohol

14.2 Ethers

Learning Objective: Analyze the structural and physical properties of ethers.

Ethers are organic compounds that contain a carbon atom bonded on each side of an oxygen atom in the general form R—O—R. The two carbon groups (R) can be the same on each side of the oxygen (R and R) or on different sides (R and R'). The oxygen atom in an ether molecule also has two lone pairs of electrons, resulting in a bent shape with a C—O—C bond angle around 109.5°. Similar to alcohols, the polar C—O bonds combined with the bent shape contribute to the overall polarity of the ether functional group. Unlike alcohols, ethers do not have a hydrogen atom bonded to an oxygen atom, therefore ethers do not form intermolecular hydrogen bonds with each other. While ether molecules do not form hydrogen bonds with each other, they do form hydrogen bonds with water and alcohols.

Key Terms

cyclic ether
ether
heterocycle

14.3 Functional Groups Containing Sulfur

Learning Objective: Analyze the structural and physical properties of sulfur functional groups (thiols, thioethers).

Thiols have a similar structure to alcohols except the thiol functional group contains a sulfur atom bonded to a hydrogen atom (R—S—H) instead of an oxygen atom. Similar to the oxygen atom in alcohols, the sulfur atom has two lone pairs of electrons. Thiols have a bent shape with R—S—H bond angle around 109.5°, two lone pairs of electrons around sulfur. Thiols are polar. Thioethers (R—S—R) are similar to ethers (R—O—R), except on each side a sulfur atom is bonded to a carbon instead of an oxygen atom. The R groups on each side of the sulfur atom can be the same or different (R or R').

Key Terms

thioether
thiol

14.4 Reactions of Alcohols and Thiols

Learning Objective: Determine the products of the reactions of alcohols and thiols (dehydration of alcohols, and oxidation of thiols).

The hydroxyl group in alcohols provides a reactive center. This center is involved in two types of reactions—dehydration and oxidation reactions. Dehydration reactions involve the loss of water from alcohol molecules and produce alkenes. The major product is the alkene that has the more-substituted double bond (in other words, the alkene that has more carbon atoms bonded to the carbons that are a part of the double bond) in accordance with Zaitsev's rule. An oxidation reaction of an alcohol involves the replacement of C—H bonds with C—O bonds on the carbon with the OH group. In the oxidation of alcohols, a carbonyl group (C=O) forms. A carbonyl group is a carbon atom, and an oxygen atom with a double bond between them. Primary (1°) alcohols can be oxidized to aldehydes, which can be further oxidized to carboxylic acids (R—CO₂H). Secondary (2°) alcohols can be oxidized to ketones. Tertiary alcohols do not undergo oxidation under the same conditions as primary and secondary alcohols. Oxidation of thiols (R—S—H) produces disulfides (R—S—S—R). Reduction of disulfides produces thiols. This reversible redox process is important in biological systems.

VisibleChem Video 14.1: **Dehydration Reactions of Alcohols**

VisibleChem Video 14.2: **Oxidation Reactions of Alcohols**

VisibleChem Video 14.3: **Oxidation Reactions of Thiols to Produce Disulfides**

BioConnect 14.2: **Disulfide Bonds in Proteins**

Key Terms

carbonyl group
dehydration reaction
disulfide
disulfide bridges (from BioConnect 14.2)
oxidation reaction
Zaitsev's rule

14.5 Three-Dimensional Shape: Chiral Molecules

Learning Objective: Distinguish between chiral and achiral molecules.

A molecule or object that is non-superimposable on its mirror image is chiral. Stereoisomers are isomers that differ only in the three-dimensional arrangement of atoms. Enantiomers are chiral mirror images that are not superimposable on each other. In contrast, a molecule or object that

is superimposable on its mirror image is achiral. Stereoisomers cannot be superimposed as enantiomers. A carbon atom bonded to four different groups is a chiral carbon center.

VisibleChem Video 14.4: Chirality of Objects

VisibleChem Video 14.5: Chiral Compounds

Key Terms

achiral	enantiomer	stereoisomer
chiral	mirror image	superimposable
chiral carbon center	nonsuperimposable	

14.6 Naming Alcohols, Ethers, and Thiols

Learning Objective: Name alcohols, ethers, and thiols according to the IUPAC system.

Chemists follow specific rules when naming compounds. This process of devising or choosing names for things is nomenclature. The International Union of Pure and Applied Chemistry (IUPAC) establishes the rules for the nomenclature of organic compounds.

Video 14.2: Nomenclature: Alcohols

Video 14.3: Nomenclature: Ethers

Video 14.4: Nomenclature: Thiols

 End-of-Chapter Quiz

Have you mastered the content of this chapter? Try the **End-of-Chapter Quiz** in the Pearson eText.

1. How many hydrogen atoms are attached to the alcohol carbon of (i) a primary (1°) alcohol, (ii) a secondary (2°) alcohol, and (iii) a tertiary alcohol?
   a) (i) zero, (ii) two, (iii) one
   b) (i) three, (ii) two, (iii) one
   c) (i) one, (ii) two, (iii) three
   d) (i) two, (ii) one, (iii) zero

2. Riboflavin is a water-soluble B vitamin (Vitamin B2) found in a number of foods. It is an essential medicine by the World Health Organization that is used as a dietary supplement to prevent and treat riboflavin deficiency. Study the skeletal structure of riboflavin, and determine the number of primary (1°), secondary (2°), and tertiary (3°) alcohol groups on the molecule.

riboflavin

a) Riboflavin contains one primary, two secondary, and one tertiary alcohol groups.
b) Riboflavin contains one primary, three secondary, and zero tertiary alcohol groups.
c) Riboflavin contains three primary, one secondary, and zero tertiary alcohol groups.
d) Riboflavin contains two primary, one secondary, and one tertiary alcohol groups.

3. Which statement correctly describes the effect that hydrogen bonding has on the boiling point of alcohols and the solubility of alcohols in water?
   a) Hydrogen bonding in alcohols results in a lower-than-expected boiling point when compared to hydrocarbons of similar mass. Hydrogen bonding decreases the solubility of alcohols in water because the carbon-hydrogen bond is nonpolar.
   b) Hydrogen bonding in alcohols results in a higher-than-expected boiling point when compared to hydrocarbons of similar mass. Hydrogen bonding decreases the solubility of alcohols in water since alcohols depend on London Dispersion forces to dissolve in water.
   c) Hydrogen bonding does not impact boiling points of alcohols, since boiling depends on atmospheric pressure and temperature only. Hydrogen bonding increases the solubility of alcohols in water because

it is a strong intermolecular force shared between the alcohol group and water.

d) Hydrogen bonding in alcohols results in a higher-than-expected boiling point when compared to hydrocarbons of similar mass. Hydrogen bonding increases the solubility of short-chain alcohols in water because the atoms in the OH group of alcohols can form hydrogen bonds with both H atoms and O atoms of water making small alcohols more soluble in water.

4. Kanamycin is an antibiotic identified by the World Health Organization as an essential medicine as a treatment for tuberculosis (Tb) and other severe bacterial infections. Study the structure of kanamycin and determine the number of primary (1°), secondary (2°), and tertiary (3°) alcohol groups on the molecule.

a) There is one primary (1°), four secondary (2°), and three tertiary (3°) alcohol groups on the kanamycin molecule.

b) There are two primary (1°), five secondary (2°), and no tertiary (3°) alcohol groups on the Kanamycin molecule.

c) There is one primary (1°), six secondary (2°), and no tertiary (3°) alcohol groups on the Kanamycin molecule.

d) There are six primary (1°), one secondary (2°), and two tertiary (3°) alcohol groups on the Kanamycin molecule.

5. Tuberculosis (Tb) is one of the top ten causes of death worldwide, making it one of the deadliest diseases, with over 90% of the TB deaths occurring in low- and middle-income countries. In 2016, over 10 million people fell ill with TB, and 1.7 million died from the disease (including an estimated 250,000 children). The medication delamanid has been identified by the World Health Organization (WHO) as an essential medicine for multi-drug resistant tuberculosis. Which of the indicated regions on the delamanid molecule are ether groups?

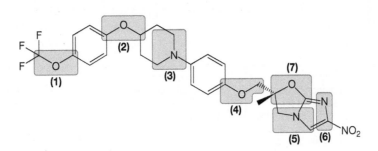

a) regions 3, 5, and 6
b) regions 1, 2, and 4
c) regions 1, 2, 4, and 7
d) There are no ether groups on the delamanid molecule.

6. Ethers cannot hydrogen bond with other ethers but can form hydrogen bonds with water. With this in mind, what is your prediction about the ability of ethers to hydrogen bond with alcohols?
a) Ethers can hydrogen bond with alcohols because alcohols and water both have a hydrogen atom bonded to an oxygen atom.
b) Ethers cannot hydrogen bond with alcohols because water is different from alcohol. Ethers can only hydrogen bond with water.
c) Ethers can hydrogen bond with alcohols because both ethers and alcohols have hydrogens on their carbon atoms that can hydrogen bond to each other.
d) Ethers cannot hydrogen bond with alcohols because ether groups have the general formula (R—O—R) or (R—O—R′), and alcohols have the general formula (R—O—H).

7. As we discuss in later chapters, coenzyme A is a molecule involved in a number of cellular processes in your body. Which shaded region on the coenzyme molecule is a thiol group?

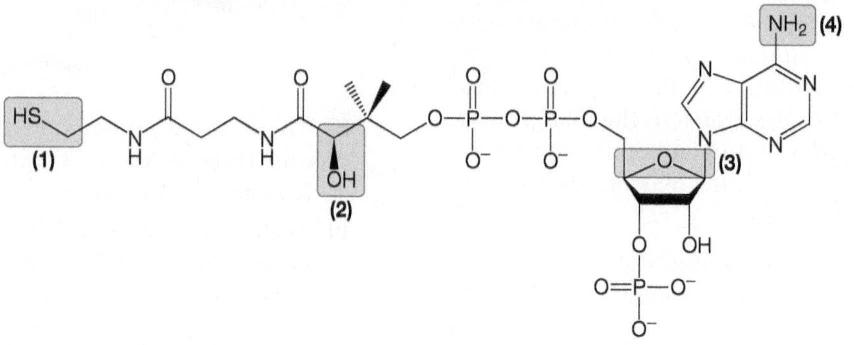

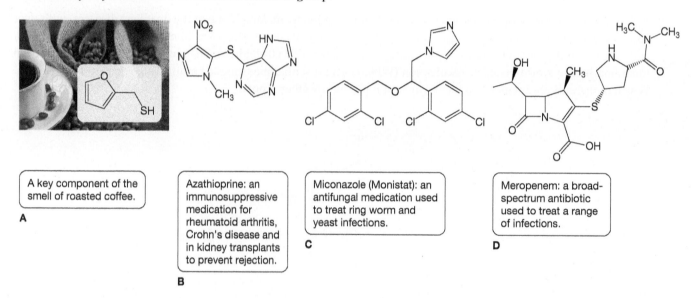

a) shaded region (1)

b) shaded region (2)

c) shaded region (3)

d) shaded region (4)

8. Identify any molecules that contain a thioether group.

| A key component of the smell of roasted coffee. | Azathioprine: an immunosuppressive medication for rheumatoid arthritis, Crohn's disease and in kidney transplants to prevent rejection. | Miconazole (Monistat): an antifungal medication used to treat ring worm and yeast infections. | Meropenem: a broad-spectrum antibiotic used to treat a range of infections. |

A

B

C

D

a) Molecule (A) contains a thioether group.

b) Molecules (B), (C) and (D) contain thioether groups.

c) Molecules (B) and (D) contain thioether groups.

d) All four molecules contain thioether groups.

9. Which statement about thiols is correct?

a) Like alcohols, thiols are able to hydrogen bond with themselves.

b) Like the oxygen atom in alcohols, the sulfur atom in thiols bonds with two tetrahedral carbon atoms, has two lone pairs of electrons, and is bent with a C—S—C bond angle around 109.5.

c) The sulfur atom in thiols can either be part of a branching group off a carbon chain or within a ring.

d) Thiols have a similar structure to alcohols except thiols contain a sulfur atom bonded to a hydrogen atom (SH), which prevents thiols from hydrogen bonding with themselves.

10. In these molecular models, sulfur is yellow, carbon is black, hydrogen is light grey, and oxygen is red. Which of the molecules is not a thiol?

a)

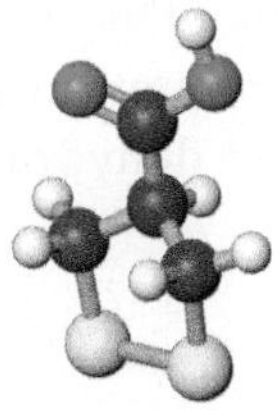

b)

c)

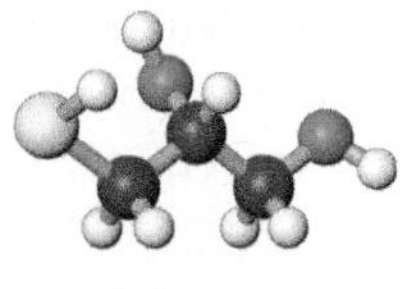

d)

11. Abacavir is used to treat HIV/AIDS and has been identified by the World Health Organization (WHO) as an essential medicine based on efficacy, safety, and comparative cost-effectiveness. What are the products of the two-step oxidation of abacavir?

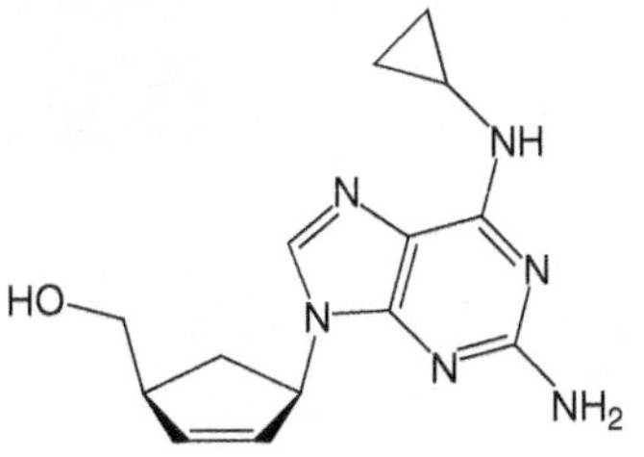

abacavir

a)

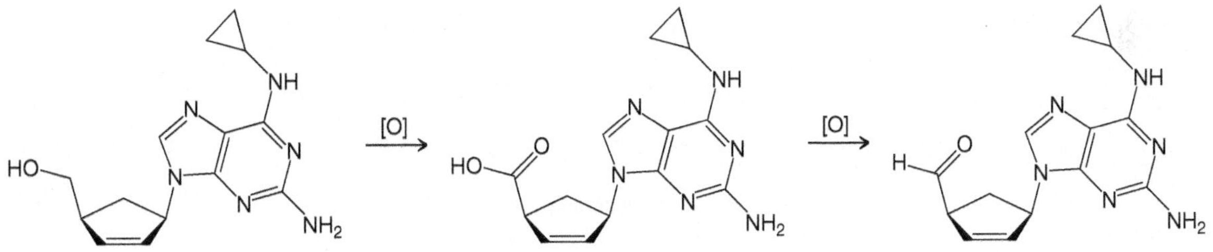

b)

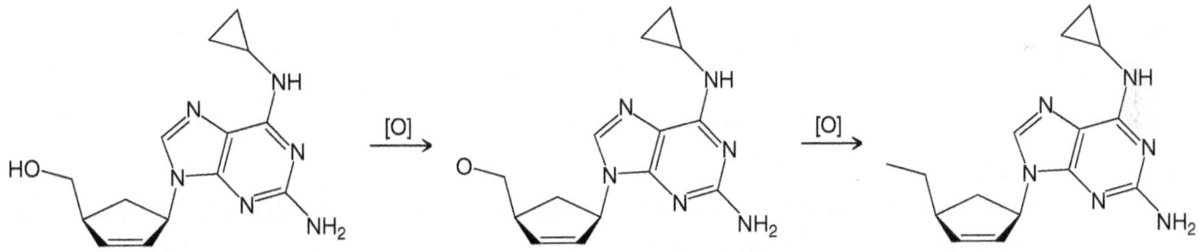

c)

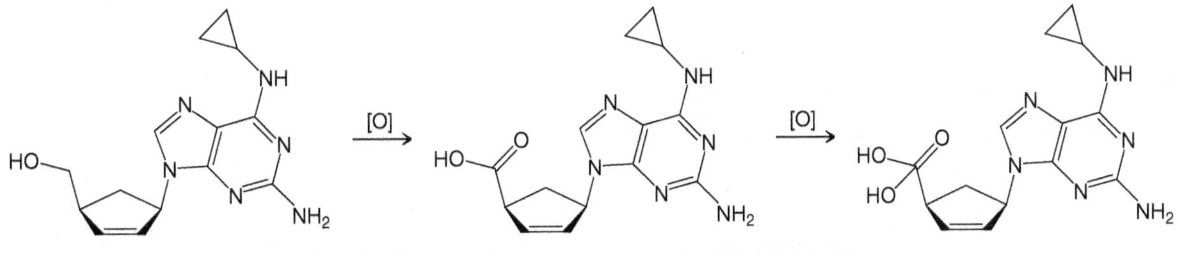

d)

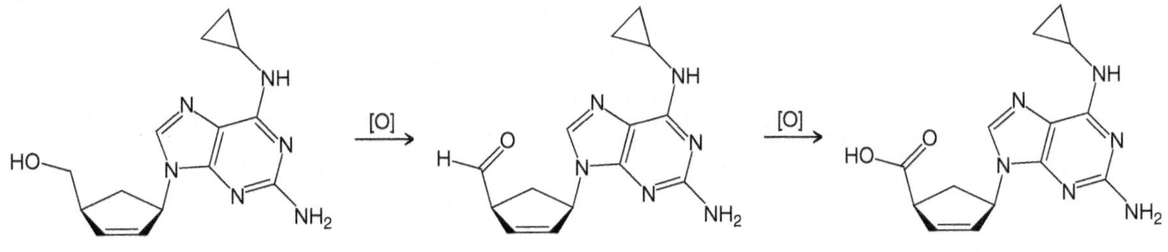

12. Diarrheal disease is a leading cause of death in children and kills approximately 500,000 children every year. Diarrheal infections are usually spread through contaminated drinking water, food, or person-to-person as a result of poor handwashing and hygiene. Diarrhea often lasts for several days and can leave the body without the water and salts that are necessary for survival. Metronidazole (also known as flagyl) is an antibiotic, and antiprotozoal medication used to treat diarrhea-causing infections. Which product is formed by the chemical dehydration of metronidazole?

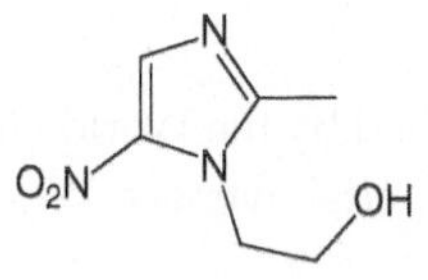

The drug metronidazole and an image of a diarrhea-causing *Giardia* cell.

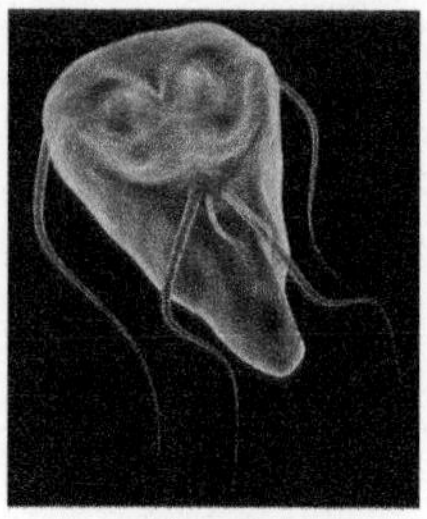

Giardia

a)

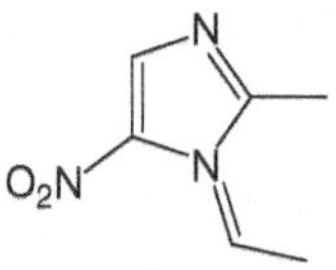

b)

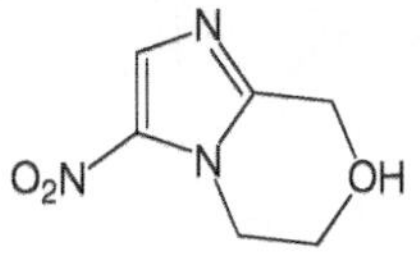

c)

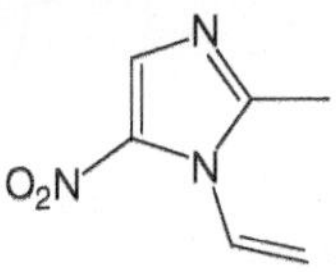

d)

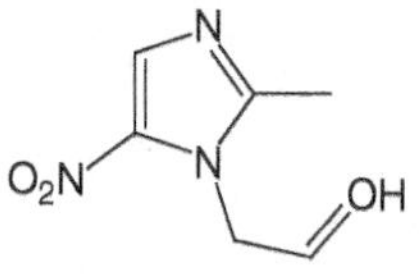

13. Which starting alcohol can be dehydrated to produce the major product shown?

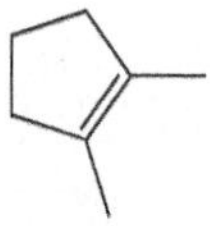

dehydration product

a)

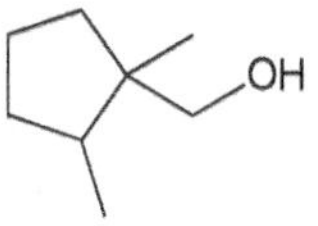

b)

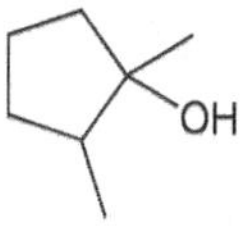

c)

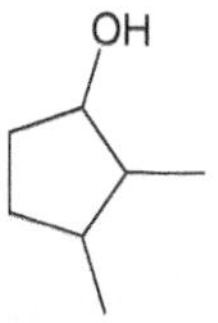

d)

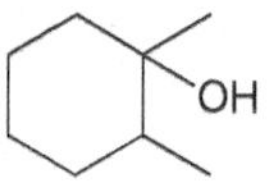

14. Glycolysis is a metabolic pathway that converts glucose (blood sugar) into energy that your body uses each day. In one step of the glycolysis pathway, 2-phosphoglycerate (2PG) is dehydrated by an enzyme-forming phosphoenolpyruvate (PEP). Which statement best describes the changes that occur in the starting material to form the product of this important biological reaction?

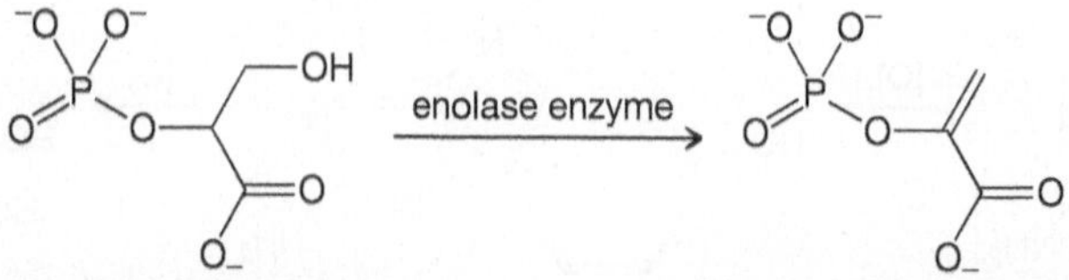

enolase enzyme

2-phosphoglycerate (2PG)   phosphoenolpyruvate (PEP)

a) The OH group and a neighboring H atom are transferred from the 2PG reactant to the PEP product during the reaction.

b) The OH group and a neighboring H atom are removed from the 2PG reactant to form an alkene in the PEP product.

c) A CH_2OH group in the 2PG reactant is removed and an alkyne group is added to form the PEP product.

d) The OH group and a neighboring H atom are removed from PEP reactant to form the alkene group in the 2PG product.

15. This molecule is a naturally-occurring thiol compound found in grapefruit. Select the product of the oxidation reaction shown.

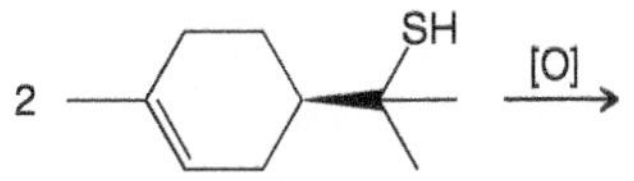

a)

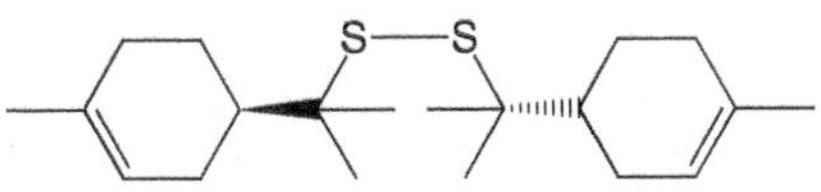

b)

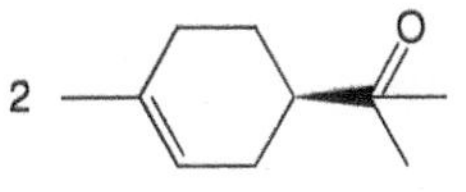

c)

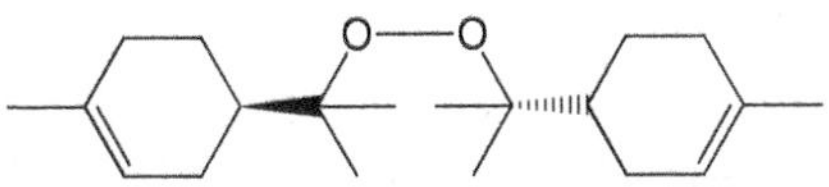

d)

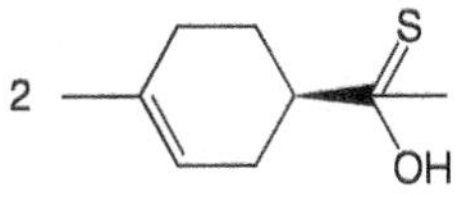

16. Which of these molecules contains at least one chiral carbon?

a)

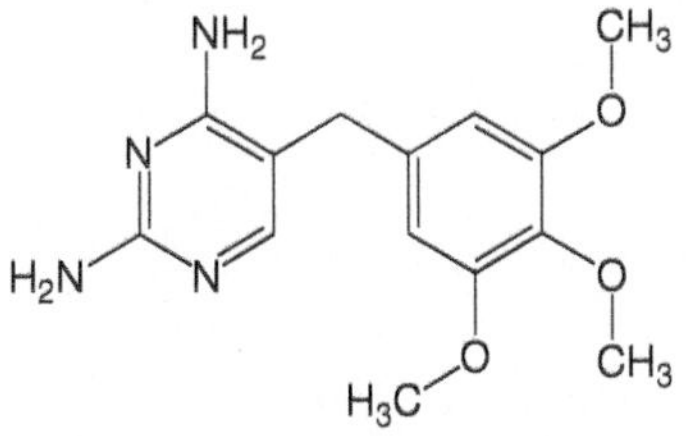

Trimethoprim: antibiotic used to treat traveler's diarrhea, ear infections, and bladder infections.

b)

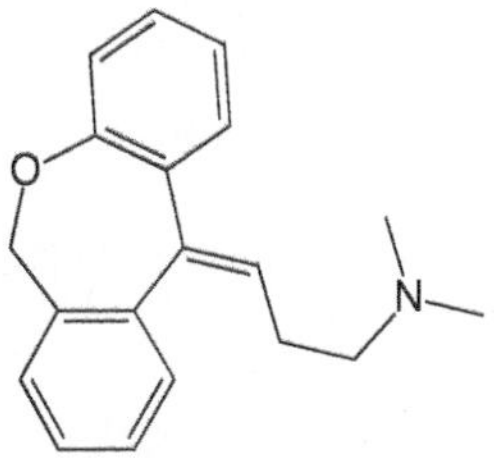

Doxepin: antidepressant used to treat depression and anxiety disorders.

c)

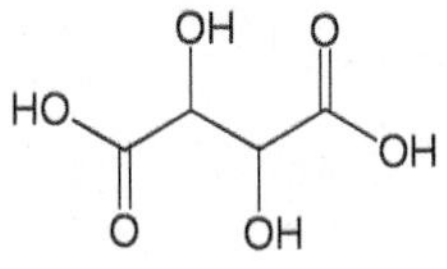

Tartaric acid: naturally occurring compound in many plants, especially grapes.

d)

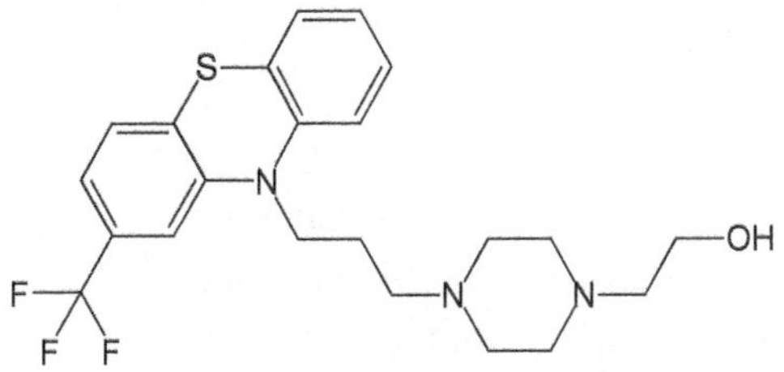

Fluphenazine (Prolixin): antipsychotic medication used to treat schizophrenia.

17. How many chiral carbons are in each molecule?

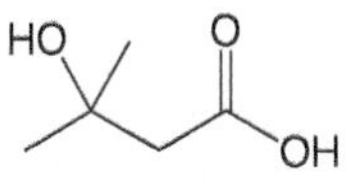

Hydroxymethylbutyrate (HMB): used to treat heart disease, high cholesterol, and high blood pressure. It is also used to increase the benefits of weight training and exercise by some athletes.

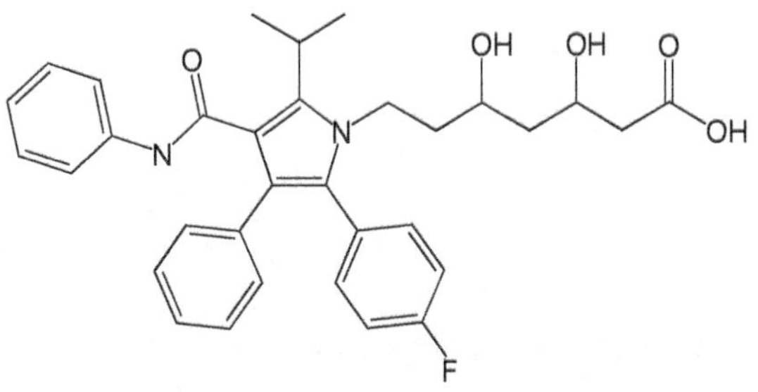

Atorvastatin (Lipitor): cholesterol lowering drug that may reduce the risk of heart attack and stroke. One of the most prescribed drugs in the US.

a) There is one chiral carbon in HMB, and there are three chiral carbons on atorvastatin.

b) There are no chiral carbons in HMB, and there are two chiral carbons on atorvastatin.

c) There is one chiral carbon in HMB, and two chiral carbons on atorvastatin.

d) There are no chiral carbons in HMB, and there are three chiral carbons on atorvastatin.

18. The molecule ribose-5-phosphate is involved in sugar metabolism. In what way are ribose-5-phosphate and the other molecule shown here related to each other?

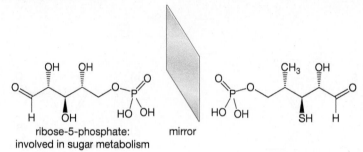

ribose-5-phosphate: mirror
involved in sugar metabolism

a) They are the same molecule.

b) They are structural isomers.

c) They are enantiomers.

d) They are unrelated.

19. Select the correct structure of 4-ethyl-5-methyl-3-octanol.

a)

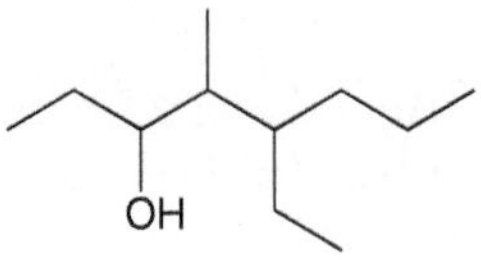

b)

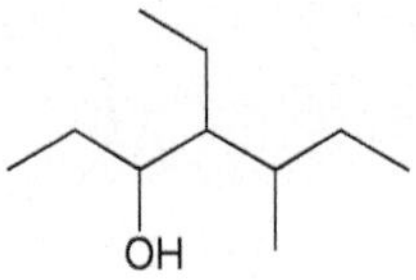

c)

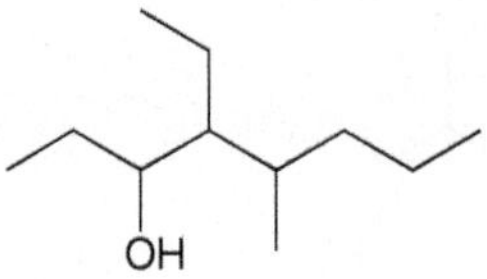

d)

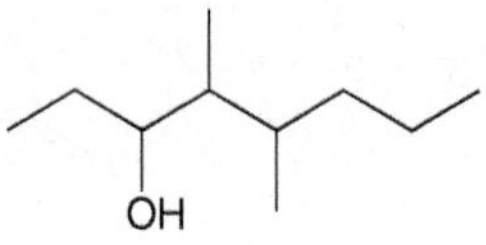

---

20. What is the IUPAC name for this molecule?

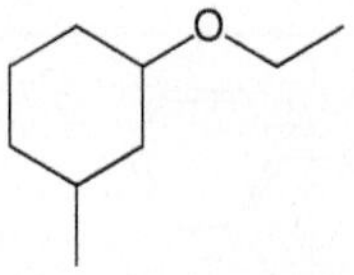

a) 1-ethoxy-3-methylcyclohexane
b) 3-ethoxy-1-methylcyclohexane
c) 1-methoxy-3-methylcyclohexane
d) 1-ethoxy-3-methylcyclopentane

21. What is the IUPAC name for this molecule?

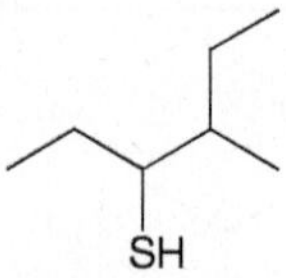

a) 4-methyl-3-hexanethiol
b) 3-methyl-4-hexanethiol
c) 3-methyl-4-pentanethiol
d) 3-methyl-4-pentanol

Unit 5

Bringing It All Together

How Can We Use Chemistry to Combat Drug-Resistant TB?

CHEMISTRY APPLICATION We opened Unit 5 with a look at the history and biology of tuberculosis (TB), including resistance to many of the drugs typically first prescribed for TB, such as ethambutol. After studying Chapters 13 and 14, we can now look more closely at the structure of ethambutol and recognize some essential features including the two alcohol groups and the chiral centers (Figure U5.6). Recall also that the polar alcohol groups and the amine groups in the molecule are able to hydrogen bond with water, helping the molecule readily dissolve in our blood and move throughout our bodies.

The increasing resistance of TB to drugs such as ethambutol is a global problem, as resistant strains can quickly move from one region of the world to another. Studies in China, for example, have documented an alarming rise in the number of resistant strains of TB among patients who were being treated for the first time (Figure U5.7). Finding resistance in these so-called primary cases is alarming as it suggests the resistant strains are abundant and circulating widely.

Figure U5.6 Key Features of Ethambutol.

The TB drug ethambutol contains two alcohol groups, two chiral centers, and two amine groups.

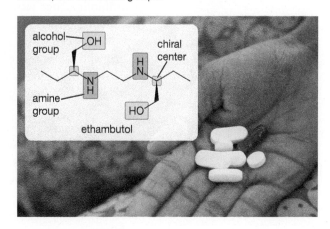

Figure U5.7 Drug Resistant TB is Common in Many Parts of the World, Including China.

A) A doctor talks to a patient with TB. **B)** Data released in 2019 show high levels of resistance to four standard TB drugs in patients in a hospital in China. (INH = isoniazid; RFP = rifampin; EMB = ethambutol; SM = streptomycin; Song *et. al.*, 2019)

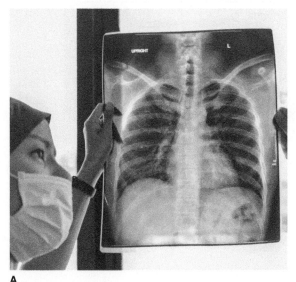

A

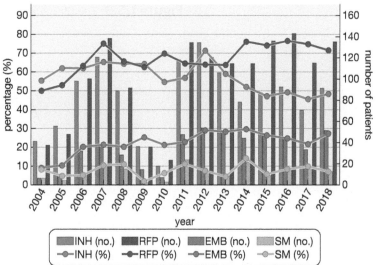

B

Figure U5.8 Drug Resistance Mechanisms.

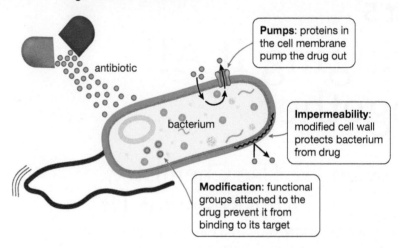

Pumps: proteins in the cell membrane pump the drug out

Impermeability: modified cell wall protects bacterium from drug

Modification: functional groups attached to the drug prevent it from binding to its target

antibiotic

bacterium

We have considered the evolutionary process that drives drug resistance in bacteria (see Fig. U5.3), but how does resistance work on a molecular level? Most antibiotic drugs work by shutting down an essential function of a bacterial cell. Examples of these essential functions include protein synthesis or the assembly of protective cell walls. Resistant bacteria may, for example, be less permeable to the drug and allow less of it to reach the drug target inside the cell (Figure U5.8). Or resistant bacteria may even actively pump the drug out. Some resistant bacteria may add new functional groups to a drug, reducing the drug's ability to bind to the target.

Understanding the molecular mechanism behind a particular form of drug resistance allows researchers to develop new strategies to combat the resistance. Chemists can design molecules to target specific, essential bacterial enzymes, for example, or search through libraries of existing molecules for compounds that might bind to essential components within the bacterial cell, interfering with its function.

For example, a group of Chinese scientists published a study that examined the ability of a molecule extracted from the plant, *Stephania tentrandra*, to combat drug-resistant TB (Zhang *et al.*, 2015). The molecule, tetrandrine, has long been used in traditional Chinese medicine to treat a wide variety of diseases (Figure U5.9). Because of

Figure U5.9 The Structure of Tetrandrine.

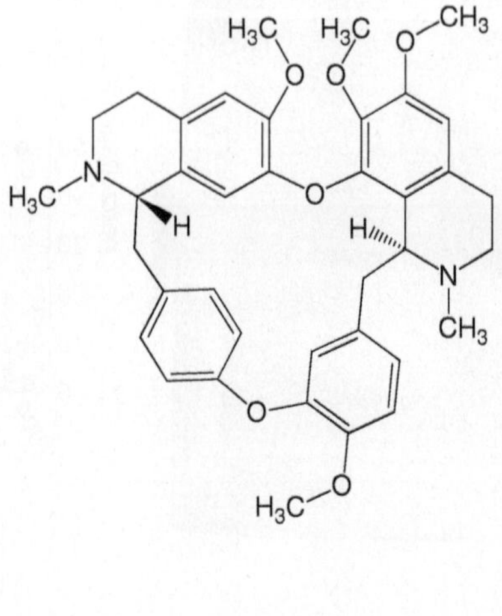

this known biological activity, the researchers hypothesized that the compound might be able to bind to, and block, a pump that allows some resistant strains of TB to transport ethambutol out of their cells.

Questions to Think About

1. Compare the molecular structures of ethambutol (see Fig. U5.6) and tetrandrine (see Fig. U5.9). What are their similarities and differences? What functional groups do you recognize? Can you find any chiral carbons in the tetrandrine molecule?

2. Based on your understanding of polarity and solubility ("like dissolves like"), do you think that ethambutol or tetrandrine is more water-soluble? Why is the solubility of a drug an important consideration?

3. The ethambutol molecule can form hydrogen bonds with water that increase solubility of this drug in body fluids. Can you locate where these hydrogen bonds will occur when ethambutol is dissolved in water? What about the tetrandrine molecule, can it form hydrogen bonds with water?

A Closer Look at the Data

To test their hypothesis that the compound from the plant, tetrandrine, might block the pump that would otherwise move ethambutol out of the cell, the researchers isolated drug-resistant TB bacteria from 200 patients. The bacteria were then grown with a dye that changes color when living bacteria remove electrons, oxidizing the dye. Growing bacteria change the solution from blue to pink. The researchers then added either ethambutol, or ethambutol and tetrandrine together, to the TB cells at various concentrations and observed the results. Figure U5.10 is from their paper. TB cells that were resistant to the drugs survived, turning the solution from blue to pink. TB cells that were susceptible to the drugs died and the solution remained blue (Zhang *et al.*, 2015).

Figure U5.10 Testing the Ability of Tetrandrine to Restore the Efficacy of Two Tuberculosis Drugs, Ethambutol and Isoniazid in Drug Resistant TB Strains.

The top numbers are the concentration of the drugs in µg/ml. Green values are the normal range of sensitivity. Red values indicate resistance (Zhang *et al.*, 2015).

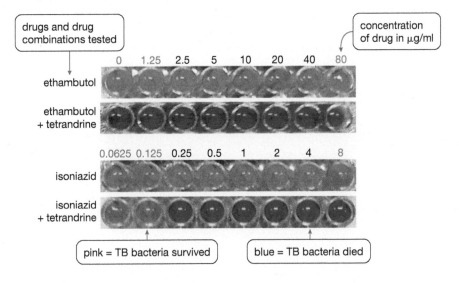

Questions to Think About

Examine Figure U5.10 and use it to answer the following questions:

1. Examine the top row of bacterial cultures. Did the bacterial cells treated with ethambutol grow well? What does this tell you about this strain of TB?

2. Now examine the second row, which are the cells grown with both ethambutol and tetrandrine. Were the bacterial cells able to grow when these two compounds were used together? What does this result tell the researchers?

3. The third and fourth rows are from a similar experiment done with another first-line TB drug, isoniazid. How do these results compare to the results for ethambutol and tetrandrine? What do they suggest about the mechanism this strain of TB uses to resist isoniazid and the mechanism it uses to resist ethambutol?

References

Song, Wm., Li, Yf., Ma, Xb. *et al.* Primary drug resistance of mycobacterium tuberculosis in Shandong, China, 2004–2018. *Respir Res* **20,** 223 (2019). https://doi.org/10.1186/s12931-019-1199-3

Zhang, Z., Yan J., Xu, K., Ji, Z., and Li, L.. 2015. Tetrandrine reverses drug resistance in isoniazid and ethambutol dual drug-resistant *Mycobacterium tuberculosis* clinical isolates. BMC Infectious Diseases. 15:153, DOI 10.1186/s12879-015-0905-0

Unit 6

Introduction
Exploring Aldehydes, Ketones, and Carbohydrates

Chapter 15: Aldehydes and Ketones

Chapter 16: Carbohydrates

Diabetes is a disease that occurs when the body loses its ability to produce or respond to the signaling molecule, insulin, which regulates blood sugar (Figure U6.1). It is the seventh leading cause of death in the U.S. In many parts of the country, more than fifteen percent of the adult population, a total of over 34 million Americans, is struggling with diagnosed diabetes. And the problem continues to escalate (Figure U6.2). The Centers for Disease Control (CDC) estimates that over a third of U.S. adults 18 and older had prediabetes in 2020.

Figure U6.1 Individuals with Diabetes Need to Carefully Monitor Their Blood Sugar Levels.

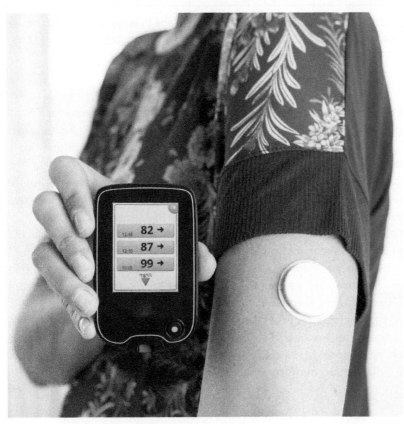

Figure U6.2 The Increasing Prevalence of Diabetes in U.S. Adults.
(CDC, 2020)

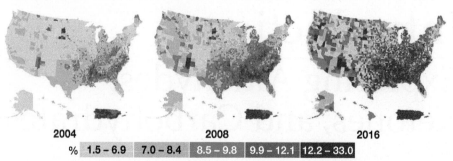

NOTES: Source: Centers for Disease Control and Prevention. National Diabetes Statistics Report, 2020.
Atlanta, GA: Centers for Disease Control and Prevention, U.S. Dept of Health and Human Services; 2020.

Patients with diabetes are at increased risk for a wide range of negative health effects including cardiovascular disease, kidney disease, eye disease, and lower-extremity amputations. In addition to these long-term consequences, diabetics face a daily struggle to regulate their blood sugar and prevent life-threatening complications.

Unit 6: Introduction
What Happens When Diabetics Develop Ketoacidosis?

 To learn more about the challenges diabetics face in acquiring enough insulin and the deadly consequences of diabetic ketoacidosis, watch **Video U6.1** in the Pearson eText.

Unit 6 opens with an example of many challenges diabetics face every day, including the potentially fatal complication, *diabetic ketoacidosis*. Diabetic ketoacidosis is a serious complication of diabetes that occurs when your body produces high levels of organic molecules called *ketones*.

Diabetics all have difficulty regulating their blood sugar (glucose), but the problem arises from two very different causes. In *type 1 diabetes*, the cells in the pancreas that produce insulin are destroyed. Insulin is a hormone that is normally released in response to high blood sugar. It signals our cells to take up sugar from the blood. Without insulin, in type 1 diabetics sugar accumulates in the blood and is not available to power their cells. In type 2 diabetes, the body still produces insulin but the cells respond poorly to the signal. This also allows sugar to accumulate in the blood of type 2 diabetics and prevents the body from absorbing and metabolizing sugar (Figure U6.3).

Type 1 diabetes occurs when our immune system attacks and destroys the insulin-producing cells in the pancreas. Scientists don't fully understand what causes this attack, but suspect that a virus or other environmental factor might be responsible. Type 1 diabetes accounts for about 5% of the diabetes in the U.S. Type 2 diabetes, in

Figure U6.3 Type 1 and Type 2 Diabetes.

In type 1 diabetes, the individual no longer produces insulin. Sugar accumulates in the blood and is not available to provide energy to the cells. In type 2 diabetes, also called insulin resistance, insulin is still produced but the cells respond poorly. Blood sugar again accumulates.

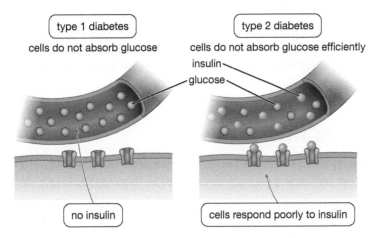

contrast, has both a genetic and an environmental factor. People are much more likely to develop type 2 diabetes if they are sedentary and/or overweight.

Fortunately, diabetics have many treatment options available to them. Most type 1 diabetics monitor their blood glucose levels multiple times a day and self-administer insulin injections to keep their levels in a healthy range (Figure U6.4). Some diabetics wear a pump that automatically administers insulin. In either case, type 1 diabetics need to carefully monitor their diet and make sure they adequately control their blood sugar.

The treatment options for type 2 diabetes are much more varied depending on the severity of the disease. Some type 2 diabetics are able to control their disease with diet and exercise while others must take oral medications and sometimes inject insulin.

Figure U6.4 Administering Insulin.

Most patients with type 1 diabetes check their blood sugar regularly and then administer the appropriate amount of insulin to keep their blood sugar in a healthy range. Insulin can be injected directly by the individual (left) or administered using a pump (right). Pumps provide better blood sugar control but are more expensive.

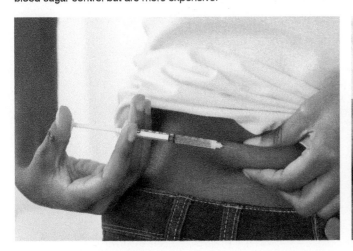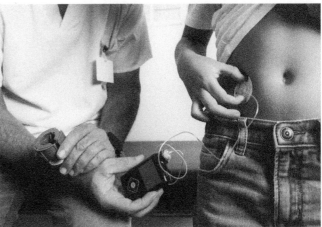

Unit 6 Chemistry Application: What Happens When Diabetics Develop Ketoacidosis?

The scale of diabetes in our communities is alarming. Treating and preventing this unfortunate disease requires multiple approaches, including a rigorous understanding of carbohydrates, blood sugar, and complications such as ketoacidosis that can arise in diabetic patients.

Questions to Think About

What chemistry do we need to know to understand the challenges of controlling diabetes? Here are some questions to consider as you move through Unit 6:

- What are ketones? How are they produced and why do they trigger diabetic ketoacidosis?

- What is blood sugar? How is it related to the other sugars in our diet?

- What are carbohydrates? How do different carbohydrates contribute to blood sugar?

What chemistry would you like to know in order to more fully understand this problem?

Now that we have an overview of this unit, let's step into Chapter 15 and learn more about the general characteristics of organic molecules such as ketones.

Reference

Centers for Disease Control and Prevention. National Diabetes Statistics Report, 2020. Atlanta, GA: Centers for Disease Control and Prevention, U.S. Dept of Health and Human Services; 2020.

Chapter 15
Aldehydes and Ketones

Aflatoxins are powerful, cancer-causing compounds produced by some types of molds that can grow on grains and nuts. Aflatoxins are ketones, one of the types of organic molecules we explore in this chapter.

 ## Chapter Outline

Learning Objectives

15.1 Analyze the structural features of aldehydes and ketones.

15.2 Compare the effects of intermolecular forces on the physical properties of aldehydes and ketones.

15.3 Predict the products of the oxidation and reduction of aldehydes and ketones.

15.4 Predict the products of the addition of alcohols to aldehydes and ketones.

15.5 Use the IUPAC system for naming organic compounds for aldehydes and ketones.

Introduction

Few types of organic molecules are more prevalent than *aldehydes* and *ketones*. Being able to recognize these types of organic compounds can help you predict the properties of a wide range of common biological molecules and drugs. In this chapter you explore these two important families of molecules and learn about their properties and reactions. You learn about molecules in our bodies, such as the hormone testosterone, and medicines, such as the blood-thinning drug warfarin used to treat and prevent blood clots (Figure 15.1). As you delve deeper into organic chemistry, it's important to start connecting ideas, reactions, and molecular properties across multiple chapters so you can better understand the complex biological processes you encounter in later chapters.

Figure 15.1 Aldehydes and Ketones in Our Lives.

Recognizing functional groups can help you predict the properties of organic molecules. **A)** Many important hormones, such as testosterone, contain aldehyde groups. **B)** Some dieters and diabetics regularly check their urine for the presence of ketones. **C)** The common blood thinner, warfarin, contains aldehyde groups. Low-dose warfarin may help prevent strokes.

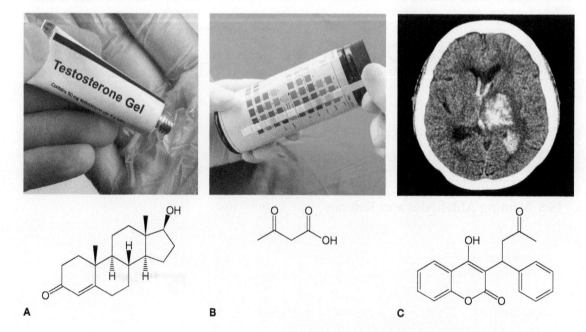

15.1 Structure of Aldehydes and Ketones

Recall from Chapter 6 that biomolecules tend to consist of a carbon backbone with a variety of groups attached to the hydrocarbon backbone. Many biomolecules contain a **carbonyl group** ($C{=}O$), which is an oxygen atom double bonded to a carbon atom. And some molecules feature more than one carbonyl group.

carbonyl group

For example, *trans*-retinal, a key molecule involved in vision, contains a carbonyl group (Figure 15.2).

Similarly, aflatoxin B1 contains two carbonyl groups (Figure 15.3). Aflatoxins are a family of toxins produced by molds that grow in soil, decaying vegetation, and improperly stored crops such as rice, corn, peanuts, wheat, and tree nuts. Aflatoxins can cause cancer and extensive liver damage.

The presence of carbonyl groups in nature is so common that much of the chemistry that occurs in living organisms is the chemistry of carbonyl compounds. You will spend several chapters learning about these molecules and how they react. The focus of this chapter is aldehydes and ketones, some of the most important common molecules that typically contain carbonyl groups, but you will encounter other types of molecules that contain carbonyl groups in other chapters as well.

Figure 15.2 *Trans*-retinal.

This molecule is essential for vision. The conversion between the *cis* and *trans* isomer sends a nerve impulse to the brain, which is then converted to a visual image.

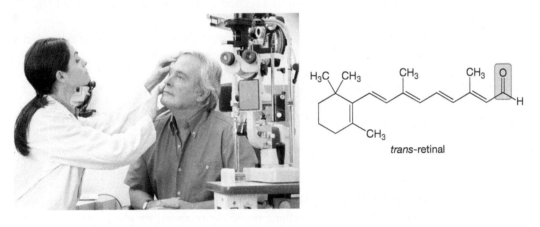

trans-retinal

Figure 15.3 Infested Corn.

Several types of molds produce toxic aflatoxins.

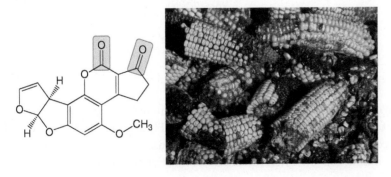

Figure 15.4 Simple Aldehydes and Ketones.

A) Formaldehyde (CH_2O) is the simplest aldehyde; it has only one carbon atom. It is widely used in industry in the production of items such as particleboard and coatings. **B)** Acetaldehyde (CH_3CHO) is a two-carbon aldehyde commonly found in nature and produced on a large scale for use in industry. The human body produces acetaldehyde when it converts ethanol to acetaldehyde in the liver. **C)** Acetone is the simplest ketone with three carbon atoms. Acetone is produced on a large scale for use as a solvent in chemical reactions. It is also naturally produced in our bodies and is present in large amounts in people with diabetes.

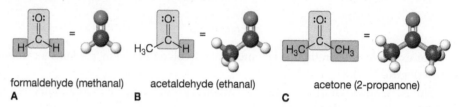

formaldehyde (methanal)   acetaldehyde (ethanal)   acetone (2-propanone)
A   **B**   **C**

Aldehydes and Ketones

An **aldehyde** contains a carbonyl group ($C{=}O$) bonded to at least one hydrogen atom and no more than one carbon group. The carbonyl groups in aldehydes are always at the end of a chain or branch directly off of a ring.

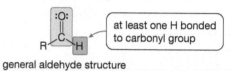

general aldehyde structure

Formaldehyde (also called methanal) is the simplest aldehyde; it has two hydrogen atoms bonded to the carbonyl group ($C{=}O$) (Figure 15.4A). Acetaldehyde (also called ethanal) has a methyl group (CH_3) and a hydrogen atom connected to its carbonyl group (Figure 15.4B).

A **ketone**, on the other hand, contains a carbonyl group ($C{=}O$) that is bonded to two carbon atoms or R groups. The carbonyl group in a ketone is therefore always within a carbon chain or a ring.

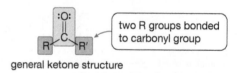

general ketone structure

Acetone is the simplest ketone and contains two methyl groups (CH_3) bonded to the carbonyl group (Figure 15.4C). Acetone is common in the laboratory where it is used as a solvent in chemical reactions and to clean laboratory glassware.

The oxygen in the carbonyl group in both aldehydes and ketones is bonded to a trigonal planar carbon with an approximate bond angle of 120°.

:O:
120°

trigonal planar

Aldehydes and Ketones in Medicine and Nature

Aldehyde and ketone groups are common in molecules throughout nature and are present in many molecules used medicinally (Figure 15.5–15.8). Many of these carbonyl-containing molecules are much larger than the simple aldehydes and ketones we just introduced and often contain other functional groups.

Figure 15.5 Cinnamaldehyde.

This molecule is an aldehyde that is produced in the bark of the cinnamon tree. It is ground up and used as a spice for cooking around the world.

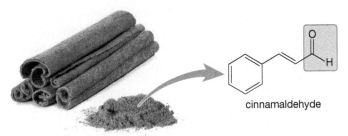

cinnamaldehyde

Figure 15.6 Aldosterone.

The hormone aldosterone contains several functional groups including an aldehyde group. This hormone helps regulate levels of sodium ions (Na^+), and potassium ions (K^+) in the body and regulate blood pressure. When levels of aldosterone are not regulated properly in the body, heart and kidney diseases can result. Antihypertensive drugs such as lisinopril are used to help lower blood pressure, by lowering aldosterone secretion in the body.

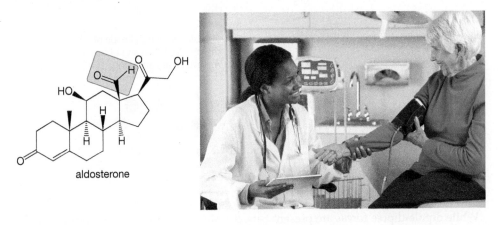

aldosterone

Figure 15.7 DHEA
dehydroepiandrosterone.

This molecule contains a ketone group and is a steroid hormone produced in the body. Some people take DHEA as a dietary supplement in an attempt to possibly reduce the effects of aging.

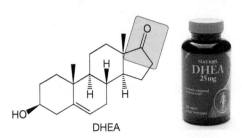

DHEA

Figure 15.8 Methadone.

This compound is an opioid pain reliever that contains a ketone group. It is used to help treat narcotic drug addiction. It reduces cravings and withdrawal symptoms.

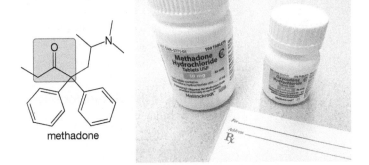

methadone

Apply what you have just learned: **Practice 15.1–15.3** in the Pearson eText.

Quiz yourself on the content of this section: **Check 15.1** in the Pearson eText.

15.2 Physical Properties of Aldehydes and Ketones

Due to the electronegativity difference between carbon and oxygen, the carbonyl group is polar. The carbon has a partial positive charge and the oxygen has a partial negative charge. The polarity of the carbonyl groups in both aldehydes and ketones plays a significant role in the properties of these molecules.

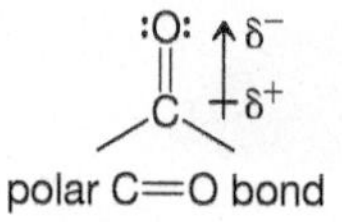

polar C=O bond

Dipole-dipole attractions between aldehyde molecules and between ketone molecules are a direct result of the polarity of the carbonyl group. The partial negative oxygen atom in one molecule forms an attraction to the partial positive side of another molecule.

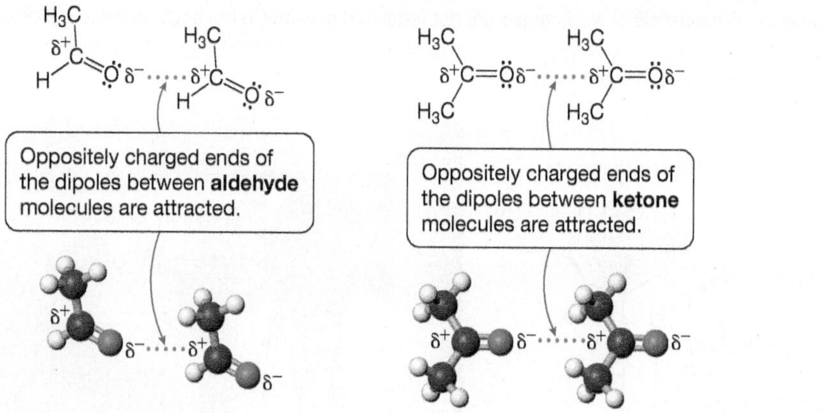

Oppositely charged ends of the dipoles between **aldehyde** molecules are attracted.

Oppositely charged ends of the dipoles between **ketone** molecules are attracted.

Boiling Points of Aldehydes and Ketones

While dipole-dipole forces are present between aldehyde molecules, hydrogen bonds do not form between aldehyde molecules. Aldehyde molecules do not have a hydrogen atom bonded to an O, N, or F and therefore do not form hydrogen bonds.

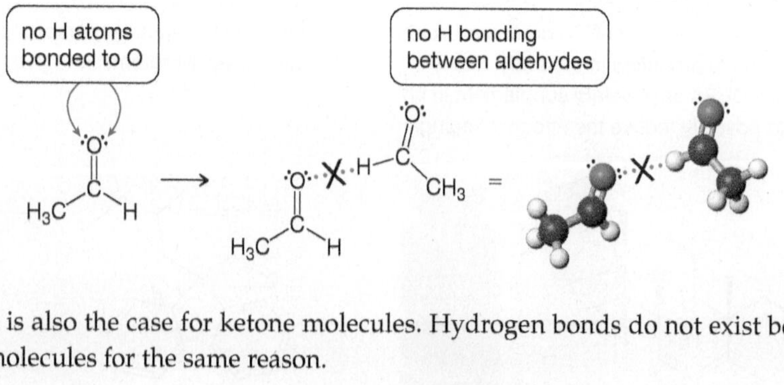

no H atoms bonded to O

no H bonding between aldehydes

This is also the case for ketone molecules. Hydrogen bonds do not exist between ketone molecules for the same reason.

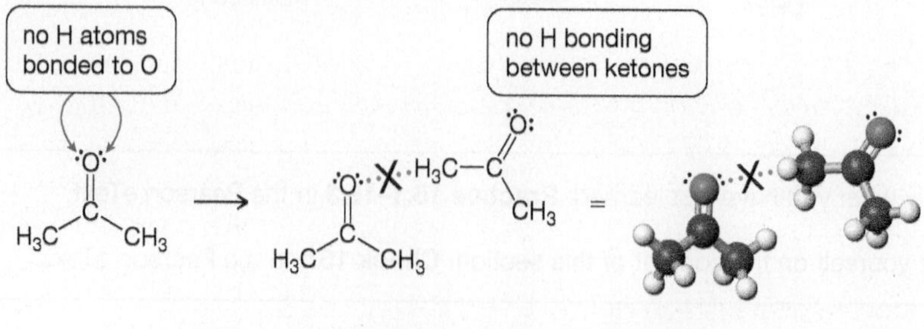

no H atoms bonded to O

no H bonding between ketones

Because hydrogen bonds are stronger than dipole-dipole forces and alcohols feature hydrogen bonds as you learned in Chapter 14, alcohols (Section 14.1) have stronger intermolecular forces than both aldehydes and ketones. Recall that the stronger the intermolecular forces, the higher the boiling point. A comparison of boiling points of molecules that are similar in size illustrates this trend. Aldehydes and ketones have lower boiling points than alcohols, but higher boiling points than alkanes, which only experience London dispersion forces. (Section 13.2).

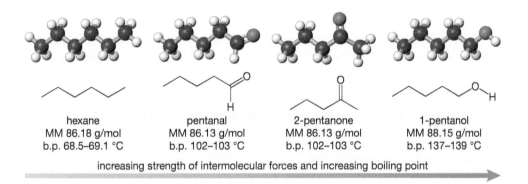

hexane	pentanal	2-pentanone	1-pentanol
MM 86.18 g/mol	MM 86.13 g/mol	MM 86.13 g/mol	MM 88.15 g/mol
b.p. 68.5–69.1 °C	b.p. 102–103 °C	b.p. 102–103 °C	b.p. 137–139 °C

increasing strength of intermolecular forces and increasing boiling point

Apply what you have just learned: **Practice 15.4** in the Pearson eText.

Solubility of Aldehydes and Ketones in Water

While aldehydes and ketones do not form hydrogen bonds with each other, both these types of organic molecules do form hydrogen bonds with water. Water has a hydrogen atom bonded to oxygen that can form a hydrogen bond with the oxygen on a carbonyl group. Because of these attractive forces aldehydes and ketones are soluble in water. This follows the principle of "like dissolves like," as both water and the carbonyl groups in aldehydes and ketones are polar.

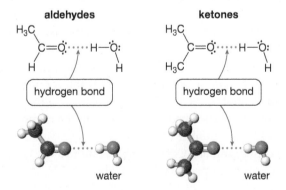

As the number of carbon atoms in their carbon backbones increases, however, the solubility of aldehydes and ketones in water decreases. Small aldehydes and ketones (fewer than five carbon atoms) are soluble in water, whereas larger aldehydes and ketones (five or more carbon atoms) are insoluble in water. As the nonpolar hydrocarbon chain of the aldehyde or the ketone increases in length, the molecule's carbonyl group is not able to hydrogen bond with water as easily, decreasing its solubility in water.

After completing the next two practice problems, select BioConnect 15.1 (contains Figures 15.9–15.18) to investigate the health effects of the aldehyde molecule called formaldehyde.

Apply what you have just learned: **Practice 15.5 and 15.6** in the Pearson eText.

Explore how Chemistry and Biology connect: **BioConnect 15.1:** Health Effects of Formaldehyde in the Pearson eText.

Quiz yourself on the content of this section: **Check 15.2** in the Pearson eText.

15.3 Reactions of Aldehydes and Ketones

The reactions of aldehydes and ketones play a significant role in how the human body functions. The oxidation of formaldehyde to a carboxylic acid is one step in a series of reactions that serve to remove formaldehyde (discussed in BioConnect 15.1) from our bodies.

The carbonyl group found in aldehydes and ketones acts as a reactive center that undergoes two primary types of reactions: 1) aldehydes are oxidized to carboxylic acids and 2) both aldehydes and ketones undergo reduction to alcohols (Table 15.1).

The oxidation of an aldehyde to a carboxylic acid involves the conversion of the C—H bond to a C—O bond. Both $K_2Cr_2O_2$ and **Tollens' reagent** (Ag_2O/NH_4OH) oxidize aldehydes to carboxylic acids. Tollens' reagent is used to test for the presence of aldehydes. Upon addition of this reagent, which includes silver ions (Ag^+), an aldehyde oxidizes to a carboxylic acid (RCO_2H) and silver metal (Ag). When you carry out this reaction in a clean glass flask, the silver metal produces a beautiful shiny mirror on the surface of the container. The presence of the silver indicates that an aldehyde is present (VisibleChem 15.1). Since ketones do not have a hydrogen atom bonded to the carbonyl group, they do not undergo oxidation.

Reduction of an aldehyde or a ketone involves the conversion of the carbonyl group (C=O) to an alcohol (C—OH). Recall in Section 8.3 the discussion of reduction reactions, which can be described as a decrease in the number of carbon-oxygen bonds or an increase in the number of carbon-hydrogen bonds. Reduction of aldehydes involves the conversion of a C=O double bond to a C—O single bond and the gain of hydrogen to produce primary (1°) alcohols (RCH_2OH). The reduction of ketones involves the conversion of a C=O double bond to a C—O single bond and the gain of hydrogen to produce secondary (2°) alcohols (R_2CHOH). These reactions are accomplished by adding hydrogen gas in the presence of a metal catalyst such as palladium (Pd), nickel (Ni), or platinum (Pt).

Explore VisibleChem Videos 15.1 and 15.2 to learn about the details of how these reactions occur and view a glimpse of the oxidation and reduction reactions of aldehydes and ketones that occur in the human body. Following these VisibleChem Videos are several practice problems to complete and BioConnect 15.2 (contains Figures 15.19–15.25), where you will explore the role of ketones in ketogenic diets.

Table 15.1 Summary Table of Aldehyde and Ketone Reactions

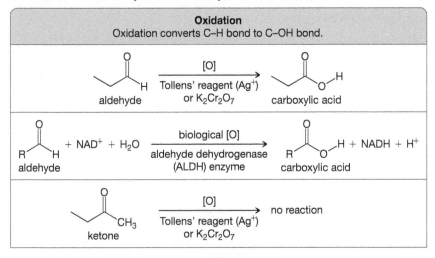

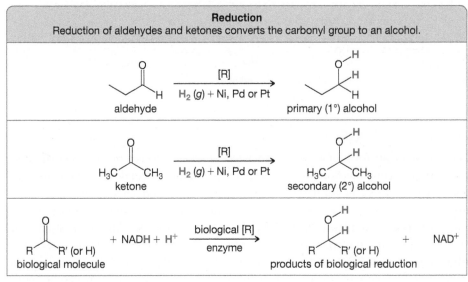

Watch this concept come to life: **VisibleChem Video 15.1:** Oxidation Reactions of Aldehydes and **VisibleChem Video 15.2:** Reduction Reactions of Aldehydes and Ketones in the Pearson eText.

Apply what you have just learned: **Practice 15.7–15.9** in the Pearson eText.

Explore how Chemistry and Biology connect: **BioConnect 15.2:** Ketogenic Diets in the Pearson eText.

Quiz yourself on the content of this section: **Check 15.3** in the Pearson eText.

15.4 Forming Hemiacetals and Acetals

As you learned in Section 15.3, the carbonyl group ($C{=}O$) on aldehydes and ketones, provides a site for reactions to take place. Aldehydes and ketones react with alcohols to form hemiacetals and acetals. A **hemiacetal** contains an OH (hydroxyl) group and an O—R group bonded to the same carbon atom. **Acetals** contain two O—R groups bonded to the same carbon.

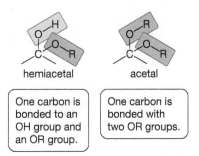

hemiacetal

acetal

One carbon is bonded to an OH group and an OR group.

One carbon is bonded with two OR groups.

A hemiacetal forms from an aldehyde or a ketone when one molecule of alcohol is added. The addition process converts the carbonyl ($C{=}O$) group into an alcohol group (OH). One of the C—O bonds in the carbonyl group in the aldehyde or ketone is broken, and two new single bonds form. When another molecule of alcohol is added, the hemiacetal is converted to an acetal.

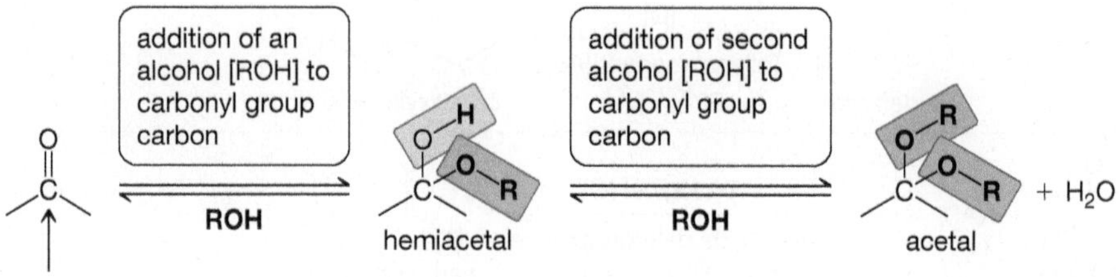

One example of hemiacetal and acetal formation from an aldehyde is the addition of the alcohol ethanol (CH_3CH_2OH) to the aldehyde ethanal.

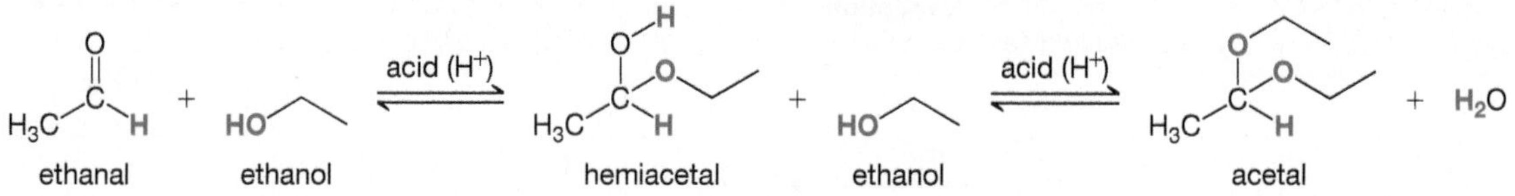

Cyclic Hemiacetals

Cyclic hemiacetals form in a similar reaction but occur through **intramolecular reactions**. Intramolecular reactions are reactions between groups contained in the same molecule. In the case of cyclic hemiacetal formation, a carbonyl and a hydroxyl group on the same molecule react to form a cyclic hemiacetal. Fructose is a sugar found in many fruits, such as mango (Figure 15.26). Fructose is readily absorbed into the bloodstream when ingested and digested. The open chain form of fructose contains a ketone group (a carbonyl group that is bonded to two carbon atoms or R groups) that reacts with an alcohol group on the same molecule in an intramolecular reaction to form a cyclic hemiacetal. In this reaction, shown in Figure 15.26, the cyclic hemiacetal closes at carbon 2.

Cyclic hemiacetals are particularly significant in carbohydrate chemistry. Glucose is the most common simple carbohydrate (Figure 15.27). Like fructose, glucose exists in both the open chain form and the cyclic hemiacetal form. There are five hydroxyl groups (OH) on the cyclic glucose molecule, but only one of the hydroxyl groups

Figure 15.26 Fructose.

Fructose is a sugar commonly found in fruit. The sugar can be found in open chain forms or as a cyclic hemiacetal.

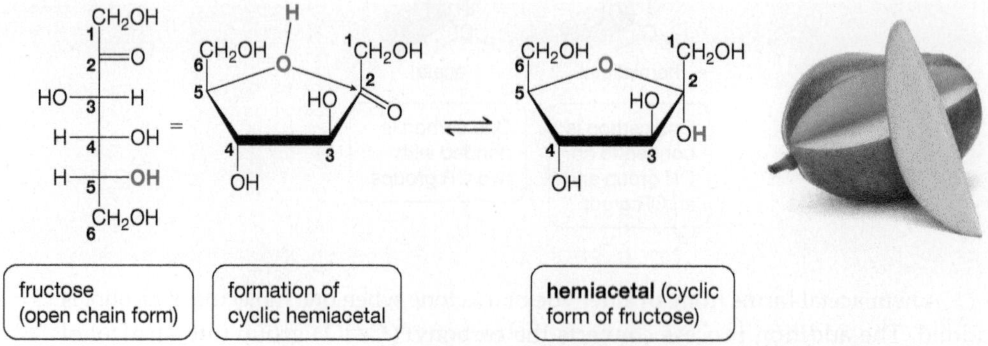

Figure 15.27 Glucose.

Glucose is a simple sugar that is an important energy source for our body. Glucose can be found in both open chain and cyclic hemiacetal forms. Honey naturally contains high levels of glucose.

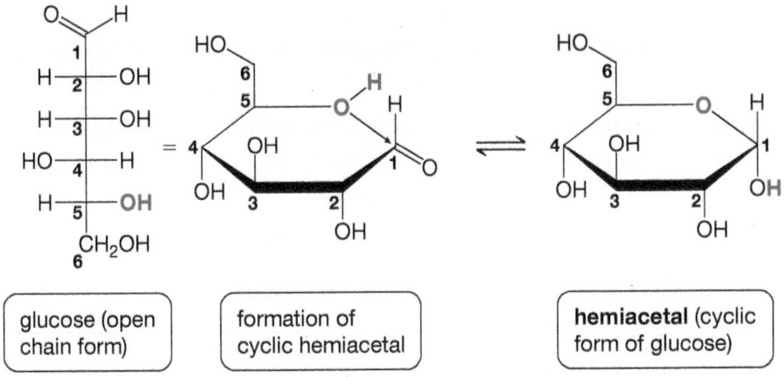

glucose (open chain form)

formation of cyclic hemiacetal

hemiacetal (cyclic form of glucose)

(shown in blue) is bonded to a carbon atom (carbon 1) that is also bonded to an oxygen atom in the ring (shown in blue), making it a cyclic hemiacetal.

Cyclic Acetals

Cyclic hemiacetals convert to **cyclic acetals** upon the addition of another alcohol (ROH). The —OR group from the alcohol replaces the —OH group on the cyclic hemiacetal to form the cyclic acetal.

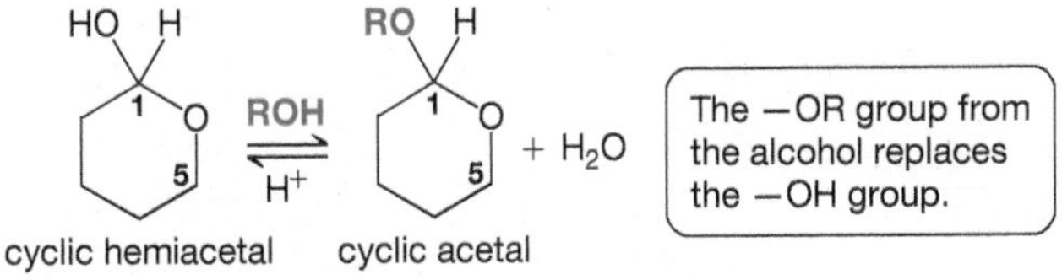

cyclic hemiacetal   cyclic acetal

The —OR group from the alcohol replaces the —OH group.

Like the reaction in Figure 15.27, this reaction is also significant in carbohydrate chemistry in molecules such as sucrose. Sucrose is a common table sugar molecule that is composed of two simple sugars, glucose and fructose (Figure 15.28). Sucrose is produced naturally in plants and refined and processed for human consumption. You learn more about these important carbohydrates in Chapter 16.

Apply what you have just learned: **Practice 15.10** in the Pearson eText.

cyclic hemiacetal: OH and OR groups bonded to the same ring carbon

glucose   fructose

Figure 15.28 Sucrose.

Sugarcane and other plants produce sucrose that is extracted, processed, and sold as sugar in grocery stores.

cyclic acetal: two OR groups bonded to the same ring carbon

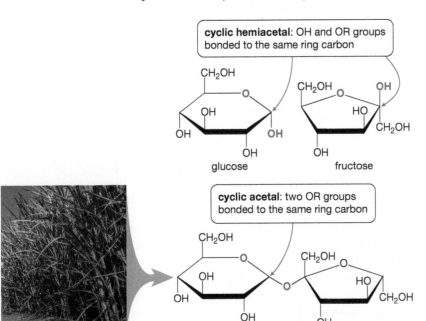

sucrose

Formation of Hemiacetals and Acetals

Table 15.2 summarizes the formation reactions of hemiacetals and acetals from aldehydes and ketones. Explore VisibleChem Videos 15.3 and 15.4 to learn more about how hemiacetals and acetals form. These reactions provide an introduction to much of the chemistry you will explore in the chapter on carbohydrate chemistry (Chapter 16).

Watch this concept come to life: **VisibleChem Video 15.3:** Forming Acetals and Hemiacetals from Aldehydes and Ketones and **VisibleChem Video 15.4:** The Formation of Cyclic Hemiacetals and Cyclic Acetals in the Pearson eText.

Apply what you have just learned: **Practice 15.11–15.13** in the Pearson eText.

Quiz yourself on the content of this section: **Check 15.4** in the Pearson eText.

Table 15.2 Formation of Hemiacetals and Acetals from Aldehydes and Ketones

Quiz yourself on the content of this section: **Check 15.5** in the Pearson eText.

Video 15.1: Nomenclature: Aldehydes

Video 15.2: Nomenclature: Ketones

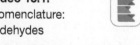

15.5 Naming Aldehydes and Ketones

Chemists follow specific rules when naming compounds. This process of devising or choosing names for things is nomenclature. The International Union of Pure and Applied Chemistry (IUPAC) establishes the rules for the nomenclature of organic compounds. The rules ensure that each compound has an unambiguous and unique name, allowing chemists from all over the world to communicate with each other. Explore Videos 15.1 and 15.2 to learn how to name the compounds discussed in this chapter. You can also review the rules for naming compounds in the nomenclature appendix.

Chapter Summary

15.1 Structure of Aldehydes and Ketones

Learning Objective: Analyze the structural features of aldehydes and ketones.

Both aldehydes and ketones contain carbonyl groups. A carbonyl group is an oxygen atom double-bonded to a carbon atom. In aldehydes, the carbonyl group is bonded to one other carbon group and a hydrogen atom. In ketones, the carbonyl group is bonded to two carbon atoms contained within a carbon chain (Figure 15.4). Both aldehydes and ketones are found in a wide variety of biological molecules and drugs.

Key Terms

aldehyde
carbonyl group
ketone

15.2 Physical Properties of Aldehydes and Ketones

Learning Objective: Compare the effects of intermolecular forces on the physical properties of aldehydes and ketones.

The carbonyl group in aldehydes and ketones is strongly polarized. This results in dipole-diploe attractions between both aldehydes and ketones. Hydrogen bonds do not form between aldehyde or ketone molecules. For this reason, aldehydes and ketones have a lower boiling point than alcohols, but higher boiling points than similarly sized alkanes. Both aldehydes and ketones form hydrogen bonds with water. Thus, small aldehydes and ketones are water-soluble. Formaldehyde is the simplest aldehyde. Exposure to formaldehyde is associated with several types of cancer.

BioConnect 15.1: Health Effects of Formaldehyde

15.3 Reactions of Aldehydes and Ketones

Learning Objective: Predict the products of the oxidation and reduction of aldehydes and ketones.

The carbonyl group in aldehydes can be oxidized to form carboxylic acids. Both aldehydes and ketones can be reduced to form alcohols. Tollens' reagent produces a shiny silver coating when aldehyde is oxidized Table 15.1.

Ketones are produced in the body when carbohydrate intake is severely limited.

VisibleChem Video 15.1: Oxidation Reactions of Aldehydes

VisibleChem Video 15.2: Reduction Reactions of Aldehydes and Ketones

BioConnect 15.2: Ketogenic Diets

Key Terms

glycogen (from BioConnect 15.2)   ketogenesis (from BioConnect 15.2)   Tollens' reagent
ketoacidosis (from BioConnect 15.2)   ketosis (from BioConnect 15.2)

15.4 Forming Hemiacetals and Acetals

Learning Objective: Predict the products of addition of alcohols to aldehydes and ketones.

The carbonyl groups on aldehydes and ketones can react with alcohols to form hemiacetals and acetals. A hemiacetal contains an OH group and an O—R group bonded to the same carbon. Acetals contain two O—R groups bonded to the same carbon. Reactions between groups on the same molecule are intramolecular reactions. Intramolecular reactions form cyclic hemiacetals or cyclic acetals when carbonyl and hydroxyl groups react (Table 15.2). Glucose is an important carbohydrate that forms a cyclic hemiacetal.

VisibleChem Video 15.3: Forming Acetals and Hemiacetals from Aldehydes and Ketones

VisibleChem Video 15.4: The Formation of Cyclic Hemiacetals and Cyclic Acetals

Key Terms

acetal

cyclic acetal

cyclic hemiacetal

hemiacetal

intramolecular reaction

15.5 Naming Aldehydes and Ketones

Learning Objective: Use the IUPAC system for naming organic compounds for aldehydes and ketones.

Chemists follow specific rules when naming compounds. This process of devising or choosing names is nomenclature. The International Union of Pure and Applied Chemistry

(IUPAC) establishes the rules for the nomenclature of organic compounds including aldehydes and ketones.

Video 15.1: Nomenclature: Aldehydes

Video 15.2: Nomenclature: Ketones

 End-of-Chapter Quiz   Have you mastered the content of this chapter? Try the **End of Chapter Quiz** in the Pearson eText.

1. Molecules that contain two aldehyde groups are called dialdehydes. Which of the molecules is *not* a dialdehyde?

a)
glutaraldehyde

b)
acetoin

c)
glyoxal

d)
succinaldehyde

2. Prednisone decreases the immune response in patients with arthritis, blood disorders, skin diseases, and severe allergies. Which statement about the prednisone molecule is true?

a) Prednisone contains one aldehyde group and two ketone groups.

b) Prednisone contains two aldehyde groups and one ketone group.

c) Prednisone contains three aldehyde groups and no ketone groups.

d) Prednisone contains three ketone groups and no aldehyde groups.

3. Ketoacids are an important class of biological molecules that are involved in several metabolic processes. The defining feature of ketoacids is that they contain both a ketone and carboxylic acid group (RCO_2H). Which molecule is *not* a ketoacid?

a) α-ketobutyric acid

α-ketobutyric acid: involved in the metabolism of the amino acids methionine and threonine

b) phosphohydroxypyruvic acid

phosphohydroxypyruvic acid: involved in the biosynthesis of the amino acid serine

c) glyoxylic acid

glyoxylic acid: used by plants, bacteria, and fungi in the conversion of fatty acids into carbohydrates

d) oxaloacetic acid

oxaloacetic acid: involved in the several metabolic processes that occur in animals

4. Why do aldehydes and ketones have higher boiling points than alkanes of similar mass?

  a) Aldehydes and ketones contain polar carbonyl groups that allow intermolecular attractions through dipole-dipole interactions. Alkane molecules are non-polar and cannot participate in dipole-interactions with each other.

  b) Aldehydes and ketones contain non-polar carbonyl groups that allow intermolecular attractions through dipole-dipole interactions. Alkane molecules are non-polar and cannot participate in dipole-interactions with each other.

  c) Aldehydes and ketones are polar and have strong London Dispersion forces of attraction. Alkane molecules are polar and can only participate in dipole-dipole interactions with each other.

  d) Aldehydes and ketones contain polar carbonyl groups that allow hydrogen bonding interactions with other aldehyde and ketone molecules. Alkanes are non-polar and only participate in London dispersion attractive intermolecular forces.

5. Which molecule is the *most* water soluble?

  a)

  benzaldehyde: found in almonds, apples, apricot, and cherry seeds. Benzaldehyde is used as a flavoring agent in the baking industry and is also a useful building block for the synthesis of many drug molecules.

b)

  anisole: used in the perfume industry to make larger and more complex molecules with a variety of smells. Anise is also used in the pharmaceutical industry as a building block molecule.

c)

  p-anisaldehyde: used as a building block molecule for the synthesis of pharmaceutical drugs and in the fragrance and flavor industry.

d)

  vanillin: extracted from the vanilla bean and used as a flavor in the food and beverage industry. Vanillin is also used for the synthesis of certain pharmaceutical drugs.

6. Which molecule is *not* water soluble?

  a)

  α-ketoglutaric acid: an important biological molecule in the class of compounds called ketoacids that are involved in several metabolic processes. Ketoacids contain both a ketone and a carboxylic acid (RCO_2H) functional group.

  b)

  vitamin K_1: a vitamin found in a variety of foods and taken as a dietary supplement. It is on the World Health Organization's Model List of Essential Medicines for the treatment of vitamin K deficiency and certain bleeding disorders.

c)

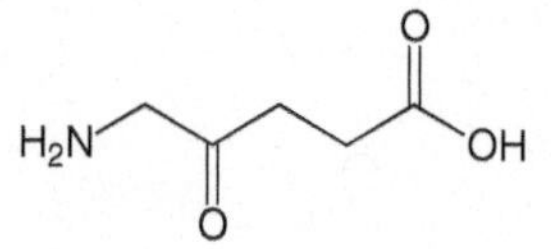

5-aminolevulinic acid: a molecule important to photosynthesis in plants and proper oxygen transport throughout the bodies of animals.

d)

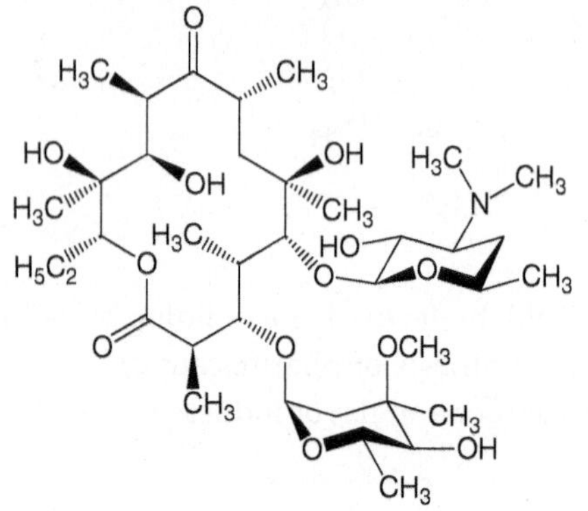

erythromycin: an antibiotic useful for the treatment of bacterial respiratory tract infections. It is also used for the treatment of pelvic inflammatory disease and sexually transmitted diseases (STDs) such as chlamydia and syphilis.

7. Retinoic acid is a naturally occurring derivative of retinal, a molecule discussed in the chapter that is essential for vision. Retinoic acid is required for proper growth and development of animal embryos. Which chemical reaction could produce retinoic acid in the laboratory using retinal as a starting material?

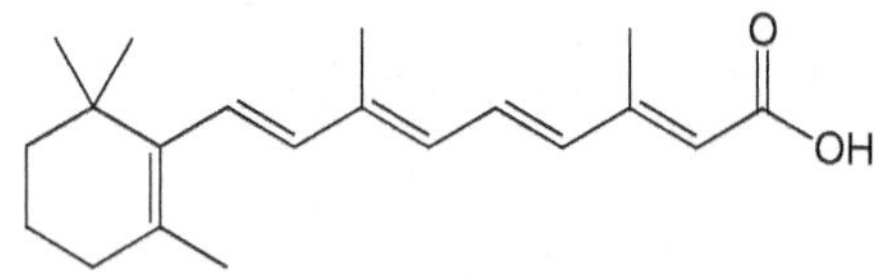

retinoic acid

a)

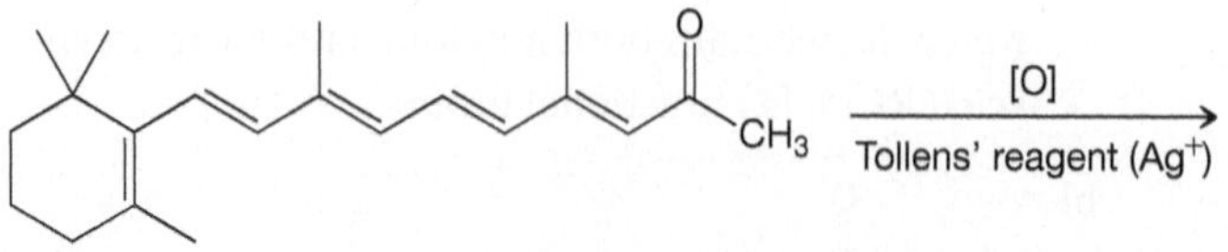

b)

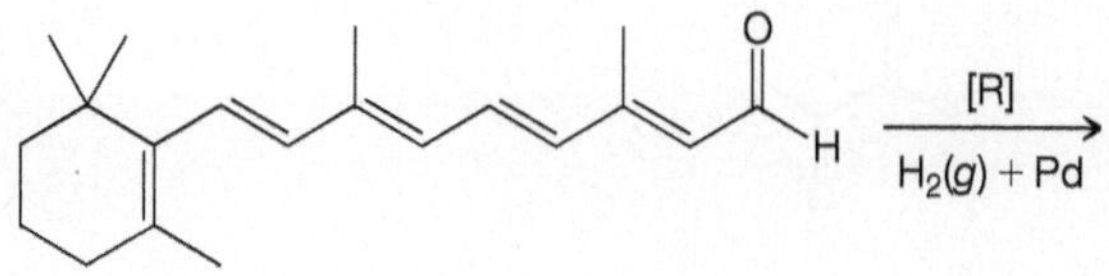

c)

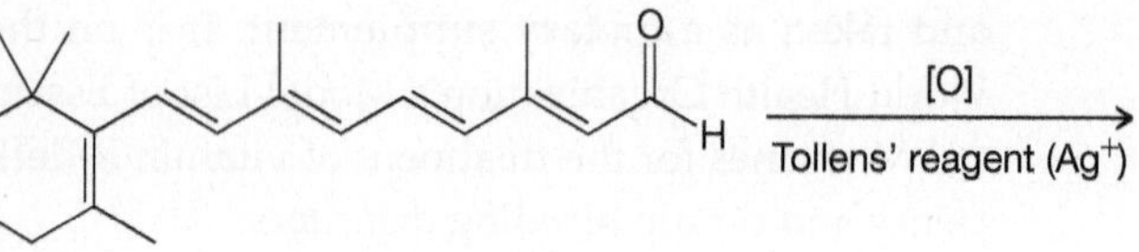

d)

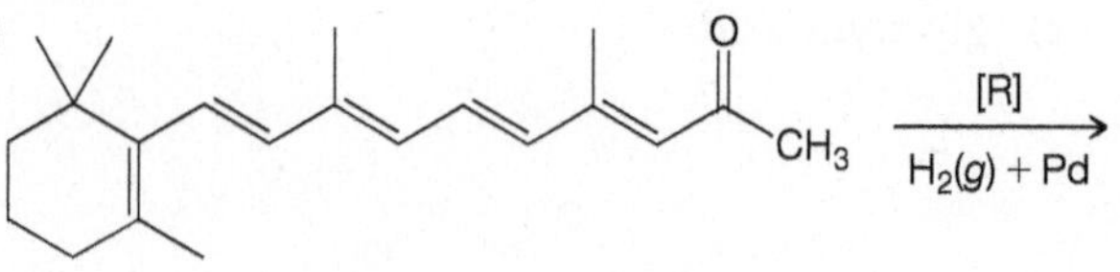

8. Morphine is a naturally occurring opiate drug found in the opium poppy. It is used medically for pain management and is also an addictive street drug. The molecule 4-hydroxyphenylacetaldehyde is a starting material in the biosynthesis of morphine. A scientist in the lab studying modifications to morphine pathway molecules wants to chemically reduce 4-hydroxyphenylacetaldehyde. Select the reaction that illustrates the correct chemical reduction of 4-hydroxyphenylacetaldehyde. Be sure to check the starting material, reagents used, and product before making your choice.

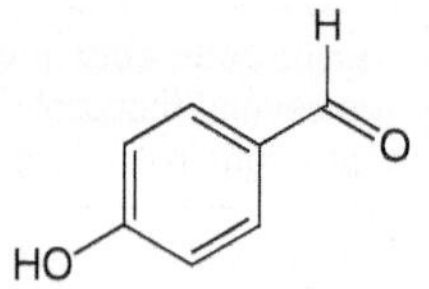

4-hydroxyphenylacetaldehyde

a)

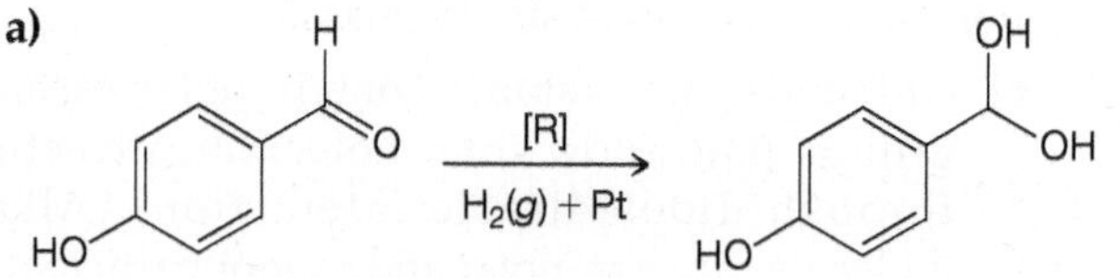

b)

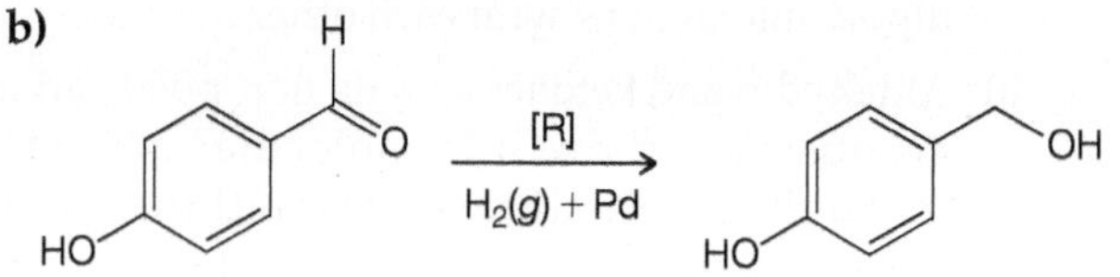

c)

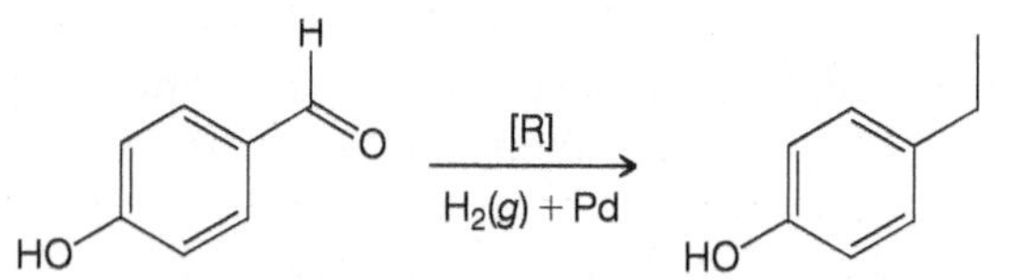

d)

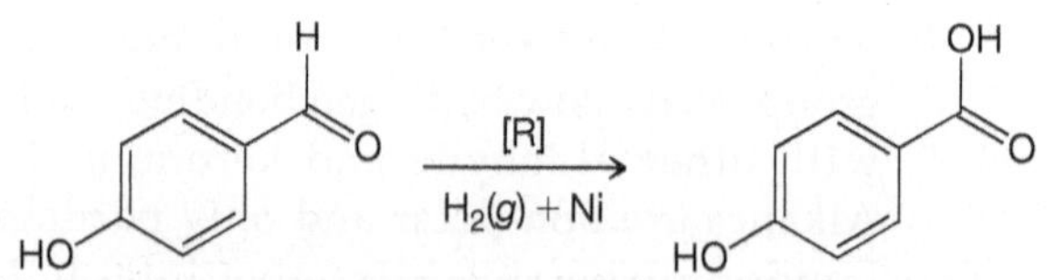

9. According to the World Health Organization (WHO), heart disease is the leading cause of death worldwide. Carvedilol (also known as Coreg) is used to treat high blood pressure and congestive heart failure. What starting material and reaction conditions are needed to produce carvedilol?

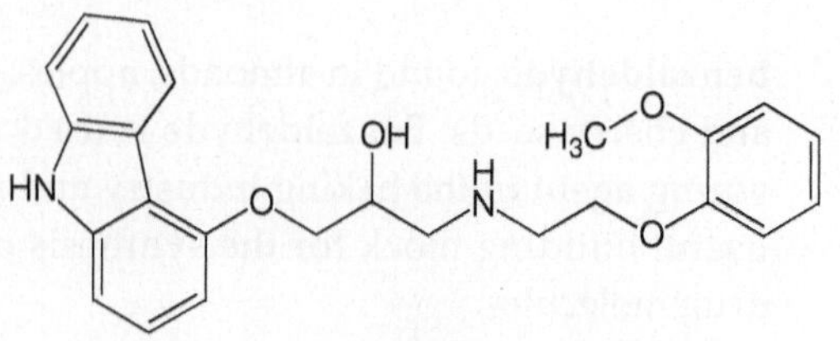

carvedilol

a)

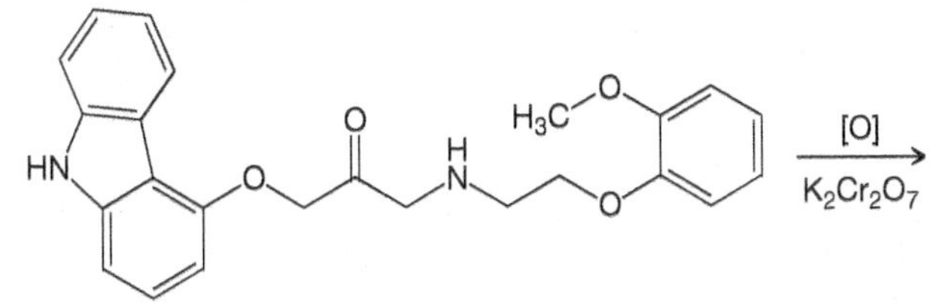

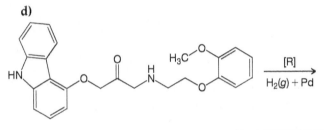

b)

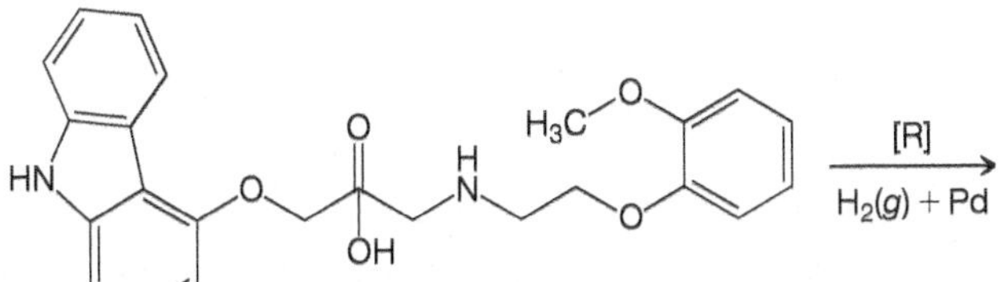

c)

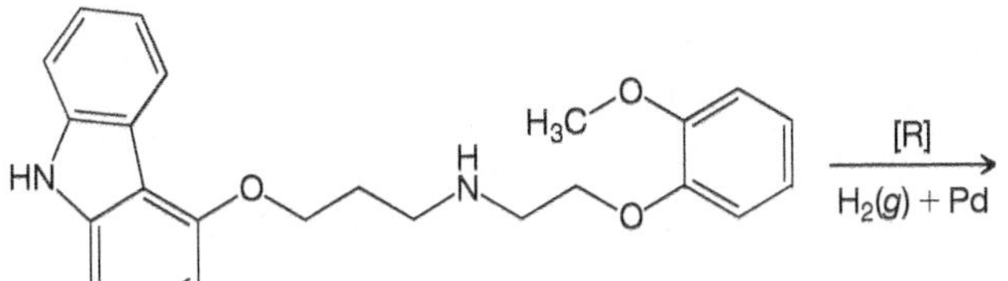

d)

10. What is the product when one molecule of an alcohol is added to a ketone?
    a) an aldehyde
    b) a hemiacetal
    c) a carboxylic acid
    d) an acetal

11. Secologanin is a naturally occurring building block molecule involved in biosynthetic pathways of an important class of molecules called terpene indole alkaloids. Which statement about secologanin is true?

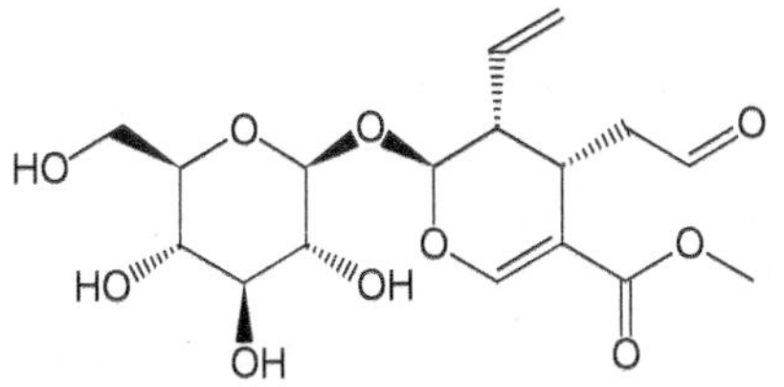

secologanin

    a) Secologanin contains an aldehyde group, two connected acetals, four alcohols, and two alkenes.
    b) Secologanin contains a ketone group, an acetal, a hemiacetal, four alcohols, and an alkene.
    c) Secologanin contains two aldehyde groups, three ether groups, four alcohols, and two alkenes.
    d) Secologanin contains an aldehyde group, three ether groups, four alcohols, and two alkenes.

---

12. What is the hemiacetal product of this reaction?

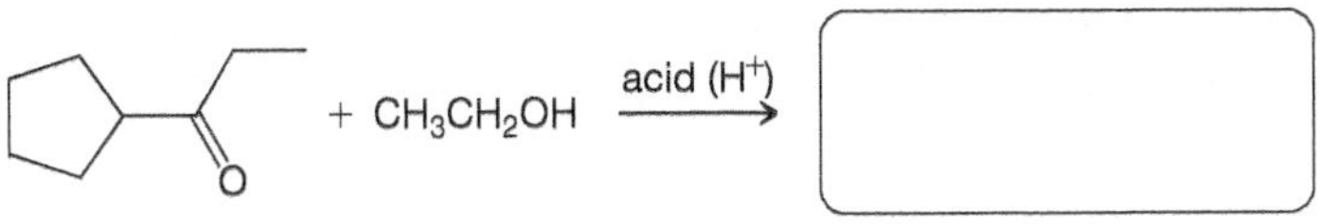

    a) 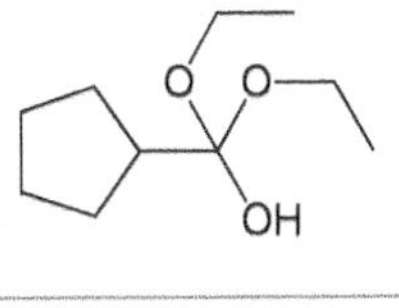 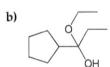   b)   c) 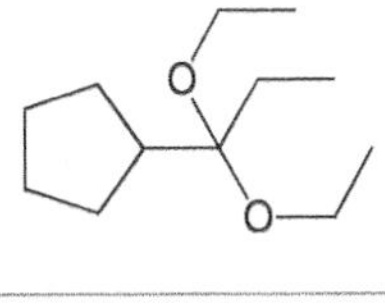   d)

---

13. The acetal 1,1-diethoxyethane is a flavoring agent in some distilled alcoholic beverages such as malt whisky. Which starting materials and reaction conditions can be used to produce 1,1-diethoxyethane?

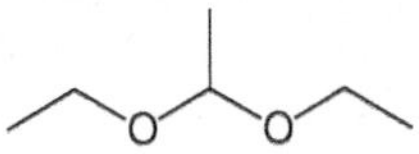

1,1-diethoxyethane

    a)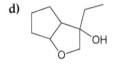

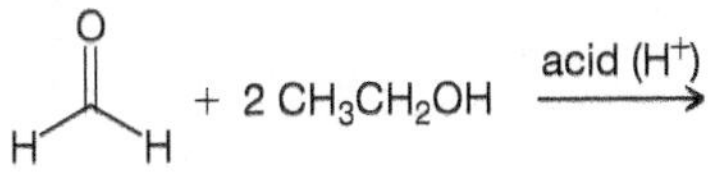

    b) H_3C—C(=O)—CH_3 + 2 CH_3CH_2OH $\xrightarrow{\text{acid (H}^+\text{)}}$

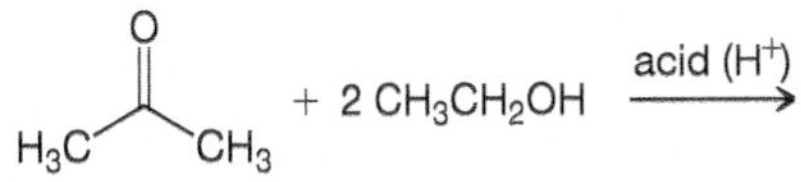

    c) H_3C—C(=O)—H + 2 CH_3CH_2OH $\xrightarrow{\text{acid (H}^+\text{)}}$

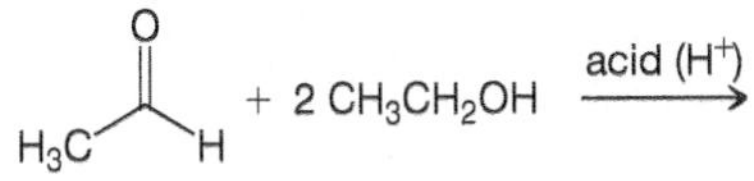

    d)

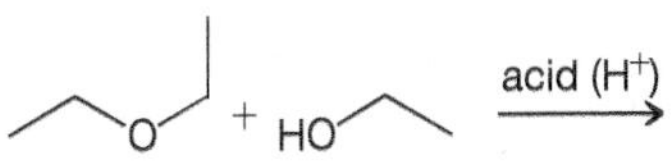

14. Molecules that contain two hemiacetal groups are dihemiacetals. The molecule ortho-phthalaldehyde (OPA) is a cyclic dihemiacetal that is formed by the addition of water (instead of an alcohol) to a molecule containing a carbonyl group. What is the missing starting material needed for the reaction that produces OPA?

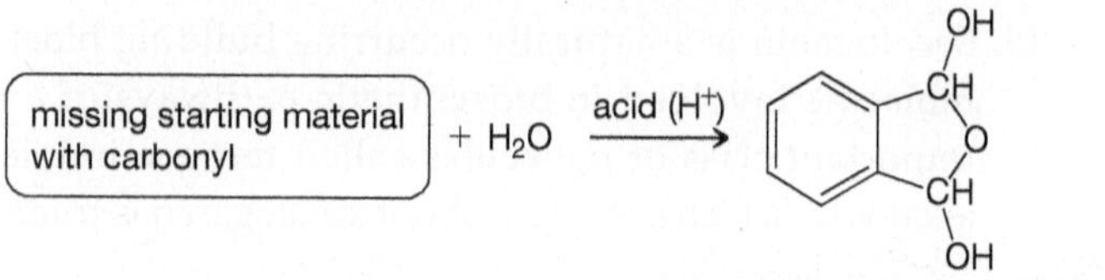

missing starting material with carbonyl + H₂O → acid (H⁺)

ortho-phthalaldehyde (OPA)

a)

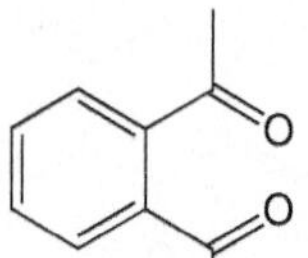

b)

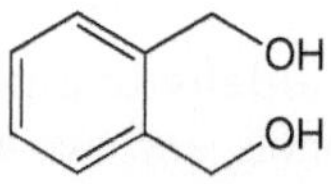

c)

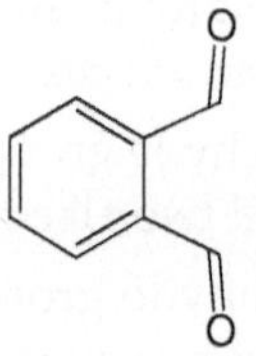

d)

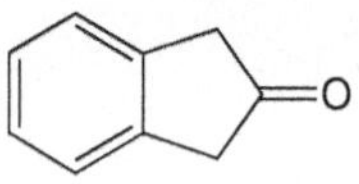

15. Which is the correct structure of 2-methylcyclopentanone?

a)

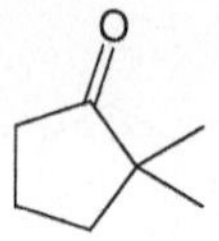

b)

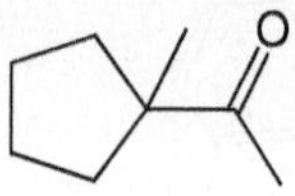

c)

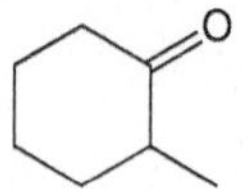

d)

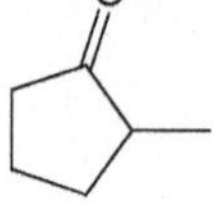

16. What is the IUPAC name for this molecule?

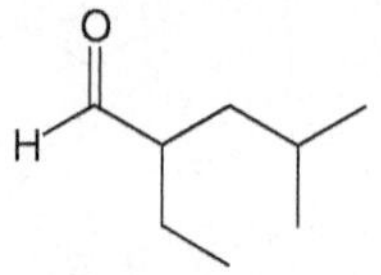

a) 2-ethyl-4-methylpenatanal
b) 2-methyl-4-ethyl-5-penatanal
c) 2-ethyl-4-methylpenatanone
d) 4,4-dimethylbutanal

17. What is the IUPAC name for this molecule?

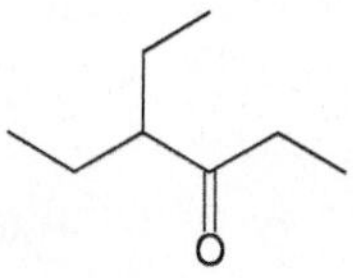

a) 3-ethyl-4-hexananone
b) 4-ethyl-3-heptanone
c) 4-ethyl-3-hexanone
d) 3-ethyl-4-hexanal

Chapter 16
Carbohydrates

Sugar cane produces most of the world's table sugar, a carbohydrate called sucrose.

Chapter Outline

Learning Objectives

16.1 Identify the three major types of carbohydrates.

16.2 Recognize and draw the major structural features of monosaccharides.

16.3 Draw the cyclic forms of monosaccharides and classify as α and β anomers.

16.4 Predict and draw the oxidation and reduction products of monosaccharides.

16.5 Recognize and draw the major structural features of disaccharides.

16.6 Recognize and draw the major structural features of polysaccharides.

Introduction

Of all the organic molecules you encounter in your chemistry courses, carbohydrates (sugars and starches) may be the most familiar due to their important, and sometimes controversial role in our diets. Carbohydrates play important roles in a variety of health, and medical applications in addition to being one of three major macronutrients (the other two are proteins and fats) in our diets. The blood tests people with diabetes use to monitor their blood sugar, for example, depend on the chemistry of carbohydrates. Blood typing, which is essential for preventing life-threatening complications from blood transfusions, relies on detecting the specific patterns of carbohydrates on the surface of our red blood cells (Figure 16.1); this is another example of an important medical role carbohydrates play.

16.1 Introduction to Carbohydrates

Carbohydrates are a group of molecules composed of carbon, hydrogen, and oxygen atoms. Historically, the term carbohydrate was used for molecules with the formula $C_n(H_2O)_n$, which were also referred to as *hydrates of carbon*. We use the subscripted letter "n" to indicate that the number of carbon atoms and H_2O units vary. The term carbohydrate is now used more broadly to refer to three groups of carbohydrate molecules: monosaccharides, disaccharides, and polysaccharides.

Figure 16.1 Carbohydrates in our Lives.

A) Carbohydrates play an important role in our diets. **B)** Diabetics must monitor the level of glucose, a carbohydrate, in their blood to prevent life-threatening complications. **C)** The type of carbohydrate on our red blood cells determines our blood type (A, B, AB, or O).

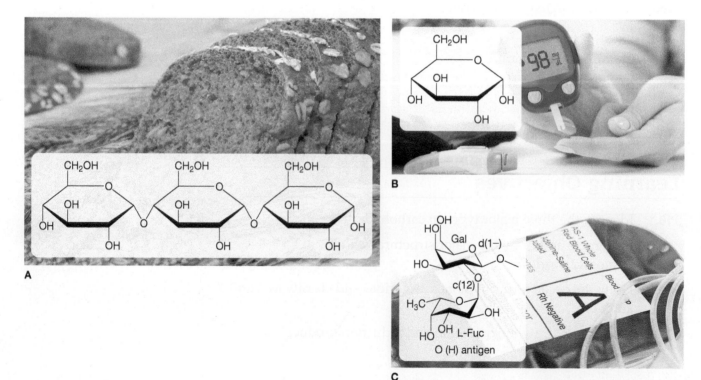

Figure 16.2 Glucose and Fructose are Monosaccharides that Exist in both the Acyclic and Cyclic Forms.

monosaccharides

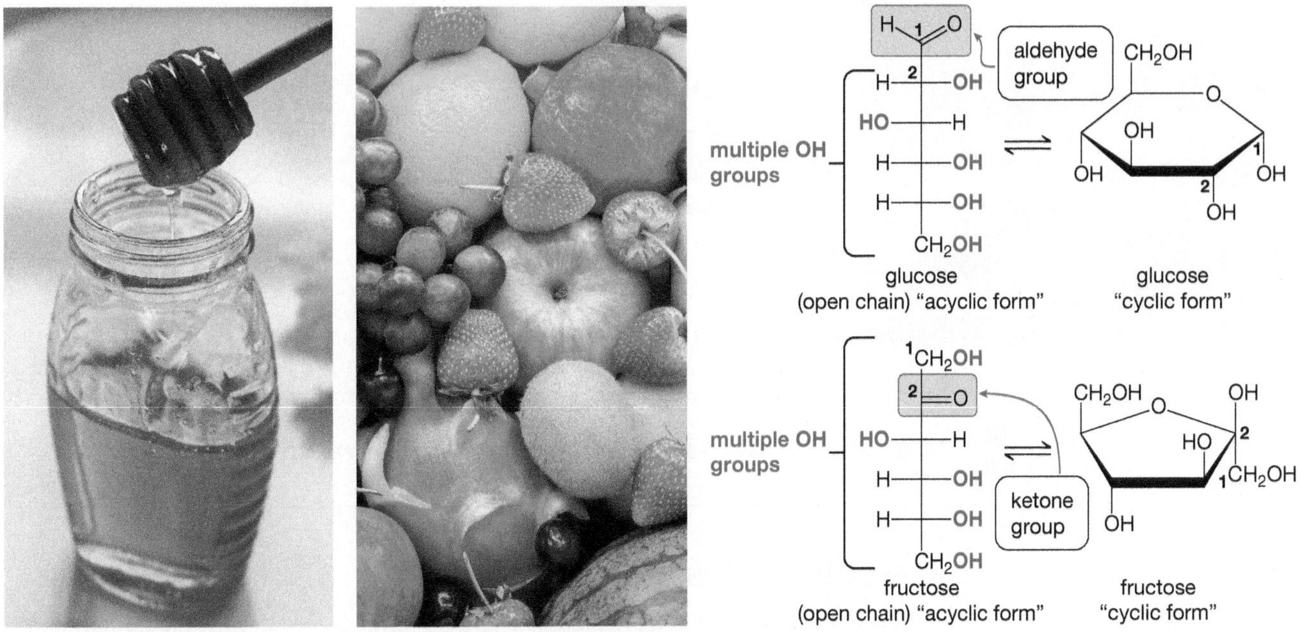

glucose
(open chain) "acyclic form"

glucose
"cyclic form"

fructose
(open chain) "acyclic form"

fructose
"cyclic form"

Monosaccharides are often called simple sugars and, as that name suggests, monosaccharides are the simplest carbohydrates. Glucose and fructose are the major monosaccharides, and they are found in items such as fruit and honey (Figure 16.2). The acyclic form of glucose, as we learned in Chapter 15, contains an aldehyde and several hydroxyl groups. Similarly, the acyclic form of fructose contains several hydroxyl groups, but in addition, fructose also contains a ketone group. Unlike the disaccharides and polysaccharides, monosaccharides cannot be split apart into smaller carbohydrates. Simple sugars, such as glucose and fructose exist in both the acyclic and cyclic forms.

Disaccharides and Polysaccharides

Disaccharides consist of two monosaccharides linked together. Table sugar, or sucrose, is an example of a common disaccharide composed of the monosaccharides glucose and fructose (Figure 16.3). Disaccharides are broken down into monosaccharides by chemical reactions during digestion.

Polysaccharides consist of three or more monosaccharides linked together. We explore three major types of polysaccharides in this chapter (starch, cellulose, and glycogen) all of which are composed of hundreds of glucose molecules linked together. The polysaccharide starch, for example, is found in common foods such as corn, rice, wheat, and potatoes (Figure 16.4).

Figure 16.3 Table Sugar (Sucrose) is a Disaccharide. The linkage between the two monosaccharides is highlighted in the box.

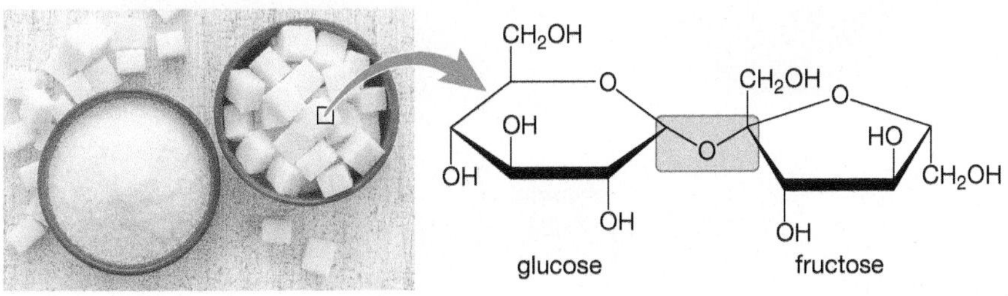

glucose   fructose

Figure 16.4 Starches Contain Chains of Monosaccharides Linked Together to Form Polysaccharides. The acetal carbon atom in each ring is highlighted in the box.

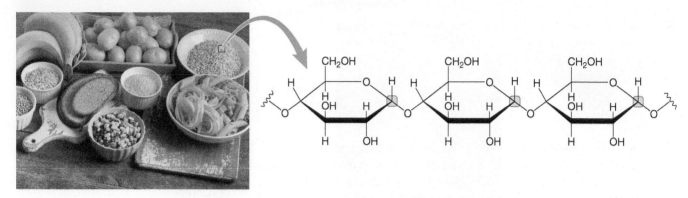

Apply what you have just learned: **Practice 16.1** in the Pearson eText.

Carbohydrates Store Energy

Carbohydrates are often described as energy storage molecules. In the human body, blood sugar (glucose) provides the stored energy for most cellular functions. During exercise, for example, our bodies use glucose from the blood for quick bursts of energy. Where does this glucose come from? There are many sources, however, ingested carbohydrates are often the source of the energy our bodies use during exercise.

Green plants and algae synthesize carbohydrates through photosynthesis using energy from the sun. Carbon dioxide (CO_2) and water (H_2O) are converted to glucose $(C_6H_{12}O_6)$ and oxygen (O_2) during photosynthesis, and then stored in the form of polysaccharides such as starch and cellulose. In the human body, polysaccharides, often from plant sources, are broken down into simple sugars during respiration. Ultimately our bodies use these simple sugars to generate energy and do work at the cellular level (Figure 16.5).

Explore BioConnect 16.1 (contains Figures 16.6–16.13) to learn more about the important role monosaccharides play in our blood.

Figure 16.5 Photosynthesis and Respiration.

Photosynthesis stores energy from the sun in carbohydrates such as glucose. This energy is released during the metabolism of carbohydrates to give us the energy we need.

Explore how Chemistry and Biology connect: **BioConnect: 16.1** Blood Sugar in the Pearson eText.

Quiz yourself on the content of this section: **Check 16.1** in the Pearson eText.

16.2 Monosaccharides

The regulation of blood sugar (glucose) is an essential function that our body carries out for us at all times. Recall from BioConnect 16.1 that feedback loops maintain blood sugar levels in the optimum range unless we suffer from a disease such as diabetes. In the hospital, an intravenous solution containing glucose, which is also called dextrose, provides patients with calories and hydration (Figure 16.14). The glucose in the IV solution eventually reaches the blood stream for uptake by our cells or is stored in the liver for later use.

Glucose is an example of a monosaccharide, which generally contain three to six carbon atoms in a chain and are often referred to as simple sugars. Several hydroxyl groups and either an aldehyde or ketone group are attached to the carbon atoms in monosaccharides. The three most common monosaccharides in biological systems are **glucose**, **fructose**, and **galactose** (Figure 16.15). All three of these common monosaccharides have the same chemical formula ($C_6H_{12}O_6$). Both glucose and galactose are aldehydes with six carbon atoms and five hydroxyl groups. They only differ in the orientation of the OH group on the fourth carbon. In contrast, fructose is a ketone, but like glucose and galactose, fructose contains six carbon atoms and five hydroxyl groups.

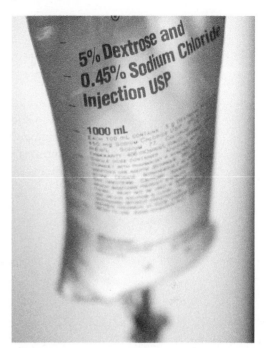

Figure 16.14 A 5% Intravenous Glucose (dextrose) Solution.

Classifying Monosaccharides by Functional Group

We can classify monosaccharides by the functional groups they contain. A monosaccharide that includes an aldehyde group is a **polyhydroxy aldehyde (aldose)**. In an aldose, the first carbon in the chain is part of an aldehyde functional group. Both glucose and galactose (see Fig. 16.15 A and C) are aldose compounds.

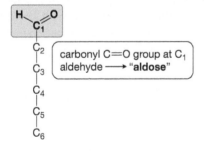

carbonyl C=O group at C_1
aldehyde ⟶ "**aldose**"

Figure 16.15 Common Six-Carbon Monosaccharides.

A) Glucose contains an aldehyde group and is the most common monosaccharide found in the blood. **B)** Fructose has a ketone group and is a monosaccharide commonly found in fruit. **C)** Galactose has an aldehyde group but differs from glucose in the orientation of the OH group on carbon 4. Galactose is commonly found in dairy products.

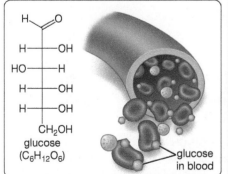

glucose
($C_6H_{12}O_6$)

glucose in blood

A

fructose
($C_6H_{12}O_6$)

B

galactose
($C_6H_{12}O_6$)

C

A **polyhydroxy ketone (ketose)** is a monosaccharide that contains a ketone group. In a ketose, the second carbon in the chain contains a ketone group. Fructose (see Fig. 16.15 B), is a ketose.

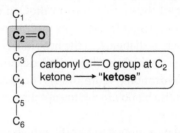

Glucose is the most common aldose and glyceraldehyde is the simplest aldose compound. Glyceraldehyde has three carbon atoms with an aldehyde group at the terminal carbon atom. Dihydroxyacetone is the simplest ketose; it has three carbon atoms and a carbonyl group on the second carbon atom.

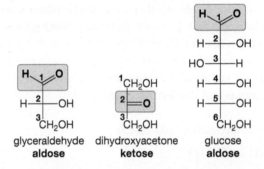

Classifying Monosaccharides by Number of Carbon Atoms

We also classify monosaccharides by the number of carbon atoms in the chain. A monosaccharide with three carbon atoms is a *triose*, one with four carbon atoms is a *tetrose*, a five-carbon monosaccharide is a *pentose*, and a *six*-carbon monosaccharide is a *hexose*.

	3 carbon atoms	*tri*	*triose*
prefix corresponds to number of carbon	4 carbon atoms	*tetra*	*tetrose*
atoms followed by "-ose" ending	5 carbon atoms	*penta*	*pentose*
	6 carbon atoms	*hexa*	*hexose*

The two classification systems are combined to indicate the aldehyde or ketone group and the number of carbon atoms (Figure 16.16). An aldotetrose, for example, is a four-carbon monosaccharide that is an aldehyde, and a ketohexose is a six-carbon monosaccharide that is a ketone.

Figure 16.16 Classifying Monosaccharides by the Number of Carbon Atoms and the Presence of an Aldehyde or Ketone Group.

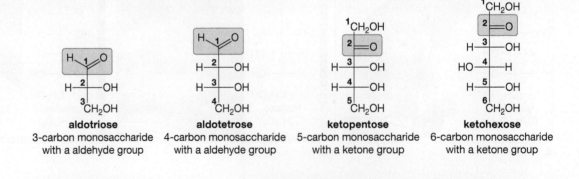

> Predict answers and see step-by-step solutions: **Learn 16.1:** Classifying Monosaccharides in the Pearson eText.
>
> Apply what you have just learned: **Practice 16.2** in the Pearson eText.

Stereoisomerism in Monosaccharides

In many biologically active molecules, the atoms are arranged in a very specific way in three-dimensional space. In these cases, only one stereoisomer (Chapter 14) elicits a biological response. This is definitely the case for carbohydrates. Most monosaccharides contain chiral carbons, yet only one of the stereoisomers are biologically active. Glucose, for example, is a major source of energy in the human body, yet the enzymes that metabolize glucose have a strong affinity for only one of the possible stereoisomers. Knowing the specific three-dimensional structure of this active stereoisomer of glucose provides a deeper understanding of how the human body works.

Recall that stereoisomers have the same chemical formula and the same atom connectivity yet differ in the way that the atoms are arranged in three-dimensional space. One example of this is molecules that are chiral—molecules that have at least one carbon atom that has four different groups attached such that the molecule is non-superimposable on its mirror image (See VisibleChem Video 14.4 for a review of chiral centers). Monosaccharides contain several chiral carbons, however, as we will see in the next few pages, only one of the isomers occurs naturally.

The simplest aldose, glyceraldehyde, contains one chiral carbon—with four different groups bonded to the second carbon in the chain. The two stereoisomers (Figure 16.17) of glyceraldehyde are non-superimposable mirror images of one another. To distinguish between a pair of monosaccharide stereoisomers, the prefixes D and L are placed in front of the name. When the OH group on carbon 2 is on the right side, the prefix D is used, and when the OH group is on the left side, the prefix L is used. In the case of glyceraldehyde, only the D isomer (D-glyceraldehyde) occurs in nature. The other isomer (L-glyceraldehyde) is considered unnatural.

Figure 16.17 Stereoisomers of Glyceraldehyde.

D-glyceraldehyde occurs naturally whereas L-glyceraldehyde is not found in nature.

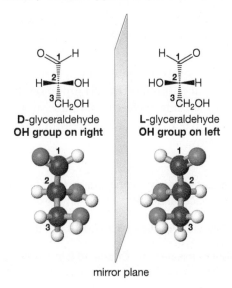

mirror plane

Fischer Projections of Monosaccharides

We use Fischer projections to draw monosaccharides molecules with chiral carbons. Recall from Section 14.5 that in a Fischer projection a cross represents a tetrahedral carbon, vertical lines represent bonds that project backwards, and horizontal lines represent bonds that project forward.

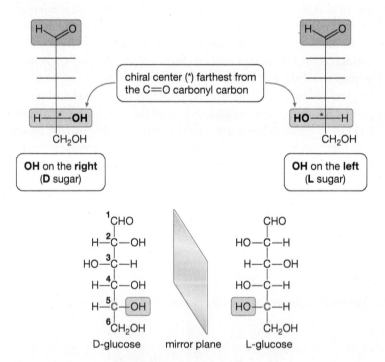

Fischer projections of monosaccharides with more than one chiral center illustrate how the stereoisomers differ at specific carbons. When more than one chiral carbon is present in a monosaccharide molecule, the chiral carbon farthest from the carbonyl group is used to determine whether the molecule is classified as D or L. Glucose, for example, contains four chiral carbons. The D monosaccharide contains an OH group on the chiral carbon that is farthest from the carbonyl (C5) on the right. The L monosaccharide, on the other hand, contains an OH group that is farthest from the carbonyl (C5) on the left.

Glucose, fructose, and all other naturally occurring sugars are D sugars. Neither L-glucose nor L-fructose occur naturally. The OH group on the carbon farthest from the carbonyl group is on the left side in these unnatural L sugars. The OH group in the D sugars is on the right side. In both bases, it is the D-form that participates in enzyme-mediated reactions in the body.

Predict answers and see step-by-step solutions: **Learn 16.2:** Determining the Stereochemistry of Monosaccharides in the Pearson eText.

Apply what you have just learned: **Practice 16.3 and 16.4** in the Pearson eText.

Quiz yourself on the content of this section: **Check 16.2** in the Pearson eText.

16.3 Cyclic Monosaccharides

Galactose is one of the most common six-carbon monosaccharides, mostly because it is found in milk products. Unfortunately, one out of every 30,000 infants is born with a genetic disorder, called galactosemia, which prevents the baby from utilizing galactose (Figure 16.18). When the body cannot absorb galactose, it accumulates in the blood causing a variety of medical conditions. Some infants with this condition suffer from failure to grow, brain damage, cataract formation in the eyes, and even death from liver damage. A defective enzyme is generally the cause of this disease. The only treatment is eliminating galactose from the diet. Infants with this disease cannot be breast fed, for example, because galactose is found in breast milk, so a soy-based formula is generally prescribed. If diagnosed early, many of the long-term effects of this disease can be prevented.

We have explored the structure of monosaccharides, such as galactose, in the open-chain form using Fischer projections. Now we turn our attention to the cyclic form of some of these same compounds. In fact, the most stable form of five- and six-carbon monosaccharides are rings. Galactose and glucose form six-carbon rings, and fructose generally forms a five-carbon ring. Keep in mind that both the open-chain form and the ring form of these monosaccharides are present in the body. In this content, we explore how the open-chain (acyclic) form of each of these monosaccharides closes during a chemical reaction to produce the ring (cyclic) form.

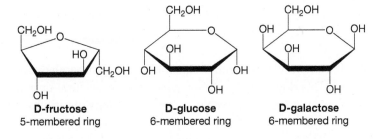

D-fructose
5-membered ring

D-glucose
6-membered ring

D-galactose
6-membered ring

Figure 16.18 Infants with Galactosemia Must be Fed a Galactose-free Diet.
Galactosemia is the result of a defective enzyme in the body that metabolizes the monosaccharide galactose.

Forming Cyclic Monosaccharides

How does the open-chain (acyclic) form of a monosaccharide convert to the ring (cyclic) form of a monosaccharide? Recall from Section 15.4. that the carbonyl groups on both aldehydes and ketones react with an alcohol to form hemiacetals.

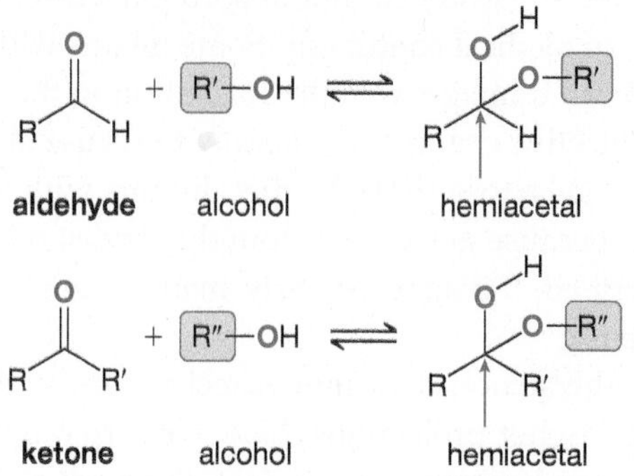

aldehyde   alcohol   hemiacetal

ketone   alcohol   hemiacetal

Cyclic hemiacetals are produced from an intramolecular reaction involving the carbonyl group and a hydroxyl group on the same molecule that produces a new chiral center.

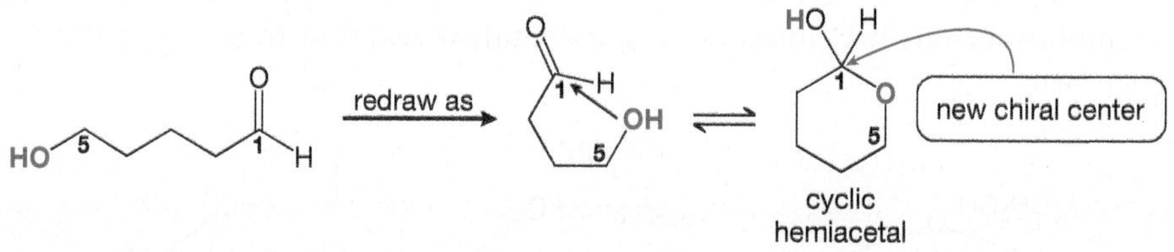

redraw as

new chiral center

cyclic
hemiacetal

When this intramolecular reaction occurs for acyclic monosaccharides, the cyclic form is produced. This ring-closing reaction generates a new chiral carbon for which two isomers, called **anomers**, are possible. In the terminology of carbohydrate chemistry, the new chiral carbon is called an **anomeric carbon**, when we draw them, the α anomer has the OH group below the ring (down) and the β anomer has the OH group above the ring (up). The flat ring structures shown here are **Haworth projections.** We use these projections to represent the cyclic hemiacetals of monosaccharides such as glucose.

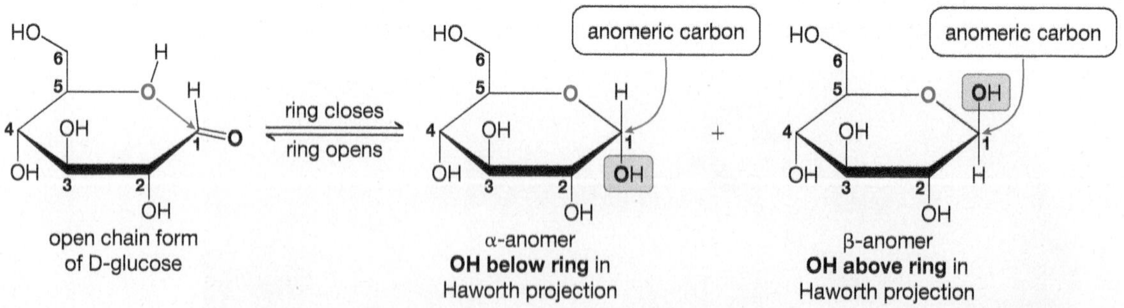

open chain form
of D-glucose

ring closes
ring opens

anomeric carbon

α-anomer
OH below ring in
Haworth projection

anomeric carbon

β-anomer
OH above ring in
Haworth projection

Explore VisibleChem Videos 16.1 and 16.2 to learn how to draw and analyze the major structural features of cyclic monosaccharides. Pay close attention to how Haworth projections are used to represent the ring closure reactions that produce α and β anomers of cyclic monosaccharides.

Watch this concept come to life: **VisibleChem Video 16.1:** Drawing the Haworth Cyclic Structure from an Acyclic Aldohexose and **VisibleChem Video 16.2:** Drawing the Haworth Cyclic Structure from an Acyclic Ketohexose in the Pearson eText.

Mutarotation

Both the acyclic and cyclic forms of monosaccharides exist in nature in known amounts. At equilibrium, a solution of glucose contains 63% of the β isomer, 37% of the α isomer, and only trace amounts of the acyclic form. Each of these three cyclic forms play a role in forming larger disaccharide and polysaccharide molecules. In some cases, the α form reacts to produce a specific larger carbohydrate molecule and in other cases the β form undergoes a reaction. Equilibrium between the three forms is maintained by the rapid conversion of the open-chain form to both ring forms. The figure shown here illustrates these equilibrium reactions for glucose.

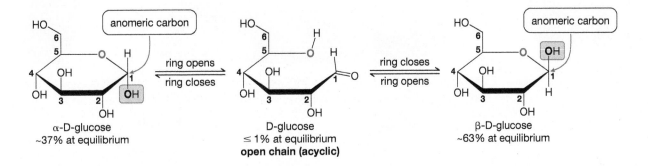

α-D-glucose
~37% at equilibrium

D-glucose
≤ 1% at equilibrium
open chain (acyclic)

β-D-glucose
~63% at equilibrium

Because we represent the molecules with Haworth projections, we can see that acyclic D-glucose (the molecule in the center) undergoes a ring-closure reaction to produce two cyclic forms of glucose (α and β; the molecules on the left and right). In aqueous solution, the ring opens and closes in a reversible process that gives rise to all three possible forms of glucose (the acyclic form in the center and the two cyclic forms on either side) in a process called **mutarotation**. As the ring closes, the OH group on carbon 1 is equally likely to end up in either position (up and down) giving rise to both the α and β anomers.

Apply what you have just learned: **Practice 16.5–16.8** in the Pearson eText.

Quiz yourself on the content of this section: **Check 16.3** in the Pearson eText.

16.4 Reactions of Monosaccharides

As we noted in the unit introduction, diabetes is a serious disease but one that can be managed. To manage their condition, diabetes patients frequently test their blood glucose levels. If glucose levels are properly controlled some of the serious complications of diabetes can be avoided. In the mid 1990s, small devices were put on the market that provided a way for diabetics to regularly monitor their blood sugar with test strips, allowing them to adjust food intake and insulin dosage as needed (Figure 16.19).

The chemical reaction that occurs in these electronic devices is the enzyme-mediated oxidation of glucose into a carboxylic acid called gluconic acid. The enzyme in this reaction is glucose oxidase. Glucose concentrations can also be measured in urine using the same glucose oxidation reaction that is employed on the test strips (Figure 16.20).

Figure 16.19 Electronic Device Measures Glucose Concentrations.

A small drop of blood is placed on the test strip that contains an embedded enzyme. The test strip is then inserted into the device and the reaction takes place and a glucose concentration reading is obtained.

Figure 16.20 Test strips that Contain Glucose Oxidase Measure Glucose Concentrations in Urine.

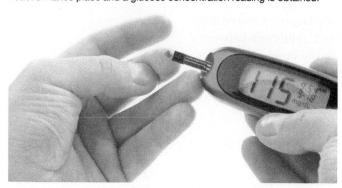

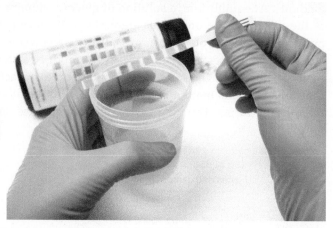

The oxidation of glucose to gluconic acid is an example of one type of chemical reaction that monosaccharides undergo. In this section we explore some of the other reactions that monosaccharides are involved in both in the laboratory and in the human body.

Oxidation of Monosaccharides

Although monosaccharides exist mostly in the cyclic form, it is the open-chain form that undergoes oxidation reactions. The aldehyde group in the open-chain form aldose monosaccharides, for example, are oxidized to a carboxylic acid by a Cu^{2+} reagent called **Benedict's reagent** (Figure 16.21). This is a similar reaction to the enzyme-mediated reaction that is central to the blood glucose test device in Figure 16.20. Benedicts' reagent converts an open-chain form aldose molecule to a carboxylic acid. In the test device, D-glucose is oxidized using Benedict's reagent to gluconic acid. In the process, a color change occurs as blue Cu^{2+} is reduced to Cu^+ and forms a red solution containing Cu_2O. This reaction increases the number of C—O bonds in the aldose molecule and is therefore considered an oxidation reaction. A carbohydrate that reacts with Benedict's reagent, such as glucose in this case, is called a **reducing sugar**.

Ketoses also react with Benedict's reagent and are reducing sugars (Figure 16.22). This may be surprising given that ketones do not have a readily available carbonyl group for oxidation to occur. Ketoses, however, contain a CH_2OH group next to the ketone group that undergoes rearrangement to form an aldose. Once the aldose is present in solution, the oxidation to a carboxylic acid by Benedict's reagent readily occurs. For example, fructose rearranges to an aldose, which is then oxidized to gluconic acid. In this roundabout way, fructose acts as a reducing sugar.

Figure 16.21 Oxidation of Acyclic Monosaccharides Produces a Carboxylic Acid.

Glucose is oxidized to gluconic acid by Benedict's reagent producing a color change from blue to red. This reaction indicates the presence of reducing sugars.

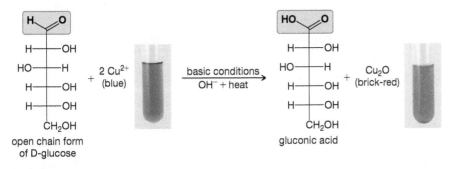

open chain form of D-glucose

gluconic acid

Figure 16.22 Rearrangement of Ketose to Aldose Produces Positive Benedict's Test.

Under conditions of Benedict's reagent, fructose can rearrange from a ketose into an aldose. The rearranged aldose product can then be oxidized by Benedict's reagent to form gluconic acid. As a result, fructose is considered a reducing sugar.

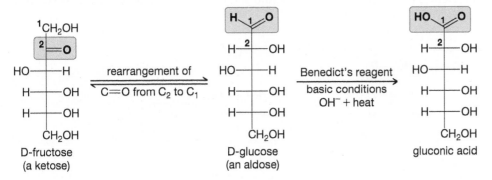

D-fructose (a ketose)

D-glucose (an aldose)

gluconic acid

Apply what you have just learned: **Practice 16.9 and 16.10** in the Pearson eText.

Reduction of Monosaccharides

Monosaccharides can also be reduced causing a reduction in the number of C—O bonds and an increase in the number of C—H bonds. NADPH is a naturally occurring molecule that assists enzymes in reducing a number of molecules within the cell by serving as the source of hydrogen atoms and electrons for reduction reactions. In the body, the reduction of glucose by NADPH is enzyme catalyzed, converting the carbonyl group to a hydroxyl group. The reduction of glucose is generally only a minor reaction in the body when blood glucose levels are normal. However, diabetics with chronic high blood sugar may have up to one third of their glucose reduced by NADPH (Figure 16.23). This process uses up significant amounts of NADPH and therefore has an impact on the synthesis of other important molecules in the body. The result is damage to the cells and further medical complications such as damage to the retina, kidneys, and nerves.

Figure 16.23 A Diabetic Patient Treated by a Nurse.

Chronic high blood sugar leads to alternate monosaccharide metabolic pathways in the body, which can cause a lot of damage to the cells. The reduction of glucose to sorbitol with NADPH is part of an alternate metabolic pathway that can be harmful when blood glucose levels are chronically high.

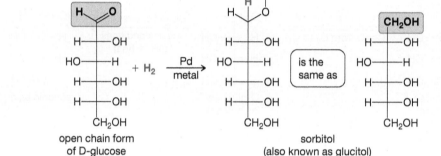

More generally, and in laboratory experiments, the carbonyl group of an aldose is reduced to a primary (1°) alcohol in the presence of hydrogen gas (H_2) and palladium metal (Pd). This reaction is similar to the reduction of aldehydes we discussed in Section 15.3. The reduction of the carbonyl group in monosaccharides to an alcohol produces what is called a **sugar alcohol** and is also referred to as an **alditol**. For example, D-glucose is reduced in the presence of H_2 (hydrogen gas) and Pd (a metal catalyst) to produce sorbitol (glucitol). Alditols, such as sorbitol, are used as artificial sweeteners in a variety of sugar-free gum and candy. Sorbitol is about 60% as sweet as sucrose (table sugar).

Apply what you have just learned: **Practice 16.11 and 16.12** in the Pearson eText.

Monosaccharide Reactions of the Primary Alcohol

The addition of a phosphate group to monosaccharides is an important step in the metabolism of sugars in the body. In the case of α-D-glucose, ATP provides a phosphate group (PO_4^{3-}) that reacts with the primary (1°) alcohol group (carbon with OH group is bonded to only one carbon atom) on glucose to produce α-D-glucose 6-phosphate.

Another reaction that readily occurs in the body is the enzyme-catalyzed oxidation of the primary (1°) alcohol at carbon 6 (C6) of D-glucose to a carboxylic acid. This reaction produces D-glucuronic acid, which plays an important role in detoxifying the body from foreign molecules, such as drug molecules.

The detoxification process occurs in the liver by converting water-insoluble compounds to water-soluble compounds that can more easily be excreted in the urine. For example, the reaction of glucuronic acid with opioids such as codeine, morphine, and naloxone, effectively removes these compounds from the body through urine excretion.

16.5 Disaccharides

Disaccharides are carbohydrates that are composed of two monosaccharides linked together. **Lactose** is a common disaccharide—composed of the monosaccharides galactose and glucose—that is found in dairy products such as milk (Figure 16.24). While the linking of two monosaccharides to produce a disaccharide is common, and thus the main focus of this section, the reverse reaction also occurs. Digestion of the disaccharide lactose, for example, produces glucose and galactose, and the enzyme **lactase** is required to accomplish this task. Disaccharides are water soluble, but they are too large to pass through the cell membrane. Therefore, disaccharides must be broken down during digestion to produce the smaller monosaccharides that can pass into the blood and through cell membranes into cells. Individuals who do not have enough of the lactase enzyme to break down lactose are diagnosed as lactose intolerant.

The joining together of two monosaccharides occurs when a hemiacetal of one monosaccharide reacts with a hydroxyl group of a second monosaccharide to form an acetal (see Section 15.4 for review). The new C—O bond that links the two rings is a **glycosidic linkage**.

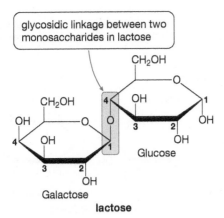

Figure 16.24 Lactose Intolerance.

Lactose is a disaccharide composed of galactose and glucose. Many adults produce the enzyme lactase that allows them to break apart the lactose molecule. Individuals who do not produce enough of this enzyme may be lactose intolerant. When lactose intolerant individuals consume products high in lactose, undigested lactose sugar is metabolized by the bacteria in the large intestine, producing gas and abdominal pain.

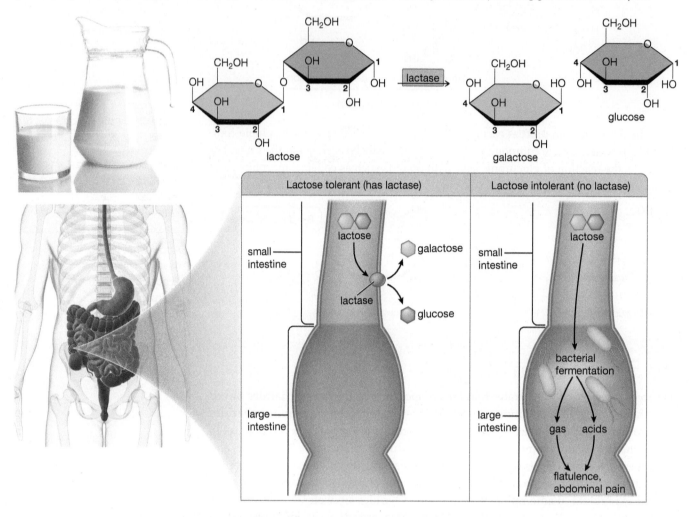

Glycosidic Linkages in Disaccharides

Disaccharides are composed of two monosaccharide rings that are either five-carbon or six-carbon. Each carbon member of the ring is numbered beginning at the carbon that is bonded to two oxygen atoms. The glycosidic linkage that joins two monosaccharides together can be oriented in two different ways as shown in these two disaccharide molecules.

An α glycosidic linkage is oriented down, whereas a β glycosidic linkage is oriented up. Numbers indicate which carbon atoms are linked in the new disaccharide. For example, we say that structure A (maltose) has a $1{\rightarrow}4$-α-glycosidic linkage because the glycosidic linkage is down and joins C1 of one ring with C4 of the other. We refer to structure B (cellobiose) as a $1{\rightarrow}4$-β-glycosidic linkage because the linkage is up and connects C1 of one ring to C4 of the other.

The three most common disaccharides are lactose, **maltose**, and **sucrose**, which are composed of the following monosaccharides:

$$\text{glucose} \;+\; \text{galactose} \;\rightarrow\; \textit{lactose}$$
$$\text{glucose} \;+\; \text{glucose} \;\rightarrow\; \textit{maltose}$$
$$\text{glucose} \;+\; \text{fructose} \;\rightarrow\; \textit{sucrose}$$

Explore VisibleChem Video 16.3 to continue your investigation of how monosaccharides link together to form disaccharides. When you encounter glycosidic linkage, be sure to note whether the linkage is α or β and which carbons are involved.

Watch this concept come to life: **VisibleChem Video 16.3:** The Structural Features of Disaccharides in the Pearson eText.

Apply what you have just learned: **Practice 16.13–16.15** in the Pearson eText.

Quiz yourself on the content of this section: **Check 16.5** in the Pearson eText.

16.6 Polysaccharides

High-fructose corn syrup (HFCS) is widely used in the U.S. food industry as a sweetener. The consumption of too much sugar of any kind, particularly HFCS, is associated with a range of health problems. Manufacturers often use HFCS because it can be cheaply produced from cornstarch. Cornstarch, which is composed of hundreds or even thousands of glucose molecules linked together, undergoes a series of processing steps to ultimately produce syrup that is a mixture of glucose and fructose (Figure 16.25). During production of HFCS, the cornstarch is broken down to mostly glucose

Figure 16.25 High Fructose Corn Syrup Production.

Enzymes break up cornstarch into glucose monomers. Additional enzymes then convert some of the glucose into fructose, forming high fructose corn syrup (HFCS). HFCS is used in a wide array of processed foods; it is valued in the processed food industries because of its low cost, high solubility, and sweet taste.

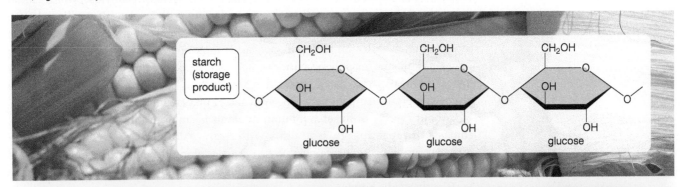

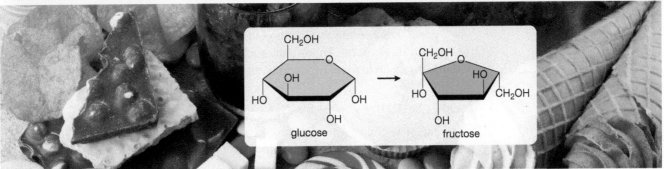

molecules, and then treated with an enzyme to convert some of the glucose to fructose. HFCS that contains 42% fructose is used to make products such as cereals, beverages, and other highly processed foods. HFCS that contains 55% fructose is mostly used to make soft drinks.

What is cornstarch and how do manufacturers produce glucose from cornstarch? Starch, including cornstarch, is a polysaccharide. Polysaccharides consist of a large number of monosaccharides bonded together by glycosidic bonds. Three common polysaccharides found in nature are **starch**, **glycogen**, and **cellulose**, each of which contains repeating glucose units. Starch and glycogen both contain glucose rings joined in $1 \rightarrow 4$-α-glycosidic linkages, whereas cellulose contains glucose rings bonded in a $1 \rightarrow 4$-β-glycosidic linkage.

Starch and glycogen repeating unit

cellulose repeating unit

Starch

Starch is an energy storage polysaccharide molecule found in the roots and seeds of plants. The two most common forms of starch are **amylose** and **amylopectin** (Figure 16.26). Between 20–25% of starch molecules in plants are amylose, which has an unbranched structure of repeating glucose molecules with $1 \rightarrow 4$-α-glycosidic linkages. This glycosidic linkage produces a helical structure in three dimensions. The number of repeating units varies for each polysaccharide molecule. We use the subscripted letter "n" to indicate that the polysaccharide contains "n" repeating units. The brackets identify the part of the molecule that is repeated in the structure. For example, the polysaccharide glycogen typically contains between seven and 11 glucose units (n = 7 – 11).

About 75–80% of the starch found in plants is amylopectin, which, like amylose, consists of repeating glucose units with α-glycosidic linkages. Unlike amylose however, amylopectin contains glucose branches along the chain. The linear linkages are formed by $1 \rightarrow 4$-α-glycosidic bonds, but the branching linkages are formed by $1 \rightarrow 6$-α-glycosidic bonds.

Both amylose and amylopectin are hydrolyzed in the body to produce only D-glucose. The enzyme **amylase** is readily available in the human digestion system to carry out this process. Food items such as pasta, bread, and corn are all sources of starch that contain these two readily digested polysaccharides.

Glycogen

Glycogen is the major carbohydrate storage molecule in animals. Similar to amylopectin, it is a branched polysaccharide consisting of a large number of glucose units bonded together with $1 \rightarrow 4$-α-glycosidic linkages and branches joined

Figure 16.26 The Two Most Common Forms of Starch—Amylose and Amylopectin.

Both amylose and amylopectin are formed by α-glycosidic bonds with the glycosidic oxygen oriented down. Branching occurs in amylopectin between C1 and C6. The brackets indicate that this part of the molecule is repeated, and the subscript "n" represents the number of times that it is repeated. The value of "n" can vary for the different starch molecules.

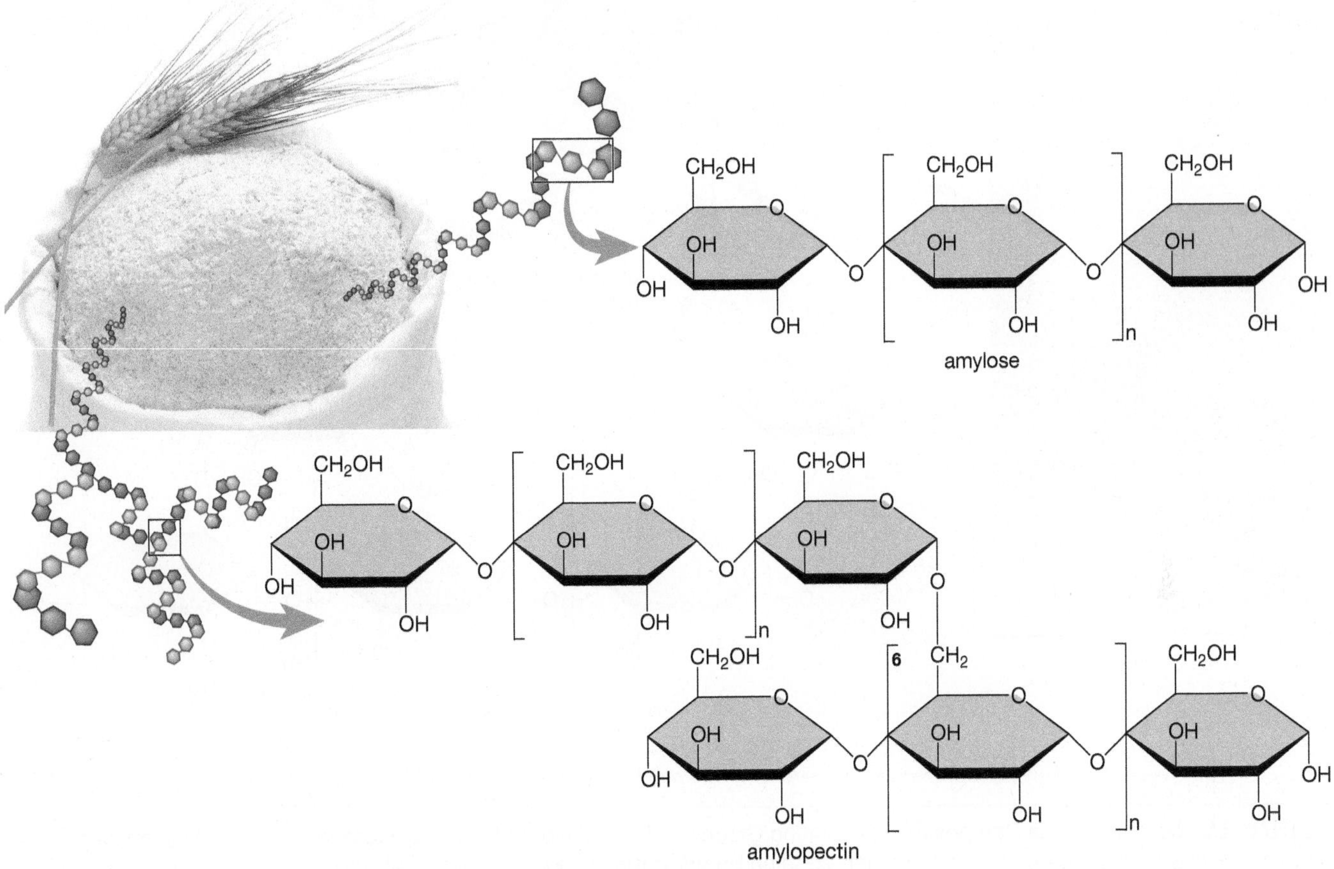

by $1 \rightarrow 6$-α-glycosidic linkages (Figure 16.27). Glycogen is highly branched compared to amylopectin and features many more branches that are shorter in length. The highly branched nature of glycogen makes it a readily available supply of glucose in our cells. Glycogen is predominantly found in the liver and muscle cells, and when energy is needed, glucose molecules can be enzymatically broken off from the branches on glycogen.

Cellulose

Cellulose is found in the cell walls of nearly all plants, providing the rigidity and support characteristic of plant stems and wood. Cellulose is an unbranched polysaccharide composed of a large number of repeating glucose units that are joined together with $1 \rightarrow 4$-β-glycosidic linkages (Figure 16.28). This type of linkage creates long chains that stack on top of one another to form well-organized water-insoluble fibers. The extensive three-dimensional structure of cellulose provides the characteristic fibrous strength of plant structure.

Humans and other animals do not have the **β-glucosidases**, which are the digestive enzymes that cleave the glycosidic bond in cellulose, and therefore are unable to digest cellulose. Instead, we have only the **α-glucosidases**, so starch and glycogen serve as our main sources of glucose. While animals usually cannot digest cellulose, many bacteria and other microorganisms do have β-glucosidases in their systems that allow them to digest cellulose. For example, while horses do not have β-glucosidases, the microorganisms present in their digestive tracts do have these enzymes and the microorganisms are able to cleave the β-glycosidic linkages found in cellulose for the horses. For this reason, horses are able to digest grass and hay.

Figure 16.27 Animals Store Carbohydrates as Glycogen in the Liver.

Similar to the starch amylopectin, glycogen has α-glycosidic linkages but the branching in glycogen is more extensive.

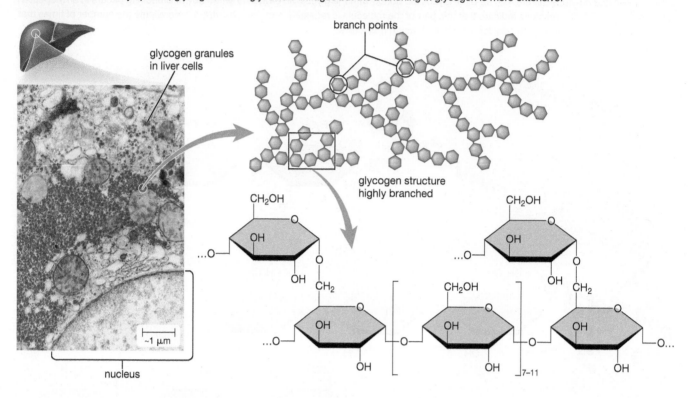

Figure 16.28 Cellulose is Composed of Repeating Glucose Units Joined by 1→4-β-glycosidic Linkages. The dashed lines shown indicate some of the extensive hydrogen bonding between the stacked chains in cellulose.

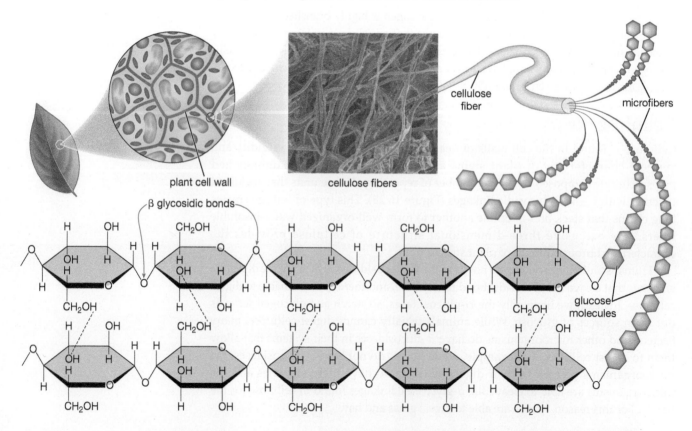

Figure 16.29 Horses Digest the Cellulose in Grass.
Microorganisms in the digestive tract of some animals provide the enzymes needed to metabolize cellulose.

After completing Practice 16.16, explore BioConnect 16.2 (contains Figures 16.30–16.36) to learn about polysaccharides in our diets.

Apply what you have just learned: **Practice 16.16** in the Pearson eText.

Explore how Chemistry and Biology connect: **BioConnect: 16.2** Carbs in Our Diet in the Pearson eText.

Examples of Polysaccharides Based on Glucose Derivatives

A variety of simple and complex polysaccharides in plants and animals carry out useful functions. Several of these polysaccharides are formed from monosaccharides that contain amino groups (NH_2) or amide groups ($NHCOCH_3$) in place of an OH group. Two examples are D-glucosamine and N-acetyl-D-glucosamine. Other polysaccharides are composed of monosaccharides that contain a COO^- group in place of the CH_2OH group such as in D-glucuronate.

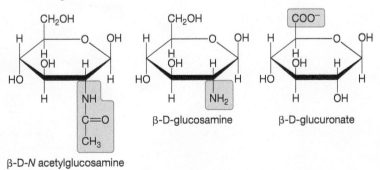

Three polysaccharides that are derived from glucose derivatives are **hyaluronate**, **heparin**, and **chondroitin** (Figure 16.37). Hyaluronate is found in the body wherever lubrication is needed between layers of tissues such as the glassy part of the eye, the joint cartilage, the fluid in the joints, and all mucous membranes. The monosaccharides in this

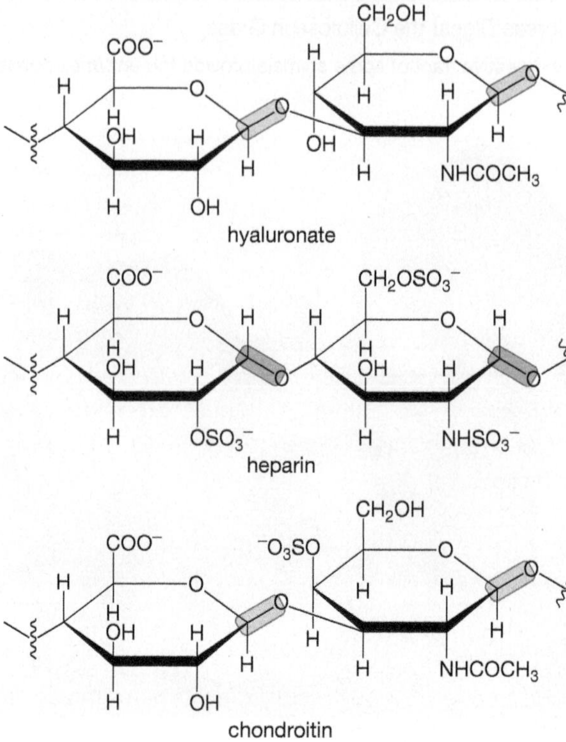

Figure 16.37 Acidic Polysaccharides.

Hyaluronate, heparin, and chondroitin are unbranched carbohydrates that are composed of alternating amino sugars and glucuronate units. Blue boxes indicate β glycosidic linkages and red boxes indicate α glycosidic linkages.

hyaluronate

heparin

chondroitin

polysaccharide are linked together with a 1→3-β-glycosidic linkage. Heparin is a mixture of sulfonated polysaccharide chains and is stored in a variety of body tissues such as the liver, lungs, and gut. Heparin is known for its ability to function as an anticoagulant and is kept on hand in hospitals to treat patients that suffer from blood clots. Chondroitin is a component of cartilage and tendons and is often taken by people suffering from arthritis as a supplement in combination with glucosamine (Figure 16.38).

Figure 16.38 Glucosamine and Chondroitin Supplement.

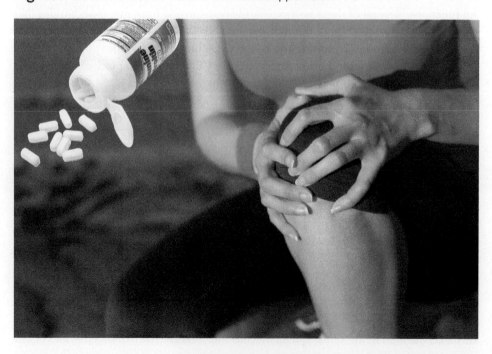

Polysaccharides Determine A, B, O Blood Type

Polysaccharides play a critical role in facilitating safe blood transfusions. The A, B, and O blood types are determined by the terminal sugar on a polysaccharide on the surface of red blood cells. Type A blood has a modified galactose, *N*-acetylgalactosamine, in the terminal position. Type B blood has a galactose sugar in the terminal position. Type AB blood has both these markers while Type O has neither additional sugar (Figure 16.39A).

Accurately typing blood is essential to prevent life-threatening attacks by the patient's immune system on the foreign blood. Individuals with type A blood, for example, recognize the A carbohydrate as self and do not produce antibodies to it. (Recall that antibodies are powerful proteins produced by the immune system to help destroy pathogens.) If a patient with type A is given a transfusion with type B blood, the patient's immune system will attack the transfused blood (see Fig 16.39B). This life-threatening reaction can trigger blood clots, potentially cutting off the supply of blood to organs or causing a stroke.

Figure 16.39 Blood Types.

A) The last sugar on a polysaccharide on the surface of red blood cells distinguishes the A, AB, B, and O blood types. **B)** Blood type must be accurately determined to prevent antibodies from the immune system from attacking foreign blood during a transfusion.

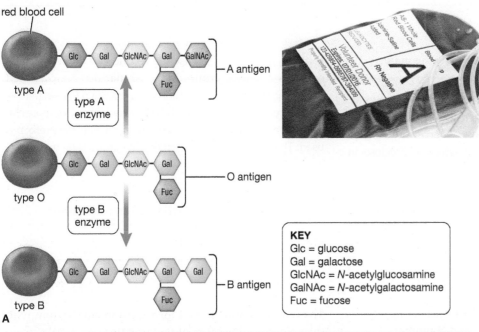

	Group A	Group B	Group AB	Group O
Red blood cell type	A	B	AB	O
Antibodies in plasma	anti-B	anti-A	none	anti-A anti-B

B

Quiz yourself on the content of this section: **Check 16.6** in the Pearson eText.

Chapter Summary

16.1 Introduction to Carbohydrates

Learning Objective: Identify the three major types of carbohydrates.

Carbohydrates are a group of molecules composed of carbon, hydrogen, and oxygen atoms. There are three types of carbohydrate molecules: monosaccharides, disaccharides, and polysaccharides. Monosaccharides (which are also called simple sugars), such as glucose, cannot be hydrolyzed into smaller carbohydrates. Disaccharides, such as sucrose, are composed of two monosaccharides linked together. Polysaccharides, such as starch, contain three or more monosaccharides linked together. Blood sugar (glucose) provides the stored energy for most of our cellular functions and is carefully regulated by feedback loops in the body.

BioConnect 16.1: Blood Sugar

Key Terms

carbohydrates
disaccharide
monosaccharide
polysaccharide

16.2 Monosaccharides

Learning Objective: Recognize and draw the major structural features of monosaccharides.

Monosaccharides generally contain three to six carbon atoms. Several hydroxyl groups are attached to the carbon atoms along with an aldehyde or ketone group. Glucose is an aldose because the first carbon is bonded to an aldehyde. Fructose, in contrast, is a ketose because the second carbon in the chain contains a ketone group. Monosaccharides are classified according to the number of carbons in the chain (triose, tetrose, pentose, etc.). Carbohydrates typically contain one or more chiral carbons. If the OH group is on the right side, the prefix D is used. The prefix L is used when the OH group is on the left.

Key Terms

fructose	hexose	polyhydroxy ketone (ketose)
galactose	pentose	tetrose
glucose	polyhydroxy aldehyde (aldose)	triose

16.3 Cyclic Monosaccharides

Learning Objective: Draw the cyclic forms of monosaccharides and classify as α and β anomers.

Acyclic monosaccharides undergo intramolecular reactions to form cyclic monosaccharides. The closing of the ring creates a new chiral carbon. Haworth projections are used to distinguish between the two anomers that form.

The α and β anomers that form exist in equilibrium with the acyclic form because of mutarotation.

VisibleChem Video 16.1: Drawing the Haworth Cyclic Structure from an Acyclic Aldohexose

VisibleChem Video 16.2: Drawing the Haworth Cyclic Structure from an Acyclic Ketohexose

Key Terms

anomeric carbon
anomers
Haworth projections
mutarotation

16.4   Oxidation and Reduction of Monosaccharides

Learning Objective: Predict and draw the oxidation and reduction products of monosaccharides.

The carbonyl group in monosaccharides undergoes three common types of reactions: 1) the aldehyde group in an aldose may be oxidized to a carboxylic acid, 2) the carbonyl group in both an aldose and a ketose are reduced to hydroxyl groups, and 3) the primary alcohol at C6 of hexoses are converted to a variety of metabolic intermediates.

Benedict's reagent oxidizes the aldehyde group in open-chain aldose monosaccharides. A carbohydrate that reacts with Benedict's reagent, such as glucose, is a reducing sugar. Monosaccharides can also be reduced causing a reduction in the number of C—O bonds. The reduction of the carbonyl group in monosaccharides to an alcohol produces a sugar alcohol (alditol).

Key Terms

Benedict's reagent
reducing sugar
sugar alcohol (alditol)

16.5   Disaccharides

Learning Objective: Recognize and draw the major structural features of disaccharides.

Two monosaccharides can be linked together to form a disaccharide when a hemiacetal of one monosaccharide reacts with a hydroxyl group of a second monosaccharide to form an acetal. The C—O bond that links the two rings is a glycosidic linkage. In an α glycosidic linkage the bond is oriented down, whereas a β glycosidic linkage is oriented up. Numbers are used to indicate which carbon atoms are linked in the new disaccharide.

VisibleChem Video 16.3: The Structural Features of Disaccharides

Key Terms

glycosidic linkage
lactase
lactose
maltose
sucrose

16.6   Polysaccharides

Learning Objective: Recognize and draw the major structural features of polysaccharides.

Starch, cellulose, and glycogen are naturally occurring polysaccharides containing repeating glucose units. Amylose is unbranched starch from plants; amylopectin is composed of branching starch molecules. $1\rightarrow4$-α-glycosidic bonds form the linear linkages while $1\rightarrow6$-α-glycosidic bonds form the branching linkages. Animals store starch in highly branched glycogen, also formed from $1\rightarrow4$-α-glycosidic linkages and $1\rightarrow6$-α-glycosidic linkages at the branch points. Cellulose is an unbranched polysaccharide composed of repeating glucose units and bonded together with $1\rightarrow4$-β-glycosidic linkages. Humans can't digest cellulose, but cellulose, and other plant fibers, plays an important role in regulating blood sugar and controlling disease.

BioConnect 16.2: Carbs in our Diet

Key Terms

α-glucosidases	cellulose	hyaluronate
amylase	chondroitin	insoluble fiber (from BioConnect 16.2)
amylopectin	complex carb (from BioConnect 16.2)	simple carb (from BioConnect 16.2)
amylose	glycogen	soluble fiber (from BioConnect 16.2)
β-glucosidases	heparin	starch

End-of-Chapter Quiz

Have you mastered the content of this chapter? Try the **End-of-Chapter Quiz** in the Pearson eText.

1. What is the difference between the open-chain structure of an aldose and a ketose?
   a) An aldose contains either an aldehyde group or a ketone group. A ketose only contains a ketone group.
   b) An aldose contains one more oxygen atom and one fewer hydrogen atoms than a ketose.
   c) An aldose contains six carbon atoms, and a ketose contains five carbon atoms.
   d) An aldose contains an aldehyde group, and a ketone contains a ketone group.

2. Which substance is known as blood sugar?
   a) fructose
   b) glucose
   c) sucrose
   d) high fructose corn syrup

3. Which statement is true about monosaccharides?
   a) Monosaccharides only exist in the open-chain (acyclic) form.
   b) Monosaccharides only exist in the cyclic form.
   c) Monosaccharides exist in equilibrium between the open-chain form and cyclic forms.
   d) Monosaccharides that are ketoses exist in the open-chain form only. Aldoses exist in open and cyclic forms.

4. Which monosaccharide shown is a ketose?
   a)
   b)
   c)
   d)

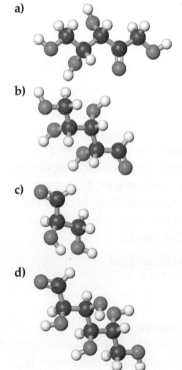

5. Which monosaccharide shown is an aldohexose?
   a)
   b)
   c)
   d)

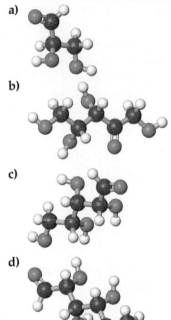

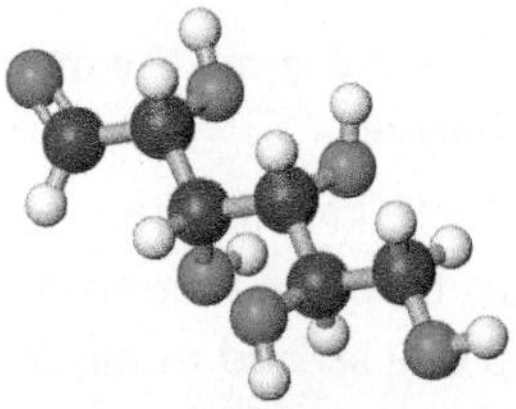

6. How many chiral centers are in the open-chain (acyclic) form of arabinose and how many are in the cyclic form?

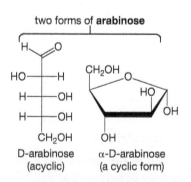

two forms of **arabinose**

D-arabinose (acyclic)   α-D-arabinose (a cyclic form)

   a) There are four chiral centers in the acyclic form and five chiral centers in the cyclic form of arabinose.
   b) There are four chiral centers in the acyclic form, and four chiral centers in the cyclic form of arabinose.
   c) There are three chiral centers in the acyclic form, and three chiral centers in the cyclic form of arabinose.
   d) There are three chiral centers in the acyclic form, and four chiral centers in the cyclic form of arabinose.

7. Which is the anomeric carbon on the monosaccharide structure shown here?

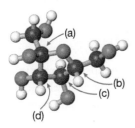

a) carbon a   **b)** carbon b

c) carbon c   **d)** carbon d

8. Which figure correctly shows the alpha (α) and beta (β) anomers of D-galactose?

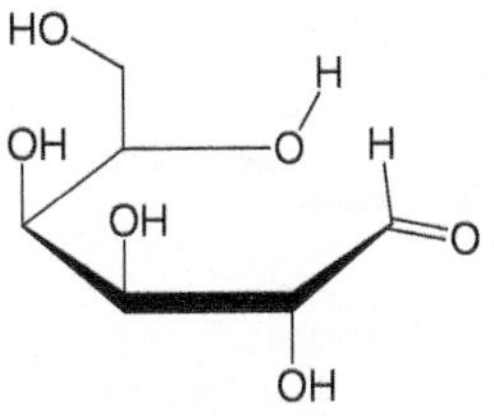

D-galactose

a) CH$_2$OH and

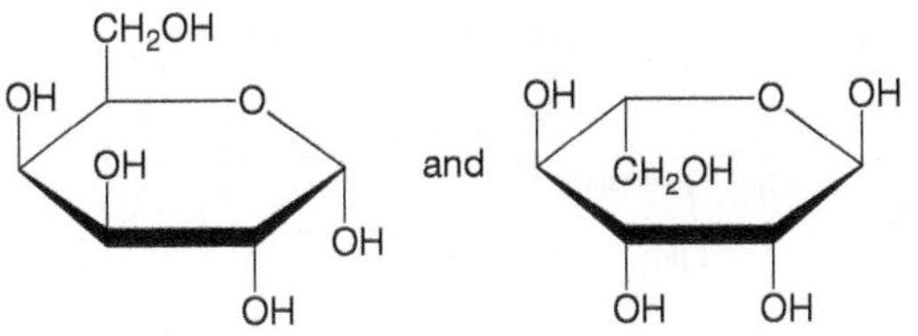

b) CH$_2$OH and

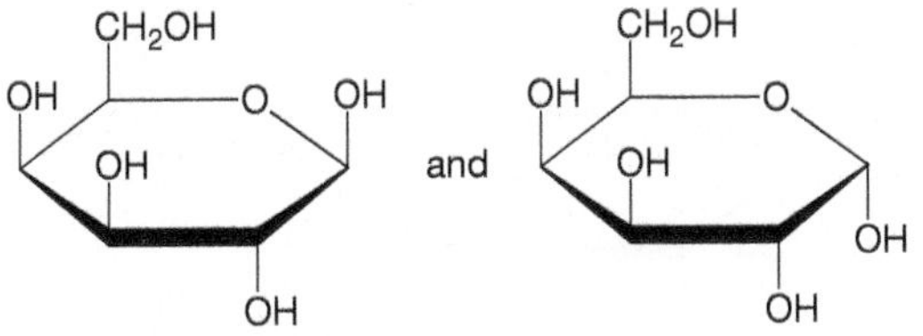

c) CH$_2$OH and

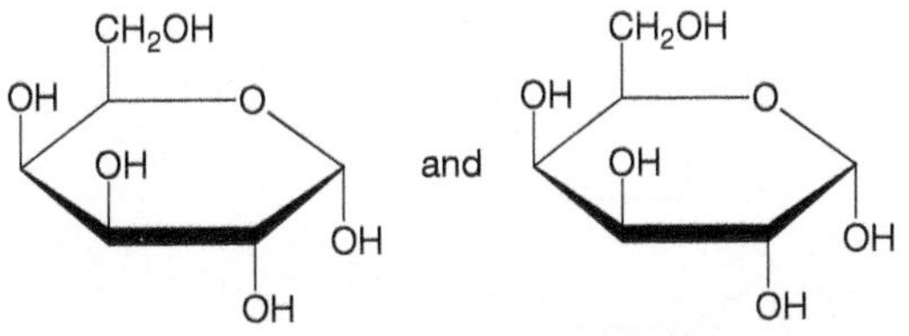

d) HO and CH$_2$OH

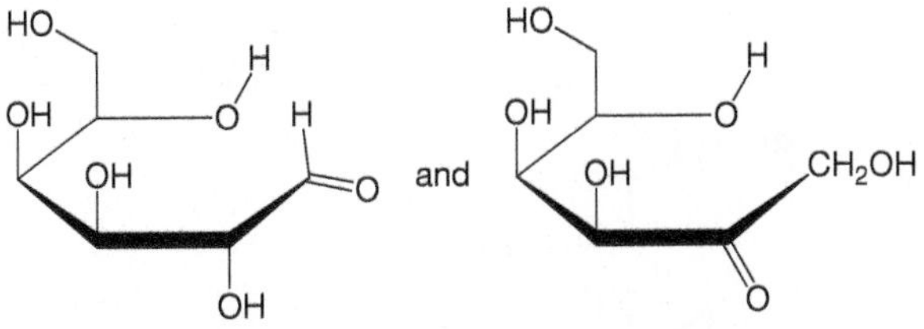

9. Which is the correct Fischer projection of D-galactose? A Haworth projection just after ring opening is shown for reference.

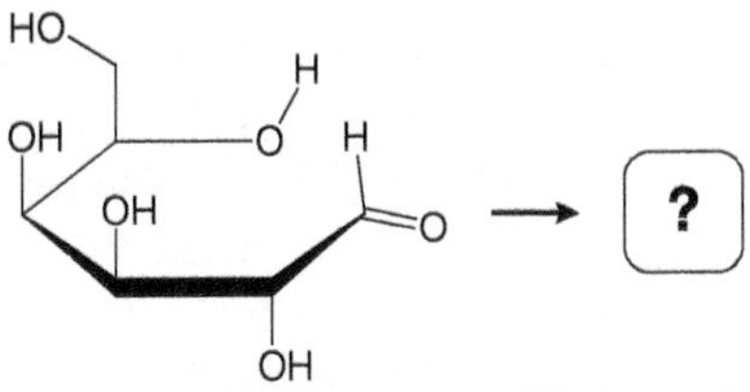

D-galactose   Fischer projection

a) CH$_2$OH
=O
H——OH
HO——H
H——OH
CH$_2$OH

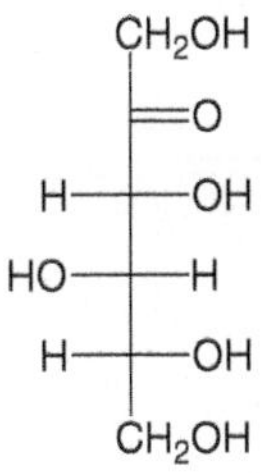

b) H、O
HO——H
HO——H
H——OH
H——OH
CH$_2$OH

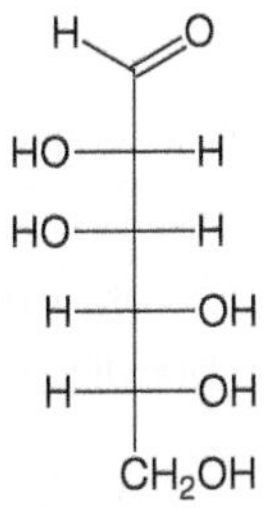

c) H、O
H——OH
HO——H
H——OH
H——OH
CH$_2$OH

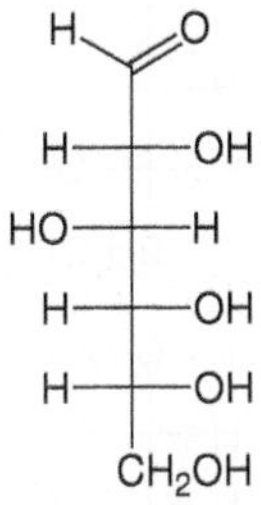

d) H、O
H——OH
HO——H
HO——H
H——OH
CH$_2$OH

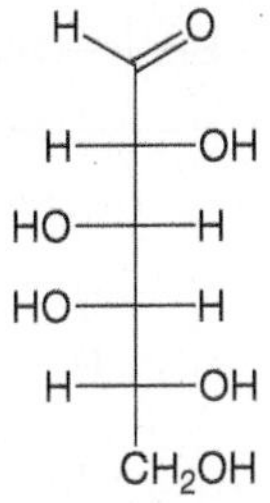

10. Which statement best describes mutarotation?
   a) Mutarotation allows for the interconversion of aldoses and ketoses through a rearrangement in the Fischer projection.
   b) Mutarotation allows for the interconversion of alpha and beta anomers through ring opening and closure.
   c) Mutarotation allows for the interconversion of the D and L forms for monosaccharides during ring closing.
   d) Mutarotation allows the OH group on the chiral carbon that is farthest from the carbonyl in the Fischer projection to twist into position during ring closure.

11. Which pair of monosaccharides are anomers of each other?
   a) α-D-glucose and β-L-glucose
   b) α-D-galactose and β-D-glucose
   c) α-D-glucose and α-L-glucose
   d) α-D-glucose and β-D-glucose

12. Erythritol is a sugar alcohol that is approximately 65% as sweet as stable sugar (sucrose). It is used in some low-calorie foods or foods consumed by diabetics since it is poorly absorbed by the body, does not significantly impact blood sugar levels, and contains fewer calories than sucrose. The chemical reduction of D-erythrose is accomplished with hydrogen gas (H_2) and palladium metal (Pd). The biological reduction is achieved by the enzyme erythrose reductases, which converts erythrose to erythritol by making use of the biological reducing agent NADPH as shown here. What is the structure of erythritol, the product of this reduction reaction?

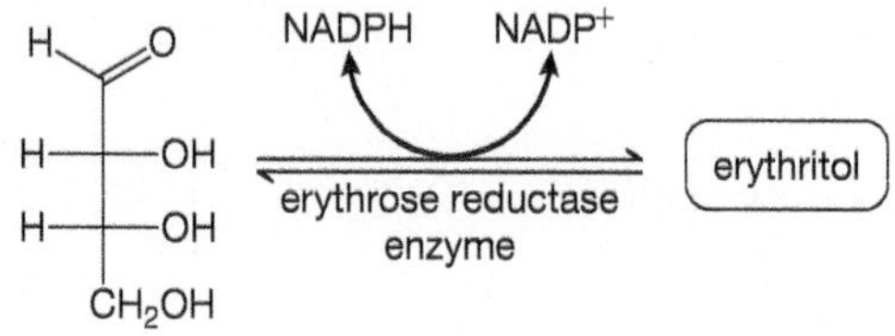

a)

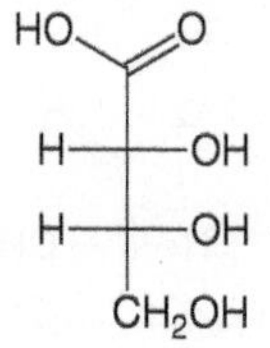

b)

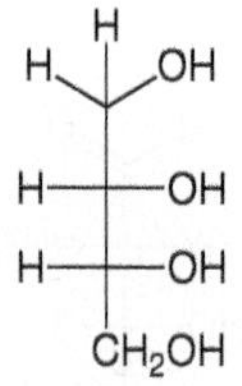

c)

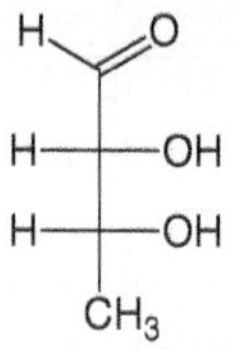

d)

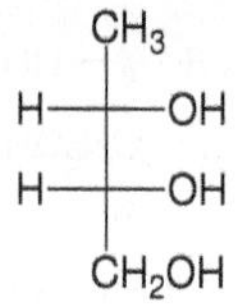

13. Threose is a four-carbon monosaccharide in the aldose family. A student in lab performs a Benedict's reagent test on a sample of D-Threose to determine if it is a reducing sugar. What reaction product should she expect to be produced when D-threose is treated with Benedict's reagent?

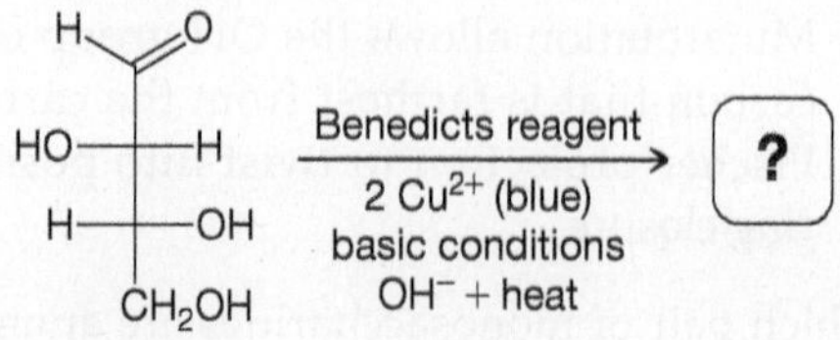

a)

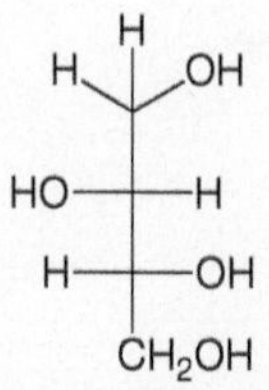

b)

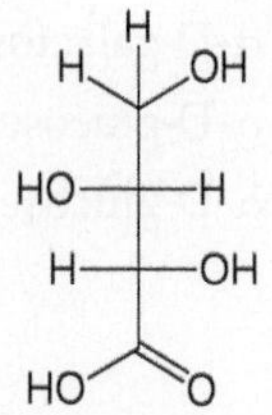

c)

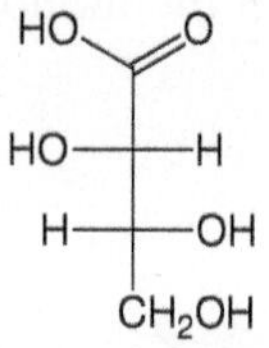

d)

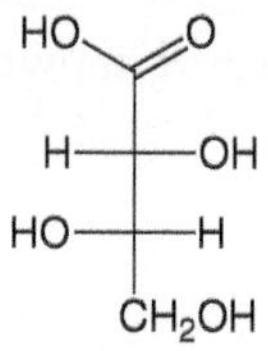

14. Altrose is a monosaccharide in the aldohexose family, and like other monosaccharides in aqueous solutions, the open-chain (acyclic) form of altrose is in equilibrium with the cyclic forms. The structure of D-altrose immediately after ring opening is shown. What is the expected product of the reaction of this molecule with hydrogen in the presence of a metal catalyst such as palladium?

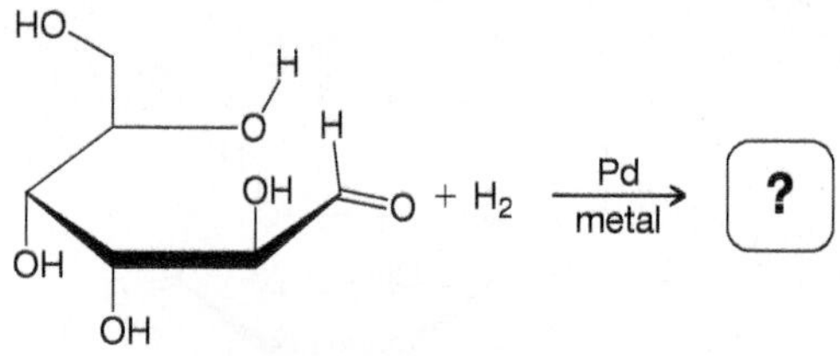

a)

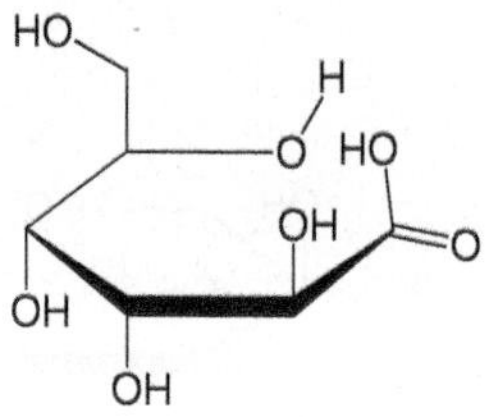

b)

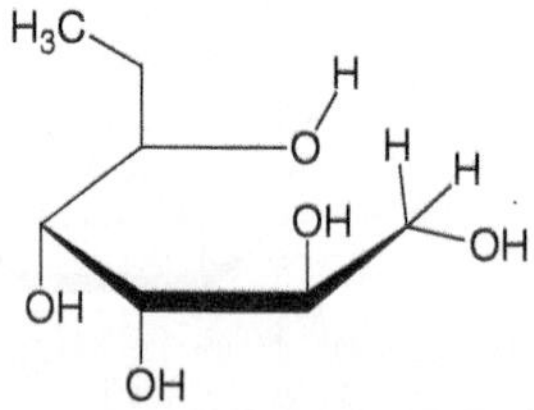

c)

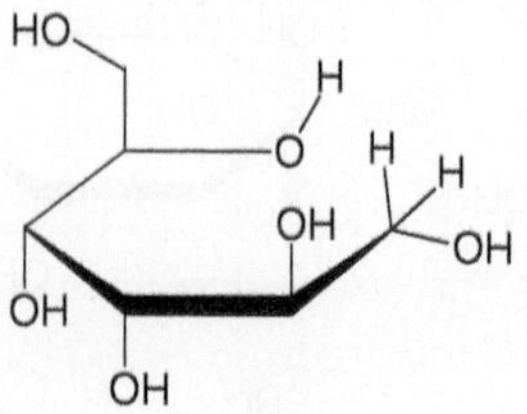

d)

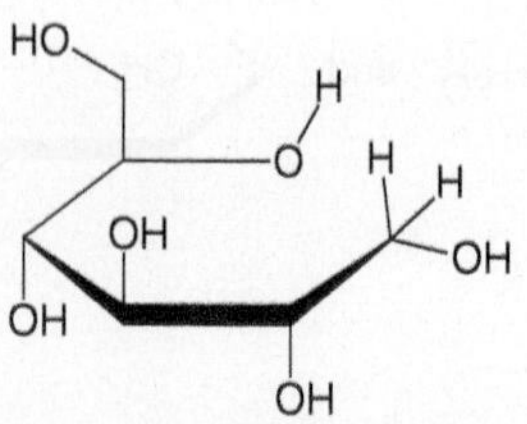

15. The glycosidic bond shown at carbon # 1 connecting the two monosaccharides in a disaccharide such as maltose is classified as a(n) _____?

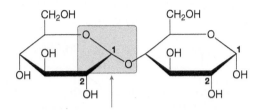

a) aldehyde   **b)** hemiacetal   **c)** ketone   **d)** acetal

16. Consider the structures of lactose and maltose shown. Which statement best describes why the disaccharides lactose and maltose both react with Benedict's reagent as reducing sugars?

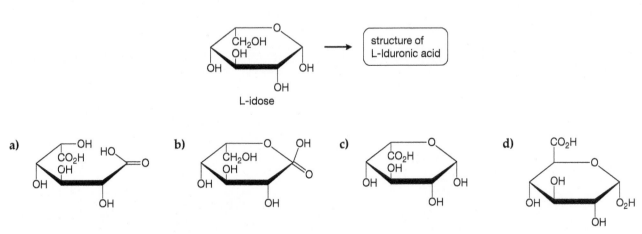

a) Even though lactose contains an 1→4-α linkage and maltose contains a 1→4-β linkage, each contain at least one glucose unit in their structures which is a requirement of reducing sugars.

b) Even though lactose contains an 1→4-α linkage and maltose contains a 1→4-β linkage, both contain monosaccharide units that can exist as six-membered rings, which is a requirement of all reducing sugars.

c) Lactose and maltose both contain glycosidic linkages that leave the anomeric carbon (C_1) of one of the monosaccharide units free as a hemiacetal that can open the ring to form an aldehyde and react with Benedict's reagent.

d) Lactose and maltose are both naturally occurring disaccharide-reducing sugars that are used to help reduce blood sugar levels in our bodies after exercise; both reducing sugars react with Benedict's reagent and are essential in our diet.

17. L-Iduronic acid (IdoA) is a component of the polysaccharide dermatan sulfate, which is found in skin, blood vessels, tendons, lungs, and other connective tissues. In this chapter, we learned that the primary (1°) alcohol on carbon number six (C_6) of D-glucose can be selectively oxidized by an enzyme to form the carboxylic acid group on D-glucuronic acid. In a similar way, L-Iduronic acid also contains a carboxylic acid on C_6 of the parent monosaccharide L-Idose. What is the structure of L-Iduronic acid?

18. Heparin sulfate, also known simply as "heparin," is used as an anticoagulant (blood thinner) to treat conditions such as thrombosis, pulmonary embolism, and arterial thromboembolism. It is also used in the treatment of heart attacks, during kidney dialysis, and to reduce clotting in blood samples collected in test tubes for clinical analysis. What type of glycosidic linkage connects monosaccharide units in heparin sulfate?

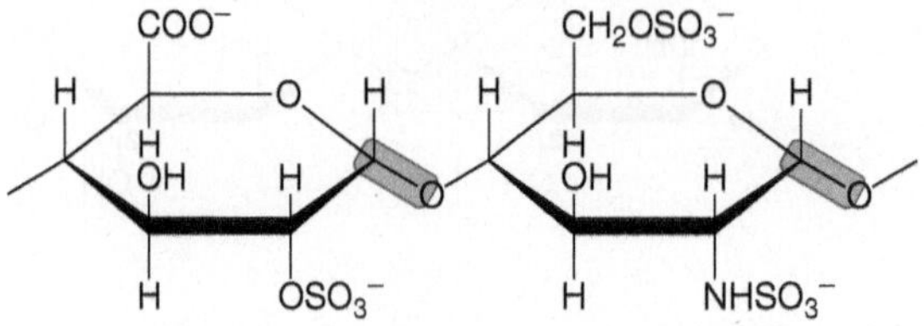

heparin

a) $1 \rightarrow 4$-α-glycosidic linkage

c) $1 \rightarrow 3$-α-glycosidic linkage

b) $1 \rightarrow 3$-β-glycosidic linkage

d) $1 \rightarrow 4$-β-glycosidic linkage

Unit 6
Bringing It All Together

What Happens When Diabetics Develop Ketoacidosis?

CHEMISTRY APPLICATION We opened Unit 6 with a look at the alarmingly high incidence of diabetes (see Fig. U6.2) and the dramatic consequences of complications like diabetic ketoacidosis (Figure U6.5). We can now look more closely at some of the chemistry driving this life-threatening complication.

Remember that insulin provides the signal for our cells to take up the monosaccharide glucose (see Fig. U6.3). This both lowers blood sugar levels and makes the sugar available to our cells to produce energy. Type 1 diabetics, however, are not able to produce enough insulin so glucose accumulates in their blood and their cells begin to run out of stored energy.

In response, the liver begins to break down the polysaccharide glycogen, releasing more glucose into the blood, driving blood sugar even higher (Figure U6.6). Without insulin however, the liver's efforts are in vain because this new sugar still isn't available to the cells and the body begins to break down proteins and fats to provide energy.

Figure U6.5 Diabetic Ketoacidosis Requires Urgent Medical Care.

Patients with diabetic ketoacidosis are often treated with IV fluids containing electrolytes and insulin.

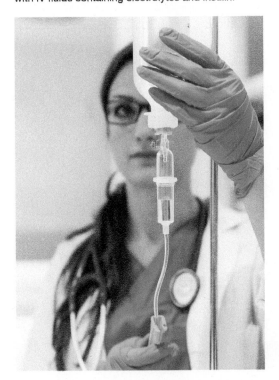

Figure U6.6 Ketones are Produced from Fats to Provide Fuel for the Brain.

Without insulin, the glucose released from the liver isn't available to fuel cells. This lack of fuel triggers the production of ketones from stored fat.

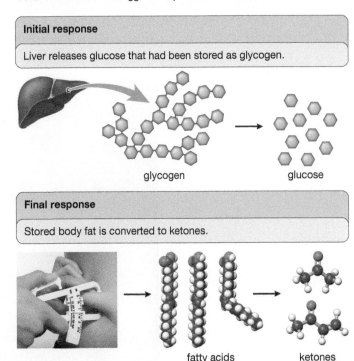

Initial response

Liver releases glucose that had been stored as glycogen.

glycogen   glucose

Final response

Stored body fat is converted to ketones.

fatty acids   ketones

Figure U6.7 Ketone Bodies Produced During Diabetic Ketoacidosis.

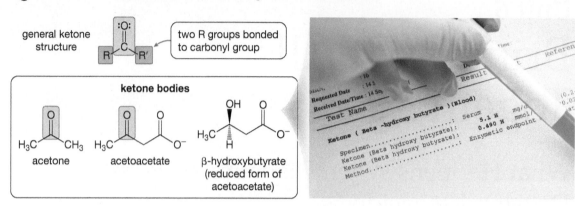

Recall from BioConnect 15.2 that breaking down fats for energy produces ketone bodies (Figure U6.7). These ketone bodies are produced in the liver at high levels when type 1 diabetes is left untreated. Two of these ketones, acetoacetate and β-hydroxybutyrate (BHB), are acidic. The —COOH on the right side of each of these molecules is a carboxylic acid functional group that we will study in more detail in the next unit. Together, the acidic characteristics of these two molecules can cause the life-threatening condition *ketoacidosis*.

Patients experiencing ketoacidosis may have a range of symptoms including abdominal pain, fatigue, and decreased consciousness. They also can get quickly dehydrated as the kidneys use water to help rid the body of excess glucose and ketones in urine. This dehydration reduces the patient's blood volume and pressure, contributing to the risk of shock (Figure U6.8).

Diabetic ketoacidosis is most common in undiagnosed diabetics and type 1 diabetics who have not been taking adequate insulin. The combination of elevated ketones and high blood glucose levels suggests a crisis that requires urgent medical care. Treatment usually involves IV fluids, electrolytes, and insulin to help restore normal blood chemistry. Thankfully diabetic ketoacidosis is rarely fatal when proper treatment is available.

Figure U6.8 Diabetic Shock.

Dehydration from diabetic ketoacidosis can cause a loss of consciousness.

Questions to Think About

1. Glucose is the most common monosaccharide in the human body. What is the molecular structure of glucose? Is it acyclic, cyclic, or both? Which functional groups are present? Which chemical reaction occurs to release glucose into the bloodstream from the breakdown of the polysaccharide glycogen?

2. Compare the molecular structures of acetone, acetoacetate, and β-hydroxybutyrate (BHB). What are their similarities and differences? Which functional groups do you recognize? How does a ketone differ in structure from an aldehyde?

3. Acetone is produced in the liver from the removal of a —COOH group from acetoacetate. BHB is also produced from acetoacetate. What type of chemical reaction converts a ketone to an alcohol (as the reaction that converts acetoacetate to BHB)?

A Closer Look at the Data

Quick access to proper treatment improves the outcomes for patients suffering from diabetic ketoacidosis. This need for rapid care is particularly urgent for individuals with newly diagnosed childhood onset type 1 diabetes as patients may not yet recognize the disease and its symptoms (Figure U6.9).

Healthcare providers have been concerned that public health emergencies such as the COVID-19 pandemic, may cause people who need medical care to delay treatment. To better understand the impact of COVID-19 on the diagnosis and treatment of diabetic ketoacidosis in children, a group of researchers compared the admissions of new pediatric type 1 diabetes patients at four hospitals in the United Kingdom just before the COVID-19 pandemic (July 2019 – March 2020) and during their first wave of infections (March 2020 – June 2020). Figure U6.10 illustrates some of their findings.

Figure U6.9 Early Symptoms of Diabetic Ketoacidosis.

Symptoms can include excessive thirst, frequent urination, weakness, stomach pain, nausea, and vomiting.

Figure U6.10 A Comparison of Pediatric Cases of Newly Diagnosed Type 1 Diabetes Before and During the First Wave of the COVID-19 Pandemic in London.

A) Incidence (%) of newly diagnosed patients presenting without diabetic ketoacidosis (DKA), with mild or moderate DKA, and with severe DKA. The absolute numbers of patients are included. **B)** Some characteristics of all patients with newly diagnosed type 1 diabetes before and during the first wave of COVID-19 (McGlacken-Byrne, *et. al.*, 2021).

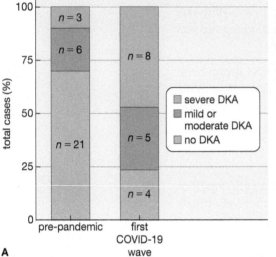

	Pre-pandemic (1 July 2019 – 22 March 2020)	First COVID-19 wave (23 March – 30 June 2020)
Sample size	30	17
Presentations per month	3.5	4.9
Age (years)	11.4 (range 2.2 – 17.6)	10.6 (range 3.2 – 16.3)
HbA$_{1c}$ %(mmol/mol) at diagnosis	10.4 ± 3.2 (90 ± 35)	13.0 ± 1.7 (119 ± 19)
pH at diagnosis	7.30 ± 0.13	7.09 ± 0.21

B

A

Questions to Think About

Examine Figure U6.10 and use it to answer the following questions:

1. Graphs can help reveal relationships between variables. What are the two variables shown in the graph in Figure U6.10A? What do the two bars represent?

2. Was there a difference in the severity of disease these children were admitted with pre-pandemic and during the first wave? Explain using specific data from the figure to support your answer.

3. Recall that HbA1c measures the percentage of a patient's hemoglobin molecules that have a glucose molecule attached to them (see Fig. 16.10) and reflects the average blood sugar levels over the last few months. How did the HbA1c values compare between the pre-pandemic group and the children admitted during the first wave? What does this suggest about the severity of their disease?

4. Recall, too, that normal blood has a pH of 7.4. How did the blood pH of the pre-pandemic and first wave groups compare? Is it more or less acidic? What might have caused this change and what does this suggest about the severity of their disease?

5. What else would you want to know in order to better understand the impact of the COVID-19 pandemic on patients seeking care for diabetes?

Reference

McGlacken-Byrne SM, Drew SEV, Turner K, Peters C, Amin R. The SARS-CoV-2 pandemic is associated with increased severity of presentation of childhood onset type 1 diabetes mellitus: A multi-centre study of the first COVID-19 wave. Diabet Med. 2021;38:e14640. https://doi.org/10.1111/dme.14640

Unit 7
Introduction
Exploring Carboxylic Acids, Esters, Amides, and Lipids

Chapter 17: Carboxylic Acids, Esters, and Amides
Chapter 18: Lipids

In 2004, the Center for Disease Control and Prevention (CDC) tested the urine from 2,517 people and found detectable amounts of the chemical bisphenol-A (BPA) in 93% of the samples. This finding launched decades of research into the source and effects of BPA in the human body. BPA has been used to make plastics and resins since the 1960s and is now present in a wide array of consumer products including polycarbonate plastics and the resin linings in food cans (Figure U7.1).

Figure U7.1 Bisphenol A (BPA) is Found in a Wide Array of Consumer Products Including Many Plastics and the Linings of Food Cans.

The use of BPA in products that contact our food suggests that our exposure is coming from our diet. Should we be concerned? What is BPA and what can we do to minimize our exposure?

Unit 7: Introduction
How Do Hormone Mimics Such as BPA Affect Our Health?

 To learn more about some of the sources of exposure to BPA and some of the reasons many scientists are concerned about its use, watch **Video U7.1** in the Pearson eText.

Unit 7 opens with a look at some of the concerns about the concentration of BPA in our bodies. The presence of BPA in our bodies is alarming, in part, because of the potential of BPA to act as a **hormone mimic**.

Hormones are chemical messengers our bodies use to regulate essential functions such as hunger and reproduction. Hormones are produced by glands in our bodies and travel through the bloodstream to one or more target receptors. They bind to their targets, triggering specific responses. Hormones are biologically active at very low concentrations and often have more than one target. Receptors for the female sex hormone, estrogen, for example, are found in many locations including the ovaries, kidneys, brain, and lungs.

Hormone mimics are molecules that are similar enough in size, shape, and charge to bind to the body's hormone receptors and trigger a response (Figure U7.2). BPA is structurally similar to one the most abundant female sex hormones, estradiol (Figure U7.3). (Males also produce estradiol, but at lower levels.) In addition, BPA and estradiol are both fat-soluble. This property makes them more likely to be retained in our tissues, unlike water-soluble compounds that we eliminate in our urine.

Our understanding of the potential risk from BPA is not new. The structural similarity between BPA and estradiol was first noticed in the 1930s and scientists have known for decades that small amounts of BPA can leach out of plastics. However, it

Figure U7.2 Hormone Mimics.

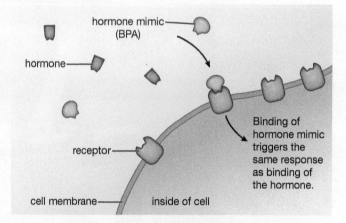

Figure U7.3 BPA and Estradiol.

BPA is similar in size, shape, and polarity to one of the female sex hormones, estradiol. The U.S. Food and Drug Administration (FDA) banned the use of BPA in baby bottles and sippy cups in 2012.

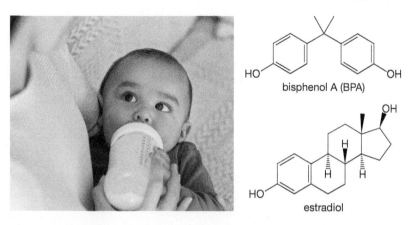

has been difficult for scientists to fully understand the health impacts of BPA. Most toxicology studies look at the effect of high doses of a chemical over short periods of time. Hormone mimics, however, may show their subtle effects at very low doses over long periods of time.

One interesting line of evidence about the potential impacts of hormone mimics comes from wildlife researchers. A study of male smallmouth bass in the Missisquoi National Wildlife Refuge in Vermont, for example, found that 85% of the male fish had eggs growing in their testes (Figure U7.4). Similar studies have confirmed this finding in fish across the country. Researchers suspect that hormone mimics in our wastewater are to blame. The so-called "feminized fish" look outwardly normal but have impaired sperm quality, impeding their ability to reproduce.

Figure U7.4 Hormone Mimics Affect Humans and Other Animals.

Male fish exposed to hormone mimics have lowered sperm counts and abnormal testes.

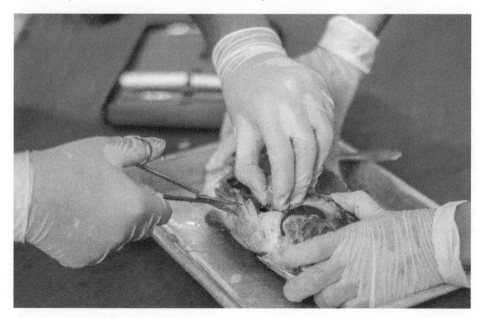

Unit 7 Chemistry Application: How Do Hormone Mimics Such as BPA Affect Our Health?

The potential effects of hormone mimics such as BPA are alarming (Figure U7.5). Assessing the risk these molecules pose to our health requires a rigorous understanding of the structure of the molecules and their behavior in both the human body and our environment.

Figure U7.5 BPA-Free Labels on Consumer Products.

 ## Questions to Think About

What chemistry do we need to know to understand the risks posed by a molecule like BPA? Here are some questions to consider as you move through Unit 7:

- What functional groups are found on BPA? How might these groups affect the molecule's biological activity?

- What are lipids? Why is BPA soluble in lipids? How would this solubility affect its biological activity?

What chemistry would you like to know in order to more fully understand this problem?

Now that we have an overview of this unit, let's step into Chapter 17 and 18 and learn more about the characteristics of some key functional groups.

Chapter 17
Carboxylic Acids, Esters, and Amides

Citrus fruits taste sour because they contain citric acid, an organic molecule that contains carboxylic acid groups. Citric acid plays important roles in energy metabolism, the absorption of minerals from the foods we eat, and in the prevention of kidney stones.

 ## Chapter Outline

Learning Objectives

17.1   Analyze the structural features of carbonyl-containing compounds: carboxylic acids, esters, and amides.

17.2   Analyze the effect of intermolecular forces on the physical properties of carboxylic acids, esters, and amides.

17.3   Evaluate reactions of carboxylic acids with bases.

17.4 Analyze reactions of carboxylic acids, esters, and amides.

17.5 Analyze the defining structural features of polyesters and polyamides.

17.6 Apply the IUPAC naming system to carboxylic acids, esters, and amides.

Introduction

We continue our exploration of key functional groups with a look at carboxylic acids, esters, and amides. These three groups are critical components of a wide range of molecules found in everyday medicines as well as the clothes that we wear (Figure 17.1). Carboxylic acids, esters, and amides are also found in familiar molecules such as fentanyl, the painkiller responsible for the deaths of Prince, Tom Petty, and so many others. Understanding the structure and shape of these molecules and the common reactions they are involved in allows us to understand their functions in biological systems and the environment.

Figure 17.1 Carboxylic Acids, Esters, and Amides in our Lives.

Recognizing functional groups helps us predict the properties of organic molecules. **A)** Many important medicines contain the carboxylic acid, ester, and amide functional groups. **B)** The painkiller fentanyl, which has been involved in a significant number of high-profile drug overdoses, contains an amide. **C)** Esters can link together to form polymers found in a variety of consumer products, including this coat.

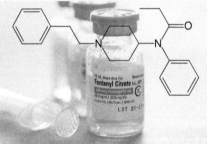

A   B   C

17.1 Structure of Carboxylic Acids, Esters, and Amides

The carbonyl group, which consists of a carbon atom double bonded to an oxygen atom, is a major structural feature of a vast array of biological molecules. Carboxylic acids, esters, and amides are three additional families of organic molecules that also contain carbonyl groups. In these three cases, however, the carbonyl group is bonded to an element that is more electronegative than carbon, such as O or N (Figure 17.2).

Carboxylic acids are organic compounds that contain a carbonyl group bonded to a hydroxyl group (OH). We write carboxylic acids as RCOOH or RCO_2H. Recall that in this notation, R represents the carbon backbone part of an organic molecule.

general carboxylic acid structure

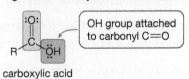

carboxylic acid

Figure 17.2 Examples of a Carboxylic Acid, Ester, and Amide.

A) Acetic acid is one of the simplest carboxylic acids. It is commonly used in industry and found in many household products such as vinegar. **B)** Methyl acetate is one of the simple esters. Its smell is familiar from glue and nail polish remover. It is sometimes used in industry as a solvent. **C)** Acetamide is a simple amide compound used in industry as a solvent and a starting material to build other molecules.

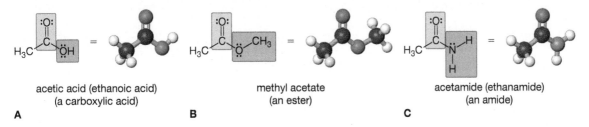

acetic acid (ethanoic acid)	methyl acetate	acetamide (ethanamide)
(a carboxylic acid)	(an ester)	(an amide)
A	**B**	**C**

Esters are organic compounds that contain a carbonyl group bonded to an OR′ group. We represent esters as RCOOR′ or RCO_2R'.

general ester structure

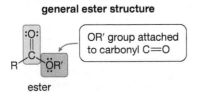

ester

Amides are organic compounds that contain a carbonyl group bonded to a nitrogen atom. The nitrogen atom is bonded to hydrogen atoms or carbon atoms. Amides are categorized as primary (1°), secondary (2°), or tertiary (3°) depending on the number of carbon atoms bonded directly to the nitrogen atom.

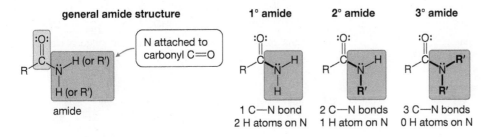

Apply what you have just learned: **Practice 17.1–17.3** in the Pearson eText.

Shape and Polarity

The central structural feature of carboxylic acids, esters, and amides—often referred to as an **acyl group (RCO)**—is shown here.

acyl group

Due to this common feature, we refer to carboxylic acids, esters, and amides as acyl compounds.

Similar to other carbonyl compounds, the carbonyl carbon has a trigonal planar shape with 120° bond angles. The carbonyl (C=O) bond is polar with a partial negative charge on the oxygen atom, and a partial positive charge on the carbonyl carbon. The shape and polarity of the acyl group plays a significant role in how carboxylic acid, ester, and amide compounds react in chemical reactions and in the human body.

$$120° \quad \overset{:\ddot{O}:}{\underset{\big/ \ \ \backslash}{\overset{\|}{C}}} \qquad \overset{:\ddot{O}: \ \delta^-}{\underset{\big/ \ \big| \ \backslash}{\overset{\|}{\underset{}{C}} {+} \delta^+}}$$

trigonal planar   polar
C=O bond

Apply what you have just learned: **Practice 17.4** in the Pearson eText.

Some molecules contain more than one of the same type of functional group (Figure 17.3). For example, a molecule can have one carboxylic acid group, as butanoic acid does, or two or more carboxylic acid groups. Succinic acid has two carboxylic acid groups, and citric acid has three carboxylic acid groups. Notice the trigonal planar shape at each carbonyl carbon in each carboxylic acid group.

Figure 17.3 Butanoic, Succinic, and Citric Acid.

Butanoic acid has a single carboxylic acid group and is found in dairy products, especially in goat milk. Succinic acid has two carboxylic acid groups and can be extracted from amber. It is also found in the human body and plays a role in many cellular processes. Citric acid, common in citrus fruit such as oranges, lemons, limes, and grapefruit, has three carboxylic acid groups. Citric acid plays an important role in the way our bodies release energy from carbohydrates, fats, and proteins.

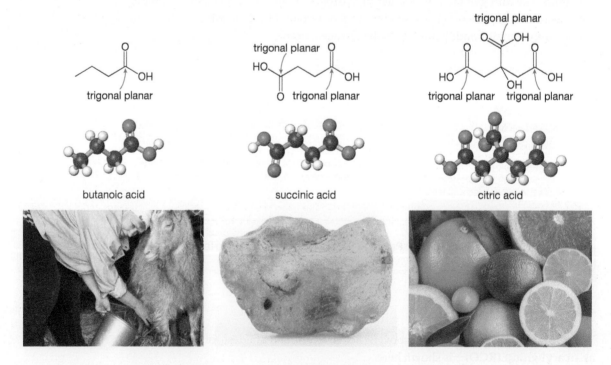

butanoic acid

succinic acid

citric acid

Carboxylic Acids, Esters, and Amides in Medicine and Nature

Carboxylic acid, esters, and amide groups are common in nature and are present in many molecules used medicinally (Figure 17.4). Explore some familiar examples in Figure 17.4 before taking a closer look at one of the world's most important medicines—penicillin—in BioConnect 17.1 (contains Figures 17.5–17.14).

Figure 17.4 A Variety of Molecules with Carboxylic Acid, Ester, and Amide Functional Groups.

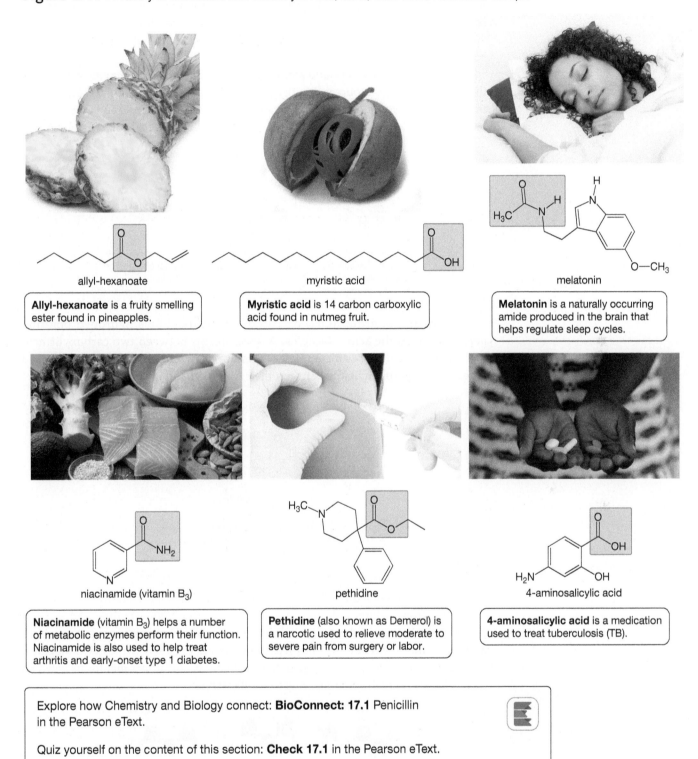

allyl-hexanoate

Allyl-hexanoate is a fruity smelling ester found in pineapples.

myristic acid

Myristic acid is 14 carbon carboxylic acid found in nutmeg fruit.

melatonin

Melatonin is a naturally occurring amide produced in the brain that helps regulate sleep cycles.

niacinamide (vitamin B₃)

Niacinamide (vitamin B₃) helps a number of metabolic enzymes perform their function. Niacinamide is also used to help treat arthritis and early-onset type 1 diabetes.

pethidine

Pethidine (also known as Demerol) is a narcotic used to relieve moderate to severe pain from surgery or labor.

4-aminosalicylic acid

4-aminosalicylic acid is a medication used to treat tuberculosis (TB).

Explore how Chemistry and Biology connect: **BioConnect: 17.1** Penicillin in the Pearson eText.

Quiz yourself on the content of this section: **Check 17.1** in the Pearson eText.

17.2 Physical Properties of Acyl Compounds

As we see repeatedly as we study organic molecules, the behavior of an organic molecule depends on the physical properties of the functional groups present on the molecule. The penicillin molecule that we discuss in BioConnect 17.1, for example, is an antibiotic containing functional groups that have a direct impact on how the molecule is able to dissolve in water and move through the body. In this section we explore the physical properties of carboxylic acids, esters, and amides and apply this information to our growing understanding of organic molecules' behavior.

Carboxylic acids, esters, and amides are polar compounds due to the presence of their polar carbonyl group and to the additional electronegative groups attached to their carbonyl carbon. Carboxylic acids have additional polar C—O and O—H bonds. Esters have an additional C—O polar bond, and amides have additional polar C—N and N—H bonds.

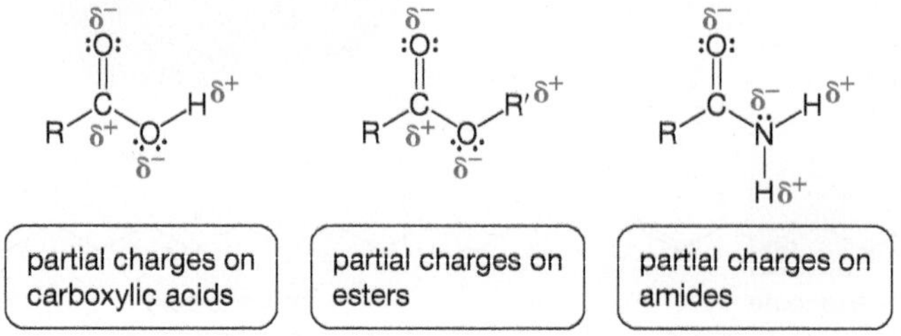

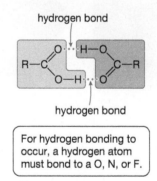

| partial charges on carboxylic acids | partial charges on esters | partial charges on amides |

The hydroxyl group (OH) on carboxylic acids allows hydrogen bonding between carboxylic acid molecules. A **dimer** forms between two carboxylic acid molecules. This dimer is a complex consisting of two identical molecules linked together by hydrogen bonds between their hydroxyl and carbonyl groups.

hydrogen bond

hydrogen bond

For hydrogen bonding to occur, a hydrogen atom must bond to a O, N, or F.

The formation of a dimer between carboxylic acids composed of hydrogen bonds results in stronger intermolecular forces and therefore higher boiling and melting points than similar sized ester and alcohol molecules. In an ester group, there is no hydrogen atom available to form hydrogen bonds between two ester molecules. Although alcohol molecules can form hydrogen bonds, the dimer that forms between carboxylic acids creates stronger intermolecular forces.

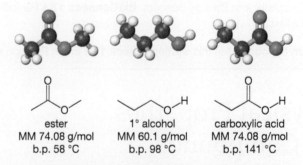

ester	1° alcohol	carboxylic acid
MM 74.08 g/mol	MM 60.1 g/mol	MM 74.08 g/mol
b.p. 58 °C	b.p. 98 °C	b.p. 141 °C

increasing strength of intermolecular forces and increasing boiling point

Hydrogen Bonding in Amides

Hydrogen bonds are possible between 1° and 2° amides. The N-H bonds on these amide molecules allow hydrogen bonds to form between amide compounds. Notice that 3° amides, in contrast, do not have a hydrogen atom available for hydrogen bonding.

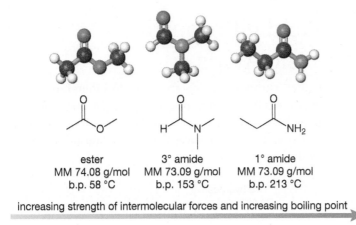

Stronger intermolecular forces in 1° and 2° amide compounds produce higher boiling and melting points compared to 3° amides and esters of similar size.

ester	3° amide	1° amide
MM 74.08 g/mol	MM 73.09 g/mol	MM 73.09 g/mol
b.p. 58 °C	b.p. 153 °C	b.p. 213 °C

increasing strength of intermolecular forces and increasing boiling point

Apply what you have just learned: **Practice 17.5 and 17.6** in the Pearson eText.

Solubility in Water

Carboxylic acids are more soluble in water than most of the organic molecule families we have encountered in previous chapters. This increased solubility is due to the ability of carboxylic acids to form hydrogen bonds with water at both their carbonyl groups and hydroxyl groups.

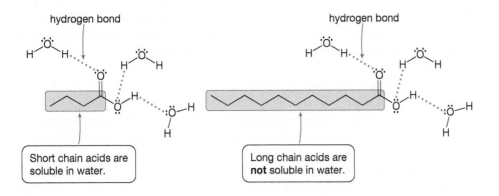

Esters and amides are also soluble in water because they also form hydrogen bonds with water. The oxygen atoms in esters, and both the oxygen and nitrogen atoms in amides, form hydrogen bonds with water molecules. Primary, secondary, and tertiary amides all form hydrogen bonds with water.

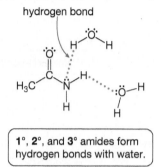

1°, 2°, and 3° amides form hydrogen bonds with water.

Apply what you have just learned: **Practice 17.7 and 17.** in the Pearson eText.

Quiz yourself on the content of this section: **Check 17.2** in the Pearson eText.

In general, carboxylic acids, esters, and amides with fewer than six carbon atoms are soluble in water. Larger acyl compounds (those that have more than six carbon atoms) are insoluble in water. As the hydrocarbon chains become larger, their ability to interact with water through attractive forces decreases. Water molecules interact with other water molecules, as opposed to interacting with the nonpolar hydrocarbon chain.

17.3 The Acidic Properties of Carboxylic Acids

As their name indicates, carboxylic acids are acids and therefore are proton (H^+) donors. In water, a carboxylic acid's hydroxyl hydrogen dissociates as a proton (H^+). Water acts as the base that accepts the proton to produce the hydronium ion (H_3O^+). This acid-base reaction also produces the **carboxylate anion**. (See Section 12.1 for review of acids and bases.)

Carboxylic acids are weak acids and therefore only partially dissociate. We represent the weak acid nature of these acids in water using a double arrow in the reaction to indicate that a dynamic equilibrium is established. Carboxylic acids have acid dissociation constants (K_a) in the range of 10^{-4} to 10^{-5}. Recall from Sections 12.1–12.3 that an acid dissociation constant (K_a) value of less than one indicates that the reactants are favored at equilibrium. This constant indicates that the reactant (the acid) is favored at equilibrium over the carboxylate anion product.

Chemists design many drug molecules to have a carboxylic acid group. This is a strategy to increase the drugs' solubility in water. Recall that plasma is made up of water, salts, and protein. An effective drug needs to be sufficiently soluble in water to dissolve in blood, so it is able to move around the body. Generating the carboxylate anion increases water solubility and therefore increases blood plasma solubility. Naproxen, for example, is an anti-inflammatory drug used to relieve pain. This drug has a carboxylic acid group that dissociates in water allowing naproxen to travel readily through the bloodstream (Figure 17.15).

Figure 17.15 Naproxen.

The carboxylic acid on the naproxen molecule dissociates to form the carboxylate anion inside the human body, which produces a more water-soluble form of the drug molecule.

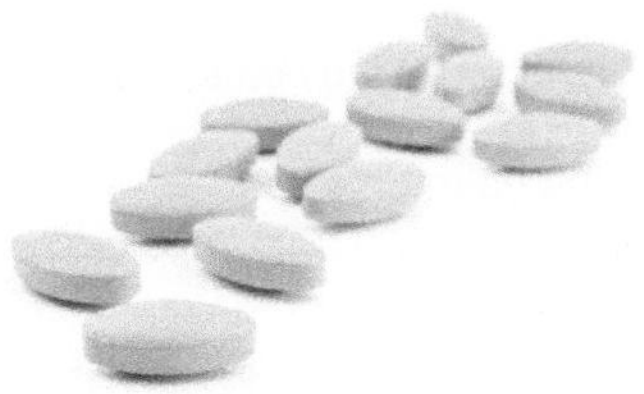

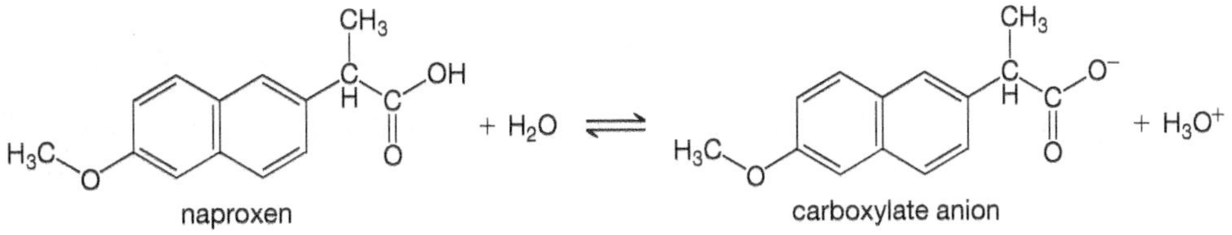

naproxen + H₂O ⇌ carboxylate anion + H₃O⁺

Carboxylate Salts

Carboxylic acids react with strong bases such as sodium hydroxide (NaOH) to form water-soluble salts called **carboxylate salts**. The hydroxide ion (OH⁻) from the base gains a proton from the carboxylic acid to form the neutral water molecule.

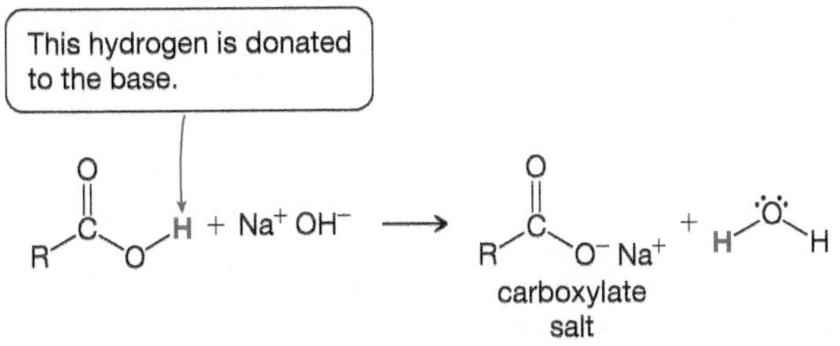

> This hydrogen is donated to the base.

carboxylate salt

Soaps are carboxylate salts that have a long hydrocarbon chain (Figure 17.16). The two distinct parts of a soap molecule are the ionic end, which is also called the **polar head**, and the nonpolar hydrocarbon chain. How does soap wash away dirt? What is it about the structure of soap molecules that allow it to clean greasy surfaces? Click on VisibleChem Videos 17.1 and 17.2 to learn more about the acidic properties of carboxylic acids and to see how the salts of carboxylic acids function as soap. Then explore BioConnect 17.2 (contains Figures 17.17–17.24) to learn more about another important carboxylate salt.

Figure 17.16 Soap Molecule.

Soaps are carboxylate salts. Soap molecules have a polar head on one end that forms from the carboxylate anion and a metal cation and a long nonpolar hydrocarbon chain on the other end.

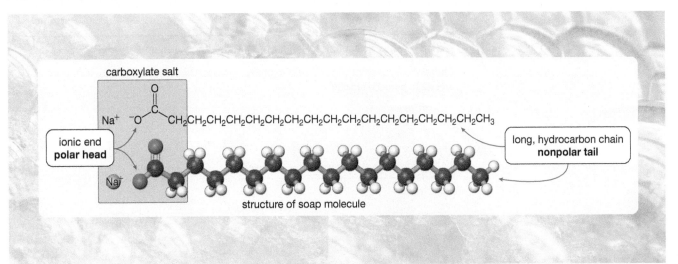

carboxylate salt

ionic end
polar head

long, hydrocarbon chain
nonpolar tail

structure of soap molecule

Watch this concept come to life: **VisibleChem Video 17.1:** Carboxylic Acids are Weak Acids and **VisibleChem Video 17.2:** Soaps in the Pearson eText.

Apply what you have just learned: **Practice 17.9–17.12** in the Pearson eText.

Explore how Chemistry and Biology connect: **BioConnect: 17.2** Aspirin in the Pearson eText.

Quiz yourself on the content of this section: **Check 17.3** in the Pearson eText.

17.4 Reactions of Carboxylic Acids, Esters, and Amides

As we have discussed, chemical reactions generally take place at the functional groups on organic molecules. Carboxylic acids, esters, and amides are no exception. For example, butyl acetate is a naturally occurring ester found in fruits. It is also synthesized industrially for the food industry by combining a carboxylic acid with an alcohol. This type of ester-forming reaction is common in nature as well as in the laboratory where it used to produce a wide range of ester compounds.

This type of reaction is common for all acyl compounds. Acyl compounds undergo substitution reactions that involve the replacement of the group containing the electronegative atom (X) bonded to the carbonyl carbon by another atom or group (Z).

general substitution reaction for acyl compounds

Z replaces X

For example, carboxylic acids react with alcohols to form esters in a general reaction type called an **esterification** (Table 17.1).

An esterification reaction is a substitution reaction because the OR′ group from the alcohol replaces the OH group on the carboxylic acid. Adding excess alcohol to the reaction drives the equilibrium mixture towards products (esters). Removing water from the reaction mixture also shifts the reaction towards the ester product. The food industry uses these strategies to increase the yield of butyl acetate in the esterification reaction shown in Figure 17.25.

Table 17.1 Substitution Reactions of Esters and Amides.

Carboxylic acids react with alcohols to produce esters. Carboxylic acids also react with amines to produce amides.

Esterification reactions	acid + alcohol ⇌ (H₂SO₄) ester + H—OH
Amide-formation reactions	acid + amine ⇌ (heat) amide + H—OH (R′ = H or C)

Figure 17.25 Production of Butyl Acetate.

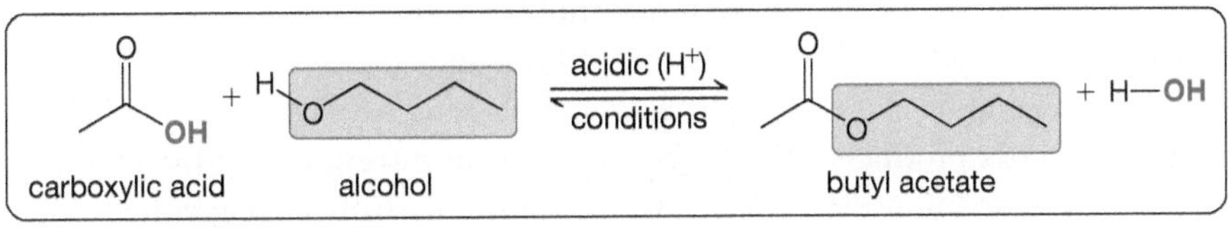

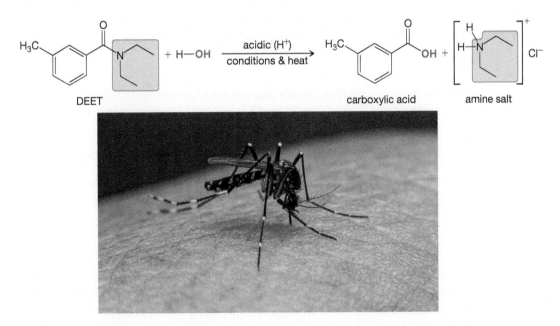

Amides form in a similar reaction by heating a carboxylic acid with ammonia (NH_3) or other amines (Table 17.1). This reaction is a substitution reaction because the OH from the carboxylic acid is once again replaced by another group—in this case, an amine.

Hydrolysis of Esters and Amides

In almost the exact reverse process, both esters and amides are broken down by **hydrolysis**. Hydrolysis is a reaction in which water is added to a substance. The powerful insect repellent DEET is an amide that breaks down to a carboxylic acid and amine salt upon the addition of acid and heat (Figure 17.26). The DEET amide can

Figure 17.26 Hydrolysis of DEET.

The insect repellent DEET is an amide that undergoes hydrolysis to produce carboxylic acid and amine salt (ammonium cation).

undergo hydrolysis in a laboratory setting. DEET is applied to clothing or skin to provide protection against mosquitoes, fleas, chiggers, and other biting insects. Ultimately it breaks down slowly in the environment.

In general, **ester hydrolysis** involves the addition of water to an ester in the presence of acid or base to form a carboxylic acid and alcohol. An excess of water drives this reaction towards products. When a base is present during the hydrolysis of an ester the carboxylate anion forms. The base-catalyzed hydrolysis reaction is called **saponification**.

Amides similarly undergo hydrolysis by a reaction with water in the presence of acid or base, but amides are much less reactive than esters (Table 17.2). The reaction of an amide with water in the presence of acid produces a carboxylic acid and an ammonium cation. The hydrolysis reaction of amides in the presence of base produces a carboxylate anion and an amine.

Table 17.2 Hydrolysis Reactions of Esters and Amides.

Ester hydrolysis: acidic and basic conditions	ester + H—OH → H⁺: carboxylic acid + alcohol OH⁻: carboxylate anion + alcohol
Amide hydrolysis: acidic and basic conditions (R′ = H or C)	amide + H—OH → H⁺: carboxylic acid + ammonium cation OH⁻: carboxylate anion + amine

Click on VisibleChem Videos 17.3 and 17.4 to learn more about the formation of esters and amides from carboxylic acids and the hydrolysis of esters and amides.

Watch this concept come to life: **VisibleChem Video 17.3:** Esterification and Amide Formation and **VisibleChem Video 17.4:** Ester and Amide Hydrolysis in the Pearson eText.

Apply what you have just learned: **Practice 17.13–17.15** in the Pearson eText.

Quiz yourself on the content of this section: **Check 17.4** in the Pearson eText.

17.5 Ester and Amide Polymers

Have you ever wondered what happens to dissolving sutures? Where do they go in the body? Are they safe? Dissolving sutures are composed of long chains of repeating units joined together by ester linkages (Figure 17.27).

Figure 17.27 Dissolving Sutures.

Dissolving sutures are made of polyesters that readily hydrolyze to products that the body can metabolize.

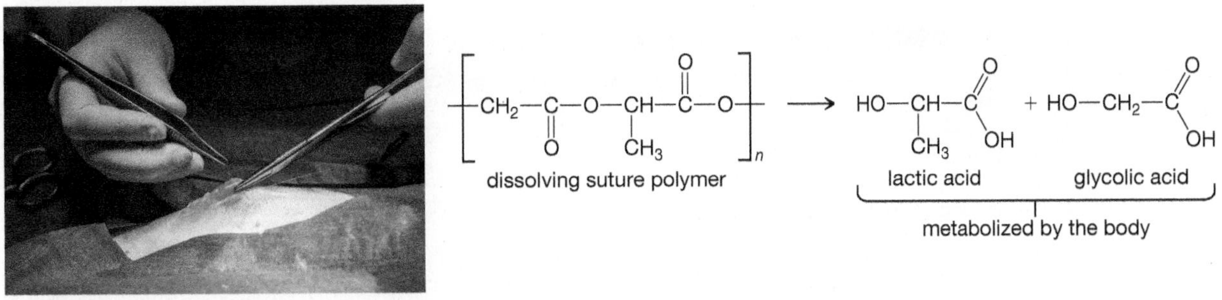

dissolving suture polymer → lactic acid + glycolic acid

metabolized by the body

Dissolving sutures hold tissue together during the healing process after surgery. Within weeks the sutures are hydrolyzed to molecules that are safely processed by the body. These sutures are made of a type of polymer that contains ester functional groups called **polyesters**. Dissolving sutures are an example of a product made from polyester that readily undergoes hydrolysis to produce two acids. The two acids—glycolic acid and lactic acid—are easily metabolized by the body.

Polylactic Acid

Variety of plastic products, similar in makeup to dissolving sutures, are now on the market that are composed of polyester molecules that readily break down (Figure 17.28).

Biodegradable plastics are slowly replacing more traditional plastic materials, which are stable in the environment for a very long time. Biodegradable plastic, in contrast to traditional plastics, decomposes naturally in the environment when microorganisms metabolize them and turn their polymers into molecules that are less harmful to the environment.

Polylactic acid (PLA) is an example of a biodegradable polymer that is gaining traction in the market as a replacement polymer. PAL is produced by the polymerization of lactic acid. The polymerization involves an esterification reaction that links lactic acid molecules together in a long chain.

Products as varied as loose-fill packaging, compost bags, food packaging, and disposable tableware are all made of PLA.

Figure 17.28 Biodegradable Tableware.

Polylactic acid (PLA) is a biodegradable polyester. PLA was engineered to be used to make a variety of products as a replacement for traditional plastic polymers.

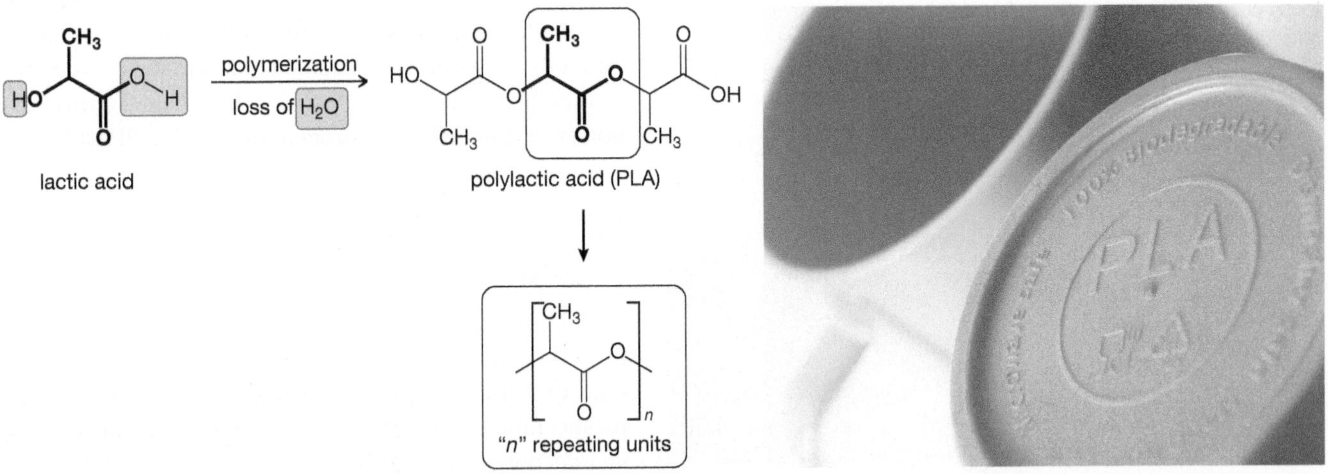

lactic acid → (polymerization, loss of H_2O) → polylactic acid (PLA) → "n" repeating units

Figure 17.29 Polyethylene Terephthalate (PET).

The polyester PET is made by the esterification reaction of a carboxylic acid group on one molecule and an alcohol group on a second molecule. For each ester linkage formed, one water molecule is lost from the starting materials. A long chain is produced by the coupling steps in the reaction.

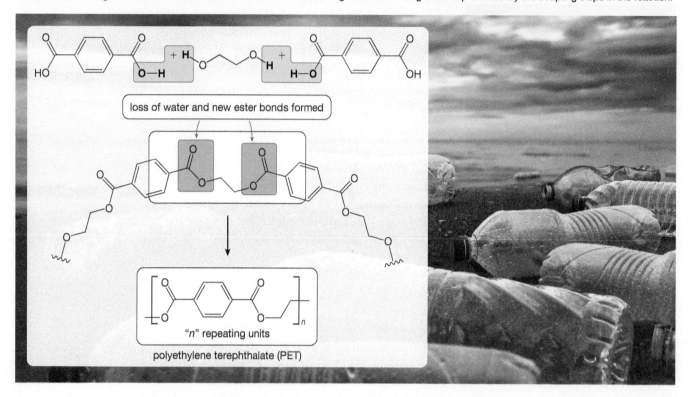

Plastic Made from Polyesters

Unlike biodegradable plastics, traditional plastic products are made from stable polymers and therefore remain in landfills and the environment, including our oceans, for long periods of time. Many traditional plastic materials made from polyesters have been produced on a large scale for many years. The most common polyester is **polyethylene terephthalate (PET)**, which is composed of polymerized repeating units called ethylene terephthalates (Figure 17.29).

PET is produced on a large scale by an esterification reaction between a carboxylic acid group and an alcohol in a series of coupling steps. For every ester linkage formed, a molecule of water is lost from the starting materials to produce long polyester chains. Once the polymer is produced it can be shaped into a variety of products including plastic bags, plastic bottles, and clothing. Estrogen mimics such as BPA are often included in these products as they help stabilize the plastics. (See Unit 7 Introduction for a discussion of estrogen mimics and BPA.)

Figure 17.30 Dead Whale.

Many dead marine mammals are found to have large quantities of plastics in their stomachs.

Environmental Consequences and Recycling

In the spring of 2018, a large sperm whale was found dead on a Spanish coast. Upon inspection, it was discovered that the young whale had ingested 64 pounds of plastic, much of it made from PET. The whale developed an infection in his digestive track and died (Figure 17.30).

Figure 17.31 Recycling Plastics.

Many plastics can be recycled into pellets that can then be used to produce new products.

To protect animals and natural environments, many researchers are working to find alternatives to traditional plastic polymers. The possible adverse health effects of chemicals that leach out of plastic containers, or result from chemical breakdown of plastics, are also a growing health concern. The biodegradable polyester plastics, such as PLA discussed earlier, are gaining traction in the market, but are not yet used on a large enough scale to protect wildlife from some of the consequences.

Recycling can also help reduce the amount of polyester plastic products that make their way into the oceans. Recycling plastic requires that items be sorted according to the different kinds of polymers they are made from. After sorting, they are melted down into pellets that can be used to make new products (Figure 17.31).

Apply what you have just learned: **Practice 17.16** in the Pearson eText.

Polyamides

Silk and wool are two natural fibers from animal sources. These natural fibers are used to make clothing and have been around for centuries. Both fibers are made up of polymers that have amide linkages called **polyamides** (Figure 17.32).

Chemists have used knowledge of the structure of these natural fibers to design and synthesize a variety of synthetic polymers that also have amide linkages. Nylon is a polyamide that was first produced in 1930 and was used in World War II to produce parachutes and parachute cord (Figure 17.33). There are many types of nylon polymers, but the most common nylon polymer is nylon-6,6.

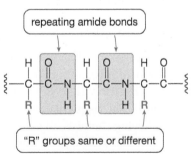

Figure 17.32 Wool from Sheep.
Natural fibers are made of polyamides.

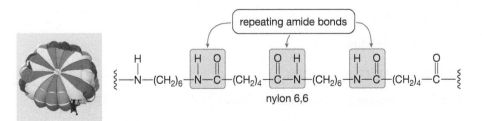

Figure 17.33 Parachute made of Nylon.

To make nylon 6,6 two molecules undergo the polymerization reaction. One of the molecules contains two carboxylic acid groups and the other molecule contains two amine groups. When these two molecules are heated together, they form amide bonds that link molecules together in a long polymer chain in a series of coupling steps. When each amide bond forms, a molecule of water is lost. Nylon is used in items such as airbags in vehicles, protective clothing, and rock-climbing rope.

loss of water and new amide bonds formed

"*n*" repeating units

Apply what you have just learned: **Practice 17.17–17.18** in the Pearson eText.

Quiz yourself on the content of this section: **Check 17.5** in the Pearson eText.

17.6 Naming Carboxylic Acids and Esters

Chemists follow specific rules when naming compounds. This process of devising or choosing names for things is nomenclature. The International Union of Pure and Applied Chemistry (IUPAC) establishes the rules for the nomenclature of organic compounds. The rules ensure that each compound has an unambiguous and unique name, allowing chemists all over the world to communicate with each other. Explore Videos 17.1 and 17.2 to learn how to name the compounds discussed in this chapter. You can also review the rules for naming compounds in the nomenclature appendix.

Video 17.1: Nomenclature: Carboxylic Acids

Video 17.2: Nomenclature: Esters

Video 17.3: Nomenclature: Amides

Quiz yourself on the content of this section: **Check 17.6** in the Pearson eText.

Chapter Summary

17.1 Structure of Carboxylic Acids, Esters & Amides

Learning Objective: Analyze the structural features of carbonyl-containing compounds: carboxylic acids, esters, and amides.

Carboxylic acids, esters, and amides each contain a carbonyl group bonded to either an O or N atom. Carboxylic acids contain a carbonyl group bonded to a hydroxyl group (OH). Esters contain a carbonyl group bonded to an alkoxy group (OR). Amides contain a carbonyl group bonded to an amine group and can be categorized as primary, secondary or tertiary depending on the number of C—H bonds. Carboxylic acids, esters, and amides are found in a wide variety of biological molecules and drugs. Penicillin contains two amides and a carboxylic acid group. One of the amide groups is part of a ring structure.

BioConnect 17.1: Penicillin

Key Terms

acyl group (RCO)
amide
carboxylic acid
ester

17.2 Physical Properties of Acyl Compounds

Learning Objective: Analyze the effect of intermolecular forces on the physical properties of carboxylic acids, esters, and amides.

Carboxylic acids, esters, and amides are polar compounds because of their polar carbonyl group and the additional electronegative groups attached to the carbonyl carbon.

Both carboxylic acids and some amides form hydrogen bonds among molecules. Because of these strong intermolecular forces, they have higher boiling points. Carboxylic acids, esters, and amides all form hydrogen bonds with water. For this reason, small molecules in each of these organic molecule families are water-soluble.

Key Term

Dimer

17.3 The Acidic Properties of Carboxylic Acids

Learning Objective: Evaluate reactions of carboxylic acids with bases.

Carboxylic acids dissociate to produce H^+ ions and carboxylate anions in aqueous solution. These compounds are classified as weak acids with K_a values in the range of 10^{-4} to 10^{-5}. Carboxylic acids react with bases to form water-soluble carboxylate salts. Soaps are carboxylate salts that have a polar head and a long hydrocarbon chain. The aspirin molecule has a carboxylic acid group that dissociates to form the carboxylate anion. This reaction increases the drug's water solubility and facilitates how aspirin is processed in the body.

VisibleChem Video 17.1: Carboxylic Acids are Weak Acids

VisibleChem Video 17.2: Soaps

BioConnect 17.2: Aspirin

Key Terms

carboxylate anion
carboxylate salt
polar head
soap

17.4 Reactions of Carboxylic Acids, Esters, and Amides

Learning Objective: Analyze reactions of carboxylic acids, esters, and amides.

Carboxylic acids, esters, and amides undergo substitution reactions. Carboxylic acids react with alcohols in the presence of acid to produce esters and react with amines to produce amides. Both esters and amides are hydrolyzed in the presence of water and either an acid or a base to produce carboxylic acids or carboxylate anions.

VisibleChem Video 17.3: Esterification and Amide Formation

VisibleChem Video 17.4: Ester and Amide Hydrolysis

Key Terms

ester hydrolysis
esterification
hydrolysis
saponification

17.5 Polyesters & Polyamides

Learning Objective: Analyze the defining structural features of polyesters and polyamides.

A variety of natural and synthetic polymers form as a result of ester and amide linkages. Polymers with ester linkages are polyesters, and polymers with amide linkages are polyamides. The most common synthetic polyester is polyethylene terephthalate (PET), which is used to make a wide variety of plastic products. PET is a stable polymer that stays around in the environment for a long time. Biodegradable polyesters, such as polylactic acid (PLA), are replacing some traditional plastic polymers. Nylon is a polyamide used to make a wide array of materials such as clothing, parachutes, and climbing rope.

Key Terms

biodegradable
polyamide
polyester
polyethylene terephthalate (PET)

17.6 Naming Carboxylic Acids and Esters

Learning Objective: Apply the IUPAC naming system to carboxylic acids, esters, and amides.

Chemists follow specific rules when naming compounds. This process of devising or choosing names for things is nomenclature. The International Union of Pure and Applied Chemistry (IUPAC) establishes the rules for the nomenclature of organic compounds including carboxylic acids and esters.

Video 17.1: Nomenclature: Carboxylic Acids

Video 17.2: Nomenclature: Esters

Video 17.3: Nomenclature: Amides

End-of-Chapter Quiz

Have you mastered the content of this chapter? Try the **End-of-Chapter Quiz** in the Pearson eText.

1. Enalapril (also known as Vasotec) is a medication used to treat high blood pressure, diabetic kidney disease, and heart failure. Which statement is true about Enalapril?

enalapril

a) Enalapril contains a carboxylic acid and an ester but does not contain an amide group.

b) Enalapril contains a carboxylic acid, a ketone, an ether group, and two amide groups.

c) Enalapril contains a carboxylic acid, an amide, and an ester group.

d) Enalapril contains two carboxylic acids and an amide but does not contain an ester.

2. Which statement best describes how the antibiotic penicillin acts to inhibit bacterial growth?
   a) Penicillin binds to the carbohydrates that bacteria use as energy sources for growth.
   b) Penicillin prevents bacteria from producing the carboxylic acids they need for proper cellular metabolism.
   c) Penicillin makes bacteria produce elevated levels of secondary amides that damage DNA and prevent cell division.
   d) Penicillin interferes with the assembly of the outer bacterial cell wall causing the cell to become vulnerable to osmosis.

3. Vitamin B$_5$ is an essential nutrient found in both plants and animals. We consume foods such as vegetables, legumes, cereal grains, eggs, milk, and meat to obtain necessary amounts of the nutrient. Which statement about the functional groups on Vitamin B$_5$ is true?

a) Vitamin B$_5$ contains a carboxylic acid, an ester, an amine, a primary alcohol, and a secondary alcohol, but does not contain an amide.

b) Vitamin B$_5$ contains a carboxylic acid, a secondary amide, a primary alcohol, and a secondary alcohol, but does not contain an ester.

c) Vitamin B$_5$ contains a carboxylic acid, a secondary amine, an ester, a primary alcohol, and a tertiary alcohol but does not contain a secondary alcohol.

d) Vitamin B$_5$ contains an ester, a primary amide, a primary alcohol, and a secondary alcohol but does not contain a ketone.

4. Which molecule contains a tertiary amide?

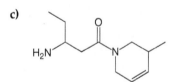

a)

b)

c)

d)

5. Which of the functional groups discussed in this chapter are polar?
   a) amides and esters only
   b) carboxylic acids, esters, and amides
   c) carboxylic acids only
   d) carboxylic acids and amides only

6. Which diagram correctly shows hydrogen bonding between secondary amides 2°?

a)

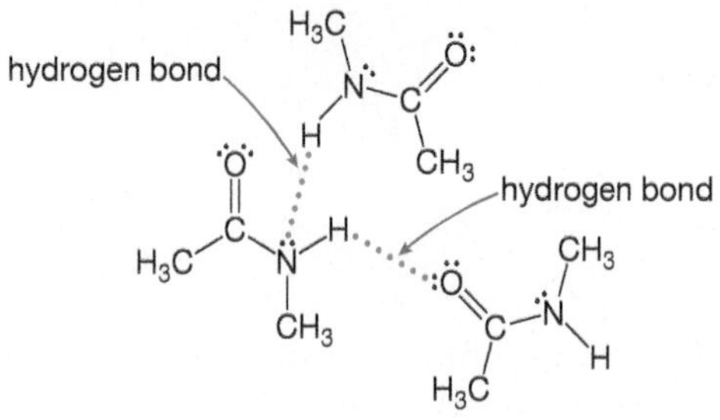

b)

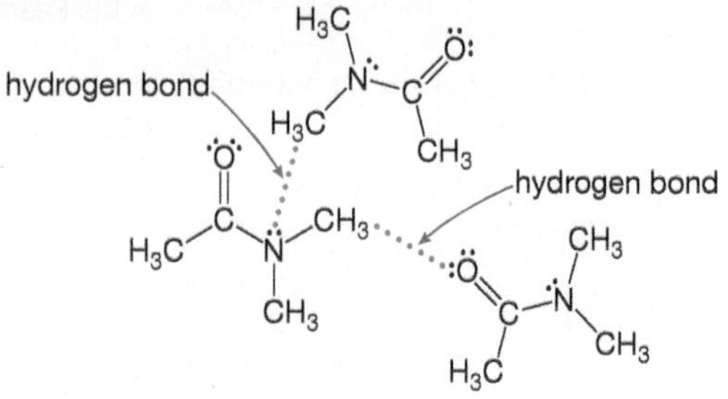

c)

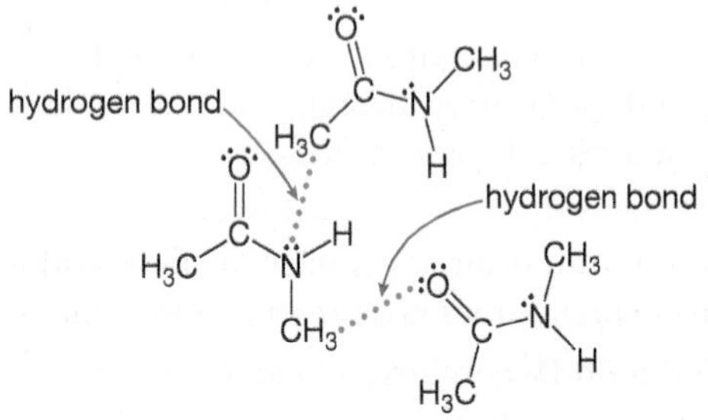

d)

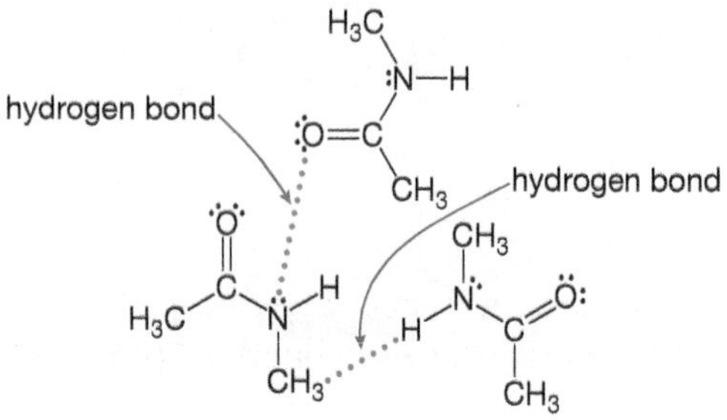

7. Which statement about the solubility of carboxylic acids in water is correct?
   a) As the carbon chain length increases, the water solubility of carboxylic acids also increases.
   b) As the carbon chain length increases, the water solubility of carboxylic acids also decreases.
   c) As the carbon chain length decreases, the water solubility of carboxylic acids also decreases.
   d) Carboxylic acids of all chain lengths can hydrogen bond with water and as a result are water-soluble.

8. Which reaction correctly shows the behavior of a carboxylic acid in water?

a)

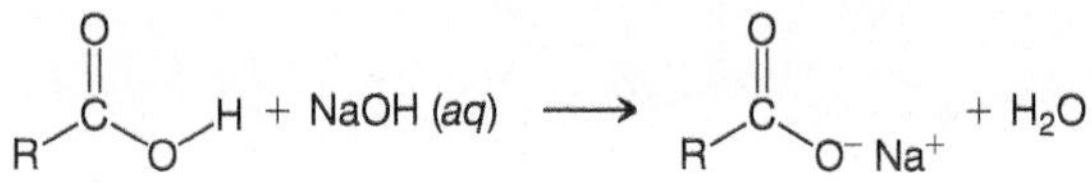

b)

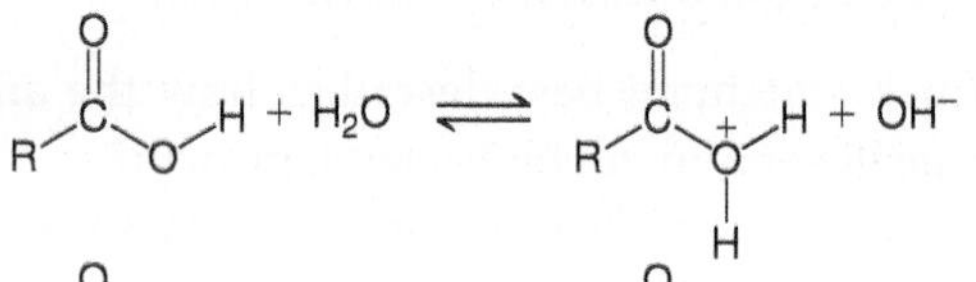

c)

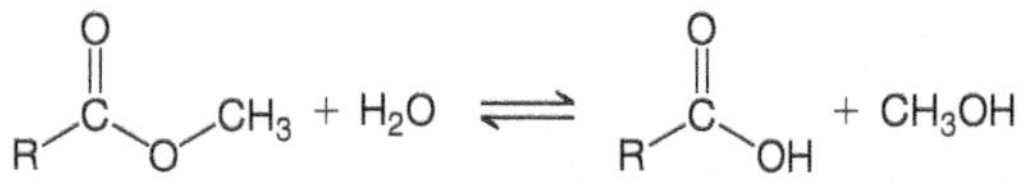

d)

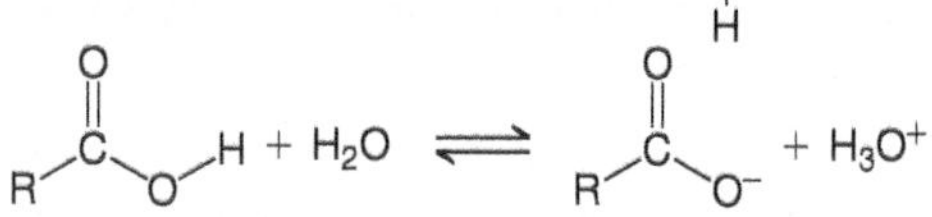

9. Examine the structures of each carboxylic acid containing biological molecule and determine the total number of acidic hydrogen atoms on each acid.

Succinic acid is involved in the in energy-yielding metabolic processes in the body.

Malic acid is a key molecule in metabolism, contributes to the pleasantly sour taste of fruits, and is used as a food additive.

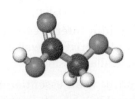

Glycolic acid is partly responsible for the flavor of apples. It is also used in a number of skin-care products.

   a) Succinic acid has two acidic hydrogen atoms, malic acid has three, and glycolic acid has two.
   b) Succinic acid has one acidic hydrogen atom, malic acid has three, and glycolic acid has two.
   c) Succinic acid has two acidic hydrogen atoms, malic acid has two, and glycolic acid has one.
   d) Each acid shown only contains one acidic hydrogen because there can only be one hydrogen lost in equilibrium.

10. Esters form in reactions between which two types of molecules?
   a) an aldehyde and an ether
   b) a carboxylic acid and an alcohol
   c) a hemiacetal and an alcohol
   d) a carboxylic acid and an amide

11. What products form when this reaction runs to completion?

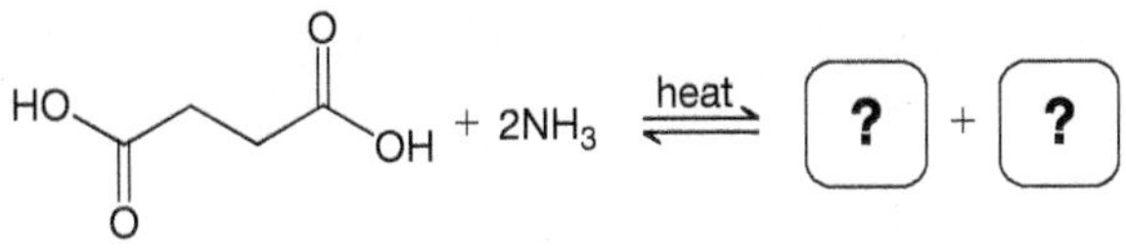

a)

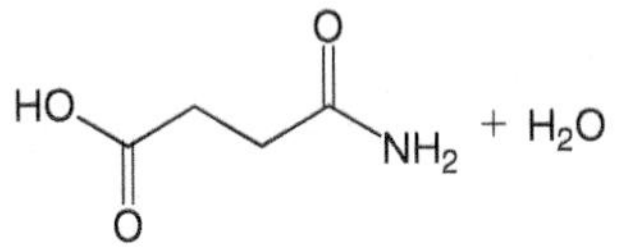

b)

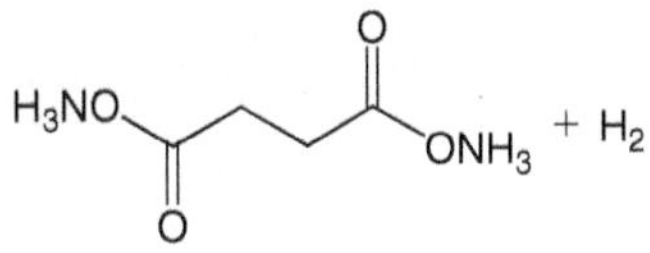

c)

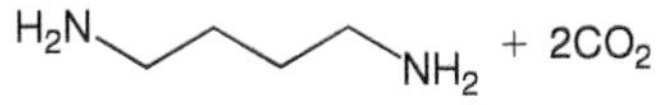

d)

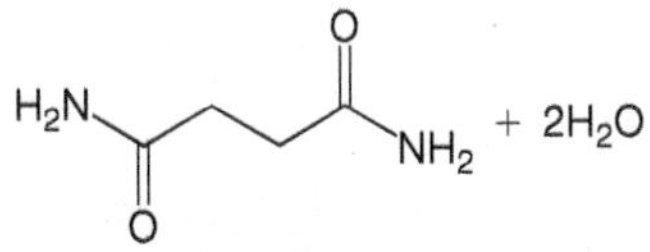

12. Tetracaine (also known as amethocaine), is a local anesthetic used to numb the eyes, nose, or throat, and the skin before starting an IV in order to lessen the pain from the procedure. A medical scientist studying the reactivity of tetracaine performs this reaction. What products does she obtain from the reaction?

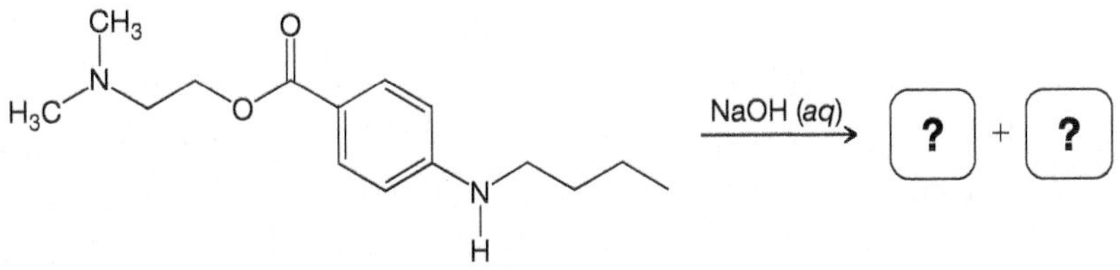

tetracaine

a)

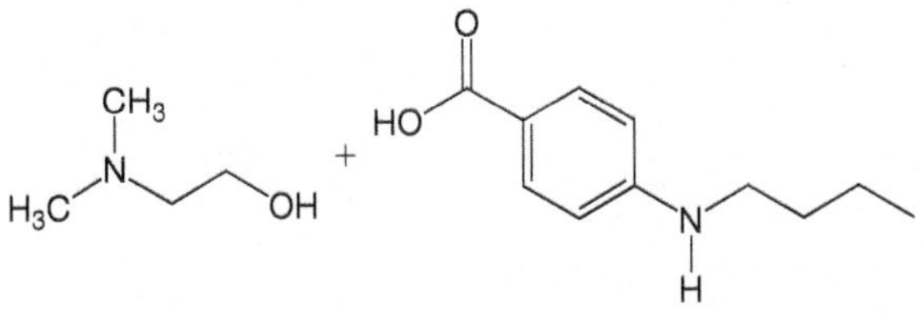

b)

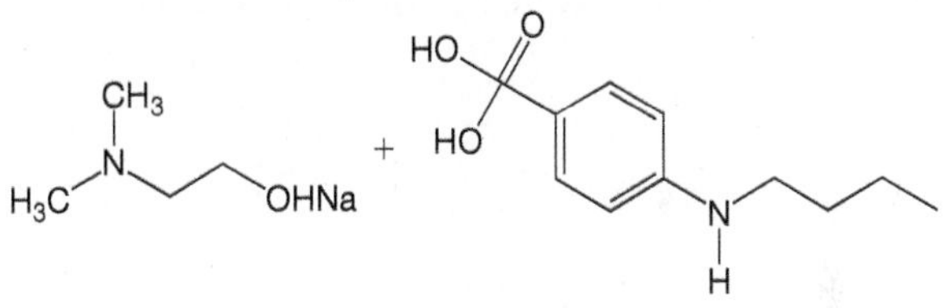

c)

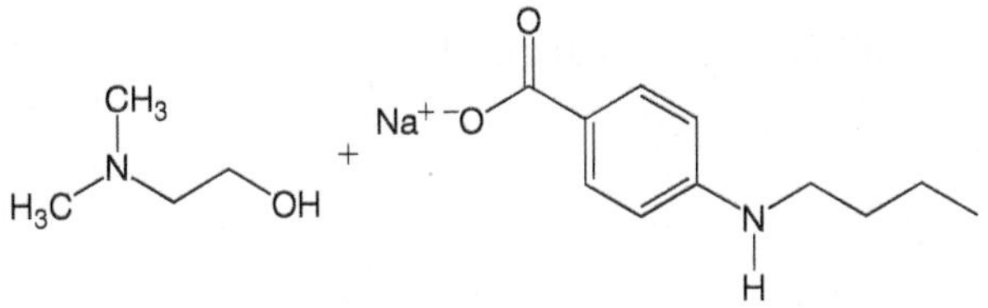

d)

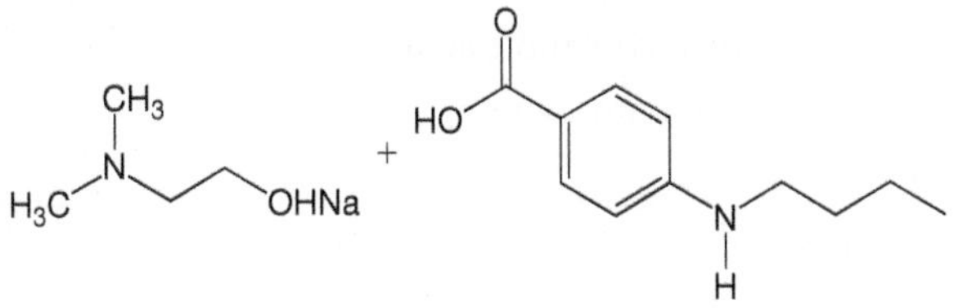

13. Identify the correct monomers needed to form this polymer.

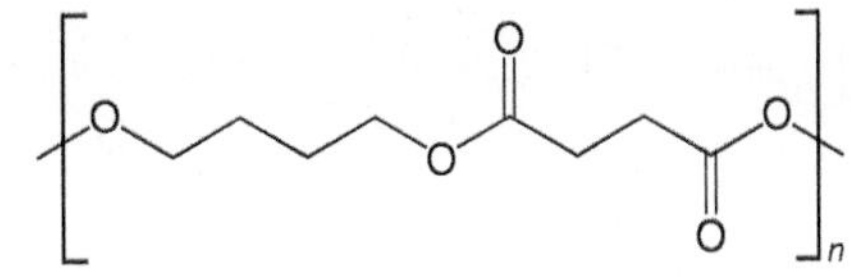

a)

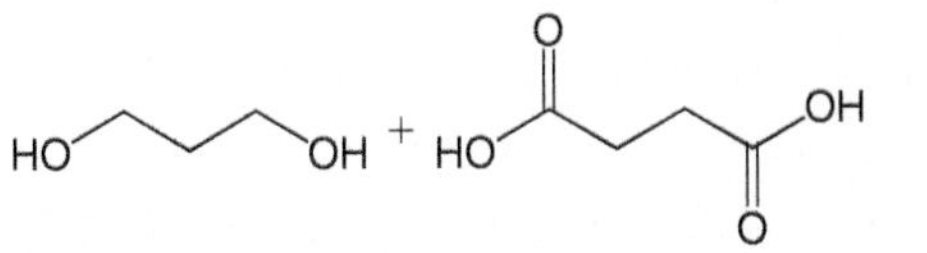

b)

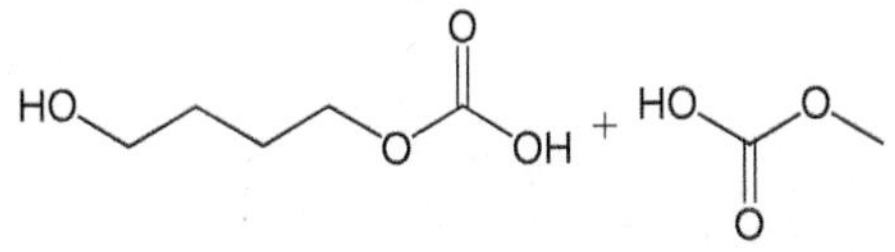

c)

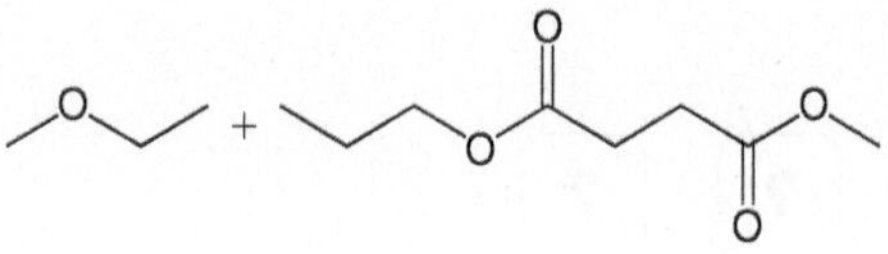

d)

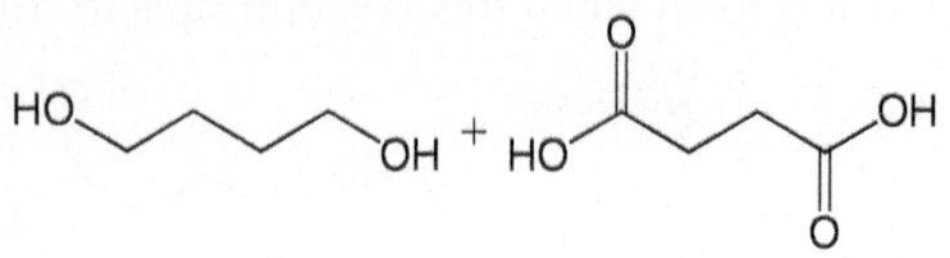

14. Identify the monomers that form this polymer.

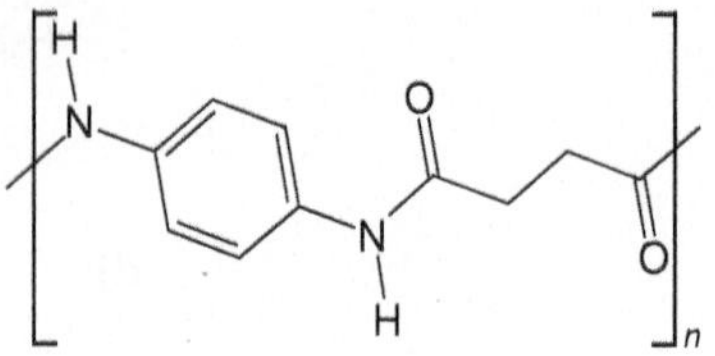

a)

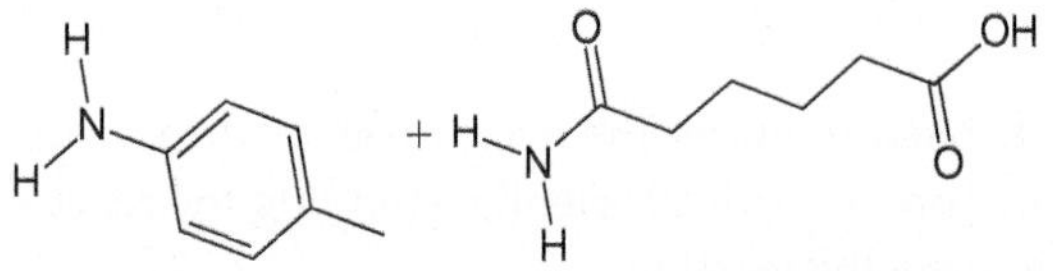

b)

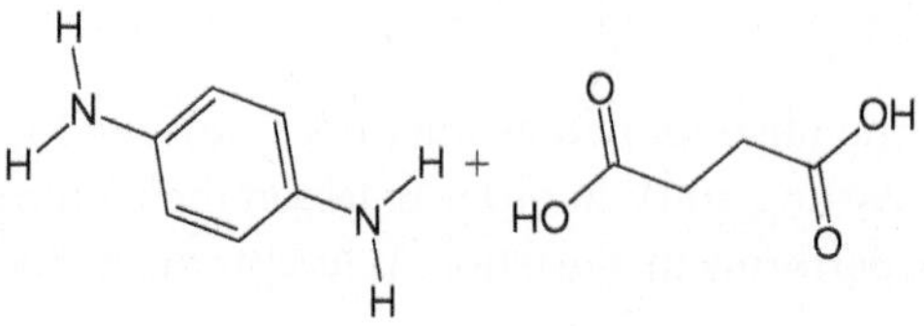

c)

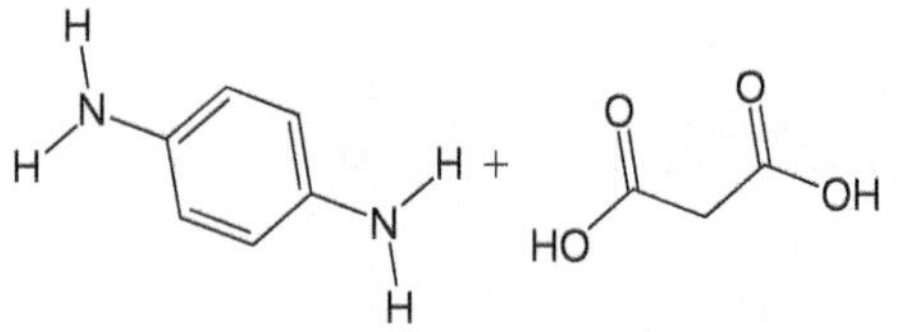

d)

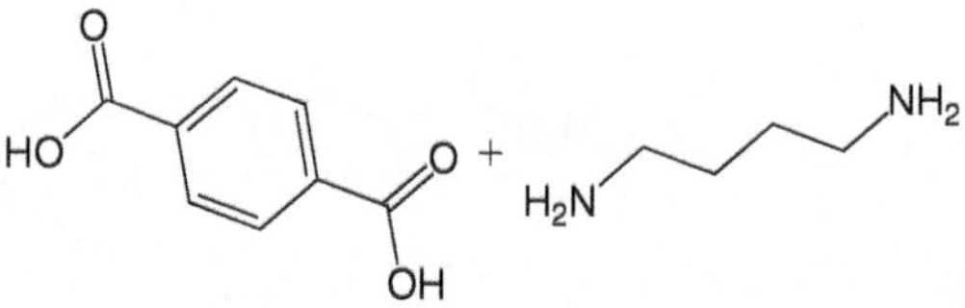

---

15. What is the IUPAC name for this molecule?

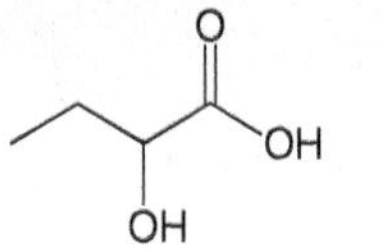

a) 1,2-dihydroxybutanone

b) 3-hydroxybutanoic acid

c) 2-hydroxybutanoic acid

d) 2-hydroxypropanoic acid

16. Which molecule has the IUPAC name methyl ethanoate?

a)

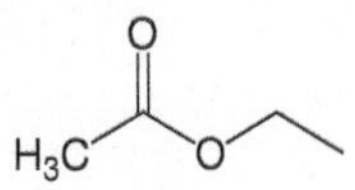

b)

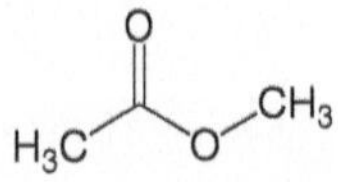

c)

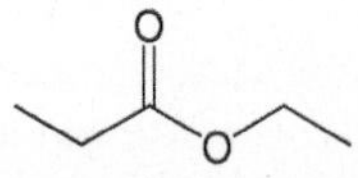

d)

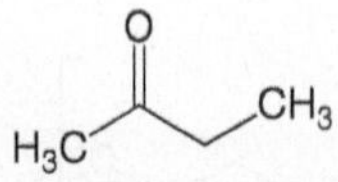

17. What is the IUPAC name for this molecule?

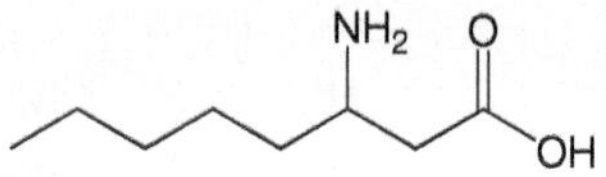

a) 2-aminooctanoic acid

b) 3-aminoheptanoic acid

c) 6-aminooctanoic acid

d) 3-aminooctanoic acid

Chapter 18
Lipids

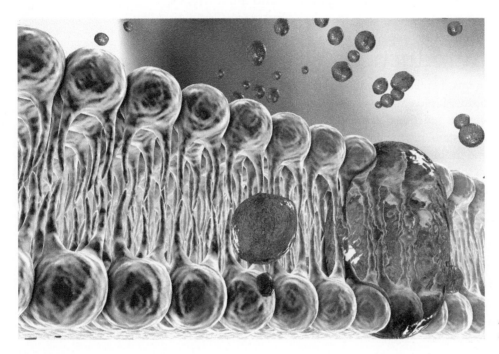

A delicate layer of lipids protects and defines each of our cells.

Chapter Outline

Learning Objectives

18.1   Classify fatty acids and describe how double bonds impact fatty acid melting points.

18.2   Recognize and draw the structure of waxes including the carboxylic acid and alcohol portions of wax molecules.

18.3   Draw the structure of triacylglycerols and predict the hydrolysis products of triacylglycerols.

18.4 Identify the two common types of phospholipids and describe the role of phosphoacylglycerols in cell membrane structure.

18.5 Recognize the general structure of steroids and steroid hormones and be familiar with several examples of each.

18.6 Describe the general structural characteristics and biological activity of prostaglandins and leukotrienes.

Introduction

In this chapter, we continue our exploration of important biomolecules by examining lipids. Lipids are a surprisingly diverse array of molecules that include familiar organic functional groups and play significant roles in the human body. The blood cholesterol many people monitor, the trans fats we are advised to avoid in our diets, and the birth control pills millions of women take every day are all lipids (Figure 18.1). In this chapter, we explore a diverse array of lipids. Understanding lipid structure, shape, and common reactions helps us better understand their functions in biological systems and the environment.

18.1 Lipids and Fatty Acids

Medical professionals routinely measure lipid levels in the blood as part of adult physical examinations. Several tests measure patient lipid levels that are associated

---

Figure 18.1 Lipids in our Lives.

A) Cholesterol is a lipid associated with increased risk of cardiovascular disease. **B)** Trans fats are also lipids and consuming them can have severe health impacts. **C)** The hormones in birth control pills are biologically active lipids.

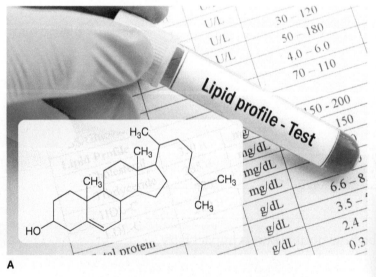

Figure 18.2 Artery Plaque.

Plaque in the arteries is a fatty, waxy substance that forms deposits in the artery wall. These deposits can narrow the artery and reduce blood flow.

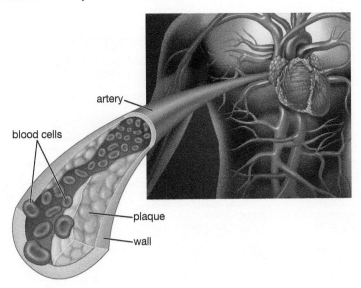

overall health. In some cases, high lipid levels lead to fatty plaque deposits in artery walls, increasing the risk of heart disease (Figure 18.2).

We often simply refer to **lipids** as fats, yet the formal definition of a lipid is broader than that. Lipids are biomolecules composed of a large hydrocarbon portion and polar groups, such as ester groups. A defining characteristic of lipids is that they are insoluble in water. Lipids serve many functions in the body including energy storage, internal organ insulation, and chemical messaging. They are also key components of our cell membranes.

carboxylic acid (polar) · hydrocarbon chain (nonpolar) · fatty acid

Because lipids are defined by their insolubility in water, a variety of molecule types are considered lipids (Figure 18.3). As we can see in Figure 18.3, almost all lipids contain between one to three **fatty acids**. A fatty acid is a molecule that contains a long unbranched hydrocarbon chain (between 12–20 carbon atoms) with a carboxylic acid group at one end.

Steroids, although in the lipid family, have a very different structure. They are not composed of fatty acids and are structurally characterized by fused carbon rings. We explore each of these lipid types in this chapter, beginning with fatty acids.

Fatty Acids

Fatty acids contain many C—C and C—H bonds. These bonds make them insoluble in water. The nonpolar part of a fatty acid molecule is *not* attracted to water, so we refer to it as **hydrophobic** (water fearing). The polar part of the fatty acid is attracted to

Figure 18.3 Types of Lipids.

Lipids are a family of naturally occurring biomolecules characterized by a lack of water solubility. Each type of lipids contains a large hydrocarbon region and a few polar groups.

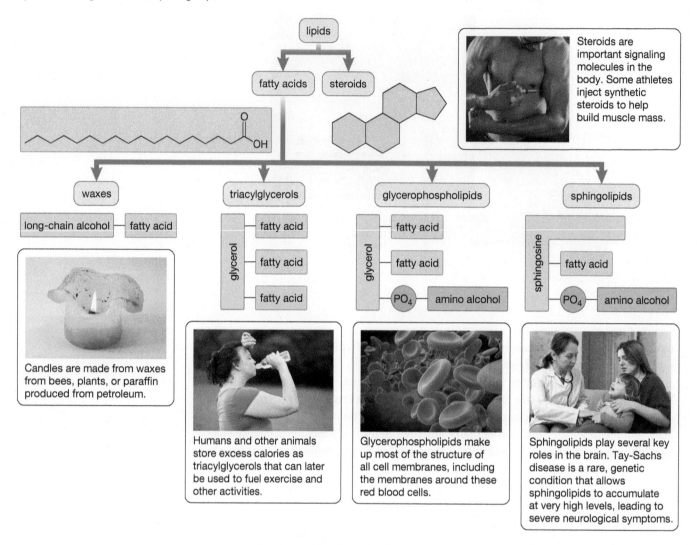

Steroids are important signaling molecules in the body. Some athletes inject synthetic steroids to help build muscle mass.

Candles are made from waxes from bees, plants, or paraffin produced from petroleum.

Humans and other animals store excess calories as triacylglycerols that can later be used to fuel exercise and other activities.

Glycerophospholipids make up most of the structure of all cell membranes, including the membranes around these red blood cells.

Sphingolipids play several key roles in the brain. Tay-Sachs disease is a rare, genetic condition that allows sphingolipids to accumulate at very high levels, leading to severe neurological symptoms.

water, so we refer to it as **hydrophilic** (water loving). Lauric acid, found in coconut, is a common fatty acid that contains 12 carbon atoms; it has a large hydrophobic region and a smaller hydrophilic region.

$$CH_3-CH_2-CH_2-CH_2-CH_2-CH_2-CH_2-CH_2-CH_2-CH_2-CH_2-C\begin{smallmatrix}O\\\\OH\end{smallmatrix}$$

lauric acid
$C_{12}H_{24}O_2$

skeletal structure

hydrophobic region
(nonpolar)

hydrophilic region
(polar)

Lauric acid does not contain any double bonds between carbon atoms and is therefore a **saturated fatty acid**. Other fatty acids do contain one or more

Figure 18.4 Food Labels.

Food product labels include, and often advertise, saturated and *trans*-fat content.

carbon-carbon double bonds and are **unsaturated fatty acids**. Oleic acid is an 18-carbon unsaturated fatty acid found in olives. The oleic acid molecule has a double bond at carbon nine. We can draw unsaturated fatty acids in both the cis and trans forms. However, the cis form is the more common isomer in nature. While the cis isomer is more likely to be found naturally, **trans fatty acids**, which are also referred to more simply as **trans fats**, are produced in the food industry and make their way into our food products (Figure 18.4). Review the discussion in BioConnect 13.1 of trans fats and how they impact health.

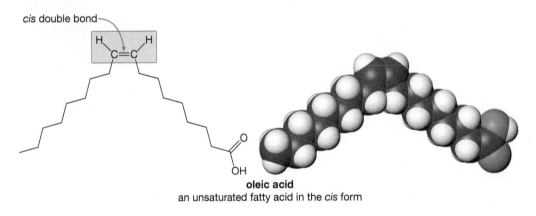

oleic acid
an unsaturated fatty acid in the *cis* form

Apply what you have just learned: **Practice 18.1–18.4** in the Pearson eText.

Physical Properties of Fatty Acids

Saturated fatty acid molecules can line up next to one another in such a way that the hydrocarbon chains interact with each other, and the polar carboxylic acid groups interact with each other. The forces between the molecules (intermolecular forces) hold the molecules in place in a regular pattern. As the length of the hydrocarbon chain increases more of these interactions occur and the molecules are harder to separate, requiring higher temperatures to melt. Saturated fatty acids are generally solids at room temperature with melting points above 25 °C (Figure 18.5).

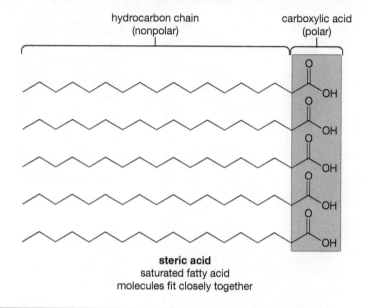

steric acid
saturated fatty acid
molecules fit closely together

Figure 18.5 Structures and Melting Points of Common Fatty Acids.

	Name	Structure	MP (°C)	Common source
Saturated fatty acids	lauric acid	12 carbons	44	coconut
	palmitic acid	16 carbons	63	palm
	stearic acid	18 carbons	69	animal fat
Unsaturated fatty acids	palmitoleic acid	*cis* double bond — 16 carbons	1	dairy
	lineoleic acid	*cis* double bonds — 18 carbons	−5	sunflower
	arachidonic acid	*cis* double bonds — 20 carbons	−49	meat, eggs, fish

Unsaturated fatty acids, on the other hand, are generally liquids at room temperature. The cis double bonds introduce kinks in the long hydrocarbon chain making it difficult for unsaturated molecules to pack closely together. The more cis double bonds, the more kinks in the chain, and the lower the molecule's melting point.

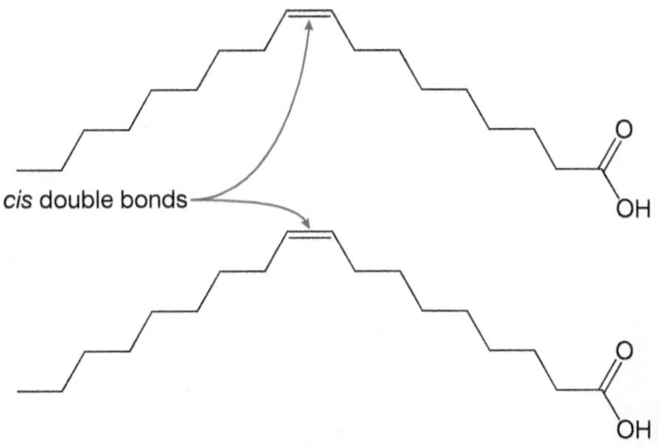

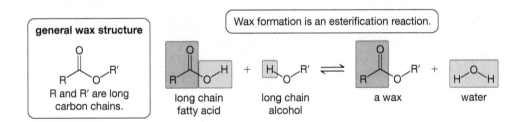

oleic acid
unsaturated fatty acid
molecules do not fit closely together

Click on BioConnect 18.1 (contains Figures 18.6–18.12) to learn more about unsaturated fatty acids in our diet including the omega fatty acids and the controversy regarding fatty acid supplements.

Apply what you have just learned: **Practice 18.5** in the Pearson eText.

Explore how Chemistry and Biology connect: **BioConnect: 18.1** Fatty Acids in Our Diet in the Pearson eText.

Apply what you have just learned: **Practice 18.6** in the Pearson eText.

Quiz yourself on the content of this section: **Check 18.1** in the Pearson eText.

18.2 Waxes

Fatty acids are lipids themselves and they are also the building blocks of several other types of lipids including **waxes**. Waxes are esters that are made up of a fatty acid and an alcohol that has a long hydrocarbon R group. A fatty acid and an alcohol undergo an esterification reaction to form a wax.

general wax structure

R and R' are long carbon chains.

Wax formation is an esterification reaction.

long chain fatty acid + long chain alcohol ⇌ a wax + water

Beeswax is composed of hundreds of molecules, but the main component is a wax called myricyl palmitate (Figure 18.13A). This wax molecule is produced from palmitic acid and a 30-carbon alcohol. A nonpolar hydrocarbon chain makes up the majority of the structure of a wax molecule, which includes only a small polar ester group. For this reason, waxes are very hydrophobic. We can represent the long hydrocarbon chains contained in waxes in a condensed format as shown here, or in expanded or skeletal forms.

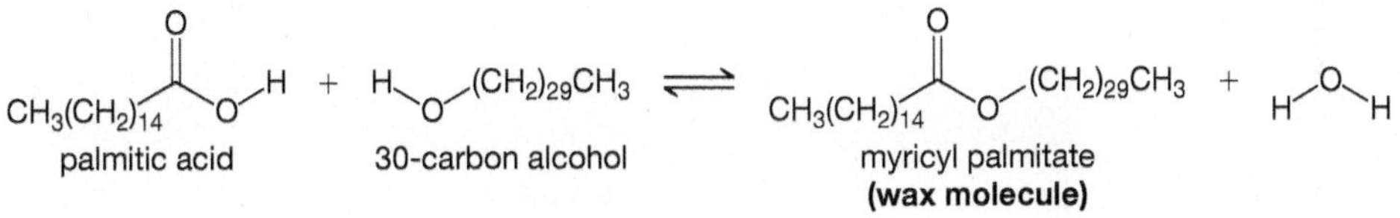

$CH_3(CH_2)_{14}$ palmitic acid + 30-carbon alcohol $H\text{--}O\text{--}(CH_2)_{29}CH_3$ ⇌ $CH_3(CH_2)_{14}$ myricyl palmitate **(wax molecule)** $O\text{--}(CH_2)_{29}CH_3$ + $H\text{--}O\text{--}H$

Figure 18.13 Wax Molecules.

A) Beeswax is a complex mixture of many different compounds including the wax myricyl palmitate, a 46-carbon wax molecule. **B)** Carnauba wax is also a complex mixture of compounds containing the wax myricyl cerotate. Carnauba wax is collected from carnauba palm tree leaves for many commercial applications. **C)** Spermaceti wax is found in the head cavity of sperm whales and contains the 32-carbon wax compound cetyl palmitate.

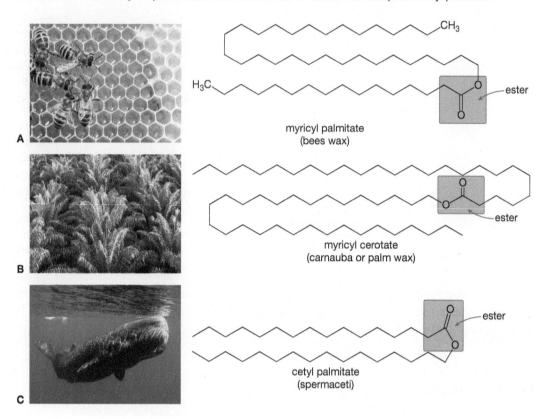

myricyl palmitate
(bees wax)

myricyl cerotate
(carnauba or palm wax)

cetyl palmitate
(spermaceti)

Apply what you have just learned: **Practice 18.7 and 18.8** in the Pearson eText.

Quiz yourself on the content of this section: **Check 18.2** in the Pearson eText.

Waxes are found in plants and animals including on the surfaces of fruit and leaves (see Fig. 18.13). Waxes help protect plants from water loss and pests. They also function as protective coatings on the skin or fur of animals. Other waxes carry out unique biological functions such as the wax compound found in the head cavity of sperm whales (spermaceti). A typical whale has up to 1900 liters of spermaceti in its head cavity. It is believed that the heating and cooling of spermaceti wax helps whales to float. The whales lower their density in order to float by heating the spermaceti and increase their density by cooling the spermaceti when it is time to dive again.

18.3 Triacylglycerols

Triacylglycerols (also called **triglycerides**) are lipid molecules that are triesters. Recall that a triester is made up of one glycerol molecule and three molecules of fatty acids.

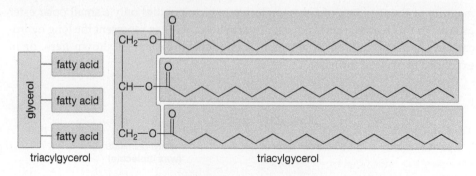

triacylglycerol   triacylglycerol

Humans and other animals store much of their energy in the form of triacylglycerols. This is particularly important for animals that hibernate (Figure 18.14). Prior to hibernation, grizzly bears consume large amounts of food. Their bodies process the food and store it primarily as triacylglycerol molecules. The stored triacylglycerols sustain the bears' bodies through their long winter hibernation.

The identity of each of the three R groups in a triacylglycerol depends on which fatty acids undergo a reaction with glycerol and can vary at each connection point.

Figure 18.14 Grizzly Bear.

Animals that hibernate, such as grizzly bears, load up on high calorie food and store it as triacylglycerols for ongoing energy.

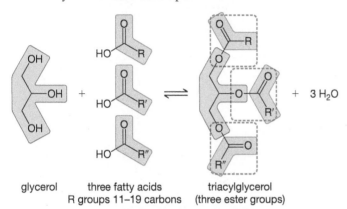

glycerol   three fatty acids   triacylglycerol
R groups 11–19 carbons   (three ester groups)

Triacylglycerols are simple, which have identical fatty acid chains, or mixed, which have two or three different fatty acid chains (Figure 18.15).

Figure 18.15 Simple and Mixed Triaclyglycerols.

Simple triacylglycerols have three fatty acids that are identical. Mixed triacylglycerol molecules contain different fatty acid chains.

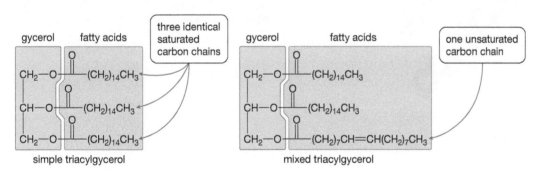

simple triacylgycerol   mixed triacylgycerol

Apply what you have just learned: **Practice 18.9** in the Pearson eText.

Fats and Oils

When we refer to **fats**, we are referring to triacylglycerols that are solid at room temperature and usually come from animal sources (Figure 18.16). Fats generally consist of fatty acids that have few carbon-carbon double bonds. **Oils**, on the other hand, are also triacylglycerol molecules but are typically liquid at room temperature. Oils consist of fatty acids that generally have a greater number of carbon-carbon double bonds and are usually from plant sources.

Monounsaturated triacylglycerols have a single carbon-carbon double bond, whereas **polyunsaturated triacylglycerols** have more than one carbon-carbon double bond. The higher the number of carbon-carbon double bonds in the fatty acid chains the lower the melting point of triacylglycerols.

Figure 18.16 Vegetable and Animal Sources of Triacylglycerols.

The fraction of saturated fats varies by the type of fat. Olive oil, for example, is 14% saturated fat while coconut oil is 82% saturated fat. Beef fat is about 50% saturated fat.

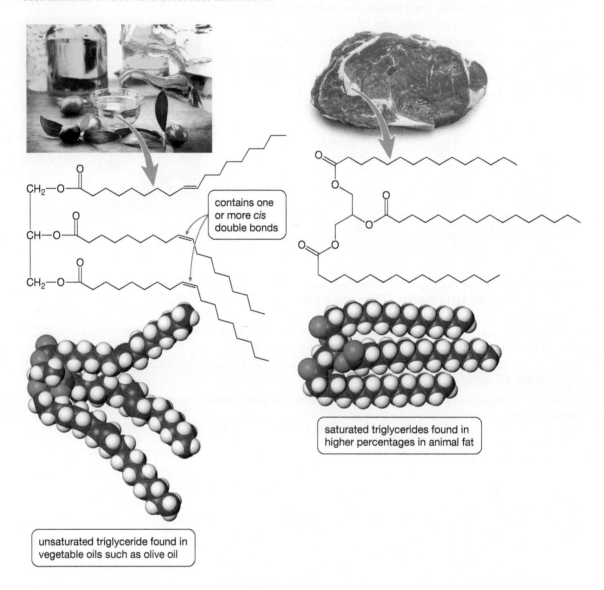

contains one or more *cis* double bonds

saturated triglycerides found in higher percentages in animal fat

unsaturated triglyceride found in vegetable oils such as olive oil

Select Learn 18.1 to explore the structure of triacylglycerols in more detail and learn a method for drawing these large molecules.

 Predict answers and see step-by-step solutions: **Learn 18.1:** Structure of a Triacylglycerol in the Pearson eText.

Apply what you have just learned: **Practice 18.10–18.12** in the Pearson eText.

Hydrogenation and Hydrolysis of Triacylglycerols

Triacylglycerols undergo three major types of chemical reactions—hydrogenation (see VisibleChem Video 13.5), hydrolysis, and saponification. Hydrogenation converts an unsaturated triacylglycerol to a saturated triacylglycerol by adding H_2 in

Figure 18.17 Hydrogenation of Vegetable Oil.

Margarine products are produced from vegetable oil using varying degrees of hydrogenation. Firmer solid margarine products have fewer carbon-carbon double bonds, whereas softer margarine products have more carbon-carbon double bonds.

hydrogenation

glyceryl trioleate
unsaturated triacylglycerol

glyceryl stearate
saturated triacylglycerol

vegetable oils
(liquids)

margarine
(solid)

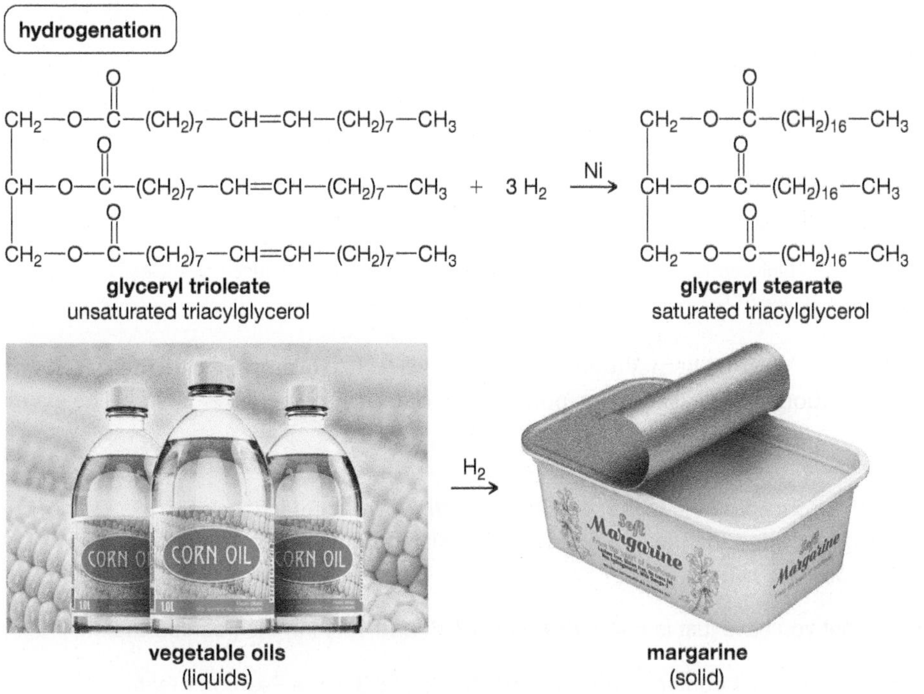

the presence of a metal catalyst such as Ni. Vegetable oils are converted to margarine using a partial hydrogenation process (Figure 18.17). Manufacturers produce a variety of products using this process including items such as soft margarine and a firmer stick of margarine. The texture of the product depends on the amount of hydrogenation that occurs.

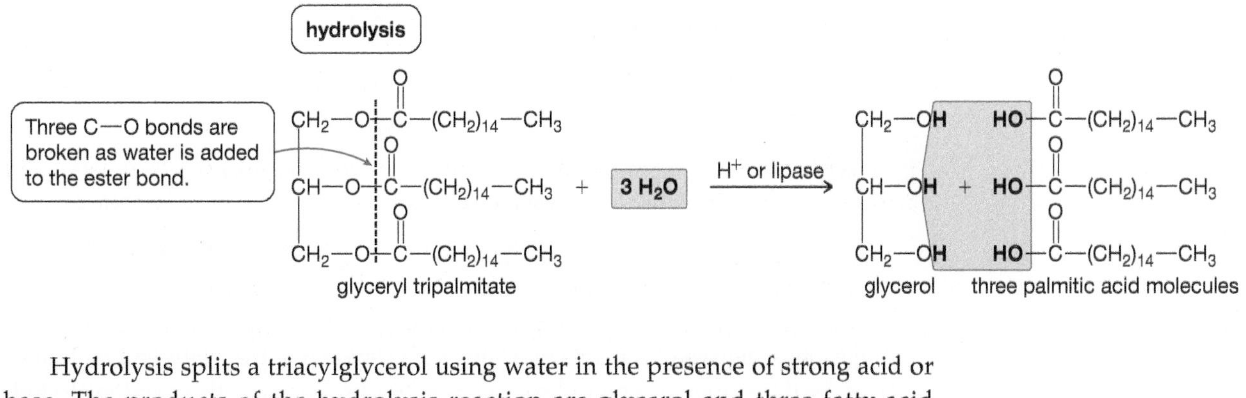

hydrolysis

Three C—O bonds are broken as water is added to the ester bond.

glyceryl tripalmitate

glycerol   three palmitic acid molecules

Hydrolysis splits a triacylglycerol using water in the presence of strong acid or base. The products of the hydrolysis reaction are glycerol and three fatty acid molecules.

In the body, the enzyme **lipase** acts as the catalyst in this hydrolysis reaction. Like grizzly bears, humans store energy in the form of triacylglycerols in a layer of fat cells called **adipose cells**. Metabolism of triacylglycerols involves a hydrolysis reaction with the lipase enzyme, followed by several additional reactions that ultimately produce CO_2, H_2O, and a great deal of energy.

Saponification occurs when a triacylglycerol is heated with water in the presence of a strong base such as NaOH or KOH. The products of saponification are glycerol and the salts of the fatty acids. This is how soap is made. The salts of the fatty acids, as shown here, are soap molecules.

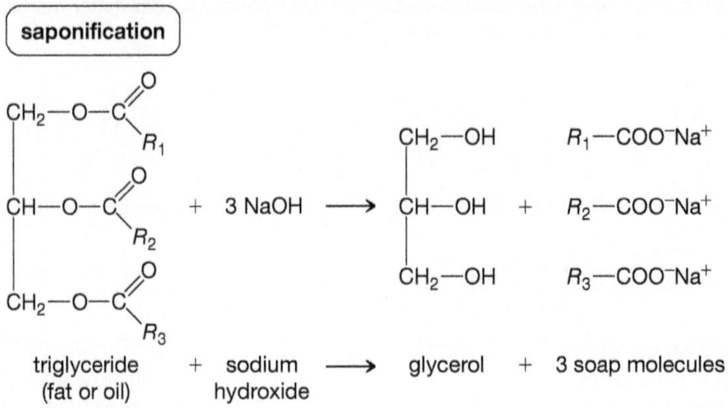

Explore VisibleChem Videos 18.1 and 18.2 to learn more about the details of hydrogenation, hydrolysis, and saponification of triacylglycerols.

Watch this concept come to life: **VisibleChem Video 18.1:** Reactions of Triacylglycerols and **VisibleChem Video 18.2:** Metabolism of Triacylglycerols in the Pearson eText.

Apply what you have just learned: **Practice 18.13 and 18.14** in the Pearson eText.

Quiz yourself on the content of this section: **Check 18.3** in the Pearson eText.

18.4 Phospholipids

In all living organisms, cell membranes—flexible, semi-permeable barriers—define and protect the contents of cells (Figure 18.18). The primary components of cell membranes are **phospholipids,** lipids that contain a phosphorus atom. The most common types of phospholipids are **phosphoacylglycerols** and **sphingomyelins,** both of which are shown in these schematic diagrams. We include a triacylglycerol molecule (discussed in the previous section) for comparison.

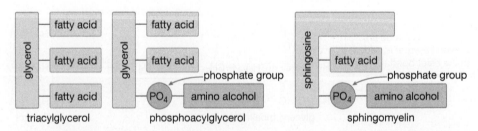

A phosphoacylglycerol contains two fatty acids similar to a triacylglycerol molecule. However, the third group in a phosphoacylglycerol is a phosphate with an **amino alcohol** group attached. An amino alcohol is a molecule that contains both an amine group and an alcohol group. Three common amino alcohols are choline, serine, and ethanolamine.

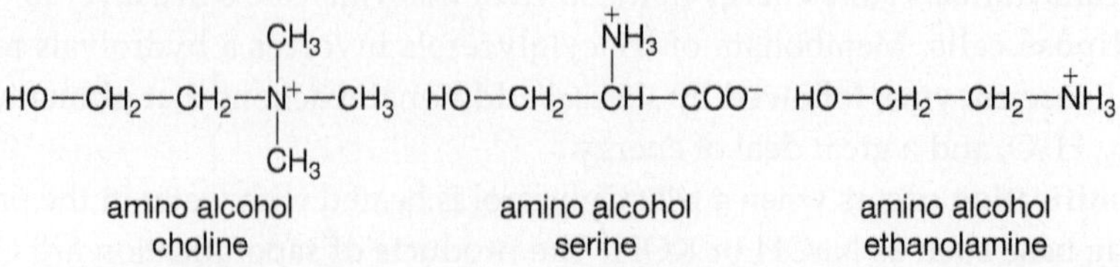

$$HO-CH_2-CH_2-\overset{CH_3}{\underset{CH_3}{\overset{|}{\underset{|}{N^+}}}}-CH_3 \qquad HO-CH_2-\overset{\overset{+}{N}H_3}{\overset{|}{CH}}-COO^- \qquad HO-CH_2-CH_2-\overset{+}{N}H_3$$

amino alcohol
choline

amino alcohol
serine

amino alcohol
ethanolamine

Figure 18.18 Cell Membranes are Composed of Two Layers of Phospholipids.

Phospholipids are fatty acids that contain a phosphorus atom.

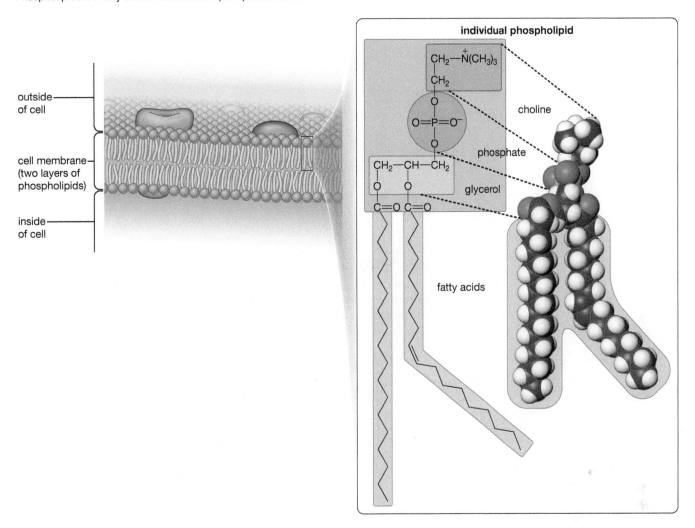

In a sphingomyelin, **sphingosine** takes the place of glycerol. Sphingomyelins are found in the cell membranes of both plant and animal cells. We explore the structure and function of these two classes of phospholipids throughout this section.

Phosphoacylglycerol and Sphingomyelin Structure

Phosphoacylglycerols contain both a polar and a nonpolar region allowing them to interact with a wide range of molecule types (Figure 18.19). The amino alcohol group, in this case choline, combined with the phosphate group is referred to as the **polar head**, the part of the molecule that is strongly attracted to water (hydrophilic). The fatty acid chains make up the **nonpolar tail**, which is the hydrophobic region of the molecule. The fatty acid chains and the amino alcohol groups vary across the many different naturally-occurring phosphoacylglycerol molecules. Some of the fatty acid chains contain carbon-carbon double bonds and some do not. The amino alcohol groups may be choline, serine, ethanolamine, or other amino alcohol groups that we have not mentioned by name in this chapter.

Sphingomyelin structure differs from the structure of phosphoacylglycerols in two significant ways (Figure 18.20). First, sphingomyelin contain a sphingosine molecule in place of glycerol. Second, the sphingosine backbone has an amine group in

Figure 18.19 Structure of a Phosphoacylglycerol.

A hydrophilic polar head and a hydrophobic nonpolar tail make up the structure of phosphoacylglycerols.

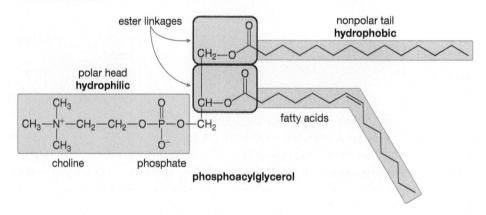

phosphoacylglycerol

Figure 18.20 Structure of Sphingomyelins.

Sphingosine replaces glycerol in the structure of sphingomyelins and an amide bond forms with a fatty acid molecule in contrast to the ester bond in phosphoacylglycerol molecules.

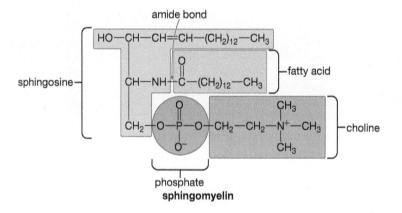

sphingomyelin

place of an OH group that forms an amide bond with the fatty acid. This bond forms where the nitrogen atom on the sphingosine molecule attaches to the carbonyl group of the fatty acid. Click on VisibleChem Videos 18.3 and 18.4 to explore the structure and function of these two common phospholipid molecules.

Watch this concept come to life: **VisibleChem Video 18.3:** Structure and Function of Phosphoacylglycerols and **VisibleChem Video 18.4:** Structure and Function of Sphingomyelin in the Pearson eText.

Apply what you have just learned: **Practice 18.15–18.17** in the Pearson eText.

Explore how Chemistry and Biology connect: **BioConnect: 18.2:** Cholera and the Cell Membrane in the Pearson eText.

Quiz yourself on the content of this section: **Check 18.4** in the Pearson eText.

18.5 Steroids and Steroid Hormones

Many lipid molecules contain a fatty acid in their structure; the steroids do not. A steroid is a lipid that contains three six-membered carbon rings and one five-membered carbon ring (Figure 18.28a). We label the rings in a steroid A, B, C, and D, and number the carbon atoms 1–17. Different steroids have different additional functional groups attached to the carbon atoms in their rings.

Cholesterol is a steroid. Most of us know someone struggling to control their **cholesterol** levels. High levels of cholesterol are associated with an increased risk of cardiovascular disease (Figure 18.28b). Cholesterol is one of the most common members of the steroid family. The cholesterol molecule has a double bond between carbons 5 and 6, a methyl group at carbons 10 and 13, an alcohol group at carbon 3, and a branched hydrocarbon chain at carbon 17. Our bodies produce cholesterol in the liver, and it can be found in almost all parts of the body. Cholesterol is an important part of cell membranes and is used to make other important steroid molecules. Our bodies also convert it to vitamin D upon exposure to direct sunlight.

In addition to the cholesterol in our body that is made in the liver, we obtain cholesterol from foods such as cheese, butter, eggs, and meat. It is recommended that adults consume less than 300 mg/day of cholesterol, although the average person in the U.S. consumes much more than that. High blood cholesterol levels increase the risk of cardiovascular disease, ultimately leading to heart attacks and strokes.

Figure 18.28 Structure of Steroids.

A) Steroids such as cholesterol contain three six-membered rings and one five-membered ring. The rings are labeled A–D and the carbon atoms are numbered 1–17. Steroids differ by the functional groups attached to the carbon atoms in the rings. **B)** Blood tests to measure cholesterol levels are an important component of physical exams.

A steroid skeleton

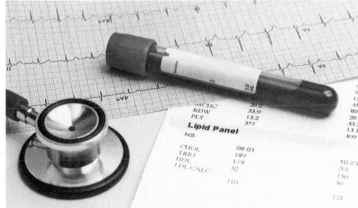

B cholesterol

Quiz yourself on the content of this section: **Check 18.18** in the Pearson eText.

Figure 18.29 Lipoprotein Structure.

The polar head groups of phospholipids orient towards the surface to interact with water. Nonpolar molecules, including cholesterol, are inside the lipoprotein.

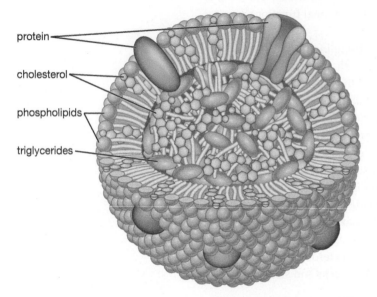

protein
cholesterol
phospholipids
triglycerides

Lipoproteins

Like other lipids that we've explored, cholesterol is not soluble in water-based solutions such as blood. The structure of cholesterol is primarily C—H bonds, and it has only one OH group. This makes the molecule mostly nonpolar and insoluble in water. Although it is insoluble in blood, cholesterol must be transported from the liver where it is made to the tissues. In order for transport to occur, cholesterol combines with other lipids and proteins to form a water-soluble spherical structure called a **lipoprotein**.

In a lipoprotein, the polar head group of the phospholipids and the polar region of the proteins are oriented towards the surface where they interact with water (Figure 18.29). The nonpolar molecules and nonpolar parts of molecules are on the inside of the lipoprotein, so they do not interfere with water solubility.

We classify lipoproteins by how dense they are. **High-density lipoproteins (HDLs)** contain more protein than **low-density lipoproteins (LDLs)** and therefore have a higher overall density. Lipoproteins with different densities serve different functions. LDLs transport cholesterol from the liver to the tissues, where it is embedded in cell membranes (Figure 18.30). HDLs transport cholesterol from the tissues back to the liver. When LDLs supply more cholesterol to the tissues than is needed, the excess cholesterol is deposited in the walls of our arteries, forming plaque. Arterial plaque leads to cardiovascular disease. As a result, people often refer to LDL cholesterol as "bad" cholesterol.

HDLs, on the other hand, transport cholesterol back to the liver where it is either eliminated or used to make hormones. This process reduces the level of cholesterol in the blood. For this reason, HDL cholesterol is referred to as "good" cholesterol.

Figure 18.30 Lipoprotein Function.

Lipoproteins help transport cholesterol in the body.

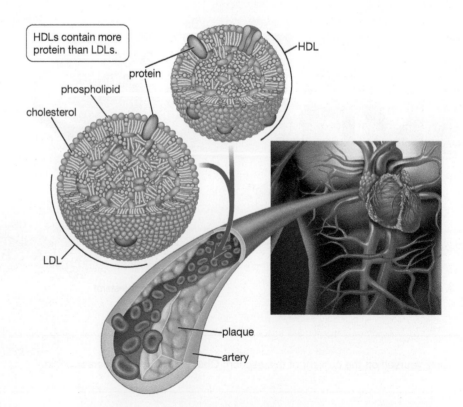

HDLs contain more protein than LDLs.

protein
phospholipid
cholesterol
HDL
LDL
plaque
artery

Figure 18.31 Female Sex Hormones.

Birth control pills contain synthetic hormones that prevent pregnancy.

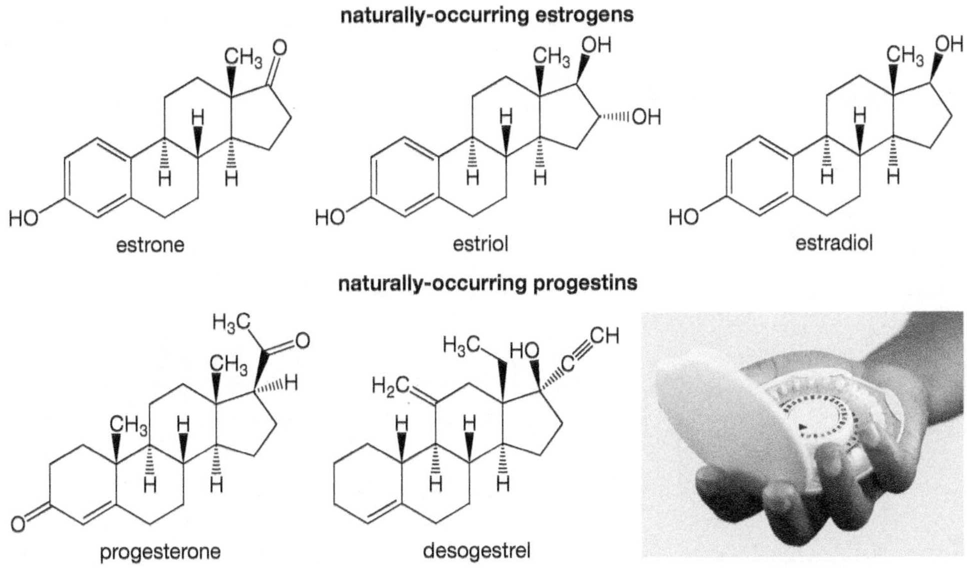

naturally-occurring estrogens

estrone

estriol

estradiol

naturally-occurring progestins

progesterone

desogestrel

Steroid Hormones

Cholesterol also is an important building block for hormones. Recall from the unit introduction that hormones are signaling molecules that regulate an array of important functions in the body. Several types of molecules act as hormones including both small proteins and steroids. In this section, we explore two categories of **steroidal hormones** that are produced in the body, the **sex hormones** and the **corticosteroids,** and several synthetic steroid hormones.

Sex hormones are perhaps some of the best-known hormones. There are two types of female sex hormones, **estrogens** and **progestins** (Figure 18.31). Estrogens signal the development and regulation of the female reproductive system as well as secondary sex characteristics such as the enlargement of breasts and the widening of the hips. Progestins also help prepare the uterus for a fertilized egg.

Male sex hormones are **androgens** (Figure 18.32). Produced in the testes, androgens drive the development of secondary sex characteristics in males such as the growth of facial hair and the deepening of the voice. Females produce lower concentrations of androgens, just as males produce lower levels of estrogens.

Each steroid hormone contains three six-membered rings and one five-membered ring. These molecules are also fairly nonpolar, allowing them to diffuse freely across cell membranes. Because they are mostly nonpolar and fat soluble, steroid hormone molecules tend to accumulate in our stored fat. This is also the case for hormone mimics such as BPA (see Unit 7 Introduction). Fat soluble toxins and hormone mimics are problematic because they can be released

Figure 18.32 Male Sex Hormones.

naturally-occurring androgens

testosterone

androsterone

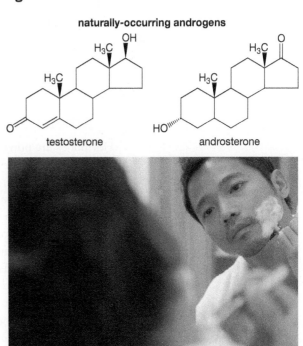

Figure 18.33 Corticosteroids.

These steroid hormones are produced in the adrenal glands on the kidneys and carry out unique functions in the body. Cortisone is released when the body is under stress. Cortisone shots are used to increase the cortisone response and reduce pain at the site of an injury. Aldosterone regulates blood pressure, and cortisol increases blood sugar and aids in metabolism.

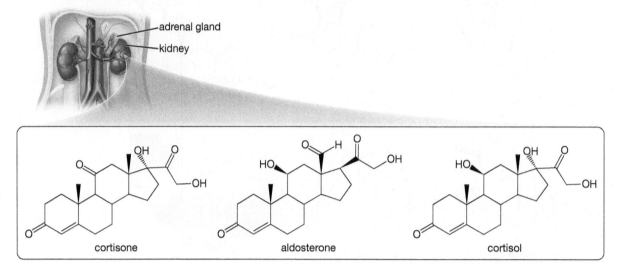

cortisone   aldosterone   cortisol

back into the body when the fat is metabolized for energy or transferred to an infant during breast feeding.

Another family of steroid hormones is the corticosteroids, which are produced in the adrenal glands located above each kidney. Aldosterone, cortisone, and cortisol are three important corticosteroids (Figure 18.33). Cortisone is released in response to stress and functions to suppress the immune system and reduce pain and swelling at the site of an injury. Cortisone injections are given by medical professionals to temporarily relieve pain and swelling. Aldosterone regulates blood pressure by controlling the concentration of Na^+ and K^+ in body fluids. Cortisol increases blood sugar and regulates carbohydrate metabolism. The structure of all of these molecules contains the characteristic four rings of steroid hormones, as well as several carbonyl and alcohol groups.

 Apply what you have just learned: **Practice 18.19 and 18.20** in the Pearson eText.

Synthetic Steroid Hormones

Hormones are powerful chemical messengers. Their ability to trigger a broad, rapid response from a very low concentration makes them great targets for drug development (Figure 18.34). Digoxin, for example, is a steroid hormone drug that is used to treat a variety of heart conditions. Prednisone is a steroid hormone medication commonly prescribed to treat allergic and autoimmune disorders.

Synthetic androgens called **anabolic steroids** are ingested to promote muscle growth and are often used by body builders and other athletes. There are many different anabolic steroids used in bodybuilding including tetrahydrogestrinone (THG), which has been used by athletes to gain an unfair advantage.

Many birth control products are also synthetic steroid hormones. To produce these drugs, the naturally occurring hormones estrogen and progesterone are synthetically manufactured and sometimes modified. Medroxyprogesterone acetate is an example of progestin-based birth control that is chemically modified to function as birth control.

Figure 18.34 Synthetic Steroid Hormones.

A) Digoxin is a synthetic steroid hormone that is prescribed for a variety of heart conditions. **B)** Prednisone is a synthetic corticosteroid drug derived from cortisone and used to treat autoimmune disorders such as rheumatoid arthritis. **C)** Medroxyprogesterone acetate (MPA) is prescribed for birth control and as an estrogen replacement therapy for post-menopausal women. **D)** Tetrahydrogestrinone (THG) is an anabolic steroid used to enhance muscle development.

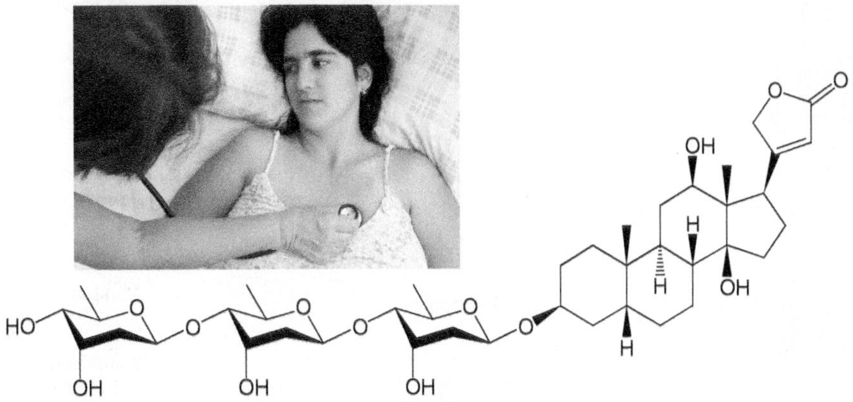

A   digoxin

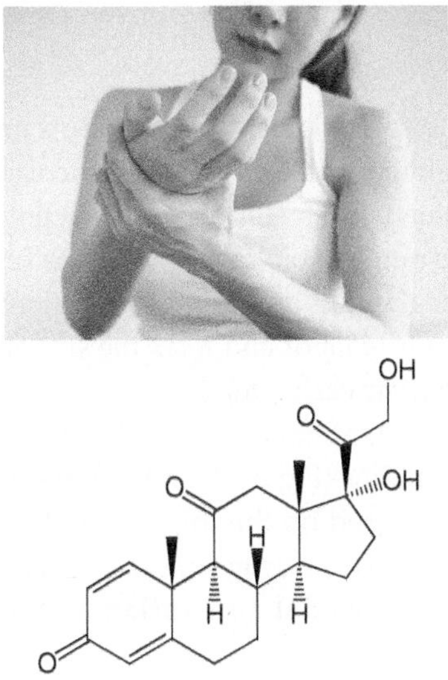

B   prednisone 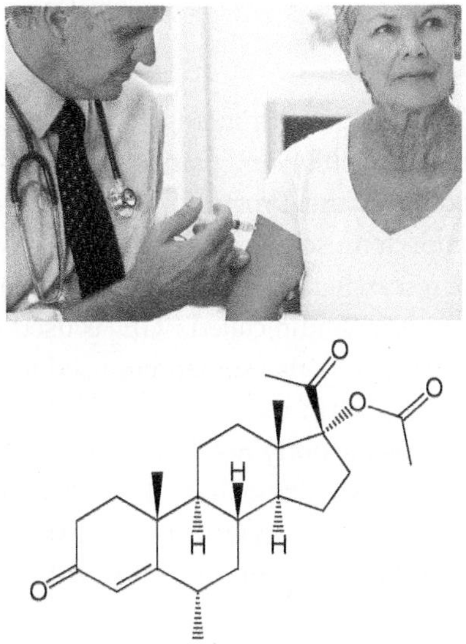   C medroxyprogesterone acetate (MPA) 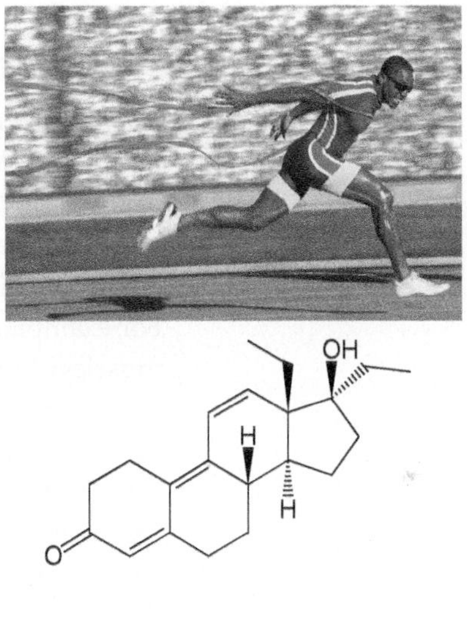   D   tetrahydrogestrinone (THG)

Quiz yourself on the content of this section: **Check 18.5** in the Pearson eText.

18.6 Prostaglandins and Leukotrienes

Have you ever stubbed your toe on a coffee table, slammed your finger in the car door, or cut yourself with a knife while chopping vegetables? If so, you probably noticed that the injury began to swell and hurt (Figure 18.35). This response by the body is due to **eicosanoids**, which are lipids that are synthesized from the 20-carbon polyunsaturated fatty acid, arachidonic acid. (Eicosanoid is derived from the Greek word for 20– eikosi). Eicosanoids function as temporary chemical messengers that act near the place in the body where they are produced. This is different from how hormones function. Hormones, in contrast, are synthesized at various locations in the body and *then* transported to other locations for action. **Prostaglandins** and **leukotrienes** are two types of eicosanoids.

Figure 18.35 Eicosanoids.

This family of lipids are produced in the body from arachidonic acid, a 20-carbon fatty acid. They are responsible for the pain and inflammation response at the site of an injury.

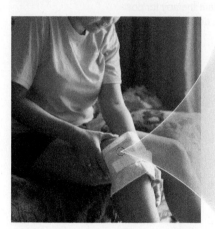

Prostaglandins

Prostaglandins are lipids with intense physiological effects. Some prostaglandins are responsible for inflammation and pain at the site of an injury, while others either increase or decrease blood pressure. Prostaglandins also function to both stimulate contractions and relax the smooth muscles of the uterus. This wide range of biological functions has enticed medical researchers to explore the use of prostaglandins as natural medications. For example, a prostaglandin called PGE_2 is used to induce labor and relax the smooth muscles of the uterus. It is also sometimes used to terminate early pregnancies.

Ibuprofen and aspirin relieve pain and decrease inflammation by inhibiting the production enzymes the body needs to make prostaglandins (Figure 18.36). A range of other anti-inflammatory drugs have been developed based on the inhibition of the enzymes responsible for the synthesis of prostaglandins. These drugs, including aspirin and ibuprofen, are commonly referred to as **nonsteroidal anti-inflammatory drugs (NSAIDs)**.

Figure 18.36 Ibuprofen.

Ibuprofen blocks the production of prostaglandins, reducing pain and inflammation.

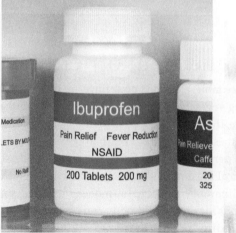

Prostaglandins are characterized by a five-membered ring at one end and a carboxylic acid group at the other end of the molecule. The structures of prostaglandins vary depending on which groups are attached to the five-membered ring. For example, prostaglandin E (PGE_1) has a ketone group on the five-membered ring and prostaglandin F (PGF_2) has a hydroxyl group. The subscripts indicate how many carbon-carbon double bonds are in the molecule.

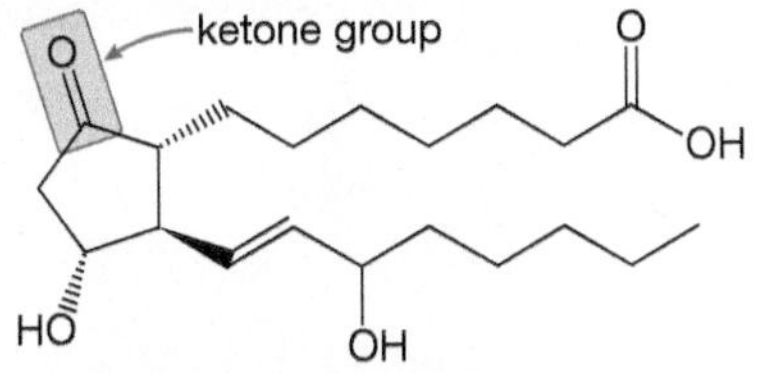

Leukotrienes

Leukotrienes are another type of lipid that the body makes from arachidonic acid to carry out a function in the location where they are produced. Leukotrienes constrict smooth muscles, especially in the lungs. For this reason, they have been identified as molecules that are involved in the asthmatic response. Asthma is a lung disease that constricts the airways making it difficult to breathe (Figure 18.37). Leukotrienes are the molecules in the body that initiate this airway constriction response. Newer asthma drugs block the synthesis of leukotrienes from arachidonic acid. For example, the drug Montelukast inhibits the enzymes involved in the synthesis of the leukotriene LTD_4. This helps to reverse the constricted airways associated with an asthma attack.

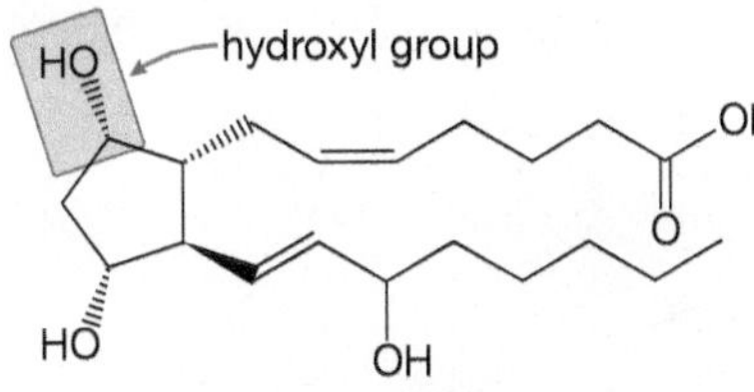

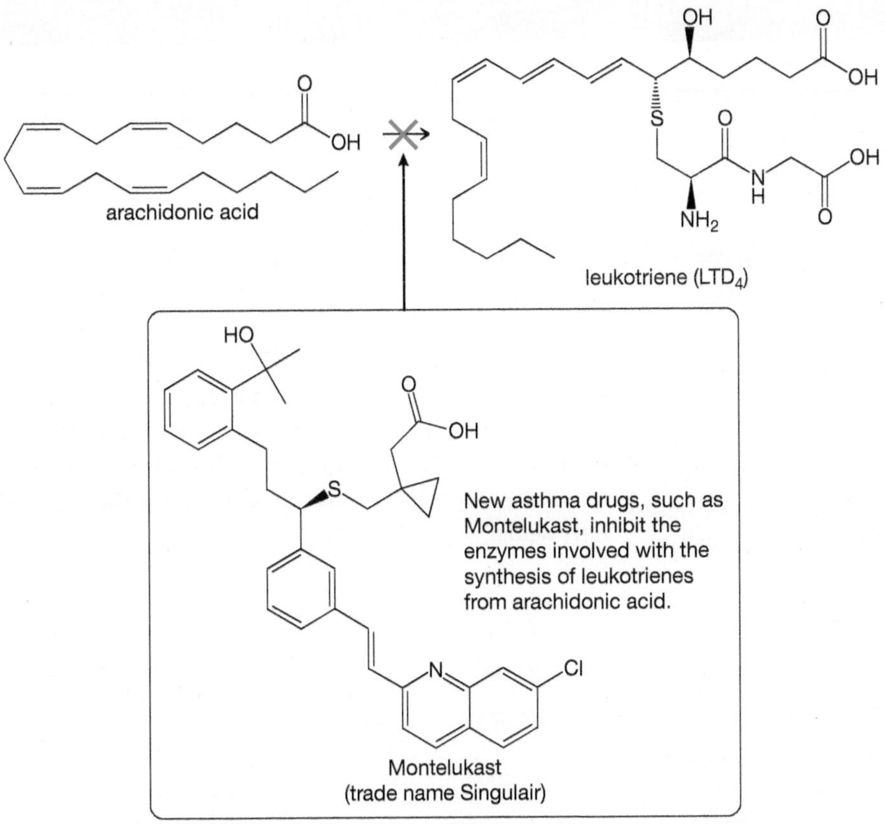

New asthma drugs, such as Montelukast, inhibit the enzymes involved with the synthesis of leukotrienes from arachidonic acid.

Montelukast
(trade name Singulair)

Figure 18.37 Asthma.

Leukotrienes can constrict the smooth muscles lining the airways in our lungs. The drug Montelukast blocks the production of these leukotrienes.

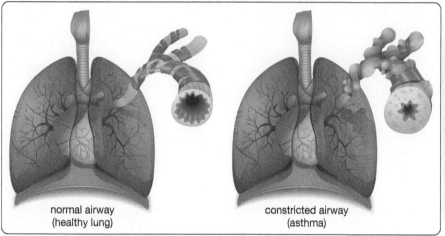

normal airway
(healthy lung)

constricted airway
(asthma)

 Quiz yourself on the content of this section: **Check 18.6** in the Pearson eText.

Chapter Summary

18.1 Lipids and Fatty Acids

Learning Objective: Classify fatty acids and describe how double bonds impact fatty acid melting points.

Each type of lipid biomolecule is composed of a large hydrocarbon region and one or more polar group. Lipids are overall nonpolar molecules and therefore are insoluble in water. Lipids serve many functions in the body including storing energy, insulating internal organs, and acting as chemical messengers. Fatty acids are lipid molecules that each contain a long unbranched hydrocarbon chain with a carboxylic acid at one end. The hydrocarbon chain of a fatty acid can be saturated (no carbon-carbon double bonds) or unsaturated (one or more carbon-carbon double bonds). Most naturally occurring unsaturated fatty acids are in the *cis* form. The kink in the chain formed by the *cis* double bond makes it difficult for unsaturated fatty acid molecules to pack closely together. For this reason, unsaturated fatty acids have lower melting points than saturated fatty acids.

Key Terms

alpha end (from BioConnect 18.1)	lipid	trans fatty acids (trans fat)
fatty acid	omega end (from BioConnect 18.1)	unsaturated fatty acid
hydrophobic	saturated fatty acid	
hydrophilic	steroid	

18.2 Waxes

Learning Objective: Recognize and draw the structure of waxes including the carboxylic acid and alcohol portions of wax molecules.

Waxes are lipids that are made up of a fatty acid and an alcohol that has a long hydrocarbon chain. The two hydrocarbon chains produce a wax molecule that is very nonpolar and therefore insoluble in water. Waxes occur naturally in plants and animals such as on the surface of fruit and leaves and on the skin or fur of animals.

Key Term

wax

18.3 Triacylglycerols

Learning Objective: Draw the structure of triacylglycerols and predict the hydrolysis products of triacylglycerols.

Fatty acids are stored in the human body as triacylglycerols. Triacylglycerols are lipid molecules that are composed of a triester made from one glycerol molecule and three molecules of fatty acids. Triacylglycerols can be saturated or unsaturated depending on the number of double bonds in the fatty acid chains. Fats that come from animal sources are triacylglycerols that are solids at room temperature. Oils are also triacylglycerols, but oils are generally derived from plants and are liquids at room temperature. Triacylglycerols undergo hydrogenation of carbon-carbon double bonds in the presence of hydrogen gas (H_2). A triacylglycerol can also undergo hydrolysis in the presence of water to produce three fatty acid molecules and glycerol. In the body, the enzyme lipase acts as the catalyst in this triacylglycerol hydrolysis reaction.

VisibleChem Video 18.1: Reactions of Triacylglycerols

VisibleChem Video 18.2: Metabolism of Triacylglycerols

Key Terms

adipose cell	monounsaturated triacylglycerols	saponification
fat	oil	triacylglycerol
lipase	polyunsaturated triacylglycerols	triglyceride

18.4 Phospholipids

Learning Objective: Identify the two common types of phospholipids and describe the role of phosphoacylglycerols in cell membrane structure.

Phospholipids are lipids that each contain a phosphorus atom. The most common phospholipids are phosphoacylglycerols and sphingomyelins. A phosphoacylglycerol contains two fatty acids similar to a triacylglycerol molecule, but the third group on the phosphoacylglycerol molecule is a phosphoric acid with an amino alcohol group attached. Phosphoacylglycerols each contain a nonpolar tail composed of two fatty acid molecules and a polar head composed of glycerol, phosphate, and an amino alcohol.

Cell membranes are composed of two layers of phosphoacylglycerol molecules. A sphingomyelin molecule contains a sphingosine in place of glycerol. Sphingomyelins are found in the myelin sheath, the coating surrounding nerve cells that increases the speed of nerve impulses and protects the nerve.

BioConnect 18.2: Cholera and the Cell Membrane

VisibleChem Video 18.3: Structure and Function of Phosphoacylglycerols

VisibleChem Video 18.4: Structure and Function of Sphingomyelin

Key Terms

amino alcohol	phosphoacylglycerol	sphingomyelin
hypertonic (from BioConnect 18.2)	phospholipid	sphingosine
nonpolar tail	polar head	

18.5 Steroids and Hormones

Learning Objective: Recognize the general structure of steroids and steroid hormones and be familiar with several examples of each.

Steroids are lipids that each contain three six-membered carbon rings and one five-membered carbon ring. Cholesterol is one of the most common members of the steroid family. Due to the insolubility of cholesterol in water, cholesterol is transferred from the liver to the tissues by lipoproteins. Low-density lipoproteins (LDLs) transport cholesterol to the tissues. When there is more LDL in the body than is needed, the excess is deposited in the arteries as plaque. High-density lipoproteins (HDLs) transport cholesterol back to the liver where it is either eliminated or used to make hormones. Hormones are molecules produced in one part of that body that elicit a response in another part. Two important classes of steroid hormones are the sex hormones and the corticosteroids.

Key Terms

anabolic steroid	estrogen	progestin
androgen	high-density lipoprotein (HDL)	steroid hormone
corticosteroid	lipoprotein	sex hormones
cholesterol	low-density lipoprotein (LDL)	

18.6 Prostaglandins and Leukotrienes

Learning Objective: Describe the general structural characteristics and biological activity of prostaglandins and leukotrienes.

Eicosanoids are lipids. They function as temporary chemical messengers that act near the place in the body where they are produced. Prostaglandins and leukotrienes are two types of eicosanoids that are both synthesized from the 20-carbon polyunsaturated fatty acid, arachidonic acid. Prostaglandin molecules are characterized by a five-membered ring at one end of the molecule and a carboxylic acid group at the other end. Some prostaglandins are responsible for inflammation and pain at the site of an injury, while other prostaglandins either increase or decrease blood pressure. Prostaglandins also function to contract and relax the smooth muscles of the uterus. Similarly, leukotrienes function to constrict smooth muscles, especially in the lungs and have been identified as molecules that are involved in the asthmatic response. A variety of drugs have been developed to block the synthesis of leukotrienes as a way to prevent asthmatic reactions.

Key Terms

eicosanoid
leukotriene
nonsteroidal anti-inflammatory drug (NSAID)
prostaglandin

End-of-Chapter Quiz

Have you mastered the content of this chapter? Try the **End-of-Chapter Quiz** in the Pearson eText.

1. Which class of lipids does this molecule belong to?

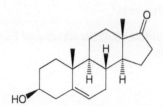

  a) wax
  b) sphingolipid
  c) triacylglycerol
  d) steroid

2. Which statement accurately describes the similarities and differences between triacylglycerols and glycerophospholipids?

  a) A glycerophospholipid consists of glycerol connected to a phosphate and an amino alcohol as well as a wax and a fatty acid. A triacylglycerol is composed of glycerol connected to three fatty acids.

  b) A glycerophospholipid consists of glycerol connected to a phosphate and an amino acid as well as three fatty acids. A triacylglycerol is composed of glycerol connected to three fatty acids.

c) A glycerophospholipid consists of glycerol connected to a phosphate and an amino alcohol as well as two fatty acids. A triacylglycerol is composed of glycerol connected to three fatty acids.

d) A glycerophospholipid is composed of glycerol connected to three fatty acids, whereas a triacylglycerol consists of glycerol connected to a phosphate and an amino alcohol and two fatty acids.

3. Saturated fatty acids have higher melting points than unsaturated fatty acids with *cis* C=C double bonds because ______.

a) saturated fatty acids have more carboxylic acid groups making them more acidic and harder to melt

b) the *cis* double bonds in saturated fatty acids introduce kinks in the long hydrocarbon chain making it difficult for molecules to pack closely together

c) saturated fatty acids always have two more carbon atoms than unsaturated fatty acids, so their carbon chain has weaker intermolecular forces

d) saturated fatty acids always have two fewer carbon atoms than unsaturated fatty acids so saturated fatty acids cannot pack as tightly together

4. Omega-3 and omega-6 fatty acids all contain ______.

a) the same number of carbon atoms in their fatty acid chains

b) *trans* carbon-carbon double bonds

c) carboxylic acid hydrogen atoms that are more acidic than those on non-omega fatty acids

d) *cis* carbon-carbon double bonds

---

5. Which molecule is a *cis* polyunsaturated fatty acid?

a)

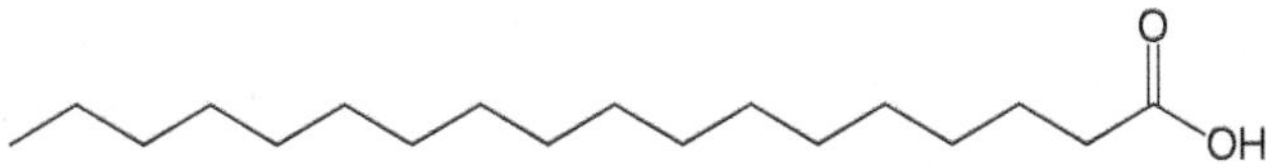
O
OH

b)

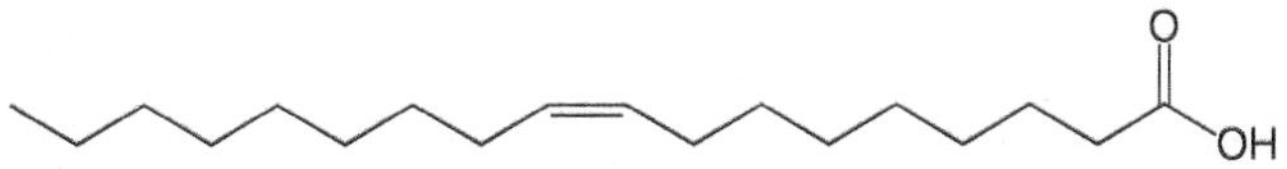
O
OH

c)

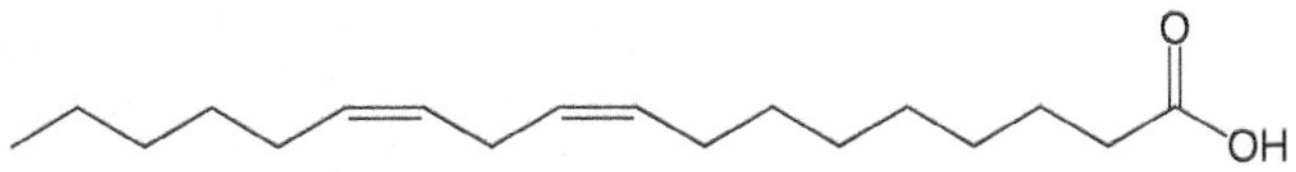
O
OH

d)

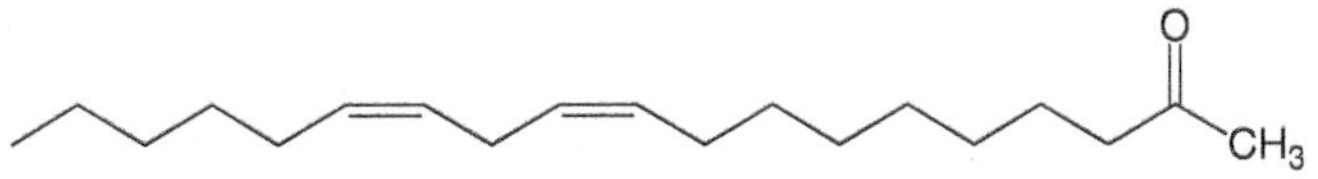
O
CH3

6. Which molecule is *not* a wax?

a)

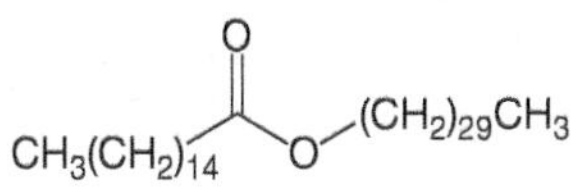
O
CH3(CH2)14
O
(CH2)29CH3

b)

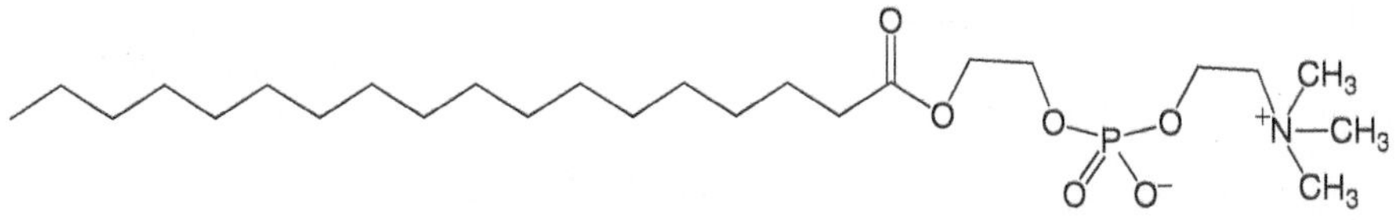
O
O
O
P
O
O
O–
+N—CH3
CH3
CH3

c)

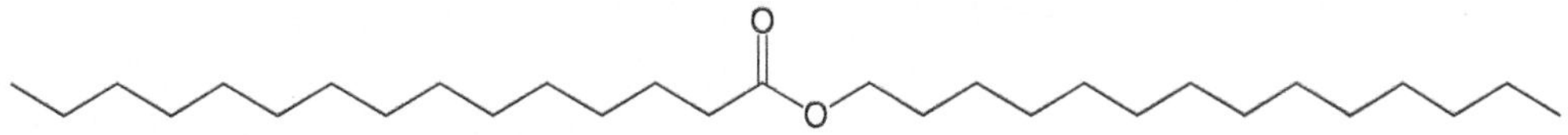
O
O

d)

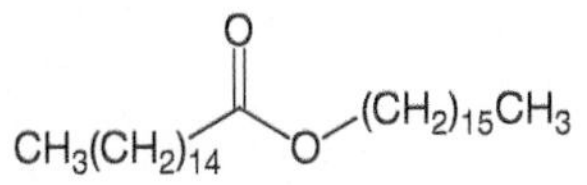
O
CH3(CH2)14
O
(CH2)15CH3

7. The chemical linkage (functional group) that connects the two building blocks of a wax molecule together is ______.

a) an ester

b) a ketone

c) a hemiacetal

d) a carboxylic acid

8. Identify the polyunsaturated triacylglycerol.

a)

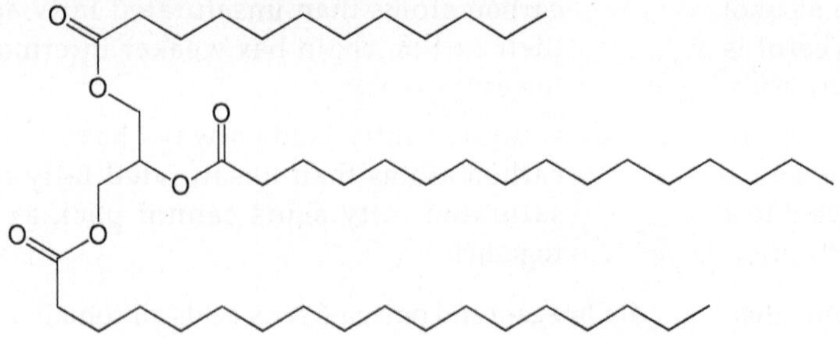

b)

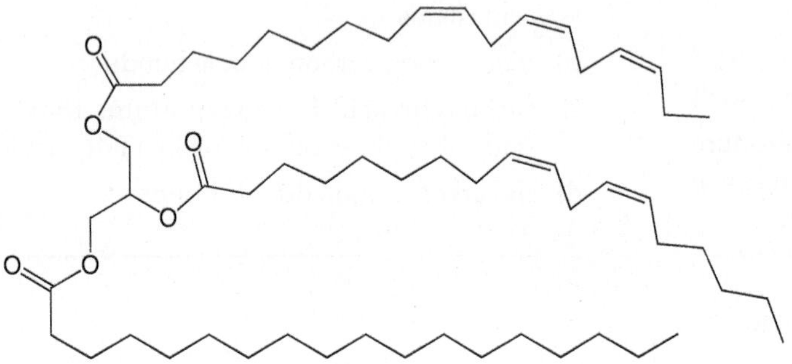

c)

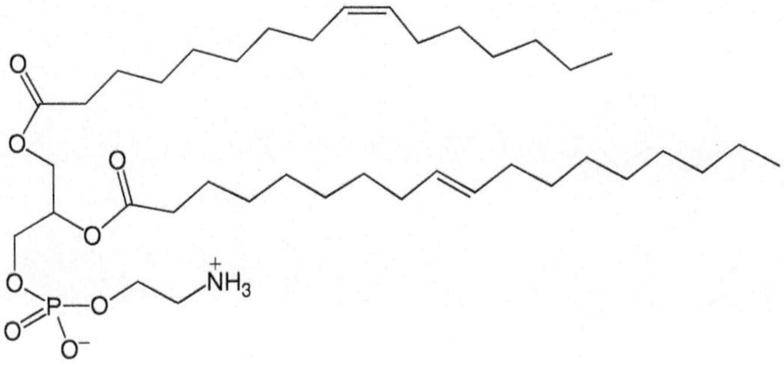

d)

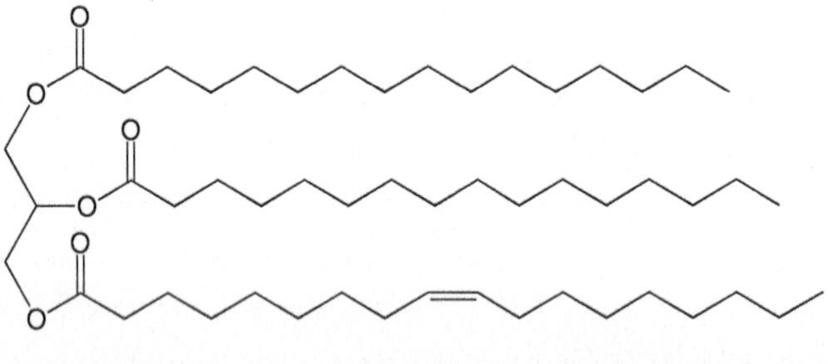

9. What products form as a result of this complete hydrolysis reaction?

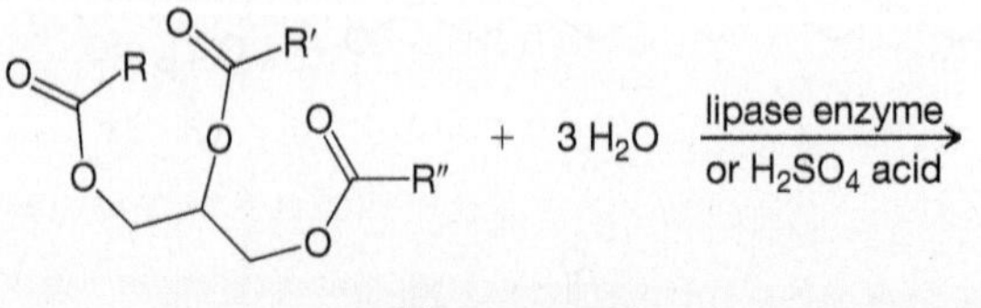

a)

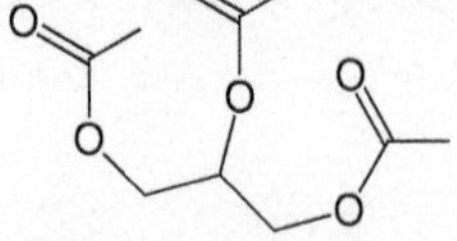 + R + R′ + R″

b)

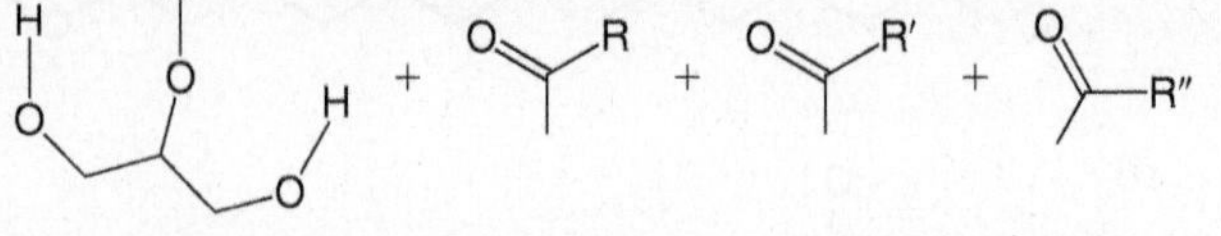

c)

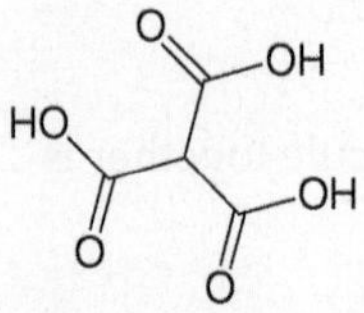

+ HOR + HOR′ + HOR″

d)

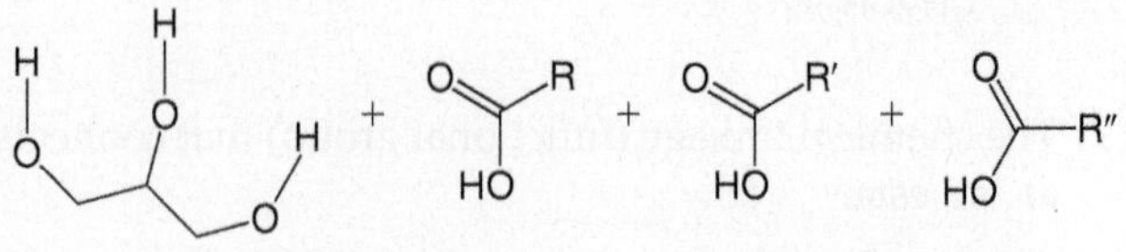

10. What is the expected product of this complete hydrogenation reaction?

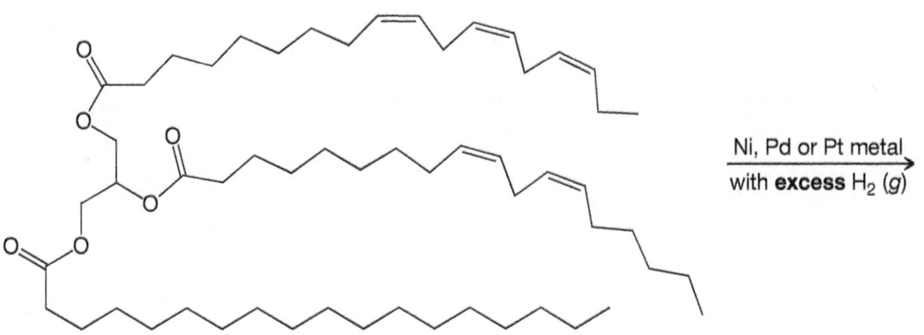

Ni, Pd or Pt metal
with **excess** H$_2$ (g)

a)

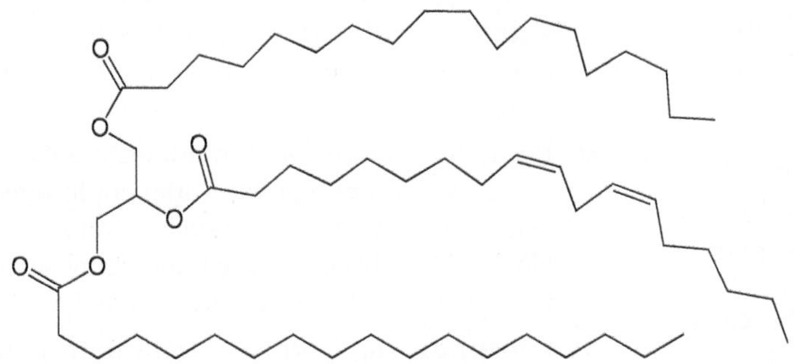

b)

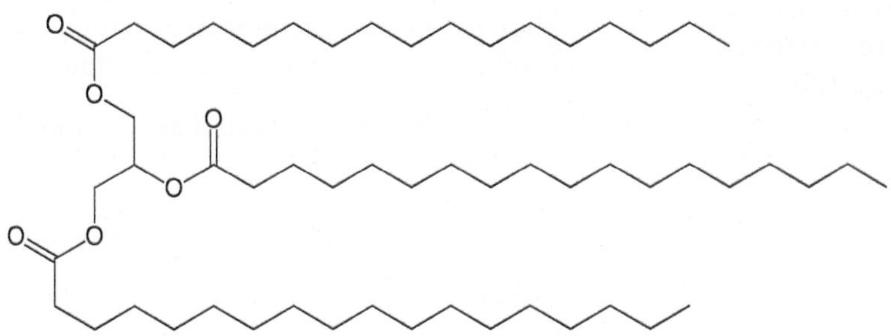

c)

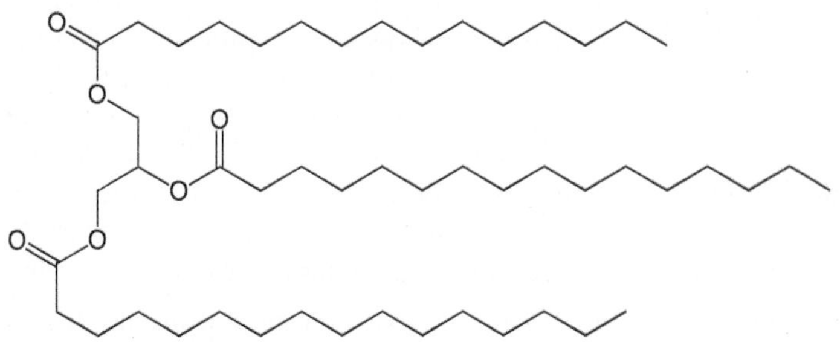

d)

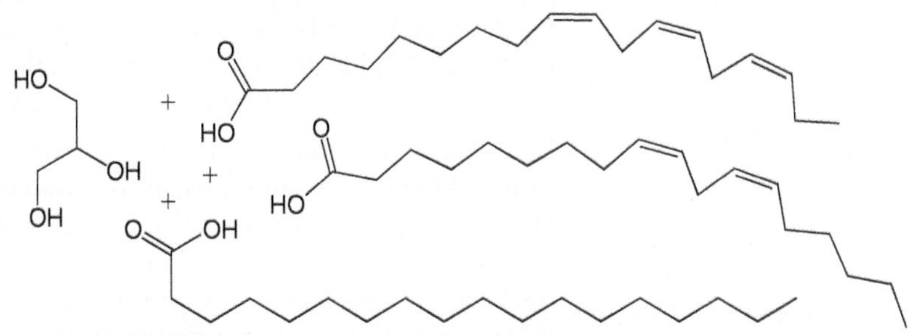

11. Select the correct description of the basic structural similarities and differences between a phosphoacylglycerol and a sphingomyelin.
    a) Both types of lipid molecules contain two ester groups and a phosphate group connected to an amino alcohol. Phosphoacylglycerols have glycerol as the backbone molecule and contain two fatty acids, whereas sphingomyelins have sphingosine as the backbone molecule and contain only one fatty acid that can only be as long as the myelin sheath.
    b) Both types of lipid molecules contain at least one fatty acid and a phosphate group connected to an amino alcohol. Phosphoacylglycerols have glycerol as the backbone molecule and contain two fatty acids, whereas sphingomyelins have sphingosine as the backbone molecule and contain only one fatty acid.
    c) Both types of lipid molecules contain only one fatty acid as well as a phosphate group connected to an amino acid. Phosphoacylglycerols have sphingosine as the backbone molecule and always contain an omega-3 fatty acid, whereas sphingomyelins have glycerol as the backbone molecule and always contain a *trans*-fat.
    d) Both types of lipid molecules contain at least two fatty acids along with a phosphate group connected to an amino alcohol. Phosphoacylglycerols have glycerol as the backbone molecule and contain two *trans* fatty acids, whereas sphingomyelins have sphingosine as the backbone molecule and contain only one saturated fatty acid.

12. Which molecule is *not* an amino alcohol commonly found in phosphoacylglycerols?

    a) b)

    c) d)

13. What are the components that make up this phospholipid?

    a) glycerol, palmitic acid, phosphate, and choline
    b) glycerol, stearic acid, phosphate, and ethanolamine
    c) sphingosine, lauric acid, phosphate, and choline
    d) glycerol, palmitic acid, phosphate, and serine

14. Which statement correctly explains how phosphoacylglycerol molecules help form cell membranes?
    a) Phosphoacylglycerols contain sphingolipid regions, which allow them to interact with both polar and nonpolar substances. The short nonpolar tails can align to form a layer with the glycerol head groups facing water on each side.
    b) Phosphoacylglycerols contain both polar and nonpolar regions, which allow them to interact with both polar and nonpolar substances. The nonpolar tails can align to form a membrane with the polar head groups facing water on each side.
    c) Phosphoacylglycerols contain only polar regions allowing them to regulate water, ionic substances, and other polar molecules such as amino acids and DNA. These dipole-dipole interactions are needed to form new cell walls during cell division.
    d) Phosphoacylglycerols contain both polar and nonpolar regions allowing them to interact with both polar and nonpolar substances. The polar tails align to form a structural layer with the nonpolar head groups facing water on each side.

15. Elevated levels of which steroid are commonly associated with heart disease?
    a) epinephrine
    b) cholesterol
    c) estradiol
    d) cortisone

16. Which statements about high-density lipoproteins (HDLs) and low-density lipoproteins (LDLs) are correct?
    a) HDLs transport cholesterol from the liver to the tissues where it is embedded in cell membranes. LDLs transport cholesterol from the tissues back to the liver. When HDLs supply more cholesterol to the tissues than is needed, the excess cholesterol is deposited in the walls of the arteries, forming plaque.
    b) LDLs transport cholesterol from the stomach to the tissues where it is embedded in cell membranes. HDLs transport cholesterol from the heart back to the kidneys. When LDLs supply more cholesterol to the tissues than is needed, the excess cholesterol is deposited in the walls of the arteries, forming plaque.
    c) LDLs transport cholesterol from the liver to the tissues where it is embedded in cell membranes. HDLs transport cholesterol from the tissues back to the liver. When LDLs supply more cholesterol to the tissues than is needed, the excess cholesterol is deposited in the walls of the arteries, forming plaque.

d) HDLs transport cholesterol from the blood to the heart where it is embedded in the arteries forming plaque. LDLs hydrolyze cholesterol and transport the fragmented fatty acids to the liver for removal. When HDLs supply more cholesterol to the heart than is needed, this sends a signal to the body to store excess fat in the body and around the waistline causing obesity.

17. Which steroid hormones are primarily involved in preparing the uterus for a fertilized egg in females?
  a) estrogens   **b)** progestins
  c) androgens   **d)** corticosteroids

18. Which molecule is a prostaglandin?

  a)

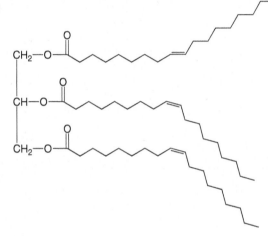

  b)

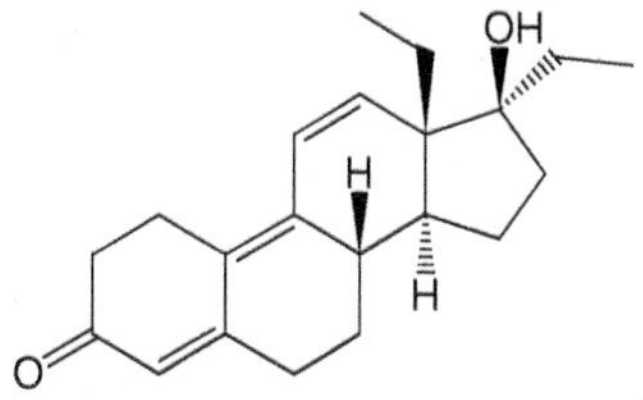

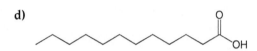

  c)

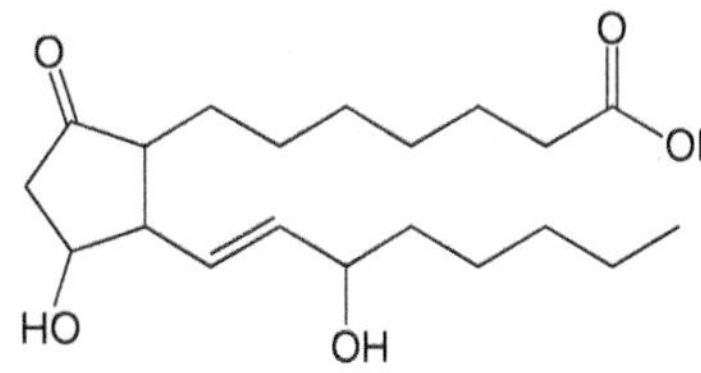

  d)

19. Prostaglandins and leukotrienes are derived from which specific fatty acid? How many carbon atoms are associated with these two classes of molecules?
  a) palmitic acid; 20 carbons
  b) oleic acid; 18 carbon atoms
  c) arachidonic acid; 20 carbons
  d) stearic acid, 18 carbons

Unit 7
Bringing It All Together

A Closer Look at the Chemistry of BPA

CHEMISTRY APPLICATION We opened Unit 7 with a look at the potential risks posed by the hormone mimic, BPA. Let's now look more closely at why so many of us are exposed to BPA and what we can do to limit this exposure.

BPA has been used for decades as an inexpensive reagent to produce the **polymer**, polycarbonate (Figure U7.6). Polycarbonate is tough and transparent, making it useful in a wide range of consumer products. Unfortunately, some residual BPA remains after polymerization, potentially contaminating our food, water, or hands. In addition, polycarbonates can break down over time and release BPA.

Regulatory agencies such as the Food and Drug Administration (FDA) and the Environmental Protection Agency (EPA) continue to study the effects of BPA. The EPA for example, recognizes that BPA is a reproductive toxin in animals but suggests that the exposure levels in humans are below the level of potential concern. Despite the limited regulation on BPA in consumer products, many companies are choosing to address consumer concerns by switching to BPA-free plastics.

Many of the newer BPA-free plastics contain *analogues,* or structurally similar molecules such as bisphenol S (BPS) or bisphenol F (BPF) (Figure U7.7). These products can be labeled "BPA-free", potentially making them more attractive to consumers.

Scientists have started studying the effects of BPS and BPF on human cells. Initial results suggest that molecules such as BPS and BPF may have as much biological activity, if not more, than the BPA they are replacing. These findings suggest that the search for a truly safe, inert, plastic may not be over yet.

Figure U7.6 Polycarbonate.

bisphenol A (BPA)

phosgene

polycarbonate

Figure U7.7 BPA Analogues such as BPS and BPF are used to Polymerize Many "BPA-free" Plastics.

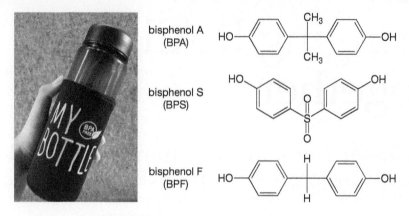

Questions to Think About

1. Examine the structure of BPA, BPS, and BPF. What similarities do you notice? Would you expect them to have similar biological activity? Why or why not?

2. What functional groups are present on BPA, BPS, and BPF? How might these functional groups affect the solubility of the molecules?

3. What is a hormone and why do scientists call BPA a hormone mimic?

4. Why are hormone mimics harmful to animals and humans even at low levels of exposure?

A Closer Look at the Data

Our exposure to BPA can come from surprising places. Most receipts, for example, contain very high levels of BPA. (Figure U7.8; BPA is used in the outer layer of the paper as a print developer.) While food containers are an obvious source of BPA in our

Figure U7.8 Most Receipts are Printed on Paper Coated with BPA.

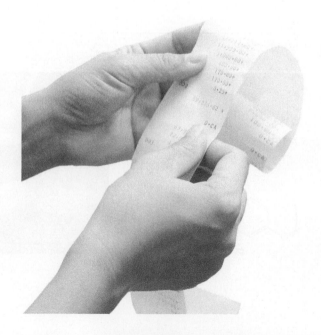

bodies, a group of researchers from Missouri wondered how much BPA we might be either absorbing directly or transferring to our food from handling these ubiquitous cash register receipts. They were also interested in understanding how the use of hand-sanitizers might affect this transfer.

To address these questions, the scientists recruited students at the University of Missouri to participate in a study. The students first handled a receipt with dry hands, and then immediately after again using a hand sanitizer to wet their hands. Researchers measured the levels of BPA on their hands at various points after they touched the receipt as well as after they used the sanitizer. The participants were then asked to again use hand sanitizer before holding a BPA-containing receipt for four minutes and eating ten French fries with the BPA-contaminated hand, modeling common behavior at fast food restaurants. The researchers collected blood samples from the individuals both before they handled the receipt and at several time points following the experiment. Figure U7.9 is from their paper.

Figure U7.9 A) Concentrations of BPA on Hands after Handling a Receipt with Hand Sanitizer (left) and Without Hand Sanitizer (right). **B)** Blood concentrations of BPA prior to (B = baseline levels) and after holding a BPA-containing receipt paper for 4 min followed by picking up and eating 10 French fries over 4 minutes with the BPA-contaminated hand.

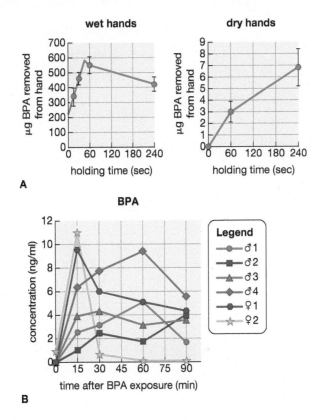

Questions to Think About

Examine Figure U7.9 and use it to answer the following questions:

1. Graphs can help reveal relationships between variables. What are the two variables shown in each graph in Figure U7.9?

2. Figure U7.9A shows the results of the dry hand vs. wet hand sanitizer comparison. What difference does the hand sanitizer seem to make? (Look carefully at the units on the vertical axis.)

3. Each line on the graph in U7.9B represents a specific individual. How are the responses of the individuals similar? What differences do you notice?

4. What does this data suggest to you about possible ways to reduce your exposure to BPA?

Reference

Horman, A. M., vom Saal, G. S., Nagel, S. C., Stahlhut R. W., Moyer, C. L., Ellersieck, M. R., Welshons, W. V., Toutain, P. L., Taylor, J. A. Holding Thermal Receipt Paper and Eating Food after Using Hand Sanitizer Results in High Serum Bioactive and Urine Total Levels of Bisphenol A (BPA). *PLOS One* (2014)

Unit 8

Introduction

Exploring Amines, Amides, Amino Acids, Proteins, and Enzymes

Chapter 19: Amines and Neurotransmitters

Chapter 20: Amino Acids and Proteins

Chapter 21: Enzymes: Biological Catalysts

In the twenty years between 1999 and 2019, nearly 500,000 people died from opioid overdoses (Figure U8.1). In addition to the personal tragedies, the economic burden of this epidemic is staggering—an estimated $1,021 billion a year in healthcare costs, lost productivity, and other expenses. With the introduction of the synthetic drug fentanyl, drug overdoses became a leading cause of death for

---

Figure U8.1 Opioids.

Opioids include illegal drugs such as heroin, synthetic opioids such as fentanyl, and an array of prescription pain medications including oxycodone, codeine, and morphine.

adults under age 55 and the overall life expectancy for Americans began falling in 2014 due to fatal overdoses.

Why are these drugs so addictive and deadly? What steps can scientists and healthcare providers take to help reverse these dangerous trends?

Unit 8: Introduction
What Is an Opioid Drug and Why Are They So Addicting?

 To learn more about the challenges of the opioid crisis, watch **Video U8.1** in the Pearson eText.

Unit 8 opens with an overview of the nature of the opioid drug crisis in the U.S. **Opioids** are a class of molecules that bind to specialized receptors in the brain, triggering the release of chemical messengers. These chemical signals help block pain, slow breathing, and trigger a sense of calmness (Figure U8.2).

Because of their action on receptors in the spinal cord, opioid drugs are often prescribed to treat pain following injury or surgery. But in addition to blocking pain, the drugs can also trigger reward centers in the brain. The drugs become less effective over time, causing users to seek out higher doses and increasing their risk of a life-threatening overdose.

The risk of overdose increased dramatically when fentanyl became common in the illicit drug supply. Heroin is produced from opium poppies and must be processed and transported to the U.S. Fentanyl, in contrast, can be produced synthetically in a lab anywhere in the world. In addition, its greater potency means that much smaller volumes of the drug need to be smuggled (Figure U8.3). This reduces the cost of fentanyl and provides an incentive for illicit drug manufacturers to add this much more addictive synthetic opioid to their products.

Figure U8.2 Opioid Receptors.

Receptors are proteins that bind specific signaling molecules and trigger a response. Opioid receptors are located throughout the body. The receptors bind both naturally-occurring endorphins and opioids.

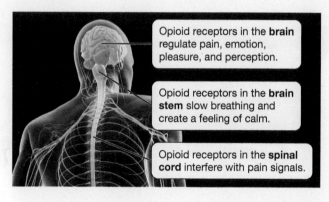

Figure U8.3 Opioid Molecules.

Both prescribed pain relievers such as oxycodone as well as illicit drugs such as heroin are driving the opioid crisis. The addition of fentanyl to the illicit drug supply has made the epidemic much more lethal.

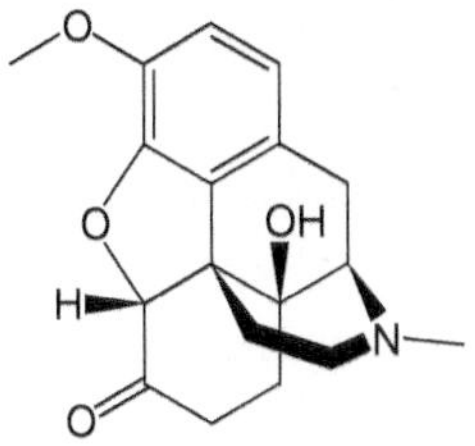

oxycodone

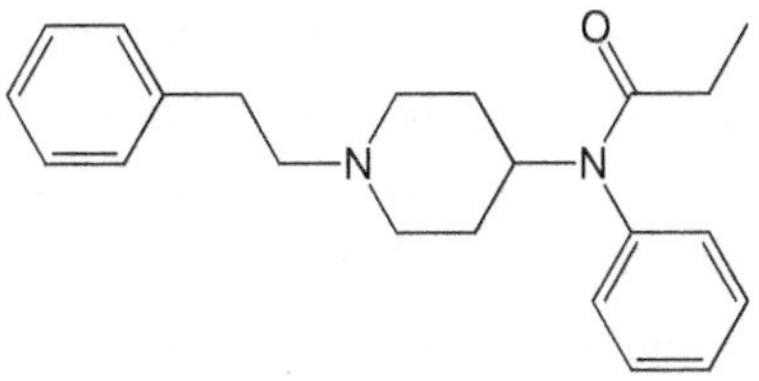

fentanyl

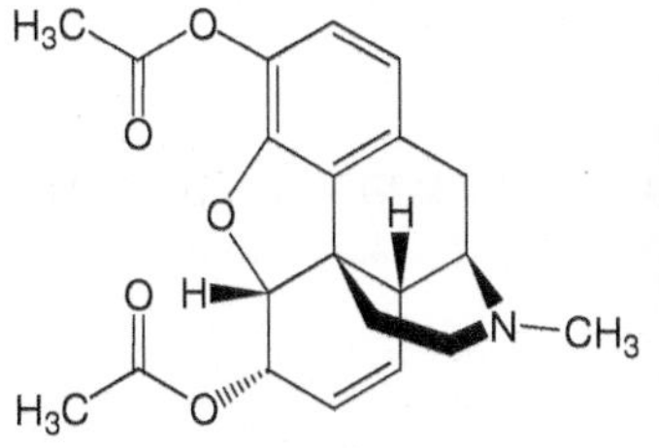

heroin

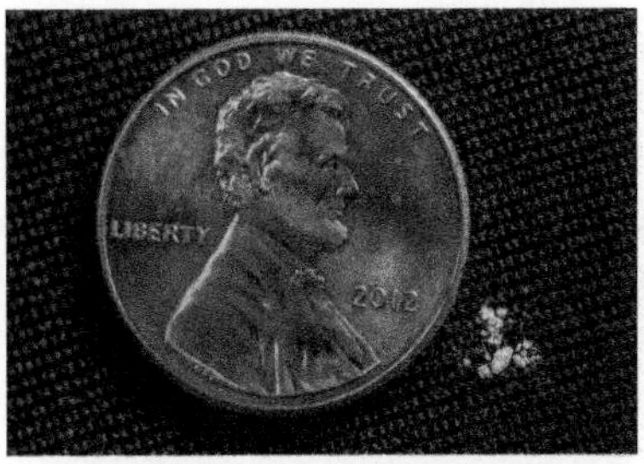

A 2 mg dose of fentanyl; 2 mg is lethal for most people.

Unit 8 Chemistry Application: What Is an Opioid Drug and Why Are They So Addicting?

The dramatic increase in opioid overdoses makes understanding the biology and chemistry of opioid addiction and treatment more urgent than ever. As in prior units, understanding this public health crisis will require an understanding of the structure and function of an array of molecules including amines, neurotransmitters, proteins, and enzymes (Figure U8.4).

Figure U8.4 Treating Opioid Addiction.

Some treatment approaches use molecules such as naloxone (Narcan) that bind and block opioid receptors in the brain.

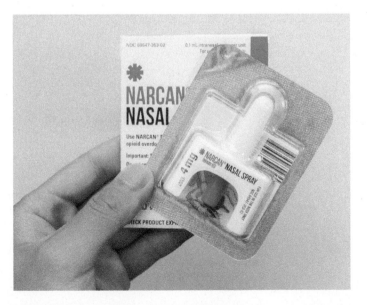

Questions to Think About

What chemistry do we need to know to better understand the opioid crisis? Here are some questions to consider as you move through Unit 8:

- What are opioid receptors? How does their structure anchor them in cell membranes and allow them to bind an array of opioids?

- What are neurotransmitters? How are they produced and recycled in the normal function of nerve cells?

- What other types of molecules are able to bind to opioid receptors and help treat addiction?

What chemistry would you like to know in order to more fully understand this problem?

Now that we have an overview of this unit, let's step into Chapters 19, 20, and 21 and learn more about the characteristics of some of the key molecules in the opioid drug crisis.

References

Wide-ranging online data for epidemiologic research (WONDER). Atlanta, GA: CDC, National Center for Health Statistics; 2020. Available at http://wonder.cdc.gov.

Florence C, Luo F, Rice K. The economic burden of opioid use disorder and fatal opioid overdose in the United States, 2017. Drug Alcohol Depend 2021;218:108350. https://doi.org/10.1016/j.drugalcdep.2020.108350

Chapter 19
Amines and Neurotransmitters

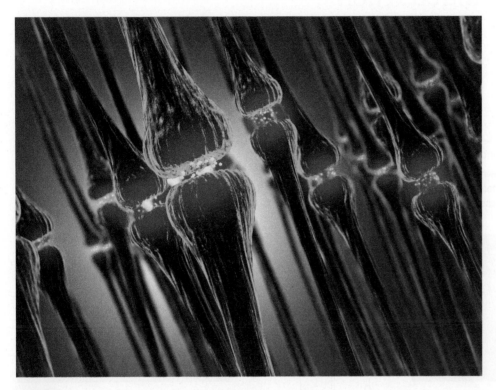

The diffusion of neurotransmitters between nerve cells provides the chemical basis for thoughts and actions.

 ## Chapter Outline

Learning Objectives

19.1 Identify amines and classify them as 1°, 2°, or 3°.

19.2 Describe how intermolecular forces affect boiling points and water solubility of amines.

19.3 Predict and draw the products of acid-base reactions of amines.

19.4 Describe the characteristics of alkaloids and provide examples.

19.5 Describe and provide examples of the general structure and physiological function of neurotransmitters.

19.6 Use the IUPAC system for naming organic compounds to convert from structure to name and from name to structure for amines and ammonium salts.

Introduction

We continue our exploration of key functional groups with a look at the structure and function of amines. These fascinating molecules play essential roles in both basic biology and the treatment of disease. Amines are found in a wide array of medicines and toxins and are important components of the DNA and proteins that make us who we are (Figure 19.1). In this chapter, we explore the diversity of amines and how amine structure and behavior can help us better understand this essential group of organic molecules.

Figure 19.1 Amines and Neurotransmitters.

A) Tranexamic acid (also known as TXA) is a medication used for the treatment of excessive blood loss from surgery, major trauma, childbirth, nosebleeds, and heavy menstruation. **B)** The highly addictive amine heroin is produced from morphine found in the sap of the poppy plant. **C)** The bases that make up the individual "letters" of our DNA (see BioConnect 6.1) and make each of us unique are also amines.

A   tranexamic acid   B   heroin   C   adenine

19.1 Structure of Amines

Amines are a diverse group of important organic molecules that contain nitrogen atoms. Amines form when one or more of the hydrogen atoms on the ammonia molecule (NH_3) is replaced with an alkyl or aromatic group. Recall that an alkyl group is a hydrocarbon missing one hydrogen atom. The basic amine functional group, therefore, is a nitrogen atom bonded to a combination of hydrogen atoms and carbon groups. We represent the general structure of amines using R for the carbon groups.

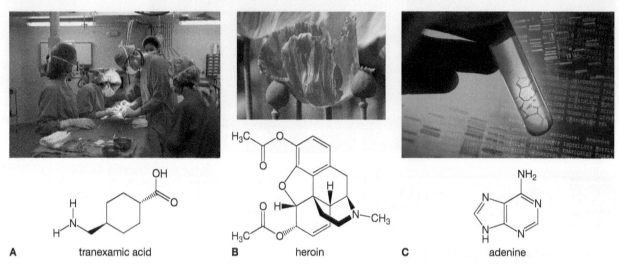

The amine functional group is distinct from the amide functional group. Recall that amides contain a nitrogen atom but also contain a carbonyl group (Section 17.1).

amide general structure

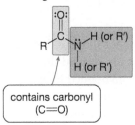

contains carbonyl
(C=O)

Methylamine, cadaverine, and triethylamine are three examples of amines (Figure 19.2). Note that we refer to these amine compounds here using their common names. We explain the IUPAC naming system for amines in Section 19.6. These three amine compounds are found in rotting fish and are responsible for much of its foul odor. Methylamine is a simple amine that has a methyl group (CH_3) bonded to the amino group. Cadaverine features two amino groups, one at each end of a five-carbon chain. Triethylamine is an amine in which the nitrogen atom is bonded to three carbon atoms and no hydrogen atoms.

Figure 19.2 Three Simple Amines.

Methylamine is the simplest amine; its nitrogen atom is bonded to a methyl group. Methylamine is used in industry and as a starting material for making many other organic molecules. Cadaverine has two amino groups and is produced as animal tissue begins to rot. Triethylamine is an amine that has a "fishy" smell. Triethylamine is also used in the production of a variety of larger molecules.

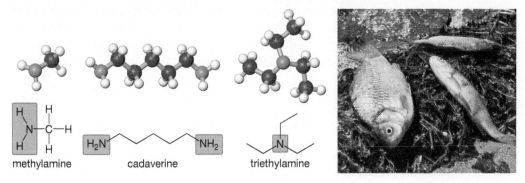

methylamine   cadaverine   triethylamine

Molecular Shape of Amines

Understanding the shape and chemical properties of amines allows us to better predict the functions of these important molecules. Similar to ammonia (NH_3), amines contain a nitrogen atom that has a lone pair of electrons. The lone pair is not always shown on the amine structure for simplicity, yet it plays a significant role in the reactions of the amine functional group. An amine nitrogen is surrounded by three atoms and one lone pair of electrons producing a trigonal pyramidal shape with bond angles approximately 109.5°.

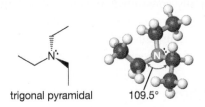

trigonal pyramidal   109.5°

Nitrogen is more electronegative than carbon and hydrogen. As a result, the C—N bond and H—N bond in an amine group are both polar bonds. Its polar bonds and bent shape contribute to the overall polarity of the amine functional group. The dipole arrows indicate bond polarity that, when summed, result in an overall dipole in the direction of the nitrogen atom.

overall dipole toward N

We classify amines as primary (1°), secondary (2°), or tertiary (3°) depending on the number of carbon atoms that are bonded directly to the nitrogen atom. A primary (1°) amine contains a nitrogen atom bonded to one carbon atom or one alkyl group. In a secondary (2°) amine, the nitrogen is bonded to two carbon atoms or two alkyl groups. A tertiary (3°) amine contains a nitrogen atom bonded to three carbon atoms or three alkyl groups. Any organic molecule with a nitrogen bonded to one, two, or three alkyl or aromatic groups is an amine.

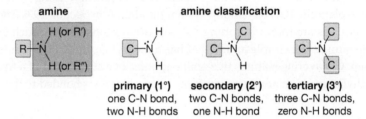

amine

amine classification

primary (1°)
one C-N bond,
two N-H bonds

secondary (2°)
two C-N bonds,
one N-H bond

tertiary (3°)
three C-N bonds,
zero N-H bonds

Predict answers and see step-by-step solutions: **Learn 19.1:** Classifying Amines as 1°, 2°, or 3° in the Pearson eText.

Apply what you have just learned: **Practice 19.1 and 19.2** in the Pearson eText.

Heterocyclic Amines

The nitrogen atoms in amine molecules can also be part of rings. Compounds that contain atoms other than carbon in the ring are **heterocycles.** In a **heterocyclic amine,** the ring contains five or six atoms of which one or two are nitrogen atoms. Pyrrolidine is the simplest five-atom heterocyclic amine. Pyrrolidine's ring contains four carbon atoms and one nitrogen atom. Pyrrole also has a five-atom ring with four carbon atoms and a nitrogen atom, but pyrrole differs from pyrrolidine in that it contains two double bonds. Imidazole is a five-atom ring with two nitrogen atoms and two double bonds.

pyrrolidine   pyrrole   imidazole

There are several types of six-atom heterocyclic amines but the two most relevant to biological systems are pyrimidine and purine. These two amines are found in DNA molecules. Their rings play a significant role in linking the two strands of DNA together through hydrogen bonding.

pyrimidine   purine

Caffeine is a commonly consumed substance that contains amine heterocycles (Figure 19.3) used in cultures around the world. Caffeine is in beverages including coffee and tea and also in consumables such as chocolate. Caffeine functions as a mild stimulant of the central nervous system giving the user a feeling of alertness.

Amines in the Diet

Amines provide essential nutrients and are found in many foods. But some of the nitrogen-containing molecules in our food are much larger than the simple amines we encountered earlier in this section and may contain other functional groups.

Figure 19.3 Caffeine in Coffee.

Caffeine is a heterocyclic amine compound that functions as a stimulant. Caffeine is naturally produced in coffee plants. Coffee beans are picked, dried, and roasted before they are brewed to produce a cup of coffee.

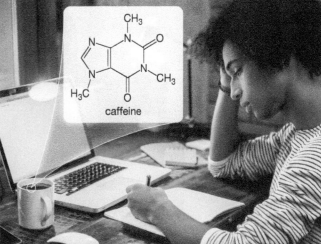

Vitamin B1 (thiamine), for example, is an essential vitamin found in an array of foods including grains, beans, nuts, and meat (Figure 19.4). Thiamine deficiency causes beriberi disease, a disease with a range of symptoms including muscle weakness, neurological problems, and heart failure. Thiamine is water-soluble and not stored in the body so it must be consumed regularly. Thankfully thiamine deficiency is rare in most developed countries where grain products are often supplemented with this essential amine.

Figure 19.4 Thiamine.

Thiamine, also known as vitamin B1, is an essential vitamin. Many grain products are supplemented with thiamine to help prevent deficiencies.

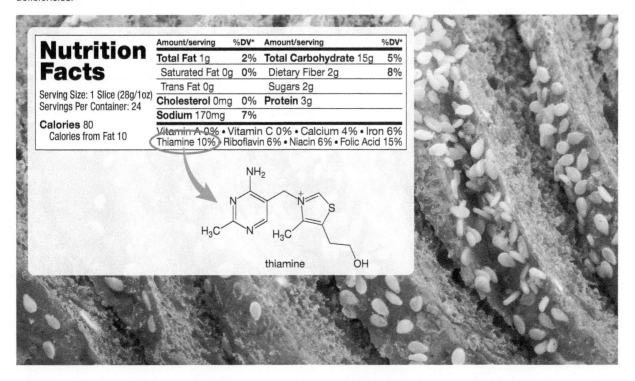

Figure 19.5 Folic Acid.

Folic acid, a B vitamin, is found naturally in some foods and is added to a variety of processed foods. Pregnant women are encouraged to consume folic acid during their pregnancy to avoid birth defects. Folic acid is sold as a dietary supplement.

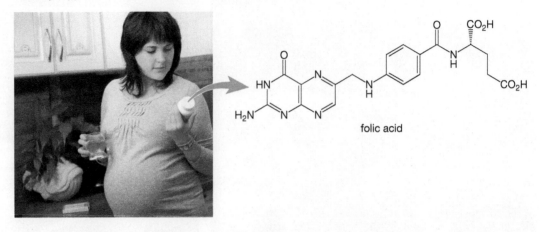

folic acid

Another important B vitamin that is also an amine is the water-soluble compound folic acid. (Figure 19.5). Folic acid occurs naturally in a range of food items. Since 1998 it has also been added to processed food products such as cereals, flour, breads, and pasta. It is particularly important for women who are pregnant to consume enough folic acid; folic acid helps prevent fetuses from developing deformities of the brain or spine.

The proteins in our body are all made up of long chains of amino acids (see BioConnect 6.1 and Section 20.1). Each amino acid contains an amino group and a carboxylic acid group (Figure 19.6). An NH_2 group named as a substituent is called an **amino group**. Amino acids are sold as nutritional supplements for people looking to increase their protein consumption. Proteins are essential biological macromolecules that participate in virtually every process in our cells.

Amines in Medicine

Amines are also found in the human body and in a wide array of medicines. Histamines, for example, are signaling molecules released by our immune cells when they recognize a foreign substance (Figure 19.7A). Histamines bind to unique receptors on

Figure 19.6 Amino Acids.

Amino acids, the building blocks of proteins, also contain an amino group. Mixtures of amino acids are sold as nutritional supplements.

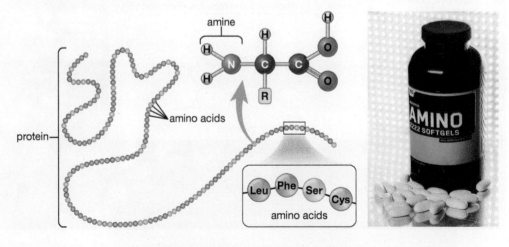

Figure 19.7 Histamine and Diphenhydramine.

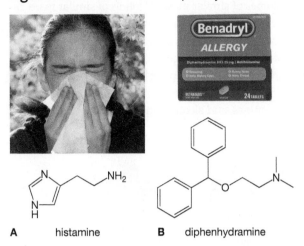

A   histamine   B   diphenhydramine

Figure 19.8 Albuterol.

This substance is taken to alleviate and prevent asthma symptoms including coughing, wheezing, and tightness in the chest.

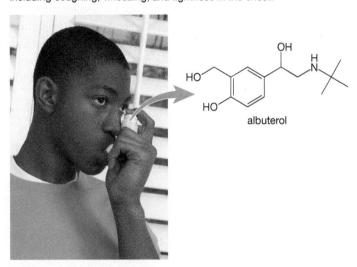

albuterol

the surfaces of cells, increasing blood flow to an area and triggering inflammation. Histamines cause mucus membranes to produce more mucus, resulting in a runny nose. You may have experienced these symptoms if you suffer from *allergies*, the over-production of histamines in response to specific substances, such as pollen or pet dander.

Many allergy sufferers combat these symptoms with another amine, diphenhydramine (Figure 19.7B). Diphenhydramine (sold under the brand name Benadryl) binds to histamine receptors without triggering a response. With many of the histamine receptors occupied by the diphenhydramine molecules, fewer histamine molecules reach their targets, reducing the symptoms of allergies.

Albuterol is a prescription drug used to treat asthma symptoms (Figure 19.8). Asthma is a chronic disease of the airways and lungs that leads to breathing difficulties. Inhaling albuterol relaxes the muscles around the airways, widening airways and making it easier for asthma sufferers to breathe normally. There are many additional medications that are amines; we encounter some of them in later sections of this chapter.

Apply what you have just learned: **Practice 19.3** in the Pearson eText.

Quiz yourself on the content of this section: **Check 19.1** in the Pearson eText.

19.2 Physical Properties of Amines

Primary (1°) and secondary (2°) amines, like hydroxyl groups (OH), have the ability to form hydrogen bonds with each other. The lone pair on the nitrogen atom of one amine molecule can form a hydrogen bond with a hydrogen atom covalently bonded to a nitrogen atom on another amine molecule. Tertiary (3°) amines do not have a hydrogen atom bonded to a nitrogen atom and therefore do not form hydrogen bonds with each other.

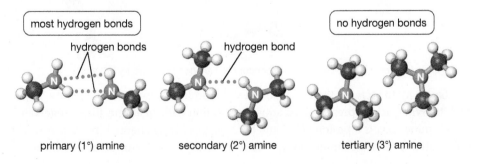

most hydrogen bonds   no hydrogen bonds

hydrogen bonds   hydrogen bond

primary (1°) amine   secondary (2°) amine   tertiary (3°) amine

Because of the ability of 1° and 2° amines to hydrogen bond, these molecules have higher boiling points than nonpolar alkanes of similar mass. Alcohols of similar mass, on the other hand, have higher boiling points than amines of similar mass. This is because nitrogen is less electronegative than oxygen. Therefore, the hydrogen bonds that form between N and H in amines are weaker than the hydrogen bonds that form between O and H in alcohols. As we just noted, tertiary (3°) amines do not have an H atom bonded to a nitrogen atom and therefore do not form H bonds. Tertiary (3°) amines therefore have lower boiling points than 1° amines, 2° amines, and alcohol molecules of similar mass.

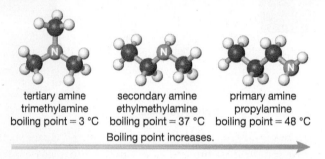

tertiary amine
trimethylamine
boiling point = 3 °C

secondary amine
ethylmethylamine
boiling point = 37 °C

primary amine
propylamine
boiling point = 48 °C

Boiling point increases.

The ability of amine compounds to form hydrogen bonds plays a significant role in the structure of DNA. Base pairing between the two strands of DNA involves one purine molecule forming hydrogen bonds with a pyrimidine molecule. The strands are held together by hydrogen bonds, forming the characteristic double helix of DNA. Explore Visible Chem Video 19.1 to zoom into the hydrogen bonds that hold the DNA strands together in a double helix.

 Watch this concept come to life: **VisibleChem Video 19.1:** Hydrogen Bonds Between Amine Molecules in the Pearson eText.

Water Solubility of Amines

All amines (1°, 2°, and 3°) form hydrogen bonds with water. These bonds increase the water solubility of amines. Primary amines form the most hydrogen bonds with water and are therefore generally more soluble than secondary and tertiary amines. The number of carbon atoms in the amine also plays a role in water solubility. Amines with fewer than six carbon atoms are water soluble. As the number of carbon atoms increases, water solubility decreases. Large amines are considered water insoluble unless additional polar functional groups are present in the molecule.

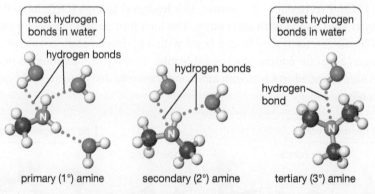

most hydrogen bonds in water

hydrogen bonds

fewest hydrogen bonds in water

hydrogen bonds

hydrogen bond

primary (1°) amine

secondary (2°) amine

tertiary (3°) amine

One way to increase the water solubility of amines is to lower the pH by adding an acid. When acid is present in an aqueous solution with an amine, the nitrogen atom of the amine accepts a proton (H^+) and becomes positively charged (protonated). This protonated form of an amine along with its counter anion forms an **ammonium salt**.

Ammonium salts are much more soluble in water than the corresponding unprotonated amine. We explore this reaction in more detail in the next section of the chapter.

$$H_3C-\overset{\overset{\displaystyle CH_3}{|}}{\underset{\underset{\displaystyle H}{|}}{N^{\pm}}}-H \quad Cl^-$$

dimethylammonium chloride
a secondary (2°) ammonium salt

Apply what you have just learned: **Practice 19.4–19.6** in the Pearson eText.

Quiz yourself on the content of this section: **Check 19.2** in the Pearson eText.

19.3 Reactions of Amines

Ammonia and amines undergo a variety of similar chemical reactions. These reactions play an important role in how molecules are made and processed in our bodies (Figure 19.9).

Figure 19.9 Ammonia in the Body.

Bacteria in the gut produce ammonia as they break down protein. The liver normally converts ammonia into urea, a water-soluble chemical that leaves the body in urine. **Urea** is a nitrogenous compound containing a carbonyl group attached to two amino groups. If the liver is not functioning properly, ammonia can build up in the body and cause a coma or death. A simple blood test can check for levels of toxic ammonia in the blood.

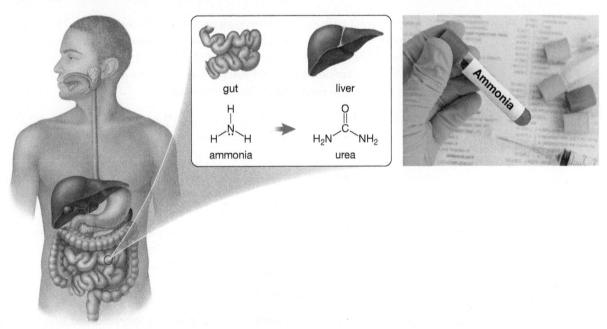

One of the most common reaction types is an acid-base reaction. Ammonia (NH_3) functions as a base by accepting a proton (H^+) from water to produce the **ammonium ion** and hydroxide ion (OH^-).

electron pair forms new bond with a proton from water

one of the protons is removed from water

$$H-\overset{\overset{\displaystyle}{|}}{\underset{\underset{\displaystyle H}{|}}{N}}-H \;+\; H-\overset{..}{\underset{..}{O}}-H \;\rightleftharpoons\; \left[H-\overset{\overset{\displaystyle H}{|}}{\underset{\underset{\displaystyle H}{|}}{N}}-H \right]^+ \;+\; {}^{..}_{..}\overset{..}{O}-H$$

ammonia   water   ammonium ion   hydroxide ion

Amines also act as bases when placed in water by accepting H^+ to produce ammonium ions and hydroxide ions (OH^-). This reaction occurs with 1°, 2°, and 3° amines. Amines are considered weak bases as indicated by the double arrow in the chemical equations. These reactions proceed in both directions until a dynamic equilibrium is reached.

reaction of primary amine with water

methylamine   methylammonium ion   hydroxide ion

reaction of secondary amine with water

dimethylamine   dimethylammonium ion   hydroxide ion

reaction of tertiary amine with water

trimethylamine   trimethylammonium ion   hydroxide ion

Amines also react with acids to form water-soluble ammonium salts. The reaction of an amine with hydrochloric acid (HCl) occurs when the lone pair of electrons on the nitrogen of the amine accepts a proton (H^+) from HCl. The H^+ transfers from the acid to the base. When an amine and an acid react, the amine gains a proton, the acid loses a proton, and the reaction produces an ammonium salt.

methylamine   methylammonium chloride

Watch this concept come to life: **VisibleChem Video 19.2:** Reactions of Amines in the Pearson eText.

Apply what you have just learned: **Practice 19.7–19.9** in the Pearson eText.

Quiz yourself on the content of this section: **Check 19.3** in the Pearson eText.

19.4 Alkaloids: Plant Amines

The plant kingdom produces thousands of molecules that are classified as **alkaloids**–naturally occurring amines derived from plant sources. For example, the ephedra plant produces an alkaloid, ephedrine, which contains a secondary (2°) amine group and has a long history in herbal supplements (Figure 19.10). In the past, the compound was widely promoted as a nutritional supplement to help with weight loss and improve athletic performance. But ephedra was the first dietary supplement to be

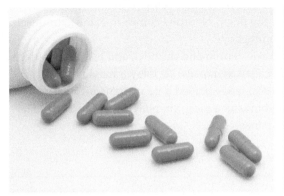

ephedra

Figure 19.10 Ephedra.

The alkaloid ephedrine, from the ephedra plant, was widely marketed as a nutritional supplement until the high-profile death of pitcher Steve Bechler in 2004.

banned by the FDA in 2004 after the high-profile death of a pitcher for the Baltimore Orioles, Steve Bechler, was linked to ephedra use. Ephedra can cause heart attack, strokes, and heart rhythm problems, and ephedra made Bechler more vulnerable to the heat stroke that killed him at just 23 years old. Deaths and poisonings from ephedra dropped by more than 98% after the FDA ban.

In addition to containing an amine functional group, alkaloids often have complex structures and are biologically active once they enter the human body. Cocaine is an alkaloid with a complex structure including several rings and a variety of functional groups (Figure 19.11). Cocaine is an addictive stimulant used as a recreational drug that is obtained from leaves of the coca plant.

The caffeine molecule, discussed in Section 19.1, is another alkaloid produced in a plant. Nicotine is an alkaloid produced by tobacco plants. Both caffeine and nicotine are biologically active alkaloids that are addictive substances. Other alkaloids have medicinal properties and are prescribed to treat a wide range of illnesses. Select BioConnect 19.1 (contains Figures 19.12–19.18) to explore some of these alkaloids in more detail.

Figure 19.11 Cocaine, Caffeine, and Nicotine.

Cocaine is an alkaloid produced by the coca plant. Caffeine is an alkaloid produced by the coffee plant and nicotine is an alkaloid produced by the tobacco plant.

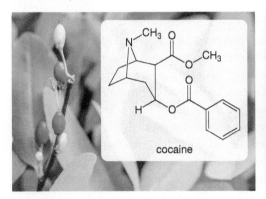

cocaine

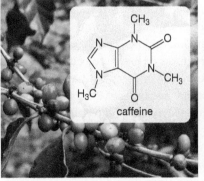

caffeine

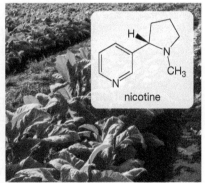

nicotine

Explore how Chemistry and Biology connect: **BioConnect: 19.1** Important Alkaloids in the Pearson eText.

Quiz yourself on the content of this section: **Check 19.4** in the Pearson eText.

19.5 Neurotransmitters

In our brains, 86 billion specialized nerve cells called **neurons** process and transmit information. Neurons contain distinct parts, including a cell body, an **axon**, and dendrites. The axon is a long fiber that transmits messages from the cell body (Figure 19.19). Neurons communicate by sending messages from one neuron to the next, as well as to target cells in muscles and organs in the body. Neurons communicate with muscle cells, for example, to trigger muscle contractions.

There are gaps, however, between one neuron and the next, and between neurons and their target cells. These gaps are called **synapses**. To relay a message across the synapse, a neuron releases a chemical messenger called a **neurotransmitter**. The neurotransmitter crosses the synapse and binds to a receptor, relaying a signal to the target cell. Many neurotransmitters are amines.

Figure 19.19 Neurons.

Neurons process and transmit information using both electrical and chemical signaling. Neurons typically have three distinct parts, the cell body, axon, and dendrites. Neurotransmitters allow messages to be transmitted across the gap (synapse) between a neuron and its target cell.

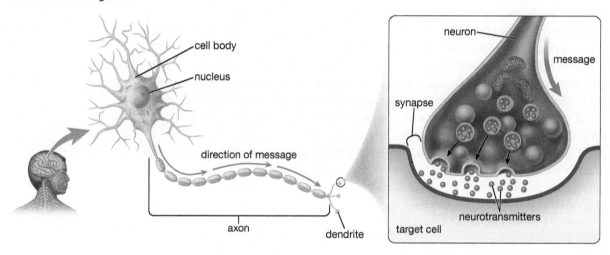

Amine Neurotransmitters

Amine neurotransmitters all contain nitrogen atoms. In some cases, the nitrogen atoms are part of amino groups and in other cases, the nitrogen atoms are part of ammonium ions. The structures of neurotransmitters vary, and the specific shapes and structures of these molecules determines each neurotransmitter's biological activity. Neurotransmitters bind and fit into receptors in the body allowing them to trigger specific responses. Most neurotransmitters are made in our bodies from amino acids, such as tyrosine and tryptophan, that we consume in our diet.

While there are many neurotransmitters, significant amine neurotransmitters include: dopamine, norepinephrine, epinephrine, serotonin, and acetylcholine (Table 19.1). These five neurotransmitters play key roles that range from regulating muscle activation to controlling alertness and feelings of pleasure.

Due to their physiological importance, chemists have designed many medicinal compounds to mimic the functions of these five neurotransmitters. Explore BioConnect 19.2 (contains Figures 19.20–19.28) to learn more about the biological functions of these neurotransmitters and how synthetic compounds impact neurotransmitter function.

Table 19.1 Key Neurotransmitters and their Functions.

Neurotransmitter		Function	Made in the body from:
Dopamine	(structure)	a natural stimulant that increases pleasurable feelings; regulates muscle movement, cognition, sleep, and mood	tyrosine
Norepinephrine	(structure)	plays a role in sleep, attention, focus, and alertness	tyrosine
Epinephrine (adrenaline)	(structure)	plays an important role in fight-or-flight response by increasing blood flow to muscles, heart rate, and blood sugar levels	tyrosine
Serotonin	(structure)	facilitates relaxation, deep sleep, rational thinking, mood, learning, and memory	tryptophan
Acetylcholine	(structure)	regulates muscle activation, learning, and short-term memory	acetyl-Co-A, choline

Explore how Chemistry and Biology connect: **BioConnect: 19.2** Neurons and Neurotransmitters in the Pearson eText.

Apply what you have just learned: **Practice 19.10 and 19.11** in the Pearson eText.

Quiz yourself on the content of this section: **Check 19.5** in the Pearson eText.

19.6 Naming Amines

Chemists follow specific rules when naming compounds. The rules ensure that each compound has an unambiguous and unique name, allowing chemists from all over the world to communicate with each other. Explore Video 19.1 to learn how to name amines and ammonium salts. You can also review the rules for naming compounds in the nomenclature appendix.

Video 19.1: Nomenclature: Amines

Quiz yourself on the content of this section: **Check 19.6** in the Pearson eText.

Chapter Summary

19.1 Structure of Amines

Learning Objective: Identify amines and classify them as 1°, 2°, or 3°.

Amines are organic molecules that contain a nitrogen atom bonded to one, two, or three carbon groups and a lone pair of electrons. Amines have a trigonal pyramidal shape with bond angles of approximately 109.5°. Amines are classified as primary (1°), secondary (2°), or tertiary (3°) depending on the number of carbon atoms bonded directly to the nitrogen atom. A primary (1°) amine contains a nitrogen atom bonded to one carbon atom; a secondary (2°) amine contains a nitrogen atom bonded to two carbon atoms or two alkyl groups; and a tertiary (3°) amine contains a nitrogen atom bonded to three carbon atoms. The nitrogen atom in an amine molecule can be a part of a ring called a heterocyclic amine.

Key Terms

amine
amino group
heterocycle
heterocyclic amine

19.2 Physical Properties of Amines

Learning Objective: Describe how intermolecular forces affect boiling points and water solubility of amines.

Primary (1°) and secondary (2°) amines form hydrogen bonds with each other. Tertiary (3°) amines, on the other hand, do not have a hydrogen atom bonded to a nitrogen atom, and therefore do not form hydrogen bonds with each other. Because of the ability of 1° and 2° amines to hydrogen bond, their boiling points are higher than nonpolar alkanes and tertiary amines (3°). The ability of amine compounds to form hydrogen bonds plays a significant role in the structure of many biological molecules, including DNA. All amines (1°, 2°, and 3°) form hydrogen bonds with water, which increases amine solubility in water.

VisibleChem Video 19.1: Hydrogen Bonds Between Amine Molecules

Key Term

ammonium salt

19.3 Reactions of Amines

Learning Objective: Predict and draw the products of acid-base reactions of amines.

Amines are weak bases and therefore accept protons (H^+) in aqueous solution to produce an ammonium ion and a hydroxide ion (OH^-). Amines also react with acids to form ammonium salts that are water soluble. Medications that contain amine groups are generally converted to ammonium salts prior to injection. This conversion increases water solubility of the medication so that the body can better absorb the medication.

VisibleChem Video 19.2: Reactions of Amines

Key Term

ammonium ion
urea

19.4 Alkaloids: Amines Found in Plants

Learning Objective: Describe the characteristics of alkaloids and provide examples.

The plant kingdom naturally produces thousands of molecules classified as alkaloids, which are naturally occurring amines. In addition to each containing an amine group, alkaloids often have complex structures and are biologically active once they enter the human body. Ephedrine, cocaine, caffeine, nicotine, and codeine are all alkaloid compounds.

BioConnect 19.1: Important Alkaloids

Key Term

alkaloid

19.5 Neurotransmitters

Learning Objective: Describe and provide examples of the general structure and physiological function of neurotransmitters.

To relay a message in the brain, a neuron releases a chemical messenger called a neurotransmitter. The neurotransmitter crosses the synapse and binds to a receptor, relaying a signal to a target cell. Many neurotransmitters are amines. The structure of neurotransmitters varies, and the specific shape of these molecules is key to their biological activity. Significant amine neurotransmitters include dopamine, norepinephrine, epinephrine, serotonin, and acetylcholine. These five neurotransmitters play physiological roles that range from regulating muscle activity to controlling alertness and feelings of pleasure.

BioConnect 19.2: Neurons and Neurotransmitters

Key Terms

axon	neurotransmitter	serotonin (from BioConnect 19.2)
neuron	receptor (from BioConnect 19.2)	synapse

19.6 Naming Amines

Learning Objective: Use the IUPAC system for naming organic compounds to convert from structure to name and from name to structure for amines and ammonium salts.

Chemists follow specific rules when naming compounds. This process of devising or choosing names for things is nomenclature. The International Union of Pure and Applied Chemistry (IUPAC) establishes the rules for the nomenclature of organic compounds.

Video 19.1: Nomenclature: Amines

 # End-of-Chapter Quiz

Have you mastered the content of this chapter? Try the **End-of-Chapter Quiz** in the Pearson eText.

1. Tamoxifen is a medication used to treat breast cancer. Tamoxifen, shown here, is which type of amine?

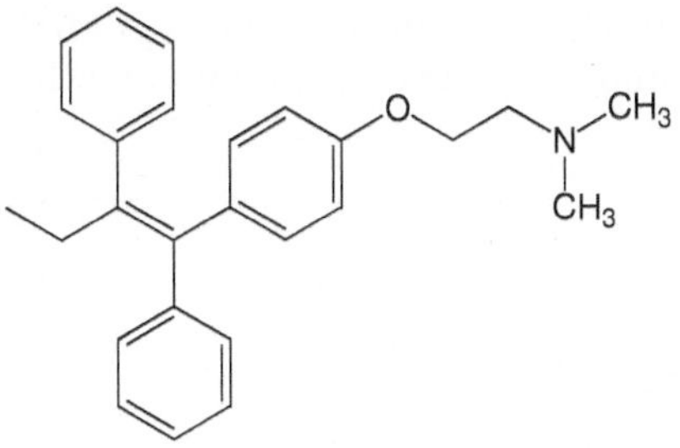

tamoxifen

a) primary (1°)
b) secondary (2°)
c) tertiary (3°)
d) heterocyclic

2. Spermine is a naturally occurring amine that is involved in cellular metabolism. Which statement best describes the spermine molecule? (Nitrogen atoms are blue, carbon is black, and hydrogen is white in this molecular model of spermine.)

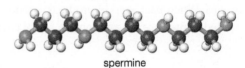

spermine

a) The spermine molecule contains four primary (1°) amine groups.

b) The spermine molecule contains two primary (1°) amine groups and two secondary (2°) amine groups.

c) The spermine molecule contains two primary (1°) amine groups and two tertiary (3°) amine groups.

d) The spermine molecule contains four secondary (2°) amine groups.

3. Bupivacaine (shown here; also known as Marcaine) is a pain medication used to reduce feeling in a specific area during surgery or other medical procedures. Which statement about the functional groups on bupivacaine is true?

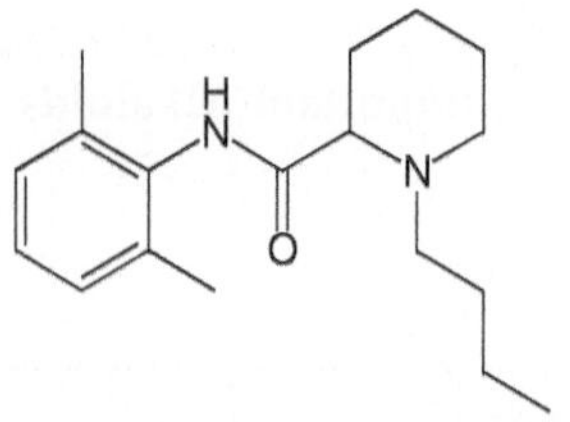

a) The bupivacaine molecule contains a secondary (2°) amine and a heterocyclic tertiary (3°) amine.

b) The bupivacaine molecule contains a primary (1°) amine and a heterocyclic tertiary (3°) amine.

c) The bupivacaine molecule contains a secondary (2°) amine and a heterocyclic primary (1°) amine.

d) The bupivacaine molecule contains a secondary (2°) amide and a heterocyclic tertiary (3°) amine.

4. Which structure correctly shows the hydrogen bonding that occurs between the given amine molecule and water?

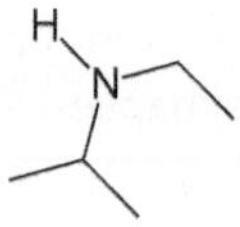

a) 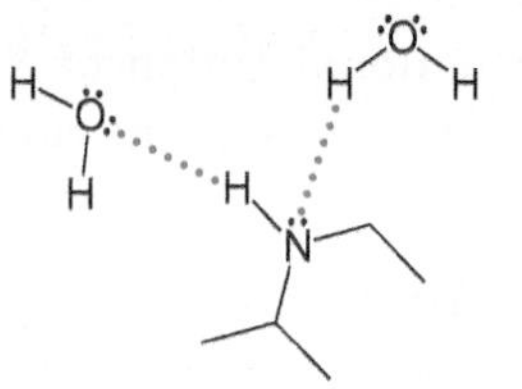   b)

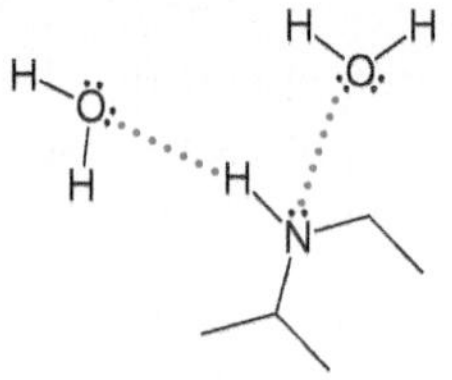

c) 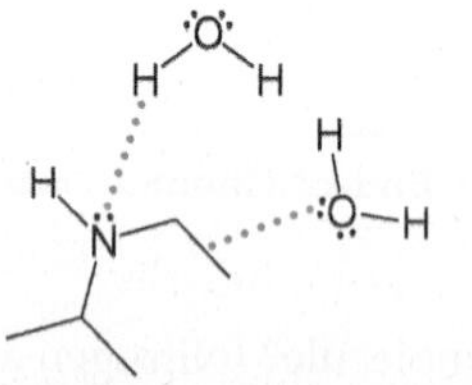   d)

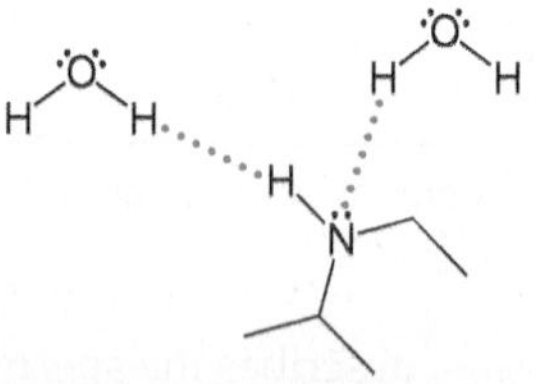

5. Which of these six-carbon diamine molecules has the highest boiling point?

a)   b)

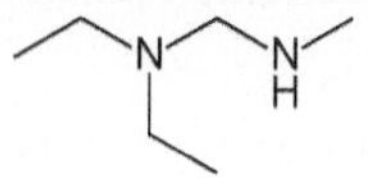

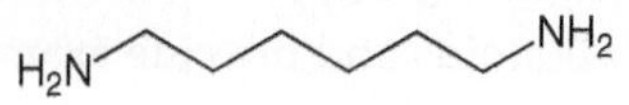

c) 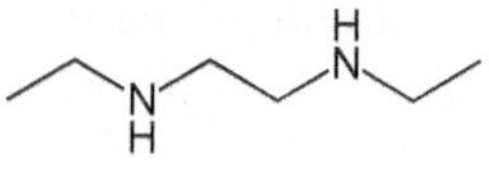   d)

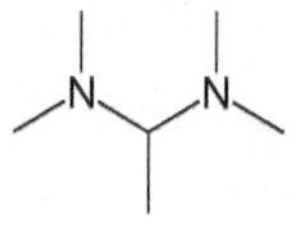

6. Which diagram correctly illustrates hydrogen bonding between secondary (2°) amines?

a)

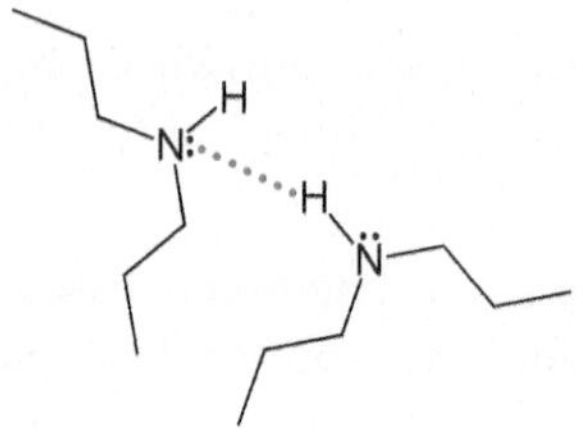

b)

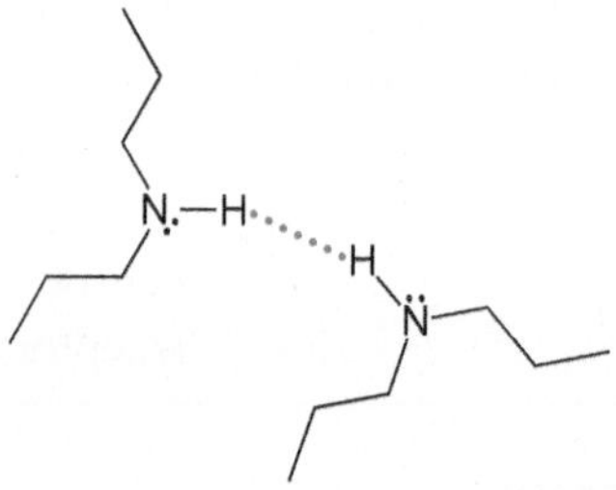

c)

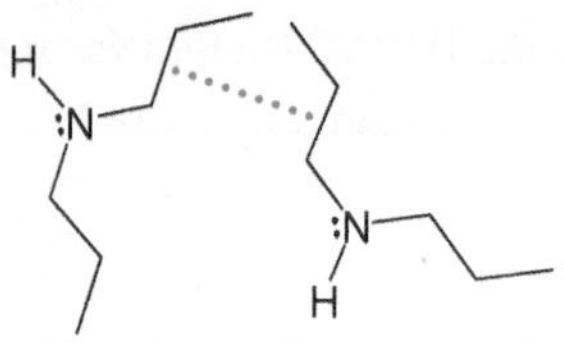

d)

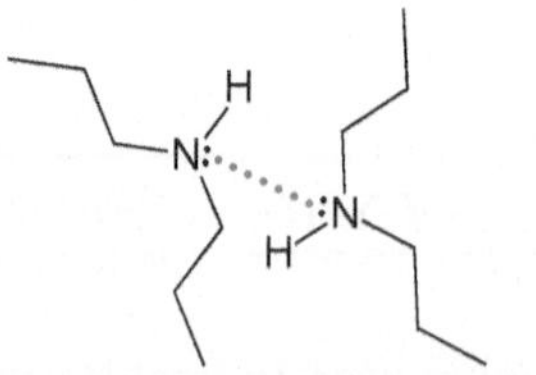

7. Pseudoephedrine is the active ingredient in several nasal and sinus decongestants that are sold in drug stores and pharmacies. When packaged in products, pseudoephedrine is often formulated as an ammonium salt. What reactants are needed to produce the ammonium salt of pseudoephedrine?

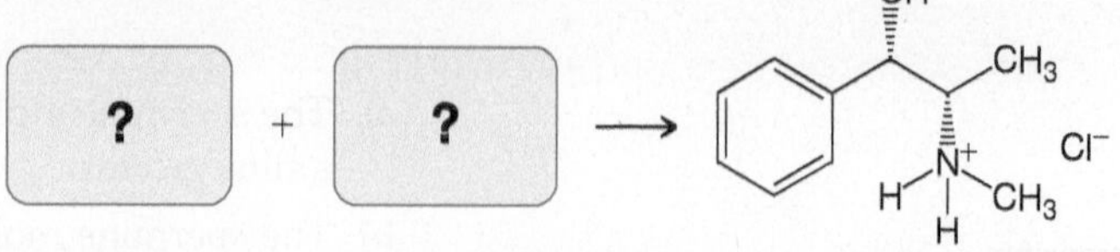

? + ? →

a)   + NaCl(aq)

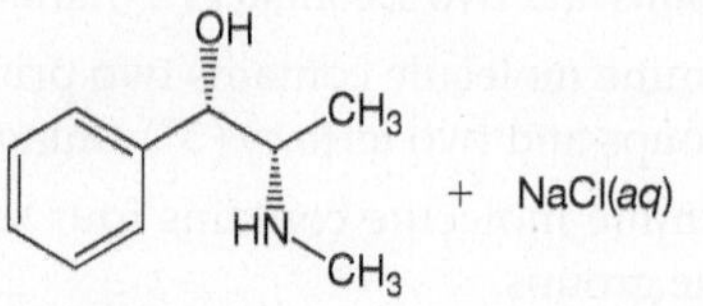

b)   + HCl(aq)

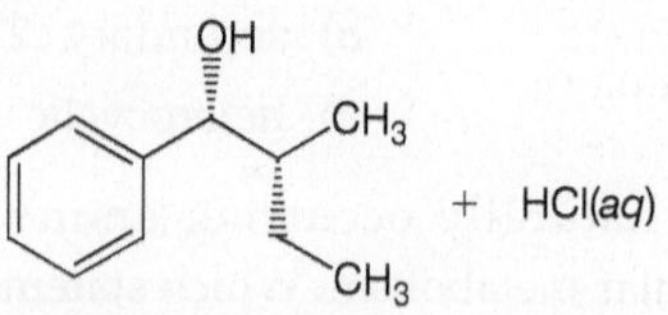

c)

+ $H_2Cl(aq)$

d)

+ $HCl(aq)$

8. When an amine reacts as a weak base in the presence of acid to form the corresponding ammonium salt, what (if anything) happens to its solubility in water?

a) The water solubility of the ammonium salt is lower than the water solubility of the amine starting material.

b) The water solubility of the ammonium salt is the same as the water solubility of the amine starting material.

c) The water solubility of the ammonium salt is higher than the water solubility of the amine starting material.

d) The water solubility of the ammonium salt cannot be predicted and must be measured by experiment.

9. Salbutamol (also known as albuterol or Ventolin) is a medication used to treat asthma and chronic obstructive pulmonary disease (COPD). It is often used with an inhaler and is also available as a pill and IV solution. Identify the correct missing products of this reaction that occurs when salbutamol reacts with water in the body.

a)

+ H_3O^+

b)

+ OH^-

c)

+ NOH_2

d)

+ H_3O^+

---

10. The dried leaves of the tobacco plant contain a number of different alkaloids including nicotine and nornicotine. Consider the chemical structures of these two alkaloids and identify the answer option that best describes their similarities and differences.

nicotine   nornicotine

a) Both alkaloids contain a six-carbon heterocyclic amine connected to a five-carbon heterocyclic amine. Nicotine contains a quinine ring system, whereas nornicotine contains a secondary opioid ring system.

b) Both alkaloids contain a six-carbon heterocyclic amine connected to a five-carbon heterocyclic amine. Nicotine contains an additional methyl group and is a secondary amine, whereas the five-carbon ring in nornicotine is a tertiary amine.

c) Both alkaloids contain a six-carbon heterocyclic amine connected to a five-carbon heterocyclic amine.

Nicotine contains an additional methyl group and is a tertiary amine, whereas the five- carbon ring in nornicotine is a secondary amine.

d) Both alkaloids contain a six- carbon heterocyclic amine connected to a five- carbon heterocyclic amine. Nicotine contains a purine ring, whereas nornicotine contains a pyrimidine ring.

11. Actinidine is a naturally occurring alkaloid found in the oil of the valerian root that acts as an attractant for a variety of insects and cats. Which structural feature of this molecule makes it an alkaloid?

actinidine

a) the double bonds in the ring

b) the two rings fused together

c) the two methyl ($-CH_3$) groups

d) the amine group

12. Caffeine is a central nervous system stimulant consumed in vast quantities around the world, often in the form of coffee or tea. The caffeine molecule is a heterocyclic amine that is metabolized in the liver into multiple different molecules. What do all three of the metabolic products of caffeine shown here have in common with each other?

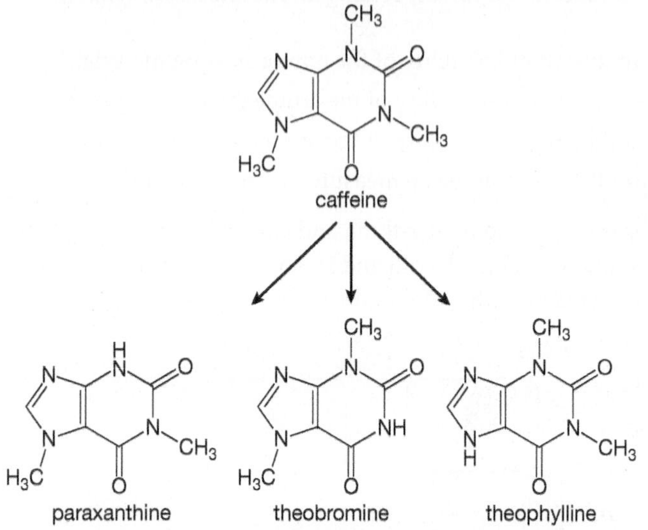

CH₃

caffeine

CH₃

paraxanthine

CH₃

theobromine

CH₃

theophylline

a) A carbonyl C=O group on the caffeine molecule is biochemically reduced during the production of paraxanthine, theobromine, and theophylline.

b) During the metabolism of caffeine, a primary amine group is converted to a secondary amine group in the production of paraxanthine, theobromine, and theophylline.

c) A methyl group on one of the nitrogen atoms of caffeine is removed during the production of paraxanthine, theobromine, and theophylline.

d) When caffeine is metabolized to produce paraxanthine, theobromine, and theophylline, secondary heterocyclic amine groups convert to tertiary heterocyclic amines.

13. Which molecule is *not* a neurotransmitter discussed in this chapter?
a) serine   **b)** norepinephrine
c) serotonin   **d)** acetylcholine

14. What primary function does the neurotransmitter acetylcholine serve?

a) Acetylcholine signals the immune system to trigger antibody production and a rapid immune response.

b) Acetylcholine signals across synapses to receptors on the surface of muscle cells to initiate muscle contractions.

c) Acetylcholine signals the pancreas to increase cellular uptake of insulin for the management of blood sugar levels.

d) Acetylcholine signals the pituitary gland to increase production of the male and female sex hormones progesterone and estrogen.

15. How do antidepressant drugs in the SSRI category (selective serotonin reuptake inhibitors), such as Prozac, function?

a) Drugs in the SSRI category, such as Prozac, work by speeding up the pump that delivers serotonin to the synapse. With the pump highly activated, serotonin levels decrease, which often decreases the symptoms of depression.

b) Drugs in the SSRI category, such as Prozac, work by pumping niacin into the serotonin junction. With high levels of niacin in the serotonin junction, dopamine re-uptake is inhibited, which leads to decreased symptoms of depression.

c) Drugs in the SSRI category, such as Prozac, work by blocking the pump that normally delivers serotonin to the adrenal gland. Without an active pump, serotonin levels in the adrenal gland remain low, often decreasing the symptoms of depression.

d) Drugs in the SSRI category, such as Prozac, work by blocking the pump that normally removes serotonin from the synapse. Without an active pump, serotonin levels in the synapse remain high, often decreasing the symptoms of depression.

16. What is the IUPAC name of the given amine molecule? (Nitrogen is blue.)

a) 4-aminobutane
b) 1-butanamine
c) aminobutene
d) N—N—dihydrobutanamine

17. Which molecule is *N*-ethyl-*N*-methyl-2-hexanamine?

a) 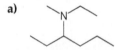   **b)**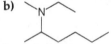

c) 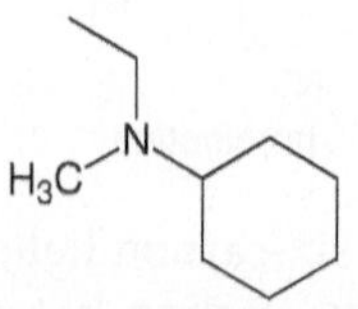   **d)**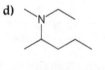

18. What is the IUPAC name of this molecule?

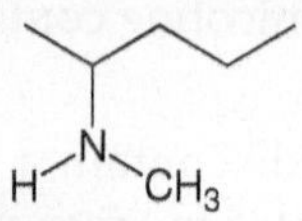

a) methyl-2-pentanamine
b) N-methyl-4-pentanamine
c) N-pentyl-methanamine
d) N-methyl-2-pentanamine

Chapter 20
Amino Acids and Proteins

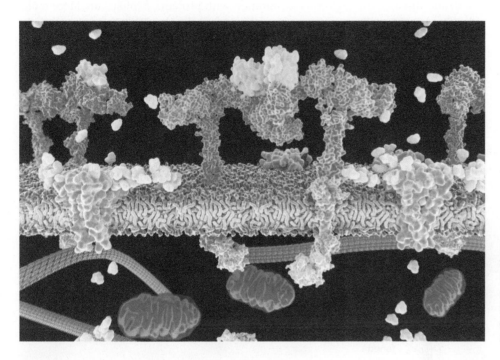

Insulin, one of the hormones that regulates blood glucose levels, is a protein. This representation shows the insulin protein (green) binding to a protein on the surface of the cell (purple), triggering the uptake of blood glucose.

 ## Chapter Outline

Learning Objectives

20.1 List the key functions that proteins carry out in the body.

20.2 Draw the charged forms of amino acids at a range of pH values and identify amino acid stereoisomers as D or L.

20.3 Draw simple peptides and identify peptide bonds.

20.4 Describe primary, secondary, tertiary, and quaternary structures of proteins.

20.5 Draw the products of protein hydrolysis and describe protein denaturation.

Introduction

In this chapter, we turn to large biological molecules and their impact on human health and disease. We begin this exploration with proteins. Proteins are large molecules that provide a diverse array of functions in our bodies. Proteins range from the structural fibers holding our skeleton together to the signaling molecules regulating our blood glucose concentration (Figure 20.1). Given the diverse roles proteins play in the body, it is not surprising that proteins also play a role in a wide range of human diseases. In this chapter, we explore the essential characteristics of proteins as well as their role in health and disease.

Figure 20.1 Examples of Important Proteins.

A) Collagen is a structural protein that provides strength to structures such as our Achilles' tendons. **B)** Insulin is a small protein; its crucial role in the body illustrates the regulatory function many proteins serve. **C)** Cataracts occur when crystallin proteins in the lens of the eye begin to aggregate, clouding vision.

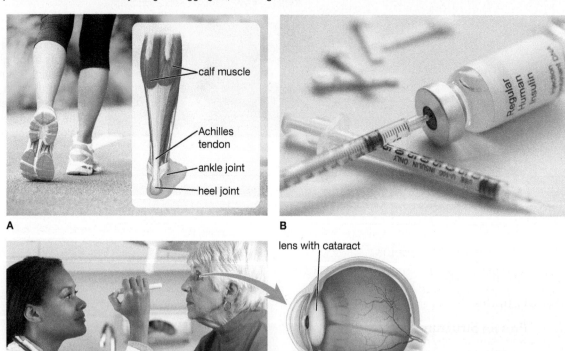

20.1 Introduction to Proteins

Proteins perform a wide array of essential dynamic and structural functions in the human body. Proteins play so many key roles that scientists sometimes refer to proteins as the most important class of biomolecules (Figure 20.2). The word protein is derived from the Greek word *proteios*, meaning "of first importance".

Figure 20.2 Vital Proteins.

Proteins serve a wide array of functions in our bodies.

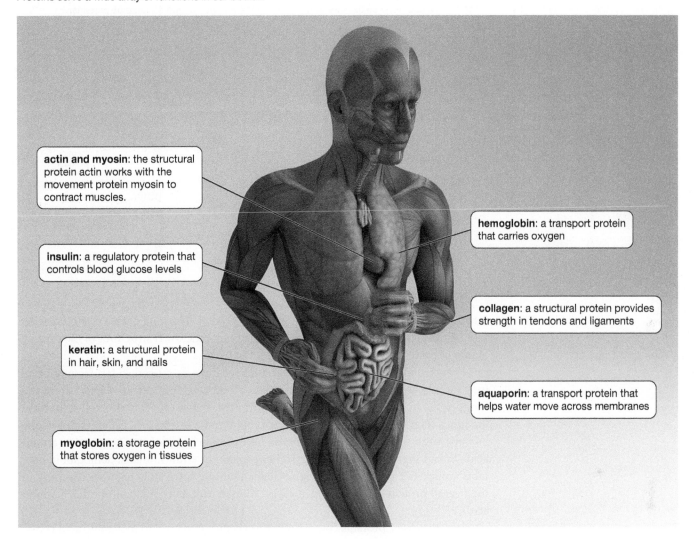

actin and myosin: the structural protein actin works with the movement protein myosin to contract muscles.

insulin: a regulatory protein that controls blood glucose levels

keratin: a structural protein in hair, skin, and nails

myoglobin: a storage protein that stores oxygen in tissues

hemoglobin: a transport protein that carries oxygen

collagen: a structural protein provides strength in tendons and ligaments

aquaporin: a transport protein that helps water move across membranes

Some proteins make up structural features of the body. For example, protein molecules such as keratin and collagen form long fibers, strengthening a variety of tissues. Other proteins function as **membrane proteins** that transport molecules and ions across cell membranes or help with cell-to-cell communication. Hemoglobin is a **transport protein** that delivers oxygen (O_2) throughout the body. Insulin is a **regulatory protein** that regulates blood glucose levels, as we learned in Chapter 16. **Enzymes** are proteins that catalyze and regulate the essential functions of the cell. Enzymes form such an important class of proteins that we dedicate the next chapter to them.

Because of this wide array of functions, scientists categorize proteins into the following classes: structural, catalysis (enzymes), movement, transport, storage, protection, and regulation. Throughout this chapter, we encounter proteins from all of these classes as we discuss this highly functional group of biomolecules.

Protein Size and Composition

Despite their diverse functions, all proteins are made of the same building blocks. All proteins are chains of the twenty common amino acids connected in an array of combinations (Figure 20.3). Amino acids are simple organic compounds containing both a

Figure 20.3 Basic Protein Structure.

All proteins are made of chains of amino acids that fold to adopt their final shape. We often represent large proteins using ribbon diagrams (right). The ribbons represent the chains of amino acids and allow us to more easily visualize the size and shape of complex proteins.

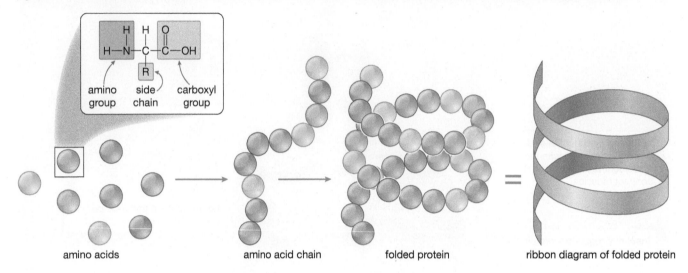

amino acids   amino acid chain   folded protein   ribbon diagram of folded protein

carboxyl group (COOH) and an amino group (NH_2). The long chains of amino acids fold in multiple intricate ways to produce the final, functional structures of the diverse family of proteins.

Proteins are by far the largest molecules we have discussed so far. Hemoglobin, for example, is the transport protein in red blood cells that carries oxygen from the lungs to the body's tissues and helps return carbon dioxide from the tissues back to the lungs (Figure 20.4). Hemoglobin has a molar mass of about 64,500 g/mol. Despite its very large size, hemoglobin is made up of long chains of the 20 common amino acids linked together just like every other protein. In adult humans, hemoglobin contains around 575 amino acids in four chains that fold intricately together resulting in the overall protein structure. On average, human proteins contain around 375 amino acids.

In some cases, proteins contain other molecules that bind to the amino acid chain. These molecules can play a significant role in protein function. Each hemoglobin

Figure 20.4 Hemoglobin in Blood.

Hemoglobin is an iron-containing oxygen transport protein in red blood cells. This protein carries oxygen from the lungs and delivers it to the rest of the body. Healthcare providers often use a blood test to measure hemoglobin concentration as a diagnostic tool.

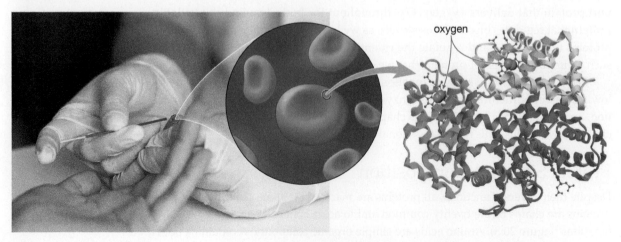

oxygen

molecule, for example, contains four **heme** molecules. Heme is a complex organic molecule containing an Fe^{2+} ion. The Fe^{2+} binds oxygen and transports oxygen in the body. Each heme contains one iron atom that is able to bind to one oxygen molecule. Each hemoglobin molecule therefore can carry a maximum of four oxygen molecules at any one time. A healthy individual has 12–16 grams of hemoglobin in every 100 mL of blood. A hemoglobin concentration test is one of the most common blood tests and is usually part of a complete blood analysis. Low hemoglobin levels suggest that a person has *anemia* and is unable to transport oxygen efficiently. This most often occurs because of blood loss or a lack of iron in the diet.

Sickle Cell Disease

The sequence of the amino acids makes each protein different from another and can have a dramatic impact on function. For example, substituting just one amino acid in the hemoglobin protein results in an abnormal hemoglobin protein. The abnormal proteins stick to each other and change the shape of the red blood cells (Figure 20.5). These "sickled" red blood cells can get stuck in small blood vessels, reducing or even blocking the flow of blood to tissues. When this happens, a person has **sickle cell disease**.

Sickle cell disease is a genetic disorder—patients inherit the gene for the sickled protein. But even individuals with the normal version of the gene need to consume the right mix of proteins to produce healthy hemoglobin and the rest of the diverse array of proteins that keep us functioning. Explore BioConnect 20.1 (contains Figures 20.6–20.12) to learn more about the role of protein in our diet.

Figure 20.5 Sickle Cell Disease.

A variation of just one amino acid from the normal hemoglobin protein sequence produces an abnormal protein that results in misshapen red blood cells.

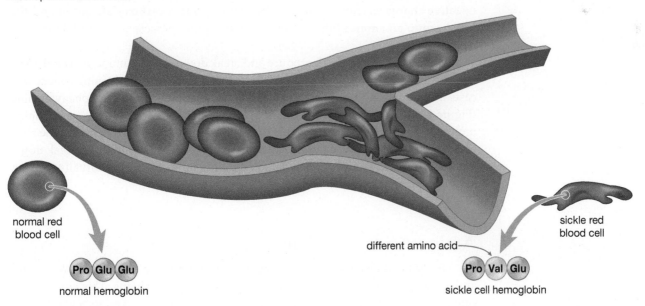

normal red
blood cell

Pro Glu Glu
normal hemoglobin

different amino acid

sickle red
blood cell

Pro Val Glu
sickle cell hemoglobin

Explore how Chemistry and Biology connect: **BioConnect: 20.1** Protein in Our Diets in the Pearson eText.

Quiz yourself on the content of this section: **Check 21.1** in the Pearson eText.

20.2 Amino Acids

Proteins are long chains made up of twenty different amino acids. In this section, we explore amino acids in more detail. Recall that amino acids are organic molecules that each contain an amino group (NH_2) and a carboxyl group (COOH). Also recall from Chapter 19 that the amino group is a nitrogen atom bonded to a combination of hydrogen atoms and carbon groups. All the amino acids the human body uses to build proteins are a **α-amino acids**. In an α-amino acid, the amino group bonds to the carbon adjacent to the carboxyl group. This carbon is the **α-carbon**. An R group also bonds to the α-carbon, giving each amino acid a unique structure.

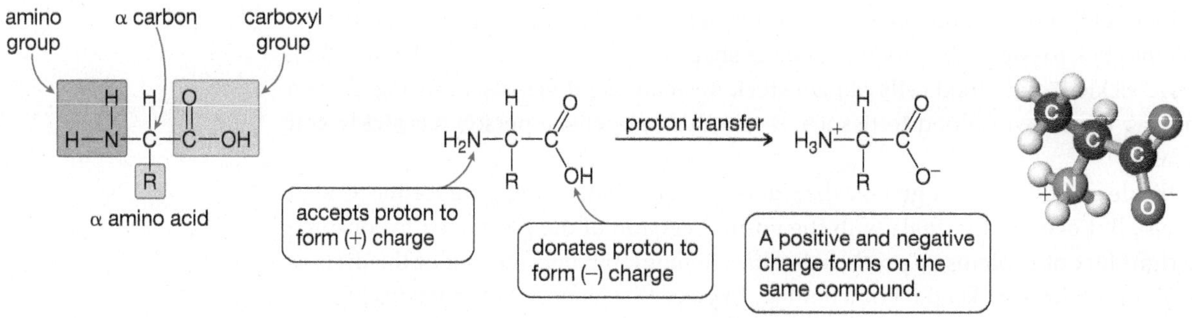

We draw the uncharged form of amino acids such as the one shown here on occasion, however, amino acids often have charged groups under certain conditions. Because amino acids contain a base and an acid, the acidic proton on the carboxyl group is transferred to the amino group leaving both a positive and negative charge as shown. We call the COO^- group a **carboxylate anion** and the NH_3^+ group an **ammonium cation**. We discuss this process in more detail in the next section.

The body's ability to both produce and break down specific amino acids is the key to some diseases. For example, *phenylketonuria (PKU)* is a life-threatening genetic disease. Individuals with PKU are unable to break down the amino acid phenylalanine (Figure 20.13). These individuals cannot break the bonds within the phenylalanine molecule, so their bodies are not able to use the atoms within the phenylalanine molecule to build other molecules. Because these people lack the ability to break down and recycle phenylalanine, phenylalanine builds up in tissues, eventually causing severe neurological symptoms.

Amino Acid Side Chains

We refer to the R group on an amino acid as the **amino acid side chain**. We classify amino acids according to the characteristics of their side chains. This creates four categories of amino acids: polar, nonpolar, acidic, and basic. Amino acids that are nonpolar contain H, alkyl, or aromatic side chains that repel water, making them hydrophobic. Polar amino acids contain functional groups such as hydroxyl (OH), thiol (SH), or amide ($CONH_2$) groups, making these molecules hydrophilic

Figure 20.13 Phenylketonuria (PKU) Disease.

About 1 in 15,000 infants in the United States is born with the genetic disease phenylketonuria. These individuals cannot break down the amino acid phenylalanine. As a result, it builds up in their tissues causing brain damage and seizures. **A)** Individuals with PKU disease must be careful to avoid foods containing phenylalanine. Many diet sodas are sweetened with an artificial sweetener, aspartame, that contains phenylalanine. **B)** All infants born in the United States are tested for PKU disease shortly after birth.

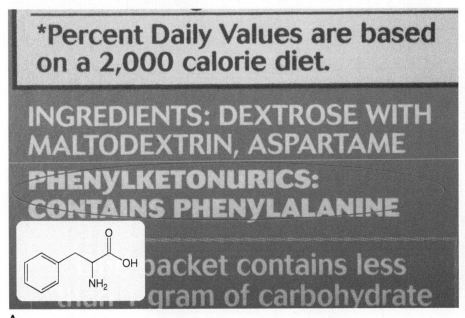
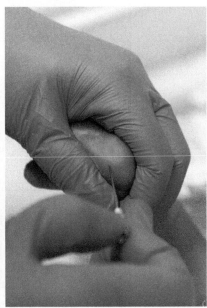

A   B

(attracted to water). We can further classify polar amino acids as polar neutral, polar acidic, or polar basic (Table 20.1). The polarity of the R group has an impact on the overall structure of a protein, a concept we explore in more detail in Section 20.4.

There are 20 amino acids present in human proteins (Table 20.1). The amino acid side chain (R group) is the primary difference among the common 20 amino acids.

Each of the twenty α-amino acids has a name and a three-letter and a one-letter abbreviated name. Glycine is the simplest of these 20 amino acids. We refer to it as Gly or G. Serine (Ser or S) is a polar amino acid. We show both here in the uncharged forms of the amino acids.

glycine (Gly)   serine (Ser)

Apply what you have just learned: **Practice 20.1–20.3** in the Pearson eText.

Table 20.1 Amino Acids in the Human Body.

The side chain of an amino acid makes one amino acid different from another. We discuss isoelectric point (pI) values in the next section.

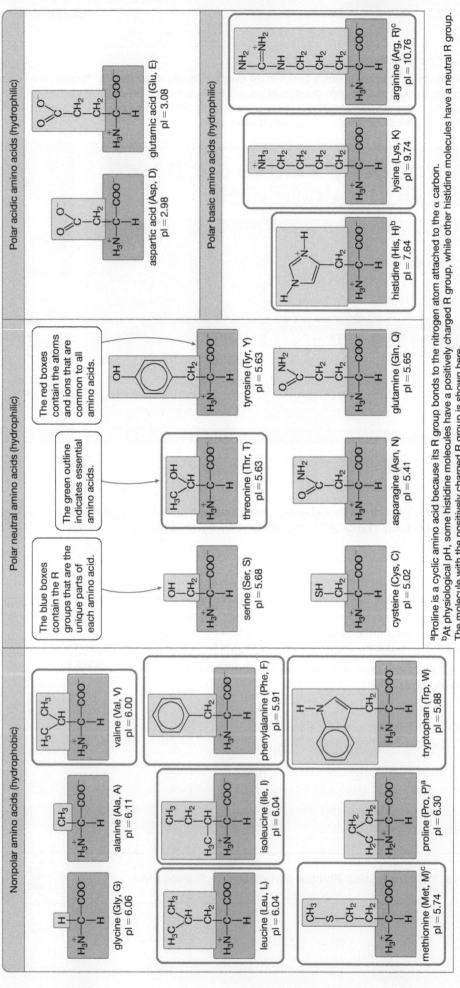

[a]Proline is a cyclic amino acid because its R group bonds to the nitrogen atom attached to the α carbon.
[b]At physiological pH, some histidine molecules have a positively charged R group, while other histidine molecules have a neutral R group. The molecule with the positively charged R group is shown here.
[c]Mammals can synthesize arginine and methionine but the biochemical demand for these amino acids by the body is generally greater than the amount biosynthesized.

Figure 20.14 Zwitterions.

A zwitterion is an amino acid that contains both a positive and negative charge. Here we show the overall neutral zwitterionic form for the essential amino acid threonine.

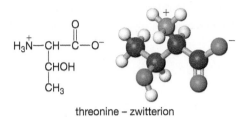

threonine – zwitterion

Acid-Base Characteristics of Amino Acids

Amino acids contain both a basic group (NH_2) and an acidic group (COOH). A proton transfers from the acidic group to the basic group to produce a **zwitterion**. A zwitterion is the form of an amino acid that contains an equal number of positively- and negatively-charged functional groups. As you can see in Figure 20.14, the zwitterion contains both a positive charge (an ammonium cation, NH_3^+) and negative charge (a carboxylate anion COO^-). The net charge on a zwitterion is zero so a zwitterion is overall neutral.

The pH of the environment in which both the positive and negative charges are present (zwitterion form) is the **isoelectric point (pI).** Isoelectric points for nonpolar and polar amino acids range between 5–7. The isoelectric points for amino acids with acidic and basic side chains vary more, depending on which R group they include. Table 20.1 includes pI values.

The pH of the aqueous solution containing an amino acid determines the charge distribution. In our bodies, at normal pH of 7.4, most amino acids are in their overall neutral zwitterionic form. When the pH drops or rises above or below the pI, the amino acid takes on an overall charge. For example, at low pH when acid is present, the negatively charged carboxylate anion on an amino acid accepts a proton and becomes neutral (Figure 20.15). As a result, the overall charge on the amino acid is positive due to the positively charged ammonium cation (NH_3^+). On the other hand, at elevated pH, when base is present, the positively charged ammonium cation donates its proton and becomes neutral (see Fig. 20.15). This results in an overall negative charge on the amino acid due to the negative charge on the negatively charged carboxylate anion.

Figure 20.15 Acid-Base Properties of Amino Acids.

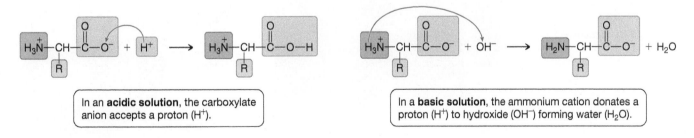

In an **acidic solution**, the carboxylate anion accepts a proton (H⁺).

In a **basic solution**, the ammonium cation donates a proton (H⁺) to hydroxide (OH⁻) forming water (H₂O).

Apply what you have just learned: **Practice 20.4 and 20.5** in the Pearson eText.

Stereochemistry of Amino Acids

Except for the simplest amino acid (glycine), all amino acids contain a chiral carbon because the α-carbon bonds to four different groups. This gives rise to enantiomers. We show the non-superimposable mirror image enantiomer molecules here for the amino acid alanine using a wedge-dash representation and a Fischer projection.

We use the prefixes D and L to indicate the specific arrangement of groups on the α-carbon (as we do with the monosaccharides we studied in Chapter 16). When we draw **L-amino acids** with the COO^- at the top of the Fischer projection and the R group on the bottom, the ammonium group (NH_3^+) is on the left side. When we draw **D-amino acids** in this same way, the ammonium group (NH_3^+) is on the right side.

The L isomers of amino acids are common in nature. In contrast, the D stereoisomers are not common in nature. L-DOPA, for example, is a modified amino acid that the human body produces from L-tyrosine. The D isomer, D-DOPA, can be made in a laboratory, but the body does not produce it. The body ultimately converts L-DOPA to the neurotransmitter *dopamine* and other important neurotransmitters (Figure 20.16). Several diseases of the nervous system are associated with dysfunctions of the

---

Figure 20.16 Dopamine Treats Parkinson's Disease.

The body produces L-DOPA from the amino acid, tyrosine. L-DOPA is converted to dopamine, a neurotransmitter that helps with motor control.

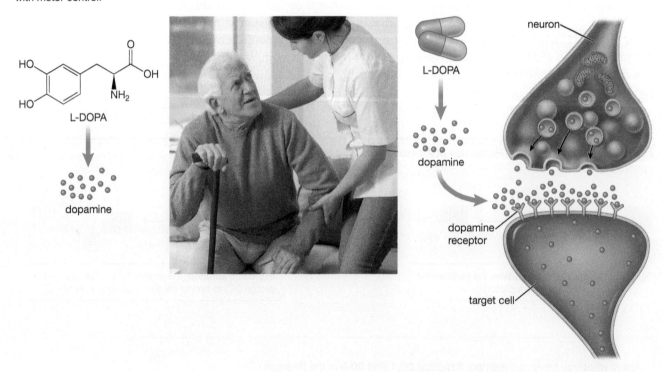

dopamine system. A loss of dopamine-secreting neurons is the cause of Parkinson's disease, for example. One of the most successful medications for Parkinson's disease is L-DOPA. Pharmaceutical companies produce L-DOPA synthetically and purify it to ensure that only the L isomer is present. It is given to patients to increase dopamine concentrations in the brain.

Apply what you have just learned: **Practice 20.6** in the Pearson eText.

Quiz yourself on the content of this section: **Check 20.2** in the Pearson eText.

20.3 Peptides

Amino acids undergo a chemical reaction that links them to each other with amide bonds. We generally refer to amide bonds between amino acids as **peptide bonds.** When amino acids link to each other in long chains they form larger molecules called **peptides**. A **dipeptide** is two amino acids joined together with one peptide bond and a **tripeptide** is three amino acids joined by two peptide bonds.

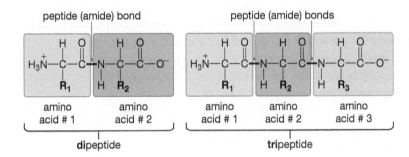

Polypeptides are many amino acids joined together in long chains. One such polypeptide is used in a drug that contains 39 amino acids linked together with peptide bonds, which treats type 2 diabetes (Figure 20.17).

Figure 20.17 Peptide Drugs.

Several drugs for type 2 diabetes are peptides. The drug Byetta, for example, contains a peptide that is 39 amino acids long. This polypeptide binds to many receptors in the body, particularly in the pancreas, which prompts the body to increase production of insulin and helps regulate blood sugar levels.

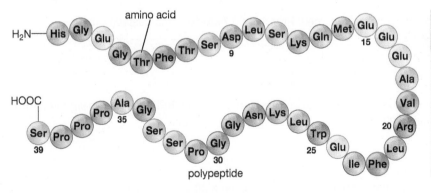
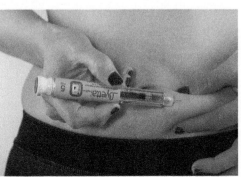

Peptide Formation Reaction

A peptide bond forms when the carboxylate anion (COO^-) of one amino acid joins with the ammonium cation (NH_3^+) of another amino acid and water (H_2O) is removed. Because water is removed, this type of reaction is a dehydration (condensation) reaction.

condensation/dehydration reaction

In the reaction between serine and alanine that forms a dipeptide, for example, the oxygen atom from the carboxylate anion on serine combines with hydrogen atoms from the ammonium cation on alanine. A peptide bond forms linking the two amino acids together to form a dipeptide.

In this particular dipeptide, the unreacted NH_3^+ group is on the left; it is the **N-terminal** amino acid-in this case serine. The alanine, on the right, contains a free COO^- group –the **C-terminal** amino acid. By convention, the N-terminal amino acid is always on the left and the C-terminal amino acid is on the right.

To name a dipeptide, we change the *-ine* or *-ic* ending of the N-terminal amino acid on the left to the suffix *-yl*. To that, we add the name of the C-terminal amino acid on the right using the names from Table 20.1. The dipeptide is called serylalanine. In the case where alanine is the N-terminal amino acid and serine is the C-terminal amino acid, the dipeptide is called alanylserine. Due to the directionality of peptide sequences (N → C), there are two different dipeptides possible when two different amino acids combine.

Click on VisibleChem Video 20.1 to explore the condensation reactions that form peptide bonds between amino acids. This video also provides additional examples of naming small peptides. After the VisibleChem Video 20.1 you can practice drawing a dipeptide beginning with individual amino acids in Learn 20.1.

Watch this concept come to life: **VisibleChem Video 20.1:** Formation of a Peptide Bond in the Pearson eText.

Predict answers and see step-by-step solutions: **Learn 20.1:** Drawing Peptide Bond Formation in the Pearson eText.

Apply what you have just learned: **Practice 20.7–20.10** in the Pearson eText.

Polypeptides in the Human Body

Polypeptides play a wide range of roles in the body, including acting as signaling molecules (Figure 20.18).

Quiz yourself on the content of this section: **Check 20.3** in the Pearson eText.

Figure 20.18 Polypeptides in the Body.

enkephalin

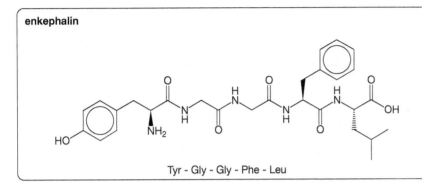

Tyr - Gly - Gly - Phe - Leu

Enkephalins are naturally-occuring polypeptides that bind to opiate receptors in the brain providing powerful pain killing activity.

oxytocin

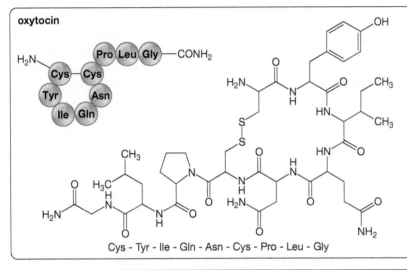

Cys - Tyr - Ile - Gln - Asn - Cys - Pro - Leu - Gly

The cyclic polypeptide **oxytocin** is a hormone that triggers contractions during childbirth and helps with lactation. Synthetic oxytocin (pitocin) can be used to induce labor.

vasopressin

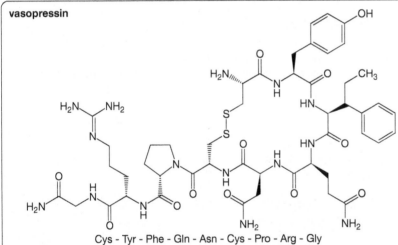

Cys - Tyr - Phe - Gln - Asn - Cys - Pro - Arg - Gly

Vasopressin, also called anti-diuretic hormone (ADH), is a cyclic polypeptide. Vasopressin increases the amount of water retained in the body by the kidneys and narrows blood vessels. Both these actions raise blood pressure.

endorphin

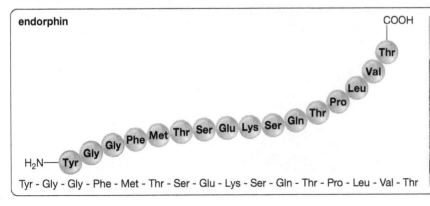

Endorphins are polypeptides widely credited with causing the "runner's high"— the feeling of euphoria some athletes experience.

Tyr - Gly - Gly - Phe - Met - Thr - Ser - Glu - Lys - Ser - Gln - Thr - Pro - Leu - Val - Thr

20.4 Protein Structure

Proteins are polypeptides composed of 50 or more amino acids. On average, each human protein contains around 375 amino acids. The amino acids in each individual protein in the human body are arranged in a unique sequence that ultimately determines that individual protein's three-dimensional structure and function. The three-dimensional shape of proteins results from extensive folding. Intermolecular forces and electrostatic attractions between amino acid side chains along the polypeptide chain stabilize the folded structures of proteins.

In many cases, protein folding results in pocket formation. Other molecules may bind to sites in these pockets, causing the protein to either function or to shut down. For example, the kappa **opioid receptor** is a protein on the surface of cells in the brain that has a binding site for opioid molecules. The folding pattern of the polypeptide chains in the protein forms this binding site (Figure 20.19).

The drug morphine, for example, binds to the kappa opioid receptor protein. This initiates a pain relief response. The opioid, morphine, is widely used across the country in hospitals for pain relief. Opioid molecules are also used as recreational drugs. Unfortunately, tens of thousands of people die each year from opiate overdose as we discussed in the Unit introduction. An opiate overdose occurs when too much of an opioid, such as heroin or oxycontin, binds to too many receptors, leading to respiratory distress and even death.

In this section, we delve into the details of how protein folding occurs and the structure of proteins. Appreciating the complexity of protein structure allows us to understand how proteins carry out their functions in the body.

Figure 20.19 Opioid Receptor Protein.

A morphine molecule (green) is bound to the binding site in the kappa opioid receptor protein. Opioids, such as morphine, are prescribed for pain relief. Many opioid drugs are used recreationally for pleasure. Heroin and oxycontin are two drugs that are responsible for a tragic number of overdose deaths in the United States.

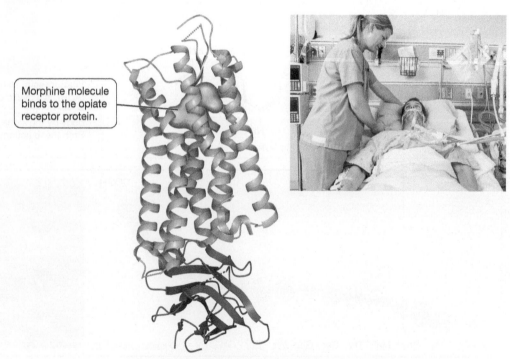

Morphine molecule binds to the opiate receptor protein.

Levels of Protein Structure

There are four levels of structure in proteins: *primary, secondary, tertiary, and quaternary.* **Primary protein structure** results from the unique sequence of amino acids that are joined together by peptide bonds (Figure 20.20). Each protein has a different sequence of amino acids. This sequence ultimately determines the structure and function of a protein.

The long chains of amino acids in proteins fold in specific repeated patterns. The repeating patterns determine the **secondary protein structure**. The two most common secondary structures in proteins are the α**-helix** and β**-pleated sheets**. Certain regions in a protein form into sheets because of hydrogen bonds between the H atom on an amino group of one amino acid and the carbonyl oxygen of another. VisibleChem Video 20.2 provides additional information about α-helices and β-pleated sheets.

Figure 20.20 Primary and Secondary Protein Structure.

The sequence of amino acids in a protein is its primary structure. Chains of amino acids form repeating hydrogen bonds with other amino acids forming two types of secondary structures, α-helices and β-pleated sheets.

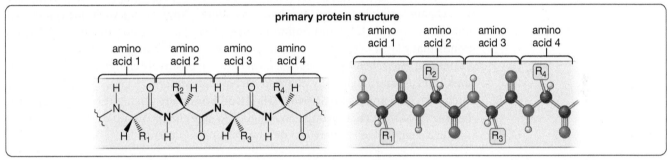

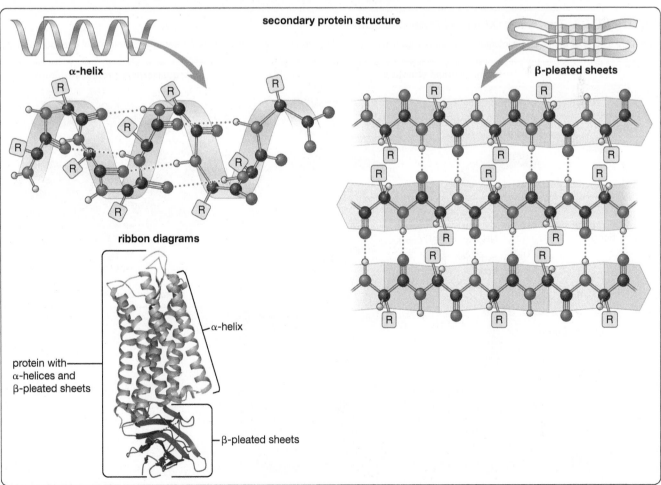

Proteins generally contain regions of both α-helix and β-pleated sheets with other regions of less predictable folding. We use a variety of representations to communicate about secondary structures, but the **ribbon diagram** is the most common representation of protein structure. A flat ribbon coiled in the shape of a helix represents α-helix secondary structure. A flat wide ribbon in the shape of an arrow represents one strand of a β-pleated sheet. While the details of primary structure are not included in ribbon diagrams, these diagrams are useful to view secondary structure.

Tertiary and Quaternary Structure

The three-dimensional shape and folding pattern of the entire protein results in **tertiary protein structure**. Tertiary structure includes interactions of the amino acid side chains. It also involves the way the secondary structures are incorporated into the larger folding context of the entire molecule. Proteins generally fold into structures that maximize stability.

Several different types of stabilizing interactions play roles in protein folding (Figure 20.21). London dispersion forces stabilize amino acids that only have nonpolar side chains containing carbon and hydrogen atoms. Amino acids with side chains that contain hydroxyl (OH) and amino groups (NH_2) form intramolecular hydrogen bonds that play a large role in stabilizing proteins. **Salt bridges**, which we also call *electrostatic interactions* or *ion bridges*, form between positively charged ammonium cations (NH_3^+) and negatively charged carboxylate anions (COO^-) on amino acids such as lysine and aspartic acid. **Disulfide bonds** are covalent bonds that form between two thiol (SH) groups on amino acid side chains. Disulfide bonds can form within a chain as well as between different chains in proteins.

Figure 20.21 Tertiary and Quaternary Protein Structure.

There are a number of stabilizing interactions in tertiary protein structure. Quaternary protein structure is illustrated in a protein that has four subunits.

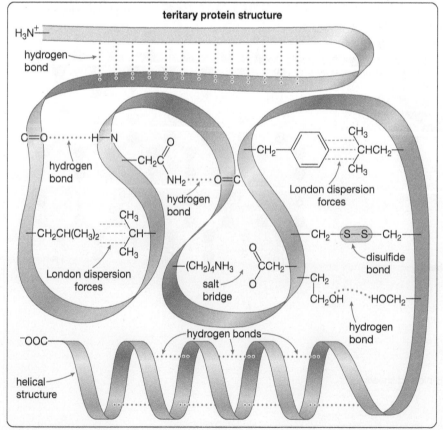

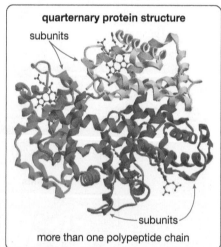

The highest level of protein structure is referred to as **quaternary protein structure**. Only proteins that have more than one polypeptide chain exhibit this level of structure. We refer to each individual polypeptide chain as a **subunit (see Fig 20.21)**. Many proteins need more than one subunit (chain) to be complete and biologically active. However, not all proteins have quaternary protein structure; many proteins contain only one polypeptide chain.

Watch VisibleChem Videos 20.2 and 20.3 to explore the four levels of protein structure.

Watch this concept come to life: **VisibleChem Video 20.2:** Overview of Protein Structure and **VisibleChem Video 20.3:** Stabilizing Interactions in Protein Folding in the Pearson eText.

Protein Folding in the Body: Collagen and Myoglobin

Proteins in the human body carry out dynamic and essential functions that are directly related back to their structure, including their intricate folding patterns.

Collagen is a structural protein and the most abundant protein in the body. Collagen is a building block in bone, cartilage, tendons, teeth, and blood vessels (Figure 20.22). Collagen has a unique secondary structure called a *triple helix*. The triple helix forms because glycine and proline, which are both amino acids with small side chains, make up a large percentage of collagen. The small side chains of glycine and proline allow the polypeptide chains in collagen to lie next to each other and form hydrogen bonds. Together the bonded chains form its characteristic triple helix structure. As humans age, not only is collagen produced in our bodies at a slower rate, but some structural features of the collagen protein also change.

Figure 20.22 Collagen.

This protein is the major structural protein in the body and has a triple helix structure. Collagen serves to help tissues withstand stretching. As people age, collagen is produced at a slower rate which ultimately leads to skin wrinkles.

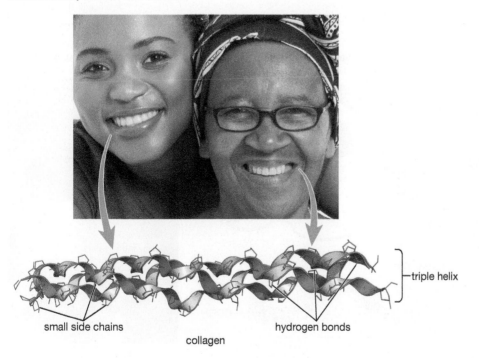

Figure 20.23 Myoglobin.

This important protein stores oxygen in muscle tissue. A positive test for myoglobin in the blood indicates severe trauma to the muscles. A normal blood test should not contain myoglobin.

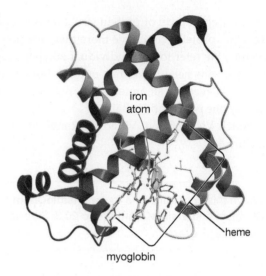

Myoglobin is the primary oxygen-carrying protein in muscle tissue (Figure 20.23). As an oxygen-transport protein, myoglobin shares similarities with hemoglobin. Both myoglobin and hemoglobin contain heme, the molecule that houses an iron atom and provides a binding site for oxygen. Healthcare workers test for myoglobin in the blood to identify severe injury to muscle tissue. A healthcare provider will order the myoglobin blood test if a heart attack, which involves damage to the heart muscle, is suspected, or in situations in which other muscles in the body are severely traumatized.

Protein Folding in the Body: Insulin and Human Serum Albumin

Insulin, another important protein in the body, regulates glucose levels in the blood. Insulin is a regulatory protein composed of two peptide chains linked together by two disulfide bonds and an additional disulfide bond within one of the chains (Figure 20.24). Diabetes occurs when the pancreas produces very little or no insulin, or when the body does not respond appropriately to insulin. Treatment for diabetes often involves regular injections of insulin.

Figure 20.24 Insulin.

The structure of insulin contains disulfide bonds that stabilize the tertiary structure of the molecule. Insulin regulates glucose in our bodies.

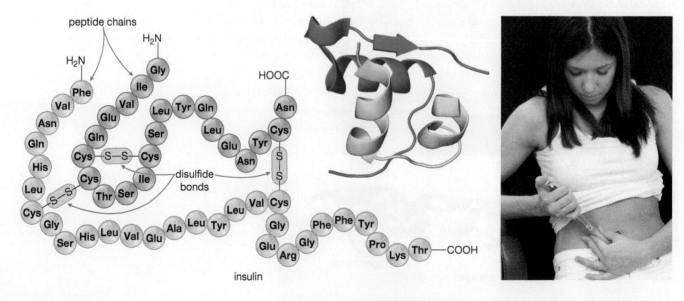

Figure 20.25 Human Serum Albumin.

The ribbon diagram of HSA shows the protein bound to a molecule of the drug ibuprofen.

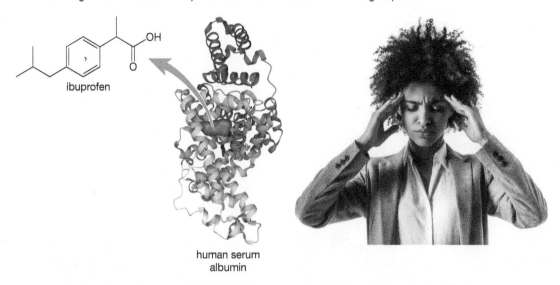

ibuprofen

human serum
albumin

Human serum albumin (HSA) is the main protein in human blood plasma (Figure 20.25). The body produces HSA in the liver and secretes it into the blood where it helps bind and transport hormones, fatty acids, and other molecules, including medications. Ibuprofen molecules, for example, bind to HSA and HSA transports them to different parts of the body through the blood. Ibuprofen is a commonly used over-the-counter pain medication that relieves mild pain from various conditions including headache, dental pain, menstrual cramps, muscle aches, and arthritis.

Apply what you have just learned: **Practice 20.11–20.14** in the Pearson eText.

Quiz yourself on the content of this section: **Check 20.4** in the Pearson eText.

20.5 Protein Hydrolysis and Denaturation

Conditions that impact any of the four levels of protein structure can disrupt or even prevent the proper function of proteins. Peptide bonds are broken, for example, when a protein encounters acids, bases, or some enzymes in an aqueous environment. The bond-breaking reaction is hydrolysis, which is the splitting of a molecule by the addition of water. When water is added to a substance and it undergoes a hydrolysis reaction, we say it is *hydrolyzed*. The hydrolysis reaction is the opposite of the condensation reaction that forms the peptide bond. A hydrolysis reaction of a protein breaks the peptide bond, releasing individual amino acids. The acid, base, or enzyme plays the role of a catalyst when water is added to the peptide bond. When each peptide bond is hydrolyzed, an ammonium cation and a carboxylate anion form.

Peptide bonds break
when water is added.

Figure 20.26 Digesting Proteins.

Proteins are broken down into peptides and then individual amino acids by hydrolysis reactions. The enzyme pepsin catalyzes many of these reactions in the stomach.

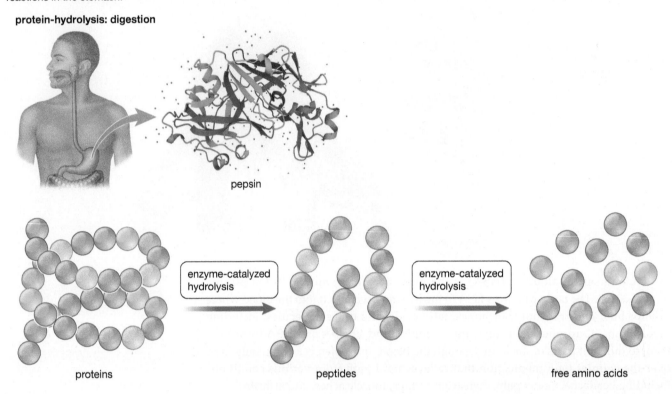

protein-hydrolysis: digestion

pepsin

enzyme-catalyzed hydrolysis

enzyme-catalyzed hydrolysis

proteins

peptides

free amino acids

An important hydrolysis reaction occurs in the stomach when enzymes promote protein breakdown to produce free amino acids (Figure 20.26). Once our bodies digest the proteins, the body absorbs the free amino acids in the intestines and transports them to the cells where the body uses them to make new proteins.

Protein Denaturation

Exposure to physical or chemical reagents can compromise the stability of secondary, tertiary, or quaternary structure in a process called **denaturation** (Figure 20.27). Denaturation can change the shape so that the protein can no longer function. The covalent peptide bonds that characterize primary structure, however, are not affected by denaturation.

High temperatures, acids and bases, heavy metals, and agitation can all disrupt the noncovalent interactions that create the intricate three-dimensional shape of a protein. Ultimately exposure to these conditions can denature a protein so much that it can no longer function correctly.

Heat, for example, breaks up London dispersion forces between nonpolar amino acids in the polypeptide chain of a protein. This generally results in a globular (spherical or globe-like) protein uncoiling to become an undefined denatured structure. We witness heat denaturation in the kitchen when we cook eggs. The heat of the stove denatures ovalbumin, the major protein in egg white, when we scramble an egg. The denatured egg white protein forms a solid.

The response of milk protein to acidic conditions is another denaturation process we may experience in the kitchen. As milk ages, lactic acid produced by enzymes in the milk denatures milk proteins. The result is sour milk that includes solids called *curds*. Another familiar example is alcohol-based hand sanitizers. These products typically contain 70% alcohol. The alcohol solution enters the bacterial cells, killing the cells by denaturing the proteins (Figure 20.28).

Figure 20.27 Protein Denaturation.

A) Various by physical and chemical factors such as heat, acids, bases, heavy metals, or agitation, disturb secondary, tertiary, or quaternary structure and denature proteins. **B)** Heat denatures the proteins in egg whites, turning them from a liquid to a solid during cooking.

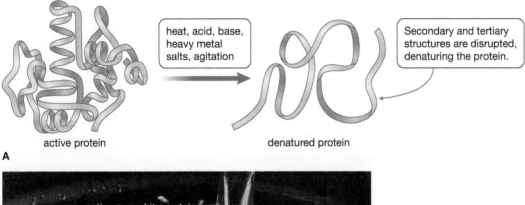

heat, acid, base, heavy metal salts, agitation

Secondary and tertiary structures are disrupted, denaturing the protein.

active protein   denatured protein

A

active egg white protein

Heat from stove denatures egg white protein.

B

Figure 20.28 Hand Sanitizer.

Most hand sanitizers contain 70% alcohol. The alcohol penetrates bacteria cells on our hands and denatures bacterial proteins by disrupting the hydrogen bonds that stabilize their secondary and tertiary structure.

Select BioConnect 20.2 (contains Figures 20.29–20.35) to learn about human diseases associated with protein misfolding and denaturation.

Explore how Chemistry and Biology connect: **BioConnect: 20.2** Protein Folding Diseases in the Pearson eText.

Quiz yourself on the content of this section: **Check 20.5** in the Pearson eText.

Chapter Summary

20.1 Introduction to Proteins

Learning Objective: List the key functions that proteins carry out in the body.

Proteins throughout the human body carry out functions that are significant in a range of essential bodily functions. Proteins are composed of long chains of amino acids that fold in intricate ways, producing the unique overall three-dimensional structure of each protein. While many amino acids exist in nature, there are twenty that produce all the proteins in the human body. Nine of these are considered essential amino acids, meaning that humans must obtain them from our diets.

BioConnect 20.1: Proteins in our Diets

Key Terms

enzymes	proteins	sickle cell disease
heme	regulatory protein	transport protein
membrane proteins		

20.2 Amino Acids

Learning Objective: Draw the charged forms of amino acids at a range of pH values and identify amino acid stereoisomers as D or L.

Amino acids are organic molecules that contain an amino group (NH_2) and a carboxyl group (COOH) (Table 20.1). A unique R group is also part of the structure. Each amino acid belongs in a specific category; the category is determined by the R group being nonpolar, polar, acidic, or basic. The zwitterion form of an amino acid contains both a positive charge (NH_3^+) and negative charge (COO^-) (Figure 20.14). Most amino acids have two enantiomers, referred to as an L-amino acid and a D-amino acid. The L isomer is commonly found in nature; the D isomer is not common in nature.

Key Terms

α-amino acid	α-carbon	carboxylate anion
L-amino acid	amino acid side chain	isoelectric point (pI)
D-amino acid	ammonium cation	zwitterion

20.3 Peptides

Learning Objective: Draw simple peptides and identify peptide bonds.

Amino acids undergo chemical reactions that link them with a peptide bond. These reactions involve the carboxylate anion of one amino acid forming a peptide bond with the ammonium cation of another amino acid to produce a peptide and water. This type of reaction is a condensation (dehydration) reaction. A dipeptide contains two amino acids, a tripeptide contains three amino acids, and a polypeptide contains many amino acids.

VisibleChem Video 20.1: Formation of a Peptide Bond

Key Terms

C-terminal	peptide	polypeptide
dipeptide	peptide bonds	tripeptide
N-terminal		

20.4 Protein Structure

Learning Objective: Describe primary, secondary, tertiary, and quaternary structures of proteins.

Protein structure is on four levels: *primary, secondary, tertiary, and quaternary.* The primary structure of a protein is the unique sequence of amino acids joined by peptide bonds. Repeating patterns of folding create secondary structure. The two most common secondary structures encountered in proteins are α-helix and β-pleated sheets. The three-dimensional shape and folding pattern of the entire protein results in tertiary structure. Tertiary structure includes interactions of the side chains, as well as the ways secondary structure is incorporated into the larger folding context of the entire molecule. Proteins generally fold into a structure that maximizes stability. The highest level of protein structure is quaternary structure; quaternary structure is only found in proteins that have more than one subunit (polypeptide chain).

VisibleChem Video 20.2: Overview of Protein Structure

VisibleChem Video 20.3: Stabilizing Interactions in Protein Folding

Key Terms

α-helix

β-pleated sheet

disulfide bonds

opioid receptor

primary protein structure

quaternary protein structure

ribbon diagram

salt bridges

secondary protein structure

subunit

tertiary protein structure

20.5 Protein Hydrolysis and Denaturation

Learning Objective: Draw the products of protein hydrolysis and describe protein denaturation.

A hydrolysis reaction of a protein breaks the peptide bond releasing individual amino acids. This reaction occurs in the stomach where enzymes facilitate the hydrolysis of proteins to produce free amino acids. Once the proteins are digested, the free amino acids are absorbed into the intestines and then transported to the cells where they are utilized to make new proteins. Protein function can be disturbed by exposure to physical or chemical reagents that compromise the stability of secondary, tertiary, or quaternary structure in a process called denaturation. High temperatures, acids and bases, heavy metals, and even agitation are all capable of disrupting and denaturing a protein.

BioConnect 20.2: Protein Folding Diseases

Key Terms

chaperone protein (from BioConnect 20.2)

denaturation

 End-of-Chapter Quiz

Have you mastered the content of this chapter? Try the **End-of-Chapter Quiz** in the Pearson eText.

1. Collagen is important in a variety of connective tissues including tendons, ligaments, and cartilage. What type of protein is collagen?

a) transport protein   **b)** regulatory protein

c) membrane protein   **d)** structural protein

2. Hemoglobin is a blood protein that carries oxygen (O_2) from the lungs to the rest of the body, where it releases the oxygen to support metabolic processes. What type of protein is hemoglobin?

a) regulatory protein   **b)** membrane protein

c) transport protein   **d)** structural protein

3. Which statement best describes proteins?

a) Proteins are biomolecules made up of many sugar molecules linked together in specific sequences.

b) Proteins are biomolecules made up of large numbers of amino acids linked together in specific sequences.

c) Proteins are biomolecules that each contain between 2 and 20 amino acids linked together in specific sequences.

d) Proteins are biomolecules that contain zwitterions connected to each other by carboxylate ions.

4. Amino acids with which type of R group are not attracted to water?
   a) hydrophilic
   b) hydrophobic
   c) essential
   d) chiral

5. What is the primary difference among the common 20 amino acids?
   a) The alpha carbon has a different number of bonded groups in each common amino acid.
   b) The carboxyl group in each common amino acid may be primary (1°), secondary (2°), or tertiary (3°).
   c) The R group varies in structure in each amino acid.
   d) The amino group in each common amino acid may be primary (1°), secondary (2°), or tertiary (3°).

6. Identify the R group type on the given amino acid.

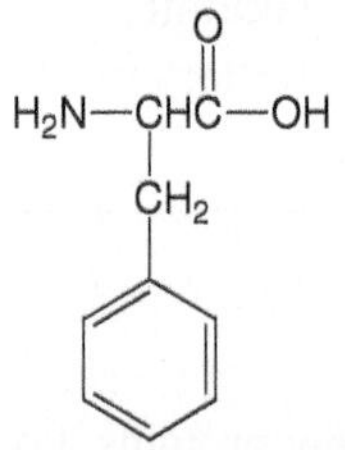

$$H_2N-CHC-OH$$
(with C=O above, and CH_2 below connecting to a benzene ring)

   a) polar
   b) ionic
   c) acidic
   d) nonpolar

7. Which functional group could be found on the R group of a basic amino acid?
   a) an amino group
   b) a carboxyl group
   c) an hydroxyl group
   d) a thiol group

8. The isoelectric point of an amino acid is the point at which:
   a) the amino and carboxyl groups are completely protonated (they have both accepted a proton).
   b) the amino acid carries an overall charge of zero.
   c) both the amino and carboxyl group are completely deprotonated (neither has accepted a proton).
   d) the amino acid has coupled to another amino acid through a peptide bond.

9. At what pH does the amino acid methionine (pI 5.7) have an *overall negative charge*?

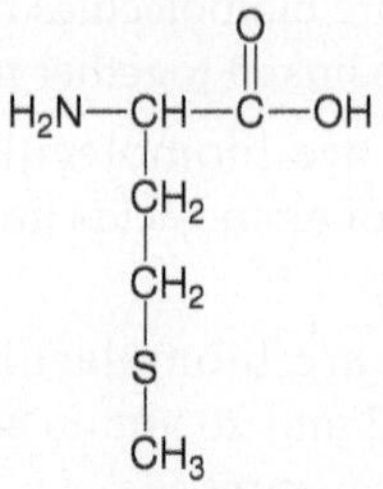

$$H_2N-CH-C-OH$$
(with C=O above, and CH_2, CH_2, S, CH_3 below)
methionine

   a) 1
   b) 4
   c) 5
   d) 9

10. Which statement about the stereochemistry of the common 20 amino acids is correct?
    a) Each of the common 20 amino acids has two chiral centers.
    b) All non-essential amino acids are non-chiral.
    c) D-amino acids are more common in nature than L-amino acids.
    d) Except for glycine, the common 20 amino acids are chiral and can occur in either the D- or L-form.

11. When amino acids undergo a chemical reaction that links them together through a peptide bond, what other product is formed in the balanced chemical reaction?
    a) NH_3
    b) H_2O
    c) H+
    d) CO_2

12. Which two groups are joined together during a peptide bond formation reaction between amino acids?
    a) two amino groups
    b) an amino group and a carboxyl group
    c) two carboxyl groups
    d) two side chain R groups

13. Which functional group links amino acids together in a peptide?
    a) ester
    b) amine
    c) hemiacetal
    d) amide

14. What is the N-terminal amino acid in the peptide Glu-Pro-Ala-Ser-Tyr?
    a) tyrosine
    b) glutamic acid
    c) tryptophan
    d) glutamine

15. Carnosine is a dipeptide molecule found in muscle and brain tissue. Which arrow is pointing at the peptide bond in carnosine?

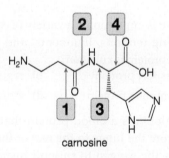

carnosine

   a) 1
   b) 2
   c) 3
   d) 4

16. Enterostatin is a peptide believed to help regulate fat intake, during and after meals. How many total amino acids are in the structure of enterostatin?

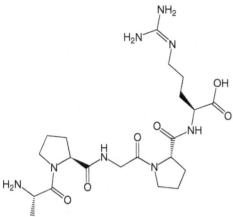

enterostatin

a) three
b) four
c) five
d) six

17. Opioid peptides are specific peptides that bind to opioid receptors in the brain. Opiates, including heroin, fentanyl, and oxycodone, mimic the effect of these peptides and are highly addictive. Which is the correct single letter amino acid sequence of the given enkephalin opioid peptide?

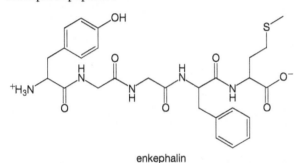

enkephalin

a) YGGFM
b) TGGWM
c) MFGGY
d) TGGFM

18. Glucagon is a peptide hormone produced by alpha cells of the pancreas. It is a medication that treats severe hypoglycemia (low blood sugar) in patients with diabetes. Glucagon helps raise the concentration of glucose and fatty acids in the bloodstream. It has the opposite effect that insulin has. The given image of glucagon features which type of protein structure?

a) primary
b) secondary
c) tertiary
d) quaternary

19. Aquaporins are multi-subunit cell membrane proteins that help regulate the transfer of water in and out of cells through water channels within their structures. The given image is an aquaporin structure. What level of protein structure is shown?

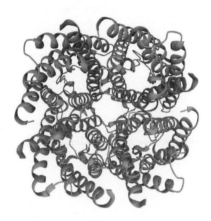

a) primary
b) secondary
c) tertiary
d) quaternary

20. Which is an example of primary protein structure?
a) a double helix
b) an α-helix
c) the sequence of amino acids
d) a β-pleated sheet

21. Copper peptide GHK-Cu is a complex formed between the tripeptide Gly-His-Lys and an aqueous copper(II) ion. It is naturally occurring and can be found in human blood plasma, saliva, and urine. Which set of reaction products forms during hydrolysis of the copper GHK complex?

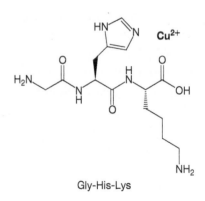

Gly-His-Lys

a)

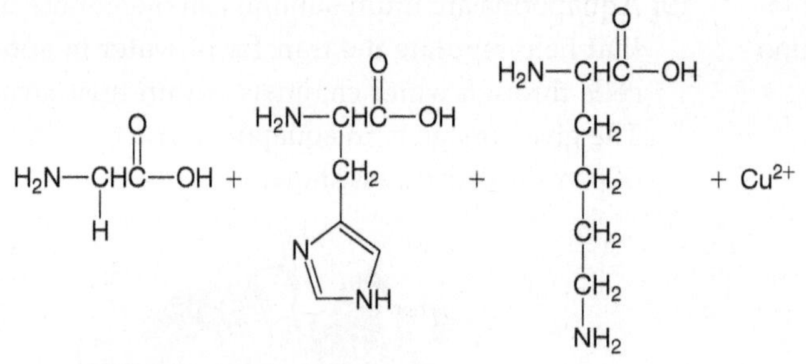

$$H_2N-CHC-OH + \;\; H_2N-CHC-OH \;\; + \;\; H_2N-CHC-OH \;\; + \; Cu^{2+}$$

b)

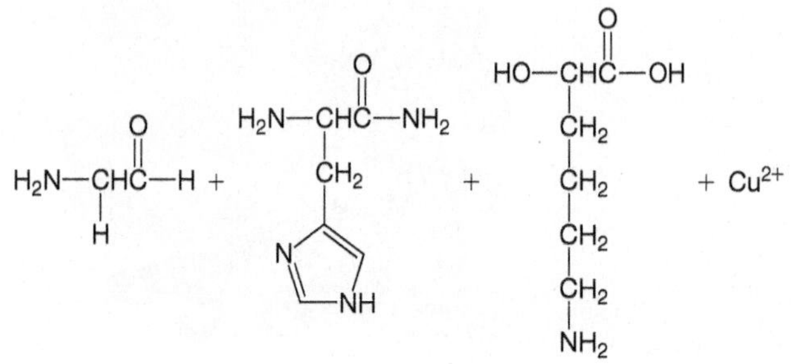

$$H_2N-CHC-H + \;\; H_2N-CHC-NH_2 \;\; + \;\; HO-CHC-OH \;\; + \; Cu^{2+}$$

c)

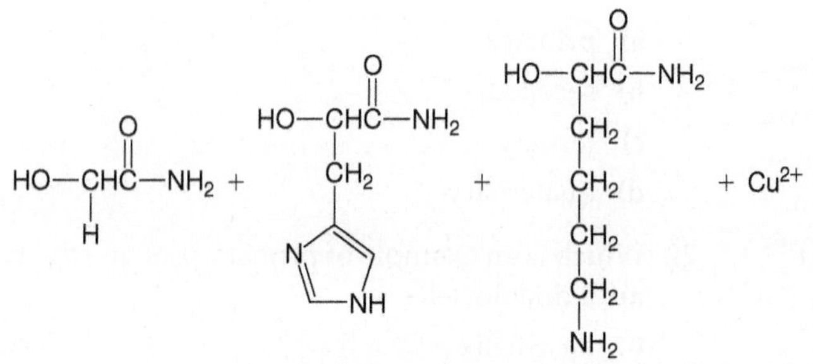

$$HO-CHC-NH_2 + \;\; HO-CHC-NH_2 \;\; + \;\; HO-CHC-NH_2 \;\; + \; Cu^{2+}$$

d)

$$H_2N-CHC-OH + \;\; H_2N-CHC-OH \;\; + \;\; H_2N-CHC-OH \;\; + \; Cu^{2+}$$

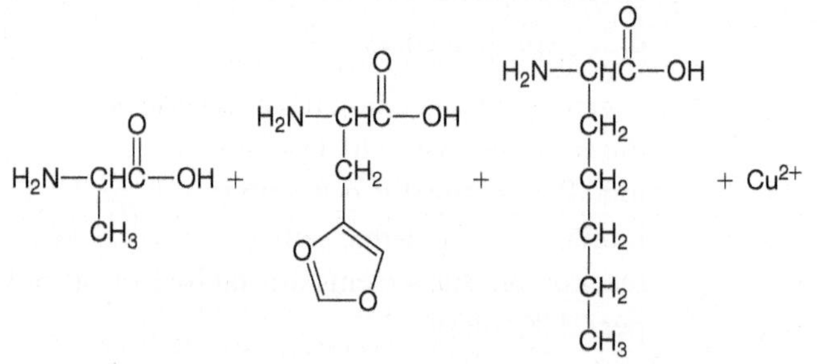

22. Which is *not* a common way that proteins become denatured?
   a) exposure to extreme heat
   b) exposure to strong detergents
   c) exposure to non-essential amino acids
   d) exposure to extremely acidic or basic conditions

Chapter 21
Enzymes: Biological Catalysts

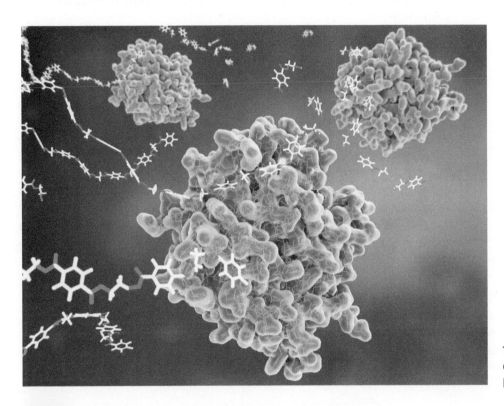

The PETase enzyme can break down PET plastics to help reduce plastic waste.

 ## Chapter Outline

21.1 Introduction to Enzymes

21.2 How Enzymes work

21.3 Factors Affecting Enzyme Activity

21.4 Enzyme Inhibition

21.5 Regulation of Enzyme Activity

21.6 Enzyme Cofactors and Vitamins

Learning Objectives

21.1 Describe the role enzymes play in biochemical reactions and recognize the six classes of enzyme function.

21.2 Explain the two models of enzyme catalysis.

21.3 Describe the effects of temperature, pH, and reaction concentrations on enzyme activity and rate of reaction.

21.4 Differentiate between reversible and irreversible inhibition and describe the processes for competitive and noncompetitive enzyme inhibition.

21.5 Identify the steps involved with allosteric control, feedback control, and covalent modification in regulating enzyme activity.

21.6 Explain the role of enzyme cofactors and vitamins in enzyme function.

Introduction

Chapter 20 is an introduction to proteins and the amino acids that bond together to form proteins. In this chapter we look more closely at a special group of proteins: enzymes. Enzymes play a critical role in biological systems. They drive and regulate millions of chemical reactions in cells each day. Enzymes are responsible for most of the day-to-day functions of our cells, from copying DNA to metabolizing the alcohol in a cold beer (Figure 21.1). Research into the role of enzymes in the body has led to the development of a wide range of drugs that speed up or slow down enzymes and help treat diseases ranging from high blood pressure to AIDS. Enzymes are also the driving force behind **bioremediation**—the use of organisms to help clean up environmental pollutants, such as oil spills and plastics.

Figure 21.1 Functions of Enzymes.

A) The enzyme alcohol dehydrogenase catalyzes the breakdown of alcohol in the liver. **B)** Many common medicines speed up or slow down enzymes. **C)** Enzymes from bacteria break down hydrocarbons after an oil spill.

Alcohol dehydrogenase in the liver and stomach detoxifies alcohol.

A

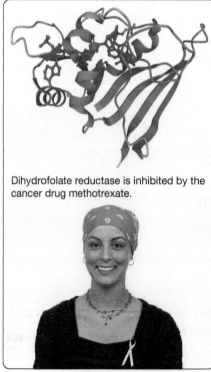

Dihydrofolate reductase is inhibited by the cancer drug methotrexate.

B

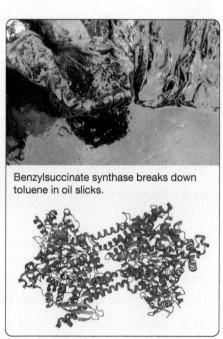

Benzylsuccinate synthase breaks down toluene in oil slicks.

C

21.1 Introduction to Enzymes

Enzymes are proteins that function as biological catalysts to speed up reactions in living organisms. Like all catalysts, enzymes are not used up in a reaction. Once they've catalyzed a reaction, enzymes are free to catalyze the next reaction. Without enzymes, the biological reactions that occur in the human body would occur much too slowly or not at all. With only a few exceptions, enzymes are water-soluble globular proteins with complex structures. You will often encounter them depicted as ribbon structures. Acetylcholinesterase, for example, is an enzyme with a complex structure that speeds up the breakdown of the neurotransmitter acetylcholine so that our nervous system functions properly (Figure 21.2). Improper function of the acetylcholinesterase enzyme can lead to paralysis, convulsions, airway constriction, and even death.

As catalysts, enzymes facilitate the breaking of bonds in reactant molecules and forming of new bonds in products. Recall from Chapter 9 that catalysts speed up reactions by lowering the activation energy (Figure 21.3) but do not affect the point that a reaction reaches dynamic equilibrium. Enzymes function as catalysts, speeding up reactions that would otherwise take a long time or never occur.

Figure 21.2 Acetylcholinesterase.

A) The acetylcholinesterase enzyme breaks down acetylcholine in the junction between neurons and muscle cells. **B)** The ribbon structure of acetylcholinesterase illustrates the complex structure of the protein. **C)** Individuals with the disease myasthenia gravis produce antibodies that attack their acetylcholine receptors. These individuals display a range of symptoms, including eye lids that are droopy due to poor muscle function. Drugs that block the activity of acetylcholinesterase can help myasthenia gravis patients maintain adequate levels of acetylcholine, restoring function despite the limited number of active receptors in their bodies.

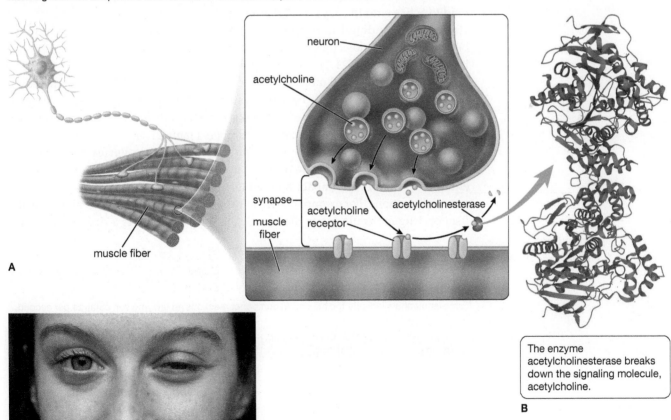

The enzyme acetylcholinesterase breaks down the signaling molecule, acetylcholine.

B

Blocking the activity of acetylcholinesterase can restore muscle function in people with the disease myasthenia gravis.

C

Figure 21.3 Impact of Enzymes on Activation Energy.

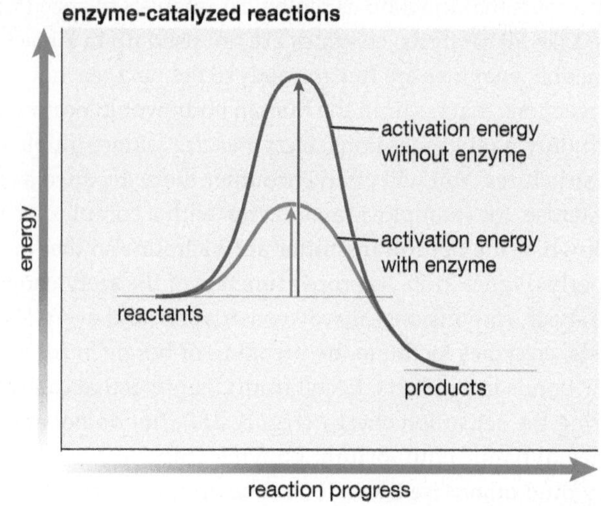

Enzyme Activity – Turnover Number

We report the activity of an enzyme in terms of its **turnover number**. The turnover number is the maximum number of substrate molecules converted to product by one enzyme molecule per unit of time. (**Substrates** are the specific molecules that bind to active sites in enzymes and are then converted to products. We discuss substrates in more detail in Section 21.2.) Most enzymes have turnover numbers between 10–1000 molecules per second, however some are much faster. Acetylcholinesterase (see Fig. 21.2), for example, has a turnover number of 25,000. This enzyme degrades 25,000 molecules of acetylcholine every second. This incredibly fast reaction rate allows our nervous system, and therefore our body, to carry out everyday movements at a pace we take for granted. Enzymes throughout the human body have a range of turnover numbers (Table 21.1).

In some cases, the turnover number of an enzyme varies by individual (Figure 21.4). In other words, in different people, the rate of catalytic events is different. This variation can impact how efficiently each individual's body carries out essential reactions. For example, there is variation among individuals in the metabolism of drug molecules once they reach the liver. Codeine is a drug in the opiate

Table 21.1 Turnover Number for a Variety of Enzymes.

Turnover numbers indicate the maximum number of reactions an enzyme can catalyze per second.

Enzyme	Turnover Number (per second)	Function
Carbonic anhydrase	600,000	Converts carbon dioxide to bicarbonate ion in red blood cells
Acetylcholinesterase	25,000	Breaks down acetylcholine in the nervous system
Lactate Dehydrogenase	1000	Converts pyruvate to lactate in the last step of glycolysis
Ribonuclease	100	Hydrolysis of phosphate ester bond in RNA
DNA polymerase	15	Synthesis of DNA molecules
Papain	10	Hydrolysis of peptide bond, found papaya plant

Figure 21.4 Enzymes Metabolize Drugs.

Our bodies metabolize many drugs, including the opioids, in the liver. **A)** Liver enzymes convert some drugs, such as codeine, to their active state. **B)** Variations in the efficiency of an individual's enzymes make people more or less susceptible to drug overdose. Studies show that the blood levels of morphine, for example, can vary more than 30-fold between individuals who don't metabolize the drug well, and those whose enzymes metabolize the drug more rapidly.

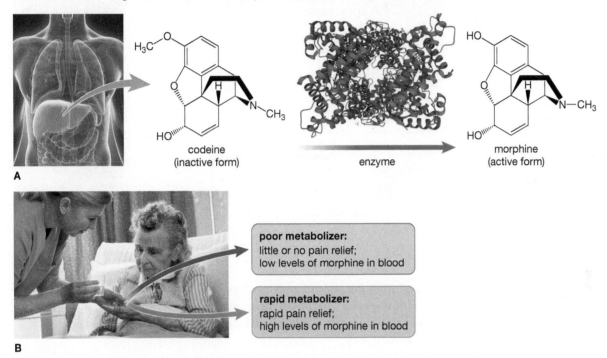

family used for pain relief. Codeine remains inactive until it undergoes an enzyme-catalyzed reaction and produces the active form called morphine. Some individuals have enzymes that are slow to convert codeine to morphine, so they experience little or no pain relief after taking these drugs. Other individuals have efficient enzymes and experience rapid pain relief when they take codeine.

The Diversity of Enzyme Function

An enormous number of proteins act as enzymes and a typical cell contains thousands of different kinds of enzymes. Each enzyme carries out a specific function and we place each enzyme into one of six major classes based on function (Table 21.2).

The name of each specific enzyme describes the reactant in the reaction the enzyme catalyzes or the general reaction type. Note the suffix *ase* at the end of the name of many enzymes. Oxidases, for example, are a type of oxidoreductase (see Table 21.2) enzymes that catalyze the oxidation of a molecule. In this case, the enzyme name includes the partial name of the reaction type (oxid-) with the suffix *ase*.

We can often determine the class and function of an enzyme from the enzyme name. The enzyme lipase, for example, is a specific type of hydrolase (see Table 12.2). Lipase catalyzes hydrolysis reactions of lipids, breaking down lipids in digestion. In this case, the reactant name (lipid) is contained in the name of the enzyme. Another example are carboxylases, a type of ligase (see Table 21.2), which catalyze the formation of a bond between CO_2 and another molecule. The *carboxyl* part of the name indicates this.

Some enzymes have common names that do not fit the naming scheme just described and others end in the suffix *in*. *Pepsin* and *trypsin* are enzymes that catalyze the hydrolysis of proteins and have the *in* ending on the name of the enzyme.

Table 21.2 Classification of Enzymes.

Classification of enzymes			
1. oxidoreductases Catalyze oxidation-reduction reactions.		**4. hydrolases** Catalyze bond breaking with the addition of water.	
2. transferases Catalyze the transfer of a functional group between two different compounds.		**5. lyases** Catalyze the addition or elimination of a functional group from a substrate.	
3. isomerases Catalyze the rearrangement of atoms in a substrate.		**6. ligases** Catalyze the bonding of two substrate molecules.	

After exploring the table of enzyme classes (Table 21.2) and completing Practice 21.1, read BioConnect 21.1 (contains Figures 21.5–21.11) to learn about important enzymes that play key roles in critical biological processes such as blood clotting.

Apply what you have just learned: **Practice 21.1** in the Pearson eText.

Explore how Chemistry and Biology connect: **BioConnect: 21.1** Using Enzymes to Treat Blood Clots in the Pearson eText.

Quiz yourself on the content of this section: **Check 21.1** in the Pearson eText.

21.2 How Enzymes Work

Every enzyme has a unique three-dimensional shape that binds small molecules called substrates in an active site (Figure 21.12). The **active site** of an enzyme is a region formed by the folds of the protein chains where a chemical reaction takes place. Each active site has a specific shape in which a substrate, or possibly several substrates, fit just right, like a foot fits in a shoe.

When a substrate binds to the active site of an enzyme, an **enzyme-substrate complex** forms. This occurs when amino acid side chains that are responsible for the shape of the active site bind with the substrate. The most common intermolecular forces that occur in an enzyme-substrate complex are hydrogen bonds, salt bridges, and in the case of nonpolar side chains, London dispersion forces.

For example, the lactase enzyme—the enzyme that is essential for digestion of the milk sugar lactose—consists of four subunits with an active site that binds the lactose sugar molecule (Figure 21.13). Lactose is held in the active site by hydrogen bonds with amino acid side chains. Once in the active site, the lactase enzyme, a hydrolase, catalyzes a hydrolysis reaction that breaks down the substrate lactose into smaller

Figure 21.12 Substrate Binding to Enzyme Active Site.

When a substrate binds to an enzyme, an enzyme-substrate complex forms, a chemical reaction occurs, and product(s) are released.

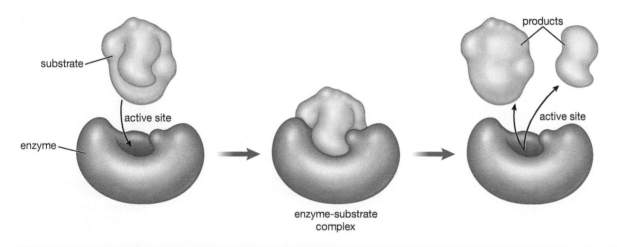

Figure 21.13 Lactase Enzyme Active Site.

Intermolecular forces hold the substrate lactose in the active site of the lactase enzyme with the amino acids that compose the active site. Lactase enzymes are essential for digesting the lactose in dairy products. Individuals that do not have lactase enzymes experience lactose intolerance symptoms.

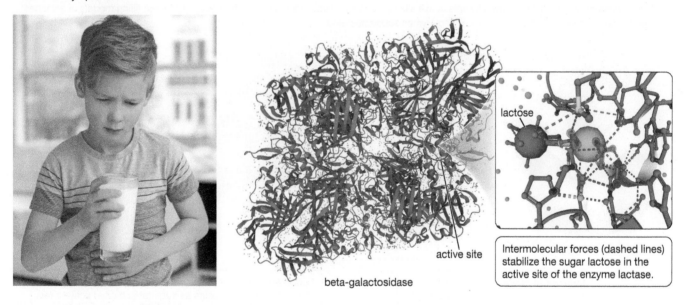

molecules that are absorbed into the bloodstream through the intestinal walls. Individuals that don't make functional lactase experience symptoms of lactose intolerance when they consume dairy products.

The Lock-and-Key and Induced-Fit Models

In some cases, only one substrate fits in an enzyme's active site, but in other cases, a group of substrates with similar shapes can bind at the enzyme's active site. We refer to the match between substrates and active sites as enzyme **specificity**.

Two models describe specificity of a substrate for an active site: the *lock-and-key model* and the *induced-fit* model (Figure 21.14).

In the **lock-and-key model**, the shape of the active site is rigid like a "lock." The three-dimensional shape of the substrate, or the "key" must exactly match the shape of the active site for the enzyme to catalyze the reaction. The lock-and-key model explains how enzymes with high specificity function.

Figure 21.14 The Lock-and-Key Model of Enzyme Function.

The lock-and-key model describes a rigid active site that must provide an exact match for a specific substrate.

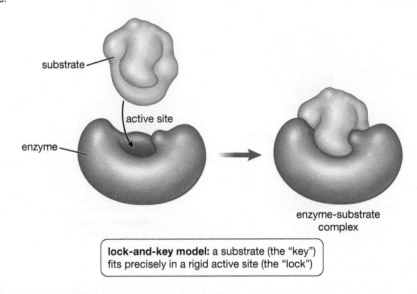

lock-and-key model: a substrate (the "key") fits precisely in a rigid active site (the "lock")

Figure 21.15 The Induced-Fit Model of Enzyme Function.

The induced-fit model explains how a flexible active site can change shape when a substrate binds to it. Space filling models of enzymes help researchers visualize the changes that occur when substrates bind.

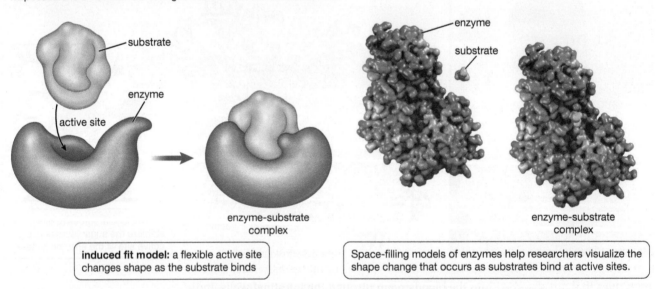

induced fit model: a flexible active site changes shape as the substrate binds

Space-filling models of enzymes help researchers visualize the shape change that occurs as substrates bind at active sites.

In the **induced-fit model**, the shape of the active site is flexible (Figure 21.15). In this model when the substrate and enzyme interact, the active site changes shape to accommodate the substrate. The induced-fit model explains why some enzymes catalyze reactions with a variety of substrates. The shape of the active site and substrate must be reasonably similar for catalysis to occur. However, the enzyme undergoes a shape change once the substrate is bound to accommodate subtle shape differences. The enzyme hexokinase, for example, undergoes a shape change once the substrate glucose binds to its active site.

Categories of Enzyme Specificity

There are several types of enzyme specificity including: *absolute, group, bond,* and *stereochemical specificity*. Explore Table 21.3 to learn more about the different ways in which enzymes fit into active sites.

Table 21.3 Types of Enzyme Specificity.

Types of enzyme specificity			
absolute specificity	**group specificity**	**bond specificity**	**stereochemical specificity**
Enzyme acts on a single, specific substrate.	Enzyme reacts with specific functional groups.	Enzyme acts on a specific bond type.	Enzyme acts on a specific steric or optical isomer.
Example: The lactase enzyme can only bind the sugar lactose but not other similar sugars.	Example: Alcohol dehydrogenases can metabolize several different alcohols including ethanol and methanol.	Example: Pepsin recognizes specific peptide bonds between amino acids to help digest protein in the stomach.	Example: Amylase enzymes in saliva break down starch but not cellulose.

Apply what you have just learned: **Practice 21.2 and 21.3** in the Pearson eText.

Quiz yourself on the content of this section: **Check 21.2** in the Pearson eText.

21.3 Factors Affecting Enzyme Activity

Several factors impact the activity of an enzyme and how fast an enzyme catalyzes a reaction. These factors include temperature, pH, and enzyme and substrate concentrations.

Effects of Temperature Changes on Reaction Rates

Enzymes are very sensitive to temperature change. In general, as temperature increases, reacting molecules move faster and collide more with enzymes, increasing the rate of the reaction. Enzymes in our body are most active at the optimum temperature of 37°C, which is body temperature, and show very little activity at low temperatures (Figure 21.16). At temperatures above 37°C, enzymes begin to denature (unfold); above 50°C most enzyme activity stops.

Some unusual organisms, known as *thermophiles*, live in environments where temperatures can be as high as 120°C (Figure 21.17). These organisms have enzymes that function at high temperatures. Research indicates that enzymes that are functional at high temperatures have additional hydrogen bonds and salt bridges, which stabilize the tertiary protein structure.

Effects of pH Changes on Reaction Rates

Like temperature, pH affects enzyme activity. Each enzyme has an optimum pH. At this optimum pH, the enzyme functions at its peak rate (Figure 21.18). When an enzyme is subjected to solutions that are not at optimal pH, tertiary protein structure interactions are disrupted. This disruption is the result of a change in the charges on specific amino acid side chains (the R groups). The result of this change is that the side chain interactions no longer stabilize the tertiary structure of the enzyme. Once this occurs, the enzyme cannot bind substrates and is no longer able to act as a catalyst and no reaction takes place.

Figure 21.16 Effect of Temperature on Rate of Enzyme-catalyzed Reactions in the Human Body.

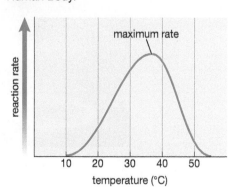

Figure 21.17 Thermophiles.

Organisms that thrive at relatively high temperatures (40°–120°C) have enzymes that function well in these temperatures. Thermophiles live in geothermally heated regions such as hot springs.

Figure 21.18 Effect of pH on Rate of Enzyme-catalyzed Biological Reactions.

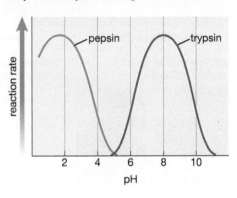

The optimum pH for most enzymes in human cells is around pH 7.4. This pH is known as *physiological* pH. Enzymes in other parts of the body, however, have a different optimum pH. Digestive enzymes, for example, have an optimum pH closer to 2.0 or even lower (Figure 21.19). When food enters the stomach, hydrochloric acid is secreted into the stomach cavity. This lowers the pH and activates digestive enzymes. Pepsin is a digestive enzyme in the stomach that performs best at a pH of 1.6.

Figure 21.19 Digestive Enzymes Breakdown Macromolecules.

Enzymes break the bonds between the monomers of carbohydrates, proteins, and fats in food. The body absorbs the small molecules produced during digestion in the small intestine and uses them to produce energy or build macromolecules. All enzymes in the body work best at or near body temperature but vary in their optimal pH depending on where enzymes are active. Pepsin, for example, is active in the stomach and functions best at pH 1.6.

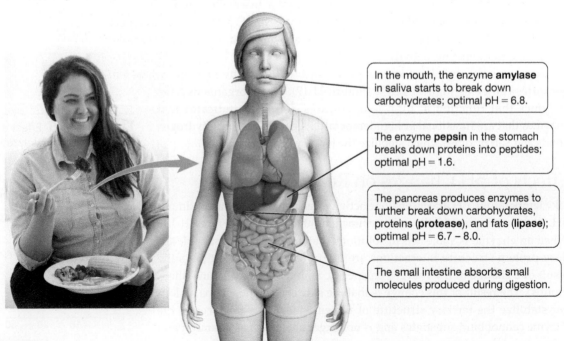

In the mouth, the enzyme **amylase** in saliva starts to break down carbohydrates; optimal pH = 6.8.

The enzyme **pepsin** in the stomach breaks down proteins into peptides; optimal pH = 1.6.

The pancreas produces enzymes to further break down carbohydrates, proteins (**protease**), and fats (**lipase**); optimal pH = 6.7 – 8.0.

The small intestine absorbs small molecules produced during digestion.

Figure 21.20 Effect of Substrate Concentration on Reaction Rate.

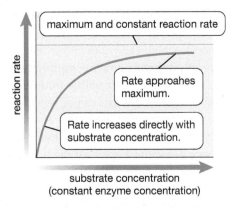

Effects of Concentration Changes on Reaction Rates

The concentration of enzyme generally does not change in our cells. However, the substrate concentration can vary quite a bit (Figure 21.20). When substrate concentrations are low compared to the enzyme, not all enzymes are in use. When this is the case, the reaction rate for enzyme-catalyzed reactions increases as substrate concentration increases. This is because more of the enzymes are working when substrate concentration increases. Eventually, as there are fewer and fewer available active sites for the substrate, the reaction rate for enzyme-catalyzed reactions begins to level out at a maximum rate. At this point, the rate of the reaction is determined by how fast the enzyme-substrate complex converts to product. Increasing the amount of substrate has no impact on reaction rate. This effect is sometimes referred to as saturation.

Although not common, it is possible for the concentration of an enzyme to vary and have an impact on reaction rate (Figure 21.21). In this case, as long as there is plenty of substrate present, the reaction rate varies directly with enzyme concentration. For example, if enzyme concentration doubles, reaction rate doubles, and if enzyme concentration triples, reaction rate triples.

Figure 21.21 Effect of Enzyme Concentration on Reaction Rate.

Adding additional enzymes causes a proportional increase in the rate of the reaction. Individuals who can't produce enough lactase enzyme, for example, can increase the concentration of this enzyme in their digestive tract by taking lactase tablets.

Apply what you have just learned: **Practice 21.4–21.6** in the Pearson eText.

Quiz yourself on the content of this section: **Check 21.3** in the Pearson eText.

21.4 Enzyme Inhibition

Enzyme **inhibitors** are molecules that prevent a substrate from binding properly to an active site of an enzyme and prevent the enzyme from carrying out its function. Many different types of molecules inhibit enzymes and inhibitors function in a variety of ways (Table 21.4). We generally separate enzyme inhibitors into two categories: *reversible inhibitors* and *irreversible inhibitors*. In **reversible inhibition,** a loss of enzymatic activity occurs but as the name suggests, this loss can be reversed. Reversible inhibition can be either **competitive** or **noncompetitive inhibitors**. A competitive inhibitor has a similar structure and polarity to a substrate and competes for the active site on an enzyme. A noncompetitive inhibitor does not compete for the active site—it binds to a different site on the molecule, distorting the shape of the enzyme so that the substrate cannot bind.

Irreversible inhibition shuts down all enzyme activity and cannot be reversed. Covalent bonds are often formed between the amino acid side chains in the active site and an irreversible inhibitor.

Once you have read about enzyme inhibitors in Table 21.4, watch VisibleChem Video 21.1 to explore the mechanism of enzyme inhibition in more detail. Then explore BioConnect 21.2 (contains Figures 21.22–21.26) to learn about how enzyme inhibitors are used as drugs to treat many diseases.

Table 21.4 Enzyme Inhibition.

Reversible inhibition	A **competitive inhibitor** is a molecule that has a similar structure and polarity to a substrate. These similarities allow the competitive inhibitor to compete for the active site on the enzyme. When the inhibitor binds it prevents the substrate from occupying the active site and no reaction occurs. Increasing substrate concentration eventually restores enzyme activity by diluting the inhibitor and increasing the likelihood of a substrate molecule binding to the active site.	
	A **noncompetitive inhibitor** does not have the same shape as a substrate and does not compete for the active site. A noncompetitive inhibitor binds to a different site on the enzyme which distorts the shape of the enzyme including the active site. Once this distortion occurs, the substrate no longer fits in the active site, and the reaction does not take place. Increasing substrate concentration does not restore enzyme activity because the noncompetitive inhibitor does not compete for the active site.	
Irreversible inhibition	In **irreversible inhibition** an enzyme loses all function in a irreversible process. Many irreversible inhibitors are toxic substances that completely shut down enzyme activity. In most cases, an irreversible inhibitor forms a permanent covalent bond with an amino acid in the active site inhibiting the substrate from binding to the active site and preventing all enzymatic activity.	

Watch this concept come to life: **VisibleChem Video 21.1:** Enzyme Inhibition in the Pearson eText.

Apply what you have just learned: **Practice 21.7–21.9** in the Pearson eText.

Explore how Chemistry and Biology connect: **BioConnect: 21.2** Enzyme Inhibitors in the Pearson eText.

Quiz yourself on the content of this section: **Check 21.4** in the Pearson eText.

21.5 Regulation of Enzyme Activity

Complex mechanisms that produce only what the body needs when it needs it, control many biochemical reactions in our body. These regulatory mechanisms vary depending on the specific cellular process as well as the substrate and enzyme. In this section, we discuss three enzyme regulation mechanisms: *allosteric control*, *feedback control, and covalent modifications.*

Allosteric Control

In the allosteric control enzyme regulation mechanism, an **allosteric enzyme** binds with a regulatory molecule (also called a regulator). The regulatory molecule is different from the substrate (Figure 21.27). The binding of the regulatory molecule does not occur at the active site. Instead, the regulatory molecule binds at an *allosteric site* that is located in a separate region of the enzyme from the active site. When the allosteric enzyme regulatory molecule binds to the allosteric site, it alters the shape of the active site. There are both positive and negative allosteric enzyme regulators. A **positive regulator** changes the shape of the active site to allow the substrate to bind more easily. This increases the rate of the reaction. A **negative regulator** changes the shape of the active site so that the substrate cannot properly bind to the enzyme. This decreases the rate of the reaction.

Feedback Control

In **feedback control**, the end product in a series of reactions inhibits an enzyme that appears earlier in the reaction series. Most biochemical reactions in the body are a part of a series of reactions that resemble assembly lines in factories. The simplest

---

Figure 21.27 Positive and Negative Allosteric Regulation.

A positive regulator binds at an allosteric site and changes the shape of the active site, allowing the substrate to bind and increasing the reaction rate. A negative regulator also binds at an allosteric site and changes the shape of the active site. However, in this case, the change prevents binding of the substrate to the active site and slows reaction rate.

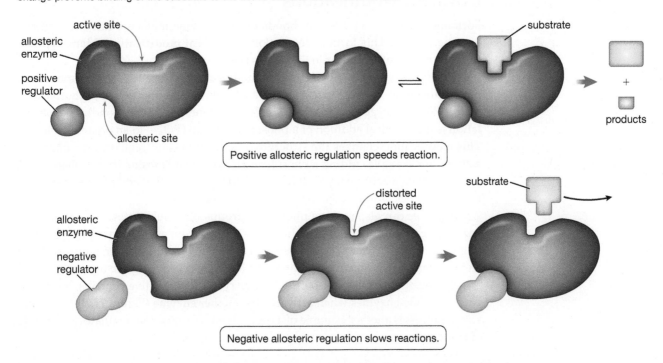

Positive allosteric regulation speeds reaction.

Negative allosteric regulation slows reactions.

Figure 21.28 Feedback Control.

In this example of feedback control, three steps and three enzymes ultimately produce an end product (the green circle at the far right) that inhibits an early step in the series of reactions. The end product binds to a site on an enzyme early in the series (bottom). When this happens, a shape change occurs in the enzyme and the process is inhibited and the series of reactions comes to a halt.

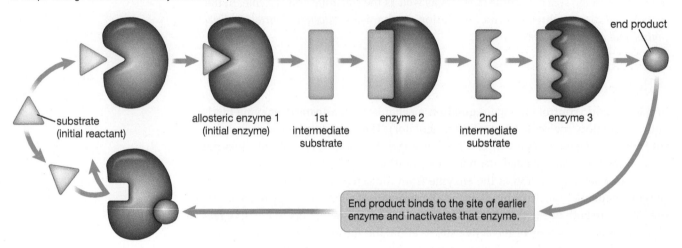

End product binds to the site of earlier enzyme and inactivates that enzyme.

pathways resemble the one shown in Figure 21.28. In the example shown in the figure, there are three steps and three enzymes that ultimately produce an end product that also functions as an inhibitor for the entire reaction.

In addition to inhibiting one process, the end product is likely to be used in another process pathway. When it is not being consumed by the other pathway, end product begins to accumulate. To avoid too much accumulation, feedback control stops the production of the end product. To stop production, a signal must be sent to the initial reaction reactants. Feedback control does exactly that. As the end product accumulates, end product binds to the initial enzyme and inactivates that enzyme. When the level of end products is low, the end product dissociates from the site of the initial enzyme and that enzyme becomes active again. Feedback control allows the enzyme-catalyzed reactions to operate only when the end product is needed. This mechanism allows the cell to conserve both energy and material.

Covalent Modifications

Forming and breaking covalent bonds on the enzyme molecule can also regulate enzyme activity. This form of regulation is **covalent modification**. Many types of covalent modifications occur in the body's cells.

The most common type of covalent modification is the addition or removal of a phosphate group. A phosphate group is a functional group with a phosphorus atom bonded to four oxygen atoms (three single bonds and one double bond). **Phosphorylation** is the chemical addition of a phosphoryl group (PO_3^-) to an organic molecule. This modification changes the structure of an enzyme and regulates the enzyme's activity. For example, adding a phosphate group from adenosine triphosphate (ATP) can activate an inactive enzyme (Figure 21.29A). Enzymes that add phosphate groups to substrates, including other enzymes, are **kinases**.

Enzymes can also remove phosphate groups from substrates, including other enzymes. Enzymes that remove phosphate groups from enzymes are **phosphatases** (Figure 21.19B). The addition or removal of phosphate groups from enzymes provides an important mechanism for regulating the biochemical pathways in our bodies.

Zymogens, which are also called **proenzymes**, are inactive proteins, which are converted into enzymes when activated by another enzyme (Figure 21.30). This activation process is another example of a covalent modification that regulates the activity of many enzymes.

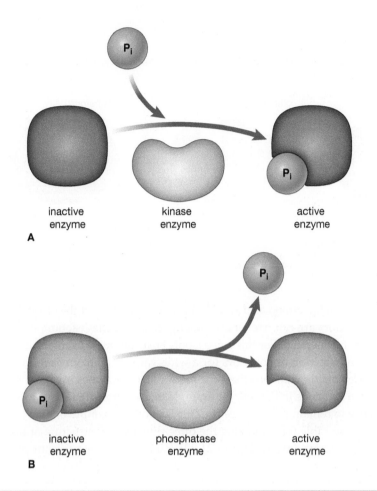

A

inactive enzyme   kinase enzyme   active enzyme

B

inactive enzyme   phosphatase enzyme   active enzyme

Figure 21.29 Phosphorylation. The addition and removal of a phosphate group is a type of covalent modification that regulates enzyme activity. **A)** A kinase enzyme activates an inactive enzyme by adding a phosphate group (phosphorylation). **B)** A phosphatase enzyme activates an inactive enzyme by removing a phosphate group (dephosphorylation).

Figure 21.30 Zymogens.

Zymogens are Inactive forms of enzymes. They are activated by the breaking of a covalent bond that leaves the active site accessible to a substrate.

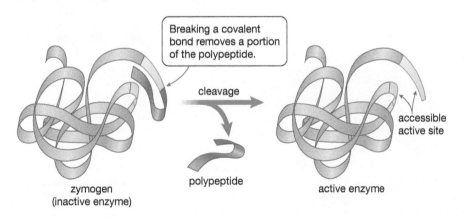

Breaking a covalent bond removes a portion of the polypeptide.

cleavage

accessible active site

zymogen (inactive enzyme)

polypeptide

active enzyme

A zymogen is converted to the active form of the enzyme when a covalent bond breaks and a portion of the polypeptide is removed. Removing this portion of the polypeptide often exposes the active site, allowing the enzyme to function.

Click on VisibleChem Video 21.2 to further explore the mechanisms and specific examples of enzyme regulation.

Watch this concept come to life: **VisibleChem Video 21.2:** Enzyme Regulation in the Pearson eText.

Apply what you have just learned: **Practice 21.10** in the Pearson eText.

Quiz yourself on the content of this section: **Check 21.5** in the Pearson eText.

21.6 Enzyme Cofactors and Vitamins

Many enzymes require the help of other small molecules or ions to carry out their functions. The metal ions or small organic molecules that are bound to enzymes for this purpose are **cofactors** (Figure 21.31). Cofactors offer additional possibilities for binding

Figure 21.31 Cofactors.

Cofactors bind in enzyme active sites along with substrates to activate enzymes. Cofactors are either metal ions or small organic molecules.

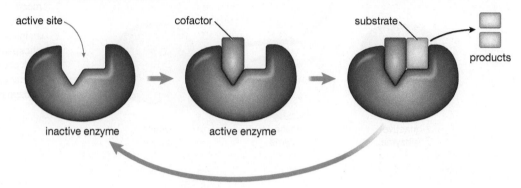

substrates beyond the amino acid side chains in the structure of the enzyme. Similar to enzymes, cofactors are not irreversibly changed during the reaction; they are either unchanged or regenerated. For this reason, only small amounts of cofactors are needed.

Metal ions function as cofactors for a wide variety of enzymes in many cellular processes. We obtain metal ions from the food we eat. Enzymes involved in oxidation and reduction reactions in the cell, for example, require iron(II). People must consume iron regularly to remain in good health. Zinc is another example of a metal ion cofactor. Zinc is responsible for stabilizing the three-dimensional structure of the digestive enzyme carboxypeptidase A (Figure 21.32). Zinc is also a significant player in the

Figure 21.32 Carboxypeptidase Active Site.

Zinc (II) ion is a cofactor for the hydrolysis of polypeptides. This enzyme-catalyzed reaction takes place as proteins are digested in the small intestine.

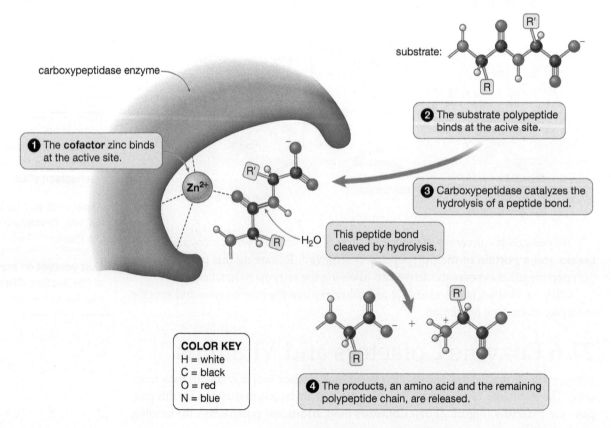

Table 21.5 Metal Ion Cofactors.

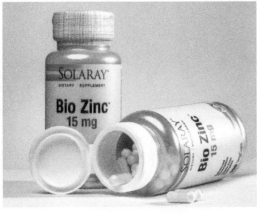

Metal ions	Enzymes requiring cofactor
Cu^{2+}/Cu^{+}	cytochrome oxidase
Fe^{2+}/Fe^{3+}	cytochrome oxidase catalase
Mg^{2+}	hexokinase glucose-6-phosphatase
Zn^{2+}	alcohol dehydrogenase carboxypeptidase A
Ni^{2+}	urease
K^{2+}	pyruvate kinase

function of alcohol dehydrogenase, the enzyme that breaks down alcohol in our body and studies have shown that taking zinc can shorten the duration of common colds by inhibiting critical enzymes in the cold virus. Table 21.5 lists some enzymes that require metal ion cofactors.

Coenzymes and Vitamins

Coenzymes are a specific type of cofactor composed of small organic molecules. Many coenzymes are vitamins or are derived from vitamins. **Vitamins** are organic molecules that are essential for normal growth and function in the human body. Like enzymes, coenzymes are not used up in the reactions they catalyze. Thus, only small amounts of coenzymes are needed. This is why we only need to consume small amounts of vitamins for normal health and growth.

We classify vitamins into two groups based on solubility. **Water-soluble vitamins** are soluble in the aqueous environment of the cell. They feature polar functional groups such as —OH and —COOH. **Fat-soluble vitamins** are nonpolar molecules that are stored in the fatty tissue of the human body.

Our bodies cannot store water-soluble vitamins and therefore we must consume them regularly in our diet. Due to the solubility of these molecules, they are excreted in urine each day. The majority of water-soluble vitamins are coenzymes or are used to produce specific coenzymes. Vitamin B_3, for example, is a component of the very important coenzyme NAD^+ (nicotinamide adenine dinucleotide). Explore Table 21.6 to learn more about the structure, function, and sources of the water-soluble vitamins.

Fat-soluble vitamins (A, D, E, and K) are mostly nonpolar and therefore stored in the body's fat deposits. These vitamins play a significant role in the chemical reactions in the body. Vitamin K, for example, is a coenzyme important for blood clotting (Figure 21.33). There is a greater risk of overdosing when consuming these vitamins (in contrast to water-soluble vitamins) because fat-soluble vitamins are stored in the body not excreted. Unlike the water-soluble vitamins, fat-soluble vitamins are not all coenzymes or components of coenzymes. Explore Table 21.7 to learn more about the fat-soluble vitamins.

Table 21.6 Water-Soluble Vitamins.

Water-soluble vitamins

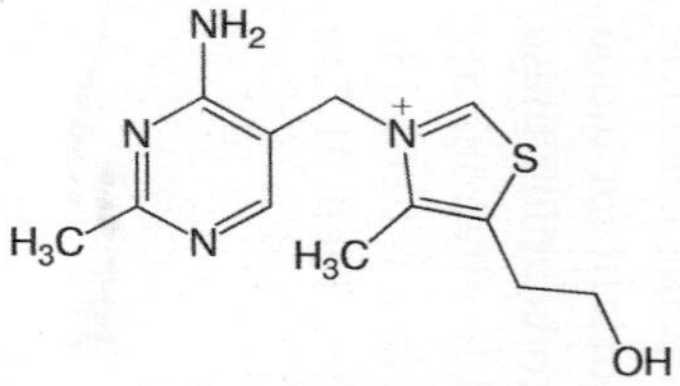

B₁₂ (cobalamin)

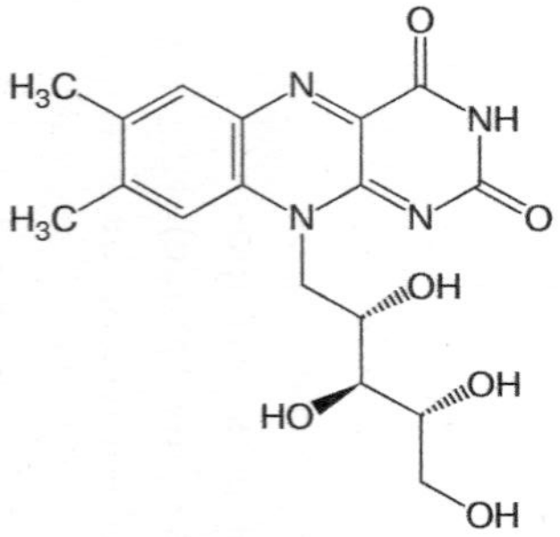

B₇ (biotin)

B₅ (pantothenic acid)

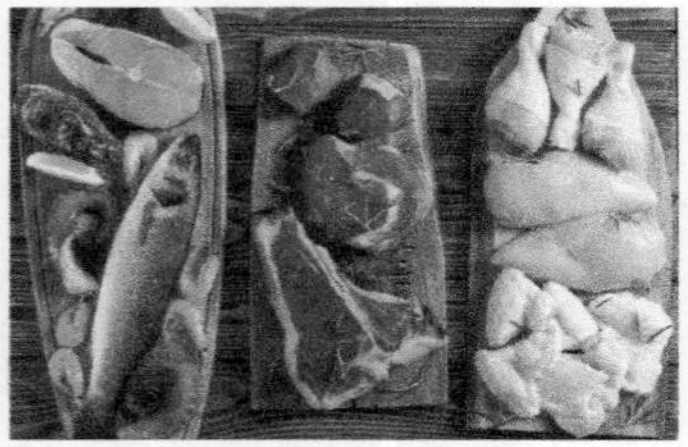

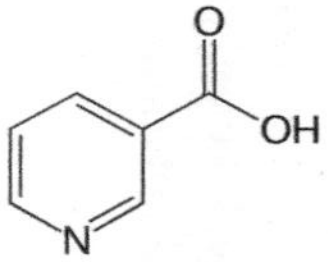

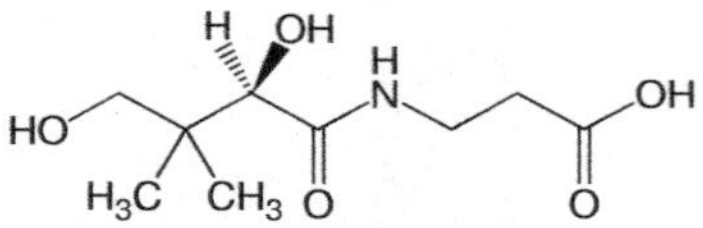

C (ascorbic acid)

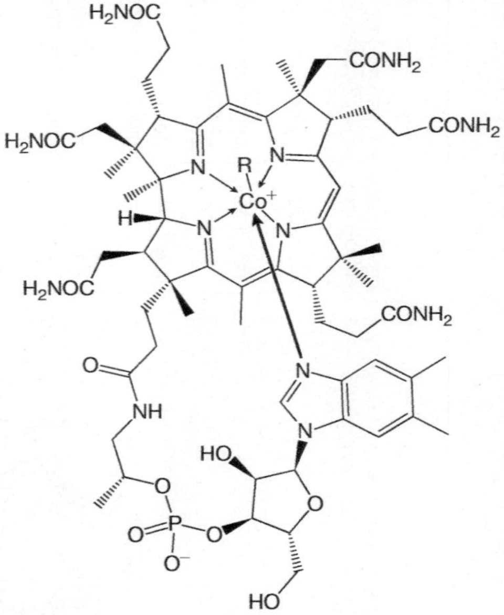

B₃ (niacin)

B₂ (riboflavin)

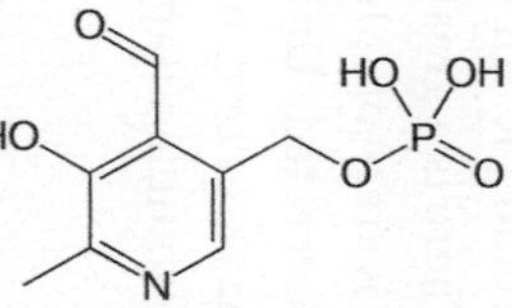

B₉ (folic acid)

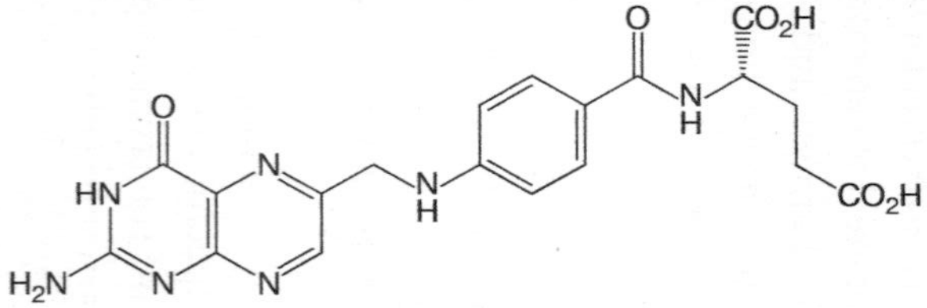

B₁ (thiamine)

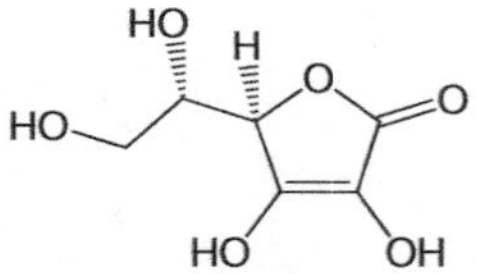

B₆ (pyridoxine)

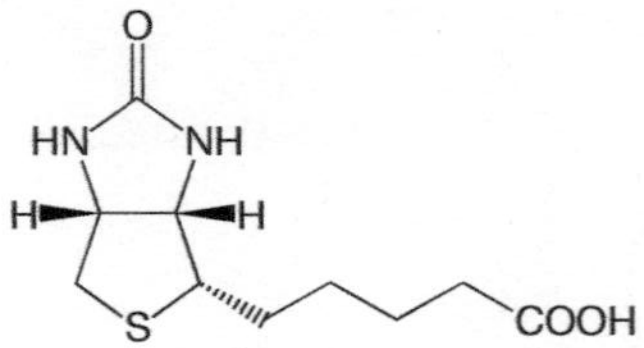

Figure 21.33 Vitamin K₁.

A) Vitamin K₁, found in many green vegetables, acts as a coenzyme for an enzyme that produces blood-clotting proteins.
B) Vitamin K₁ does not cross the placenta, so all infants are vitamin K₁ deficient at birth. This deficiency leaves them vulnerable to severe bleeding in the brain and intestines. A simple shot provides enough vitamin K₁ to last until a baby begins to eat solid food. **C)** Two million adults in the U.S. take the "blood thinner" coumadin (warfarin) to reduce the risk of stroke and heart attack from blood clots. Coumadin blocks the activity of vitamin K₁, reducing the number of clotting proteins in the blood.

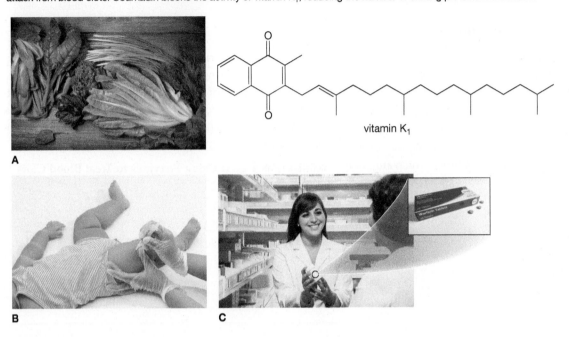

vitamin K₁

A

B

C

Table 21.7 Fat-Soluble Vitamins.

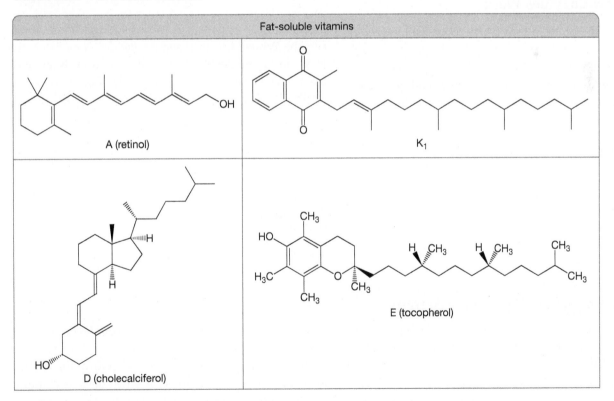

Fat-soluble vitamins

A (retinol)

K₁

D (cholecalciferol)

E (tocopherol)

 Apply what you have just learned: **Practice 21.11 and 21.12** in the Pearson eText.

Quiz yourself on the content of this section: **Check 21.6** in the Pearson eText.

Chapter Summary

21.1 Introduction to Enzymes

Learning Objective: Describe the role enzymes play in biochemical reactions and recognize the six classes of enzyme function.

Enzymes are proteins that function as biological catalysts to speed up reactions without being altered in the process. With only a few exceptions, enzymes are water-soluble globular proteins with complex structures, which are often represented using ribbon structures. Enzymes speed up reactions by lowering activation energy (Figure 21.3). The turnover number for enzymes indicates the number of catalytic events per second. Enzymes are classified into six major classes: *oxidoreductases, transferases, isomerase hydrolases, lyases. and ligases (Table 21.2).*

BioConnect 21.1: Using Enzymes to Treat Blood Clots

Key Terms

bioremediation
enzyme
plasmin (from BioConnect 21.1)
substrate
turnover number

21.2 How Enzymes Work

Learning Objective: Explain the two models of enzyme catalysis.

Each enzyme has a unique three-dimensional structure with an active site where a substrate binds and undergoes a reaction to produce products. Two models have been proposed to describe specificity of a substrate for an active site: the *lock-and-key model* and the *induced-fit* model. In the lock-and-key model the shape of the active site is nonflexible. In the induced-fit model the shape of the active site is flexible (Table 21.3).

Key Terms

active site
enzyme-substrate complex
induced-fit model
lock-and-key model
specificity

21.3 Factors Affecting Enzyme Activity

Learning Objective: Describe the effects of temperature, pH, and reaction concentrations on enzyme activity and rate of reaction.

Several factors affect how fast an enzyme catalyzes a reaction. As temperature increases, molecules move faster causing more collisions with enzymes and increasing the rate of a reaction. Enzymes in the human body are most active at body temperature (37°C) and begin to denature as temperatures rise. Most enzymes in our bodies function optimally at physiological pH (7.4), however, enzymes in some parts of the body have a different optimum pH. Reaction rates generally increase when the concentration of substrate increases until a maximum rate is reached. Maximum rate occurs when all active sites are occupied. Reaction rates also increase as the concentration of enzyme increases, provided plenty of substrate is present.

21.4 Enzyme Inhibition

Learning Objective: Differentiate between reversible and irreversible inhibition and describe the processes for competitive and noncompetitive enzyme inhibition.

Enzyme inhibitors are molecules that bind to enzymes and prevent them from carrying out their intended functions. Inhibitors are either reversible or irreversible. There are two types of reversible inhibitors: competitive and noncompetitive. A competitive inhibitor is a molecule that competes for the active site of an enzyme because it has a similar shape as the substrate. A noncompetitive inhibitor does not compete for the active site. A noncompetitive inhibitor binds to a different site on the enzyme and changes the shape of the active site, preventing the substrate from binding. Irreversible inhibitors generally form covalent bonds to the enzyme, shutting down enzyme activity.

VisibleChem Video 21.1: Enzyme Inhibition

BioConnect 21.2: Enzyme Inhibitors

Key Terms

inhibitor
competitive inhibitor
irreversible inhibition
noncompetitive inhibitor
reversible inhibition

21.5 Regulation of Enzyme Activity

Learning Objective: Identify the steps involved with allosteric control, feedback control, and covalent modification in regulating enzyme activity.

Prominent enzyme regulation mechanisms are *allosteric control, feedback control, and covalent modifications.* Allosteric control involves the binding of a regulatory molecule (regulator) at a separate region from the active site called an allosteric site. A positive regulator changes the shape of the active site to allow the substrate to bind more easily and a negative regulator changes the shape of the active site so that the substrate is prevented from binding. Feedback control involves a series of reactions for which the end product inhibits an initial enzyme produced early in the reaction series. Enzyme regulation also occurs by covalent modifications, which involves the making or breaking of covalent bonds on an enzyme. These modifications render the enzyme either inactive or active.

VisibleChem Video 21.2: Enzyme Regulation

Key Terms

allosteric enzyme	negative regulator	proenzyme
covalent modification	phosphatase	zymogen
feedback control	phosphorylation	
kinase	positive regulator	

21.6 Enzyme Cofactors and Vitamins

Learning Objective: Explain the role of enzyme cofactors and vitamins in enzyme function.

Metal ions and small organic molecules called cofactors often help enzymes function. Similar to enzymes, cofactors are not irreversibly changed during the reaction; they are either unchanged or regenerated (Figure 21.31).

Coenzymes are a type of cofactor that are small organic molecules. The body derives many coenzymes from vitamins. Vitamins are either water-soluble or fat-soluble. Water soluble vitamins are excreted from the body daily, whereas fat-soluble vitamins are stored in fat deposits.

Key Terms

coenzyme	fat-soluble vitamin	water-soluble vitamin
cofactor	vitamin	

End-of-Chapter Quiz

Have you mastered the content of this chapter? Try the **End-of-Chapter Quiz** in the Pearson eText.

1. You can often identify when a biological molecule is an enzyme by _____.
   a) the "–ate" ending to its name
   b) the prefix "poly" in its name
   c) the "–ase" ending to its name
   d) the term "amino" in its name
   e) the "–yne" ending to its name

2. The turnover number of an enzyme is _____.
   a) the maximum number of times one molecule of enzyme rotates per unit of time per molecule of substrate
   b) the maximum number of times the substrate is not reacted upon by one enzyme molecule per unit of time
   c) the maximum number of times the substrate is rotated in the active site of one enzyme molecule per unit of time
   d) the maximum number of substrate molecules acted upon by one molecule of enzyme per unit of time
   e) the minimum number of times the substrate fails to react in the active site of one enzyme molecule per unit of time

3. Select the correct statement.
   a) Ligases catalyze the breaking of bonds using water (hydrolysis).
   b) Transferases catalyze the conversion of one isomer to another using stereochemistry.
   c) Hydrolases catalyze the production of hydrogen gas and water.
   d) Ligases catalyze the bonding of two substrates using ATP energy.

4. Dopamine is a neurotransmitter involved in mood, attention, motivation, and memory. Dopamine is produced in the body when the enzyme DOPA decarboxylase removes the carboxyl group (a carboxyl functional group consisting of a carbon atom double-bonded to an oxygen atom and singly bonded to a hydroxyl group) from the substrate in a step that also requires a coenzyme pyridoxal phosphate (PLP) from vitamin B_6. What class of enzyme does DOPA decarboxylase belong to?

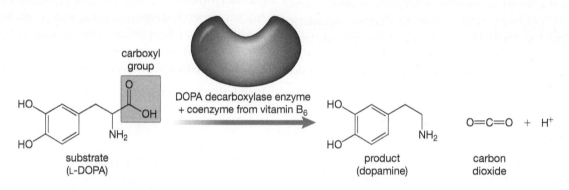

a) transferase   b) lyase   c) isomerase   d) ligase

5. The molecule kyotorphin (Tyr-Arg) is a dipeptide active in the brain. Kyotorphin was discovered in Kyoto, Japan and named after that city. It plays a role in pain regulation in the brain. Which class of enzyme catalyzes the given reaction of kyotorphin?

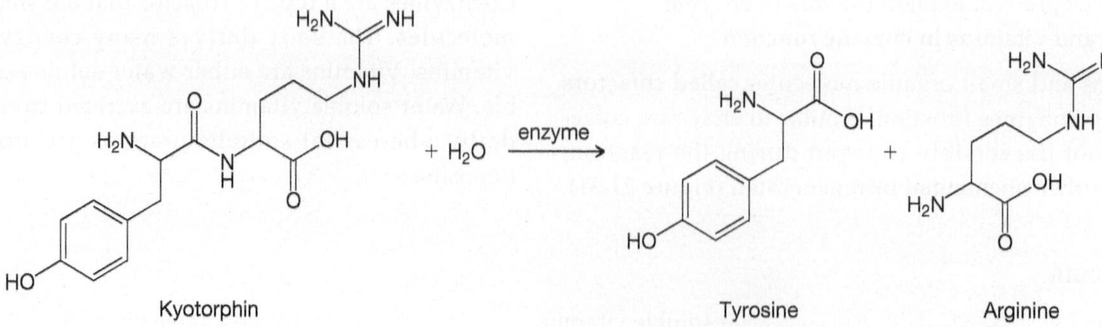

a) hydrolase   b) transferase   c) oxidoreductase   d) ligase

6. Which type of forces hold together enzyme-substrate complexes?
   a) catalyst forces
   b) intermolecular forces
   c) substrate forces
   d) enzyme forces

7. Which is *not* a general characteristic of an enzyme-catalyzed reaction?
   a) The enzyme-substrate complex is converted to free enzyme plus released products.
   b) A substrate hydrolyzes enzyme to form the substrate-product complex plus free enzyme available for the next reaction.
   c) When an enzyme is present, a reaction produces products faster than the same reaction does when carried out without an enzyme present.
   d) The substrate binds to the active site of the enzyme to form an enzyme-substrate complex.

8. Which statement describes a primary difference between the lock and key model of enzyme specificity and the induced fit model?
   a) In the lock-and-key model, the shape of the active site is flexible, but in the induced-fit model, the shape of the active site is not flexible.
   b) In the lock-and-key model, the shape of the enzyme is not flexible, but in the induced-fit model, the entire enzyme becomes the active site.
   c) In the lock-and-key model, the shape of the active site is not flexible, but in the induced-fit model, the shape of the active site is flexible.
   d) In the lock-and-key model, the shape of the active site is nonflexible and in the induced-fit model, the enzyme must be cut into two pieces producing two active sites.

9. The enzyme pepsin helps digest the foods we eat by breaking the peptide bonds that connect amino acids. Pepsin is able to recognize when any two aromatic side chain groups (an amino acid side chain is aromatic when it contains an aromatic ring system) such as phenylalanine, tryptophan, and tyrosine are located next to each other. When pepsin encounters this situation, it cuts the protein backbone between these two aromatic groups in the peptide chain, breaking down the proteins we eat. Which term best describes the level of specificity of pepsin?
   a) absolute specificity
   b) limited specificity
   c) group specificity
   d) stereochemical specificity

10. If substrate concentrations are very low, the rate of enzyme-catalyzed reactions often doubles when the concentration of the substrate is doubled. Consider the given curve illustrating the rate of a certain enzyme-catalyzed reaction and how it changes with substrate concentration. In a situation where the substrate concentration is very high relative to enzyme

concentration, would you expect the rate to double if the substrate concentration is doubled?

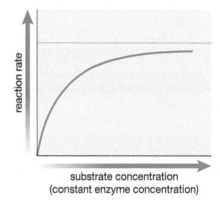

substrate concentration
(constant enzyme concentration)

   a) Yes, if the rate doubles when substrate concentration doubles in the very low range of substrate concentrations, it is also true this rate doubling effect will occur in the range of very high substrate concentrations.
   b) No, although the reaction rate may double when substrate concentrations are doubled within the very low range of possible substrate concentrations, the rate begins to level off at very high substrate concentrations.
   c) Yes, as shown by the curve, reaction rates have a consistent and linear response to substrate concentrations across the entire range of substrate concentrations.
   d) No, the rate of enzyme-catalyzed reactions is inversely proportional to substrate concentration. As the substrate concentration increases, the rate of enzyme-catalyzed reactions decreases.

11. You are working in a clinical laboratory and want to determine the ideal reaction conditions for an enzyme you are studying. Which list includes the conditions you want to optimize?
   a) temperature, pH, and substrate concentration
   b) substrate concentration, temperature, and enzyme concentration
   c) enzyme concentration, pH, and temperature
   d) substrate concentration, enzyme concentration, pH, and temperature

12. If an enzyme-catalyzed reaction has excess substrate present, what is the effect of increasing the concentration of enzyme?
   a) The rate slows down because this inhibits the formation of additional enzyme-substrate complexes.
   b) The rate remains unchanged since there is already excess substrate present.
   c) The rate slows down because increasing the enzyme concentration accelerates the reverse reaction.
   d) The rate increases because excess substrate is present that reacts with the added enzyme.

13. A medical researcher studying a certain enzyme wants to double the rate of an enzyme-catalyzed reaction in her experiments. Can she achieve this by increasing the temperature?
a) Possibly. Depending on where the new temperature is on the temperature versus reaction rate curve, it may be possible to increase the rate with this action, but this action could also slow the reaction down.
b) Yes. Increasing the temperature increases the rate of reaction by providing the additional energy reactants need to overcome the energy of activation.
c) No. Simply increasing the temperature will not have a large effect. Other variables such as substrate concentration, pH, and enzyme concentration must be optimized as well.

d) No. Temperature and reaction rate are inversely proportional. Reaction rates always increase with decreasing temperature, but increasing substrate concentration, pH, and enzyme concentration could also be used to achieve this effect.

14. A reversible inhibitor _____.
a) reverses the order of the last two amino acids in the protein sequence of the enzyme catalyzing the reaction
b) inhibits the enzyme catalyzed reaction in such a way that the inhibited forward reaction cannot be reversed
c) inhibits the reverse reaction of an enzyme, therefore catalyzing the forward reaction
d) inhibits enzyme activity when bound to an enzyme, but enzyme activity returns to normal when the inhibitor is released

---

15. People have long used the drug aspirin (acetyl salicylic acid) to help treat pain, fever, headache, and inflammation. Aspirin acts as an inhibitor when it transfers an acetyl group from aspirin to a serine amino acid in the active site of the enzyme cyclooxygenase. An acetyl group contains a carbonyl group $(C=O)$ and a methyl group (CH_3). This covalently bonded acetyl group modifies the active site in such a way that the cyclooxygenase enzyme cannot perform its function properly. What type of inhibitor is the drug aspirin in this example?

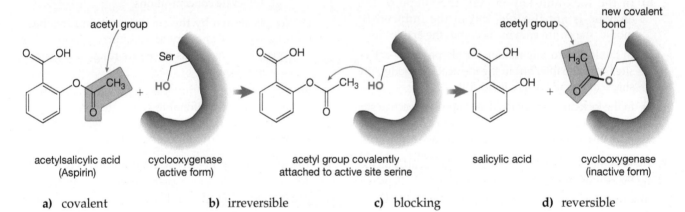

| acetylsalicylic acid (Aspirin) | cyclooxygenase (active form) | acetyl group covalently attached to active site serine | salicylic acid | cyclooxygenase (inactive form) |

a) covalent   b) irreversible   c) blocking   d) reversible

16. What form of enzyme regulation does the given diagram illustrate?

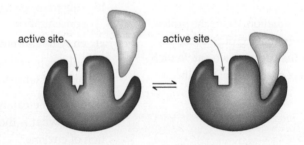

a) allosteric regulation   b) competitive inhibition   c) substrate control   d) active site regulation

17. How do allosteric enzymes control the amount of product produced?
a) Allosteric enzymes bind both the product at the active site and the substrate at a site away from the active site.
b) Allosteric enzymes use irreversible inhibition with the product as the inhibitor and the substrate as the cofactor.
c) Allosteric enzymes bind either a positive or negative regulator at a noncompetitive site.
d) Allosteric enzymes use acidic and basic amino acid side chains to adjust the pH up or down to control reaction rate.

18. The enzyme phosphofructokinase (PFK) is involved in metabolism. PFK catalyzes the conversion of fructose-6-phosphate (F6P) to fructose-1,6-bisphosphate (FBP) by adding a phosphate group to carbon number one on the fructose-6-phosphate molecule as shown in the given reaction. In mammals, the molecule citrate can act as a negative allosteric regulator by inhibiting this reaction. Given this information, do you predict that citrate acts as a competitive inhibitor to PFK?

phosphofructokinase (PFK)

ATP   ADP

fructose-6-phosphate
(F6P)

new phosphate
group

fructose-1,6-bisphosphate
(FBP)

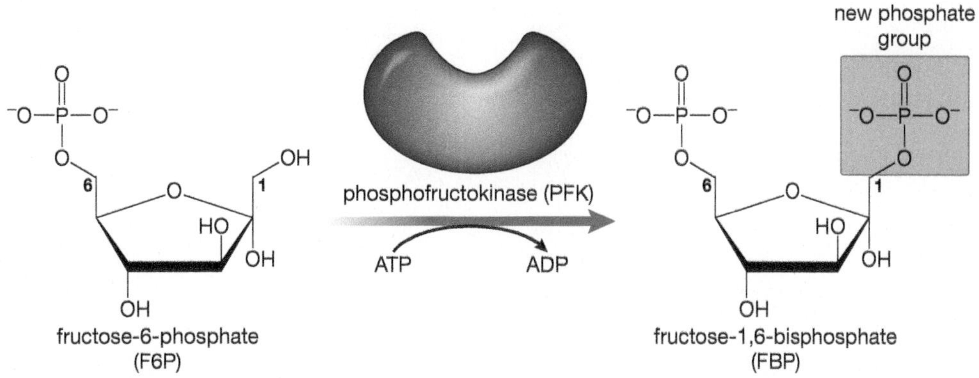

a) No. Negative allosteric regulators bind to a site on the enzyme other than the active site and change the shape of the active site so that the substrate cannot bind as effectively. Competitive inhibitors bind to the active site of an enzyme.

b) Yes. Negative allosteric regulators bind to the active site of an enzyme. Competitive inhibitors bind to a site on the enzyme other than the active site and change the shape of the active site so that the substrate cannot bind as effectively.

c) There is not enough information provided in the question to predict if citrate acts as a competitive inhibitor to PFK. Negative allosteric regulators generally bind to the active site of enzymes, so they are able to act as either competitive or noncompetitive inhibitors depending on the enzyme.

d) Yes. Citrate can act as a negative allosteric regulator by binding to the active site of the PFK enzyme. In doing so, it changes the shape of the active site so that the PFK enzyme becomes more efficient at processing substrate molecules.

19. Which statement about vitamins is true?
  a) All vitamins are water soluble because they need to be transported through the blood.
  b) Vitamins are sometimes chemically modified in the body to become active coenzymes.
  c) Vitamins typically serve as competitive inhibitors of metabolic enzymes.
  d) Vitamins are required for effective positive allosteric regulation.

20. Which statement best describes why small amounts of cofactors are needed in the cell?
  a) Cofactors are able to react with other cofactors and in doing so they have an amplifying allosteric effect.
  b) Cofactors are able to catalyze the reactions needed to reproduce themselves, so they are able to reproduce in the cell.
  c) Cofactors are only needed for a very small percentage of enzymatic reactions within the cell.
  d) Cofactors are not irreversibly changed during the reaction. They are either unchanged or regenerated like a catalyst.

Unit 8

Bringing It All Together

What Is an Opioid Drug and Why Are They So Addicting?

CHEMISTRY APPLICATION We opened Unit 8 with a look at some of factors driving the devastating opioid epidemic. Now let's look more closely at some of the ways to treat an opioid overdose.

The ready availability of kits containing the drug naloxone (Narcan) has been one of the most powerful tools in reducing deaths from opioid overdoses (Figure U8.5). Naloxone, like morphine, is a heterocyclic amine. It is structurally very similar to morphine and binds to the same receptors in the nervous system (Figure U8.6). Naloxone, however, has a greater affinity for opioid receptors and can displace opioids bound to the receptors.

Recall that opioid receptors are found in many places in the body, including the brain stem (see Fig. U8.3). When powerful opioid drugs bind to these receptors, they slow the breathing rate, a process called *respiratory depression*. In a severe overdose, the

---

Figure U8.5 Opioid Overdose Kit.

Many first responders now carry kits containing an easy-to-administer nasal spray containing the drug naloxone.

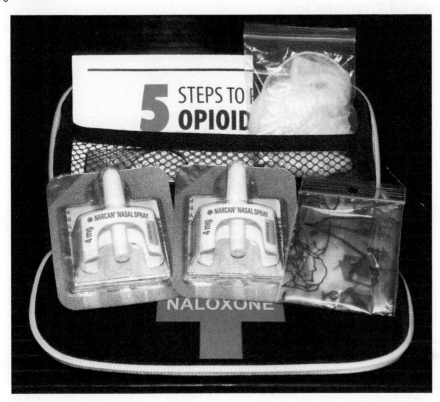

Figure U8.6 Naloxone.

The drug naloxone (Narcan) binds to opioid receptors in the brain, displacing opioids and reversing the symptoms of an overdose.

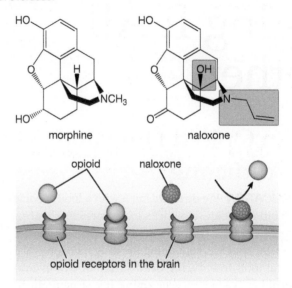

victim can lose consciousness and stop breathing. In these cases, rapid treatment with naloxone can temporarily displace the opioids. Naloxone, however, does not trigger the receptor so breathing returns to normal. Many police, fire, and medical workers now carry naloxone to ensure they can quickly respond to an overdose.

The devastation from the opioid crisis has renewed interest in the structure and function of opioid receptors and the molecules that bind to them. Opioid receptors are large proteins with intricate secondary and tertiary structures (Figure U8.7). Our bodies contain several forms of opioid receptors. The desire to

Figure U8.7 Opioid Receptors.

Opioid receptors are large proteins in the membranes of nerve cells. Like enzymes, receptors have unique binding sites that typically recognize a specific molecule, triggering a response from the cell. The opioid receptor can be activated by both our own naturally produced opiates as well as drugs like morphine, heroin, and fentanyl.

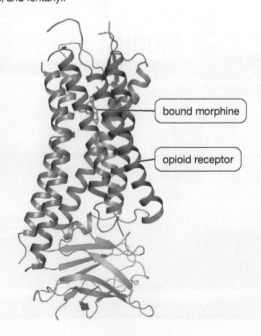

better understand the structural differences between receptor types along with how opioids bind to receptors has inspired many new areas of research. For example, scientists are working to design new pain-relieving drugs that block pain without triggering the rewarding effects or respiratory depression associated with opioids. In theory, these drugs would be less likely to trigger addiction and cause overdose.

There are many important players in the effort to curb the opioid crisis. And chemistry, too, has a critical role to play.

Questions to Think About

1. Examine the structure of naloxone and morphine (Figure U8.6). What similarities do you notice? What functional groups do you recognize? Would you expect these two molecules to have similar biological activity? Why or why not?

2. The structure of an opioid receptor is shown in Figure U8.7. What protein secondary structures do you recognize in this representation?

3. What types of intermolecular forces might be binding the morphine molecule or other opioids to the receptor?

4. Do you expect the binding of the opioid to its receptor to be reversible or irreversible? Why? (Consider how naloxone would function if it were competing with a reversibly vs irreversibly bound opioid.)

A Closer Look at the Data

First responders, especially emergency medical technicians (EMTs) are often the ones administering life-saving naloxone to people suffering from reverse opioid overdoses (Figure U8.8).

Rapid access to naloxone can be limited, however, by a phenomenon called the *rural paramedic paradox*. In rural areas, the time it takes to get an ambulance to a patient and then the patient to a hospital is often much longer due to greater distances. In addition, the EMTs staffing rural response centers are often volunteers and may have

Figure U8.8 EMTs May Administer Naloxone to Reverse Opioid Overdoses.

lower certifications that don't include authorization to dispense naloxone*. The longer response times and lower levels of training combine to reduce survival rates from a variety of emergencies, including opioid overdoses.

A team of researchers from the Centers for Disease Control (CDC) and two emergency medicine centers recently examined the impact of geographical location on both the rate of opioid overdose fatalities and the likelihood of naloxone use by emergency medical workers. To do this, the researchers examined the records from over 19 million emergency responses collected in a national database. Figure U8.9 is from their paper.

Figure U8.9 Overdose Rates and Odds of Naloxone Use by EMS Providers in Urban, Suburban, and Rural Locations

(from Faul, *et al.*, 2015).

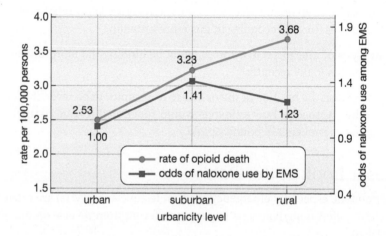

Questions to Think About

Examine Figure U8.9 and use it to answer the following questions:

1. Graphs can help reveal relationships between variables. This graph shows two different variables on the Y (vertical) axes. What are these variables, how do they compare with each other, and what are each compared to on the X (horizontal) axis?

2. Which of the three environments examined had the greatest rate of opioid-related deaths? Where were patients most likely to be treated with naloxone by emergency medical personnel?

3. What does this data suggest to you about possible ways to decrease the incidence of fatal opioid overdoses? What additional variables do you think should be examined?

Reference

Faul, M, Dailey, MW, Sugerman, DE, Sasser, SM, Levy, B, and LJ Paulozzi. (2015) Disparity in Naloxone Administration by Emergency Medical Service Providers and the Burden of Drug Overdose in US Rural Communities. *American Journal of Public Health.* 105 (S3): 26-32. doi: 10.2105/AJPH.2014.302520

---

*Many states have now adopted new regulations allowing EMT-basic certified responders to administer naloxone nasal sprays.

Unit 9

Introduction

Exploring DNA, RNA, and Protein Synthesis

Chapter 22: Nucleic Acids, DNA, and Genetic Testing
Chapter 23: RNA and Protein Synthesis

An estimated 100,000 people in the U.S. suffer from a painful, life-threatening blood disorder, sickle cell disease. Sickle cell disease is a genetic disorder that arose on the African continent; thus, most patients with sickle cell disease in the U.S. have African ancestry as a result of the transatlantic slave trade.

Because of the unusual demographics of sickle cell disease, it provides an important opportunity to think critically about racial disparities in healthcare (Figure U9.1). Cystic fibrosis, for example, is also an inherited, progressive,

---

Figure U9.1 Sickle Cell Disease Provides a Powerful Example of Racial Inequities in Healthcare.

The 2020 murder of George Floyd by a White policeman helped catalyze the Black Lives Matter movement and foster a closer look at racial injustice in many arenas including healthcare.

life-threatening disease but cystic fibrosis primarily affects White Americans. Despite affecting far fewer Americans than sickle cell disease, cystic fibrosis receives roughly 3.5 times the research funding per patient from the National Institute of Health (NIH) and 75 times the funding from medical charities (Farooq et al, 2020). In addition, fewer therapies are available for the primarily Black sickle cell patients who must often also navigate the additional challenges of structural and interpersonal racism in our healthcare system.

Diseases with clearly defined genetic causes, such as sickle cell disease, are a prime target for gene therapy—an approach that modifies genes to help treat or even cure disease. While gene therapy has been attempted on a range of genetic diseases since the 1990s, the approach became much more promising in 2012 with the discovery of a new approach to editing DNA called CRISPR-Cas9.

What is CRISPR-Cas9, and does it have the potential to help alleviate the historical inequities of sickle cell disease in the U.S.?

Unit 9: Introduction
Can Genetic Technology Cure Sickle Cell Disease?

 To learn more about the promise of CRISPR-Cas9, watch **Video U9.1** in the Pearson eText.

Unit 9 opens with a look at the exciting potential of the gene editing technique CRISPR to launch a new, potentially more equitable era of healthcare by significantly expanding genetic treatment options for a wide range of diseases including sickle cell disease.

Patients with sickle cell disease inherit tiny changes in their DNA that dramatically modify the structure of their red blood cells. While normal red blood cells are plump and round, delivering oxygen efficiently through our blood vessels, the red blood cells in individuals with sickle cell disease contain an abnormal form of hemoglobin and adopt a "sickled" shape (Figure U9.2). These cells are hard and sticky; they can get stuck when traveling through small blood vessels causing severe pain as well as strokes and other life-threatening conditions.

While several drugs are available to treat some of the symptoms and complications of sickle cell disease, until recently the only true cure was a bone marrow transplant—an expensive, risky procedure that requires a close genetic match, often from a disease-free sibling. A gene therapy approach such as CRISPR, in contrast, has the opportunity to be more widely available to patients.

Figure U9.2 Sickle Cell Disease.

Symptoms of sickle cell disease usually appear in early childhood. The sickled red blood cells die quickly, leaving a shortage of red blood cells to transport oxygen and causing fatigue. Sickled cells can also clump together, blocking blood flow to tissues and causing painful episodes and potentially life-threatening complications.

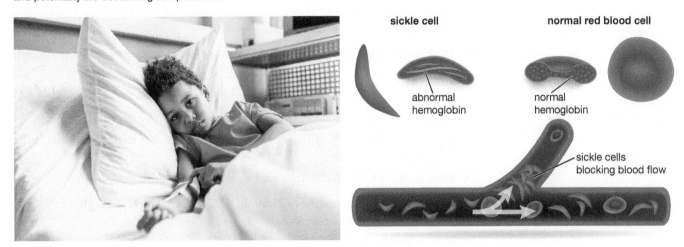

Unit 9 Chemistry Application: Can Genetic Technology Cure Sickle Cell Disease?

The enormous potential of CRISPR to truly cure genetic diseases such as sickle cell disease hinges on our ability to understand the mechanisms that drive the production of the hemoglobin protein. We must both deeply understand the structure of DNA as well as the process our cells use to build proteins from the information encoded in our DNA (Figure U9.3). With this understanding, we can continue to develop novel strategies to provide innovative, long-overdue treatment options for patients with sickle cell disease.

Figure U9.3 CRISPR-Cas9.

The CRISPR-Cas9 gene editing system can precisely target specific regions of DNA using an enzyme called Cas9.

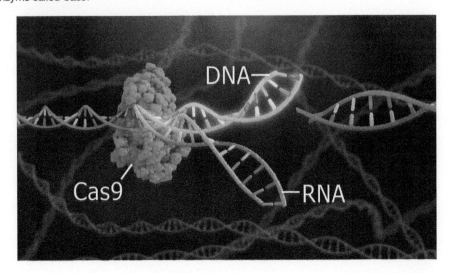

Questions to Think About

What chemistry do we need to know to better understand the promise of CRISPR-based gene therapy? Here are some questions to consider as you move through Unit 9:

- What is DNA made of? How does the structure of DNA provide information about our individual genes? What is a gene?

- How do mistakes or mutations happen in DNA and how does this lead to disease?

- What techniques do scientists use to study the human genome?

- What biochemical processes in our body convert a gene into a protein? How does a better understanding of these processes allow scientists to discover treatments, or even cures, for diseases?

- How does the CRISPR-Cas9 system target specific regions of DNA?

What chemistry would you like to know in order to more fully understand this new approach to treating genetic diseases?

Now that we have an overview of this unit, let's step into Chapter 22 and 23 and learn more about how DNA affects our health.

Reference

Farooq F, Mogayzel PJ, Lanzkron S, Haywood C, Strouse JJ. Comparison of US federal and foundation funding of research for sickle cell disease and cystic fibrosis and factors associated with research productivity. JAMA Netw Open 2020;3(3):e201737-e201737.

Chapter 22
Nucleic Acids, DNA, and Genetic Testing

DNA is an amazing molecule that both encodes the directions to produce all the proteins in the human body and copies itself quickly and accurately.

Chapter Outline

Learning Objectives

22.1 Describe and draw the building blocks of nucleosides and nucleotides.

22.2 Describe the structure and draw segments of a single strand of DNA including phosphodiester linkages.

22.3 Describe the structure and fundamental features of the DNA double helix.

22.4 Explain the process of DNA replication and the role of DNA polymerase.

22.5 Explain the mechanism and utility of several common DNA technologies.

Introduction

In this chapter we take a closer look at one of life's most essential and fascinating molecules, **deoxyribonucleic acid (DNA)**. This long, complex molecule carries the information that makes each individual on Earth unique. DNA also allows us to pass this information down to our children and their children. DNA plays an increasingly important role in forensics, agriculture, pharmaceutical production and development, and in the genetic therapy approach to potentially cure sickle cell disease we began to explore in the Unit 9 introduction (Figure 22.1). In this chapter, we explore the structure of this molecule, how it replicates, and some of the many technologies rooted in the structure and function of DNA.

Figure 22.1 DNA.

A) Representations of DNA, such as this sculpture, are common in art. **B)** Health care workers can use a blood draw from a pregnant mother to analyze fetal DNA, providing a low-risk option for prenatal genetic testing. **C)** Forensic scientists can recover small amounts of DNA from common items such as cigarette butts and coffee cups to generate genetic profiles of criminal suspects.

A   B   C

22.1 Building Blocks of DNA

Deoxyribonucleic acid (DNA) is a large polymer molecule that stores the genetic information found in the nuclei of cells. A polymer consists of a large number of repeating units (monomers) bonded to each other. The DNA molecule is a long chain of repeating monomers called **nucleotides**. DNA is a member of the class of molecules called **nucleic acids**.

Ribonucleic acid (RNA) is another nucleic acid that is also present in all living cells. RNA is responsible for a variety of functions including carrying instructions from DNA that synthesize proteins. We explore the structure and function of RNA in Chapter 23.

In this chapter, we explore the question: What are the monomers that the complex DNA polymer molecules are made of and how do they link together to make each individual unique?

Nucleotides

One DNA molecule can contain as many as several million nucleotides linked together in two long strands. Each nucleotide is an organic molecule that contains three parts- a *five-carbon sugar*, a *nitrogen-containing base,* and a *phosphate group* (Figure 22.2). We explore these three parts of a nucleotide one at a time beginning with the five-carbon sugar.

The five-carbon sugar in DNA is **deoxyribose** (Figure 22.3). Recall from the discussion in Chapter 16 about monosaccharides, that a pentose sugar is a sugar molecule containing five carbon atoms. To differentiate between the carbon atoms in a pentose sugar, we number them with primes ($1'$, $2'$, $3'$, $4'$, $5'$). We begin with the carbon atom on the right side of the ring. Deoxyribose means "without oxygen." This reflects the lack of a hydroxyl group (—OH) on carbon number 2 ($C2'$) in the deoxyribose molecule. In contrast, the five-carbon sugar **ribose** does contain a hydroxyl group on $C2'$. Ribose is the pentose sugar in ribonucleic acid (RNA). We explore the structure of RNA further in Chapter 23.

Nitrogen-Containing Bases

We sometimes refer to the **nitrogen-containing bases** in DNA as **nitrogenous bases.** The bases in DNA fall into two categories of molecules, **pyrimidines,** and **purines.** Each pyrimidine has a single ring with two nitrogen atoms. Each purine contains two rings with two nitrogen atoms in both ring structures. In DNA, the pyrimidine bases are **cytosine** (C) and **thymine** (T) and the purine bases are **adenine** (A) and **guanine** (G) (Figure 22.4). We often abbreviate the names of the bases to just the first letter.

Figure 22.2 Nucleotides.

Each nucleotide contains a sugar, a nitrogen-containing base, and a phosphate group.

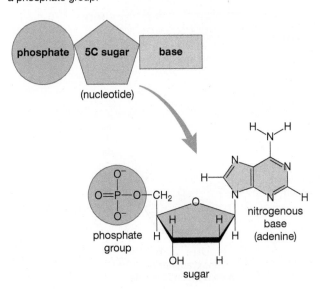

Figure 22.3 The Sugars in DNA and RNA.

DNA contains the pentose sugar deoxyribose. RNA contains the pentose sugar ribose. Note the carbons are numbered in each molecule beginning with the carbon atom on the right side of the ring ($1'$–$5'$).

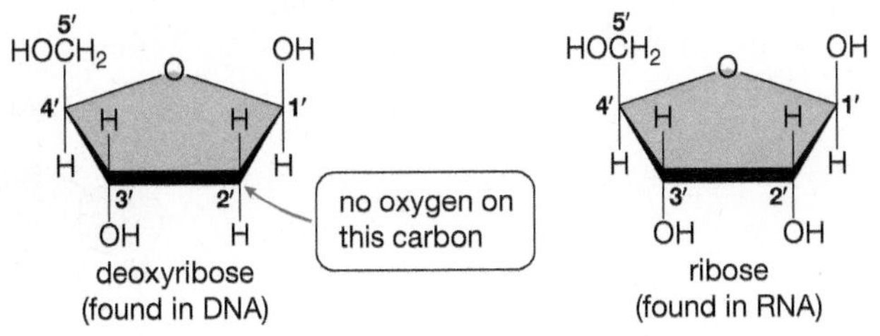

Figure 22.4 The Nitrogen-Containing Bases in DNA: Pyrimidines and Purines.

Pyrimidines have a single ring while purines have two rings.

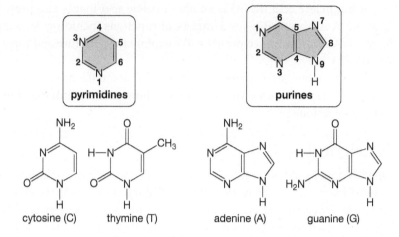

cytosine (C)   thymine (T)   adenine (A)   guanine (G)

Apply what you have just learned: **Practice 22.1** in the Pearson eText.

To synthesize DNA, the body requires that both purine bases and pyrimidine bases be present in the cell in approximately equal amounts. We consume both types of molecules in our diet and our bodies can also produce these molecules. A complex feedback control mechanism regulates the amount of purine and pyrimidine bases and ensures that there are nearly equal amounts of both types in the body's cells.

Nucleosides

A **nucleoside** is similar to a nucleotide but does not contain a phosphate group. A nucleoside is made up of a nitrogenous base (a purine or pyrimidine) linked to a pentose sugar. It is useful to explore how the two parts of a nucleoside molecule are linked together. The linkage occurs between the first carbon atom (C1′) on the sugar and a nitrogen atom on the base. The new bond that forms through a condensation reaction is a **β-N-glycosidic bond**. Figure 22.5 illustrates how the linkage of the nitrogenous base adenine (A) and the sugar deoxyribose produces the nucleoside deoxy*adenosine*. The general term for this type of molecule is a **deoxyribonucleoside**.

Figure 22.5 The Nucleoside Adenosine Forms from a Condensation Reaction Between a Five-Carbon Sugar and a Nitrogen-Containing Base.

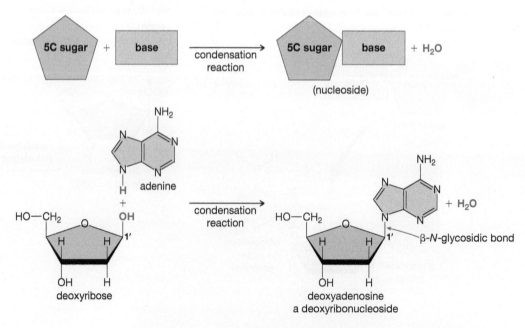

The names for nucleosides are derivatives of the names of the bases in the structure. Follow these rules to name these molecules:

1. When the base in the nucleoside is a pyrimidine base, use the suffix *-idine* (for example, cytosine forms cyt*idine*).

2. When the base in the nucleoside is a purine base, use the suffix *-osine* (for example, adenine forms aden*osine*).

3. When the sugar in the nucleoside is deoxyribose, add the prefix *deoxy-*.

Click on Learn 22.1 to apply these rules to name a nucleoside and identify the two parts of a nucleoside.

Predict answers and see step-by-step solutions: **Learn 22.1:** Forming and Naming Nucleosides in the Pearson eText.

Apply what you have just learned: **Practice 22.2 and 22.3** in the Pearson eText.

Formation of Nucleotides

Nucleotides form when the C5′ hydroxyl group of the pentose sugar in a nucleoside forms a bond with a phosphate group (Figure 22.6). If the bonded sugar is a deoxyribose sugar, then the nucleotide that forms is a **deoxyribonucleotide**. Recall that the prefix deoxy indicates "without oxygen." This prefix indicates the lack of a hydroxyl group (—OH) on carbon 2 (C2′). A **ribonucleotide**, on the other hand, is a nucleotide that has a hydroxyl group (—OH) on carbon 2 (C2′).

We name nucleotides by adding 5′-monophosphate to the name of the nucleosides from which they form. (Recall that mono indicates one, di indicates two, and tri indicates three. Poly means many.) For example, adenosine 5′ monophosphate contains a single phosphate group, a ribose sugar, and adenine. Deoxycytidine 5′-monophosphate is another example of a nucleotide that contains a single phosphate group, deoxyribose sugar, and cytosine. We use three- or four-letter abbreviations to refer to nucleotides. Adenosine 5′ monophosphate is abbreviated as AMP and deoxycytidine 5′-monophosphate is dCMP. Note that a lowercase d in a nucleotide name abbreviation indicates a deoxyribose. Table 22.1 summarizes the nucleosides and nucleotides in DNA.

adenosine 5′-monophosphate (AMP)
(a ribonucleotide)

deoxycytidine 5′-monophosphate (dCMP)
(a deoxyribonucleotide)

Figure 22.6 Nucleotides Form when a Phosphate Group bonds to the Sugar in a Nucleoside in a Condensation Reaction.

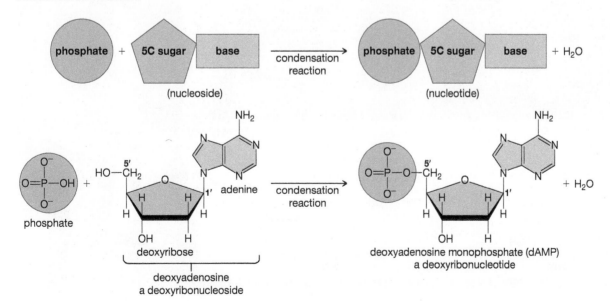

(nucleoside)   (nucleotide)

phosphate

deoxyribose

deoxyadenosine
a deoxyribonucleoside

deoxyadenosine monophosphate (dAMP)
a deoxyribonucleotide

Table 22.1 Nucleosides and Nucleotides in DNA.

Base	Nucleosides	Nucleotides
DNA		
Adenine (A)	Deoxyadenosine (A)	Deoxyadenosine-5′-monophosphate (dAMP)
Guanine (G)	Deoxyguanosine (G)	Deoxyguanosine-5′-monophosphate (dGMP)
Cytosine (C)	Deoxycytidine (C)	Deoxycytidine-5′-monophosphate (dCMP)
Thymine (T)	Deoxythymidine (T)	Deoxythymidine-5′-monophosphate (dTMP)

Diphosphates and Triphosphates

Diphosphates and triphosphates are also produced from nucleosides by adding additional phosphate groups to the 5′-hydroxyl group. For example, adenosine is converted to the nucleotides adenosine 5′-diphosphate (ADP) and adenosine 5′-triphosphate (ATP). These two molecules are central to energy production in the body, and we discuss them in more detail in Chapter 24 (Figure 22.7).

After completing Practice 22.4, explore BioConnect 22.1 (contains Figures 22.8–22.15) for an overview of how the building blocks discussed in this section make each of us unique.

Figure 22.7 ADP and ATP.

Adenosine triphosphate (ATP) provides energy to drive many processes in living cells including muscle contraction. The molecular structure of ATP is similar to one of the nucleotides of DNA but the diphosphate molecule ADP contains one additional phosphate group and ATP contains two additional phosphate groups that DNA lacks.

adenosine 5′-diphosphate
ADP

adenosine 5′-triphosphate
ATP

Apply what you have just learned: **Practice 22.4** in the Pearson eText.

Explore how Chemistry and Biology connect: **BioConnect: 22.1** Our DNA in the Pearson eText.

Quiz yourself on the content of this section: **Check 22.1** in the Pearson eText.

22.2 Structure and Formation of Nucleic Acids

Recall that nucleic acids are polymers made up of nucleotide monomers. Nucleic acids, such as DNA and RNA, form when nucleotides link together to form long **polynucleotide** chains. To form the chains, the 3'-OH group of one nucleotide joins with the 5'-phosphate of a second nucleotide to form a **phosphodiester** linkage (Figure 22.16). Phosphodiester linkages are the key to forming long polynucleotide chains.

A polynucleotide chain grows as the nucleotides in the chain form new phosphodiester linkages to additional nucleotides. The polynucleotide chain contains

Figure 22.16 Formation of Phosphodiester Linkages.

Nucleotides form polynucleotides, such as DNA and RNA, when the 3' end of one nucleotide joins to the 5' end of another nucleotide with a phosphodiester linkage.

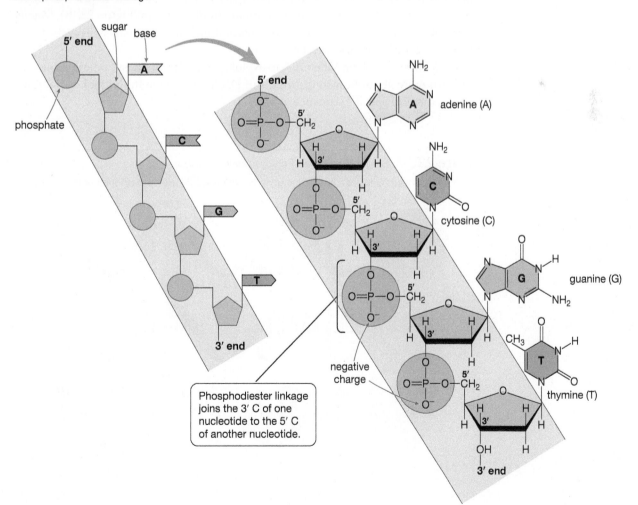

multiple nucleotides in an alternating sugar and phosphate pattern that forms a **sugar-phosphate backbone**. One end of the chain contains a phosphate group on carbon 5, referred to as the **5′ end** and the other end of the chain contains a hydroxyl group (—OH), referred to as **3′ end.** Polynucleotides form in the direction 5′ → 3′. Identifying the 5′ and 3′ ends is useful as we learn about how a chain of DNA makes a copy of itself.

DNA Sequences

The sequence of the nucleotides in a DNA polynucleotide makes each of us unique. We indicate the sequence using upper case letters that represent the base part of the nucleotides in the sequence. For example, a sequence of DNA nucleotides that includes the bases guanine, adenine, and cytosine is GAC. Variations in the order of sequences within genes are important. As we discover in Chapter 23, variations in the DNA sequence within a gene can have dramatic effects on the proteins cells make.

Some diseases are due to a change of just a single nucleotide within a gene. If you compare the genomes of any two individuals, most of the sequence is identical. There are, however, locations in the genome where individuals may have different nucleotides. These are known as **single nucleotide polymorphisms (SNPs)** (Figure 22.17).

Cystic fibrosis, for example, is a serious genetic lung disease. Individuals with cystic fibrosis inherited a single SNP from each of their parents. While most of the human population has a guanine (G) at this site, most people with cystic fibrosis have a cytosine (C). This changes the structure of a critical protein in the lungs. The difference in structure allows mucus to accumulate in the airways (Figure 22.18). Mucus interferes with oxygen transport in the lungs and makes individuals with cystic fibrosis very susceptible to lung infections.

Click on VisibleChem Video 22.1 to explore the details of phosphodiester linkages and learn more about how long strands of DNA form when individual nucleotides link together in a specific sequence of bases.

Figure 22.17 Single Nucleotide Polymorphisms (SNPs).

A SNP (pronounced "snip") is a spot in the genome where individuals have different nucleotides.

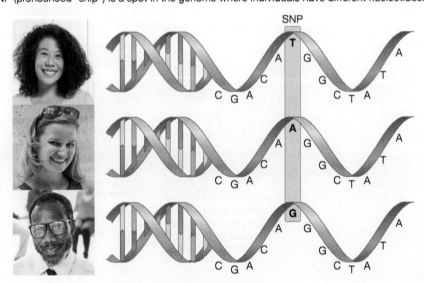

Figure 22.18 Cystic Fibrosis.

Individuals with cystic fibrosis inherit two copies of a specific SNP, one from each parent. The single nucleotide change dramatically changes the structure of a protein in the lungs. Excess mucus builds up in their airways, interfering with lung function and making them vulnerable to infections.

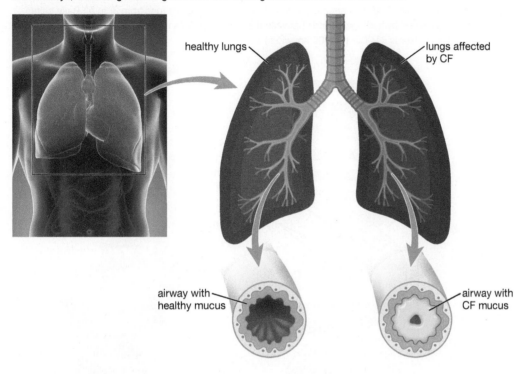

healthy lungs

lungs affected by CF

airway with healthy mucus

airway with CF mucus

Watch this concept come to life: **VisibleChem Video 22.1:** Linking Nucleotides in the Pearson eText.

Apply what you have just learned: **Practice 22.5 and 22.6** in the Pearson eText.

Quiz yourself on the content of this section: **Check 22.2** in the Pearson eText.

22.3 The DNA Double Helix

In 1953, the scientists Jim Watson and Francis Crick published a ground-breaking paper describing the structure of DNA. Their model was based on the pioneering work of another scientist, Rosalind Franklin. Franklin had created the world's first image of the structure of DNA–an image shared with Watson and Crick without Franklin's permission. Franklin did not originally receive credit for her role in the discovery (Video 22.1).

Despite the controversy surrounding their methods, Watson and Crick's model has withstood the test of time. In this model, DNA is a **double helix** formed by two polynucleotide strands that twist together. In a DNA molecule, the sugar-phosphate backbone is on the outside and the bases are inside the double helix, forming "rungs" that connect the two strands. The phosphate groups that connect each nucleotide along the DNA strands are negatively charged and are part of the sugar-phosphate backbone. The two strands that make up the backbone line up opposite one another—one strand is lined up from 5′ to 3′ end while the other strand is lined

Video 22.1: TED-ED:
Rosalind Franklin
—DNA's Unsung Hero

Figure 22.19 DNA Double Helix Structure.

Two strands of DNA twist together to form a double helix structure with a sugar phosphate backbone. The sugar-phosphate backbone is represented using a ribbon diagram in **(A)** and with a three- dimensional molecular model in **(B)** where oxygen atoms are red, carbon atoms are black and H atoms are white. One DNA strand runs from 5′ to 3′ and the other runs from 3′ to 5′. Base pairs form rungs joined by hydrogen bonds between the strands. A DNA molecule is just 2 nm wide. (A single human hair is 80,000–100,000 nm wide.)

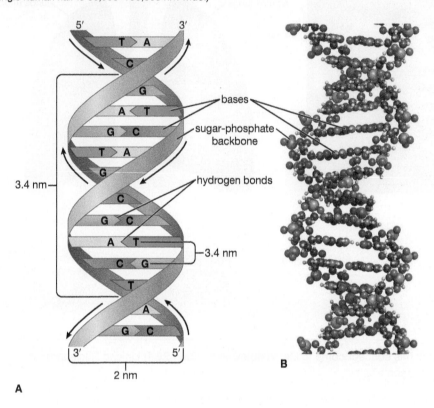

up from 3′ to 5′ end. The base A(adenine) pairs with the base T (thymine) and the base C (cytosine) pairs with the base G (guanine). All base pairs are joined to each other with hydrogen bonds (Figure 22.19).

Complementary Base Pairing

The bases form hydrogen bonds with one specific base on the opposite strand of DNA. Thymine forms two hydrogen bonds with adenine and cytosine forms three hydrogen bonds with guanine (Figure 22.20) to create **complementary base pairs.** Because there are three hydrogen bonds between guanine (G) and cytosine (C), the additional hydrogen bond makes this the stronger of the two pairings. Interestingly, many bacteria found in very warm environments such as hot springs have unusually high fractions of guanine and cytosine in parts of their genome. This high guanine and cytosine content may help stabilize the nucleic acids at high temperatures.

Hydrogen bonds also occasionally form between other bases. These alternate pairings are called **mismatches**. Our cells are able to detect and repair most mismatches. If mismatches are not repaired, however, they can create **mutations** that may cause disease. We explore how mistakes in DNA cause disease in Chapter 23.

Figure 22.20 Base Pairing Within the DNA Double Helix.

The base adenine (A) forms two hydrogen bonds with the base thymine (T). The base guanine (G) forms three hydrogen bonds with cytosine (C). Organisms such as the bacteria found in hot springs have more G-C pairs in parts of their genome, possibly helping to stabilize their structures at high temperatures.

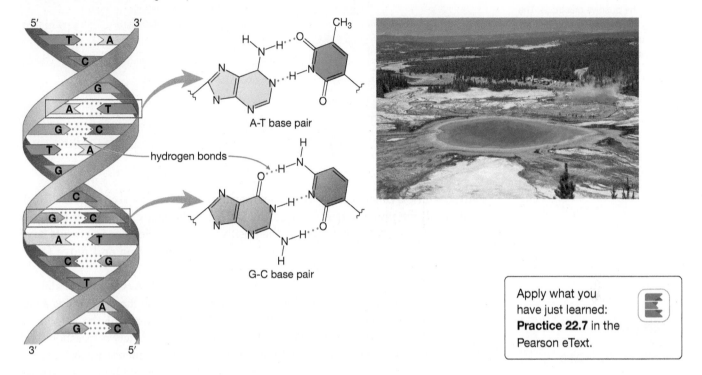

A-T base pair

hydrogen bonds

G-C base pair

> Apply what you have just learned: **Practice 22.7** in the Pearson eText.

Electrophoresis

Many DNA technologies and laboratory techniques take advantage of the structural features of DNA, especially the negative charges on the phosphate groups. **Gel electrophoresis**, for example, is a common technique that separates DNA molecules based on their size and charge (Figure 22.21). In electrophoresis, technicians load DNA fragments into small pockets, which are called *wells*, at one end of a thick

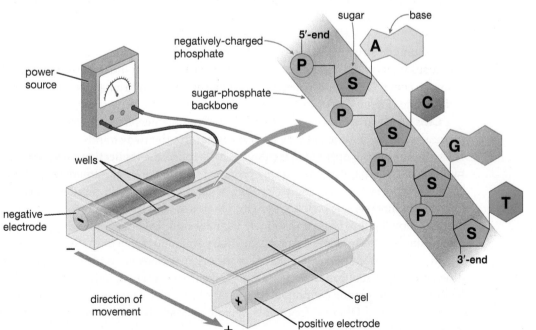

Figure 22.21 DNA Electrophoresis.

DNA electrophoresis helps us to separate DNA molecules based on their size and electrical charge. DNA is negatively charged so it migrates through the gel towards the positive electrode. Smaller molecules move faster and thus travel farther than larger molecules.

Figure 22.22 A Technician Loads DNA onto a Gel and Examines the Results.

The DNA has moved from the wells towards the positive electrode. The glowing bands at the bottom of the gel contain smaller DNA molecules. The bands at the top of the gel contain larger DNA molecules.

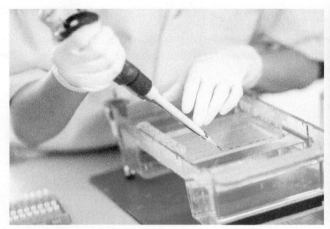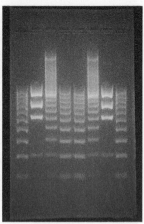

Quiz yourself on the content of this section: **Check 22.3** in the Pearson eText.

matrix, which is called a *gel*. A technician then applies an electrical current to the gel. Because all the phosphate groups on the DNA backbone are negatively charged, DNA flows through the gel towards the positive electrode. Smaller fragments have less mass. Therefore the small molecules experience less drag and move faster through the gel than larger molecules.

Once the current is turned off, technicians stain the DNA. Clusters of stained DNA molecules of the same size migrate to the same position in the gel, forming a visible band or line on the gel that represents DNA fragments of the same size (Figure 22.22). The pattern formed by the bands can answer a variety of questions and address issues that range from matching suspects to crime scenes to identifying the pathogen responsible for a disease outbreak. We learn more about how scientists use these patterns of DNA fragments in Section 22.5.

22.4 DNA Replication

Scientists estimate that the average human body contains 37 trillion cells. All of the cells in each of our bodies come from a single fertilized egg cell. The DNA in that single cell is copied again and again in a process called **DNA replication** to create the body each of us inhabits today. Even in an adult body, cells are constantly dividing, and copying their DNA, every time our bodies repair or replace tissues. All of these cell divisions require that DNA must replicate (copy) itself both quickly and accurately.

The unique structure of the DNA molecule allows the two strands to separate so that replication can take place. Once separated, each of the strands can serve as a template. An enzyme, **DNA polymerase**, joins nucleotides to build a new, complementary DNA strand (Figure 22.23).

Cells use an array of enzymes to build new complementary strands of DNA. The process begins when the enzyme **helicase** separates the two strands of the double-helix. This creates an opening in the double-helix called the **replication fork.** Once the two strands are separated, the enzyme **primase** binds to the single-stranded DNA and creates a short temporary single-stranded sequence of nucleotides called a **primer.** Primers are short segments of RNA or DNA that provide a binding site for DNA polymerase, allowing it to begin to assemble the new complementary strand. DNA polymerase then begins to create the complementary strand to match the parental template strand of DNA. Because the two halves of the original DNA molecule run in opposite directions, DNA replication occurs a bit differently on each strand. One strand, the **leading strand**, is made continuously. The other so-called **lagging strand** is made in short pieces called **Okazaki fragments** that are later stitched together by yet another enzyme, **ligase** (Figure 22.24).

Figure 22.23 An Overview DNA Replication.

The DNA in a cell must copy itself before cells can divide. An enzyme called DNA polymerase uses separated single-stranded molecules as templates and attaches nucleotides to the newly forming complementary strands. Note that the enzymes in Figure 22.23 and Figure 22.24 are much larger relative to DNA than shown in these representations.

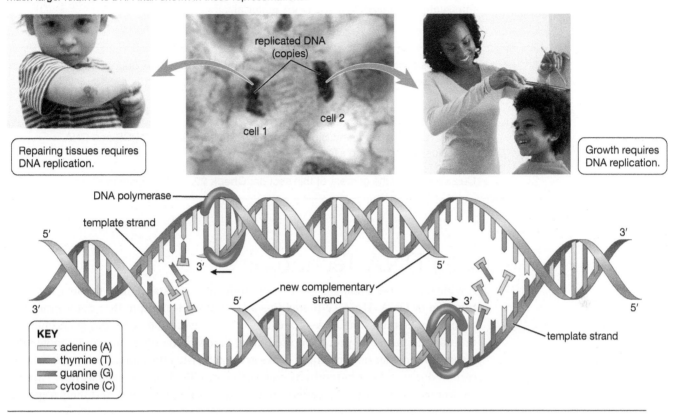

Repairing tissues requires DNA replication.

replicated DNA (copies)

cell 1   cell 2

Growth requires DNA replication.

DNA polymerase

template strand

new complementary strand

template strand

KEY
- adenine (A)
- thymine (T)
- guanine (G)
- cytosine (C)

Figure 22.24 A Detailed View of DNA Replication

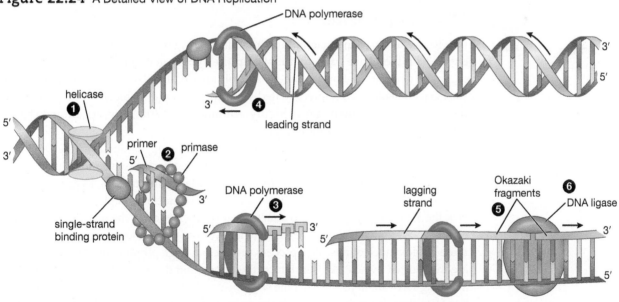

DNA polymerase

helicase

leading strand

primer   primase

single-strand binding protein

DNA polymerase

lagging strand

Okazaki fragments

DNA ligase

❶ Helicase separates the two halves of the DNA helix.

❷ Primase creates a short, complimentary sequence, the primer.

❸ DNA polymerase binds at the primer and begins attaching complimentary bases to the 3′ end of the primer.

❹ On the **leading strand**, DNA polymerase continues adding to the 3′ end of the new complimentary strand.

❺ On the **lagging strand**, DNA polymerase must build the complimentary strand in short pieces called **Okazaki fragments**.

❻ The enzyme **ligase** joins the Okazaki fragments together, completing the complimentary strand.

KEY
- adenine (A)
- thymine (T)
- guanine (G)
- cytosine (C)

Check out VisibleChem Videos 22.2 and 22.3 to review the structure of DNA and the many enzymes required to accurately copy DNA. After exploring the videos, proceed to BioConnect 22.2 (contains Figures 22.25–22.29) to learn about the **polymerase chain reaction (PCR)**- a reaction that produces millions of copies of DNA in a lab from miniscule amounts of starting DNA material.

Watch this concept come to life: **VisibleChem Video 22.2:** DNA Double Helix and **VisibleChem Video 22.3:** DNA Replication in the Pearson eText.

Apply what you have just learned: **Practice 22.8 and 22.9** in the Pearson eText.

Explore how Chemistry and Biology connect: **BioConnect: 22.2** PCR and DNA Forensics in the Pearson eText.

Quiz yourself on the content of this section: **Check 22.4** in the Pearson eText.

22.5 DNA Technology

A wide range of technologies have come from our understanding of the structure and function of DNA. **DNA sequencing**—a laboratory technique that determines the order of nucleotides in DNA—for example, has revolutionized biology and helped unleash the power of **precision medicine**. Precision medicine expands on genetic testing to consider how multiple genes act together to affect an individual's risk for certain diseases, how individuals metabolize specific drugs, as well as how various environmental factors might affect an individual's risk of disease and their response to treatment.

DNA Sequencing

Video 22.3:

DNA Sequencing

In 1990, the international scientific community launched a bold project to sequence the entire 3.3 billion base pairs that make up the human genome. Sequencing the first complete genome cost an estimated $2.7 billion dollars. This sequence, released in 2004, gave scientists an unprecedented view into the building blocks of life. Today the process of DNA sequencing is highly automated—a full human genome can be sequenced for just a few hundred dollars (Figure 22.30).

The chemistry involved in DNA sequencing technology is similar to the DNA replication process. A DNA polymerase builds complementary new strands. But a typical sequencing reaction includes a few fluorescent **dideoxynucleotides**. In contrast to the typical nucleotides DNA polymerase uses to build the strands, dideoxynucleotides lack the 3′ OH group required to attach the next nucleotide in the growing DNA molecule. DNA synthesis therefore stops whenever the polymerase incorporates one of these dideoxynucleotides. This process produces a large population of molecules that are then sorted by size. A laser detects the fluorescent dye on each dideoxynucleotide allowing software to reconstruct the sequence of the template DNA molecule. The output from the sequencing process is the correct order of the nucleotides in a particular DNA fragment.

DNA Fingerprinting

Although the cost of sequencing a genome has dramatically reduced since 2004, this approach generates an enormous data set and is not practical for the quick identification of an individual. When rapid identification is needed, as it is in the forensic

Figure 22.30 DNA Sequencing.

A) DNA sequencing has become both rapid and affordable in recent years. **B)** A technician operates a room of automated DNA sequencing machines. See the Pearson eText to view an animation of this figure.

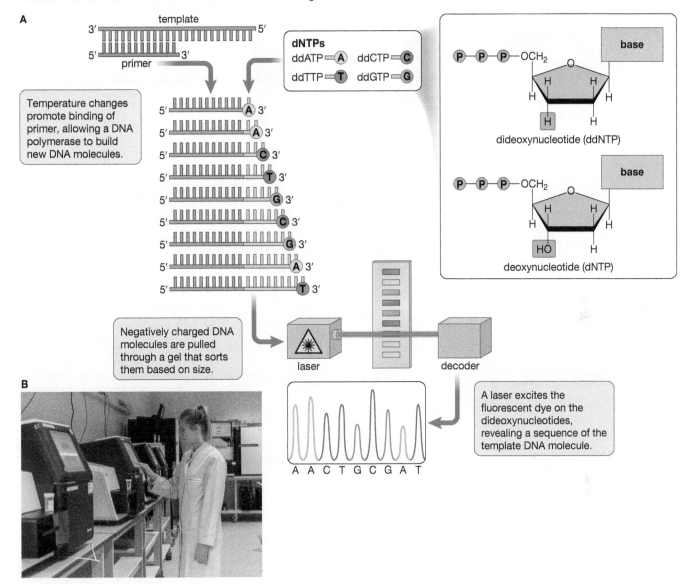

applications explored in BioConnect 22.2, scientists often instead utilize a **DNA finger-print.** DNA fingerprinting refers to a range of techniques that all yield specific genetic signatures that can be used to identify individuals. Many of these techniques use PCR to copy specific regions of DNA that vary between individuals. Technicians can then compare the copied regions to known samples or DNA collected from a crime scene to look for matches (Figure 22.31).

While we often think about DNA fingerprinting in the context of identifying criminals, it has many other important applications. All living things have DNA, allowing these technologies to be used in many different situations. For example, public health officials can use DNA fingerprints to rapidly identify the bacterium causing a disease outbreak or help identify the source of bacteria responsible for contaminating a food source (Figure 22.32).

Figure 22.31 DNA Fingerprinting.

A DNA fingerprint is a unique genetic signature used to identify individuals. In this example, law officials extract DNA from a crime scene and two suspects. The lab copies a region of DNA with PCR. The products are visualized using gel electrophoresis. In this example, the pattern of bands from suspect B's DNA matches the DNA sample found at the crime scene.

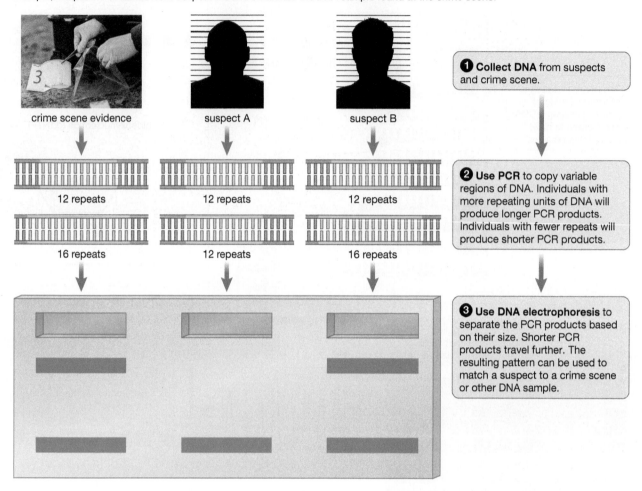

crime scene evidence   suspect A   suspect B

12 repeats   12 repeats   12 repeats

16 repeats   12 repeats   16 repeats

❶ **Collect DNA** from suspects and crime scene.

❷ **Use PCR** to copy variable regions of DNA. Individuals with more repeating units of DNA will produce longer PCR products. Individuals with fewer repeats will produce shorter PCR products.

❸ **Use DNA electrophoresis** to separate the PCR products based on their size. Shorter PCR products travel further. The resulting pattern can be used to match a suspect to a crime scene or other DNA sample.

Figure 22.32 Field of Lettuce.

Crops such as lettuce are particularly vulnerable to contamination with disease-causing bacteria because they grow close to the soil and are consumed raw. DNA fingerprinting can help trace the source of an outbreak of food-borne disease minimizing the number of victims.

Figure 22.33 DNA Microarrays.

A DNA Microarray contains specific single-stranded DNA sequences attached at known locations on a glass slide.

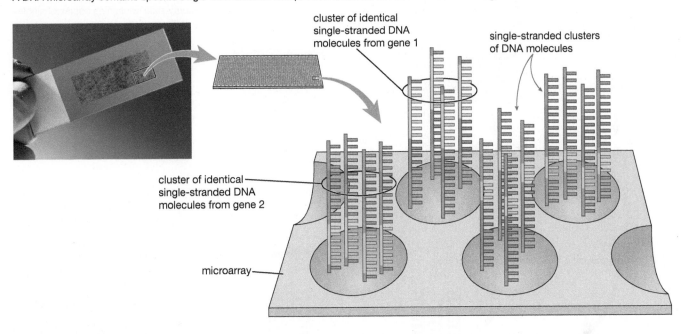

DNA Microarrays

The wealth of information from the human genome project led to a pressing need to rapidly screen DNA samples in order to examine thousands of genes. Much of this screening work is done using **DNA microarrays** (Figure 22.33). DNA microarrays are used to identify whether different genes are present in different samples as well as how often a specific gene is being used in various samples. For example, a researcher might compare the results of a DNA microarray from healthy cells to one from cancerous cells to help determine the underlying cause of a specific cancer.

DNA microarrays are small glass slides with thousands of microscopic spots of DNA in specific locations (see Figure 22.33). Each dot contains multiple identical copies of single-stranded DNA from a specific gene.

To compare DNA from a healthy tissue sample and a cancerous sample using a microarray, a researcher would first extract DNA from each sample (Figure 22.34). She would then attach two different fluorescent molecules to the DNA, one color for the healthy cells and one color for the cancerous cells. The researcher then washes the labeled DNA over the microarray slide, which has multiple identical copies of single-stranded DNA the lab wants to know more about. The color-coded labeled DNA sticks to the slide wherever it finds a complementary sequence. A laser scans the slide, recording if one color is observed, both colors are observed, or neither fluorescent DNA molecule is present. This information rapidly reveals which genes are unique to the cancer. Many types of mutations can cause cancer. Using a microarray to identify which particular mutations are present in a patient's cancer can help a healthcare practitioner develop a more effective treatment strategy.

CRISPR-Cas9 Technology

No discussion of DNA technology is complete without considering the alluring possibility of **gene editing**. Gene editing allows scientists to replace regions of DNA with other corrected, or more desirable, DNA sequences. A patient with cystic fibrosis, for example, might be cured if scientists could replace the one mutant nucleotide in the patient's DNA sequence (see Fig. 22.18).

Figure 22.34 Comparing Genes Using a DNA Microarray.

DNA is isolated from two samples, normal and cancerous cell tissue in this example. Technicians copy the DNA and attach a different fluorescent dye molecule tag to the DNA from each tissue type. The DNA is then washed across a microarray slide containing copies of single-stranded DNAs with known sequences. If a complementary match is found, the two DNAs stick and the spot glows (fluoresces).

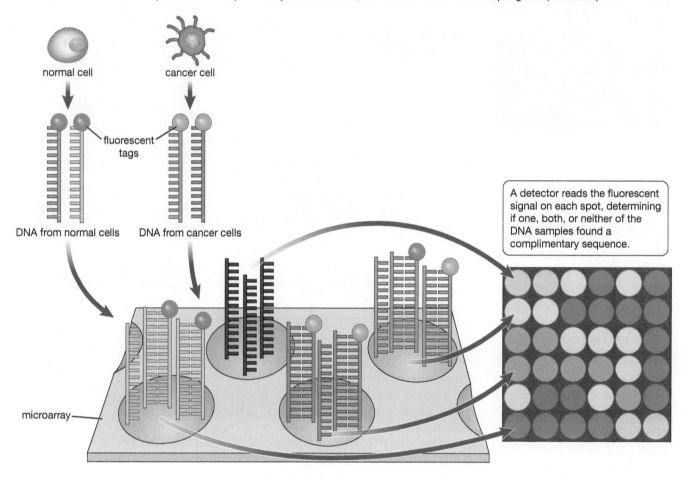

normal cell

cancer cell

fluorescent tags

DNA from normal cells   DNA from cancer cells

A detector reads the fluorescent signal on each spot, determining if one, both, or neither of the DNA samples found a complimentary sequence.

microarray

Scientists have been pursuing safe, effective gene therapy for decades. The potential for gene editing grew dramatically in 2013 when scientists announced that they had successfully edited the DNA of human cells using the new technology, **CRISPR-Cas9,** we explored in the Unit introduction. **CRISPR** (pronounced "crisper") stands for clusters of regularly interspaced short palindromic repeats. These clusters are repeating groups of nucleotides first observed in bacteria as a defense against viral infection.

In the CRISPR-Cas9 process, the enzyme **Cas9** cuts DNA at specific sequences that are complementary to a piece of guide RNA packaged within the enzyme's structure (Figure 22.35). In bacteria in the natural world, guide RNA helps bacteria destroy viral DNA. During the CRISPR-Cas9 process scientists manipulate the guide RNA and direct the DNA-cutting Cas9 enzyme to any part of the genome. This targeted approach allows scientists to remove or add specific sequences of DNA anywhere in the genome.

The ease and accuracy of CRISPR-Cas9 has led to a variety of exciting applications. In 2019, for example, scientists used CRISPR-Cas9 to rid bananas of a virus that has plagued farmers for decades. But just months earlier, a Chinese scientist, He Jiankui, announced he had used CRISPR-Cas9 to modify the DNA of two human embryos that had been implanted and carried to term (Figure 22.36). The international scientific community widely denounced He Jiankui's application of CRISPR-Cas9. Changes made to the DNA of embryos are permanent and will be inherited by all the future offspring of those individuals. Most scientists feel we do not yet understand enough about the potential risks of CRISPR-Cas9 to use the technology in this permanent, irreversible way.

Figure 22.35 CRISPR-Cas9.

CRISPR-Cas9 is a powerful technology for editing genes. Cas9, a DNA-cleaving enzyme, uses single stranded guide RNA molecules to target specific, complementary sites in the genome, allowing regions of DNA to be removed and replaced.

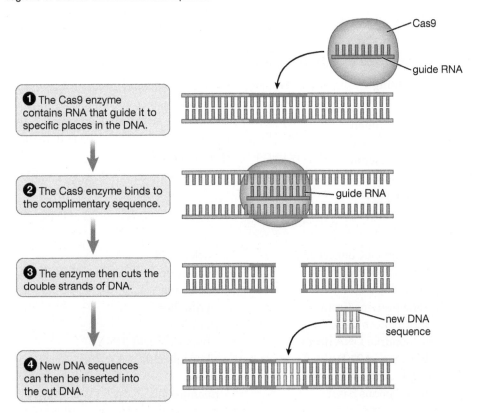

❶ The Cas9 enzyme contains RNA that guide it to specific places in the DNA.

❷ The Cas9 enzyme binds to the complimentary sequence.

❸ The enzyme then cuts the double strands of DNA.

❹ New DNA sequences can then be inserted into the cut DNA.

Cas9
guide RNA
guide RNA
new DNA sequence

Figure 22.36 CRISPR Applications.

A) CRISPR-Cas9 was used to eradicate a virus that has long infected banana plants, threatening crops. **B)** in 2018, geneticist He Jiankui announced he had used CRISPR-Cas9 to permanently edit the DNA of two baby girls, research widely considered to be unethical.

A

B

Quiz yourself on the content of this section: **Check 22.5** in the Pearson eText.

Chapter Summary

22.1 Building Blocks of DNA: Nucleosides and Nucleotides

Learning Objective: Describe and draw the building blocks of nucleosides and nucleotides.

Every one of the estimated 37 trillion cells in a human body contains a complete set of DNA (deoxyribonucleic acid). This collection of all an individual's genetic material is the person's genome. DNA molecules are made of monomers called nucleotides, which contain three parts–*a*

five-carbon sugar, a nitrogen-containing base, and a phosphate group (Figure 22.7). The nitrogen-containing bases in DNA have a pyrimidine or purine structure. Cytosine (C) and thymine (T) are pyrimidines and adenine (A) and guanine (G) are purines (Figure 22.5).

BioConnect 22.1: Our DNA

Key Terms

adenine (A)	gene (from BioConnect 22.1)	nucleic acid
β-*N*-glycosidic bond	genome (from BioConnect 22.1)	nucleoside
chromosomes (from	guanine (G)	nucleotide
BioConnect 22.1)	histone proteins (from	pyrimidine
cytosine (C)	BioConnect 22.1)	purine
dexoyribonucleic acid (DNA)	mitochondrial DNA (from	ribonucleic acid (RNA)
deoxyribonucleoside	BioConnect 22.1)	ribonculeotide
deoxyribonucleotide	nitrogen-containing base	ribose
deoxyribose	(nitrogenous base)	thiamine (T)

22.2 Structure and Formation of Nucleic Acids

Learning Objective: Describe the structure and draw segments of a single strand of DNA including phosphodiester linkages.

Phosphodiester linkages join nucleotides together to form long polynucleotide chains (Figure 22.17). Each polynucleotide chain has a 5′ end and a 3′ end. The 3′ end of the chain contains an —OH group and links to the 5′ end containing a

phosphate group. The polynucleotide chain contains alternating sugar and phosphate groups that form a sugar-phosphate backbone. The order of bases in the chain distinguishes one strand of DNA from another and makes humans and other living things unique as individuals. Some diseases are due to a change of just a single base within a gene.

VisibleChem Video 22.1: Linking Nucleotides

Key Terms

3′ end	polynucleotide	sugar-phosphate backbone
5′ end	single nucleotide polymorphism	
phosphodiester	(SNP)	

22.3 The DNA Double Helix

Learning Objective: Describe the structure and fundamental features of the DNA double helix.

DNA is made up of two polynucleotide strands that twist together into a double helix structure (Figure 22.21). The two strands line up opposite one another—one strand is oriented from 5′ to 3′ end while the other strand is oriented from 3′ to 5′ end. Each of the bases form

hydrogen bonds with one specific complementary base on the opposite strand of DNA. Thymine forms hydrogen bonds with adenine and cytosine forms hydrogen bonds with guanine; these are complementary base pairs (Figure 22.22).

Video 22.1: TED-ED: Rosalind Franklin—DNA's Unsung Hero

Key Terms

complementary base pair   gel electrophoresis   mutations
double helix   mismatches

22.4 DNA Replication

Learning Objective: Explain the process of DNA replication and the role of DNA polymerase.

As cells divide, they produce copies of DNA through DNA replication. During the replication process, strands in the original DNA molecule separate to allow the synthesis of new complementary strands. In each new DNA molecule one strand of the double helix is from the original DNA and one is a newly synthesized strand (Figure 22.26).

VisibleChem Video 22.2: DNA Double Helix

VisibleChem Video 22.3: DNA Replication

BioConnect 22.2: PCR and DNA Forensics

Key Terms

dideoxynucleotide   leading strand   primase
DNA polymerase   ligase   primer
DNA replication   Okasaki fragment   replication fork
helicase   polymerase chain reaction
lagging strand   (PCR) (from BioConnect 22.2)

22.5 DNA Technology

Learning Objective: Explain the mechanism and utility of several common DNA technologies.

DNA sequencing technology led to the sequencing of the human genome (Figure 22.34). DNA fingerprinting is a method for determining an individual's identity using DNA. DNA fingerprinting is often helpful in forensic investigations, but it can also identify a specific species of bacteria linked to disease outbreak (Figure 22.35). DNA microarrays allow us to rapidly search for the presence of thousands of different genes at one time. A researcher might, for example, compare the DNA of a healthy and a cancerous cell to determine the underlying cause of a specific cancer. Gene editing allows scientists to replace regions of DNA with corrected, or more desirable, DNA sequences. CRISPR-Cas9 is a gene editing technology that recently has been used to successfully edit the DNA of human cells (Figure 22.39).

Video 22.3: DNA Sequencing

Key Terms

Cas9   dideoxynucleotides   DNA sequencing
CRISPR   DNA fingerprint   gene editing
CRISPR-Cas9   DNA microarray   precision medicine

 End-of-Chapter Quiz

Have you mastered the content of this chapter? Try the **End-of-Chapter Quiz** in the Pearson eText.

1. Which structural component does a nucleotide contain that a nucleoside does not?
    a) a sugar   **b)** a nitrogen-containing base
    c) a β-N-glycosidic bond   **d)** a phosphate group

2. What is the difference between a ribose and a deoxyribose ring?
    a) A ribose ring has two OH groups bonded to C2′, and a deoxyribose ring has only one OH group bonded to C2′.

b) A ribose ring contains no OH group attached to C2′, and a deoxyribose ring does contain an OH group at C2′.

c) A ribose ring contains an OH group attached to C2′, and a deoxyribose ring does not contain an OH group at C2.

d) A ribose ring contains an OH group attached to C2′ and a deoxyribose ring contains two OH groups attached to carbon number two of the ring.

3. Which statement about DNA is correct?
   a) Human cells contain 23 chromosomes, each containing DNA.
   b) DNA is folded into beta sheets within chromosomes.
   c) Mitochondrial DNA is inherited almost exclusively from mothers.
   d) DNA is wrapped around the amino acid histidine.

4. Which is the smallest component that contains genetic information?
   a) histone
   b) gene
   c) DNA in the nucleus
   d) chromosome

5. Consider the given structure of the base thymine (T) and identify the correct structure of the molecule dTDP.

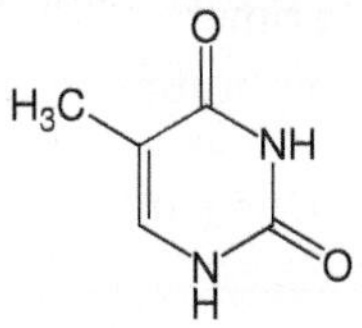

thymine (T)

a)

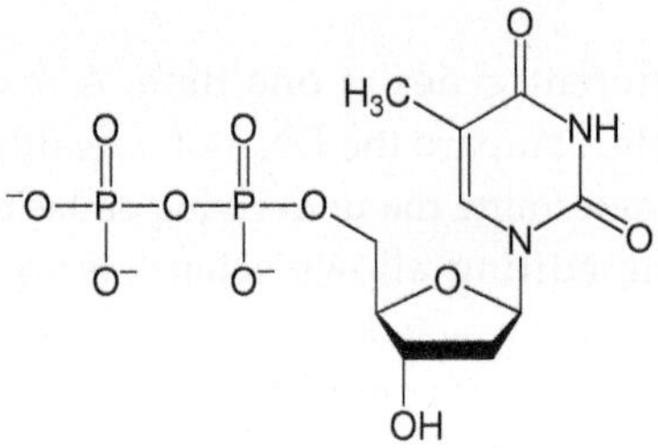

b)

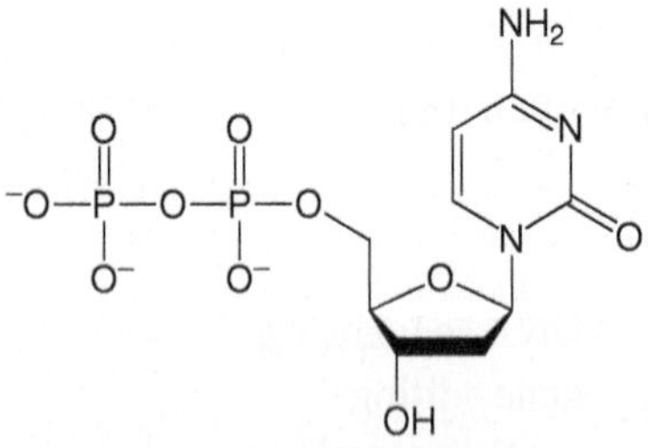

c)

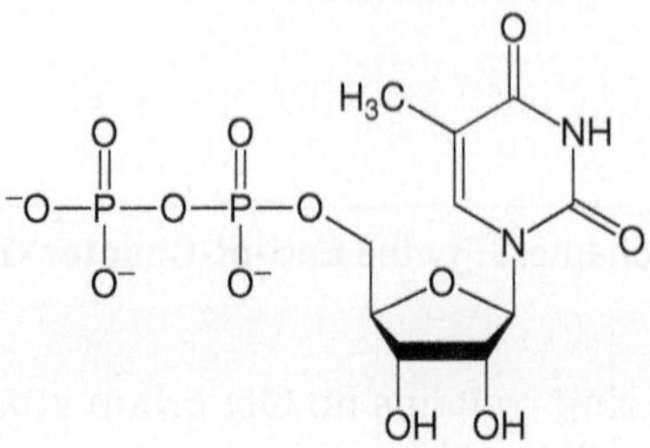

d)

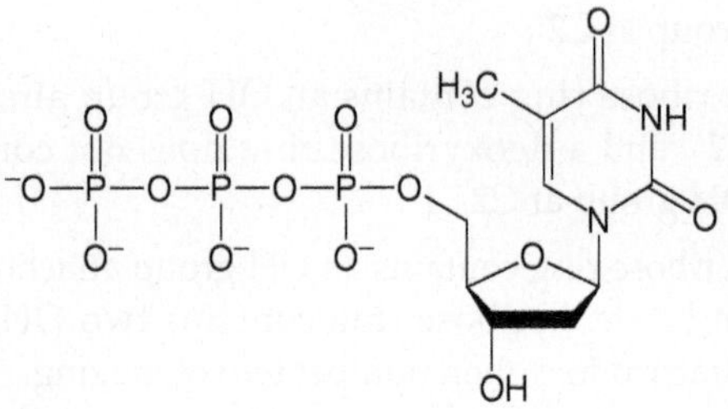

6. Which group covalently links the multiple nucleotides together in DNA and RNA strands?
   a) hydroxyl
   b) β-N-glycosidic
   c) purine and pyrimidine
   d) phosphodiester

7. Select the structure that correctly shows the phosphodiester linkage between dTMP and dCMP that produces the dinucleotide TC?

a)

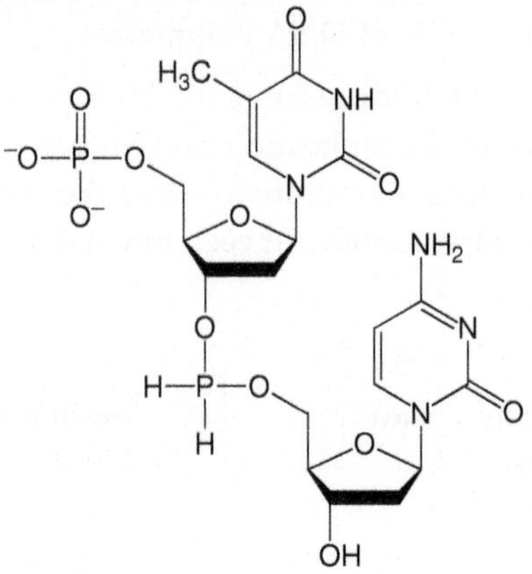

b)

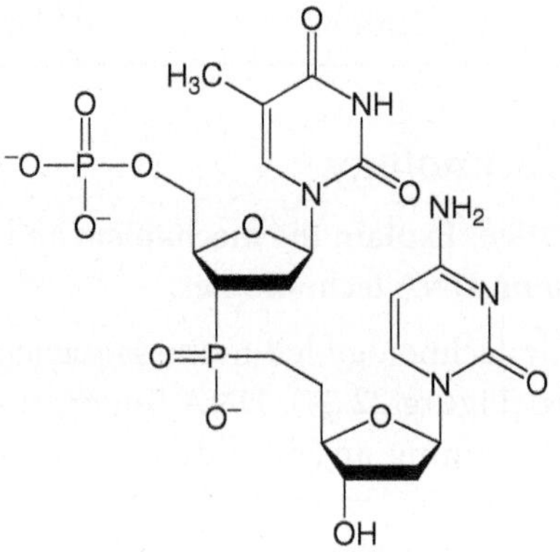

c)

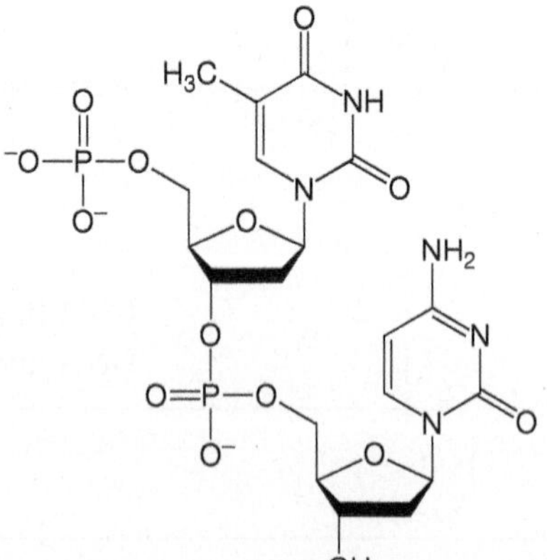

d)

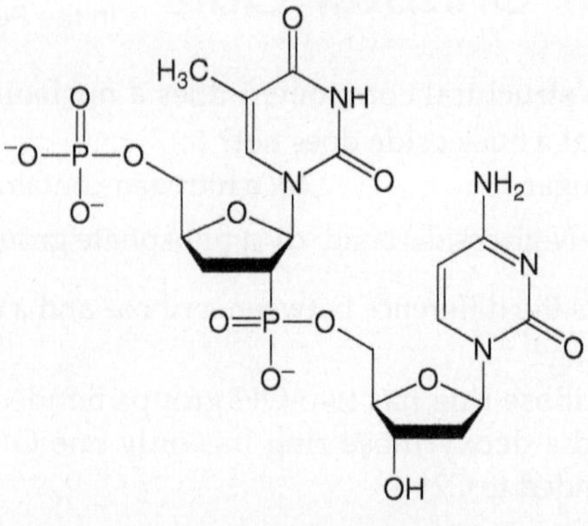

8. Select the correct structure of the dinucleotide that forms when the 3'OH group of AMP joins with the 5' phosphate in CMP? The structures of the bases adenine and cytosine are given for reference.

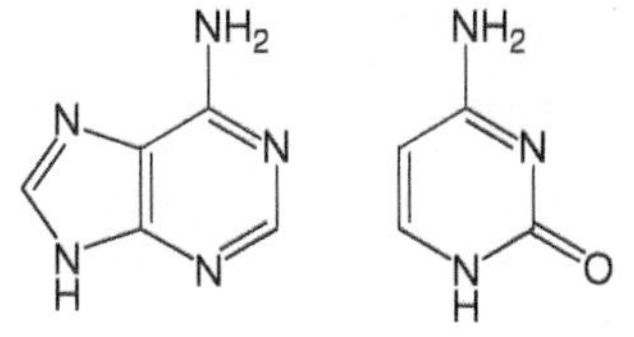

adenine (A)   cytosine (C)

a)

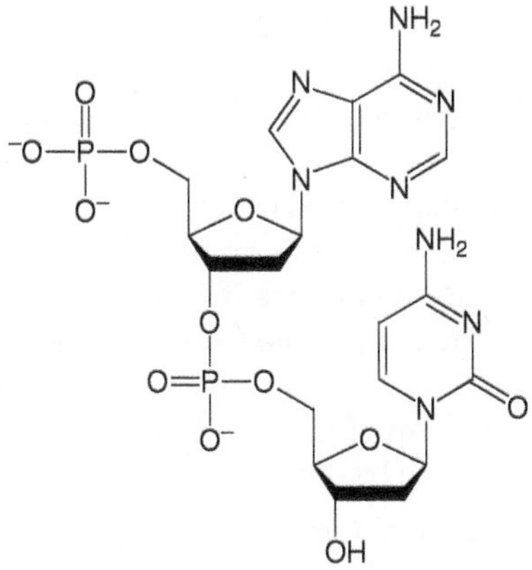

b)

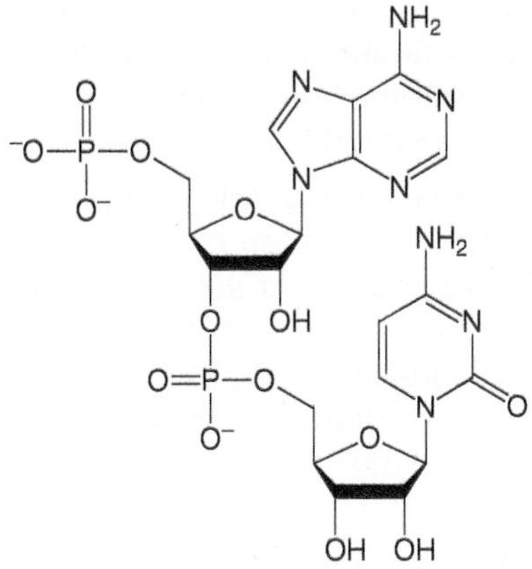

c)

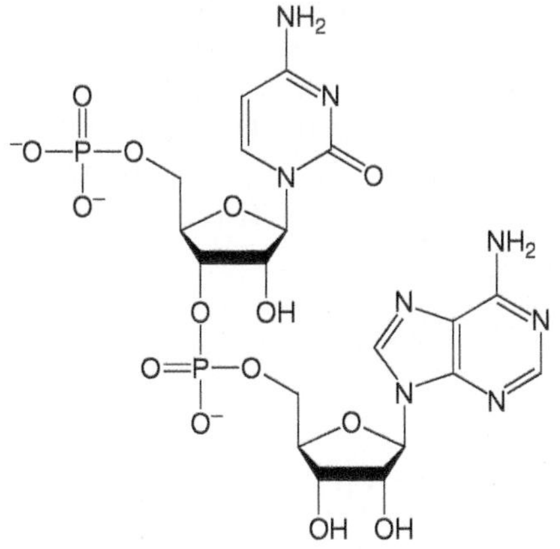

d)

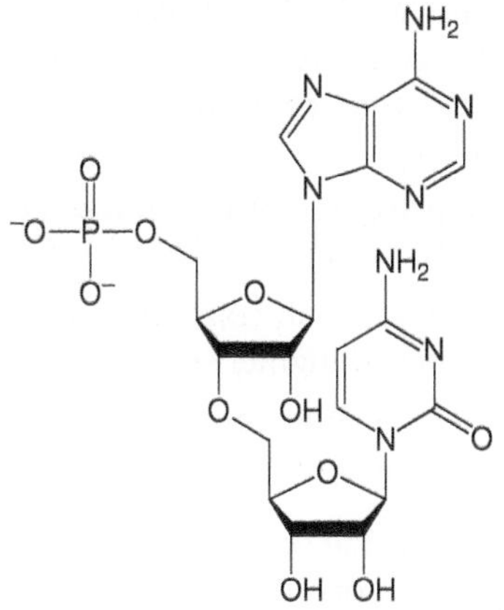

9. Which statement best describes the backbone of a DNA strand?

   a) The backbone of a DNA strand contains alternating sugar units and nitrogen bases joined together with hemiacetal bonds.

   b) The backbone of a DNA strand is made up of complementary bases joined together with hydrogen bonds.

   c) The backbone of a DNA strand contains sugar molecules bonded to each other with glycosidic linkages between C3' of one unit and C5' of the next sugar unit.

   d) The backbone of a DNA strand contains alternating sugar and phosphate groups joined together by phosphodiester linkage.

10. Select the two complementary DNA strands.

   a) 5'-GTGCAC-3'   **b)** 5'-TCAAGC-3'
       3'-CACGTG-5'   3'-GCTTGG-5'

   c) 5'-CCGATA-3'   **d)** 5'-CGCAGT-3'
       3'-ATAGCC-5'   5'-GCGTCA-3'

11. What is the role of DNA polymerase in the DNA replication process?

   a) DNA polymerase separates the DNA strands at the replication fork.

   b) DNA polymerase connects the lagging strand fragments to form a complete lagging strand.

   c) DNA polymerase catalyzes the formation of phosphodiester linkages on new DNA strands.

   d) DNA polymerase reconnects the base pairing in the newly formed DNA strands to complete the DNA replication process.

12. When DNA is replicated, the two resulting double-stranded DNA molecules are:
    a) four identical strands consisting of two pairs of double helices.
    b) four double helices, two of which consist of two daughter strands.
    c) two double helices, each containing one parent strand and one new daughter strand.
    d) two double helices, one containing two parent strands and one containing two daughter strands.

13. What is the primary role of the polymerase chain reaction (PCR) in the laboratory?
    a) PCR optimizes the enzyme activity of specific hydrolysis reactions.
    b) PCR enhances viral replication mechanisms used by the cell to amplify DNA.
    c) PCR allows scientists to produce many copies of a DNA sample of interest.
    d) PCR efficiently degrades non-template strand DNA thus increasing the rate of template strand duplication.

14. Which is the sequence of a newly synthesized DNA strand if it is made from a template strand with the sequence 3'-CGGTCA-5'?
    a) 3'-CGGTCA-5'
    b) 5'-GCCAGT-3'
    c) 5'-CGGTCA-3'
    d) 3'-ACTGGC-5'

15. What is the purpose of heating samples to 95°C in laboratory experiments using the polymerase chain reaction (PCR)?
    a) Heating samples to 95 °C quickly heat denatures DNA polymerase so that replication is more efficient.
    b) Heating samples to 95 °C denatures double-stranded DNA into separate single strands.
    c) 95 °C is the optimum temperature for the PCR primers to bind to the longer DNA strands.
    d) 95 °C is the optimum temperature for the elongation process in PCR.

16. In a typical DNA microarray experiment, what is attached to the surface of the microarray slide?
    a) fluorescent dideoxynucleotides and PCR primers
    b) single-stranded DNA sequences
    c) DNA polymerase for template replication
    d) double-stranded DNA sequences

17. Which DNA technology do researchers use to edit genes?
    a) DNA sequencing
    b) CRISPR-Cas9
    c) DNA fingerprinting
    d) DNA microarrays

18. DNA polymerase uses deoxyribonucleotide triphosphates (dNTPs) to build new DNA strands during the replication process. DNA sequencing experiments often use a mixture of both deoxyribonucleotides and fluorescently labeled dideoxyribonucleotide triphosphates (ddNTPs). What purpose do fluorescently labeled ddNTPs serve in DNA sequencing experiments?
    a) The ddNTPs have an extra CH_2OH group in the sugar at position C3', which halts DNA synthesis whenever the polymerase incorporates a ddNTP into a growing chain. The fluorescent label helps scientists detect the length of each strand and the sequence position of labeled ddNTP, allowing the DNA sequence to be determined.
    b) The ddNTPs have a branching point in the sugar at position C3', which allows a short branching DNA sequence to form at CRISPR sites in the DNA sequence. The fluorescently labeled ddNTP helps scientists detect the branch point on each strand and determine the DNA sequence.
    c) The ddNTPs lack the 3' OH group required to attach the next nucleotide in the growing DNA molecule, so synthesis stops whenever the polymerase incorporates a ddNTP into a growing chain. The fluorescent labels help scientists detect the length of each strand and the sequence position of the labeled ddNTP and determine the DNA sequence.
    d) The ddNTPs lack the 3' OH group required to attach the next nucleotide in the growing DNA molecule, so synthesis stops whenever the polymerase incorporates a ddNTP into a growing chain. The fluorescent label on the ddNTP helps scientists interpret the DNA microarray, allowing CRISPR enzymes to fingerprint the DNA sequence.

Chapter 23
RNA and Protein Synthesis

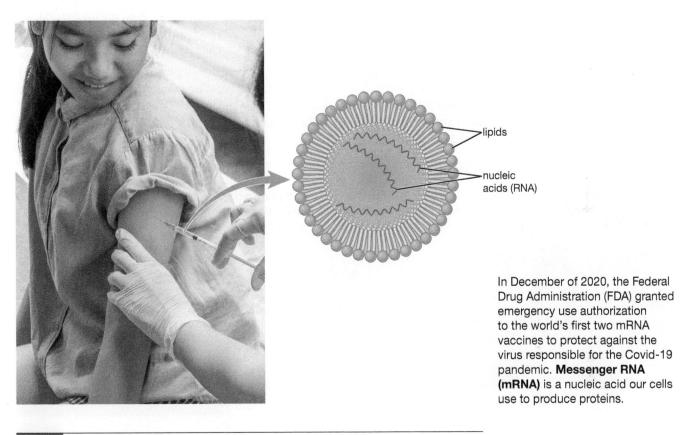

lipids

nucleic
acids (RNA)

In December of 2020, the Federal
Drug Administration (FDA) granted
emergency use authorization
to the world's first two mRNA
vaccines to protect against the
virus responsible for the Covid-19
pandemic. **Messenger RNA
(mRNA)** is a nucleic acid our cells
use to produce proteins.

 ## Chapter Outline

Learning Objectives

23.1 Describe how RNA structure differs from DNA structure.

23.2 Explain the key steps of transcription.

23.3 Use the genetic code to convert mRNA codons to a sequence of amino acids.

23.4 Explain the key steps of translation.

23.5 Describe types of point mutations and how they affect protein structure.

Introduction

In this chapter we build on our discussion of the DNA molecule in the previous chapter and learn how DNA produces the wide array of proteins that make individuals unique. Understanding how bodies produce proteins from DNA unlocks the secrets of a wide range of important topics from vaccine development to the inheritance and treatment of genetic diseases (Figure 23.1). Harnessing the protein production process also makes possible the development of a fascinating array of biomaterials, including solar panels made from bacterial proteins and body armor made from genetically modified spider silk.

Figure 23.1 Applications of Protein Synthesis.

A) A child receives a treatment for cystic fibrosis, a serious genetic disease that disrupts the production of a protein needed for proper lung function. **B)** Many vaccines, such as the vaccines for hepatitis B and whooping cough are made from genetically modified proteins. **C)** The military has been experimenting with body armor made from spider silk, a protein up to ten times stronger than Kevlar.

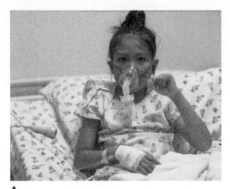
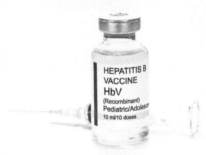

A B C

23.1 Structure of RNA

In Chapter 22, we discussed how DNA is copied, quickly and accurately, every time our cells divide. DNA replication is critical to survival because DNA provides the instructions for creating the tens of thousands of unique proteins that keep cells functioning.

Chromosomes in every cell in the body contain DNA packaged with proteins. The short regions of this DNA that code for specific proteins are **genes**. To create proteins, cells must first make a working copy of the individual genes on chromosomes (Figure 23.2). This working copy of the specific section of DNA that makes up a gene is in the form of a very similar molecule, **ribonucleic acid (RNA)**. RNA is responsible for a variety of functions including carrying instructions from DNA that synthesize proteins. The process of assembling an RNA molecule from a gene (DNA) is **transcription.** The body uses most of the RNA molecules it makes to build proteins in a process called **translation.**

We explore some of RNA's other functions later in this chapter. In this section, we look more closely at the structure of RNA before delving deeper into transcription and translation.

Figure 23.2 Using the Information in Genes to Build Proteins.

A gene is a specific region of DNA that contains the directions for making a specific protein. To make proteins, the body copies individual genes in a process known as transcription to create working copies in the form of RNA. The body then converts this information in the RNA to proteins in a process known as translation.

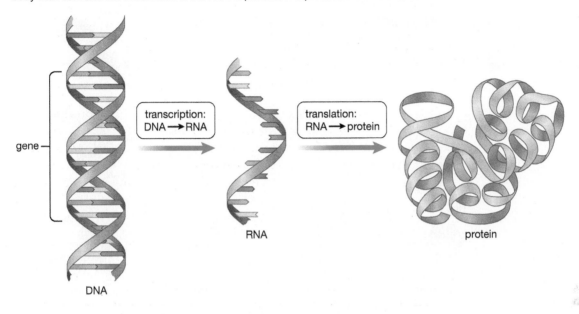

RNA Structure

DNA and RNA are both nucleic acids and share many structural similarities. Both of these polymers consist of a backbone of alternating five-carbon (pentose) sugars with attached nitrogenous bases. Like DNA, RNA is a directional molecule, with a 5′ and 3′ end. DNA molecules, however, contain a deoxyribose sugar in their backbone—hence the name deoxyribonucleic acid—while RNA contains ribose, a slightly different sugar (Figure 23.3).

Figure 23.3 The Sugars in DNA and RNA.

DNA contains a deoxyribose sugar while RNA contains a ribose sugar. Deoxyribose lacks the hydroxyl group (OH) on the 2′ carbon that ribose contains.

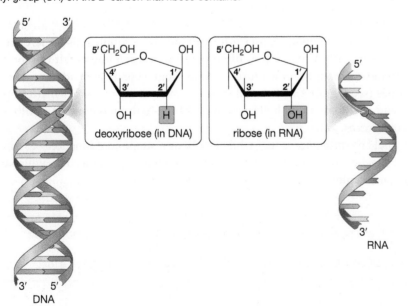

Figure 23.4 Comparing DNA and RNA.

DNA is a double-stranded molecule with the bases adenine, guanine, cytosine, and thymine. RNA contains a different sugar (ribose), is single-stranded, and instead of thymine includes the base uracil. Uracil forms hydrogen bonds with adenine, just as thymine does.

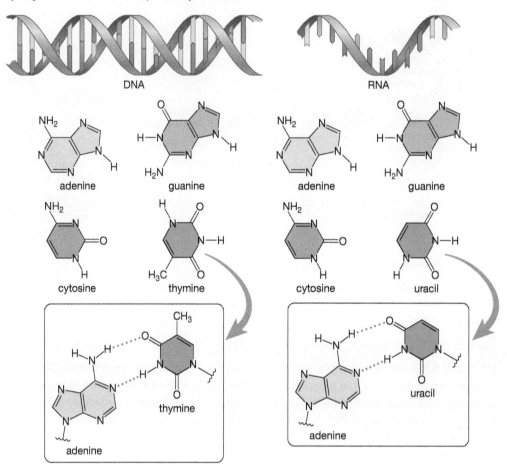

In addition, RNA molecules contain a nitrogenous base not found in DNA called **uracil**. Uracil is structurally similar to thymine and replaces thymine in RNA polymers (Figure 23.4). RNA molecules, therefore, contain the four bases adenine (A), cytosine (C), guanine (G), and uracil (U).

The third difference between RNA and DNA is that RNA almost always occurs as a single-stranded molecule, in contrast to the DNA double helix. There are many similarities too. RNA, like DNA, often forms hydrogen bonds with other nucleic acids. In these situations, uracil forms two hydrogen bonds with adenine just as thymine does (see Fig. 23.4). RNA molecules form an array of shapes including folds, loops, and single-stranded helices because of the hydrogen bonds and other intermolecular forces.

A final key difference is that while DNA has a single core function—to carry and pass on genetic information—there are many different RNA molecules, which we discuss in this chapter, and each one has a unique function.

 Apply what you have just learned: **Practice 23.1 and 23.2** in the Pearson eText.

Quiz yourself on the content of this section: **Check 23.1** in the Pearson eText.

Figure 23.5 Producing Insulin.

Insulin is a protein that regulates blood sugar. When a person ingests sugars, cells in the pancreas transcribe the insulin gene to produce messenger RNA. The mRNA is transported out of the nucleus and used to make the insulin protein.

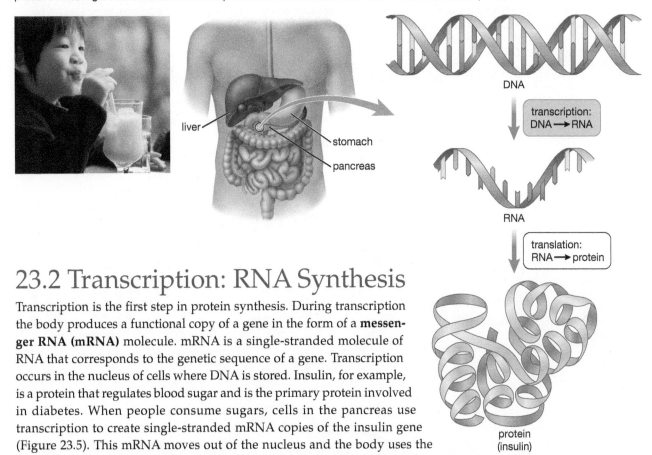

liver

stomach

pancreas

DNA

transcription:
DNA → RNA

RNA

translation:
RNA → protein

protein
(insulin)

23.2 Transcription: RNA Synthesis

Transcription is the first step in protein synthesis. During transcription the body produces a functional copy of a gene in the form of a **messenger RNA (mRNA)** molecule. mRNA is a single-stranded molecule of RNA that corresponds to the genetic sequence of a gene. Transcription occurs in the nucleus of cells where DNA is stored. Insulin, for example, is a protein that regulates blood sugar and is the primary protein involved in diabetes. When people consume sugars, cells in the pancreas use transcription to create single-stranded mRNA copies of the insulin gene (Figure 23.5). This mRNA moves out of the nucleus and the body uses the mRNA to produce the insulin protein. In this section, we look at this first step in protein synthesis– transcription– in more detail.

Transcription occurs in three steps. The first step, **initiation**, assembles the needed molecules at the start of a gene. This region of DNA at the beginning of a gene is a **promoter.** Promoters play a significant role in the initiation step of transcription. **Transcription factors** are proteins that bind to promoters and attract the key molecule RNA polymerase to the promoter region. **RNA polymerase** is an enzyme that catalyzes the reaction that eventually makes the new mRNA molecule (Figure 23.6).

Once the RNA polymerase binds to the start of the gene, it unzips the two strands of the DNA molecule forming a temporary "bubble". The two halves of the DNA helix are exposed in the bubble, allowing the second step, **elongation**, to begin. In this step, one strand, the **template strand,** is used to build a complementary mRNA sequence. (The other strand that is not copied is the **informational strand.**) Free floating complementary nucleotides temporarily pair with the nucleotides of the template strand, which is held in place by hydrogen bonds. The RNA polymerase then catalyzes the formation of new phosphodiester bonds between adjacent nucleotides, assembling the new mRNA one nucleotide at a time as RNA polymerase moves down the gene being transcribed.

The elongation of the mRNA molecule continues until RNA polymerase reaches a termination sequence encoded in the DNA. This sequence causes RNA polymerase to release the newly constructed mRNA. This is the **termination** step of transcription. The DNA double-helix closes again, and RNA polymerase is free to transcribe the next gene.

Figure 23.6 Key Steps in Transcription.

Transcription factors and RNA polymerase bind at a specific sequence of DNA, the promoter. (Note that both transcription factors and the RNA polymerases are much larger than shown in this representation.) RNA polymerase can then temporarily separate the DNA double helix to use one strand as a template. RNA polymerase elongates (builds) the complementary mRNA sequence. The process terminates (ends) when the RNA polymerase is released after encountering a stop sequence in the DNA.

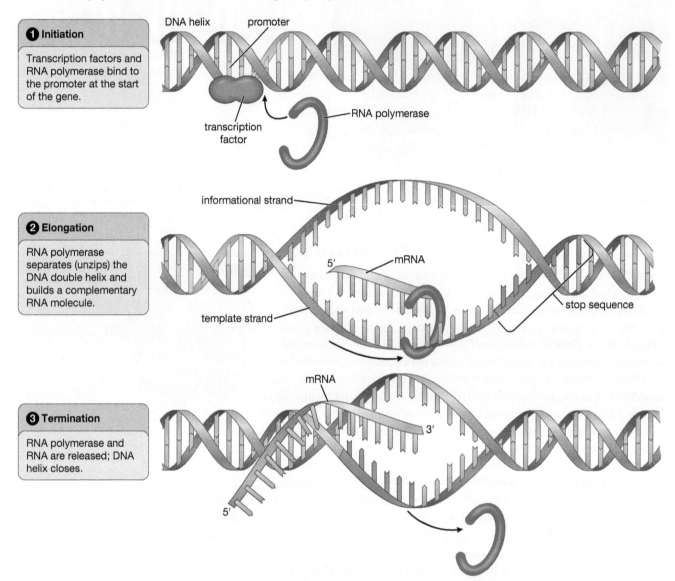

1 Initiation

Transcription factors and RNA polymerase bind to the promoter at the start of the gene.

DNA helix — promoter

RNA polymerase

transcription factor

2 Elongation

RNA polymerase separates (unzips) the DNA double helix and builds a complementary RNA molecule.

informational strand

5′ — mRNA

template strand

stop sequence

3 Termination

RNA polymerase and RNA are released; DNA helix closes.

mRNA

3′

5′

Explore VisibleChem Videos 23.1 and 23.2 to review the structure of RNA and consider the process of transcription more closely. Then explore BioConnect 23.1 (contains Figures 23.7–23.13) to investigate viral transcription and how scientists develop powerful antiviral medications using their knowledge of viral transcription.

Watch this concept come to life: **VisibleChem Video 23.1:** Overview of Transcription and **VisibleChem Video 23.2:** A Closer Look at Transcription in the Pearson eText.

Apply what you have just learned: **Practice 23.3–23.5** in the Pearson eText.

Explore how Chemistry and Biology connect: **BioConnect: 23.1** Targeting Viral Transcription in the Pearson eText.

Quiz yourself on the content of this section: **Check 23.2** in the Pearson eText.

23.3 Translation: The Genetic Code

Once a gene has been transcribed to form a messenger RNA, the mRNA is sent out of the nucleus and used to synthesize a protein in translation. This translation process is aptly named—we now transition from the "language" of nucleic acids to the "language" of proteins. In this section, we explore the coding system that allows our cells to do this work of translating. We examine the molecular-level mechanisms of translation in the next section.

Recall that proteins are composed of 20 amino acids in a specific sequence. Each protein's specific sequence ultimately leads to a complex three-dimensional structure. A coding system—the **genetic code**—converts each molecule of mRNA into a specific sequence of amino acids (Table 23.1).

In this system, each set of three nucleotides, or **triplet**, on an mRNA is a **codon**. Each codon corresponds to a specific amino acid. For example, the codon UGA in a mRNA molecule codes for the amino acid cysteine, and the codon GUA codes for the amino acid valine.

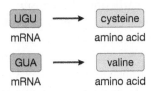

Table 23.1 The Genetic Code.

To use the codon table, find the letter for the first nucleotide on your codon of interest on the left side of the table. Follow the row across until you reach the column containing your second nucleotide. The right side of the table shows all possible nucleotides for the third position of your codon of interest. Note that each three-letter codon corresponds to a specific amino acid. More than one codon may code for each amino acid.

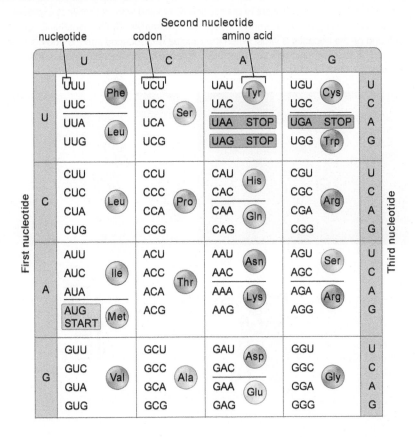

Predict answers and see step-by-step solutions: **Learn 23.1:** Using the Genetic Code to Determine an Amino Acid Sequence from mRNA in the Pearson eText.

Apply what you have just learned: **Practice 23.6 and 23.7** in the Pearson eText.

One-by-one each amino acid is coded for and linked together in the long chains that form the primary structure of a protein during translation. By convention, codons are written from the 5′ to 3′ end of an mRNA molecule.

There are 64 different ways to combine A, C, G, and U into groups of three and therefore 64 different codons. Because there are far fewer than 64 amino acids in organisms, more than one codon frequently corresponds to each amino acid as shown in Table 23.1. For example, the codons UCU, UCC, UCA, UCG, AGU, and AGC all correspond to the amino acid serine (Ser). In contrast, there is only one codon (UGG) for the amino acid tryptophan (Trp). The **start codon** (AUG) is the first codon of a mRNA molecule that is translated and always codes for the amino acid methionine (Met). Three codons (UAA, UAG, and UGA) are **stop codons** that signal the termination of protein synthesis. Click on Learn 23.1 to use the genetic code table to determine amino acid sequences from mRNA molecules.

Recombinant Proteins

Scientific understanding of the genetic code has made possible a wide array of technologies. The genetic code is nearly universal, meaning that almost all life forms use the same codons for the amino acid sequences of proteins. The universal nature of DNA and proteins has allowed scientists to recombine DNA from diverse organisms to create **recombinant DNA**. Scientists place this recombinant DNA in other organisms that then transcribe and translate the new DNA to form **recombinant proteins.** Recombinant proteins have a wide variety of applications including biomaterials, research tools, therapeutic drugs, and vaccines (Figure 23.14).

Figure 23.14 Applications of Recombinant Proteins.

A) Spider silk is an extraordinarily strong and versatile material. Because the silk is difficult to obtain from spiders, scientists place the gene for the spider silk protein in goats. The goats produce milk that contains the recombinant spider silk protein. **B)** The green fluorescent protein (GFP), originally from jellyfish, is a widely-used research tool that allows scientists to quickly see where and when a protein is expressed. Recombinant GFP has been expressed in many organisms including bacteria, worms, insects, and mammals. **C)** The hepatitis B vaccine contains a recombinant version of a surface protein found on the hepatitis B virus. When the vaccine is introduced into the body, the body launches an immune response to the recombinant viral protein. The antibodies that the body produces during the immune response protect the individual from future infection with the hepatitis B virus.

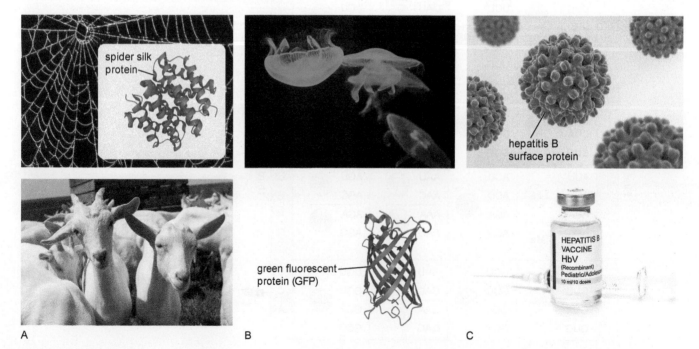

A

B

C

mRNA Vaccines

The universal nature of the genetic code has changed how we design and develop vaccines. In December of 2020, the Federal Drug Administration (FDA) granted emergency use authorization to the world's first two **mRNA vaccines** to protect against the virus responsible for the Covid-19 pandemic (Figure 23.15). These two vaccines were produced in record time, taking just one year to develop. Vaccines have historically taken 10–15 years to develop. This rapid development was facilitated by both the substantial investment by the U.S. federal government and by decades of prior work exploring the use and delivery of mRNA vaccines.

Humans naturally produce antibodies, large proteins that bind to and help destroy disease-causing bacteria and viruses, when we are exposed to disease-causing agents. All vaccines similarly train our immune system to recognize and inactivate specific disease-causing agents and produce antibodies. Most vaccines contain a weakened or inactivated bacteria or virus, or a specific piece of a protein from the disease-causing agent. mRNA vaccines, in contrast, contain the mRNA for a specific protein on the outer surface of the disease-causing agent. When this mRNA is injected into our cells, we translate the mRNA and produce just that single protein from the disease-causing agent. In the mRNA vaccines for Covid-19, the mRNA codes for a portion of the spike protein on the surface of the SARS-CoV-2 virus (Figure 23.16). Our immune system recognizes this protein as foreign and produces antibodies to bind to and inactivate it. These antibodies persist in our bodies, allowing us to more quickly fight off future infections, preventing more serious disease.

Figure 23.15 Covid-19 Vaccination Clinic at Dodger Stadium in Los Angeles in January 2021.

The first two approved vaccines for Covid-19 in the U.S. were both mRNA vaccines.

Figure 23.16 mRNA Vaccines.

mRNA vaccines contain mRNA for a single protein. Once inside our cells, the mRNA is translated to produce the single protein from the disease-causing agent. The bodies of vaccinated people produce antibodies that bind to and inactivate any virus we're exposed to, preventing serious disease.

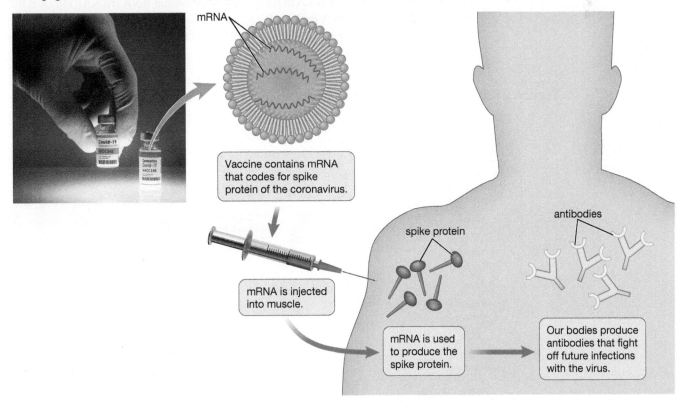

In contrast to conventional vaccines, small changes can quickly be made to the mRNA sequence used in mRNA vaccines when new versions of a virus evolve, making mRNA vaccines an important tool for combating emerging diseases.

 Quiz yourself on the content of this section: **Check 23.3** in the Pearson eText.

23.4 A Closer Look at Translation: Protein Synthesis

The genetic code (see Table 23.1) helps us translate the sequence of a protein from a gene, but it does not tell us how cells accomplish the function of protein synthesis. Once a gene has been transcribed to create a messenger RNA, the mRNA exits the nucleus and synthesizes a protein (Figure 23.17). The order of the amino acids that make up any given specific protein is determined by the information in the DNA that is transcribed in the mRNA molecule.

Recall that translation is the process that occurs in cells that *translates* mRNA into a protein. To produce insulin for diabetics to use, for example, scientists place the gene for the insulin protein in bacteria. Large vats of bacteria provide ideal conditions for rapid growth. As the bacteria grow, they transcribe and translate the insulin gene, producing the life-saving insulin diabetics need (Figure 23.18).

In many ways, translation is a more complex process than transcription. Several key molecules must be present for translation to occur.

Key Players in Translation

Translation takes place at **ribosomes** in the body's cells. Ribosomes are enzymes composed of two subunits, a large subunit and a small subunit, both made of RNA and proteins (Figure 23.19). The RNA in ribosomes is **ribosomal RNA (rRNA).** rRNA is the most abundant type of RNA in the cell.

Another key player, **transfer RNA (tRNA),** helps with the translation process. Transfer RNAs deliver the correct amino acid to the ribosomes according to the sequence specified

---

Figure 23.17 Translation Converts the Information in mRNA into Protein.

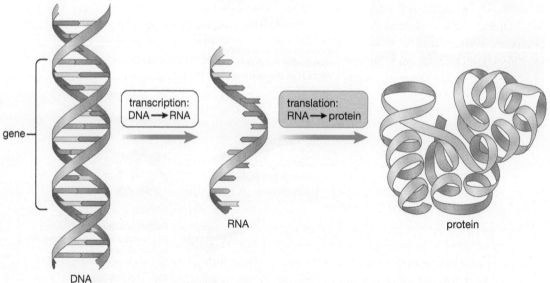

Figure 23.18 Insulin Production.

Insulin (A) is produced in large tanks called bioreactors (B). Bacteria in the bioreactors transcribe and translate the insulin protein, which is then purified.

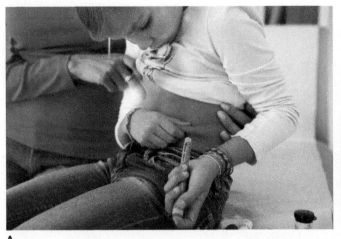

A

B

Figure 23.19 Representations of Ribosomes.

Ribosomes are composed of two subunits, a large and a small subunit. The subunits are made of protein and a unique form of RNA called ribosomal RNA (rRNA).

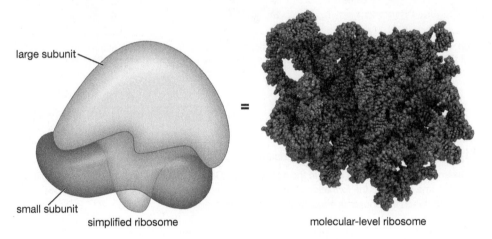

in the mRNA. tRNAs are able to accomplish this task because of their unique structure. The three-dimensional folded structure of single-stranded tRNAs exposes two important sites. At one end is an amino acid attachment site. On the other end, three nucleotides form an **anticodon** (Figure 23.20). An anticodon is a nucleotide sequence complementary to that of a corresponding codon in mRNA sequence. The anticodon of the tRNA forms complementary base pairs with the specific set of three bases in the mRNA—the codons we introduce in Section 23.3—and delivers the correct amino acid to the correct location.

Building Proteins

Like transcription, we can think of translation occurring in three steps: initiation, elongation, and termination. Initiation begins when the ribosome assembles at the start codon on the mRNA. Additional tRNAs bind at the ribosome, each carrying a unique amino acid coded for by the anticodon. If the anticodon is complementary to the codon in the mRNA, hydrogen bonds temporarily form. These bonds hold the tRNA in position while at the ribosome, an enzyme catalyzes the formation of a new peptide bond between amino acids, elongating the protein (Figure 23.21). Once each new

Figure 23.20 Representations of tRNA.

Transfer RNA (tRNA) is single-stranded RNA with a structure on one end that binds to specific amino acids. Three bases are exposed on the opposite end of the folded tRNA molecule, forming an anticodon that hydrogen bonds with the codon on an mRNA.

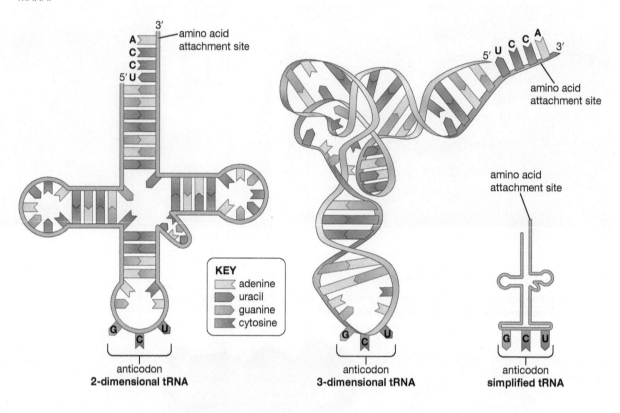

Figure 23.21 An Overview of Translation.

Transfer RNA delivers amino acids in the correct order. Once each tRNA and amino acid is in place, the ribosome catalyzes the formation of new peptide bonds between amino acids. The process terminates when the ribosome encounters a stop codon.

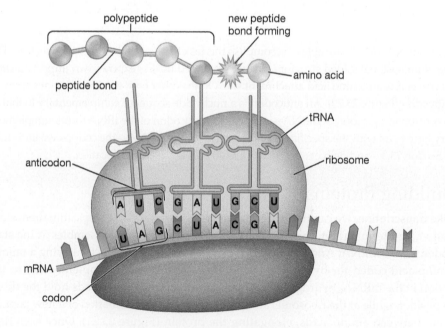

peptide bond attaches the amino acid to the growing polypeptide chain, the tRNA that delivered the amino acid is released. That same tRNA may deliver another amino acid later in the growing peptide, much like a taxi might drop off a passenger at a concert and return again later with another passenger. The process of translation ends when the ribosome encounters a stop codon, triggering the release of the mRNA, ribosome, and finished polypeptide protein.

Select VisibleChem Video 22.3 to explore the process of translation in more detail.

Watch this concept come to life: **VisibleChem Video 23.3:** Translation and Protein Synthesis in the Pearson eText.

Apply what you have just learned: **Practice 23.8 and 23.9** in the Pearson eText.

Quiz yourself on the content of this section: **Check 23.4** in the Pearson eText.

23.5 Mutations and Genetic Disease

In 2013, actress Angelina Jolie announced that she carried a mutation in a gene called *BRCA1* (breast cancer 1; Figure 23.22). According to her physicians, the mutation indicated that she had an 87% chance of developing breast cancer. Jolie opted to have a double mastectomy, preventatively having both breasts removed to reduce her risk of developing breast cancer. While many women have faced similar difficult decisions, her international fame and the candor with which Jolie discussed her situation cast a spotlight on testing for genetic mutations.

While the popular press often describes women such as Jolie as "having *BRCA1*," this description is a bit misleading. All humans have the *BRCA1* gene. When it is working correctly, the *BRCA1* gene codes for a protein that helps repair damage to DNA. Jolie carries a mutation in her *BRCA1* gene that prevents it from doing this repair. **Mutations** are changes in the structure or sequence of a gene that turn off or reduce the activity of a protein and potentially cause disease, or on rare occasions,

---

Figure 23.22 Angelina Jolie.

The actress had a double mastectomy after finding out she carried a genetic mutation associated with a high risk of breast cancer.

Figure 23.23 Environmental Causes of Acquired Mutations.

Exposure to certain chemicals, radiation, and a few specific bacteria and viruses are all associated with an increased risk of acquired DNA mutations.

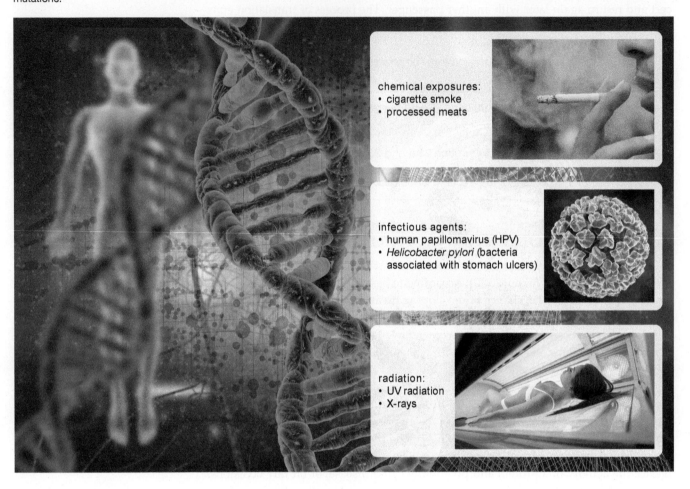

chemical exposures:
• cigarette smoke
• processed meats

infectious agents:
• human papillomavirus (HPV)
• *Helicobacter pylori* (bacteria associated with stomach ulcers)

radiation:
• UV radiation
• X-rays

may convey a benefit. The mutation in Jolie's in *BRCA1* gene predisposes her to cancer, which occurs when damaged cells divide uncontrollably.

Mutations can be *hereditary* (passed on from parent to child) or *acquired* during a lifetime affecting just a small fraction of a person's cells during that lifetime. Some *acquired* mutations result from mistakes made during DNA replication while others are the result of environmental factors such exposure to ultraviolet (UV) radiation from the sun, infectious agents, or certain chemicals (Figure 23.23).

Point Mutations

Many common acquired and hereditary DNA mutations, including several of those affecting the function of the *BRCA1* gene, are **point mutations**. Point mutations are changes in a single nucleotide within a gene (Figure 23.24). Point mutations include substitution, insertion, and deletion mutations. We discuss each of these in this section.

Substitution mutations are point mutations where one nucleotide is substituted for another. Such a substitution changes a codon and may change the resulting amino acid and therefore change the protein. Substitutions that change an amino acid in a protein are **missense mutations**. For example, a common missense substitution mutation changes an amino acid in one of the enzymes that helps break down caffeine. Individuals with this substitution do not break down caffeine as quickly and often find they need to limit their consumption of coffee, soda, and other caffeinated food to avoid the unpleasant side effects of excess caffeine. (Figure 23.25).

Figure 23.24 Types of Point Mutations.

Point mutations are changes in a single nucleotide in a DNA sequence. They can include substitutions that replace one nucleotide with another, or insertions or deletions in which a nucleotide is added or lost from a sequence.

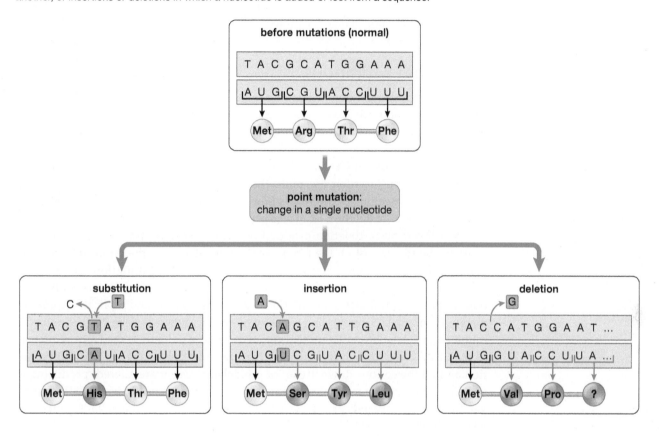

Figure 23.25 A Substitution Affects Caffeine Metabolism.

The *CYP12A* gene produces an enzyme that helps break down caffeine. A common substitution mutation in this gene changes one amino acid in the sequence, reducing the effectiveness of the enzyme protein. Individuals with this mutation take longer to break down caffeine.

In some cases, however, a substitution mutation does not change the amino acid sequence of a protein. This type of mutation is a **silent substitution mutation**. A substitution that changes the codon GUU to GUC, for example, does not affect the protein as both codons code for the amino acid valine. This silent mutation changes the DNA sequence but does not change the protein.

Frameshift Mutations

A mutation that changes how the pattern of three nucleotides are translated is a **frameshift mutation** and can have significant effects on the structure of a protein. Point mutations also occur when an extra nucleotide is incorporated into a DNA sequence, a frameshift mutation known as an **insertion** (see Fig. 23.25). Inserting a single base changes not only the single corresponding codon in the mRNA but also everything downstream of the insertion site, much the way inserting an extra letter in a sentence can change the meaning of the words (Figure 23.26). A point mutation that deletes a single nucleotide—a **deletion**—can also cause a frameshift mutation.

Any insertion or deletion of a number of nucleotides *not* divisible by three, changes the identity of all the amino acids downstream of the mutation site. The gene *CCR5* provides a fascinating example of a frameshift mutation. The normal CCR5 protein is a receptor on the surface of white blood cells. HIV has evolved to bind to this receptor, using it as a doorway to get into cells and replicate. Approximately 1% of the U.S. population carries a mutation known as delta-32. The delta-32 mutation is a deletion mutation that removes 32 base pairs from the DNA sequence of the *CCR5* gene. As 32 is not divisible by three, this deletion is a frameshift mutation and all the codons downstream of the deletion event are altered, producing a protein that is a nonfunctional receptor. Without this receptor/doorway, HIV cannot get into the white blood cells (Figure 23.27). Individuals with the delta-32 mutation cannot get HIV or AIDS.

Explore BioConnect 23.2 (contains Figures 23.28–23.35) to learn more about other more common genetic disorders in humans.

Figure 23.26 Frameshift Mutations.

The insertion or deletion of any number of bases not divisible by three changes the identity of all the codons that follow it, dramatically altering the amino acid sequence of the protein.

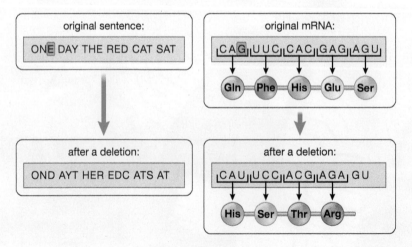

Figure 23.27 The Delta-32 CCR5 Mutation.

This frameshift mutation is a 32-base-pair deletion in one of the white blood cell's receptors for HIV. The deletion results in the production of a nonfunctional protein. When this receptor does not function, HIV cannot get inside white blood cell and replicate. Individuals with two copies of the delta-32 mutation cannot get HIV and AIDS.

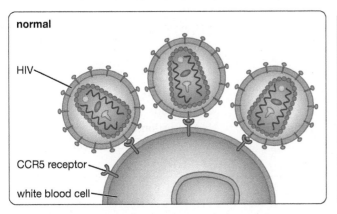
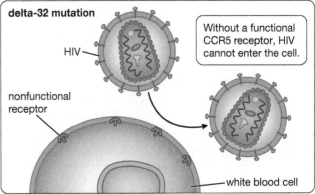

Explore how Chemistry and Biology connect: **BioConnect: 23.2** Genetic Disease in the Pearson eText.

Quiz yourself on the content of this section: **Check 23.5** in the Pearson eText.

Chapter Summary

23.1 Structure of RNA

Learning Objective: Describe how RNA structure differs from DNA structure.

DNA and RNA are both nucleic acids and have many structural similarities (Figure 23.4). DNA molecules contain a deoxyribose sugar in their sugar phosphate backbone while RNA molecules contain ribose, a slightly different sugar. RNA contains uracil, a nitrogenous base not found in DNA. Uracil is structurally similar to thymine and takes the place of thymine in RNA polymers. RNA molecules, therefore, contain the four bases adenine (A), cytosine (C), guanine (G), and uracil (U).

Key Terms

chromosomes	ribonucleic acid (RNA)	translation
genes	transcription	uracil (U)

23.2 Transcription: RNA Synthesis

Learning Objective: Explain the key steps of transcription.

Transcription occurs in three steps: initiation, elongation, and termination. The first step of transcription, initiation, is the assembly of transcription factors and RNA polymerase. Transcription factors are proteins that bind to special regions of DNA at promoters, the beginning of genes. The binding of transcription factors attracts the enzyme RNA polymerase that is key to the creation of mRNA. The RNA polymerase temporarily separates the two strands of the DNA molecule. In the next step, elongation, RNA polymerase uses one strand of the DNA as a template to build a complementary mRNA sequence that is identical to the DNA strand (except that it contains the base uracil (U) instead of thymine (T). The elongation of the mRNA molecule continues until the RNA polymerase reaches a termination sequence encoded in the DNA.

VisibleChem Video 23.1: Overview of Transcription

VisibleChem Video 23.2: A Closer Look at Transcription

BioConnect 23.1: Targeting Viral Transcription

Key Terms

antibiotics (from BioConnect 23.1)
elongation
informational strand
initiation
messenger RNA (mRNA)

phosphodiester bonds
promoter
reverse transcription (from
    BioConnect 23.1)
RNA polymerase

template strand
termination
transcription factors
viruses (from BioConnect 23.1)

23.3 Translation: The Genetic Code

Learning Objective: Use the genetic code to convert mRNA codons to a sequence of amino acids.

The genetic code translates a molecule of RNA into a specific sequence of amino acids (Table 23.1). In this system, each sequence of three nucleotides on RNA, called a triplet or a codon, codes for a specific amino acid. There are 64 different ways to combine A, C, G, and U into groups of three and therefore 64 different codons. There are fewer than 64 amino acids, so each amino acid corresponds to more than one codon. A start codon initiates protein synthesis and stop codons terminate protein synthesis.

Key Terms

codon
genetic code
mRNA vaccines

recombinant DNA
recombinant proteins
start codon

stop codon
triplet

23.4 A Closer Look at Translation: Protein Synthesis

Learning Objective: Explain the key steps of translation.

Translation occurs at the ribosomes. Ribosomes are composed of two subunits, a large subunit and a small subunit, both made of RNA and proteins. Like transcription, translation occurs in three steps: initiation, elongation, and termination. Initiation begins when the ribosome assembles at the start codon on the mRNA. The ribosome binds tRNAs, each carrying the unique amino acid coded for by an anticodon (Figure 23.20). A peptide bond forms between the collected amino acids. Translation proceeds until the ribosome encounters a stop codon in termination, the final step.

VisibleChem Video 23.3: Translation and Protein Synthesis

BioConnect 23.2: Genetic Diseases

Key Terms

anticodon
ribosomal RNA (rRNA)
ribosomes
transfer RNA (tRNA)

23.5 Mutations and Genetic Disease

Learning Objective: Describe types of point mutations and how they affect protein structure.

Point mutations are changes in a single nucleotide within a gene. In a substitution mutation, one nucleotide is substituted for another. If this substitution changes the amino acid sequence, it is a missense mutation. If the substitution does not change the amino acid sequence, the mutation is a silent substitution. Insertions or deletions of any number of nucleotides not divisible by three cause frameshift mutations. When a frameshift mutation occurs all the amino acids downstream of the mutation are changed. Mutations can be inherited or acquired.

Key Terms

deletion	missense mutation	silent substitution mutation
frameshift mutation	mutation	substitution mutation
insertion	point mutation	

 # End-of-Chapter Quiz

Have you mastered the content of this chapter? Try the **End-of-Chapter Quiz** in the Pearson eText.

1. Which is *not* a difference between RNA and DNA?
   a) In RNA the base uracil (U) replaces the thymine (T) in DNA.
   b) RNA molecules are single-stranded; DNA is double-stranded.
   c) The sugar in RNA is ribose; the sugar in DNA is deoxyribose.
   d) RNA molecules contain only purine bases whereas DNA molecules contain both purine and pyrimidine bases.

2. Select the correct structure of the nucleotide uracil triphosphate (UTP). The nitrogen-containing bases found in nucleic acids are given for reference.

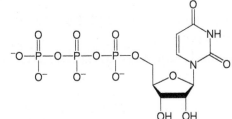

3. Consider the hexanucleotide with the sequence GATATC. Which statement about this polynucleotide is correct?
   a) This polynucleotide has a G on the 5′ end and could be found in RNA.
   b) This polynucleotide has a G on the 3′ end and could be found in DNA.
   c) This polynucleotide has a C on the 3′ end and could be found in DNA.
   d) This polynucleotide has a G on the 3′ end and could be found in RNA.

4. Consider the diagram of transcription and select the correct statement.

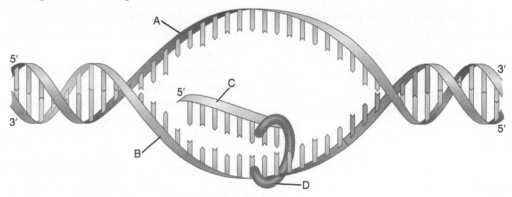

a) Transcription proceeds from left to right in the diagram.
b) The growing mRNA attaches to the informational strand through complementary base pairing.
c) The template strand is oriented 5′ to 3′ in the diagram.
d) The informational strand is oriented from 3′ to 5′ in the diagram.

---

5. The BRCA1 gene has been linked to increased risk for breast cancer. A medical researcher studying breast cancer and variations in the BRCA1 gene identifies the given DNA fragment as a possible sequence of interest. What mRNA sequence results from transcription of this short double-stranded DNA fragment?

informational strand 5′— TCGTATGACA —3′

template strand 3′— AGCATACTGT —5′

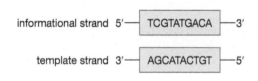

a) 5′-TCGTATGACA-3′
b) 5′-AGCAUACUGU-3′
c) 5′-UCGUAUGACA-3′
d) 3′-AGCATACTGT-5′

6. Select the correct statement about viruses.
a) Some viruses convert their proteins into RNA in a process known as reverse transcription.
b) Some viruses use the base uracil (U) in their DNA in a process known as reverse replication.
c) Some viruses convert their RNA into DNA in a process known as reverse transcription.
d) Some viruses use deoxyribonucleotides in their RNA in a process known as reverse translation.

7. Which amino acid has more than three codons? You may need to refer back to Table 23.1: The Genetic Code to answer this question.
a) cysteine (Cys)
b) threonine (Thr)
c) asparagine (Asn)
d) glutamic acid (Glu)

8. Which codon triplet shown does *not* code for the amino acid threonine (Thr)? You may need to refer back to Table 23.1: The Genetic Code to answer this question.
a) UAU b) ACA c) ACC d) ACG

9. Which nucleic acid contains the genetic information that codes for the sequence of a protein formed during translation?
a) ribosomal RNA (rRNA)
b) transfer RNA (tRNA)
c) template DNA
d) messenger RNA (mRNA)

10. Which nucleic acid carries amino acids to the site of protein chain growth in the ribosome?
a) ribosomal RNA b) recombinant RNA
c) transfer RNA d) messenger RNA

11. The molecule angiotensin II is a peptide hormone our bodies produce to regulate blood pressure. Physicians sometimes prescribe synthetic angiotensin II to treat hypotension (low blood pressure) resulting from severe bacterial infections in the blood and septic shock. Consider the given angiotensin II peptide sequence and identify the mRNA sequence that could code for this sequence. Refer to Table 23.1 The Genetic Code to answer this question.

N-terminal **Asp-Arg-Val-Tyr-Ile-His-Pro-Phe** C-terminal

a) mRNA sequence: 5′-GAC CGU GUA UAG AUC CAU CCC UUC-3′
b) mRNA sequence: 5′-GAC CGU GUA UAC AUC CAU CCC UUC-3′
c) mRNA sequence: 5′-CUU CCC UAC CUA CAU AUG UGC CAG-3′
d) mRNA sequence: 5′-GAC CGU GUA UAC AUC CAU CGC UUC-3′

12. A medical researcher is studying genes potentially involved in Alzheimer's disease. She is interested in proteins coded for by a gene that has the given DNA sequence. Which peptide sequence does this short piece of DNA code for?

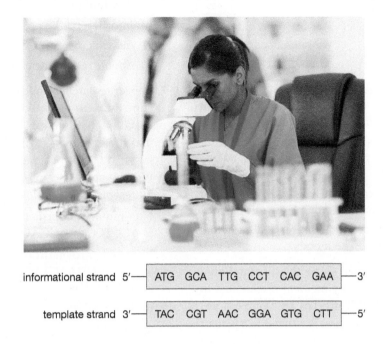

informational strand 5'— | ATG GCA TTG CCT CAC GAA | —3'

template strand 3'— | TAC CGT AAC GGA GTG CTT | —5'

   a) N-terminal   Tyr-Arg-Asn-Gly-Val-Leu   C-terminal
   b) N-terminal   Met-Ala-Leu-Pro-His-Glu   C-terminal
   c) N-terminal   Glu-His-Pro-Leu-Ala-Met   C-terminal
   d) N-terminal   Met-Gly-Leu-Pro-Pro-Glu   C-terminal

13. Insulin is a hormone that regulates the transport of blood glucose into cells, providing cells with the energy to function properly. A lack of sufficient and effective insulin plays a role in the development of diabetes. The insulin molecule is a relatively small protein made up of two peptide chains linked together by disulfide bonds. The first six amino acids of one of the peptide chains are given here. Select the double-stranded DNA segment that could be transcribed and translated into this peptide sequence?

N-terminal   Gly-Ile-Val-Glu-Gln-Cys   C-terminal

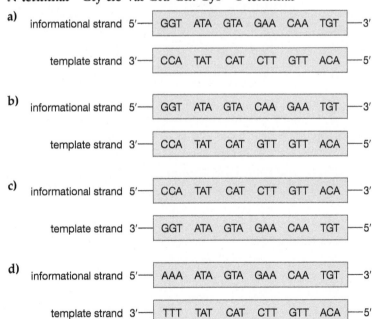

a)
informational strand 5'— | GGT ATA GTA GAA CAA TGT | —3'

template strand 3'— | CCA TAT CAT CTT GTT ACA | —5'

b)
informational strand 5'— | GGT ATA GTA CAA GAA TGT | —3'

template strand 3'— | CCA TAT CAT GTT GTT ACA | —5'

c)
informational strand 5'— | CCA TAT CAT CTT GTT ACA | —3'

template strand 3'— | GGT ATA GTA GAA CAA TGT | —5'

d)
informational strand 5'— | AAA ATA GTA GAA CAA TGT | —3'

template strand 3'— | TTT TAT CAT CTT GTT ACA | —5'

14. Genetic mutations in the *BRCA1* gene have been associated with which condition?
    a) ribosomal disorders
    b) brain cancer
    c) tRNA disorders
    d) breast cancer

15. Select the *incorrect* statement about genetic mutations.
    a) Genetic mutations can be hereditary and passed down from one or more of your parents.
    b) Genetic mutations can result from exposure to certain chemicals, radiation, or infectious agents such as HPV.
    c) Genetic mutations cannot be hereditary and cannot be passed down from one or more of your parents.
    d) Genetic mutations are sometimes repaired by the natural mechanisms in your body.

16. Part of the DNA sequence along the informational strand of a gene is found by medical researchers to have the sequence 5'-ATGACGTACCCTGCTATC-3'. A mutation in this sequence was identified in a patient carrying a metabolic disease, whose mutated sequence was 5'-ATGACCGTACCCTGCTATC-3'. Which type of DNA point mutation does this represent?
    a) substitution
    b) insertion
    c) deletion
    d) double replacement

17. Cancer researchers studying gene mutations that may contribute to elevated risk of disease identified a mutation that interests them. The informational (coding) strand sequences of both the non-mutated and the mutated DNA in the region of interest are given. Identify the specific type of DNA point mutation this represents.

    Non-mutated informational (coding) DNA sequence: 5'-AGCTCCGAACGAGTCCTT-3'

    Mutated informational (coding) DNA sequence: 5'-AGCTCCGAACTAGTCCTT-3'
    a) substitution
    b) termination
    c) deletion
    d) insertion

Unit 9
Bringing It All Together

Can Genetic Technology Cure Sickle Cell Disease?

CHEMISTRY APPLICATION We opened Unit 9 with a look at the promise of CRISPR-Cas9 to offer novel cures to historically understudied diseases such as sickle cell disease. Recall that individuals with sickle cell disease have inherited a mutation in their DNA. When this DNA is transcribed and translated, their cells produce a version of the hemoglobin protein that polymerizes, dramatically altering the structure and function of their red blood cells (Figure U9.4).

The advent of CRISPR-Cas9 has unleashed a new opportunity to reexamine therapeutic approaches to genetic disease. Scientists can now leverage our understanding of the structure and function of the human genome to develop carefully targeted therapies that offer the promise of a true cure for several devastating diseases.

Sickle cell disease is an attractive target for gene therapy, including CRISPR-Cas9 based approaches, for several reasons. Our red blood cells are produced by stem cells in our bone marrow (Figure U9.5). This can simplify gene therapy as bone marrow cells can be removed from a patient, genetically modified, and returned to the same patient. The genetically modified stem cells will persist in the bone marrow, continuing to produce and release new, genetically-modified red blood cells.

In addition, we all have multiple versions of the hemoglobin gene. Recall that the hemoglobin protein has quaternary structure—it consists of four folded polypeptides or subunits. Adult hemoglobin (HbA) is composed of two α subunits and two β subunits. In the womb, however, we produce a slightly different version of hemoglobin called fetal hemoglobin (HbF). This fetal version is composed of two α subunits and two γ subunits (Figure U9.6).

Figure U9.4 Transcription and Translation of the Hemoglobin Gene.

Individuals with sickle cell disease have most often inherited a single nucleotide substitution that dramatically alters the structure of their hemoglobin proteins. Individuals with sickle cell disease require frequent blood transfusions and are at risk for serious complications such as organ failure and stroke.

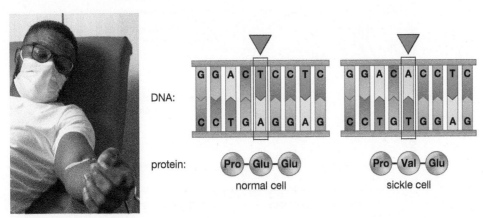

Figure U9.5 Red Blood Cells are Produced in the Bone Marrow.

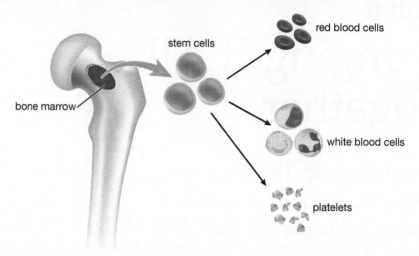

Figure U9.6 Fetal and Adult Hemoglobin.

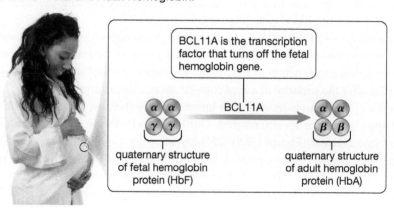

The switch from the fetal version to the adult version of hemoglobin occurs around the time of birth as a transcription factor, BCL11A, turns off the fetal hemoglobin gene. Over the course of a few months, fetal hemoglobin levels in the blood drop as they are replaced by the adult version (Figure U9.7). Importantly, the mutation that causes most forms of sickle cell disease occurs in the gene for the β subunit of the

Figure U9.7 Production of Fetal and Adult Hemoglobin.

Fetal hemoglobin levels begin to drop shortly before birth as the fetal version is replaced by adult hemoglobin.

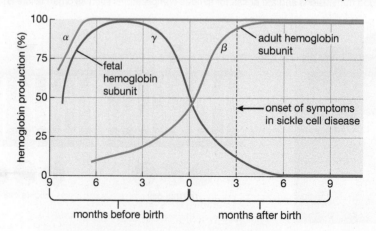

adult hemoglobin protein. Individuals with sickle cell disease still have the gene for the functional γ subunit in their DNA; the functional γ subunit has just been turned off by the transcription factor BCL11A.

The presence of the functional but silenced gene for fetal hemoglobin provides an exciting opportunity for gene therapy. If the functional fetal gene can be reactivated using CRISPR, then sickle cell patients might be able to produce their own, fully functional red blood cells, freeing patients from a lifetime of blood transfusions and the dangerous, painful consequences of sickle cell disease. This CRISPR-based approach also provides an important step towards a more equitable investment of our research efforts to treat genetic diseases.

Questions to Think About

1. Examine the amino acid change described in Figure U9.4. How similar are these two amino acids? Would you expect this change to dramatically affect the structure of the protein? Why or why not?

2. What is a transcription factor? What role do they play in transcription?

3. At birth, approximately what fraction of hemoglobin is HbF? What fraction is HbA? What does this tell you about the transcription and translation of these two genes?

A Closer Look at the Data

In 2021 an international group of physicians and medical researchers published a paper describing the use of CRISPR-Cas9 to potentially cure sickle cell disease and another closely related blood disorder (Frangoul *et al.*, 2021). The researchers created genetically modified stem cells in which the transcription factor that normally turns off the fetal hemoglobin gene was itself turned off. They hoped this genetic modification would allow their patients to again produce the functional fetal hemoglobin protein. Figure U9.8 is from their paper.

Figure U9.8 Hemoglobin Fractionation in a Patient Receiving CRISPR-Cas9 Gene Therapy (Frangoul *et al.*, 2021).

This patient, a 19-year-old female, was receiving 34 blood transfusions a year prior to treatment. She received a single blood transfusion 30 days after treatment and did not require any additional transfusions during the 21.5-month follow-up period.

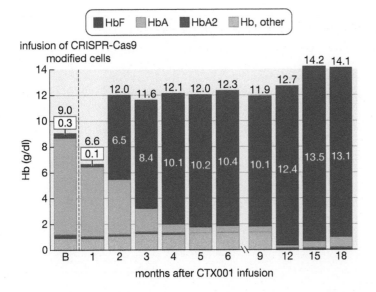

Questions to Think About

Examine Figure U9.8 and use it to answer the following questions:

1. Graphs can help reveal relationships between variables. The X axis follows this patient through time. What does the Y axis illustrate? What do the different colors in the bars represent?

2. Normal hemoglobin levels are 12.0 to 15.5 grams per deciliter (g/dl) in women. How did this patient's level compare prior to treatment? How did this patient's hemoglobin level compare to the normal range in the months after treatment? Based on what you know about the function of hemoglobin, what symptoms might she have experienced because of her initial total hemoglobin levels?

3. There is a striking difference in this patient's hemoglobin fractionation between months 1 and 2. What has changed? What must be happening at the molecular level to drive this change?

4. This graph illustrates the findings from a single patient over the course of a year and a half. What types of follow-up studies do you think should be done next?

Reference

Frangoul Haydar; Altshuler, David; Domenica, Cappellini M; Yi-Shan, Chen; Domm, Jennifer; et al. (2021) CRISPR-Cas9 Gene Editing for Sickle Cell Disease and β-Thalassemia. *The New England Journal of Medicine; Boston* Vol. 384, Iss. 3: 252-260. DOI:10.1056/NEJMoa2031054.

Unit 10
Introduction
Exploring Metabolism

Chapter 24: Metabolism: Generating Energy from Carbohydrates
Chapter 25: Metabolism of Lipids and Amino Acids

*The U.S. is facing a largely unseen public health crisis. The CDC estimates that over a third of adults in the U.S. now have **metabolic syndrome** (Moore et al, 2017). Metabolic syndrome is a group of risk factors that occur together and increase an individual's risk of heart disease, stroke, and type 2 diabetes (Figure U10.1). The more of these risk factors you have, the greater your risk of having a heart attack, stroke, or developing type 2 diabetes.*

Metabolic syndrome is becoming more common due to rising obesity rates around the world and is a leading cause of heart disease. Understanding both the complexity of combatting obesity as well as the details of our metabolism can help us better understand this increasingly common medical condition.

Figure U10.1 Metabolic Disease.

The five conditions that contribute to metabolic syndrome are excess body fat around the waist (visceral obesity), high blood pressure (hypertension), insulin resistance, high triglycerides, and low HDL-cholesterol.

VISCERAL OBESITY   HYPERTENSION   INSULIN RESISTANCE   HIGH TRIGLYCERIDES   LOW HDL-CHOLESTEROL

Unit 10: Introduction

What Is Metabolic Syndrome and How Does It Affect Our Health?

Watch Video U10.1 to learn more about the global challenge and causes of obesity, one of the leading risk factors associated with metabolic syndrome.

 To learn more of the global challenge and causes of obesity, one of the leading risk factors associated with metabolic syndrome, watch **Video U10.1** in the Pearson eText.

Unit 10 opens with a sobering look at the growing incidence of obesity around the world. This increase is alarming because a person's **body mass index (BMI)** is closely associated with their risk of metabolic syndrome (Figure U10.2).

Obesity is a complex public health challenge. Our **metabolism**—the collection of all the chemical reactions that support life—certainly plays a key role. But a myriad of other interacting factors including our built environment, dietary habits, level of physical activity, socioeconomic status, and genetics all influence the likelihood that we'll be overweight or obese (Figure U10.3). The built environment, for example, includes variables such as whether an individual has easy access to safe places to

Figure U10.2 Body Mass Index (BMI).

An individual's body mass index is calculated by dividing their weight by the square of their height. BMI values above 25 are generally considered overweight.

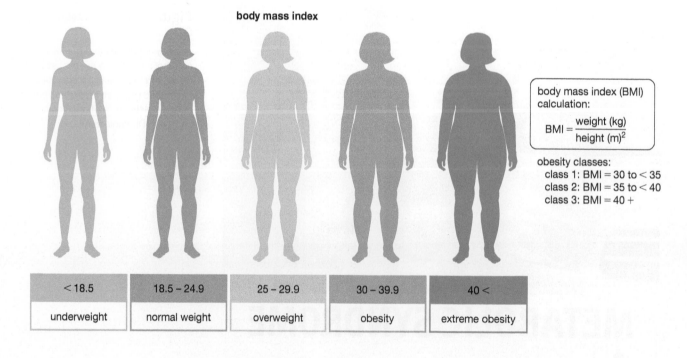

body mass index

body mass index (BMI) calculation:

$$BMI = \frac{weight\ (kg)}{height\ (m)^2}$$

obesity classes:
class 1: BMI = 30 to < 35
class 2: BMI = 35 to < 40
class 3: BMI = 40 +

< 18.5	18.5 – 24.9	25 – 29.9	30 – 39.9	40 <
underweight	normal weight	overweight	obesity	extreme obesity

Figure U10.3 An Array of Factors Contribute to Obesity and the Accompanying Risk of Metabolic Syndrome.

Multiple, interacting factors contribute to an individual's risk of developing metabolic syndrome including their built environment, their dietary habits and physical activity, their socioeconomic status, and several environmental and genetic influences.

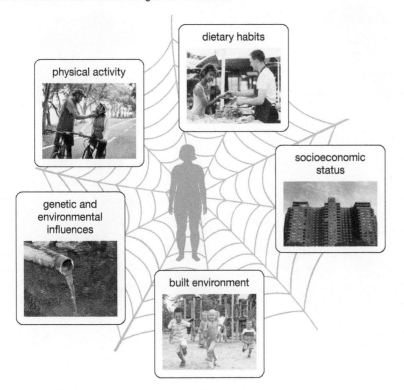

exercise and reasonably priced healthy food choices. This, in turn, influences their dietary habits and level of physical activity. Factors like socioeconomic status also play an important role as it often dictates a person's built environment and access to medical care.

Unit 10 Chemistry Application: What Is Metabolic Syndrome and How Does It Affect Our Health?

Our ability to take a comprehensive approach to preventing and treating metabolic syndrome will require an interdisciplinary approach that includes a solid understanding of the biochemistry that drives our metabolism. We must both deeply understand the nature of biochemical pathways as well as how our body uses the food we consume. With this understanding, we can continue to address some of the many variables that make individuals susceptible to obesity and metabolic disease, potentially improving the quality of life for millions of patients (Figure U10.4).

Figure U10.4 Preventing and Treating Metabolic Disease.

Effectively preventing and treating metabolic disease requires a holistic approach that considers the many factors that contribute to obesity.

 ## Questions to Think About

What chemistry do we need to know to better understand the challenge of combatting metabolic syndrome? Here are some questions to consider as you move through Unit 10:

- How does our body make energy from the food we eat? How do we use the carbohydrates, protein, and fats in our diets?
- How does our body digest the food we consume and how is this useful to us?
- What are the biochemical reactions that occur in our body that will help us understand the obesity epidemic?
- What happens in our body if we eat too much? What happens if we eat too little?
- How do we store energy if we do not need it at the moment we consume food?
- How does the body regulate metabolism? How is energy stored in the body?

What chemistry would you like to know in order to more fully understand this public health threat?

Now that we have an overview of this unit, let's step into Chapter 24 and 25 and learn more about how our bodies process the food we eat to generate energy.

References

Moore JX, Chaudhary N, Akinyemiju T. Metabolic Syndrome Prevalence by Race/Ethnicity and Sex in the United States, National Health and Nutrition Examination Survey, 1988–2012. Prev Chronic Dis 2017;14:160287. DOI: http://dx.doi.org/10.5888/pcd14.160287external icon.

Chapter 24
Metabolism: Generating Energy from Carbohydrates

sugar

transport protein

cell membrane

Transport proteins move sugars from the blood into cells where the sugars are broken down to produce the energy that supports life.

⌄ Chapter Outline

Learning Objectives

24.1 Distinguish between anabolic and catabolic pathways and describe where metabolic pathways occur in the body.

24.2 Describe the basic structure and function of ATP, NAD^+, FAD, and coenzyme A.

24.3 Describe the inputs, outputs, and role of glycolysis.

24.4 Describe the inputs, outputs, and role of the citric acid cycle.

24.5 Explain the process of oxidative phosphorylation and the role of the electron transport chain.

24.6 Describe the processes that produce glucose from lactate, triglycerides, and amino acids.

Introduction

In this chapter we explain and explore some of the complex chains of chemical reactions that are involved in human metabolism. **Metabolism** is the combined set of chemical reactions in an organism. Metabolic reactions help humans digest food to capture the energy and building blocks within food and construct the many complex molecules that support life such as DNA, glycogen, and proteins. In this chapter, we focus on the metabolic reactions that help us break down carbohydrates to harvest energy and building blocks in our food. Chapter 25 explores the reactions that help us break down other large molecules in our diet, including proteins and fats. The information in these two chapters explain an array of everyday activities from what happens to the food we eat as it's broken down in our bodies to how diet can affect our risk of the potentially life-threatening diseases associated with metabolic syndrome (Figure 24.1).

Figure 24.1 Understanding Metabolism.

A) Our bodies digest a diverse collection of molecules after every meal. **B)** Most of the chemical reactions that generate energy from food happen in the mitochondria within cells. A single mitochondrion is shown here as viewed through an electron microscope. **C)** People with metabolic syndrome have an increased risk of several life-threatening diseases including type 2 diabetes and cardiovascular disease.

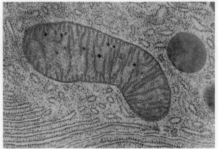

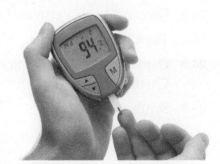

A B C

24.1 Overview of Metabolism

Food is the fuel that produces the energy bodies need to function. When you eat lunch, for example, your body breaks down the carbohydrate, fat, and protein molecules in your meal in a series of chemical reactions that produce smaller molecules, releasing energy along the way (Figure 24.2).

The term metabolism refers to all of the reactions in the body that are involved with energy production and cell growth. Two additional terms differentiate between the breakdown of large molecules and the production of large molecules in the body. The breakdown of large biomolecules into smaller molecules is **catabolism**–a series of biochemical reactions that ultimately produces energy (Figure 24.3). Large biomolecules are synthesized from smaller molecules in a process called **anabolism**.

Figure 24.2 Eating Lunch.

We break down the carbohydrates, fats, and proteins in each meal to produce both energy and building blocks to support our cells.

Figure 24.3 Catabolism and Anabolism.

Catabolism reactions break larger molecules, often from food, into smaller molecules, releasing energy. The energy that is produced by the catabolism of a certain food is listed on that food's nutrition labels in units of Calories. Anabolism reactions build complex molecules from smaller molecules.

Anabolism generally consumes energy. In this chapter, we focus primarily on catabolism. Specifically, we closely investigate the reactions and processes that produce energy from carbohydrates in food.

Representing Metabolic Pathways

Imagine the diverse array of molecules you could consume for lunch. Given the diversity, it makes sense that a complex series of reactions is needed to fully break down the molecules found in your food. A series of chemical reactions that breaks down biomolecules in the body is a **metabolic pathway.** The intermediates–the products produced throughout these metabolic pathways–are **metabolites**. Enzymes catalyze most of the reactions in a metabolic pathway. The product of each enzyme-mediated reaction is the starting material of the next reaction in the pathway. Enzymes both speed up the rates of reactions and regulate individual pathways.

Metabolic pathways can be extraordinarily complex. Rather than memorizing most of these pathways, focus on being able to interpret and understand critical portions of complex pathways. We represent metabolic pathways using a unique set of symbols: arrows, boxes and circles, chemical structures, and representations of energy. A metabolic pathway is either linear or cyclic. We introduce both linear and cyclic pathways throughout this unit. A linear pathway is a series of reactions that generates a final product. In contrast, a cyclic pathway is a series of reactions that regenerates the first reactant (Figure 24.4).

Figure 24.4 Linear and Cyclic Metabolic Pathways.

Linear pathways convert reactants into products in a series of enzyme-mediated steps. Cyclic pathways, in contrast, regenerate the initial reactant, allowing the reactions to proceed again.

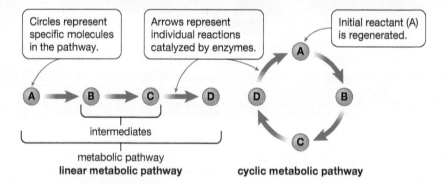

Overview of Catabolism

The foods we eat progress through a series of linked biochemical reactions that ultimately produce energy (Figure 24.5). Catabolism begins with digestion (Stage 1) and progresses to two stages that occur in cells (Stages 2 and 3). Each of these stages consists of a series of chemical reactions. We explore each of these stages and reactions in this chapter.

The specific focus of this chapter is carbohydrate catabolism. In the next chapter (Chapter 25), we explore how proteins and fats are catabolized in more detail. In each section of this chapter, we look more closely at the key steps in Figure 24.5. In this section, we provide an overview of the pathways that make up the whole process of carbohydrate catabolism.

Explore BioConnect 24.1 (contains Figures 24.6–24.9) to learn more about where the first essential stage of catabolism takes place in the body.

Figure 24.5 Stages of Catabolism.

We divide catabolism of the food we eat into three essential stages. In stage 1, our bodies digest food, such as carbohydrates, in the digestive tract (see BioConnect 24.1) to form small molecules (such as sugars) that enter cells (stages 2 and 3) and produce energy.

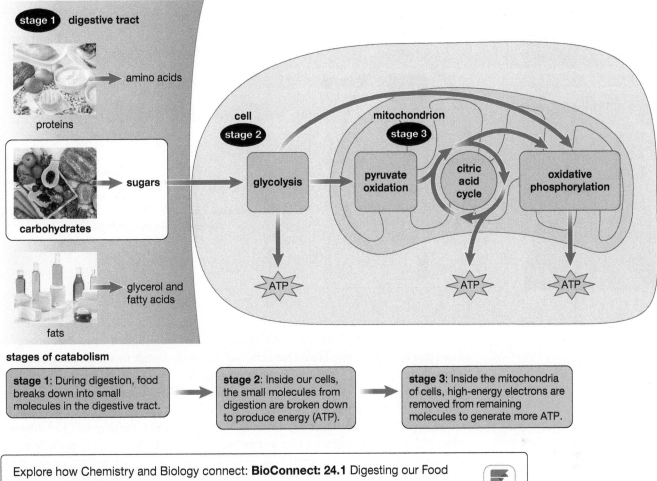

stages of catabolism

stage 1: During digestion, food breaks down into small molecules in the digestive tract. → **stage 2**: Inside our cells, the small molecules from digestion are broken down to produce energy (ATP). → **stage 3**: Inside the mitochondria of cells, high-energy electrons are removed from remaining molecules to generate more ATP.

Explore how Chemistry and Biology connect: **BioConnect: 24.1** Digesting our Food in the Pearson eText.

Quiz yourself on the content of this section: **Check 24.1** in the Pearson eText.

24.2 Important Components of Metabolic Pathways

Several compounds repeatedly function as key intermediates in metabolic pathways. Their job is to capture and store energy so that the cell, and therefore the body, has a constant supply of energy. These compounds are worth getting to know before moving on to learn more about the pathways. These compounds have diverse structures, but we classify them into three groups based on function. The three groups are compounds that:

1. store energy and transfer phosphate groups
2. transfer electrons
3. transfer carbon atoms in the form of acetyl groups

ATP and ADP

The catabolic reactions that break down food release energy. Our cells must capture this energy and make it available to do work later. This process is similar to how the

Figure 24.10 Adenosine Triphosphate (ATP).

Cells capture and store energy in the form of ATP. ATP is the "charged" high-energy form of the molecule. When a phosphate group is removed from ATP, the low-energy form of the molecule, adenosine diphosphate (ADP) results. Our cells constantly cycle a pool of molecules between the "charged" ATP state and the "discharged" ADP state. We refer to this cycling back and forth as the interconversion between ATP and ADP.

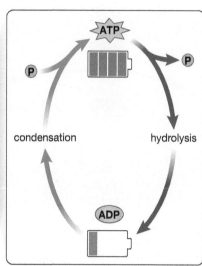

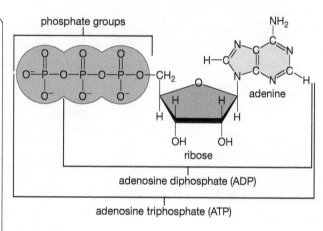

battery in your cell phone captures energy when it is plugged in so that energy is available to your phone later. Our cells use the high-energy molecule **adenosine triphosphate (ATP)** for short term energy storage (Figure 24.10). ATP consists of three phosphate groups, a ribose sugar, and an adenine. ATP loses a phosphate group to form **adenosine diphosphate (ADP)** in a hydrolysis reaction that releases energy.

The phosphate group that is removed from ATP is often transferred to an intermediate in a metabolic pathway. One example of this is the transfer of a phosphate group from ATP to glucose–an intermediate in the first step of the metabolism of glucose (a pathway we explore in Section 24.3). The addition of a phosphate group to a molecule is called phosphorylation.

The body uses the energy released when a phosphate is removed from ATP to form ADP to generate heat, contract muscles, and drive a wide array of chemical reactions in cells. A single one of the 37 trillion cells that make up the human body can use a staggering 10 million molecules of ATP per second. Thankfully ATP is readily recycled when needed. As you will learn later in this chapter, energy from the food we consume is used to add a phosphate to ADP, regenerating ATP.

In metabolic pathways, the interconversion between ATP and ADP is the key to the storage and release of energy. The hydrolysis of one ATP molecule to ADP releases 7.3 kcal/mol (31kJ/mol) of energy. The reverse reaction, phosphorylation of one ADP molecule to regenerate ATP, requires 7.3 kcal/mol (31kJ/mol) of energy. The addition and removal of the phosphate group in the interconversion between ATP and ADP is one of the most significant chemical reactions that our body carries out continuously to keep us alive and functioning.

Apply what you have just learned: **Practice 24.1** in the Pearson eText.

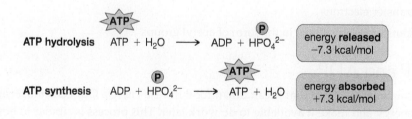

Figure 24.11 Coupled Reactions.

The hydrolysis of ATP releases energy that fuels other reactions. In this example, the energy released when ATP converts to ADP is used to convert glucose into glucose-6-phosphate in a phosphorylation reaction.

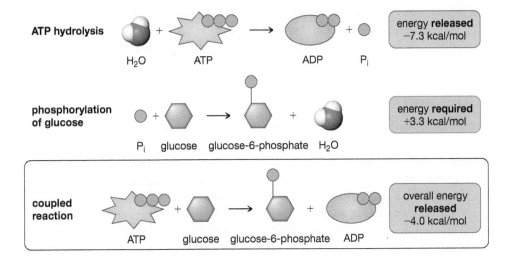

Coupled Reactions

Many reactions that occur in the cell require energy in order to go forward. The hydrolysis of ATP to ADP releases energy that drives energetically unfavorable processes by coupling reactions together. **Coupled reactions** are pairs of reactions that occur together. The energy released by one of the coupled reactions provides the energy to drive the other reaction.

For example, consider the first steps in metabolism of glucose, which we discuss in detail in Section 24.3. This process involves coupling the phosphorylation reaction that changes glucose to glucose-6-phosphate with the hydrolysis reaction of ATP to ADP. The energy released from the hydrolysis reaction provides the energy to drive the phosphorylation reaction (Figure 24.11). When individual reactions are coupled, identical substances on opposite sides of the reactions cancel out in the overall reaction. We add the reaction energies associated with the individual steps to determine the overall energy of the coupled reaction. Recall from Chapter 9 that a positive value indicates that the reaction absorbs energy and therefore the reaction is not energetically favorable. A negative energy indicates that the reaction generates energy, and the reaction is energetically favorable.

We represent coupled reactions using a curved arrow above or below the reaction arrow. In this case, ATP converts to ADP, as shown above the arrow, as glucose is converted to glucose-6-phosphate. You will encounter this representation of coupled reactions throughout this chapter and in Chapter 25.

Apply what you have just learned: **Practice 24.2** in the Pearson eText.

Coenzymes

Metabolic reactions often involve coenzymes. Recall that coenzymes are organic compounds that must be present for enzyme-catalyzed reactions to occur. There are many different coenzymes. Several coenzymes in metabolism act as oxidizing and reducing agents that transfer electrons in oxidation-reduction (redox) reactions. Another coenzyme plays a large role in metabolism by transferring an acetyl group (CH_3CO^-) to other substrates. In this section, we explore the structure and function of some important coenzymes to gain a better understanding of how metabolic pathways work.

NAD^+ and NADH

Four of the coenzymes we discuss in this section serve as oxidizing and reducing agents in many metabolic pathways. Recall that oxidation results in the loss of electrons (e^-), the loss of hydrogen (H^+), or the gain of oxygen. Reduction, on the other hand, involves the gain of electrons (e^-), the gain of hydrogen (H^+), or the loss of oxygen. (See Section 8.3 for review of redox reactions.)

NAD^+ (nicotinamide adenine dinucleotide) is a coenzyme with a **nicotinamide group** bonded to ribose and to ADP (Figure 24.12A). A nicotinamide group contains a pyridine ring with a primary amide. NAD^+ is an oxidizing agent that reacts with an H^+ ion and two electrons and becomes the high-energy, reduced form of itself, abbreviated **NADH**. A new carbon-hydrogen bond forms and the NAD^+ compound is reduced to become NADH. One example of how NAD^+ and NADH function in the human body occurs in our muscles. Our muscles couple the reaction of NADH to NAD^+ to the reduction of **pyruvate** to lactate during periods of intense exertion (see Figure 24.12B). Pyruvate is an intermediate in several metabolic pathways and contains both a carboxylic acid group and a ketone group (see Figure 24.12B).

This coupled pair of reactions is like the conversion between ATP and ADP. Our cells constantly cycle a pool of molecules between oxidized NAD^+ and reduced NADH forms to facilitate numerous essential metabolic pathways. Individuals without enough NAD^+ develop pellagra, a potentially fatal disease (Figure 24.13). Millions of Americans suffered from pellagra during the early 20th century until it was discovered that the disease is caused by a lack of niacin (vitamin B$_3$) in the diet. The body uses niacin to produce NAD^+. The U.S. began enriching flour with niacin in the 1940s, ending the epidemic of pellagra. This largely eliminated the disease in many countries. Unprocessed dietary sources of niacin include meats, peanuts, avocados, and whole grains.

Figure 24.12 NAD^+ and NADH.

A) NAD^+ is an oxidizing agent. It can pick up an H^+ and two electrons to form NADH. This reaction is reversible; NADH can serve as a reducing agent, releasing electrons to form NAD^+. **B)** Our muscles, for example, convert pyruvate into lactate during periods of intense energy demand in a reaction coupled to the conversion of NADH to NAD^+.

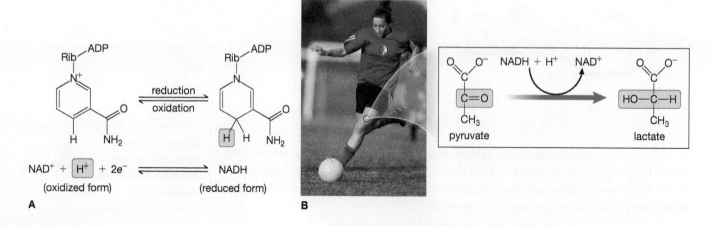

Figure 24.13 Pellagra and Niacin.

A) Insufficient niacin in the diet prevents the production of adequate NAD^+ and causes the disease pellagra, characterized, in part, by skin lesions. **B)** Manufacturers enrich flour with niacin, which has largely eliminated pellagra in most industrialized countries.

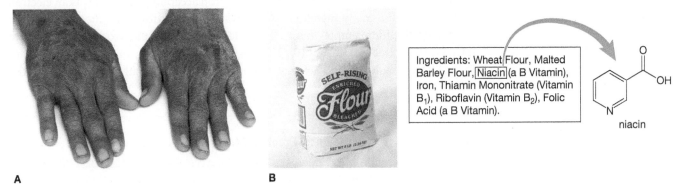

Ingredients: Wheat Flour, Malted Barley Flour, Niacin (a B Vitamin), Iron, Thiamin Mononitrate (Vitamin B_1), Riboflavin (Vitamin B_2), Folic Acid (a B Vitamin).

niacin

A   B

FAD and $FADH_2$

FAD (flavin adenine dinucleotide) is another important coenzyme that helps shuttle electrons between molecules in metabolic pathways. Like NAD^+, FAD is also derived from a vitamin–vitamin B_2 called **riboflavin**. Riboflavin is a molecule that has a complex structure with multiple rings and both nitrogen and oxygen functional groups. Many of the same foods that are good sources of vitamin B_3 (niacin) also contain high levels of vitamin B_2 (riboflavin).

FAD has a complex structure made up of adenine, ribose, two phosphate groups and riboflavin (Figure 24.14A). Only part of the FAD molecule is shown in Figure 24.14 so that you can focus on the part of this large molecule that undergoes a reaction. The R group bonded to the nitrogen atom represents the part of the molecule not shown,

Figure 24.14 Flavin Adenine Dinucleotide (FAD).

A) FAD is a riboflavin molecule bound to adenine, ribose and two phosphate groups. The R group represents the part of this large molecule for clarity. FAD reacts with two H^+ and two electrons to produce the reduced form, $FADH_2$. Like NAD^+, FAD molecules cycle repeatedly between their oxidized and reduced forms. **B)** Much of the breakdown of glucose occurs inside the mitochondria, including the oxidation of succinate to fumarate. The electrons captured in $FADH_2$ power the production of ATP.

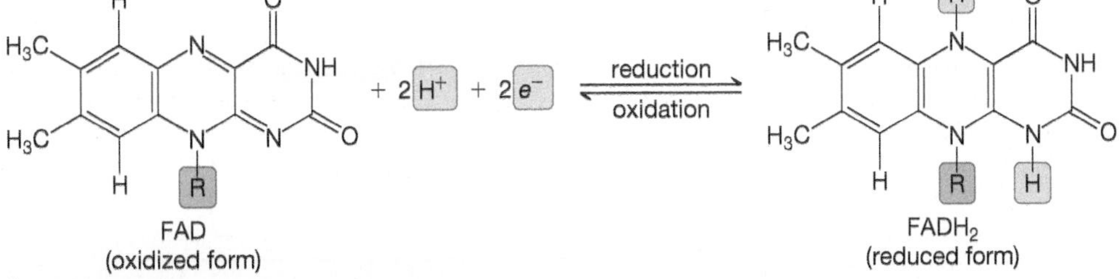

FAD
(oxidized form)

$$+\ 2\,H^+ + 2\,e^-$$

$$\xrightleftharpoons[\text{oxidation}]{\text{reduction}}$$

$FADH_2$
(reduced form)

A

succinate

FAD $FADH_2$

fumarate

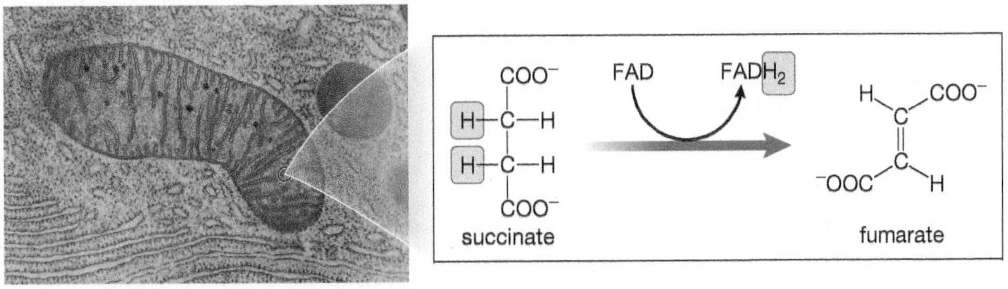

B

including part of riboflavin, adenine, ribose, and two phosphate groups. FAD is reduced when two nitrogen atoms react with two hydrogen atoms and two electrons to produce the high-energy reduced form, **FADH$_2$**.

Coupled reactions in which FAD is an electron acceptor and FADH$_2$ is an electron donor are vital to many metabolic pathways. The breakdown of glucose and other carbohydrates, for example, involves an intermediate step that oxidizes succinate to form fumarate **(see Figure 24.14B)**. The electrons from the succinate molecule transfer to the FADH$_2$ molecule and are used in another subsequent pathway to generate ATP for the cell.

 Apply what you have just learned: **Practice 24.3 and 24.4** in the Pearson eText.

Coenzyme A

Coenzyme A (CoA) is a large complex molecule made in the body from another B vitamin, B$_5$ (pantothenic acid). Coenzyme A is different from the other coenzymes we have discussed because it is not involved in redox reactions. It does not move electrons between molecules in metabolic pathways. Instead, coenzyme A transfers carbon atoms in the form of acyl groups (RCO-).

Coenzyme A is made up of aminoethanethiol, pantothenic acid, and phosphorylated ADP (Figure 24.15). The reactive region of the CoA molecule is the thiol group (-SH). We highlight the thiol group by abbreviating its structure and represent the coenzyme A molecule as HS-CoA in equations.

Figure 24.15 Coenzyme A.

Coenzyme A transfers carbon atoms between reactions. When the coenzyme A compound is bound to carbon atoms in the form of an acetyl group, it forms acetyl-CoA.

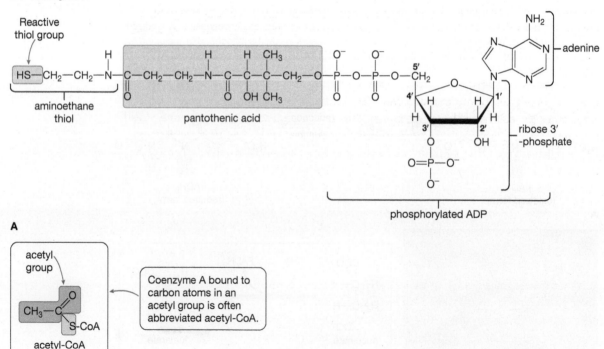

Figure 24.16 Coenzyme A is Formed in Many Metabolic Pathways.

When we consume alcohol (ethanol), for example, enzymes in our liver convert it to acetaldehyde and then acetate in a series of enzyme-mediated, coupled reactions. The body transports acetate to the mitochondria where it converts acetate to acetyl CoA and uses it to generate ATP.

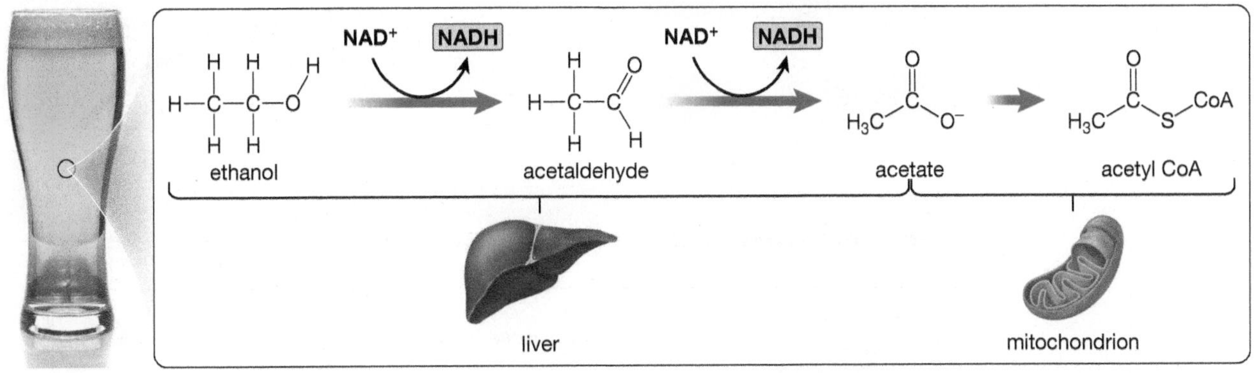

When an acetyl group (CH_3CO) bonds to CoA the product is **acetyl coenzyme A (acetyl-CoA;** see Figure 24.15). Many different types of molecules are converted to acetyl-CoA before being metabolized in our mitochondria. In this chapter, we follow glucose through this process, but fats and other molecules, such as ethanol, are also converted to acetyl-CoA (Figure 24.16).

Quiz yourself on the content of this section: **Check 24.2** in the Pearson eText.

24.3 Glycolysis and Pyruvate Oxidation

In Sections 24.1 and 24.2, we explored metabolic pathways and the structure and function of some of the most significant compounds in metabolism. In this section, we will zoom in and examine the breakdown of glucose into smaller molecules.

The breakdown of glucose to produce ATP using oxygen is **cellular respiration** (Figure 24.17). Cellular respiration is related to breathing. The oxygen we inhale when we breathe is used in a series of reactions that break down the food we consume in cellular respiration. This same series of reactions produces the carbon dioxide we exhale.

During digestion, larger carbohydrate molecules from food or stored reserves in the body break down into monosaccharides, such as glucose. Then the monosaccharides enter the cell from the bloodstream. This is accomplished when a protein that transfers glucose in the cell membrane launches the first step of cellular respiration. Once in the cell, glucose is catabolized in the biochemical pathway called **glycolysis.** Glycolysis is a ten-reaction linear metabolic pathway that converts glucose to two three-carbon molecules of pyruvate (Figure 24.18). The glycolysis pathway includes **energy-consuming reactions,** during which ATP drives reactions, and **energy-generating reactions,** during which both NADH and ATP are produced.

Reactions of Glycolysis

The first five reactions **(Reactions 1-5 in Figure 24.19)** of glycolysis require an energy investment of two molecules of ATP. During these reactions, phosphate groups from ATP molecules are added to the glucose molecule. These reactions in the first part of the pathway are the reactions that require energy. We refer to them as the energy-consuming reactions. The glucose molecule is split into two smaller sugar phosphate molecules in Reactions 1-5. Figure 24.19 details these five chemical reactions.

Figure 24.17 Cellular Respiration.

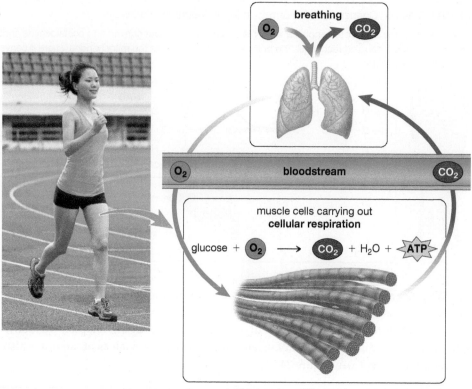

Figure 24.18 An Overview of Glycolysis.

Glycolysis breaks down the 6-carbon sugar glucose to form two 3-carbon pyruvate molecules. This ten-reaction process involves energy-consuming reactions, in which two ATP molecules are consumed per molecule of glucose. The energy-generating reactions, in contrast, generate four molecules of ATP per molecule of glucose. The net yield of glycolysis is therefore two molecules of ATP per molecule of glucose.

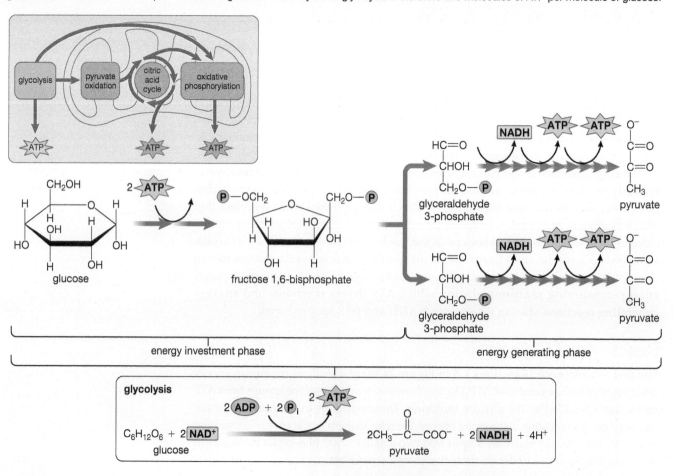

Figure 24.19 A Detailed View of the Ten-Reaction Glycolysis Pathway.

The first five reactions require an investment of energy and split the glucose molecule into two molecules of glyceraldehyde 3-phosphate (G3P). Both of the two G3P molecules then enter the energy-generating phase (Reactions 6–10). VisibleChem Videos 24.1 and 24.2 explain each of these reactions in more detail.

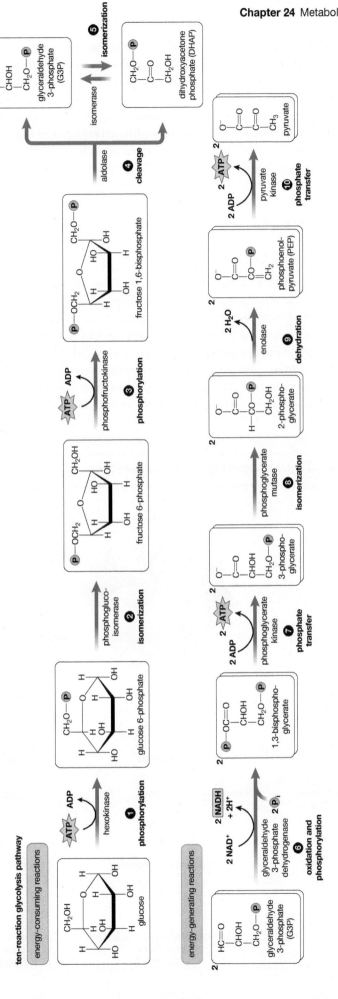

The energy-generating reactions of glycolysis (Reactions 6 to 10 in Fig. 24.19) produces two electron-rich NADH molecules when two more phosphate groups are added. Four ATP molecules are produced when four phosphate groups from glycolysis metabolites transfer to ADP (see reactions 7 and 10 in Figure 24.19).

The net energy output for one molecule of glucose in the ten reactions of glycolysis is two NAHD and two ATP. Note that additional energy and electrons are captured from the remaining pyruvate molecules produced in Reactions 9 and 10. We explore this process of pyruvate oxidation later in the chapter.

Click on VisibleChem Video 24.1 to explore the energy-consuming reactions of glycolysis (Reactions 1 to 5 in Fig. 24.19) and VisibleChem Video 24.2 to explore the energy-generating reactions of glycolysis (Reactions 6 to 10 in Fig. 24.19).

Fructose and Galactose

People consume other monosaccharides in addition to glucose. And the body also metabolizes these other sugars in the glycolysis pathway to provide energy. These sugars must first, however, be converted to metabolites that are able to enter somewhere in the glycolysis pathway. Fructose, for example, is a monosaccharide found in many foods. As its name indicates, fructose is especially abundant in fruit (Figure 24.20). When humans consume fructose, our bodies convert it to fructose-1-phosphate in the liver and then to 2 glyceraldehyde-3-phosphate molecules. The 2 glyceraldehyde-3-phosphate molecules enter glycolysis at Reaction 6 in the glycolysis pathway

---

Figure 24.20 Metabolism of Fructose and Galactose.

Fructose and galactose form intermediates that enter the glycolysis pathway to be metabolized.

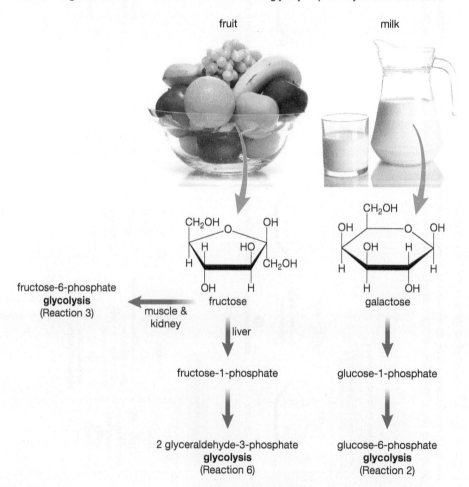

(see Figure 24.20). Our bodies can also convert fructose directly to fructose-6-phosphate, which enters glycolysis at Reaction 3 in the glycolysis pathway.

Galactose is a monosaccharide that produces the disaccharide lactose when combined with glucose. Lactose is found primarily in milk and milk products. When lactose is broken down to monosaccharides, galactose is one of the monosaccharides produced. Galactose must undergo further processing in order to be fully metabolized. Our bodies first convert galactose to glucose-1-phosphate and then to glucose-6-phosphate. This metabolite enters glycolysis at Reaction 2 (See Fig. 24.20). Some individuals lack the enzymes to carry out these reactions and are diagnosed with galactosemia, a condition characterized by the build-up of galactose in the body. This condition leads to symptoms that are sometimes fatal. Newborn screening often can detect galactosemia, which can be managed by eliminating galactose in the diet.

Pyruvate Oxidation and Pyruvate Reduction

After Reaction 10 of the glycolysis pathway is complete, the pyruvate generated in glycolysis proceeds through additional biochemical reactions to produce more energy in the body. The two molecules of pyruvate produced by glycolysis end up in the **cytosol**, the liquid found inside cells. After this, the pathway the pyruvate takes in our bodies depends on the availability of oxygen in the cell. Under **aerobic** conditions—when oxygen is available—the pyruvate is oxidized (loses electrons) and converted to acetyl CoA in the mitochondria of our cells. Under **anaerobic** conditions—when very little oxygen is present—pyruvate reduces to lactate in the cytosol (Figure 24.21). In yeast cells, under anaerobic conditions, pyruvate also reduces to ethanol in the **fermentation** process. Let us discuss each of these paths in more detail.

AEROBIC CONDITIONS   The cardiovascular system can normally maintain an adequate supply of oxygen to the cells. Under aerobic conditions, when oxygen is present in the cell, the pyruvate produced in glycolysis continues on to the next phase—pyruvate oxidation. The reaction in the next phase removes a CO_2 from pyruvate and

Figure 24.21 Aerobic and Anaerobic Pathways of Pyruvate.

When oxygen is present, pyruvate is oxidized to form acetyl CoA. When oxygen is limited, pyruvate is reduced to form lactate. We explore the fate of acetyl CoA in the citric acid cycle in Section 24.3.

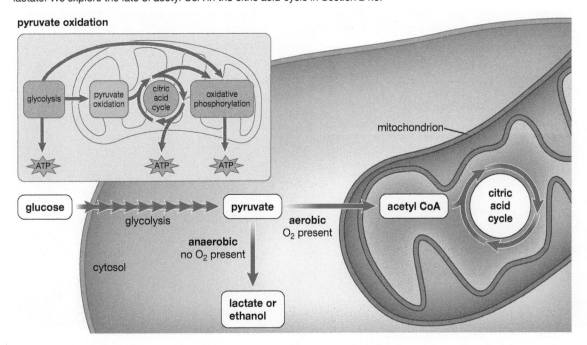

Figure 24.22 Aerobic Production of Acetyl CoA from Pyruvate.

When oxygen is present, pyruvate is transported from the cytosol of the cell into the mitochondria where it is converted to acetyl CoA.

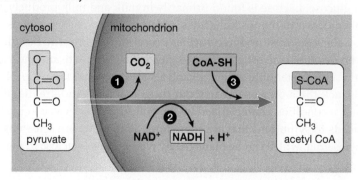

reduces NAD$^+$ to NADH. The resulting two-carbon acetyl compound attaches to CoA-SH producing acetyl CoA (Figure 24.22). In the next phase of metabolism, the body uses this acetyl CoA to generate ATP. (See Section 24.4.)

ANAEROBIC CONDITIONS What happens when the heart and lungs are not able to deliver enough oxygen to a cell? Fortunately, the body is able to carry out glycolysis in the absence of oxygen and provide ATP to power critical functions, such as muscle contraction. During anaerobic respiration, the body produces ATP without oxygen.

The body's ability to carry out anaerobic respiration is limited by the pool of available NAD$^+$ molecules. Recall that NAD$^+$ accepts electrons to form NADH. (See Section 24.2.) Once all the available NAD$^+$ molecules have been reduced to NADH, glycolysis shuts down. When this happens, anaerobic respiration occurs, and our cells regenerate NAD$^+$ by unloading the excess electrons into pyruvate to form lactate (Figure 24.23). This replenishes the pool of NAD$^+$ molecules available to accept electrons during glycolysis and keeps this important source of ATP operating.

Figure 24.23 Lactate Production from Pyruvate during Anaerobic Respiration.

Our bodies produce ATP to fuel important processes including muscle contraction even when oxygen cannot be delivered to our cells fast enough. Under these circumstances, NAD$^+$ can become depleted. Excess electrons from NADH form lactate from pyruvate allowing glycolysis to continue and providing a source of ATP during periods of rapid exertion.

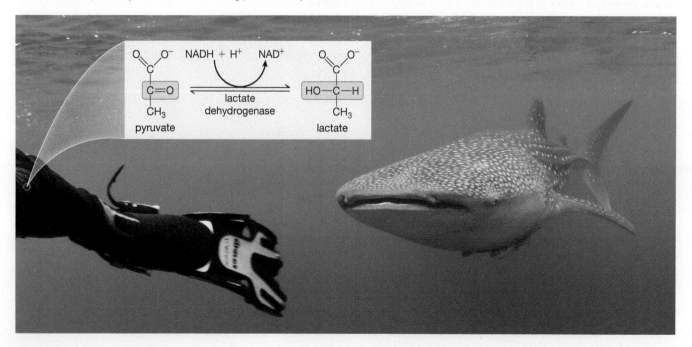

Figure 24.24 Brewing Beer.

Beer is produced in large, air-tight containers. When yeast in the containers run out of oxygen, they carry out fermentation. This process produces CO_2 and ethanol. NAD^+ is reduced to NADH as it picks up electrons from glycolysis and then oxidized to NAD^+ as it passes the electrons to acetaldehyde.

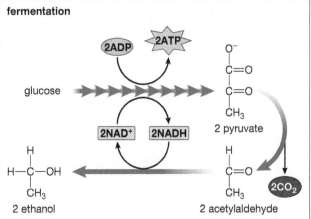

Our muscles are not the only place anaerobic respiration occurs. A wide range of other organisms break down glucose without using oxygen in a process called fermentation. Yeast, common single-celled organisms, for example, undergo fermentation and produce ATP in the absence of oxygen. For centuries, people have added yeast to grain mixtures. When kept in large, airtight containers the yeast and grain ferments to produce beer (Figure 24.24). As the yeast run low on oxygen, they carry out fermentation and the excess electrons from NADH are used to produce ethanol, the alcohol in beer and wine.

Quiz yourself on the content of this section: **Check 24.3** in the Pearson eText.

24.4 The Citric Acid Cycle

In this chapter, we are tracking glucose as it makes its way through the stages of metabolism. So far, we have considered how, during the glycolysis pathway, glucose produces two molecules of pyruvate in the cytosol of the cell. After glycolysis, if oxygen is present, the pyruvate oxidation converts the pyruvate to acetyl CoA in the mitochondria of the cell.

The next major stage of catabolism is a series of enzyme-catalyzed reactions that also occurs in the mitochondria of the cell. This series of reactions is the **citric acid cycle** (Figure 24.25). Acetyl CoA produced by the aerobic oxidation of pyruvate enters the citric acid cycle and ultimately produces CO_2, H_2O, ATP, and the high-energy reduced molecules NADH and $FADH_2$. Each turn of the citric acid cycle produces two molecules of CO_2, four molecules of reduced coenzymes (3 NADH and 1 $FADH_2$) and one high-energy **guanosine triphosphate (GTP)** molecule that is converted to one ATP molecule. The carbon in the CO_2 we exhale with each breath comes from pyruvate molecules as they are metabolized in the reactions of the citric acid cycle.

The citric acid cycle includes eight reactions, each catalyzed by a specific enzyme. The metabolism of both proteins and fats also involves the citric acid cycle. We discuss proteins and fat metabolism in Chapter 25.

Figure 24.25 An Overview of the Citric Acid Cycle.

The citric acid cycle completes the breakdown of pyruvate, releasing CO_2, ATP, and reducing NAD^+ and FAD.

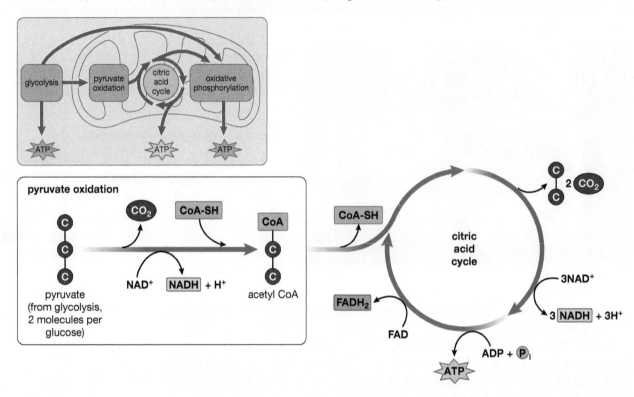

Reactions of the Citric Acid Cycle

The citric acid cycle is also sometimes called the **Krebs cycle** after Hans Krebs, the Jewish scientist who deciphered the details of this metabolic pathway after fleeing Nazi Germany in 1933. We use the term citric acid cycle throughout this unit. This name provides a convenient reminder of the first reaction of the cycle.

After pyruvate is converted to acetyl CoA, the acetyl group of acetyl CoA enters the cycle. It combines with oxaloacetate, forming citrate, a six-carbon molecule that is the conjugate base of citric acid **(Reaction 1 in Figure 24.26)**. Citrate undergoes two **decarboxylation** reactions that result in the loss of two carbon atoms in the form of CO_2 in Reaction 2. These decarboxylation reactions ultimately produce the four-carbon molecule succinyl CoA in Reaction 4. Energy is transferred in Reactions 3 and 4 to produce NADH from the coenzyme NAD^+. Succinyl CoA then undergoes a series of reactions in Reactions 5 through 8 that regenerates oxaloacetate, and the cycle begins again with Reaction 1. In many cells in the body, the reaction in Reaction 5 produces a guanosine triphosphate (GTP) molecule, which is similar to ATP in its structure and function. GTP can be used to make an ATP molecule as shown below Reaction 5 (see Fig. 24.26). The cell can also use GTP directly as energy. *Overall, each turn of the citric acid cycle produces three NADH molecules, one $FADH_2$ molecule and one ATP molecule.*

Select VisibleChem Video 24.3 to explore the detailed reactions of the citric acid cycle.

Figure 24.26 A Detailed View of the Citric Acid Cycle.

The citric acid cycle completes the breakdown of acetyl CoA in eight enzyme-mediated reactions. Note that the cycle regenerates oxaloacetate in Reaction 8 allowing the next molecule of acetyl CoA to react in Reaction 1 as the cycle begins again.

citric acid cycle

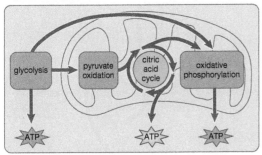

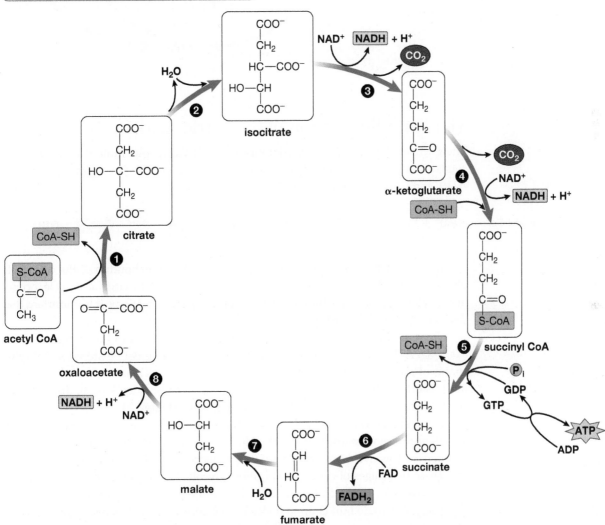

Watch this concept come to life: **VisibleChem Video 24.3:** The Reactions of the Citric Acid Cycle in the Pearson eText.

Apply what you have just learned: **Practice 24.7** in the Pearson eText.

Figure 24.27 Regulating Energy Production.

Glycolysis and the citric acid cycle are regulated to keep the two pathways operating efficiently. ATP and citrate inhibit one of the enzymes early in glycolysis. The presence of AMP, which indicates an energy shortage in the cell, stimulates glycolysis.

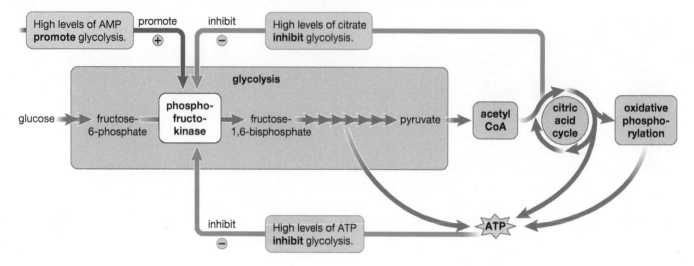

Yield and Regulation of the Citric Acid Cycle

The citric acid cycle produces two molecules of CO_2, four molecules of reduced coenzymes (3 NADH and 1 $FADH_2$), one molecule of GTP (an energy carrier like ATP), and CoA:

$$\text{acetyl-CoA} + 3NAD^+ + FAD + GDP + \textcircled{P} + 2H_2O \longrightarrow 2CO_2 + 3\boxed{NADH} + 3H^+ + \boxed{FADH_2} + GTP + CoA$$

Remember that the citric acid cycle occurs in the mitochondria of the cell while glycolysis, the pathway that provides the pyruvate to run the citric acid cycle, occurs in the cytosol of the cell. Although they occur in separate locations, it is important that these two pathways coordinate.

This coordination occurs through the use of feedback control of enzymes. If, for example, ATP levels are high in the cell, excess glucose must be stored in complex chains of glycogen to provide energy later. In this case, ATP acts as an inhibitor and inhibits one of the early enzymes in glycolysis, phosphofructokinase, dramatically slowing the rate of glycolysis and conserving glucose (Figure 24.27).

If energy levels in the cell are very low, two phosphates are removed from ATP, forming **adenosine monophosphate (AMP)**. The presence of AMP activates the enzymes that function early in glycolysis, stimulating the production of ATP (see Fig. 24.26).

These two stages of cellular respiration, glycolysis, and the citric acid cycle, must be synchronized. Notice in Figure 24.27 that citrate inhibits one of the early enzymes in glycolysis. Citrate builds up in the cell if the citric acid cycle is overwhelmed. This build-up slows the process of glycolysis, allowing the citric acid cycle to catch up with the incoming acetyl CoA.

In addition to small amounts of ATP, the citric acid cycle produces reduced coenzymes that go on to ultimately produce ATP as we discuss in Section 24.5.

 Quiz yourself on the content of this section: **Check 24.4** in the Pearson eText.

24.5 Oxidative Phosphorylation: The Electron Transport Chain and Chemiosmosis

During the pathways we have discussed so far in the chapter, much of the energy available from the glucose has not yet been made available to do work. Glycolysis produced a net yield of two molecules of ATP per molecule of glucose. The citric acid cycle provides another two molecules of ATP per molecule of glucose. This yield is still much too low to support the body's high energy demands.

The bulk of the ATP the body produces during cellular respiration is harvested in the final step of metabolism—**oxidative phosphorylation**. The reduced coenzymes NADH and FADH$_2$ are energy-rich molecules because each contains a pair of electrons that can be transferred to other molecules during metabolism. When the electrons from NADH and FADH$_2$ reduce oxygen (O$_2$) to water, a large amount of energy is released that is used to generate ATP. Oxidative phosphorylation is the process that captures this energy from the electrons carried by NADH and FADH$_2$. The energy is then used to produce ATP in the mitochondria. The process of oxidative phosphorylation involves two key steps: the electron transport chain and chemiosmosis

The Electron Transport Chain

In the first step of oxidative phosphorylation, the electrons carried by NADH and FADH$_2$, are unloaded in the **electron transport chain** (Figure 24.28). The electron transport chain is an array of molecules in the inner membrane of the mitochondria called **complexes I, II, III, and IV**. Each of these complexes is composed of enzymes,

---

Figure 24.28 The Electron Transport Chain.

The final stage of cellular respiration–oxidative phosphorylation–occurs in two steps. In the first step of oxidative phosphorylation, electrons are passed down an electron transport chain in a series of redox reactions. Oxygen is the final electron acceptor in this chain. If there is not enough oxygen present, our cells cannot continue adequate ATP production.

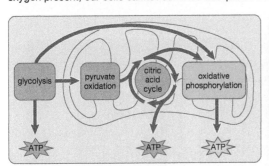

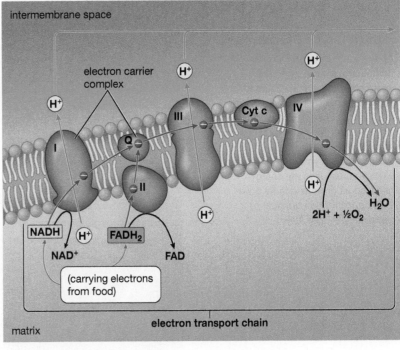

proteins, and metal ions that act as electron carriers as they gain and lose electrons in oxidation-reduction (redox) reactions. (See Section 8.3 Oxidation-Reduction Reactions.) Two additional electron carriers, *coenzyme Q (CoQ)* and *cytochrome c (Cyt c)*, function as mobile carriers, shuttling electrons between the complexes that are not bound to the inner membrane.

NADH gives up its high-energy electrons to the first complex in the chain and $FADH_2$ releases electrons (e^-) to the second complex. The electrons (e^-) are transferred from one complex to another by a series of oxidation-reduction reactions releasing energy as they progress. At the end of the chain, the electrons (e^-) and hydrogen ions (H^+) react with oxygen to produce water. This reaction occurs at complex IV. We can write the reaction in two ways:

$$4e^- + 4H^+ + O_2 \rightarrow 2H_2O$$
$$\text{or simplified to}$$
$$2e^- + 2H^+ + \tfrac{1}{2}O_2 \rightarrow H_2O$$

The electron transport chain is explored in more detail in VisibleChem Video 24.4.

Chemiosmosis

The second step of oxidative phosphorylation is **chemiosmosis**. In chemiosmosis, energy released by the flow of electrons through the electron transport chain pumps hydrogen ions (H^+) into the space between the two membranes of the mitochondria (the intermembrane space; see Fig. 24.28). Charged protons (H^+) cannot diffuse across the phospholipid bilayer and accumulate in the space, creating a reservoir of H^+. This build-up of hydrogen ions (H^+), like water behind a dam, stores potential energy that synthesizes ATP by the phosphorylation of ADP (Figure 24.29).

ATP synthase is an enzyme that catalyzes the phosphorylation of ADP. Like all substances, the hydrogen ions diffuse spontaneously down their concentration

Figure 24.29 Chemiosmosis.

A) The electron transport chain pumps protons (H^+) into the intermembrane space. Charged protons cannot diffuse across the phospholipid bilayer and accumulate in the space, like water behind a dam. **B)** The protons diffuse out through the enzyme ATP synthase. ATP synthase uses the energy released as protons diffuse down their concentration gradient to produce ATP from ADP.

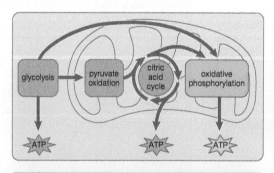

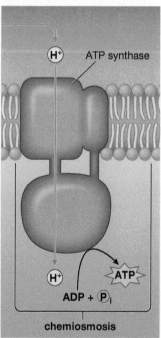

A   B

gradient, releasing energy in the process. In this case, the hydrogen ions diffuse from the intermembrane space into the mitochondrial matrix through a channel in the ATP synthase enzyme (see Fig. 24.29B). The energy released as hydrogen ions (H^+) moves through ATP synthase drives the phosphorylation of ATP to ADP.

$$ADP + HPO_4{}^{2-} \longrightarrow ATP + H_2O$$

> Energy released from H^+ movement drives phosporylation.

The entire two-stage process is called oxidative phosphorylation because the energy from the oxidation of coenzymes transfers a phosphate group.

Note that this second step of oxidative phosphorylation is called chemiosmosis. Osmosis is the diffusion of water down its concentration gradient across a cell membrane. Chemiosmosis refers to a chemical diffusing down its concentration gradient across a cell membrane. In this case, the chemical is the H^+ ions that diffuse through ATP synthase.

Each NADH that enters the electron transport chain at complex I produces enough energy to phosphorylate 2.5 ADP molecules, forming ATP. When $FADH_2$ enters the electron transport chain at complex II, its oxidation provides energy for the phosphorylation of an additional 1.5 ADP molecules. Click on VisibleChem Video 24.4 to review the important features of the electron transport chain and chemiosmosis in more detail.

***

Watch this concept come to life: **VisibleChem Video 24.4:** Oxidative Phosphorylation in the Pearson eText.

Apply what you have just learned: **Practice 24.8 and 24.9** in the Pearson eText.

***

Overall Production of ATP Energy from Glucose

Now that we have followed the catabolism of carbohydrates through the key stages, let us see how much ATP one molecule of glucose produces.

Carbohydrates break down to monosaccharides during digestion. The monosaccharide glucose enters glycolysis and produces two ATP molecules as well as two NADH electron carriers. In pyruvate oxidation, pyruvate, the product of glycolysis, is oxidized to acetyl CoA. Acetyl CoA enters the citric acid cycle, which produces two more ATP molecules along with six NADH and two $FADH_2$ electron carriers. In oxidative phosphorylation—the final stage of catabolism—NADH and $FADH_2$ are shuttled to the electron transport chain where they function as reducing agents (electron sources). Recall that each NADH produces 2.5 ATP molecules and each $FADH_2$ produces 1.5 ATP. The electron transport chain produces between 26-28 ATP. In sum, each molecule of glucose produces a maximum of 30-32 ATP molecules (Figure 24.30).

As you can see, the total yield from catabolism is a much larger yield of ATP than from glycolysis alone. The electron transport chain in oxidative phosphorylation, which takes place in the mitochondria, is responsible for the bulk of ATP production. For this reason, tissues with long-term high-energy demands need many mitochondria and efficient oxygen delivery. Only short bursts of energy, in contrast, can be supported with just glycolysis. This difference is reflected in the structure of slow twitch and fast twitch muscles (Figure 24.31).

See BioConnect 24.2 (contains Figures 24.32–24.37) to explore the electron transport chain.

Figure 24.30 The Energetic Yield of Cellular Respiration.

Each glucose molecule fuels the production of 32 ATP molecules.

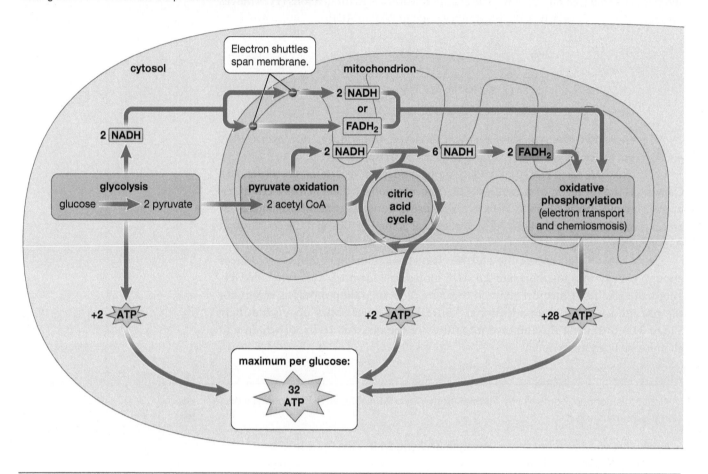

Figure 24.31 Slow Twitch and Fast Twitch Muscle.

Endurance athletes tend to have more slow twitch muscles, which have large numbers of mitochondria, than average people. Athletes that depend on short bursts of energy tend to have more fast twitch muscles, which have fewer mitochondria and rely more heavily on glycolysis alone to produce their ATP.

slow twitch muscle
• fatigue resistant
• abundant mitochondria and oxygen stores

fast twitch muscle
• easily fatigued
• fewer mitochondria oxygen stores

Explore how Chemistry and Biology connect: **BioConnect: 24.2** Brown Fat and UCPs in the Pearson eText.

Quiz yourself on the content of this section: **Check 24.5** in the Pearson eText.

24.6 Synthesis of Glucose

As we discuss in Chapter 25, the body also metabolizes fats and proteins, in addition to carbohydrates such as glucose, to produce ATP. Many of our tissues however, including our brains, use glucose as their primary energy source. This makes maintaining a steady supply of glucose an essential function.

Part of the solution to keeping blood sugar constant lies in utilizing glycogen stores in the liver and muscle when glucose levels drop. But what happens when glycogen stores are depleted when someone undergoes a prolonged fast or follows a low carb diet, for example? Fortunately, our body has metabolic pathways that can synthesize glucose from non-carbohydrate sources including lactate, amino acids, or glycerol (Figure 24.38).

Recall, for example, that working muscles anaerobically produce lactate (see Fig. 24.23). Our bodies can recycle lactate to produce additional glucose. This recycling is a form of **gluconeogenesis**, the synthesis of glucose from sources other than carbohydrates. Unlike the pathways we have studied so far in this chapter, gluconeogenesis is an anabolic pathway not a catabolic one. In other words, gluconeogenesis produces glucose from smaller molecules.

Before gluconeogenesis can begin, the lactate produced by muscles working anaerobically is transported in the blood to the liver. The liver then uses lactate to produce glucose in a series of enzyme-mediated reactions. This glucose returns to the blood and can be used again to produce ATP in muscles (Figure 24.39). The cycling of these compounds to the liver and back to the muscle is the **Cori cycle.** The production of glucose from lactate derived from pyruvate is in many ways the reverse process of glycolysis. The pyruvate molecule passes through ten enzyme-mediated reactions and all the same intermediates found in glycolysis. Three of the ten enzymes, however, are unique to the Cori cycle.

Making Glucose from Fats

Fats can also serve as an important source of glucose. During periods of starvation or low-carbohydrate intake, fat stores can provide important fuel in the form of glucose to our cells. Humans store most of their fats in the form of triacylglycerides. Recall from Chapter 18 that a triacylglyceride molecule is composed of glycerol and three fatty acids (Figure 24.40).

Our bodies can break down stored triacylglycerols into glycerol and fatty acids. And our bodies can metabolize glycerol and fatty acids to produce ATP. We discuss fatty acids in the citric acid cycle in Chapter 25.

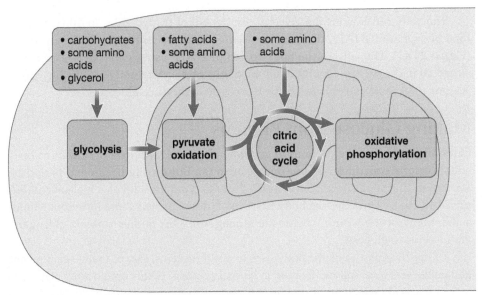

Figure 24.38 Other Sources of ATP.

Proteins and fats can also be used to generate ATP in cellular respiration.

Figure 24.39 Recycling Lactate.

Lactate is produced by cells during anaerobic respiration. The liver can recycle lactate during gluconeogenesis, which provides glucose to fuel glycolysis.

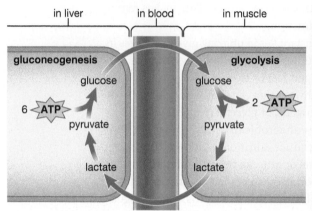

Figure 24.40 Triglycerides.

Triacylglycerols (also known as triglycerides) are composed of a glycerol molecule covalently bonded to three fatty acid chains. A check of blood triglycerides is often included as part of wellness exams. Excess carbohydrates in the diet are converted to triacylglycerols and increase the risk of cardiovascular disease.

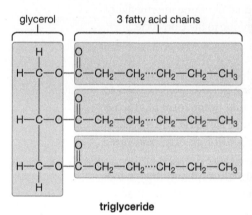
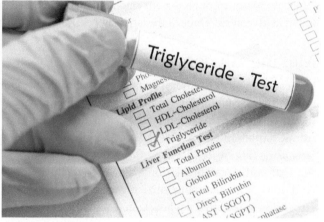

The body can convert the glycerol component of triglycerides to dihydroxyacetone phosphate (DHAP), the same molecule produced in Reaction 5 of glycolysis (Figure 24.41). This allows the body to produce ATP using glycerol released from stored fat in the energy-generating phase of glycolysis. Alternatively, the dihydroxyacetone phosphate can be used in the Cori cycle to produce glucose.

Making Glucose from Proteins

Our bodies can also use proteins to generate glucose. During short periods of inadequate calorie consumption, our bodies burn fat. But during prolonged periods of starvation, our bodies begin to consume proteins from muscles as a fuel source (Figure 24.42). In this process, the body first breaks down proteins into individual amino acids. Many of these amino acids are **glucogenic**. Our bodies convert glucogenic amino acids to glucose.

Of the 20 amino acids the body uses to build proteins, two of them—alanine and glutamine—are most commonly used in gluconeogenesis. (Other amino acids play a role in the citric acid cycle; we will explore in Chapter 25.) Alanine travels in the blood to the

Figure 24.41 Metabolizing Glycerol.

Glycerol from either stored fat or dietary fat can be converted to dihydroxyacetone phosphate (DHAP), the molecule produced in Reaction 5 of glycolysis. Dihydroxyacetone phosphate can then be used to generate ATP in glycolysis or glucose in the Cori cycle.

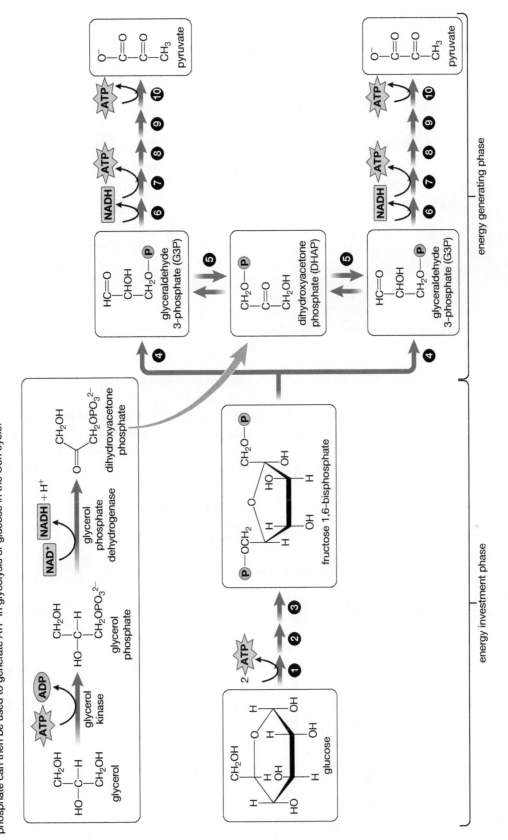

Figure 24.42 Metabolizing Protein to Produce Glucose.

A) The man shown here was a conscientious objector in World War II who volunteered for a starvation study in Minnesota. People with severe, prolonged calorie deficits break down proteins, especially those found in muscle. **B)** The amino acid alanine is transported from muscle cells to the liver where it is converted to pyruvate and then glucose.

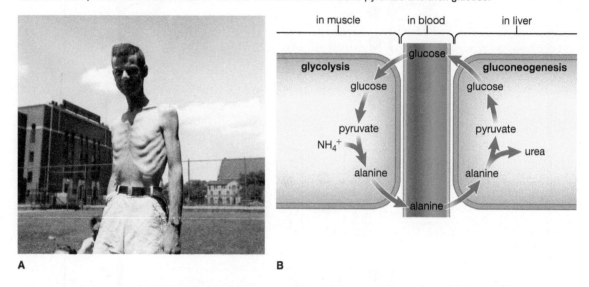

A

B

liver. There, the enzyme alanine aminotransferase (ALT) converts the alanine to pyruvate. This pyruvate generates the glucose needed to support other key functions in the body.

   Together the body's ability to use lactate, amino acids, and glycerol to produce glucose allows us the flexibility to both consume a wide range of foods and to keep the brain fueled during periods of prolonged calorie deficits (Figure 24.43). We take a closer look at other mechanisms to generate energy from fats and proteins in Chapter 25.

Figure 24.43
Gluconeogenesis Pathways.

An array of anabolic pathways allows us to build glucose from diverse starting materials including lactate, amino acids, and the glycerol molecules produced from stored fats.

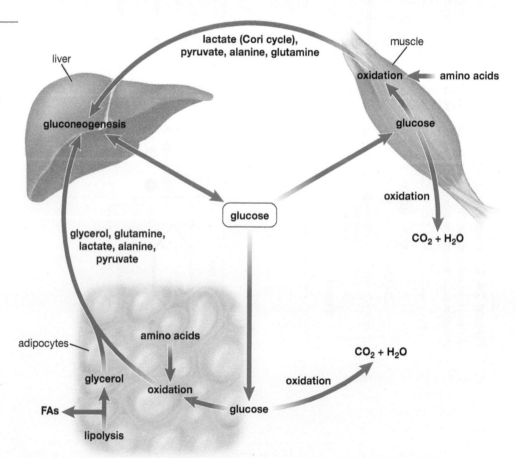

As you might imagine, the process of synthesizing glucose, gluconeogenesis, and breaking down glucose, glycolysis, need to be carefully balanced. When glucose is widely available, glycolysis should be ongoing. But when glucose is scarce, gluconeo-genesis should begin.

Quiz yourself on the content of this section: **Check 24.6** in the Pearson eText.

Chapter Summary

24.1 Overview of Metabolism

Learning Objective: Distinguish between anabolic and catabolic pathways and describe where metabolic pathways occur in the body.

Metabolism is a summary term for all the reactions in the body that are involved with energy production and cell growth. We divide metabolism into two types of processes: catabolism and anabolism. Catabolism is the breakdown of large molecules in the body to ultimately release energy (Figure 24.5). Anabolism is the synthesis of larger molecules from small molecules and generally requires energy. Metabolic pathways are series of reactions that are either linear or cyclic. Metabolic pathways are generally very complex but are made up of smaller pathways that we can characterize by inputs and outputs. Catabolism is the focus of this chapter and involves four stages: glycolysis, pyruvate oxidation, the citric acid cycle, and oxidative phosphorylation.

BioConnect 24.1: Digesting Our Food

Key Terms

anabolism	intermembrane space	metabolism
catabolism	(from BioConnect 24.1)	metabolites
digestive tract	matrix (from BioConnect 24.1)	mitochondria
(from BioConnect 24.1)	metabolic pathway	(from BioConnect 24.1)

24.2 Important Compounds of Metabolic Pathways

Learning Objective: Describe the basic structure and function of ATP, NAD⁺, FAD, and coenzyme A.

There are several metabolites that repeatedly function as key intermediates in metabolic pathways. ATP and ADP, for example, are molecules that store energy and transfer phosphate groups. ATP is a significant high-energy molecule metabolite in metabolism. Other compounds transfer electrons between molecules. NAD^+ (nicotinamide adenine dinucleotide) is one of these. NAD^+ is a coenzyme composed of a nicotinamide group bonded to ribose and ADP. NAD^+ serves as a biological oxidizing agent and

reacts with an H^+ ion and $2e^-$ to produce the reduced form, NADH. FAD is another important coenzyme that helps shuttle electrons between molecules in metabolic pathways. FAD is reduced when the two nitrogen atoms in the flavin portion of the molecule react with two hydrogen atoms and two electrons to produce the reduced form, $FADH_2$. Coupled reactions are pairs of reactions that occur together. The energy released by one of the coupled reactions provides the energy to drive the other reaction. The energy released from the hydrolysis of ATP to ADP for example, drives energetically unfavorable reactions.

Key Terms

acetyl coenzyme A (acetyl CoA)
adenosine diphosphate (ADP)
adenosine triphosphate (ATP)
coenzyme A (CoA)
coupled reactions

FAD (flavin adenine dinucleotide)
$FADH_2$
NAD^+ (nicotinamide adenine dinucleotide)
NADH

nicotinamide group
pyruvate
riboflavin

24.3 Glycolysis and Pyruvate Oxidation

Learning Objective: Describe the inputs, outputs, and role of glycolysis.

The breakdown of glucose to produce ATP using the oxygen we inhale is cellular respiration. In our cells, glucose is catabolized through glycolysis, a ten-reaction biochemical pathway (Figure 24.18). Glycolysis includes an energy-consuming phase during which ATP drives reactions and an energy-generating phase during which NADH, ATP, and pyruvate are produced (Figure 24.19). After glycolysis, pyruvate proceeds on to one of two pathways (Figure 24.21). Under aerobic conditions (when oxygen is available) pyruvate oxidation produces acetyl CoA. Under anaerobic conditions (when little to no oxygen is present) pyruvate is reduced to lactate. Under anaerobic conditions, yeast cells convert pyruvate to ethanol in the fermentation process.

VisibleChem Video 24.1: The Energy-Consuming Reactions of Glycolysis

VisibleChem Video 24.2: The Energy-Generating Reactions of Glycolysis

Key Terms

aerobic
anaerobic
cellular respiration

cytosol
energy-consuming reactions
energy-generating reactions

fermentation
glycolysis

24.4 The Citric Acid Cycle

Learning Objective: Describe the inputs, outputs, and role of the citric acid cycle.

The citric acid cycle follows glycolysis (Figure 24.25). The citric acid cycle consists of a series of enzyme-catalyzed reactions that occurs in the mitochondria of the cell. Acetyl CoA, produced from the aerobic oxidation of pyruvate, enters the citric acid cycle, and combines with oxaloacetate, forming citrate. Citrate undergoes two decarboxylation reactions that result in the loss of two carbon atoms in the form of CO_2. These decarboxylation reactions produce a four-carbon molecule called succinyl CoA. Succinyl CoA undergoes a series of reactions that regenerates oxaloacetate, and the cycle begins again (Figure 24.26). Overall, each turn of the citric acid cycle produces two molecules of CO_2, four molecules of reduced coenzymes (three NADH and one $FADH_2$), and one molecule of GTP, an energy carrier that functions much like ATP. Glucose catabolism is regulated in several ways. Excess ATP acts as an inhibitor to an enzyme in an early step of glycolysis, conserving glucose. Likewise, citrate inhibits one of the enzymes early in glycolysis so that the build-up of citrate slows down glycolysis until the citric acid cycle can catch up. And AMP activates enzymes early in glycolysis, which stimulates the production of ATP.

VisibleChem Video 24.3: The Reactions of the Citric Acid Cycle

Key Terms

adenosine monophosphate (AMP)
citric acid cycle

decarboxylation
guanosine triphosphate (GTP)

Krebs cycle

24.5 Oxidative Phosphorylation: The Electron Transport Chain and Chemiosmosis

Learning Objective: Explain the process of oxidative phosphorylation and the role of the electron transport chain.

The bulk of the ATP produced during cellular respiration is harvested in the last step of catabolism: oxidative phosphorylation. Oxidative phosphorylation consists of two steps: the electron transport chain and chemiosmosis. In the electron transport chain, complexes I, II, III and IV, which are built into the inner membrane of the mitochondria and composed of enzymes, proteins, and metal ions, gain and lose electrons (Figure 24.28). Electrons, carried by NADH and $FADH_2$, enter the electron transport chain and are transferred from one molecule to another by a series of oxidation-reduction reactions that release energy. At the end of the chain, the electrons and H^+ react with oxygen to produce water. The energy released by the flow of electrons through the electron transport chain pumps hydrogen ions (H^+) from the mitochondrial matrix into the intermembrane space of the mitochondria, creating a reservoir of H^+. These H^+ diffuse through a channel in the ATP synthase enzyme and produce energy. The energy–in the form of hydrogen ions (H^+)—moves through ATP synthase and fuels the phosphorylation of ADP to ATP. This final state of catabolism produces between 26-28 ATP. One molecule of glucose produces a maximum of 30-32 ATP molecules in the pathways of catabolism (Figure 24.30).

VisibleChem Video 24.4: Oxidative Phosphorylation

BioConnect 24.2: Brown Fat and UCPs

Key Terms

ATP synthase
chemiosmosis
coenzyme Q (CoQ)
complex I, II, II and IV

cytochrome c (Cyt c)
electron transport chain
oxidative phosphorylation
uncoupled protein (UCP) (from BioConnect 24.2)

24.6 Synthesis of Glucose

Learning Objective: Describe the processes that produce glucose from lactate, triglycerides, and amino acids.

Gluconeogenesis is an anabolic pathway that involves the synthesis of glucose from non-carbohydrate sources, such as lactate, amino acids, or glycerol. The production of glucose from lactate occurs in the liver in a series of reactions that produces pyruvate along the way. The series of reactions from pyruvate to glucose is essentially the reverse of glycolysis. Glucose returns to the blood to be used again to produce ATP in muscles. The cycling of compounds to the liver and back to the muscles is the Cori Cycle. During periods of starvation or low-carbohydrate intake, the body can use fat stores to provide glycerol. Glycerol is converted to dihydroxyacetone phosphate and enters Reaction 5 of glycolysis. Amino acids, that result from the breakdown of proteins, can also generate glucose in the gluconeogenesis pathway. Alanine and glutamine are most commonly used in gluconeogenesis. Alanine, for example, is transported by the blood to the liver and can then be converted to pyruvate and used to generate glucose. The processes of gluconeogenesis and glycolysis need to be carefully balanced. When glucose is widely available, glycolysis should be operating. But when glucose is scarce, gluconeogenesis should occur. Signals that activate one pathway tend to inhibit the other.

Key Terms

Cori cycle
glucogenic
gluconeogenesis

End-of-Chapter Quiz

Have you mastered the content of this chapter? Try the **End-of-Chapter Quiz** in the Pearson eText.

1. Which process characterizes anabolism?
   a) the generation of chemical energy by converting H_2O to CO_2, which drives glucose synthesis
   b) the use of biochemical energy to convert ATP to ADP to break down large molecules
   c) the generation of biochemical energy from the hydrolysis of glucose and ATP
   d) the use of biochemical energy to synthesize large molecules from smaller molecules

2. Select the correct sequence for the complete metabolism of glucose under aerobic conditions.
   a) glycolysis → citric acid cycle → pyruvate oxidation → oxidative phosphorylation
   b) glycolysis → acetyl CoA formation → pyruvate oxidation → citric acid cycle → oxidative phosphorylation
   c) glycolysis → pyruvate oxidation → citric acid cycle → oxidative phosphorylation
   d) pyruvate oxidation → glycolysis → citric acid cycle → oxidative phosphorylation

3. Which is *not* the reduced form of a coenzyme that participates in the redox reactions of metabolism?
   a) acetyl CoA   b) NADH   c) $CoQH_2$ d) $FADH_2$

4. When the two reactions shown here are coupled, what is the chemical equation and energy value of the overall reaction?

   Energy

   $$\text{1,3-bisphosphoglycerate} + H_2O \rightarrow \text{3-phosphoglycerate} + HPO_4{}^{2-} - 11.8 \text{ kcal/mol}$$
   $$ADP + HPO_4{}^{2-} \rightarrow ATP + H_2O + 7.3 \text{ kcal/mol}$$

   a) 1,3-bisphosphoglycerate + ADP → 3-phosphoglycerate + ATP (overall energy = −19.1 kcal/mol, favorable)
   b) 1,3-bisphosphoglycerate + ADP → 3-phosphoglycerate + ATP (overall energy = −4.5 kcal/mol, favorable)
   c) 1,3-bisphosphoglycerate + ATP → 3-phosphoglycerate + ADP (energy change = +4.5 kcal/mol, unfavorable)
   d) 1,3-bisphosphoglycerate + ADP → 3-phosphoglycerate + 2ATP (energy change = +19.1 kcal/mol, unfavorable)

5. Which coenzyme contains a thiol (-SH) group and enters the citric acid cycle as a thioester?
   a) NADH   b) $FADH_2$
   c) coenzyme A   d) coenzyme Q

6. Which coenzyme contains riboflavin as part of its structure?
   a) coenzyme Q   b) ATP
   c) coenzyme A   d) FAD

7. In the context of organic and biochemical reactions, the term *reduction* means
   a) the gain of oxygen atoms or increase in carbon-oxygen bonds by a molecule
   b) the gain of electrons or hydrogen by a molecule
   c) the fragmentation of a molecule through breaking the carbon chains in a molecule
   d) the loss of electrons or hydrogen by a molecule

8. When oxygen is not present, or is severely limited, what is the pyruvate generated during glycolysis converted into?
   a) citrate   b) glycogen
   c) acetyl CoA   d) lactate

9. Which molecule is *not* directly produced as a reaction product during glycolysis?
   a) ADP   b) H_2O c) ATP   d) CO_2

10. Glucose is the six-carbon starting sugar for glycolysis. A friend notices that the product of glycolysis only contains three carbon atoms and asks you what happened to the other three carbon atoms in the reactant six-carbon glucose. Select the best explanation.
    a) During glycolysis, the six-carbon glucose breaks down and three of the carbon atoms are used to produce three molecules of carbon dioxide (CO_2) gas that is exhaled.
    b) During glycolysis, the six-carbon glucose breaks down into a molecule containing three carbon atoms and the other carbon atoms become attached to ATP in the form of three acetate groups.
    c) During glycolysis, the six-carbon glucose breaks down into two molecules each containing three carbon atoms. These two fragments become the identical products that are produced during the last several steps of glycolysis.
    d) During glycolysis, the six-carbon glucose breaks down into a three-carbon glyceraldehyde-3-phosphate molecule, and a three-carbon glycerol molecule.

11. During glycolysis, what is NAD^+ converted into?
a) ATP
b) $NAD^{2+} + H^+$
c) $ADP + 2H^+$
d) NADH

12. Under aerobic conditions, what is the pyruvate generated during glycolysis converted into before entering the citric acid cycle?
a) citrate
b) acetyl CoA
c) lactate
d) NADH

13. Which molecule is regenerated at the end of each round of the citric acid cycle?
a) acetyl CoA
b) citrate
c) oxaloacetate
d) NAD^+

14. In the second reaction of the citric acid cycle, the enzyme aconitase acts as a catalyst. What kind of reaction is Reaction 2?

a) decarboxylation
b) isomerization
c) decomposition
d) combination

15. In Reaction 8 of the citric acid cycle, the enzyme malate dehydrogenase catalyzes the conversion of malate to oxaloacetate. Which kind of reaction is Reaction 8?

a) isomerization
b) hydrogenation
c) dehydration
d) redox

16. In Reaction 4 of the citric acid cycle, the enzyme a-ketoglutarate dehydrogenase catalyzes the conversion of a-ketoglutarate to succinyl CoA. Predict the missing product.

a) OH^-
b) CO_2
c) H_2O
d) ATP

17. Select the correct description of cellular respiration that includes the electron transport chain and oxidative phosphorylation.
a) aerobic
b) anabolic
c) anaerobic
d) antigenic

18. Which stage of the complete metabolic breakdown of glucose generates the largest net yield of ATP molecules to fuel our cells?
a) citric acid cycle
b) glycolysis
c) pyruvate oxidation
d) oxidative phosphorylation

19. During oxidative phosphorylation, which enzyme catalyzes the phosphorylation of ADP?
a) ATP oxidase
b) ATP synthase
c) ATP reductase
d) ATP citrase

20. How are electrons transferred from complex I to complex III in the electron transport chain?
a) FAD is the mobile electron carrier between complex I and III in the electron transport chain.
b) Coenzyme Q is the mobile electron carrier between complex I and III in the electron transport chain.
c) NADH is the mobile electron carrier between complex I and III in the electron transport chain.
d) Cytochrome C (Cyt c) is the mobile electron carrier between complex I and III in the electron transport chain.

21. During the production of glucose from fats, what is glycerol converted into?

a) coenzyme Q

b) fructose-6-phosphate

c) dihydroxyacetone phosphate

d) phosphoenolpyruvate

22. Select the process that converts the lactate formed during anaerobic respiration in the liver back into glucose.

a) glycosylation

b) oxidative phosphorylation

c) catabolism

d) Cori cycle

Chapter 25
Metabolism of Lipids and Amino Acids

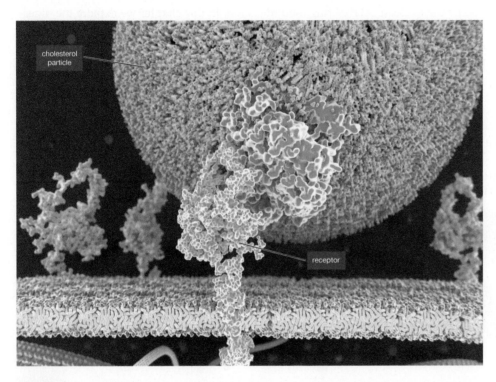

cholesterol particle

receptor

Cholesterol from the food we consume enters the cells of the body by binding to specific receptors on cell surfaces.

Chapter Outline

Learning Objectives

25.1 Describe how fats and cholesterol are digested in the body.

25.2 Describe β oxidation of fatty acids and determine the ATP yield from fatty acid oxidation.

25.3 Describe the catabolism of amino acids including the removal of the amino group and the pathways involved in the breakdown of the amino acid carbon skeleton.

25.4 Describe the synthesis of fatty acids from acetyl CoA.

25.5 Describe the general pathways involved with the synthesis of nonessential amino acids from the intermediates of glycolysis and citric acid cycle.

Introduction

In Chapter 24 we followed glucose through the essential biochemical pathways our bodies use to create ATP during food digestion. In this chapter we explore the digestion and metabolism of proteins and fats, some of the other important components of our diets. Like glucose, fats and proteins generate important energy and building blocks in catabolic pathways. And like glucose, the amount and type of proteins and fats we consume profoundly impacts our health and our body chemistry (Figure 25.1).

Figure 25.1 Metabolism of Fats and Proteins.

A) The metabolism of fat plays a critical role in metabolic syndrome and diabetes. **B)** Cholesterol is an important fat that the body needs for an array of essential functions, but cholesterol is also associated with significant health risks. **C)** When our bodies metabolize proteins, they produce toxic ammonia that is converted to urea and excreted in urine.

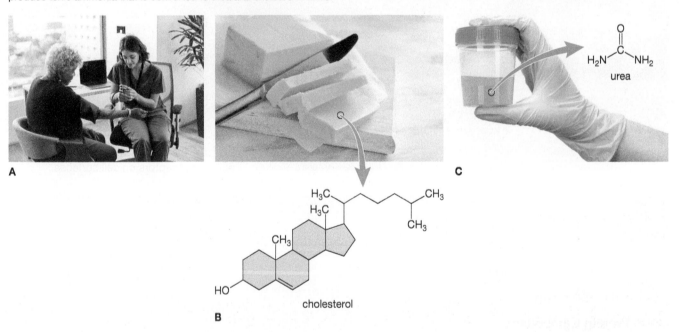

25.1 Digestion of Fats and Cholesterol

This chapter explores how our body processes fats and proteins. Parts of the metabolic pathways we discuss in this chapter are familiar from Chapter 24, which focuses on the metabolism of carbohydrates, because the pathways are the same ones that metabolize carbohydrates (Figure 25.2). For example, metabolites from both protein and fat catabolism enter the citric acid cycle and oxidative phosphorylation and ultimately produce energy.

Our bodies metabolize fats from the fat stores in our body as well as the fats in our diet to produce energy. Most of the fats we consume are triacylglycerols (which we also refer to as triglycerides). Each triacylglycerol molecule is composed of three fatty acid molecules bound to a **glycerol** ($C_3H_8O_3$) molecule (Figure 25.3).

Figure 25.2 Proteins and Fats can Power the Citric Acid Cycle and Oxidative Phosphorylation.

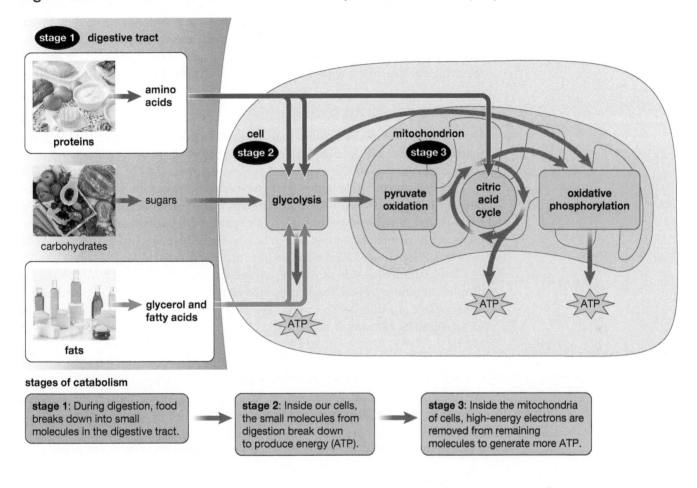

stages of catabolism

stage 1: During digestion, food breaks down into small molecules in the digestive tract.

stage 2: Inside our cells, the small molecules from digestion break down to produce energy (ATP).

stage 3: Inside the mitochondria of cells, high-energy electrons are removed from remaining molecules to generate more ATP.

Figure 25.3 Triacylglycerols.

Most of the fats we consume are triacylglycerols, which are made up of glycerol molecules covalently bound to three fatty acid chains. The fatty acids in triacylglycerols may be saturated or unsaturated.

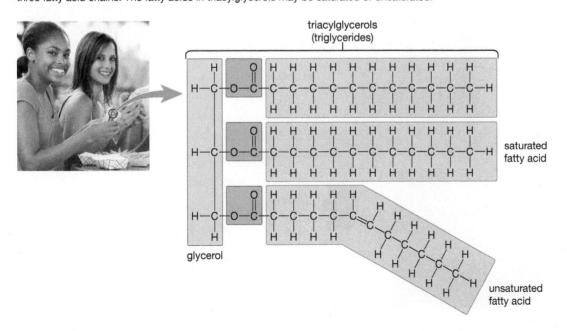

Digesting and absorbing fats is challenging because lipids are not soluble in either the aqueous environment of our digestive tract nor in our blood. Fat molecules are hydrophobic and not soluble in solutions of polar water molecules. Recall that polar molecules are soluble in polar solvents and nonpolar molecules are insoluble in polar solvents. For this reason, lipids pass largely unchanged through the stomach and into the small intestine where digestion and absorption can begin.

Getting Fats into Cells

Hydrophobic fat molecules clump together in the aqueous environment of the digestive tract, forming fat globules. Our bodies must break down fat globules to make fat accessible to our digestive enzymes.

The first step in breaking down fat globules occurs when the gallbladder secretes bile into the upper stretch of the small intestine. **Bile** is a greenish brown fluid made in the liver and stored in the gallbladder. Bile contains **bile salts** that have both hydrophobic and hydrophilic regions. Bile salts help emulsify (break up) the fat globules to form small fat droplets called **micelles** (Figure 25.4).

The hydrophobic side of the bile salt assembles around small hydrophobic fat droplets to form micelles. The hydrophilic ends of the bile salts are exposed on the outer surface of a micelle. This makes the micelle structure water-soluble and easier for fat-digesting enzymes to access.

Figure 25.4 Bile Salts Make Fat Globules More Water-Soluble.

Bile salts have both hydrophobic and hydrophilic ends, allowing the salts to break large fat globules into micelles –water-soluble fat droplets. Cholic acid is an example of a bile salt, shown here as the potassium salt.

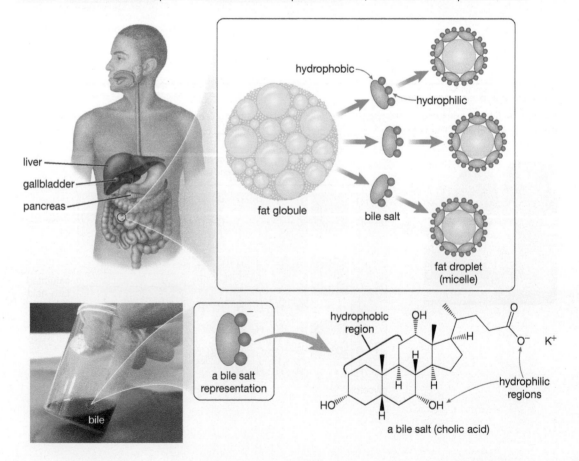

Once the fat globules form micelles, the pancreas releases a class of enzymes called **lipases** into the small intestine. Lipase helps cleave (split apart) the triacylglycerols within the micelles into glycerol and fatty acids.

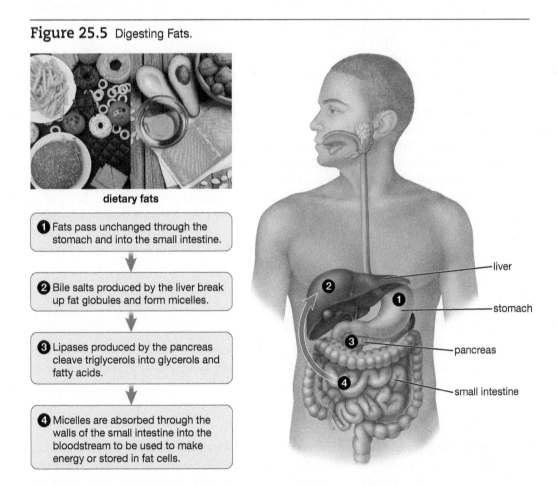

The micelles contain glycerol and fatty acids along with fat-soluble vitamins and cholesterol from our food. The small size of the micelles allows them to cross the cell membrane into the cells lining the small intestine (Figure 25.5).

Lipoproteins and Cholesterol

Once inside the cells lining the small intestine, glycerol and fatty acids recombine to reform triacylglycerols. These triacylglycerols then join together in large numbers and become part of **lipoproteins**. Lipoproteins are not molecules. They are particles composed of thousands of molecules including phospholipids, proteins, cholesterol, and triacylglycerols. Lipoproteins have a single layer of phospholipid molecules on their outside. The polar portion of each phospholipid faces out where

Figure 25.5 Digesting Fats.

dietary fats

❶ Fats pass unchanged through the stomach and into the small intestine.

❷ Bile salts produced by the liver break up fat globules and form micelles.

❸ Lipases produced by the pancreas cleave triglycerols into glycerols and fatty acids.

❹ Micelles are absorbed through the walls of the small intestine into the bloodstream to be used to make energy or stored in fat cells.

liver

stomach

pancreas

small intestine

Figure 25.6 Lipoproteins.

A) Lipoproteins are composed of phospholipids, proteins, cholesterol, and triacylglycerols. **B)** Two forms of lipoproteins, high-density and low-density lipoproteins, are associated with cardiovascular disease and are thus often measured in blood draws.

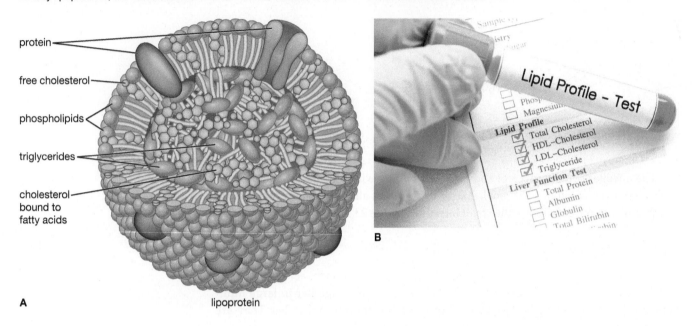

protein

free cholesterol

phospholipids

triglycerides

cholesterol bound to fatty acids

A   lipoprotein

B

it can interact with the polar water molecules in the cytosol of the cell. The nonpolar portion faces inward towards the triacylglycerols and other nonpolar components of the lipoprotein (Figure 25.6). The lipoproteins transport the absorbed triacylglycerols to the cells of the body where the triacylglycerols can be stored or used to produce ATP.

The cholesterol in our body, like other fats, cannot circulate freely in the blood as it is not water soluble. It, too, must first be packaged into lipoproteins just as triacylglycerols are. Lipoproteins are found in many sizes. The two most widely recognized forms of lipoprotein are low-density lipoproteins (LDL) and high-density lipoproteins (HDL). LDL is sometimes called "bad cholesterol" because high levels of LDL can form **plaques**—fatty deposits on the walls of blood vessels—which increase the risk of heart disease and stroke. HDL, in contrast, plays a positive role in the body so we sometimes call it "good cholesterol." HDL transports the cholesterol it contains to the liver where it can be broken down and ultimately passed out of the body. Because of this ability to remove excess cholesterol, high levels of HDLs are associated with a decreased risk of heart attack and stroke.

Explore BioConnect 25.1 (contains Figures 25.7 – 25.13) to explore the important roles cholesterol plays in our bodies.

Explore how Chemistry and Biology connect: **BioConnect: 25.1** Cholesterol in our Diets in the Pearson eText.

Quiz yourself on the content of this section: **Check 25.1** in the Pearson eText.

25.2 Fat Catabolism

After fats have been transported through the blood to the cells, they can be metabolized to produce ATP. Both the glycerol component and the fatty acid component of triacylglycerols fuel cellular respiration (Figure 25.14).

Breakdown of Glycerol

Most of the glycerol that results from the breakdown of fats metabolizes in the liver. In the liver, two enzyme-mediated reactions convert the glycerol into dihydroxyacetone phosphate. In the first reaction, ATP phosphorylates glycerol to produce

Figure 25.14 Glycerol and Fatty Acids can Fuel Cellular Respiration.

A) Glycerol and fatty acids can feed into glycolysis and the citric acid cycle to generate ATP. **B)** Glycerol is included in many processed foods. Glycerol tastes sweet but has fewer calories and less of an effect on blood sugar compared to other carbohydrates.

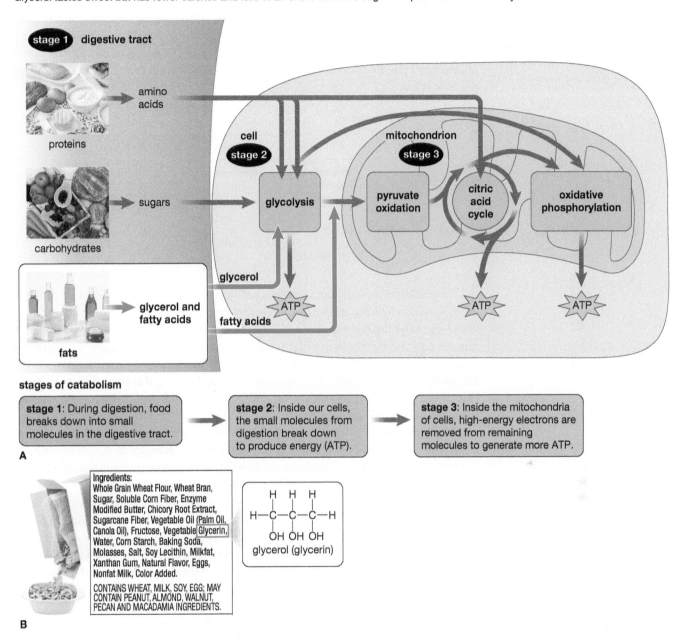

glycerol-3-phosphate. In the second reaction, the hydroxyl group is oxidized and becomes dihydroxyacetone phosphate, an intermediate in several pathways including glycolysis and glucogenesis (see Fig. 24.20, Reaction 5). The energy needs of the body determines the next step. If dihydroxyacetone phosphate enters the glycolysis pathway, each glycerol molecule produces a net yield of 20 ATP molecules.

β Oxidation of Fatty Acids

The fatty acids from triacylglycerols undergo a process called β **oxidation or beta oxidation (fatty acid oxidation)** to produce acetyl coenzyme A (acetyl CoA). This oxidative process removes two-carbon segments from the carboxyl end of the fatty acid during each round of β oxidation. This process produces a fatty acid molecule that is shorter by two carbon atoms. The shorter molecule then undergoes additional rounds of cleavage between the α and β carbons. We discuss this process in more detail in the pages to come.

beta oxidation

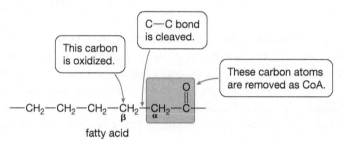

The reaction repeats until the original fatty acid is completely broken down to acetyl CoA. Each of the acetyl CoA molecules produced in this process enters the citric acid cycle to be further metabolized. The citric acid cycle is where the metabolism of glucose and the metabolism of fatty acids converge. Recall that acetyl CoA derived from glucose enters the citric acid cycle followed by oxidative phosphorylation. The fate of the acetyl CoA molecule produced in β oxidation is the same: for every molecule of acetyl CoA that completes the citric acid cycle and oxidative phosphorylation, ten molecules of ATP are produced.

Many metabolic disorders are fatty acid oxidation disorders (FAODs). An estimated one in every 5000–10,000 children is born with a disorder in the ability to carry out fatty acid β oxidation (Figure 25.15). In most of these genetic disorders, the body is unable to either produce or utilize one of the enzymes required to oxidize fatty acids. Individuals with these disorders exhibit an array of symptoms including sleepiness, moodiness, muscle weakness, and enlarged hearts. Medium-chain acyl-coenzyme A dehydrogenase deficiency (MCADD) is the most common FAOD. MCADD prevents the body from breaking down medium-chain fatty acids into acetyl-CoA. This severe disorder can lead to sudden death if not treated.

Figure 25.15 Newborn Screening for Fatty Acid Oxidation Disorders (FAODs).

Enzymes necessary to fatty acid metabolism are sometimes missing or defective. Fatty acid build-up in the body produces a range of symptoms that can be life-threatening. Newborn screening allows these disorders to be treated before symptoms become severe.

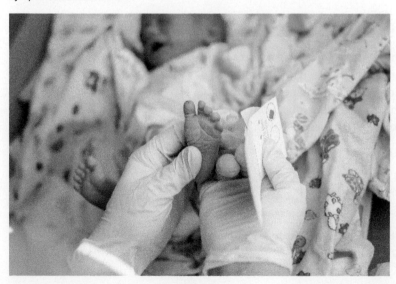

Fatty Acid Activation and Transport

Before β oxidation can occur, fatty acids must be transported through the mitochondrial membranes. For this to happen, each molecule of fatty acid combines with CoA to produce a **fatty acyl CoA.** The fatty acyl CoA is an activated form of the fatty acid with a CoA attached. The fatty acyl CoA is transported across the outer membrane of the mitochondria. The acyl CoA synthetase enzyme catalyzes this activation step, which requires energy. The energy for this reaction comes from the hydrolysis of two phosphate bonds in ATP to form AMP. This is the energy-consuming step of fatty acid catabolism. The energy it consumes is equivalent to the energy needed to convert two ADP molecules to ATP.

R—C(=O)—OH + [ATP] + [HS—CoA] $\overset{\text{acyl CoA}}{\underset{\text{synthetase}}{\rightleftharpoons}}$ (R—C(=O)—S—CoA) + [AMP + 2P$_i$] + H$_2$O

fatty acid

fatty acyl CoA
(transported across outer mitochondrial membrane)

A transport system called the **carnitine shuttle** then carries fatty acyl CoA into the mitochondria matrix. To facilitate transfer, the fatty acyl CoA molecule is converted to fatty acyl carnitine. The enzyme carnitine acyltransferase catalyzes this reaction. The fatty acyl carnitine molecule passes through the inner mitochondrial membrane into the matrix where β oxidation takes place (Figure 25.16). The carnitine shuttle molecule then returns back to the cytoplasm where it can bind another fatty acyl CoA and shuttle it into the mitochondrion.

Fatty Acid β Oxidation

After they enter the mitochondrial matrix, fatty acyl CoA molecules undergo β oxidation. We also refer to the β oxidation process more simply as fatty acid oxidation. Recall that the goal of β oxidation is to break down the fatty acid to produce acetyl coenzyme A molecules. This oxidative process removes two-carbon segments from

Figure 25.16 Carnitine Shuttle.

A) Activated fatty acids in the form of fatty acyl CoA must be transported into the mitochondrial matrix where β oxidation occurs. **B)** When fatty acids are activated, the resulting fatty acyl CoAs are converted to fatty acyl carnitines and transported from the cytoplasm through the inner mitochondrial membrane into the matrix. The carnitine molecules return to the outer membrane where they can shuttle additional molecules of fatty acyl CoA into the matrix.

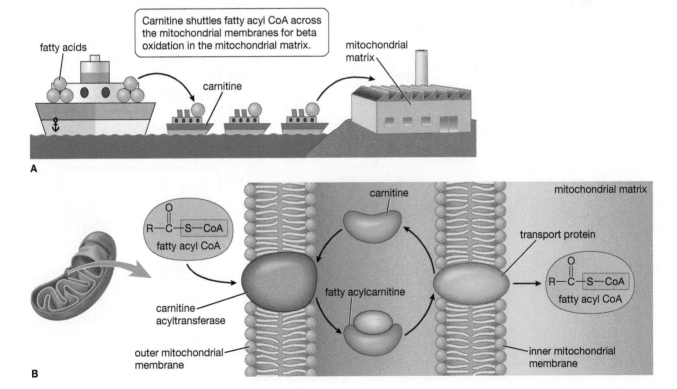

Figure 25.17 Overview of Fatty Acid β Oxidation Pathway.

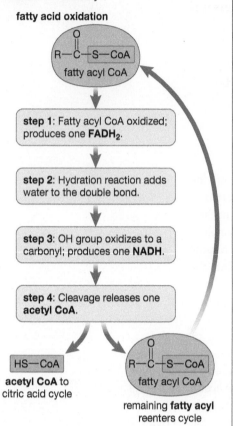

the carboxyl end of the fatty acid, producing a fatty acid molecule that is shorter by two carbon atoms. The β oxidation process involves four steps to cleave (split apart) a two-carbon unit (Figure 25.17). Each four-step series of reactions forms one molecule each of acetyl CoA, NADH, and $FADH_2$. The acetyl CoA enters the citric acid cycle, where it will produce ATP and additional high-energy electrons. The NADH and $FADH_2$ transfer electrons to the electron transport chain to generate additional ATP.

The resulting shorter fatty acid chain is now shorter by two carbon atoms (the two that were cleaved and became acetyl CoA during β oxidation). The shorter fatty acid chain enters the fatty acid oxidation cycle again and another two-carbon unit is removed by progressing through the four reactions again. This continues until the final cycle produces two molecules of acetyl CoA. For example, a 10-carbon fatty acyl CoA produces five acetyl CoA molecules and requires a total of four cycles (Figure 25.18).

Figure 25.18 Detailed View of Fatty Acid β Oxidation Pathway.

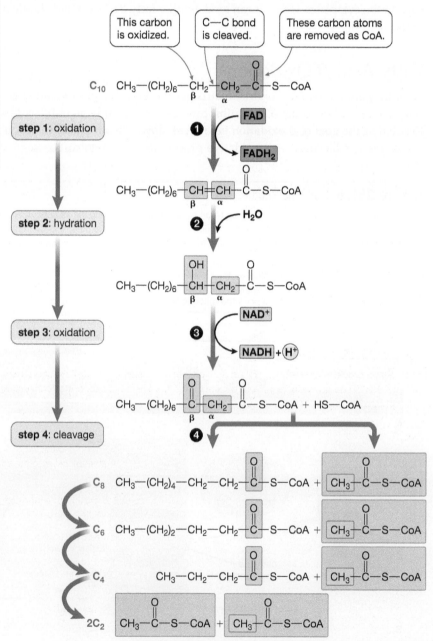

Oxidation of unsaturated fatty acids occurs in a similar way to oxidation of saturated fatty acids. However, an enzyme first converts a *cis* double bond to a trans double bond in the unsaturated fatty acid. The product with the *trans* double bond can then enter the beta oxidation pathway at step 2. This progression bypasses step 1 and therefore unsaturated fatty acids produce slightly less energy overall compared to saturated fatty acids. The $FADH_2$ count is decreased by one for every double bond found in an unsaturated fatty acid. Watch VisibleChem Video 25.1 to investigate the details of how fatty acid oxidation of both saturated and unsaturated fatty acids occurs to produce acetyl CoA.

Watch this concept come to life: **VisibleChem Video 25.1:** Beta Oxidation of Fatty Acids in the Pearson eText.

Apply what you have just learned: **Practice 25.1 and 25.2** in the Pearson eText.

Energy Yield from Fatty Acid Oxidation

Fatty acid β oxidation is an important source of ATP in our cells, particularly during moderate to light exercise (Figure 25.19).

The energy yield from a fatty acid depends on the number of carbon atoms in the original fatty acid. After the initial energy input of two molecules of ATP in the activation stage (when the fatty acid is converted to fatty acyl CoA), each fatty acid oxidation cycle produces one NADH, one $FADH_2$ and one acetyl CoA. Recall from Chapter 24, that each NADH yields 2.5 ATP molecules and each $FADH_2$ yields 1.5 ATP molecules. In addition, each CoA that proceeds through the citric acid cycle yields 10 ATP molecules. The overall equation for the β oxidation of the fatty acid palmitoyl-CoA is shown here.

$$CH_3(CH_2)_{14}C\overset{O}{\underset{SCoA}{\big\langle}} + 7FAD + 7NAD^+ + 7CoASH + 7H_2O \longrightarrow 8CH_3C\overset{O}{\underset{SCoA}{\big\langle}} + 7FADH_2 + 7NADH + 7H^+$$

16 carbon atoms

products after seven cycles of β oxidation

Figure 25.19 The "Fat Burning" Zone.

Fat oxidation provides most of our ATP production when we exercise at 60-70% of our maximum intensity. As ATP demands increase, our bodies switch from using fats for fuel to consuming carbohydrates for rapid ATP production.

Effort	Effect
maximum 90 – 100%	benefit: helps fit athletes develop speed
hard 80 – 90%	benefit: increases maximum performance capacity for shorter sessions
moderate 70 – 80%	benefit: improves aerobic fitness
light 60 – 70%	benefit: improves basic endurance and fat burning
very light 50 – 60%	benefit: helps with recovery

Explore Learn 25.1 to determine the number of ATP the 22-carbon fatty acid behenic acid produces.

Predict answers and see step-by-step solutions: **Learn 25.1:** Determining the Number of ATP Molecules Produced from a Fatty Acid in the Pearson eText.

Apply what you have just learned: **Practice 25.3** in the Pearson eText.

Ketone Bodies and Ketogenesis

When the catabolism of carbohydrates does not meet the body's energy needs, the body undergoes catabolism of fatty acids to produce the energy to carry out normal functions. As we just explored, acetyl-CoA is the major product from fatty acid β oxidation. Acetyl-CoA enters the citric acid cycle to produce ATP. As the production of acetyl CoA from fatty acid oxidation exceeds the amount of acetyl-CoA the citric acid cycle is able to process, high levels of acetyl CoA begin to accumulate in the liver. When this occurs, excess acetyl CoA proceeds down an alternative pathway called ketogenesis (Figure 25.20). This pathway produces compounds collectively known as **ketone bodies.** Ketone bodies are water-soluble molecules that contain ketone functional groups and are produced from fatty acids by the liver. Acetoacetate, β-hydroxybutyrate, and acetone are all ketone bodies. Ketone bodies are ultimately eliminated in urine and can be detected using a simple urine test.

Figure 25.20 Ketogenesis and Ketone Bodies.

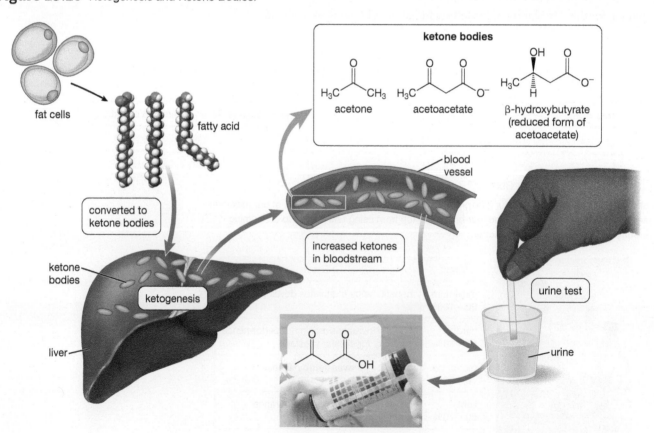

In some cases, ketone bodies accumulate in a condition called ketosis. Recall from Chapter 15 that ketosis is a metabolic state that occurs in the body during periods of starvation to ensure that the brain continues to receive enough fuel. This condition can occur during starvation, extreme dieting, or uncontrolled diabetes. All of these are associated with glucose being unavailable. In some situations, high levels of ketone bodies can be deadly. Ketoacidosis, for example, is a life-threatening condition. It is associated with low blood pH that results from the acidic nature of the ketone bodies. (See BioConnect 15.2 to review how ketosis and ketoacidosis occurs in the body.)

Quiz yourself on the content of this section: **Check 25.2** in the Pearson eText.

25.3 Protein Catabolism

Our bodies use the proteins we consume in our diets, in the same way they use fats and carbohydrates, to generate ATP (Figure 25.21).

The process of protein catabolism begins in the acidic environment of the stomach. There the proteins in our food are denatured and their molecular structure is altered. **Pepsin**, an acid-tolerant enzyme, begins to break peptide bonds between

Figure 25.21 Proteins Generate ATP in the Citric Acid Cycle and Oxidative Phosphorylation.

stage 1 · digestive tract

proteins → amino acids

carbohydrates → sugars

fats → glycerol and fatty acids

cell · stage 2

mitochondrion · stage 3

glycolysis → pyruvate oxidation → citric acid cycle → oxidative phosphorylation

glycerol

fatty acids

ATP

ATP

ATP

stages of catabolism

stage 1: During digestion, food breaks down into small molecules in the digestive tract.

stage 2: Inside our cells, the small molecules from digestion break down to produce energy (ATP).

stage 3: Inside the mitochondria of cells, high-energy electrons are removed from remaining molecules to generate more ATP.

Figure 25.22 Digesting Proteins.

Protein digestion begins in the stomach where acids denature proteins, allowing the enzyme pepsin to break peptide bonds between adjacent amino acids. The pancreas produces additional enzymes that continue to break down proteins in the small intestine. Small peptides are then transported into cells where they are digested into individual amino acids and enter the bloodstream. This process efficiently captures the amino acids from the protein we ingest, leaving little dietary protein in feces.

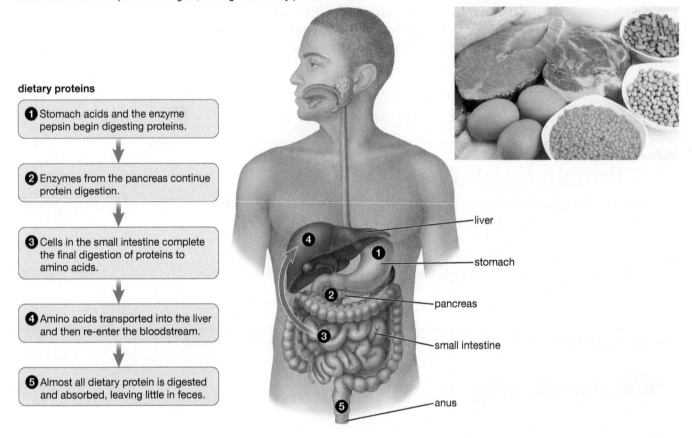

dietary proteins

1 Stomach acids and the enzyme pepsin begin digesting proteins.

2 Enzymes from the pancreas continue protein digestion.

3 Cells in the small intestine complete the final digestion of proteins to amino acids.

4 Amino acids transported into the liver and then re-enter the bloodstream.

5 Almost all dietary protein is digested and absorbed, leaving little in feces.

liver

stomach

pancreas

small intestine

anus

amino acids in the denatured polypeptides in the stomach. This process continues as polypeptides move into the small intestine. In the small intestine, additional enzymes produced in the pancreas hydrolyze peptide bonds to produce free amino acids. The amino acids are absorbed through the intestinal wall into the bloodstream and transported first to the liver and then to cells throughout the body (Figure 25.22).

The resulting amino acids are primarily used to synthesize new proteins. Explore BioConnect 25.2 (contains Figures 25.23 – 25.29) to learn more about some of the health and environmental implications of the proteins we choose to consume.

 Explore how Chemistry and Biology connect: **BioConnect: 25.2** Choosing Your Protein Sources in the Pearson eText.

Catabolism of Amino Acids

When a person consumes excess amino acids, the body does not store them like it stores carbohydrates and fats. Instead, our bodies catabolize amino acids for energy production. The catabolism of amino acids involves two parts: the removal of the amino group through the urea cycle and the reactions of the carbon skeleton once the amino group is removed (Figure 25.30).

Figure 25.30 Catabolism of Amino Acids.

A series of reactions breaks down both the amino group and the carbon skeleton of amino acids.

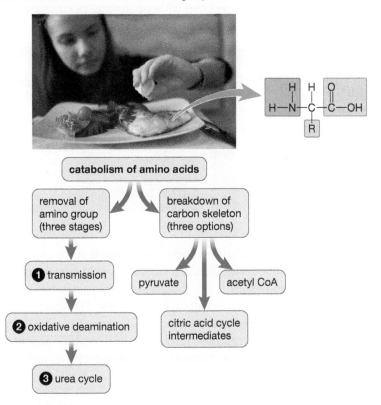

Removal of the Amino Group

The removal of the amino group from the carbon skeleton of an amino acid is the first step of amino acid catabolism. This process involves a series of reactions that ultimately produces urea and occurs in three steps: *transamination, oxidative deamination,* and the *urea cycle.* Urea is excreted in our urine.

TRANSAMINATION   In the body, amino groups freely move from one amino acid to another in the enzyme-mediated reaction **transamination.** Transamination occurs when the amino group (in the form of an ammonium cation) on an amino acid exchanges places with the carbonyl oxygen of an alpha-keto acid. Alpha-keto acids are compounds that contain a carboxylic acid group and a ketone group. For example, the amino acid alanine transfers an ammonium cation to the alpha-keto acid alpha-ketoglutarate as shown here. The product of the transamination reaction is a different alpha-keto acid (in this case pyruvate) and glutamate.

The amino group from alanine is transferred to alpha ketoglutarate.

$$CH_3-\overset{\overset{+}{N}H_3}{\underset{H}{C}}-CO_2^- \;+\; ^-OOC-\overset{O}{\overset{\|}{C}}-CH_2-CH_2-COO^- \xrightarrow{\text{transaminase}} CH_3-\overset{O}{\overset{\|}{C}}-CO_2^- \;+\; ^-OOC-\overset{\overset{+}{N}H_3}{\underset{}{CH}}-CH_2-CH_2-COO^-$$

alanine   α-ketoglutarate   pyruvate   glutamate

Figure 25.31 Processing Ammonia Waste.

Animals with access to large volumes of water, such as fish, excrete ammonium directly into their environment. Our bodies consume ATP to convert ammonium into less-toxic urea. Birds and many insects use even more ATP to further refine their ammonium wastes producing uric acid, visible here as white deposits on the rocks.

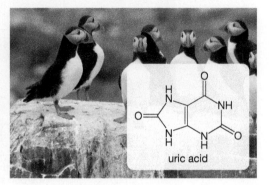

OXIDATIVE DEAMINATION The next step in the removal of the amino group from the carbon skeleton of an amino acid during catabolism is **oxidative deamination.** This process breaks the bonds and removes the nitrogen atom from glutamate to form ammonium (NH_4^+). This reaction regenerates alpha-ketoglutarate. The alpha-ketoglutarate is then available to participate again in transamination. In other words, the product alpha-ketoglutarate is recycled. This reaction also produces NADH and H^+ both of which proceed to the oxidative phosphorylation pathway and eventually produce ATP.

The ammonium (NH_4^+) produced by this stage is highly toxic to all animals. Fish and other aquatic animals often excrete ammonium directly into their environment to clear it from their bodies. Other animals, including humans and birds, invest ATP to process the ammonium into less toxic forms (Figure 25.31). In humans, ammonium enters the urea cycle, the third and final step of the removal of the amino group, which we discuss next in this section.

 Apply what you have just learned: **Practice 25.4 and 25.5** in the Pearson eText.

THE UREA CYCLE The next step in the removal of the ammonium cation features the urea cycle. The ammonium ion (NH_4^+) produced by oxidative deamination reacts with carbon dioxide in the mitochondrial matrix to produce carbamoyl phosphate. Energy from ATP drives this reaction forward. Carbamoyl phosphate enters the **urea cycle** and is converted in this four-reaction pathway to urea in the liver (Figure 25.32). Urea moves to the kidneys and our bodies excrete it in urine. The urea cycle is the primary metabolic pathway that eliminates the excess nitrogen from amino acid catabolism.

Figure 25.32 The Urea Cycle.

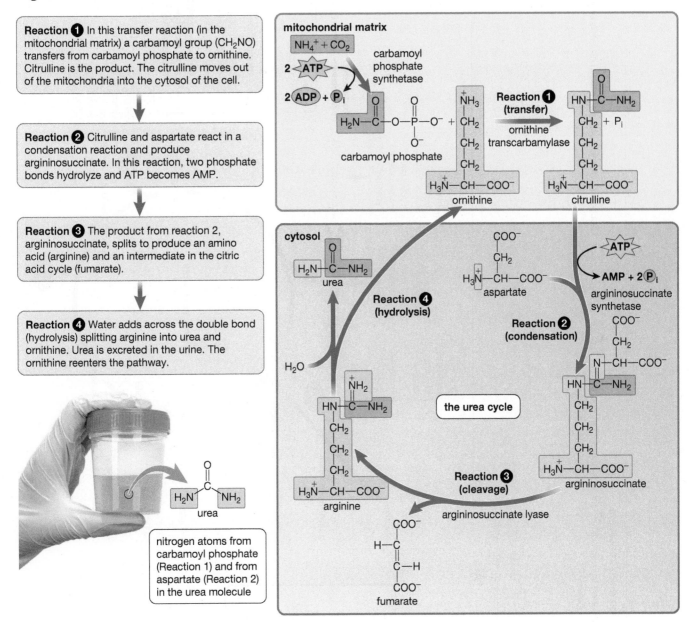

Reaction ❶ In this transfer reaction (in the mitochondrial matrix) a carbamoyl group (CH₂NO) transfers from carbamoyl phosphate to ornithine. Citrulline is the product. The citrulline moves out of the mitochondria into the cytosol of the cell.

Reaction ❷ Citrulline and aspartate react in a condensation reaction and produce argininosuccinate. In this reaction, two phosphate bonds hydrolyze and ATP becomes AMP.

Reaction ❸ The product from reaction 2, argininosuccinate, splits to produce an amino acid (arginine) and an intermediate in the citric acid cycle (fumarate).

Reaction ❹ Water adds across the double bond (hydrolysis) splitting arginine into urea and ornithine. Urea is excreted in the urine. The ornithine reenters the pathway.

nitrogen atoms from carbamoyl phosphate (Reaction 1) and from aspartate (Reaction 2) in the urea molecule

Carbon Skeleton Breakdown

After the amino group is removed in the first part of amino acid catabolism, the carbon skeleton from the amino acid continues to be catabolized through several pathways. We do not study the detailed reactions involved with these pathways here. However, we do discuss what happens to each carbon skeleton. In general, there are three common fates of the carbon skeleton. It is converted to pyruvate, acetyl CoA, or another intermediate in the citric acid cycle (Figure 25.33).

In some of these production paths, the carbon skeleton of the amino acid generates energy and in other paths, the skeleton is a building block for other molecules that the body needs. For example, when a carbon skeleton catabolizes to pyruvate, it can be broken down for energy or used to synthesize glucose. **Glucogenic** amino acid skeletons produce pyruvate or other metabolites that can be converted into glucose through gluconeogenesis.

In contrast to glucogenic amino acids, many amino acid skeletons produce acetyl CoA and do not go on to produce glucose. However, they can produce ketone bodies. These

Figure 25.33 Amino Acid Carbon Skeletons in Amino Acid Catabolism.

The carbon skeletons from broken down amino acids are converted to metabolites, such as acetyl-CoA and pyruvate, of the citric acid cycle. Glucogenic amino acids (red boxes) go on to produce glucose. Ketogenic amino acids (blue boxes) produce ketone bodies.

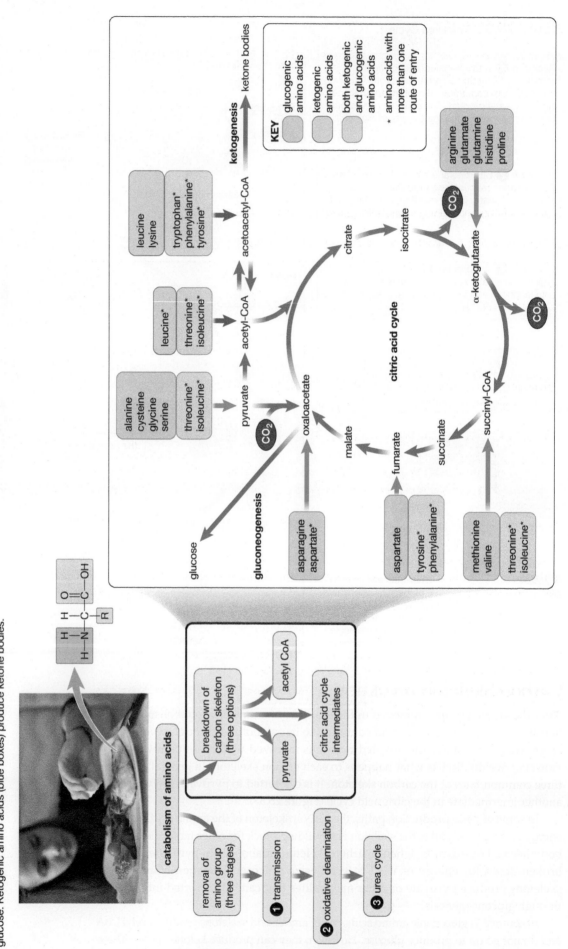

amino acids are **ketogenic**. Leucine is an example of a ketogenic amino acid. Some amino acids are both glucogenic and ketogenic, such as phenylalanine. Figure 25.33 illustrates where each amino acid carbon skeleton feeds into the cycle as well as indicating which amino acids are glucogenic, ketogenic, or both. After studying the figure, explore VisibleChem Videos 25.2 and 25.3 to investigate the reactions in the urea cycle in more detail and learn more about the fate of the carbon skeleton once the amino group is removed.

Watch this concept come to life: **VisibleChem Video 25.2:** Removing Amino Groups from Amino Acids and **VisibleChem Video 25.3:** The Fate of the Carbon Skeletons from Amino Acids in the Pearson eText.

Apply what you have just learned: **Practice 25.6–25.8** in the Pearson eText.

Quiz yourself on the content of this section: **Check 25.3** in the Pearson eText.

25.4 Fatty Acid Synthesis

In addition to catabolizing amino acids, our bodies synthesize fatty acids. This is a critical function as fatty acids help form cell membranes and serve as signaling molecules in our cells. Unlike the catabolism of fatty acids, which occurs in the mitochondria, the synthesis of fatty acids occurs in the cell cytoplasm. While synthesis involves a different pathway with different enzymes than catabolism, there are some similarities between fatty acid catabolism and synthesis. Recall that in fatty acid catabolism, fatty acids are broken down two-carbons at a time. Similarly, in fatty acid synthesis, two-carbon units from acetyl CoA are added one at a time. This process of synthesizing fatty acids two carbons at a time is called **lipogenesis.**

In general, our bodies make fatty acids when excess food is available. When we eat more food than the body needs for energy production, our bodies convert the excess acetyl CoA to fatty acids and then to fats for storage. A malfunction in the balance of the degradation of fats and the synthesis of fats is at the heart of obesity and many other conditions that contribute to metabolic syndrome. Non-alcoholic fatty liver disease (NAFLD), for example, occurs when excess fats accumulate in the liver (Figure 25.34). Fatty livers overproduce both glucose and triacylglycerides, contributing to obesity and metabolic syndrome.

Figure 25.34 Non-Alcoholic Fatty Liver Disease (NAFLD).

Excess lipogenesis in the liver leads to fatty liver disease. Fatty livers overproduce glucose and triglycerides, contributing to metabolic syndrome. About 100 million people in the U.S. are believed to have NAFLD.

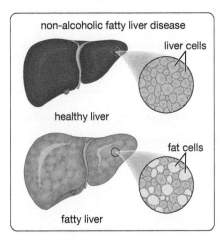

Acyl Carrier Protein

The process of lipogenesis cannot begin until the two initial reactants, acetyl CoA and malonyl CoA, are activated. These two molecules are activated when an **acyl carrier protein (ACP)** is transferred, forming acetyl ACP and malonyl ACP respectively. The enzymes acetyl transacylase and malonyl transacylase catalyze these reactions.

$$CH_3-\overset{\overset{\displaystyle O}{\|}}{C}-S-CoA + HS-\boxed{ACP} \xrightarrow{\text{acetyl-CoA transacylase}} CH_3-\overset{\overset{\displaystyle O}{\|}}{C}-S-\boxed{ACP} + HS-CoA$$

acetyl-CoA   acetyl-ACP

activated starting reactants for fatty acid synthesis

$$^-O-\overset{\overset{\displaystyle O}{\|}}{C}-CH_2-\overset{\overset{\displaystyle O}{\|}}{C}-S-CoA + HS-\boxed{ACP} \xrightarrow{\text{malonyl-CoA transacylase}} {}^-O-\overset{\overset{\displaystyle O}{\|}}{C}-CH_2-\overset{\overset{\displaystyle O}{\|}}{C}-S-\boxed{ACP} + HS-CoA$$

malonyl-CoA   malonyl-ACP

Once these two molecules are produced, the lipogenesis cycle begins. In the first step of fatty acid synthesis, an ACP-activated acyl group (malonyl ACP) combines with an ACP-activated acetyl group (acetyl ACP).

Fatty Acid Synthesis Reactions

The rest of the fatty acid synthesis process is a cycle of four reactions that add two carbon acetyl units from acetyl CoA to a continuously growing carbon chain (Figure 25.35). The four reactions proceed in the following order: *condensation, reduction, dehydration,* and *reduction.*

The cycle repeats, adding a two-carbon unit each time. Chains up to 16 carbon atoms long (palmitic acid) are produced this way. In this specific example, after seven cycles, C_{16} palmitoyl ACP is produced and ultimately hydrolyzed to palmitate (C_{16}). The overall reaction is given. If the body needs longer fatty acid chains, another fragment is added to palmitic acid using a different pathway.

$$8\text{acetyl CoA} + 14\text{NADPH} + 14\text{H}^+ + 7\text{ATP} \longrightarrow \text{palmitate} + 14\text{NADP}^+ + 8\text{HS-CoA} + 7\text{ADP} + 7\text{P}_i + 6\text{H}_2\text{O}$$

 Quiz yourself on the content of this section: **Check 25.4** in the Pearson eText.

Figure 25.35 Fatty Acid Synthesis.

Fatty acids are synthesized by the addition of two carbon atoms at a time in a four-reaction cycle.

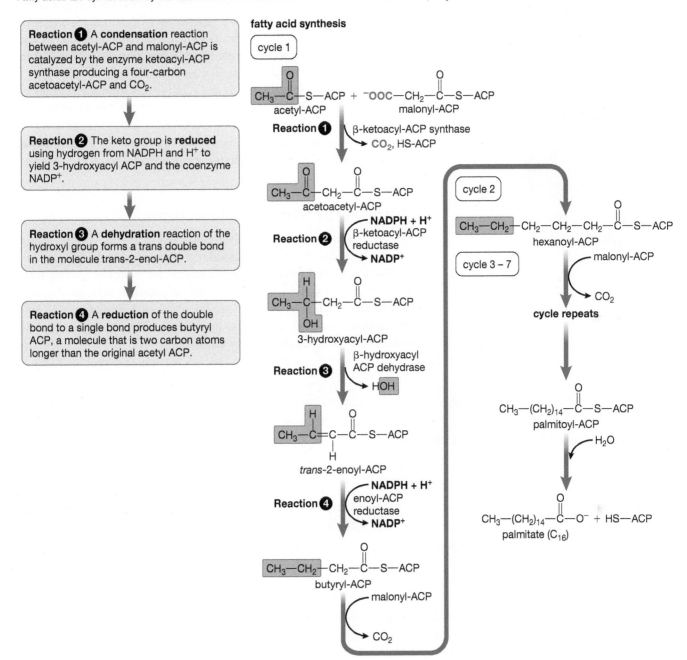

Reaction ❶ A **condensation** reaction between acetyl-ACP and malonyl-ACP is catalyzed by the enzyme ketoacyl-ACP synthase producing a four-carbon acetoacetyl-ACP and CO_2.

Reaction ❷ The keto group is **reduced** using hydrogen from NADPH and H^+ to yield 3-hydroxyacyl ACP and the coenzyme $NADP^+$.

Reaction ❸ A **dehydration** reaction of the hydroxyl group forms a trans double bond in the molecule trans-2-enol-ACP.

Reaction ❹ A **reduction** of the double bond to a single bond produces butyryl ACP, a molecule that is two carbon atoms longer than the original acetyl ACP.

25.5 Amino Acid Synthesis

Our body needs 20 different amino acids to make the protein chains we need. A lack of any of these amino acids can be life threatening. Serine deficiency, for example, can occur if an individual inherits nonfunctional versions of any of the enzymes involved in serine synthesis. Serine deficiency causes severe neurological symptoms (Figure 25.36). If patients are diagnosed early, they can reduce their symptoms by taking daily oral doses of serine.

Figure 25.36 Serine Deficiency.

Individuals who cannot synthesize serine can have severe neurological defects, including microcephaly, a condition where the brain does not develop fully, and the head is unusually small.

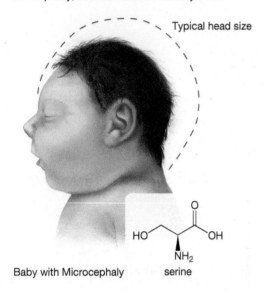

Baby with Microcephaly   serine

Eleven of the 20 amino acids our bodies use to build proteins are described as nonessential because we do not need to get them from our diet. These eleven are synthesized in the body from other compounds. Therefore, it is not essential that we obtain them from food. Serine is an example of an amino acid that is nonessential. The remaining nine amino acids are essential, and we must get them in our diet. (See Table 20.1 to review all the essential and nonessential amino acids.)

Most nonessential amino acids are synthesized from metabolites of either glycolysis or the citric acid cycle (Figure 25.37). For example, the citric acid cycle intermediates oxaloacetate and α-ketoglutarate are precursors to the amino acids aspartate, glutamate, asparagine, glutamine, and proline. Glycolysis intermediates are precursors to serine, alanine, glycine, and cysteine.

Amino Acid Synthesis Reactions

Some nonessential amino acids are synthesized in the body by reversing the transamination reaction discussed in the amino acid catabolism section (Section 25.3). Pyruvate from glycolysis, for example, undergoes a transamination reaction with glutamate to produce alanine. Alanine transaminase (ALT) enzyme catalyzes the reaction. A similar transamination reaction converts oxaloacetate to aspartate. The enzymes aspartate transaminase (AST) catalyzes that reaction.

$$^-OOC-\overset{\overset{+}{N}H_3}{\underset{|}{C}H}-CH_2-CH_2-COO^- + CH_3-\overset{\overset{O}{||}}{C}-COO^- \xrightarrow{\text{alanine aminotransferase}} CH_3-\overset{\overset{+}{N}H_3}{\underset{|}{C}H}-COO^- + {}^-OOC-\overset{\overset{O}{||}}{C}-CH_2-CH_2-COO^-$$

glutamate   pyruvate   alanine   α-ketoglutarate

$$^-OOC-\overset{\overset{+}{N}H_3}{\underset{|}{C}H}-CH_2-CH_2-COO^- + {}^-OOC-\overset{\overset{O}{||}}{C}-CH_2-COO^- \underset{\text{transaminase}}{\overset{\text{aspartate}}{\rightleftharpoons}} {}^-OOC-\overset{\overset{+}{N}H_3}{\underset{|}{C}H}-CH_2-COO^- + {}^-OOC-\overset{\overset{O}{||}}{C}-CH_2-CH_2-COO^-$$

glutamate   oxaloacetate   aspartate   α-ketoglutarate

Figure 25.37 Synthesis of Non-Essential Amino Acids.

Our cells can synthesize 11 of the 20 amino acids we use to produce proteins. (Tyrosine is considered a non-essential amino acid because mammals produce it during the degradation of phenylalanine.)

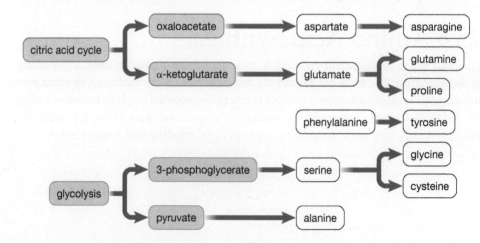

For the body to synthesize other nonessential amino acids, additional reactions must occur. One such reaction is the conversion of glutamate to glutamine by the addition of a second amino group. The glutamine synthetase enzyme catalyzes this reaction using energy from the hydrolysis of ATP.

Amino group is transferred to glutamate forming glutamine.

$$\overset{\overset{+}{N}H_3}{^-OOC-CH-CH_2-CH_2-COO^-} + \boxed{NH_3} \xrightarrow[\text{ATP} \quad \text{ADP + P}_i]{\text{Glutamine synthetase}} \overset{\overset{+}{N}H_3 \qquad\quad O}{^-OOC-CH-CH_2-CH_2-C-\boxed{NH_2}}$$

glutamate

glutamine

Quiz yourself on the content of this section: **Check 25.5** in the Pearson eText.

Chapter Summary

25.1 Digestion of Fats and Cholesterol

Learning Objective: Describe how fats and cholesterol are digested in the body.

Our bodies metabolize fats from stores in our bodies as well as the foods in our diet to produce energy. Most of the fats we consume are in the form of triacylglycerols. Hydrophobic fat globules form in our digestive tract. Bile salts emulsify the fat globules to form micelles – small fat water soluble droplets that are easier for fat-digesting enzymes to access. A class of enzymes called lipases, which are released from the pancreas into the small intestine, split the triacylglycerols into glycerol and fatty acids. Once inside the cells lining the small intestine, glycerol and fatty acids recombine to reform triacylglycerols. The body packages these triacylglycerols as low-density lipoproteins (LDL) and high-density lipoproteins (HDL). LDL is commonly called "bad" cholesterol because high levels of LDL can form plagues on blood vessels, increasing risk of heart disease and stroke. HDL, however, absorbs cholesterol and carries it to the liver. High levels of HDLs are associated with a decreased risk of heart attack and stroke.

BioConnect 25.1: Cholesterol in Our Diets

Key Terms

bile	lipases	micelles
bile salts	lipoproteins	plaque
glycerol		

25.2 Fat Catabolism

Learning Objective: Describe β oxidation of fatty acids and determine the ATP yield from fatty acid oxidation.

The body metabolizes both glycerol and fatty acids in cells to produce ATP. Glycerol is metabolized in the liver where it is converted to dihydroxyacetone phosphate in two enzyme-mediated reactions. If dihydroxyacetone phosphate enters the glycolysis pathway, there is a net yield of 20 ATP molecules from each glycerol molecule. Fatty acids undergo a four-step process called beta oxidation (β oxidation) which removes two-carbon segments from the carboxyl end of the fatty acid. The cycle repeats until the original fatty acid is completely broken down to acetyl CoA. Every four-step series of reactions forms one molecule each of acetyl CoA, NADH, and $FADH_2$. The acetyl CoA enters the citric acid cycle to be further metabolized. The length of the fatty acid carbon chain determines how many cycles occur and therefore how much ATP is produced in the citric acid cycle. When the production of acetyl CoA exceeds the processing capacity of the citric acid cycle, acetyl CoA proceeds down an alternative pathway called ketogenesis. Ketogenesis produces compounds collectively known as ketone bodies.

VisibleChem Video 25.1: Beta Oxidation of Fatty Acids.

Key Terms

beta oxidation (fatty acid β oxidation)
carnitine shuttle
fatty acyl CoA
ketone bodies

25.3 Protein Catabolism

Learning Objective: Describe the catabolism of amino acids including the removal of the amino group and the pathways involved in the breakdown of the amino acid carbon skeleton.

The catabolism of amino acids has two parts: the removal of the amino group (in the form of an ammonium cation) and the breakdown of the carbon skeleton. The removal of the amino group involves transamination, oxidative deamination, and the urea cycle. The urea cycle is a series of four reactions that ultimately produces urea to be excreted in urine. The remaining carbon skeleton has three possible fates. Skeletons may be converted to pyruvate, to acetyl CoA, or into another intermediate in the citric acid cycle.

In some cases, the carbon skeleton generates energy but in other cases the skeleton becomes a building block for other molecules that the body needs. Glucogenic amino acids break down into metabolites that produce glucose. Ketogenic amino acids break down into metabolites that produce ketone bodies.

BioConnect 25.2: Choosing Your Protein Sources

VisibleChem Video 25.2: Removing Amino Groups from Amino Acids.

VisibleChem Video 25.3: The Fate of the Carbon Skeletons from Amino Acids.

Key Terms

complete protein (from BioConnect 25.2)	ketogenic	transamination
	oxidative deamination	urea cycle
glucogenic	pepsin	

25.4 Fatty Acid Synthesis

Learning Objective: Describe the synthesis of fatty acids from acetyl CoA

Fatty acids are synthesized by adding two-carbon units at a time in a process called lipogenesis. This process is activated by the acyl carrier protein (ACP) to which the growing fatty acid chain is attached. In the first step of fatty acid synthesis, an ACP activated acyl group (malonyl ACP) combines with an ACP activated acetyl group (acetyl ACP). Once these two molecules are prepared, the lipogenesis cycle begins. The remainder of a fatty acid synthesis involves a cycle of four reactions that adds two carbon acetyl units from acetyl CoA to a continuously growing carbon chain (Figure 25.35). The four reactions proceed in this order: condensation, reduction, dehydration, and reduction. The cycle repeats until the fatty acid chain has been synthesized.

Key Terms

acyl carrier protein (ACP)
lipogenesis

25.5 Amino Acid Synthesis

Learning Objective: Describe the general pathways involved with the synthesis of nonessential amino acids from intermediates of glycolysis and the citric acid cycle.

Eleven amino acids are synthesized in the body. We must consume the remaining nine so-called essential amino acids in our diet. Amino acids are synthesized from the *intermediate* metabolites of glycolysis or the citric acid cycle, which undergo enzyme-catalyzed transamination reactions.

 End-of-Chapter Quiz

Have you mastered the content of this chapter? Try the **End-of-Chapter Quiz** in the Pearson eText.

1. Which statement best describes the role of bile salts in digestion?

a) Bile salts are hydrophobic and help break up fat globules into small fat droplets called micelles. As a result, the hydrophobic ends of the fat droplets in micelles become more lipid-soluble and easier for fat-digesting enzymes in the cell membrane to access.

b) Bile salts contain both hydrophobic and hydrophilic regions that help break up fat globules into small fat droplets called micelles. The hydrophilic ends of the bile salts make micelles more water-soluble and easier for fat-digesting enzymes to access.

c) Bile salts react with fatty acids to form triacylglycerols that break up fat globules to form small fat droplets called micelles. The hydrophilic ends on the triacylglycerols make micelles more water-soluble and easier for fat-digesting enzymes to access.

d) Bile salts attach to lipase enzymes through ester linkages that hydrolyze micelles into fat droplets. The fat droplets then bind and free bile salts to form oxidative micelles that catabolize long chain fatty acids to form ATP, acetyl CoA, and complex III.

2. Which reaction represents hydrolysis between a lipase enzyme and a triacylglycerol molecule?

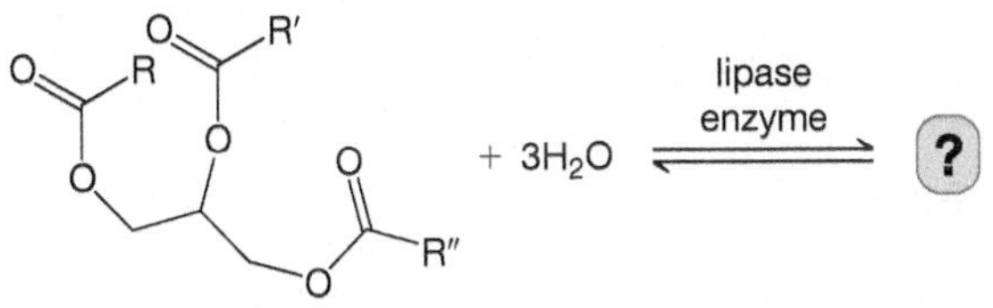

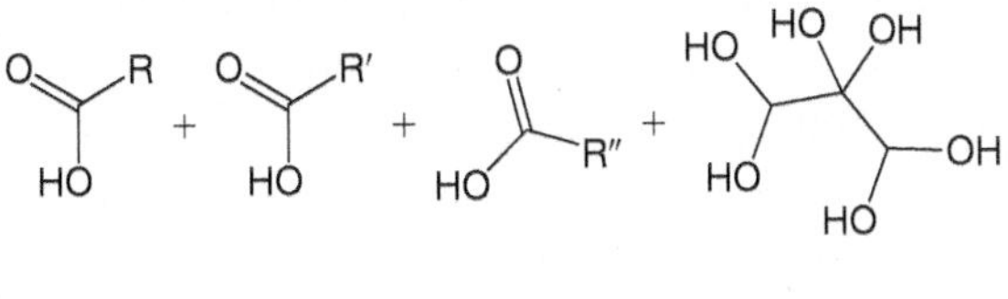

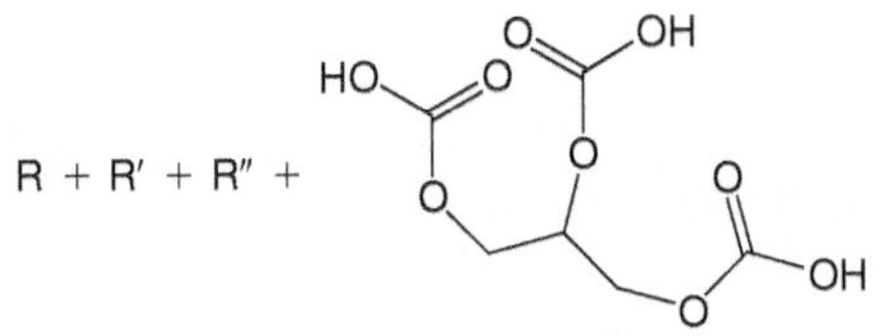

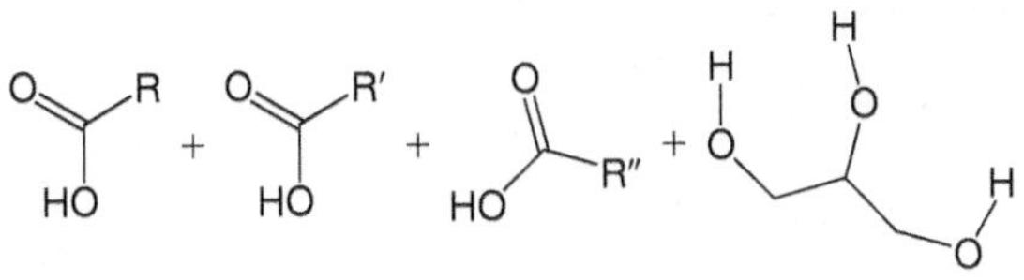

d)

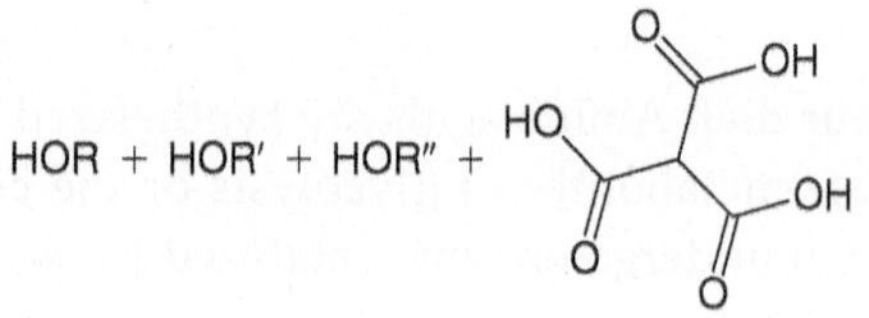

HOR + HOR' + HOR'' +

e)

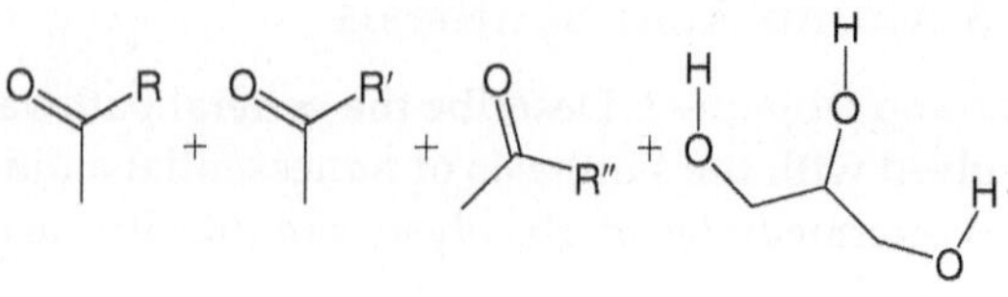

3. Most of the glycerol resulting from the breakdown of triacylglycerols is metabolized in the liver where it is converted in two enzymatic reactions into which molecule?

a) α-ketoglutarate   b) phosphoserine   c) dihydroxyacetone phosphate

d) oxaloacetate   e) β-hydroxybutyric acid

4. The alpha (α) and beta (β) positions are two important sites on a fatty acid for the β-oxidative process. Which diagram correctly identifies these two sites on the palmitic acid molecule?

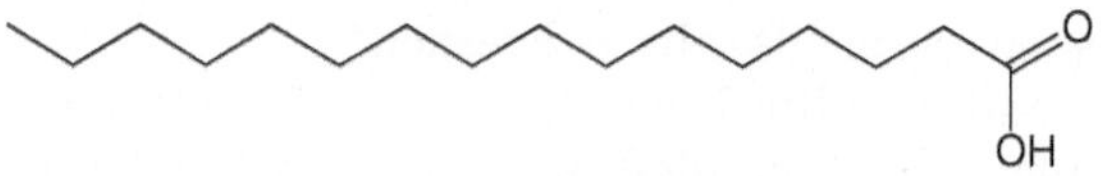

C_{16} palmitic acid

a)

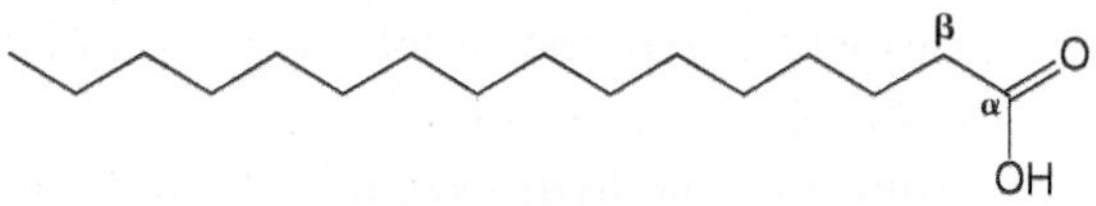

C_{16} palmitic acid

b)

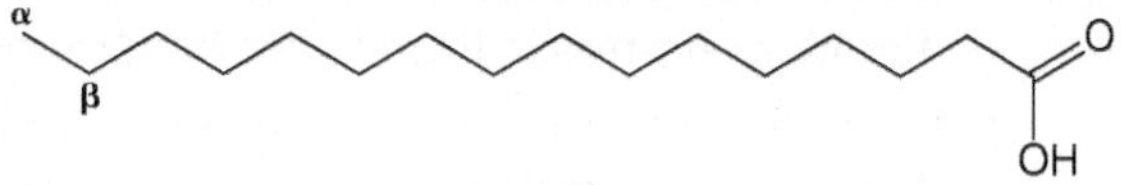

C_{16} palmitic acid

c)

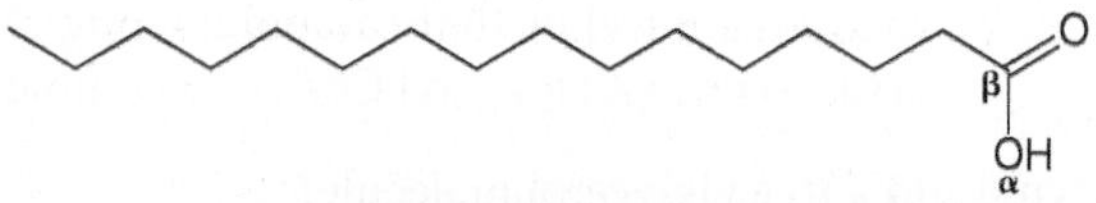

C_{16} palmitic acid

d)

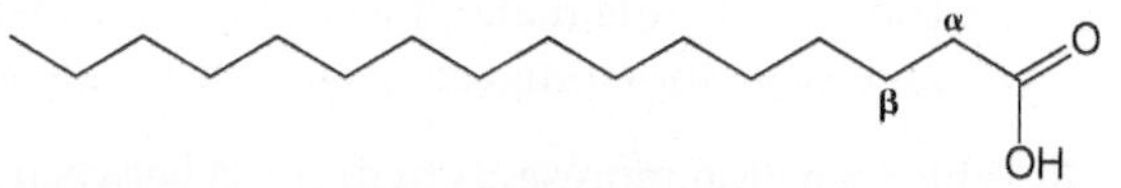

C_{16} palmitic acid

e)

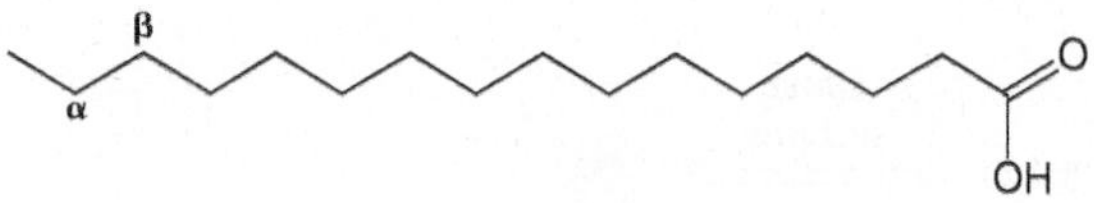

C_{16} palmitic acid

5. Before β oxidation can occur, fatty acids are transported through the inner mitochondrial membrane. For this to happen, a molecule of fatty acid combines with CoA to produce a fatty acyl CoA, which is transported across the outer membrane of the mitochondria. The acyl CoA synthetase enzyme catalyzes this step, which requires energy. Lauric acid $CH_3(CH_2)_{10}COOH$ is a fatty acid found in coconut milk, coconut oil, human breast milk, cow's milk, and goat's milk. Identify the products of the given fatty acid activation reaction.

$$CH_3(CH)_{10}-C-OH + ATP + HS-CoA \underset{synthetase}{\overset{Acyl\ CoA}{\rightleftharpoons}} CH_3(CH)_{10}-C-S-CoA + \boxed{?} + H_2O$$

a) AMP + 2 phosphate (P_i) groups   b) glycerol + CO_2

c) ADP + 1 phosphate (P_i) group   d) NAD$^+$ + 2 phosphate (P_i) groups

6. Stearic acid is one of the most common fatty acids in nature. During the first round of β oxidation of stearic acid, which two carbon atoms are removed from the C_{18} carbon chain?

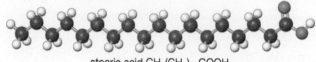

stearic acid $CH_3(CH_2)_{16}COOH$

a)

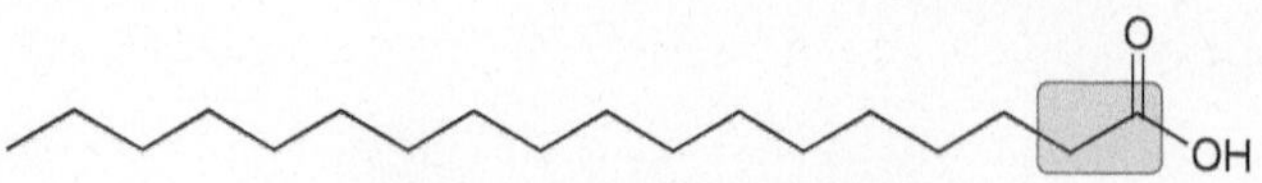

stearic acid $CH_3(CH_2)_{16}COOH$

b)

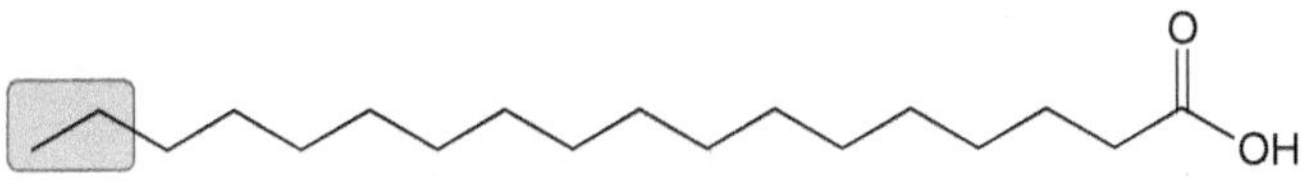

stearic acid $CH_3(CH_2)_{16}COOH$

c)

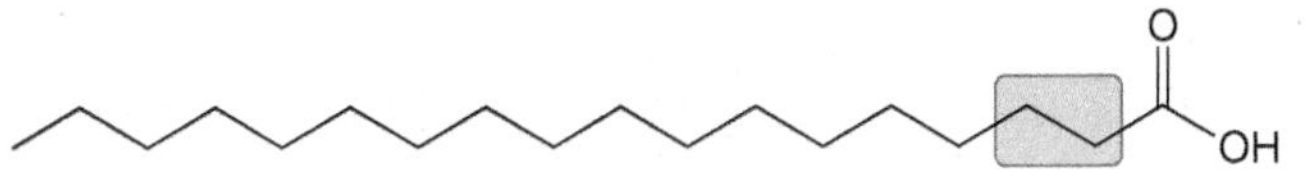

stearic acid $CH_3(CH_2)_{16}COOH$

d)

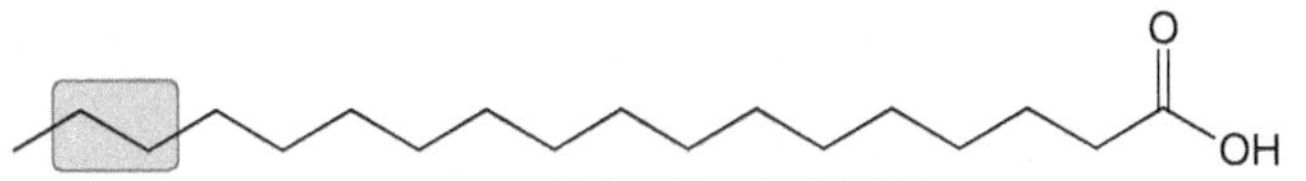

stearic acid $CH_3(CH_2)_{16}COOH$

7. When the body produces more acetyl CoA from fatty acid oxidation than the citric acid cycle is able to process, excess acetyl CoA proceeds down the alternative ketogenesis pathway. This pathway produces compounds collectively known as ketone bodies. In some cases, ketone bodies accumulate in a condition called ketosis. This condition occurs when the body experiences starvation, extreme dieting, and diabetes, all of which are associated with the unavailability of glucose. Which of the molecules shown is *not* a ketone body?

a)

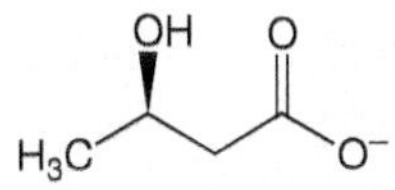

β-hydroxybutyrate

b)

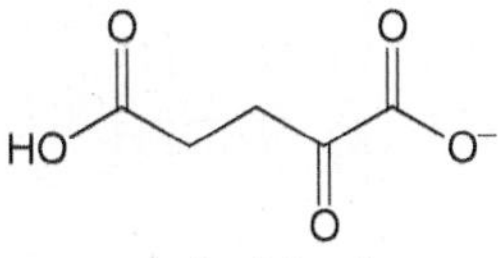

α-ketoglutarate

c)

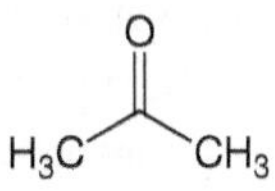

acetone

d)

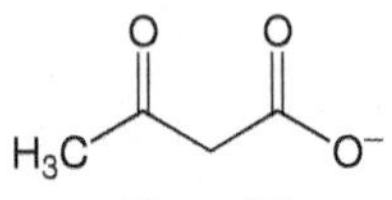

acetoacetate

8. How many phosphate bonds of ATP form or break (hydrolyze) when a fatty acid molecule converts to a fatty acyl CoA molecule?
   a) Conversion to an activated fatty acyl CoA molecule involves the formation of two phosphate bonds in ATP.

   b) Conversion to an activated fatty acyl CoA molecule involves the hydrolysis of four phosphate bonds in ATP.

   c) Conversion to an activated fatty acyl CoA molecule involves the formation of three phosphate bonds in ATP.

   d) Conversion to an activated fatty acyl CoA molecule involves the formation of two phosphate bonds in ATP.

9. How many molecules of ATP ultimately form or are consumed in each cycle of β oxidation after the initial activated fatty acyl CoA molecule has been produced and the products of β oxidation have gone through the oxidative phosphorylation process?
   a) One molecule of ATP forms from each cycle of β oxidation after the initial activated fatty acyl CoA molecule is produced.

   b) Four molecules of ATP ultimately form from each cycle of β oxidation after the initial activated fatty acyl CoA molecule is produced.

   c) Two molecules of ATP are ultimately consumed in each cycle of β oxidation after the initial activated fatty acyl CoA molecule is produced.

   d) Three molecules of ATP are ultimately consumed in each cycle of β oxidation after the initial activated fatty acyl CoA molecule is produced.

10. Which is *not* a step in the β oxidation of fatty acids?
    a) oxidation
    b) cleavage
    c) hydration
    d) hydrogenation

11. Which is *not* a product of β oxidation?
    a) NH_3 **b)** $FADH_2$
    c) acetyl CoA   **d)** NADH

12. Which products form during the transamination of the amino acid serine?

a)

b)

c)

d)

---

13. During the catabolism of amino acids, what are the carbon skeletons of amino acids converted to after the amino groups are removed from the amino acids?
  a) pyruvate, acetyl CoA, or another intermediate in the citric acid cycle
  b) uric acid, glycerol, and an intermediate in the citric acid cycle
  c) oxalate, coenzyme Q (CoQ), and an intermediate in glycolysis
  d) pyruvate, stearate, and an intermediate in carbonic acid synthesis

14. Choose the correct statement about the role of the urea cycle in the body.
  a) A primary role of the urea cycle is to reduce the body's need for ammonia during amino acid synthesis and transamination.
  b) A primary role of the urea cycle is to enhance the body's ability to convert urea into ammonia so that it is rapidly absorbed by the mitochondria.
  c) A primary role of the urea cycle is the absorption of additional nitrogen for the synthesis of fatty acids.
  d) A primary role of the urea cycle is the elimination of excess nitrogen from amino acid degradation.

15. Which amino acids do not go on to produce glucose but instead produce ketone bodies?
  a) glucogenic amino acids
  b) ketogenic amino acids
  c) β-oxidative amino acids
  d) ketoglutamic amino acids

16. Select the process that requires the acyl carrier protein (ACP).
  a) β oxidation
  b) glycolysis

  c) fatty acid synthesis
  d) gluconeogenesis
  e) oxidative phosphorylation

17. Which two molecules must form before the first cycle of lipogenesis can begin?
  a) hexanoyl-ACP and acetyl-ACP
  b) acetyl-CoA and NADH
  c) malonyl-ACP and acetyl-ACP
  d) pantothenic acid and $FADH_2$
  e) malonyl-ATP and acetyl-ATP

18. Which coenzyme(s) is involved in chain elongation in fatty acid synthesis?
  a) $FADH_2$ **b)** NADH
  c) Acetyl CoA and CoQ   **d)** NADPH
  e) AMP and $FADH_2$

19. Which enzyme involved in fatty acid synthesis is responsible for the combination of malonyl Co-A with ACP to produce malonyl ACP? Hint: Review the equations and diagrams in Section 25.4 to answer this question.
  a) Acetyl CoA transacylase
  b) Enoyl ACP reductase
  c) malonyl CoA transacylase
  d) 3-ketoacyl ACP reductase

20. Which enzyme catalyzes the formation of an alkene during fatty acid synthesis? Hint: Refer to the equations and diagrams in Section 25.4 to answer this question.
  a) 3-ketoacyl ACP synthase
  b) 3-hydroxyacyl ACP dehydratase
  c) 3-ketoacyl ACP reductase
  d) enoyl ACP reductase

Unit 10
Bringing It All Together

What Is Metabolic Syndrome and How Does It Affect Our Health?

CHEMISTRY APPLICATION We opened Unit 10 with a look at the looming public health threat associated with rising rates of obesity and metabolic syndrome (MetS). Individuals with MetS are encouraged to make several lifestyle changes to help reverse their risk factors including eating a balanced diet, incorporating at least 150 minutes of moderate physical activity into their schedule each week, and losing weight (Figure U10.5).

Figure U10.5 Lifestyle Changes.

For many patients, long-term lifestyle changes such as incorporating moderate exercise can help reduce the risk factors associated with metabolic syndrome.

Figure U10.6 Statins are Structurally Similar to HMG-CoA, an Intermediate Required for Cholesterol Synthesis.

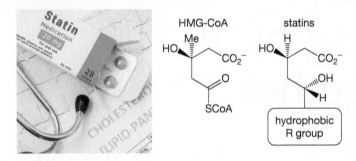

If these efforts aren't enough, an array of medications are available to help control blood pressure, reduce cholesterol levels, and increase insulin sensitivity. Many of these drugs target enzymes and pathways we've examined in this unit. Statins, for example, are a class of molecules commonly prescribed to help improve the blood lipids of patients with metabolic syndrome. Statins are structurally similar to the substrate for HMG-CoA reductase, an enzyme involved in cholesterol synthesis. Statins bind at the active site of HMG-CoA reductase, reducing the amount of cholesterol produced by the liver (Figure U10.6).

Metformin is another commonly prescribed drug that helps increase insulin sensitivity in patients with MetS and type 2 diabetes. An estimated 80 million adults in the U.S. are taking metformin. Metformin is an alkaloid originally derived from the French lily (Figure U10.7). While the precise mechanisms are well-described for most modern drugs, some older products, such as metformin, are still relatively poorly understood.

Figure U10.7 Metformin.

Metformin is a widely used drug originally derived from the French lily.

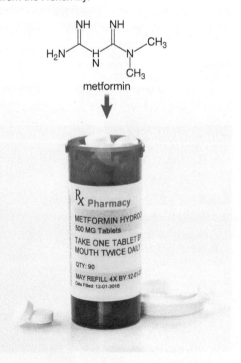

Figure U10.8 A Possible Mechanism for Metformin.

Metformin is believed to interfere with the electron transport chain in oxidative phosphorylation. This increases the AMP:ATP ratio in the cell, ultimately decreasing gluconeogenesis in the liver and increasing fatty acid oxidation.

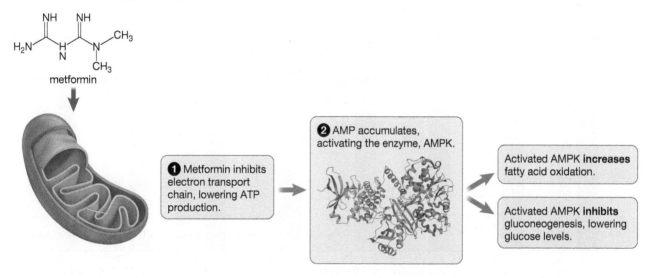

Metformin has been shown to accumulate in the mitochondria where it inhibits the electron transport chain in the inner mitochondrial membrane. This shuts down oxidative phosphorylation and causes low-energy ADP and AMP to accumulate in the cell. The elevated levels of AMP indicate that energy balance is compromised in the cell and activates an enzyme called AMP-activated protein kinase (AMPK). Activated AMPK increases fatty acid oxidation in the liver and muscle. This enzyme also helps regulate glucose levels in the body by triggering a negative feedback loop that inhibits gluconeogenesis, lowering the amount of glucose produced in the liver (Figure U10.8).

Understanding the basic structure of common metabolic pathways can help us understand some of the approaches to treating and preventing complex disorders such as MetS. It also opens the door to understanding how many common medications work and the steps we can all take towards better health.

Questions to Think About

1. Does gluconeogenesis produce or consume ATP? Why might a cell shut down gluconeogenesis in response to metformin?

2. Does fatty acid oxidation produce or consume ATP? Why might a cell increase the rate of fatty acid oxidation in response to metformin?

A Closer Look at the Data

Scientists have been looking for a reliable *marker* for metabolic syndrome. Markers are measurable values that can be used to accurately diagnose or predict disease. In addition, they can often help scientists better understand the underlying causes of a given disease.

In 2019, a group of researchers in Taiwan published the results of an exciting study that identified a new protein marker, called S14, associated with metabolic syndrome (Chen *et al*, 2019). The authors collected blood samples from 327 individuals, including 98 (30%) with MetS. They then compared the levels of S14 in the blood of individuals with and without MetS. Figure U10.9 is from their paper.

Figure U10.9 S14 Levels in the Blood of Individuals with and Without Metabolic Syndrome.
(from Chen, *et al.*, 2019).

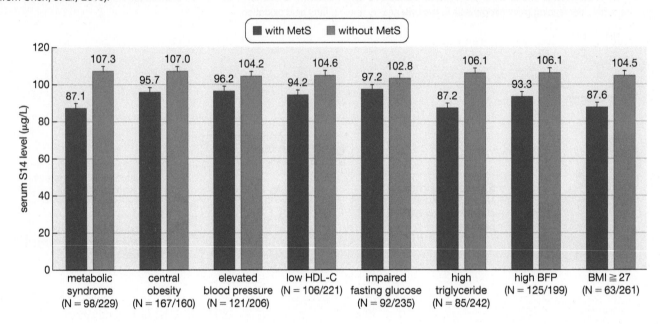

Questions to Think About

Examine this Figure U10.9 and use it to answer the following questions:

1. Graphs can help reveal relationships between variables. What are the variables on each axis of this graph?

2. What is the approximate difference in the average blood levels of S14 in an individual with MetS and one without MetS?

3. Is the level of S14 consistently different in individuals with individual risk factors for metabolic syndrome such as obesity and elevated blood pressure?

4. If the levels of S14 could be controlled with a drug, would you want to increase or decrease levels of this protein in the blood? Explain.

Reference

Chen Y-T, Tseng P-H, Tseng F-Y, Chi Y-C, Han D-S, Yang W-S (2019) The serum level of a novel lipogenic protein Spot 14 was reduced in metabolic syndrome. PLoS ONE 14(2): e0212341. https://doi.org/10.1371/journal.pone.0212341

Appendix A

End-of-Chapter Problems

For instructor-assigned homework go to **Mastering Chemistry**.

Chapter 1

1.1 What is Chemistry?

LO 1: Recognize chemistry as the central science that studies matter on the atomic level.

1.01 Which statement best describes chemistry?

  a) the study of how animals live and behave on earth

  b) the study of earth's physical structure and history

  c) the study of the properties, structure, and transformations of matter

  d) the study of how medicines impact human behavior

1.02 Which statement best describes the term *matter*?

  a) Matter is defined as only those objects that are large enough to see.

  b) Matter is defined as only those objects that we can feel with our hands.

  c) Matter is defined as anything that can be imagined.

  d) Matter is defined as anything that has mass and takes up space.

1.03 Which statement best describes atoms?

  a) Atoms are extremely tiny particles that can be broken down further into molecules.

  b) Atoms are extremely tiny particles that are the basic units of matter.

  c) Atoms are extremely tiny particles that combine to form subatomic particles.

  d) Atoms are extremely large particles that are the basic units of matter.

1.04 Select the smallest object.

  a) a pill taken as a medication

  b) a grain of sand

  c) the period at the end of a sentence

  d) an atom

1.05 Classify each statement as an observation, hypothesis, or experiment.

  a) I earn better grades when I dedicate myself to my studies in school.

  b) I added five grams of ice to the 20 grams of warm water and recorded the temperature change.

  c) Leaves on some types of trees change color in autumn.

Target boxes: observation, hypothesis, experiment

1.06 Classify each statement as an observation, hypothesis, or experiment.

  a) If I exercise regularly, then I will lose weight.

  b) My cell phone battery level is low.

  c) Attending more yoga classes each week will help me feel better.

Target boxes: observation, hypothesis, experiment

1.07 Classify each statement as an observation, hypothesis, or experiment.

  a) Blood from 271 patients will be analyzed for an increased white blood cell count during a leukemia study.

  b) Levels of depression have increased as a result of watching the news.

  c) I can see two wildfires burning in the hills surrounding my town.

Target boxes: observation, hypothesis, experiment

1.08 Classify each statement as an observation, hypothesis, or experiment.

  a) Maria's mother, brother, and father are allergic to peanuts, so she probably is, too.

  b) Maria ate one peanut then increased the number of peanuts by two each day to determine if she was allergic.

  c) After eating three peanuts, Maria did not have an allergic reaction to them.

Target boxes: observation, hypothesis, experiment

1.09 Classify each statement as an observation, hypothesis, or experiment.

a) By eating less meat and dairy, in combination with regular exercise, cholesterol levels will decrease over time.

b) A patient had a severe cough and elevated heart rate.

c) Cholesterol levels of 275 patients were measured weekly and correlated to their body mass index.

Target boxes: observation, hypothesis, experiment

1.10 Which statement best describes a hypothesis?

a) a highly controlled procedure designed to better understand a system being investigated

b) a statement describing something that you saw, heard, smelled, or felt

c) a tentative explanation of an observation, data, or experiment

d) an explanation based on a set of well-established hypotheses that offers a model of the way nature behaves and why

1.11 Which statement best describes an experiment?

a) an explanation based on a set of well-established hypotheses that offers a model of the way nature behaves and why

b) a tentative explanation of an observation, data, or experiment

c) a statement describing something that you saw, heard, smelled or felt

d) a highly controlled procedure designed to better understand a system being investigated

1.12 Which statement about the scientific method is correct?

a) Once established, a theory cannot be disproved or revised.

b) Once established, a law cannot be disproved.

c) A theory is generally formed before a hypothesis is developed and tested.

d) A theory is formed after a hypothesis has been well-established.

1.13 Classify each statement about the scientific method as true or false.

a) Once a theory has been commonly accepted, it cannot be disproved.

b) Results of experiments may support a hypothesis or nullify it.

c) Every hypothesis becomes a law.

d) The scientific method is based on observations and experimentation.

e) Scientific theories provide the foundation for scientific knowledge.

Target boxes: true, false

1.2 Matter

LO 2: Describe matter by its composition and physical state.

1.14 Classify each mixture as homogeneous or heterogeneous.

Answer choices: fruit salad, butter, pile of identical white balls, ice cream with dark colored chunks

Target boxes: homogeneous mixture, heterogeneous mixture

1.15 Which statement best describes a compound?

a) a mixture of two or more substances that have the same melting point, boiling point, density, and color

b) a pure substance that forms when two or more elements combine in constant proportions to make a new substance

c) a pure substance that forms when two or more elements combine in variable proportions depending on the day of the week

d) an individual pure element that contains atoms capable of combining with two or more other pure substances upon heating

1.16 Complete each statement.

a) _____ is a compound.

b) _____ is an element.

c) _____ is an abundant gas in the atmosphere.

d) _____ is a heterogeneous mixture.

Answer choices: calcium, the food in your stomach, $NaCl$, N_2

1.17 Classify each as an example of a physical or chemical change.

Answer choices: breaking a glass, digesting your breakfast, water freezing, water evaporating

Target boxes: physical change, chemical change

1.18 Classify each image and its description as a solid, liquid, or gas.

Answer choices:

a) the most closely packed spheres that are shown in a regular highly organized pattern

b) closely packed spheres with a little bit of space between them and are not presented in a highly organized regular pattern

c) spheres that are well separated and are not packed in an organized pattern

Target boxes: liquid, gas, solid

1.19 Which statement best describes the properties of a liquid sample of matter?

   a) A sample fills the entire volume of the container it occupies.

   b) Particles are close together and a sample takes the shape of its container.

   c) Particles are close together and a sample holds its own shape.

   d) Particles are far apart on average and a sample can be compressed.

1.20 Identify each property of a substance as a physical property or chemical property.

   a) Pure alcohol is flammable.

   b) Gold (Au) is a shiny metal.

   c) Water (H_2O) boils at 100°C.

   d) Iron (Fe) reacts with oxygen (O_2) to form "rust" (Fe_2O_3).

Target boxes: physical property, chemical property

1.21 Which statement best describes the properties of a solid sample of matter?

   a) Particles are far apart on average and a sample can be compressed.

   b) A sample fills the entire volume of the container it occupies.

   c) Particles are close together and a sample holds its own shape.

   d) Particles are very close together but can move randomly.

1.22 Identify each property of a substance as a physical property or chemical property.

   a) Water (H_2O) freezes at 0°C.

b) Sodium (Na) metal reacts with chlorine gas (Cl_2) to produce NaCl (table salt).

c) Nitrogen gas (N_2) is odorless.

d) Magnesium (Mg) reacts with sulfur (S) to produce MgS (magnesium sulfide).

Target boxes: physical property, chemical property

1.23 Which statement best describes the properties of gaseous matter?

   a) Particles are very close together but can move randomly.

   b) Particles are close together and the sample holds its shape.

   c) The sample fills the entire volume of the container it occupies.

   d) The sample has both a defined volume and a defined shape.

1.3 Elements and Compounds

LO 3: Describe elements and explain how they differ from compounds.

1.24 Which is the chemical symbol for the element cesium?

   a) Cs   b) Ce   c) C   d) Cm

1.25 Which is the chemical symbol for the element sodium?

   a) S   b) So   c) Na   d) Sd

1.26 Which is the name for the element with symbol Ru?

   a) rubidium   b) ruthenium

   c) radium   d) rhenium

1.27 Which is the name for the element with symbol Ga?

   a) gadolinium   b) germanium

   c) gallium   d) gambium

1.28 Provide the chemical symbol for each element listed. The first letter of element symbols should be upper-case (a capitalized letter).

   a) sulfur   b) potassium

   c) magnesium   d) phosphorous

   e) gold   f) iron

1.29 Provide the chemical symbol for each element. An uppercase letter is always used for the first letter of element symbols.

   a) barium   b) boron

   c) fluorine   d) argon

   e) manganese   f) nickel

1.30 Provide the name of each element (given its chemical symbol).

   a) Cr   b) Rb   c) Si

   d) I   e) Ag

1.31 Provide the name of each element (given its chemical symbol).

a) Pb   b) Pd   c) N

d) Ni   e) C   f) Ca

1.32 Provide the name of each element (given its chemical symbol).

a) H   b) He   c) Cu

d) Co   e) Ti   e) Sn

1.33 Classify each image as an element, compound, or mixture. Each sphere represents an atom. Atoms of different elements are represented by different colors.

a)   b)   c)

Target boxes: mixture, element, compound

1.34 Classify each substance as an element or a compound.

Answer choices: C, NaCl, Ca, copper, H_2O

Target boxes: element, compound

1.35 Classify each substance as an element or a compound.

Answer choices: He, Cs, NH_3, Mg, Si, KCl

Target boxes: element, compound

1.36 Classify each substance as an element or a compound.

Answer choices: Co, CO, CH_4, Sr, HF, Al

Target boxes: element, compound

1.37 Enter the chemical formula for each compound, such as CH_4N_2O. If there is only one of any given atom type, do not enter the number "1" (because It is implied).

a)

b)
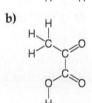

c)
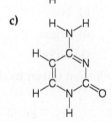

1.4 The Periodic Table

LO 4: Explain the general characteristics and organization of the periodic table.

1.38 Which element is a halogen?

a) B   b) Br

c) Ar   d) Rb

e) Be

1.39 Which of the following elements is a noble gas?

a) chlorine   b) nitrogen

c) nickel   d) strontium

e) radon

1.40 Which of the following elements is an alkali earth metal?

a) lithium   b) iodine

c) barium   d) vanadium

e) zinc

1.41 Which is the first period with transition metals?

a) period 2   b) period 3

c) period 4   d) period 5

1.42 Classify each element as a metal, nonmetal, or metalloid.

Answer choices: calcium, cobalt, sulfur, nitrogen

Target boxes: metal, nonmetal, metalloid

1.43 Classify each element as a metal, nonmetal, or metalloid.

Answer choices: Na, C, Fe, Mg, O, Si, Zn

Target boxes: metal, nonmetal, metalloid

1.44 Classify each element as an alkali metal, alkali earth metal, or transition metal.

Answer choices: Pd, Fr, Sr, Ba, Na, Cd

Target boxes: alkali metal, alkali earth metal, transition metal

1.45 Classify the element tungsten (W).

a) alkali metal   b) alkali earth metal

c) transition metal   d) halogen

e) noble gas

1.46 Classify the element krypton (Kr).

a) alkali metal   b) alkali earth metal

c) transition metal   d) halogen

e) noble gas

1.47 Classify the element fluorine (F).

a) alkali metal   b) alkali earth metal

c) transition metal   d) halogen

e) noble gas

1.48 Provide the period number for each element. Enter a number between 1 and 7 in the space provided. (Do not spell out the number.)

a) Cs

b) V

c) Li

d) Co

e) Rn

f) N

1.49 Provide the chemical symbol for each element given its period and group. The first letter of a chemical symbol is always uppercase (capital).

a) period 2, group 1A (1)

b) period 5, group 8A (18)

c) period 3, group 4A (14)

d) period 4, group 7A (17)

1.50 Which pair of elements belong to the same group or family?

a) selenium and oxygen

b) sulfur and sodium

c) calcium and cobalt

d) hydrogen and helium

1.51 Which pair of elements belong to the same period of the periodic table?

a) scandium and strontium

b) copper and cesium

c) yttrium and tin

d) bromine and iodine

1.52 Write the chemical name for each element whose period and group are provided. Use only lowercase letters for the element names.

a) period 5, group 4B (4)

b) period 2, group 2A (2)

c) period 5, group 8B (9)

d) period 4, group 4A (14)

1.53 Write the chemical name for each element whose period and group are provided. Use only lowercase letters for the element names.

a) period 1, group 1A (1)

b) period 6, group 4A (14)

c) period 4, group 3A (13)

d) period 2, group 6A (16)

1.54 Drag each type of element to the location in the periodic table where it is located.

a) halogen

b) alkali metal

c) noble gas

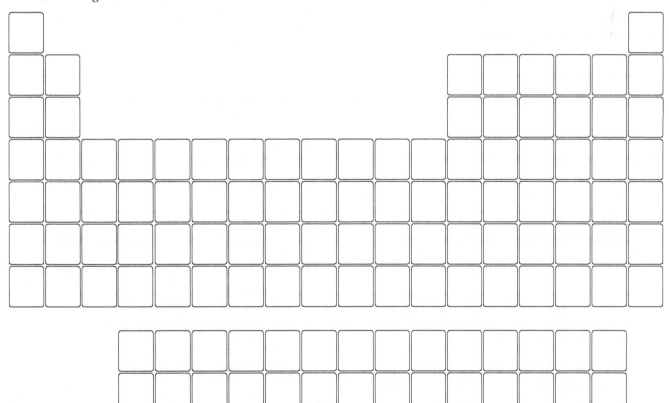

1.55 Drag each type of element to the location in the periodic table where it is located.

a) an alkali earth metal

b) a transition metal

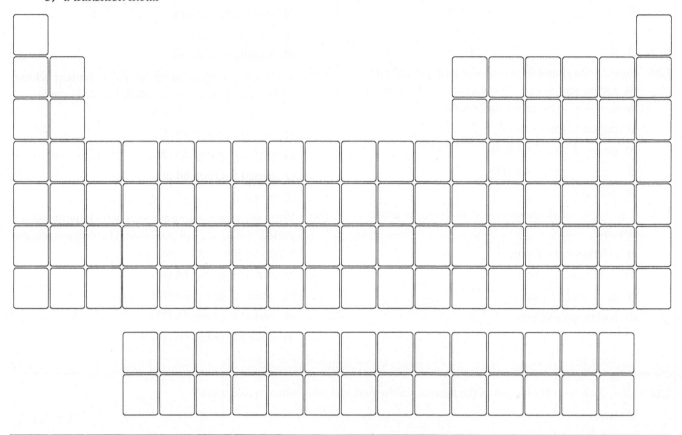

Chapter 2

2.1 Units of Measurement

LO 1: Report measurements of length, mass, and volume in metric units.

2.01 A nurse in a hospital works with many measurements. Sort each of these measurements into the appropriate category.

a) The tumor removed from a cancer patient was measured to be 4.3 g.

b) A cut along a child's foot was measured to be 6.5 cm.

c) A urine sample was measured to be 81.5 mL.

Target boxes: volume, mass, length

2.02 Match each definition with the appropriate type of measurement.

a) the amount of matter an object contains

b) the amount of space a substance occupies

Target boxes: volume, mass, length

2.03 How many micrograms are in one gram?

a) one thousand   b) one hundred

c) one million   d) ten

2.04 Which is a measurement of length?

a) 11.3 L   b) 39.2 g

c) 74.4 m   d) 96.7 s

2.05 Identify the types of measurements.

A. Which type of measurement is a value of 26.6 mL?

a) time   b) volume

c) length   d) mass

B. Which type of measurement is a value of 17.5 mm?

a) volume   b) temperature

c) mass   d) length

2.06 Match the correct scientific *metric* unit with the correct measurement type. One or more of the units are not a match for the measurement types.

Answer choices: meter, pound, gallon, gram, hour, inch, liter, Celsius

Target boxes: volume, mass, length

2.07 Classify the type of information in each example.

A. A hospital patient is given a 10 mL injection of morphine for pain management.

a) mass   b) volume

c) length   d) time

B. A newborn baby delivered in a clinic is 3.1 kg.

a) length   b) temperature

c) time   d) mass

C. A child with a bacterial infection is given 125 mg of the antibiotic, amoxicillin.

a) time   b) length

c) mass   d) volume

2.08 Match the correct scientific *metric* unit abbreviation with the correct measurement type. One or more of the units are not a match for the measurement types.

Answer choices: kg, lb, °F, m, L, gal, °C, sec

Target boxes: time, temperature, volume

2.09 Select the best answer for each of the following.

A. How many mL are in one L?

a) 0.001   b) 0.01

c) 100   d) 1000

B. There are _____ grams in one kilogram.

a) 0.001   b) 0.01

c) 100   d) 1000

C. 100 cm = _____ m

a) 1   b) 100

c) 0.1   d) 0.01

2.10 Match each measurement with the correct measurement type.

Answer choices: 37°C, 68 sec, 4.1 cm, 6.8 milliliters, 26 grams, 98.6°F, 2.6 L, 24 hr, 3.1meters, 38 kg

Target boxes: mass, length, volume

2.11 Match each image to the type of measurement being made.

Answer choices:

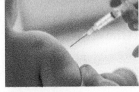 

Target boxes: mass, length, volume

2.12 Which sequence ranks the values from smallest to largest?

a) microgram, gram, milligram, kilogram

b) milligram, microgram, gram, kilogram

c) kilogram, gram, milligram, microgram

d) microgram, milligram, gram, kilogram

2.13 Which sequence ranks the values from smallest to largest?

a) milliliter, microliter, liter, deciliter

b) microliter, milliliter, deciliter, liter

c) microliter, milliliter, liter, deciliter

d) liter, deciliter, milliliter, microliter

2.14 Consider the information given and determine the appropriate answer for the hospital patient in each case.

A. A patient is given 2.2×10^2 mg of a drug to help reduce pain. How many grams does this represent?

a) 2200 g   b) 220 g

c) 22 g   d) 0.22 g

e) 0.022 g

B. A tumor biopsy was taken from a patient and measured to be 4.5×10^{-4} g. How many micrograms (μg) does this represent?

a) 4.5×10^6 mg   b) 45 mg

c) 450 mg   d) .045 mg

e) .00045 mg

2.15 A. During an eye surgery, a patient's retina is injected with 7.5×10^{-5} L of fluid. How many microliters (μL) is this?

a) 7.5×10^{-6} μL   b) 7.5×10^{-11} μL

c) 7.5×10^{-1} μL   d) 7.5 μL

e) 75 μL

B. In the clinical laboratory, 0.4 deciliters (dL) of a patient's blood is centrifuged and analyzed. How many milliliters (mL) were analyzed?

a) 4×10^3 mL   b) 4×10^{-2} mL

c) 40 mL   d) 0.4 mL

e) 400 mL

2.2 Communicating about Measurements

LO 2: Use scientific notation and significant figures when problem-solving and communicating about measurements.

2.16 Which option has the *fewest* significant figures?

a) 7.05 cm   b) 0.075 cm

c) 7.50 cm   d) 70.5 cm

2.17 Which option has the *greatest* number of significant figures?

a) 0.287 mg   b) 2.14 mg

c) 61.00 mg   d) 9100 mg

2.18 Which value has the *greatest* number of significant figures?

a) 9.8×10^{12} atoms   b) 8.500×10^4 atoms

c) 1.50×10^{23} atoms   d) 2.05×10^{25} atoms

2.19 Which value has the *greatest* number of significant figures?

a) 210.00 mL   b) 0.800 L

c) 61.00 mL   d) 12.5 L

2.20 Classify each value as measured or exact.

a) The volume of an infected kidney is 250 cm^3.

b) There are 1000 mL in 1 L.

c) A drunk driver had a blood alcohol level of 0.24% (mass/volume).

Target boxes: measured, exact

2.21 Classify each value as measured or exact.

a) There are 24 pills of medication in a prescription bottle at the pharmacy.

b) A newborn baby weighs 3.82 kg.

c) A patient's cholesterol level is 265 mg/dL.

Target boxes: measured, exact

2.22 Which option shows the measured value 6.0448 mL correctly rounded to three significant figures?

a) 6.00 mL   b) 6.045 mL

c) 6.04 mL   d) 6.05 mL

2.23 Which option shows the measured value 5.46×10^6 cells correctly rounded to two significant figures?

a) 5.46×10^6 cells   b) 5.40×10^6 cells

c) 5.50×10^6 cells   d) 5.5×10^6 cells

2.24 Match each value with its number of significant figures.

Answer choices: 0.0019, 902.6, 1.011, 6.27×10^{-3}, 60.00, 2140, 2.6×10^3, 702.0

Target boxes: 2 significant figures, 3 significant figures, 4 significant figures

2.25 Answer each question about significant figures.

A. Which number is 806.052 g rounded to four significant figures?

     a) 806.05 g   b) 806.0 g

     c) 806.1 g   d) 8060 g

B. Which number has three significant figures?

     a) .001 mL   b) .101 mL

     c) 1.001 mL   d) 100 mL

C. For the value 0.00204 g, which of the following is presented in scientific notation expressed to two significant figures?

     a) 2.0×10^{-2} g

     b) 2.04×10^{-3} g

     c) 2.0×10^3 g

     d) 2.0×10^{-3} g

2.26 Answer each question about significant figures.

A. How many significant figures are in 600.10 mL?

     a) 3   b) 4   c) 5   d) 6

B. Which number contains four significant figures?

     a) 0.008 km

     b) 200.6 g

     c) 5000 mL

     d) 7.4×10^4 sec

C. Which has the greatest number of significant figures?

     a) 6,000 g   b) 1×10^8 g

     c) 0.101 g   d) 2.9 g

2.27 Which option correctly shows the measured value 1494.79 grams expressed in scientific notation and rounded to three significant figures?

a) 1.49×10^{-3} g

b) 1.50×10^3 g

c) 1.49×10^3 g

d) 149×10^3 g

2.28 Which correctly shows the measured value 0.000605 meters expressed in scientific notation and rounded to two significant figures?

a) 6.1×10^{-4} m

b) 6.0×10^{-4} m

c) 6.1×10^4 m

d) 6.05×10^{-4} m

2.29 A biologist studying ice sheets measured a movement rate of 7.041×10^{-2} m/d. Which is the correct decimal form of the value 7.041×10^{-2} m/d?

a) 704.1 m/d   b) 7.041 m/d

c) 07041 m/d   d) 0.07041 m/d

e) 70.41 m/d

2.30 An environmental scientist determined that 7.25×10^4 m^3 of soil downstream of an industrial site has become contaminated with arsenic. Which is the correct decimal form of this value?

a) 72500 m^3 b) 72500. m^3

c) 7.25 m^3 d) 0.000725 m^3

e) 725104 m^3

2.31 In China, the government is currently expanding the city of Beijing to become a "super city" called "Jing-Jin-Ji" that is expected to have a population of approximately 130 million people. What is the correct way to express 130 million in scientific notation?

a) 1.3×10^8 b) 1.30×10^{-6}

c) 13.0×10^6 d) 1.30×10^6

2.32 When $161.3 \text{ g} + 9.2 \text{ g} + 2.34 \text{ g}$ are added, the answer to the correct number of decimal places is _____.

a) 172.84 g   b) 173 g

c) 172.8 g   d) 1.7×10^2 g

2.33 Which value is correctly rounded for the subtraction sequence: $29.031 \text{ mL} - 3.8 \text{ mL} - 4.16 \text{ mL}$?

a) 21.071 mL   b) 36.991 mL

c) 21 mL   d) 21.1 mL

2.34 What is the correctly rounded answer for the following calculation?

$$8.24 \times 2.2 \times 6.875 \times 0.116 =$$

a) 14.45708   b) 14

c) 14.5   d) 14.4

2.35 What is the correctly rounded final answer for the following calculation?

$$884.6 \div 19.00 \div 0.68 \div 2.00 =$$

a) 34.2   b) 34.2337461

c) 34   d) 34.23

2.36 Perform each calculation and enter the result in scientific notation with the correct number of significant figures.

a) $1.33 \times 0.00234 = ?$

b) $1.09 \div 0.3332 = ?$

2.37 Perform each calculation and enter the result with the correct number of significant figures.

a) $2.3 + 0.0017 + 8.14 = ?$

b) $24.891 - 0.72 = ?$

2.38 What is the correctly rounded final answer for this calculation?

$$\frac{(92.650)(3.710)}{(6.00)} = ?$$

a) 57.28   b) 57.29

c) 60   d) 57.289

e) 57.3

2.39 a) A medical technician receives these measurements of cancerous mole removed from a patient. Perform the calculation shown to determine the volume of the mole. Enter your answer in standard decimal form with the correct number of significant figures and units of mm³.

$$1.45 \text{ mm} \times 2.0 \text{ mm} \times 3.054 \text{ mm} = ?$$

b) A nurse helped an average of 24.6 patients per day for 19 consecutive days during a COVID-19 outbreak in 2020. How many total patients did she see during this period of time? Enter your answer in scientific notation with the correct number of significant figures and units of patients.

$$24.6 \frac{\text{patients}}{\text{d}} \times 19 \text{ d} = ?$$

2.40 a) Perform the calculation shown below for a patient receiving medication through an IV. Enter your answer in scientific notation with the correct number of significant figures and units of mL.

$$2.5 \frac{\text{mL}}{\text{min}} \times 135 \text{ min} = ?$$

b) A doctor recommends her pregnant patient drink at least 7.5 liters of water each day. How many liters of water should she drink each week? Enter your answer in standard decimal form rounded to two significant figures and units of L/wk. For this calculation we are treating 7 d/wk as a perfect conversion that does not impact significant figures.

$$7.5 \frac{\text{L}}{\text{d}} \times 7 \frac{\text{d}}{\text{wk}} = ?$$

2.41 Perform the calculation and report the result in standard decimal form with the correct number of significant figures.

a) $\dfrac{7.24(1.5 + 6.11 + 0.58)}{4.287} =$

b) $\dfrac{(4.28 \times 10^3)(6.879 \times 10^{-5})}{(4.2 - 1.5)} =$

2.42 Perform the calculation and report the result in standard decimal form with the correct number of significant figures and units.

a) $2.740 \text{ cm} \times 4.81 \text{ cm} \times 0.692 \text{ cm} = ?$

b) $\dfrac{(8.22 \text{ m})(1.285 \text{ m})(3.6 \text{ m})}{4.2 \text{ m}^2} = ?$

2.3 Units Conversions

LO 3: Use conversion factors to convert between units.

2.43 There are 1000 milliliters (mL) in one liter (L). A nurse administers 400 mL of IV fluids. How many L does this represent?

a) 40 L   b) 4 L

c) 0.4 L   d) 0.04 L

2.44 Which option shows a correctly written equality and two correctly written conversion factors?

a) Equality: 10 mm = 1 cm.   Conversion factors $\dfrac{1\ mm}{10\ cm}$ and $\dfrac{1\ cm}{10\ km}$

b) Equality: 1 cm = 100 m.   Conversion factors $\dfrac{1\ cm}{100\ m}$ and $\dfrac{100\ m}{1\ m}$

c) Equality: 1000 mm = 1 m.   Conversion factors $\dfrac{1000\ mm}{1\ m}$ and $\dfrac{1\ m}{1000\ mm}$

d) Equality: 1 m = 10 cm.   Conversion factors $\dfrac{1\ cm}{10\ m}$ and $\dfrac{10\ cm}{1\ m}$

2.45 If a piece of pizza contains 450 Calories and a hungry student eats three pieces of pizza while studying for an exam, how many total calories were in the pizza he ate?

a) 150 Calories
b) 135 Calories
c) 13,500 Calories
d) 1,350 Calories

2.46 An incision along the chest of a man in surgery is 14.5 inches (in) long. How many centimeters (cm) is this? There are 2.54 cm/in. Express your answer with three significant figures and in units of cm.

2.47 An elderly man takes one heart medication pill each day. His prescription contains 12 pills per bottle. If he will be gone on a 72-day trip to visit his family oversees, how many bottles of heart medication pills does he need to request from his doctor for his trip? Express your answer in units of bottles to the nearest whole number.

2.48 Enter an answer for each of the following.

a) A sick child received medication in a clinic. Perform the calculation to determine the amount of medication the child received. Enter your answer with the correct number of significant figures and units.

$$\frac{1.5\ mL}{8.0\ h} \times \frac{24\ h}{d} \times \frac{14\ d}{1} = ?$$

b) A humanitarian agency is delivering 1.5 bags of rice to each family each day during a drought. Each bag contains 525 grams of rice. Perform this calculation to determine how many grams of rice per week the agency should plan to deliver to each family. Enter your answer in scientific notation with two significant figures and units of (g/week).

$$\frac{1.5\ bag}{d} \times \frac{7\ d}{wk} \times \frac{525\ g}{bag} = ?$$

2.49 A city has a population of 1.3 million people. At one point during an outbreak of the COVID-19 virus, it was estimated that one of every 28 people had become infected. Which conversion shows the correct setup to approximate the number of people that had become infected at that time in the city?

a) 1.3×10^6 people $\times \dfrac{28\ people}{1\ infected\ person} =$

b) 28 people $\times \dfrac{1\ infected\ person}{1.3 \times 10^6\ people} =$

c) 1.3×10^6 people $\times \dfrac{1\ infected\ person}{28\ people} =$

d) $\dfrac{28\ people}{1\ infected\ person} \times \dfrac{1}{1.3 \times 10^6\ people} =$

2.50 You want to convert a measured number of micrometers to meters. Select the conversion factor that is correctly written and does not need to be inverted (flipped over) to be used to solve the problem.

a) $\dfrac{1 \times 10^{-6}\ \mu m}{1\ m}$
b) $\dfrac{1 \times 10^{-6}\ m}{1\ \mu m}$
c) $\dfrac{1\ m}{1 \times 10^{-6}\ \mu m}$
d) $\dfrac{1\ \mu m}{1 \times 10^{-6}\ m}$

2.51 A college student is participating in a fundraiser to help provide school supplies for low-income families. A donor agrees to pay $2.50 for each kilometer (km) that the student runs in a three-week period of time. The student successfully ran 5 kilometers each day for three weeks. Which conversion correctly shows how to calculate the total amount of money she raised in this effort?

a) $\dfrac{2.50\ dollars}{5\ km} \times \dfrac{5\ km}{1\ d} \times \dfrac{7\ d}{1\ wk} \times \dfrac{3\ wk}{1} =$

b) $\dfrac{2.50\ dollars}{1\ km} \times \dfrac{5\ km}{1\ d} \times \dfrac{7\ d}{1\ wk} \times \dfrac{3\ wk}{1} =$

c) $\dfrac{2.50\ dollars}{1\ km} \times \dfrac{5\ km}{1\ d} \times \dfrac{3\ wk}{1} =$

d) $\dfrac{1\ km}{2.50\ dollars} \times \dfrac{1\ d}{5\ km} \times \dfrac{1\ wk}{7\ d} \times \dfrac{1}{3\ wk} =$

2.52 Vitamin B_{12} occurs in a variety of foods and is available as a dietary supplement. It is an essential vitamin, meaning that the body requires vitamin B_{12} to be obtained in the diet to function properly. A pregnant woman takes one vitamin B_{12} supplement pill each day during her 40-week pregnancy. Each vitamin B_{12} pill contains 850 micrograms (mcg). Which conversion sequence correctly shows how the total number of grams of vitamin B_{12} consumed during the pregnancy is calculated?

a) $\dfrac{850 \text{ mcg}}{1 \text{ pill}} \times \dfrac{1 \text{ g}}{1 \times 10^6 \text{ mcg}} \times \dfrac{1 \text{ pill}}{1 \text{ d}} \times \dfrac{7 \text{ d}}{1 \text{ wk}} \times \dfrac{40 \text{ wk}}{1}$

b) $\dfrac{850 \text{ mcg}}{1 \text{ pill}} \times \dfrac{1 \text{ pill}}{1 \text{ d}} \times \dfrac{7 \text{ d}}{1 \text{ wk}} \times \dfrac{40 \text{ wk}}{1}$

c) $\dfrac{850 \text{ mcg}}{1 \text{ pill}} \times \dfrac{1 \times 10^6 \text{ mcg}}{1 \text{ g}} \times \dfrac{1 \text{ pill}}{1 \text{ d}} \times \dfrac{7 \text{ d}}{1 \text{ wk}} \times \dfrac{40 \text{ wk}}{1}$

d) $\dfrac{850 \text{ mcg}}{1 \text{ pill}} \times \dfrac{1 \text{ g}}{1 \times 10^6 \text{ mcg}} \times \dfrac{1 \text{ pill}}{1 \text{ d}} \times \dfrac{1 \text{ d}}{7 \text{ wk}} \times \dfrac{40 \text{ wk}}{1}$

2.53 An overweight man took his doctor's advice and made adjustments to his lifestyle that included better eating habits and regular exercise. If he lost an average of 2.5 pounds (lbs) each week for 27 weeks, how many pounds did he lose in this period of time? Express your answer in standard decimal form with two significant figures and units of lbs.

2.54 A scientist wants to convert a flow rate of 2.5 liters per hour (L/h) to milliliters per second (mL/s). What is the correct result?

a) 2.5×10^3 mL/s

b) 6.9×10^{-7} mL/s

c) 1.4 mL/s

d) 0.69 mL/s

2.55 Which of the following is a correct conversion factor between the units of deciliters and liters. Select all answers that are correct.

a) $\dfrac{1 \text{ dL}}{10 \text{ L}}$

b) $\dfrac{1 \text{ dL}}{10^{-1} \text{ L}}$

c) $\dfrac{1 \text{ L}}{10^{-1} \text{ dL}}$

d) $\dfrac{1 \text{ L}}{10 \text{ dL}}$

e) $\dfrac{10 \text{ L}}{1 \text{ dL}}$

2.56 Answer each of the following.

A. Blood glucose levels are often expressed in units of milligrams of glucose per deciliter of blood (mg/dL). How is the amount of glucose expressed in these units?

a) a mass to mass ratio

b) a volume-to-temperature ratio

c) a volume to volume ratio

d) a mass-to-volume ratio

B. If a patient with a blood glucose level of 215 mg/dL has 4.75 L of blood in her body, approximately how many mg of glucose are in

her body at the time the measurements were taken? For this calculation, treat the conversion factor 10 dL/L as a perfect conversion that does not impact significant figures. Express your answer in scientific notation with three significant figures and units of mg.

2.57 Order these hospital patient IV flow rates from least to greatest.

a) 1.75 mL per minute

b) 100 mL per hour

c) 2250 mL per 24-hour day

Target boxes: flow rate

2.58 In the Unit 1 Introduction, we learned that congenital hyperinsulinism (HI) is the most common cause of persistent low blood sugar or hypoglycemia in children. A hypoglycemic child weighing 70 lbs has a blood glucose level of 50 mg/dL. A child of that weight has an estimated total blood volume of 2.4L. Calculate the total number of milligrams (mg) glucose in the child's blood. Express your answer in scientific notation with two significant figures.

Conversion factor: 10 dL = 1 L

2.59 Answer each of the following.

a) If a modern train in China travels at an average speed of 225 kilometers per hour, how many hours will it take to travel the 819 miles between the cities of Beijing and Shanghai? The conversion factor $\dfrac{1 \text{ mi}}{1.609 \text{ km}}$ *might* be useful in solving this problem.

b) If the train in Part A travels at an average speed of 225 kilometers per hour, how many miles can it travel in 8 hours? Express your answer in scientific notation with three significant figures and units of mi. The conversion factor $\dfrac{1 \text{ mi}}{1.609 \text{ km}}$ *might* be useful in solving this problem.

2.60 A smoker consumes 2 packs of cigarettes each day for 30 years.

a) How many total cigarettes does this represent? Base your calculations on 365 days in a year and 20 cigarettes in each pack. Express your answer in scientific notation with three significant figures and units of cigarettes.

b) If there is an average of 12 mg nicotine in each cigarette, how many milligrams (mg) of nicotine are consumed in the 30 years of smoking? Express your answer in scientific notation with three significant figures and units of mg nicotine.

2.61 If Americans recycle and compost approximately 1.5 pounds of waste per person per day, calculate the number of kilograms of recycled and composted material that a city with a population of 3,500,000 would produce in a week. Express your answer in scientific notation with two significant figures and units of kg/wk.

Possibly useful conversion factors: $\dfrac{1 \text{ kg}}{2.205 \text{ lb}}$, $\dfrac{1 \text{ lb}}{0.4536 \text{ kg}}$.

2.62 Uric acid is produced during the breakdown of purine, a substance found in many foods. Most uric acid is carried in your blood and passes through your kidneys, where it leaves your body in urine. A high uric acid level, or hyper-uricemia, is an excess of uric acid in your blood, and can result in the condition known as gout. If the results of a uric acid blood test for a 48-year-old male patient indicates a level of 13.8 mg/dL, and the total volume of blood in the patient is 5.0 L, how many total grams of uric acid does the patient have in his blood? Express your answer in scientific notation with two significant figures and units of g.

Possibly useful conversion factors: 10 dL = 1 L, 1000 mg = 1 g.

2.63 Answer each of the following.

a) If the average heart rate of a woman is 78 beats per minute, how many beats will her heart pump in one 365-day year? Express your answer in scientific notation with two significant figures and units of beats/yr.

Possibly useful conversion factors: $\dfrac{24 \text{ h}}{1 \text{ d}}$, $\dfrac{1 \text{ yr}}{365 \text{ d}}$, $\dfrac{60 \text{ min}}{1 \text{ h}}$.

b) If a man's heart is pumping 3.92 gallons of blood per minute on average throughout the day, how many liters (L) will his heart pump in a 7-day week? Express your answer in scientific notation with two significant figures and units of L/wk.

Possibly useful conversion factors: $\dfrac{1 \text{ d}}{24 \text{ h}}$, $\dfrac{1 \text{ gal}}{3.785 \text{ L}}$, $\dfrac{60 \text{ min}}{1 \text{ h}}$, $\dfrac{7 \text{ d}}{1 \text{ wk}}$.

2.4 Dosage Calculations

LO 4: Apply ratio and proportion conversion factors for medical dosage calculations.

2.64 A dosage for an antibiotic is 400 mg per 50 kg of body weight. Select the conversion sequence that determines the dosage needed for a patient weighing 85 kg.

a) $\left[\dfrac{1}{85 \text{ kg patient weight}}\right] \times \left[\dfrac{400 \text{ mg antibiotic}}{50 \text{ kg patient weight}}\right]$

b) $\left[\dfrac{85 \text{ kg patient weight}}{1}\right] \times \left[\dfrac{50 \text{ kg patient weight}}{400 \text{ mg antibiotic}}\right]$

c) $\left[\dfrac{85 \text{ kg patient weight}}{1}\right] \times \left[\dfrac{400 \text{ mg antibiotic}}{50 \text{ kg patient weight}}\right]$

d) $\left[\dfrac{50 \text{ kg patient weight}}{1}\right] \times \left[\dfrac{400 \text{ mg antibiotic}}{85 \text{ kg patient weight}}\right]$

2.65 A child experiencing pain while recovering from a broken arm is to take 160 mg of ibuprofen each day. If liquid Children's Motrin contains 100 mg of ibuprofen per 5 mL, how many milliliters should the child take each day? Express your answer with one significant figure and units of mL.

2.66 An elderly woman in the hospital develops a bacterial infection after surgery. She is prescribed 0.6 g of clindamycin added to her IV fluid every 12 hours. If the bottle of clindamycin contains 300 mg/2 mL, which conversion correctly calculates the number of mL of antibiotic that should be added to her IV fluid every 12 hours?

a) $\left[\dfrac{0.6 \text{ g}}{1}\right] \times \left[\dfrac{1000 \text{ g}}{1 \text{ mg}}\right] \times \left[\dfrac{2 \text{ mL}}{300 \text{ mg}}\right]$

b) $\left[\dfrac{0.6 \text{ g}}{1}\right] \times \left[\dfrac{1000 \text{ mg}}{1 \text{ g}}\right] \times \left[\dfrac{300 \text{ mg}}{2 \text{ mL}}\right]$

c) $\left[\dfrac{300 \text{ mg}}{2 \text{ mL}}\right] \times \left[\dfrac{1000 \text{ mg}}{1 \text{ g}}\right] \times \left[\dfrac{12 \text{ h}}{0.6 \text{ mg}}\right]$

d) $\left[\dfrac{0.6 \text{ g}}{1}\right] \times \left[\dfrac{1000 \text{ mg}}{1 \text{ g}}\right] \times \left[\dfrac{2 \text{ mL}}{300 \text{ mg}}\right]$

2.67 Haldol (haloperidol decanoate) is a medication used to help treat mood and mental disorders such as schizophrenia. A doctor prescribes 2,500 micrograms (written as mcg or μg) injected into a patient monthly. If the bottle of the medication has a concentration of 5 mg/1 mL, which conversion sequence correctly determines the number of milliliters to be injected for a monthly dose?

a) $\left[\dfrac{2500 \text{ mcg}}{1}\right] \times \left[\dfrac{1 \text{ mg}}{1000 \text{ mcg}}\right] \times \left[\dfrac{1 \text{ mL}}{5 \text{ mg}}\right]$

b) $\left[\dfrac{2500 \text{ mcg}}{1}\right] \times \left[\dfrac{1000 \text{ mg}}{1 \text{ mcg}}\right] \times \left[\dfrac{1 \text{ mL}}{5 \text{ mg}}\right]$

c) $\left[\dfrac{2500 \text{ mcg}}{1}\right] \times \left[\dfrac{1 \text{ mg}}{1000 \text{ mcg}}\right] \times \left[\dfrac{5 \text{ mg}}{1 \text{ mL}}\right]$

d) $\left[\dfrac{1 \text{ mL}}{5 \text{ mg}}\right] \times \left[\dfrac{1 \text{ mg}}{1000 \text{ mcg}}\right] \times \left[\dfrac{1}{2500 \text{ mcg}}\right]$

2.68 A 143-pound (lb) patient in the hospital has been diagnosed with methicillin-resistant *Staphylococcus aureus* (MRSA). MRSA infections are caused by staph bacteria that have become resistant to many antibiotics. The doctor orders a dose of 15 mg/1 kg of a new antibiotic every 12 hours. The concentration on the drug bottle is 1 g/20 mL. Which conversion sequence correctly determines the number of milliliters the patient should receive every 12 hours? Note that 1 kg = 2.2 lb.

a) $\left[\dfrac{20 \text{ mL}}{1 \text{ g}}\right] \times \left[\dfrac{1 \text{ g}}{1000 \text{ mg}}\right] \times \left[\dfrac{15 \text{ mg}}{1 \text{ kg}}\right] \times \left[\dfrac{2.2 \text{ lb}}{1 \text{ kg}}\right] \times \left[\dfrac{1}{143 \text{ lb}}\right]$

b) $\left[\dfrac{20 \text{ mL}}{1 \text{ g}}\right] \times \left[\dfrac{1 \text{ g}}{1000 \text{ mg}}\right] \times \left[\dfrac{15 \text{ mg}}{1 \text{ kg}}\right] \times \left[\dfrac{1 \text{ kg}}{2.2 \text{ lb}}\right] \times \left[\dfrac{143 \text{ lb}}{1}\right]$

c) $\left[\dfrac{20 \text{ mL}}{1 \text{ g}}\right] \times \left[\dfrac{1 \text{ g}}{1000 \text{ mg}}\right] \times \left[\dfrac{15 \text{ mg}}{1 \text{ kg}}\right] \times \left[\dfrac{2.2 \text{ kg}}{1 \text{ lb}}\right] \times \left[\dfrac{143 \text{ lb}}{1}\right]$

d) $\left[\dfrac{1 \text{ mL}}{20 \text{ g}}\right] \times \left[\dfrac{1 \text{ g}}{1000 \text{ mg}}\right] \times \left[\dfrac{15 \text{ mg}}{1 \text{ kg}}\right] \times \left[\dfrac{1 \text{ kg}}{2.2 \text{ lb}}\right] \times \left[\dfrac{143 \text{ lb}}{1}\right]$

2.69 A 27-kilogram (kg) child with HIV is prescribed 150 mg of the drug Abacavir *daily* to help treat her disease. If she is given an oral liquid containing 100 mg/5 mL, how many mL should the nurse give her to take home each week? Select the correct sequence of conversions.

a) $\dfrac{100 \text{ mg}}{5.0 \text{ ml}} \quad \dfrac{150 \text{ mg}}{d} \quad \dfrac{7 \text{ d}}{1 \text{ wk}}$

b) $\dfrac{5.0 \text{ ml}}{100 \text{ mg}} \quad \dfrac{150 \text{ mg}}{d} \quad \dfrac{7 \text{ d}}{1 \text{ wk}}$

c) $\dfrac{5.0 \text{ ml}}{100 \text{ mg}} \quad \dfrac{1 \text{ d}}{150 \text{ mg}} \quad \dfrac{7 \text{ d}}{1 \text{ wk}}$

d) $\dfrac{5.0 \text{ ml}}{100 \text{ mg}} \quad \dfrac{150 \text{ mg}}{d} \quad \dfrac{1 \text{ wk}}{7 \text{ d}}$

2.70 A 67-year-old patient is prescribed 20 mg daily of the drug Lisinopril daily to help treat his hypertension (high blood pressure). How many 10 mg pills should the nurse give him for a 30-day supply? Express your answer in standard notation with two significant figures and units of pills.

2.71 A patient with Chronic Obstructive Pulmonary Disease (COPD), a serious lung disease, needs a 40 mg IV per dose of the drug Solu-Medrol. A solution of the drug contains 12.5mg/2ml. How many ml of this solution should the nurse give to the patient per dose? Express your answer in standard notation with two significant figures and units of mL/dose.

2.72 A physician in the emergency room has ordered an IV drip of Fentanyl for sedation and pain management of a patient in a severe car accident. The concentration of the drug in the IV bag is 1 mg/100 mL. If the dose needs to be 0.100 mg/h, what should the flow rate in mL/h be in the patient's IV?

A. Select the two conversion factors needed to solve the problem.

a) $\dfrac{100 \text{ mL}}{1 \text{ mg}}$

b) $\dfrac{1 \text{ h}}{0.100 \text{ mg}}$

c) $\dfrac{1 \text{ mg}}{100 \text{ mL}}$

d) $\dfrac{0.100 \text{ mg}}{1 \text{ h}}$

B. Now use the conversion factors selected in Part A to calculate the flow rate. Express the answer in standard decimal form with three significant figures and units of mL/hr.

2.73 An elderly patient with an eye infection has been prescribed 50 mg of gentamicin by injection. The label on the drug vial states the concentration is 20 mg/5 mL. How many mL should the nurse administer to the patient by injection? Express your answer in standard decimal form with three significant figures and units of mL.

2.74 A 12-year-old girl with asthma is prescribed the drug Solumedrol to help manage her condition. The prescription is for 1.5 mg/kg and the girl weighs 82 pounds (lB). Solumedrol is available in liquid form at a concentration of 125 mg/2 mL liquid. How many mL should the nurse administer to the girl?

A. Select the two conversion factors needed to complete the conversion to mL.

$$\left[\frac{82 \text{ lb}}{1}\right] \times \left[\frac{1 \text{ kg}}{2.2 \text{ lb}}\right] \times [?] \times [?]$$

a) $\dfrac{1.5 \text{ mg}}{1 \text{ kg}}$

b) $\dfrac{2.0 \text{ mL}}{125 \text{ mg}}$

c) $\dfrac{1 \text{ kg}}{1.5 \text{ mg}}$

d) $\dfrac{125 \text{ mg}}{2.0 \text{ mL}}$

B. Now use the completed conversion sequence above to calculate the final answer and express it in standard decimal form with two significant figures and units of mL.

2.75 A 52 kilogram, 28-year-old patient in the hospital needs to receive a dosage of Diazepam through an IV drip to help treat her seizures and anxiety. The doctor prescribes 0.4 mg/kg/h by continuous IV infusion. If the IV bag contains 0.1 mg/mL drug, what should the IV flow rate be in mL/h to administer the drug properly?

A. Select the conversion factor needed to complete the conversion to mL/h.

$$\left[\frac{52 \text{ kg}}{1}\right] \times \left[\frac{0.4 \text{ mg}}{\text{kg} \cdot \text{hr}}\right] \times [?]$$

a) $\dfrac{1}{28 \text{ y}}$

b) $\dfrac{0.1 \text{ mg}}{1 \text{ mL}}$

c) $\dfrac{28 \text{ y}}{1}$

d) $\dfrac{1 \text{ mL}}{0.1 \text{ mg}}$

B. Now use the completed conversion sequence above to calculate the final answer and express it in standard notation with three significant figures and units of mL/h.

2.5 Common Units in Environmental Science

LO 5: **Solve problems with conversion factors and units commonly used in environmental science.**

2.76 What does the abbreviation ppm stand for in environmental science?

a) pounds per meter

b) pressure per minute

c) parts per million

d) proton precession magnetometer

2.77 What does the abbreviation ppb stand for in environmental science?

a) protons per boson

b) parts per billion

c) production-possibility boundary

d) plasma protein binding

2.78 Which value is expressed in units of ppm for a soil sample contaminated with a toxic heavy metal?

a) $\dfrac{0.005 \text{ g}}{\text{min}}$

b) $\dfrac{3.0 \text{ mL}}{100 \text{ mL}}$

c) $\dfrac{8 \text{ mg}}{\text{kg}}$

d) $\dfrac{2.5 \text{ lb}}{\text{kg}}$

2.79 Which value is expressed in units of ppm for a sample of contaminated drinking water?

a) $\dfrac{0.5 \text{ g}}{\text{kg}}$

b) $\dfrac{0.005 \text{ mL}}{1000 \text{ dL}}$

c) $\dfrac{0.2 \text{ g}}{\text{mL}}$

d) $\dfrac{6.4 \text{ mg}}{\text{L}}$

2.80 Which value is expressed in units of ppb for a soil sample contaminated with a pesticide?

a) 9 micrograms per kilogram

b) 2 kilograms per liter

c) 5 milligrams per kilogram

d) 8 milliliters per deciliter

2.81 Which value is expressed in units of ppb for a sample of lake water contaminated with dioxin?

a) 3 grams per microliter

b) 8 milligrams per milliliter

c) 4 micrograms per liter

d) 1 microgram per milliliter

2.82 Which option shows two values representing the same concentration of a nutrient in the soil?

a) 5 mg/kg and 5 ppm   b) 5 mg/g and 5 ppb

c) 5 g/kg and 5 ppm   d) 5 mg/kg and 5 ppb

2.83 Which option shows two values representing the same concentration of lead at an industrial site?

a) 8 μg/mg and 8 ppm

b) 8 ppm and 8,000 ppb

c) 8 g/kg and 8 ppb

d) 8 mg/kg and 8 ppb

2.84 Identify the option that shows two values having the same concentration of a rare metal in the soil?

a) 25 g/kg and 2.5 ppb

b) 4 mg/dL and 4,000 ppb

c) 1.4 μg/mg and 1.4 ppm

d) 2,000 ppb and 2,000 μg/kg

2.85 Which option shows two values representing the same concentration of a toxin in the ground water below a town?

a) 0.1 ng/dL and 0.1 ppm

b) 0.1 mL/L and 0.1 ppb

c) 0.1 mg/L and 0.1 ppm

d) 5 mg/kg and 5 ppb

2.86 Which option shows two values representing the same concentration of a mineral that was measured in drinking water?

a) 9,000 mg/L and 9 ppb

b) 9,000 μg/L and 9 ppm

c) 9,000 mg/L and 9 ppm

d) 9 μg/L and 9 ppm

2.87 The fluoride level in a sample of drinking water was determined to be 0.75 milligrams of fluoride per liter of water. Calculate the total number of milligrams of fluoride a child who drinks 1.5 L of water each day will consume in a 7-day week. Express your answer in standard decimal form with two significant figures and units of mg/wk.

2.88 Green chemistry is the design of chemical products and processes that reduce or eliminate the generation of hazardous substances. If a company develops a method to eliminate 248 liters of hazardous materials each day, how many liters are eliminated every year if the production facility operates 305 days per "production year"? Express your answer in scientific notation to three significant figures with units of L/yr.

2.89 Dichloromethane is one of the most commonly used solvents in manufacturing. Annually, its use is in the hundreds of millions of pounds, yet the U.S. Environmental Protection Agency (EPA) has set the maximum contamination level (MCL) in drinking water at 0.005 mg/L.

A. Select the two conversion factors needed to calculate the maximum number of milligrams allowed (MCL) in a 465-gallon drinking water storage tank used on a family farm.

$$\left[\frac{465 \text{ gal}}{1}\right] \times [?] \times [?]$$

a) $\dfrac{1 \text{ L}}{0.005 \text{ mg}}$ **b)** $\dfrac{1 \text{ gal}}{3.785 \text{ L}}$

c) $\dfrac{0.005 \text{ mg}}{1 \text{ L}}$ **d)** $\dfrac{3.785 \text{ L}}{1 \text{ gal}}$

B. Now use the completed conversion sequence above to calculate the final answer and express it in standard decimal form with three significant figures with units of mg.

2.90 A pregnant woman eats an average of 8.0 ounces of salmon each week for the 39 weeks of her pregnancy. If the fish she is eating has an average mercury concentration of 2.0 micrograms (μg) per 4.0 ounce serving, how many total micrograms will she have consumed during her pregnancy? Express your answer in scientific notation to two significant figures with units of μg.

2.91 If a solar panel can provide an average of 4800 Watts of energy to your home each day, how many kW could the solar panel produce each 365-day year? Express your answer in scientific notation with two significant figures and units of kW/yr. 1 kW = 1000 W.

2.92 Bioremediation is a treatment that uses naturally occurring organisms or substances to break down hazardous materials into less toxic or non-toxic substances. In San Francisco Bay, an area known as Hunters Point is heavily contaminated with polychlorinated biphenyls (PCBs). The concentration of PCBs in the sediment of this area was measured to be 1,570 ppb. If a bioremediation effort using activated carbon filtration was found that could reduce the levels by 70% under ideal conditions, what would be the resulting PCB contamination if the entire area could be treated in this way? Express your answer in scientific notation with two significant figures and units of ppb.

2.6 Measuring Temperature

LO 6: Convert temperature measurements from one scale to another.

2.93 What is the freezing point of water on the Celsius temperature scale?

a) 37 °C   **b)** −32 °C

c) −100 °C   **d)** 0 °C

2.94 What is the boiling point of water on the Celsius temperature scale?

a) 212 °C   **b)** 32 °C

c) 100 °C   **d)** 373 °C

2.95 What is the freezing point of water on the Fahrenheit temperature scale?

a) 32 °F   **b)** 0 °F

c) 273 °F   **d)** −100 °F

2.96 What is the boiling point of water on the Fahrenheit temperature scale?

a) 100 °F   **b)** 373 °F

c) 212 °F   **d)** 273 °F

2.97 Select the temperature scales whose units have the same magnitude.

a) Kelvin and Fahrenheit

b) Celsius and Kelvin

c) Celsius and Fahrenheit

d) Celsius, Kelvin, and Fahrenheit

2.98 Determine the temperature on the Celsius thermometer then identify this same temperature expressed in Kelvin.

a) 53.8 K   b) 153.8 K

c) 219.2 K   d) 326.8 K

2.99 Convert the temperature value 35.5 °C into the corresponding temperature in °F. Express your answer with three significant figures and units of °F.

2.100 Convert 76.2 °C into the corresponding temperature in °F. Express your answer with three significant figures and units of °F.

2.101 Convert 121 °F into the corresponding temperature in °C. Express your answer with three significant figures and units of °C.

2.102 Convert 177 °F into the corresponding temperature in °C. Express your answer with three significant figures and units of °C.

2.103 Convert 68.5 °C into the corresponding temperature in Kelvin. Express your answer with three significant figures and units of K.

2.104 Convert 298 K into the corresponding temperature in °C. Express your answer with three significant figures and units of °C.

2.105 A woman from the United States that is visiting Spain is not feeling well. She calls the local clinic and explains that she has a fever of 104 °F. The nurse needs to convert this temperature in Fahrenheit to a temperature in Celsius because Spain uses the metric system. What is the woman's temperature in Celsius? Calculate the answer and express it in standard decimal form to two significant figures.

$$T_C = \frac{T_F - 32}{1.8}$$

2.106 Although the sun, solar wind, and gases around stars can be quite hot, much of "empty space" is very cold. The so-called "cosmic background temperature" is around minus 455 degrees Fahrenheit. Calculate the cosmic background temperature in Celsius and express your answer in standard decimal form to three significant figures with units of °C.

$$T_C = \frac{T_F - 32}{1.8}$$

2.107 A family from Japan is visiting the United States, and their young daughter is sick with a fever. The mother measures her temperature to be 39.5 °C and calls the doctor's office with the information. The physician's assistant in the hospital needs to convert the Celsius temperature to Fahrenheit in order to assess the situation. What is the child's temperature in Fahrenheit? Calculate the answer and express it in standard decimal form to three significant figures with units of °F.

$$T_F = 1.8(T_C) + 32$$

2.108 Convert 425 K into the corresponding temperature in °F. Express your answer with three significant figures and units of °F.

2.109 Convert 98.8 °F into the corresponding temperature in K. Express your answer with three significant figures and units of K.

2.110 Four buckets contain water with temperatures measured as 197 °F, 93 °C, 362 K, 98.6 °F. Which is the warmest temperature?

a) 197 °F   b) 93 °C

c) 362 K   d) 98.6 °F

2.7 Density and Specific Gravity

LO 7: Explain the concept of density and specific gravity, and solve problems involving density, mass, and volume measurements.

2.111 In 2010, a tragic explosion of an oil well at the bottom of the Gulf of Mexico resulted in the Deepwater Horizon/BP oil spill that released 200,000–2,000,000 gallons of oil a day into the Gulf. It took 87 days to stop the flow and the oil company was found to be responsible for the release of 3.1 million barrels (about 490 million liters). The oil was a mixture of petroleum-based materials with an average density of 0.95 g/cm³. The surrounding seawater has a density of 1.03 g/cm³. How can this information help you explain the images of the oil spill?

   a) The oil released has a greater density than sea water.

   b) The oil released has the same density as the sea water.

   c) The oil released is less dense than the sea water.

   d) Not enough information is provided.

2.112 Which of the following best describes density?

   a) a chemical property

   b) a physical change

   c) a physical property

   d) a chemical change

2.113 Calculate the density of an 89.5 mL liquid sample that has a mass of 93.7 g. Express your answer with three significant figures and units of g/mL.

2.114 What is the mass of a 38.2 mL sample of ethanol? The density of ethanol is 0.789 g/mL. Express your answer with three significant figures and units of g.

2.115 The density of aluminum (Al) is 2.7 g/cm³. What volume in cm³ is occupied by 9.8 g of aluminum? Express your answer with two significant figures and units of cm³.

2.116 Specific gravity is the ratio of which two values?

   a) mass of a substance and the density of water

   b) density of water and the density of a substance

   c) volume of water and the mass of a substance

   d) density of a substance and the mass of water

2.117 What units do specific gravity values have?

   a) g/mL   **b)** ppm

   c) mg/kg   **d)** no units

2.118 The volume of a solid can be determined by a method known as volume displacement. When a solid is completely submerged in water for example, it displaces a volume that is equal to the volume of the solid object. The volume of the object is determined by measuring the water level before and after an object is submerged in a measuring device such as a graduated cylinder. If an object displaces 25.0 mL of water and has a mass of 64.3 g, what is its density?

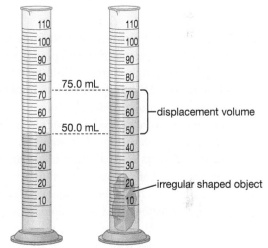

   a) 1.17 g/mL   **b)** 0.389 g/mL

   c) 2.57 g/mL   **d)** 1.29 g/mL

2.119 The volume of an object is determined using water displacement. The initial volume of water in a graduated cylinder is determined to be 17.5 mL. After the object is placed in the graduated cylinder, the water level is found to be 43.1 mL. If the dry object has a mass of 95.2 g, what is the density of the object? Express your answer with three significant figures and units of g/mL.

2.120 If a bag of intravenous (IV) glucose solution being administered to a hospital patient has a volume of 1.50 L and a density of 1.15 g/mL, what mass of fluid is the patient receiving? Express your answer in scientific notation with three significant figures and units of grams. Hint: You may need to convert mL to L.

$$D = \frac{m}{V}$$

2.121 The density of lead contaminated soil that is being removed from a hazardous site is 2450 kg/m³. If the truck hauling away the contaminated dirt can carry 48,500 kg per load, what volume of contaminated soil can be removed each trip the truck takes? Express your answer in standard decimal form with three significant figures and units of m³.

$$D = \frac{m}{V}$$

2.122 Hospitals and clinics near mountainous areas or at high elevation sometimes see patients suffering from HAPE (High Altitude Pulmonary Edema). Although HAPE is not completely understood, it can be induced by rapidly climbing to high elevations where oxygen levels are significantly lower than at lower elevations. For example, the city of Lhasa in Tibet is at an altitude of almost 12,000 ft above sea level and hosts a large number of tourists seeking adventures in the Himalayan Mountains. If the air we breathe at sea level contains around 78% nitrogen and 21% oxygen, and the percentage of oxygen decreases with increasing altitude, what is your prediction about the relative density of nitrogen gas compared with oxygen gas?

a) Nitrogen gas is more dense than oxygen gas.

b) Nitrogen gas has the same density as oxygen gas.

c) Nitrogen gas is less dense than oxygen gas.

d) Not enough information is provided to predict.

2.123 Patients suffering from bladder problems often need a catheter connected to a urine bag to collect and hold urine. A nurse is monitoring the mass of urine produced by a patient every eight hours.

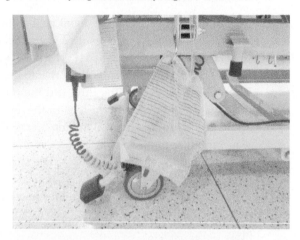

A. If a patient produces 0.210 L of urine in eight hours, and the mass of this urine is 0.231 kg, calculate the density of the patient's urine. Express your answer in standard decimal form to three significant figures with units of kg/L:

$$D = \frac{m}{V}$$

B. If the average density range of urine is between 1.002 and 1.030 kg/L, and the density of pure water is 1.00 kg/L, does your answer to part A indicate that the patient in this example is properly hydrated, dehydrated, or overhydrated?

a) The patient is properly hydrated.

b) The patient is overhydrated.

c) The patient is dehydrated (under hydrated).

d) Not enough information is provided to predict.

2.124 Blood is a precious and perishable resource needed by patients around the world. Hospitals and clinics depend on healthy caring citizens to donate blood in order to keep their reserves fresh and ready to use. In a typical blood donation, a nurse draws a one pint "unit" from a donor.

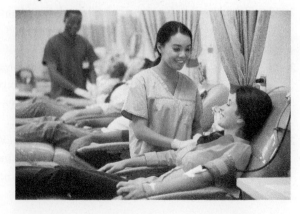

A. Select the two conversion factors needed to calculate how many kilograms each one pint "unit" of blood weighs. A typical blood sample has a density of 1060 kg/m³.

$$(1 \text{ pt}) \times \left[\frac{473.176 \text{ mL}}{1 \text{ pt}} \right] \times [?] \times \left[\frac{1 \text{ m}^3}{1000 \text{ L}} \right] \times [?]$$

a) $\dfrac{1 \text{ m}^3}{1060 \text{ kg}}$ **b)** $\dfrac{1060 \text{ kg}}{1 \text{ m}^3}$

c) $\dfrac{1000 \text{ mL}}{1 \text{ L}}$ **d)** $\dfrac{1 \text{ L}}{1000 \text{ mL}}$

B. Now use the completed conversion sequence above to calculate the final answer and express it in standard decimal form with three significant figures with units of kg.

2.125 Tissue engineering scientists use cells imbedded into a three-dimensional scaffold to produce a functional organ or tissue. If a scientist is able to grow heart cells at a density of 6.8×10^7 cells/cm³ in a scaffold, how many cells occupy an engineered heart tissue sample that is 34.5 cm³ in volume? Express your answer in scientific notation to two significant figures with units of cells. Hint: You can treat the number of cells as if it were the "mass" term in the standard density relationship.

$$\text{cell density} = \frac{\text{number of cells}}{V}$$

2.126 Your body mass index (BMI) is a key indicator of overall health. The formula for measuring BMI is given below and is a slight variation on the standard density formula. Note: the numerator in both cases is a mass term, but the denominator has units of height (in meters) squared for BMI instead of cubed for density.

A. Calculate the BMI of a 45-year-old man that is 167 cm tall and weighs 73.8 kg. Express your answer in standard decimal form to three significant figures with units of kg/m².

Useful relationships:

$$D = \frac{m}{V} = \frac{g}{cm^3}$$

$$BMI = \frac{(\text{weight in kg})}{(\text{height in meters})^2}$$

B. Consult the BMI chart below and determine if he is considered underweight, normal, overweight, or obese.

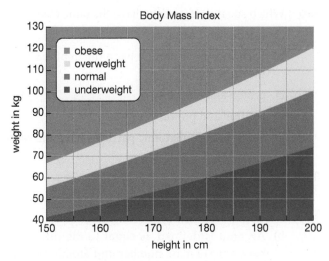

Body Mass Index

■ obese
■ overweight
■ normal
■ underweight

a) underweight   **b)** normal

c) overweight   **d)** obese

e) clinically obese

Chapter 3

3.1 The Atom

LO 1: Identify and describe the structure of atoms.

3.01 Which statement best describes the atom?

a) An atom is a compound with a unique chemical property characteristic of that isotope.

b) An atom is the nucleus of an isotope without the surrounding electrons and having a distinct chemical property.

c) An atom is the smallest component of an element that maintains the chemical properties of that element.

d) An atom is the sum of the atomic number and mass number of an element that is assigned to a specific location on the periodic table.

3.02 Which subatomic particles have similar masses?

	Mass (kg)	Mass (amu)	Charge (relative)
Proton	1.67262×10^{-27}	1.00727	+1
Neutron	1.67493×10^{-27}	1.00866	0
Electron	0.00091×10^{-27}	0.00055	−1

©2014 Pearson Education, Inc.

a) neutron and proton

b) proton and electron

c) electron and neutron

d) Each subatomic particle has a similar mass but different charge.

3.03 Which subatomic particles have the same charge?

a) electron and neutron

b) Each subatomic particle has a different mass but the same charge.

c) proton and electron

d) neutron and proton

e) None of the subatomic particles have the same charge.

3.04 Which best defines the term amu?

a) An amu is defined as equal to the atomic motion unit of the carbon atom.

b) An amu is defined as equal to the difference between the mass number and atomic number of the carbon atom.

c) An amu is defined as equal to one-twelfth the mass of a carbon atom.

d) An amu is defined as equal to the number of protons in the nucleus of the carbon atom.

3.05 An electrically neutral atom must have:

a) the same number of protons and neutrons

b) the same number of electrons and neutrons

c) the same number of electrons as the sum of the protons and neutrons

d) the same number of protons and electrons

3.06 The atomic number of an element is equal to the number of _____ in its nucleus.

3.07 Match each particle to the location where it is found.

Answer choices: electron, neutron, proton

Target boxes: inside the nucleus, outside the nucleus

3.08 Consider the simplified diagram of the atom shown. Drag each subatomic particle into the correct region of the atom. This representation is not drawn to scale.

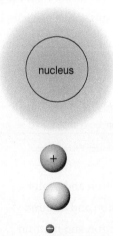

Answer choices: proton, neutron, electron

Target boxes: inside the nucleus, outside the nucleus

3.09 Match the electrical charge to each subatomic particle.

Answer choices: proton, neutron, electron

Target boxes: negative charge, positive charge, not charged

3.10 Match each item to the type of particle it describes.

Answer choices: −1 charge, +1 charge, inside the nucleus, mass is similar to a proton

Target boxes: proton and neutron, proton only, proton and electron, electron only, neutron only

3.11 Which statement best defines the atomic number (Z)?

a) The atomic number (Z) is the total number of protons and neutrons of a specific element.

b) The atomic number (Z) is the number of protons in an atom of a specific element.

c) The atomic number (Z) is the weighted mass average of the isotopes of a specific element.

d) The atomic number (Z) is the numeric difference between the number of protons and neutrons of a specific element.

3.12 Which statement best defines the mass number (A)?

a) The mass number (A) is the numeric difference between the number of protons and neutrons of a specific element.

b) The mass number (A) is the weighted mass average of the isotopes of a specific element.

c) The mass number (A) is the total number of protons and neutrons of a specific element.

d) The mass number (A) is the number of protons in an atom of a specific element.

3.13 Consult the periodic table, then write the *atomic symbol* for each element.

a) The symbol of the element with atomic number 82 is _____.

b) The symbol of the element with atomic number 44 is _____.

c) The symbol of the element with atomic number 31 is _____.

3.14 Consult the periodic table, then write the correctly spelled element name (not symbol) for each of the following.

a) The name of the element with atomic number 14 is _____ .

b) The name of the element with atomic number 19 is _____ .

c) The name of the element with atomic number 12 is _____ .

3.15 Consult the periodic table, then write the correctly spelled element name (not symbol) for each of the following.

    a) The name of the element with mass number 16 is _____ .

    b) The name of the element with mass number 19 is _____ .

3.16 What is the mass number of an element with 49 neutrons and 37 protons?

    a) 49   **b)** 12

    c) 86   **d)** 37

3.17 How many neutrons are in an atom with mass number 90 and atomic number 39?

    a) 129

    b) More information is needed.

    c) 39

    d) 51

3.2 Isotopes

LO 2: Determine the number of subatomic particles present in specific isotopes and define the atomic mass of elements.

3.18 Select the correct statement about the element $^{12}_{6}X$.

    a) It contains 12 protons.

    b) It contains 12 neutrons.

    c) Its atomic number is 6.

    d) Its mass number is 6.

3.19 Select the correct statement about the element $^{60}_{27}X$.

    a) Its mass number is 27.

    b) Its atomic number is 33.

    c) Its atomic number is 60.

    d) Its mass number is 60.

3.20 The atomic number for ^{197}Au is _____ .

3.21 The mass number of a vanadium isotope having 28 neutrons is _____ .

3.22 The mass number of an osmium isotope having 116 neutrons is _____ .

3.23 The fluorine isotope (F-18) can be attached to the neurotransmitter dopamine and used to study neurotransmitter function in the body. Drag the atomic number and mass number into the boxes to complete the isotope symbol.

Answer choices: 19, 18, 9, 10, 27, 48, 28, 8

Target boxes: two boxes stacked to the left of the Fluorine symbol

3.24 How many protons, neutrons, and electrons are in a neutral atom of aluminum (Al) with mass number 27?

    a) 27 protons, 14 neutrons, 27 electrons

    b) 14 protons, 13 neutrons, 14 electrons

    c) 13 protons, 14 neutrons, 13 electrons

    d) 13 protons, 14 neutrons, 14 electrons

3.25 How many protons, neutrons, and electrons are in a neutral atom of potassium (K) with mass number 39?

    a) 19 protons, 39 neutrons, 19 electrons

    b) 20 protons, 20 neutrons, 20 electrons

    c) 39 protons, 20 neutrons, 39 electrons

    d) 19 Protons, 20 neutrons, 19 electrons

3.26 Consider this representation of an atomic nucleus. Enter the correct atomic number, mass number, and number of protons and neutrons.

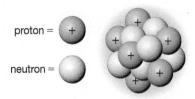

Input boxes: boxes for atomic number, mass number, number of protons, number of neutrons

3.27 Consider the representations of each nucleus. Identify the pair of isotopes of the same element.

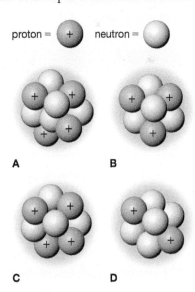

Answer choices: isotope A, isotope B, isotope C, isotope D

Target box: an isotope pair

3.28 Which is the correct nuclear symbol for the atom with 17 protons, 20 neutrons, and 17 electrons?

    a) $^{20}_{17}Cl$ **b)** $^{17}_{20}Cl$

    c) $^{37}_{17}Cl$ **d)** $^{37}_{20}Ca$

3.29 Consider the two nuclei. In the space provided, enter the atomic number, mass number, and element name for each.

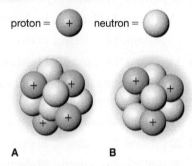

proton = (+) neutron = (○)

A   B

Input boxes for each nuclei: atomic number, mass number, element name

3.30 The element carbon is an essential building block for all biological molecules. Complete the table for the three isotopes of carbon.

	Isotope		
	$^{12}_{6}C$	$^{13}_{6}C$	$^{14}_{6}C$
Number of protons			
Number of neutrons			
Number of electrons			
Atomic number			
Mass number			

3.31 The element phosphorus is essential for life and is contained in several important biological molecules such as DNA. Complete the table for the three isotopes of phosphorus.

	Isotope		
	$^{31}_{15}P$	$^{32}_{15}P$	$^{33}_{15}P$
Number of protons			
Number of neutrons			
Number of electrons			
Atomic number			
Mass number			

3.32 How many protons, neutrons, and electrons are in an atom of rubidium (Rb) with mass number 85 and a *charge* of 1+?

a) 37 protons, 48 neutrons, 37 electrons

b) 37 protons, 48 neutrons, 36 electrons

c) 37 protons, 48 neutrons, 38 electrons

d) 48 protons, 37 neutrons, 36 electrons

3.33 How many protons, neutrons, and electrons are in an atom of chlorine (Cl) with mass number 37 and a *charge* of 1−?

a) 17 protons, 20 neutrons, 18 electrons

b) 17 protons, 20 neutrons, 17 electrons

c) 20 protons, 17 neutrons, 17 electrons

d) 17 protons, 20 neutrons, 16 electrons

3.3 Electron Arrangements

LO 3: Describe the arrangement of electrons in atoms.

3.34 Select the true statement.

a) All orbitals have the same shape.

b) Every orbital can hold two electrons and two neutrons.

c) Orbitals can have different shapes, but each can hold only two electrons.

d) Orbitals are located in the nucleus along with protons.

3.35 What is the maximum number of electrons that can occupy the first energy level $(n = 1)$? Enter a number between 0 and 32 in the box provided. Refer to Figure 3.22.

3.36 How many *orbitals* are in a p-sublevel? Enter a number between 0 and 7 in the box provided. Refer to Figure 3.22.

3.37 How many *orbitals* are in an s-sublevel? Enter a number between 0 and 7 in the box provided. Refer to Figure 3.22.

3.38 How many *orbitals* are in a f-sublevel? Enter a number between 0 and 7 in the box provided. Refer to Figure 3.22.

3.39 How many *orbitals* are in a d-sublevel? Enter a number between 0 and 7 in the box provided. Refer to Figure 3.22.

3.40 Which sublevel can hold a maximum of two electrons? Refer to Figure 3.22.

a) s b) p
c) d d) f
e) none f) all

3.41 Which sublevel can hold a maximum of six electrons? Refer to Figure 3.22.

a) s b) p
c) d d) f
e) none f) all

3.42 Which sublevel can hold a maximum of ten electrons? Refer to Figure 3.22.

a) s b) p
c) d d) f
e) none f) all

3.43 Which sublevel can hold a maximum of 14 electrons? Refer to Figure 3.22.

a) s b) p
c) d d) f
e) none f) all

3.44 What is the maximum number of *electrons* that can occupy the p-sublevel? Enter a number between 0 and 14 in the box provided. Refer to Figure 3.22.

3.45 What is the maximum number of *electrons* that can occupy the s-sublevel? Enter a number between 0 and 14 in the box provided. Refer to Figure 3.22.

3.46 What is the maximum number of *electrons* that can occupy the d-sublevel? Enter a number between 0 and 14 in the box provided. Refer to Figure 3.22.

3.47 What is the maximum number of *electrons* that can occupy the f-sublevel? Enter a number between 0 and 14 in the box provided. Refer to Figure 3.22.

3.48 Which sublevel of an electrically neutral sodium (Na) atom contains only one electron?

   a) 2s   **b)** 2p   **c)** 3s   **d)** 3p

3.49 Which sublevel of an electrically neutral sulfur (S) atom contains four electrons?

   a) 2s   **b)** 2p   **c)** 3s   **d)** 3p

3.50 Which sublevel of an electrically neutral fluorine (F) atom contains five electrons?

   a) 2s   **b)** 2p   **c)** 3s   **d)** 3p

3.51 How many electrons does a neutral atom of nitrogen (N) have in the 2p sublevel? Enter a number between 0 and 8 in the box provided. Refer to Figure 3.22.

3.52 How many electrons does a neutral atom of argon (Ar) have in the 3p sublevel? Enter a number between 0 and 14 in the box provided. Refer to Figure 3.22.

3.53 What is the maximum number of electrons that can occupy the third energy level ($n = 3$)? Enter a number between 0 and 32 in the box provided. Refer to Figure 3.22.

3.54 Match the phrases with the correct number.

   a) the total number of electrons the second energy level can hold

   b) the maximum number of electrons an individual orbital can hold

   c) the total number of electrons in a magnesium atom

   d) the number of electrons that can be held in the 2p sublevel

   Number choices: 8, 18, 10, 2, 6, 12, 4, 24

3.55 Complete the figure by 1) identifying the correct number of sublevels for each energy level, and 2) dragging the colored sublevel, as needed, into the diagram to indicate the number and type of orbitals within each sublevel.

Energy level	Number of sublevels	Types of sublevels and number of orbitals			
		s	p	d	f
$n = 4$	4	☐	☐☐☐	☐☐☐☐☐	☐☐☐☐☐☐☐
$n = 3$	◯				
$n = 2$	◯				
$n = 1$	◯				

Answer choices I:

☐   ☐☐☐   ☐☐☐☐☐   ☐☐☐☐☐☐☐

Answer choices II: 1, 2, 3, 4

Target boxes: number of sublevels, type of sublevels and number of orbitals

3.4 Valence Electrons

LO 4: Identify valence electrons and represent them using electron-dot symbols.

3.56 Identify the number of valence electrons contained by atoms in each group. Drag the correct number of valence electrons into the circle at the top of each group on the periodic table.

Answer choices: 1, 2, 3, 4, 5, 6, 7, 8, 9, 10

Target boxes:

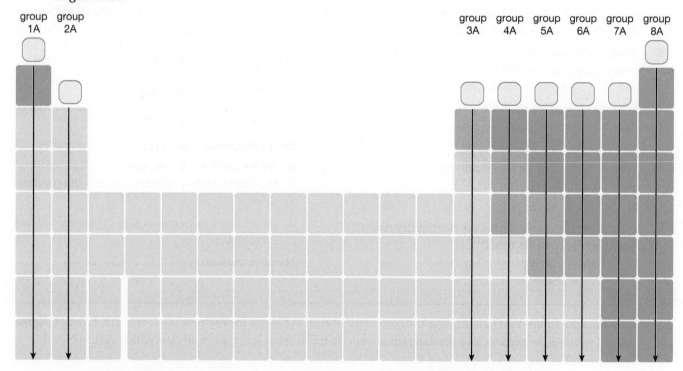

3.57 Carbon forms the backbone of most biological molecules. How many valence electrons does a carbon atom have?

   a) 2   **b)** 4   **c)** 6   **d)** 8

3.58 The cells in our bodies require a continuous supply of oxygen. How many valence electrons does an oxygen atom have?

   a) 2   **b)** 4   **c)** 6   **d)** 8

3.59 Match each element "X" electron-dot symbol with the element having the same number of valence electrons. One element has no name match.

Answer choices:

Target boxes: chlorine, phosphorous, potassium

3.60 Match each element "X" electron-dot symbol with the element having the same number of valence electrons.

Answer choices:

Target boxes: carbon, argon, boron, oxygen

3.61 Match each element "X" electron-dot symbol with the element having the same number of valence electrons.

Answer choices:

Target boxes: nonmetal, alkali earth, halogen

3.62 Match each element "X" electron-dot symbol with the element having the same number of valence electrons.

Answer choices:

Target boxes: alkali, noble gas, nonmetal

3.63 Ionization energy is best described as _____.

   a) the energy released when an atom accepts an electron

   b) the energy required to remove an electron from a neutral atom

   c) the energy released when a neutron is removed from a neutral atom

   d) the energy required to remove a proton from a neutral atom

3.64 Complete each statement.

 A. Going down a column of the periodic table, the ionization energy _____.

 a) increases

 b) decreases

 c) stays the same

 B. Going from left to right across the periodic table, the ionization energy _____.

 a) increases

 b) decreases

 c) stays the same

3.65 Complete each statement.

 A. Going from left to right across the periodic table, the atomic size _____.

 a) increases

 b) decreases

 c) stays the same

 B. Going down a column of the periodic table, the atomic size _____.

 a) increases

 b) decreases

 a) stays the same

3.66 Which has the *smallest* atomic size?

 a) C b) Li c) Al d) Si

3.67 Which has the *largest* atomic size?

 a) Cl b) K c) S d) Ca

3.68 Which has the *greatest* ionization energy?

 a) Br b) I c) Se d) Cl

3.69 Which has the *lowest* ionization energy?

 a) Rb b) Sr c) Cs d) Ba

3.70 Which correctly ranks the atoms in each group in order of *increasing* size?

 a) Al < Si < P < S

 b) S < P < Si < Al

 c) Ge < Si < Al < P

 d) Mg < Be < Al < Si

3.71 Which correctly ranks the atoms in each group in order of *increasing* ionization energy?

 a) Cl < S < P < N **b)** S < Cl < Br < I

 c) Se < Br < Cl < F **d)** F < Cl < Br < Se

3.72 Drag the correct element into each box.

 Answer choices: Si, Mg, K, P, Br, O

 Target boxes: halogen, smallest atom, smallest ionization energy, group 2A row 3

3.73 Drag the correct element into each box.

 Answer choices: Zn, Li, Sr, S, O, N

 Target boxes: largest atom, requires the most energy to remove an electron, alkali metal, has 5 valence electrons.

3.74 Drag the correct element into each box.

 Answer choices: N, C, H, He, F, Be

 Target boxes: has 7 valence electrons, group 2A row 2, has 4 valence electrons, requires the least amount of energy to remove an electron.

3.5 How Electrons Fill Orbitals

LO 5: Write electron configurations for elements.

3.75 Which statement is *not* correct?

 a) Electrons fill the lowest energy orbitals available beginning with 1s, which is closest to the nucleus.

 b) Each orbital can hold two electrons, but the electrons in the same orbital must have opposite orientations.

 c) When orbitals are equal in energy, one electron fills each orbital before they pair up.

 d) When writing electron configurations of atoms, the sublevels are listed in order of decreasing energy.

3.76 Which element has the electron configuration $1s^2 2s^2$?

 a) Li b) N c) Be d) C

3.77 Which element has the electron configuration $1s^2 2s^2 2p^6$?

 a) B b) Ar c) P d) Ne

3.78 Which element has the electron configuration $1s^2 2s^2 2p^6 3s^1$?

 a) Na b) Ne c) O

 d) P e) Sc

3.79 Which is the correct abbreviated electron configuration for an electrically neutral calcium (Ca) atom?

 a) $[Ne]3s^2$ **b)** $[Ar]4s^2$

 c) $[Ca]4s^2$ **d)** $[Ar]3s^2$

3.80 Which is the correct abbreviated electron configuration for an electrically neutral phosphorus (P) atom?

 a) $[Ne]3s^2$ **b)** $[Ar]4s^2$

 c) $[Ne]3s^2 3p^3$ **d)** $[Ar]3s^2$

3.81 Consider an atom with the electron configuration $1s^2 2s^2 2p^6 3s^2$. How many valence electrons does this atom have and what group does this element belong to?

 a) 2, group 2A **b)** 3, group 2A

 c) 5, group 3A **d)** 6, group 3A

3.82 Consider an atom with the electron configuration $1s^2 2s^2 2p^1$. How many valence electrons does this atom have and what group does this element belong to?

a) 2, group 1A

b) 1, group 2A

c) 2, group 3A

d) 3, group 3A

3.83 Determine the number of valence electrons for each electron configuration. Enter a number between 0 and 8.

a) In the electron configuration $1s^2 2s^2 2p^2$, the number of valence electrons is _____ .

b) In the electron configuration $1s^2 2s^2 2p^6 3s^1$, the number of valence electrons is _____ .

3.84 Determine the number of valence electrons for each electron configuration. Enter a number between 0 and 8.

a) In the electron configuration $1s^2 2s^2 2p^6 3s^2 3p^3$, the number of valence electrons is _____ .

b) In the electron configuration $1s^2 2s^2 2p^6 3s^2 3p^6 4s^1$, the number of valence electrons is _____ .

3.85 Drag the correct element into each box.

Answer choices: Ca, N, Mg, Si

Target boxes: electron configuration $1s^2 2s^2 2p^6 3s^2$, electron configuration $1s^2 2s^2 2p^6 3s^2 3p^2$, electron configuration $1s^2 2s^2 2p^3$, electron configuration $1s^2 2s^2 2p^6 3s^2 3p^6 4s^2$

3.86 Identify the energy sublevel (such as 1s, 2p, etc.) for each of the following.

a) Which sublevel fills after the 3s sublevel is complete?

b) Which sublevel fills after the 2p sublevel is complete?

c) Which sublevel fills after the 1s sublevel is complete?

3.87 Identify the energy sublevel (such as 1s, 2p, etc.) for each of the following.

a) Which sublevel fills after the 2p sublevel is complete?

b) Which sublevel fills after the 3d sublevel is complete?

c) Which sublevel fills after the 4p sublevel is complete?

3.88 Drag each element into the correct box.

Answer choices: O, H, C and Ne

Target boxes: the element with electron configuration $1s^2 2s^2 2p^6$, the element with electron configuration $1s^1$, the element with electron configuration $1s^2 2s^2 2p^2$, the element with electron configuration $1s^2 2s^2 2p^4$

3.89 Write the name of the neutral atom that corresponds to each orbital energy diagram.

a)

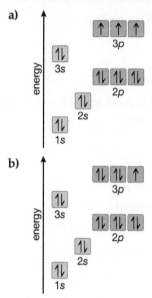

b)

3.90 Write the name of the neutral atom that corresponds to each orbital energy diagram.

a)

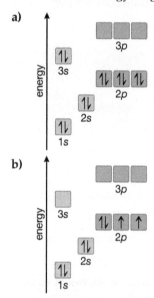

b)

3.91 Construct an orbital diagram to show the electron configuration for a neutral atom of *carbon*. Add single electrons or a pair of electrons as needed to each orbital box until the diagram is complete.

Answer choices:

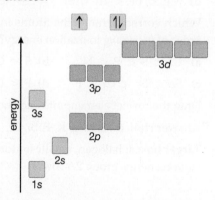

3.92 Construct an orbital diagram to show the electron configuration for a neutral atom of *silicon*. Add single electrons or a pair of electrons as needed to each orbital box until the diagram is complete.

Answer choices:

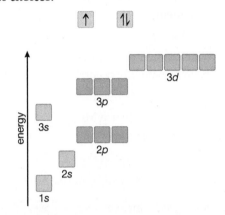

3.93 Construct an orbital diagram to show the electron configuration for a neutral atom of *sodium*. Add single electrons or a pair of electrons as needed to each orbital box until the diagram is complete.

Answer choices:

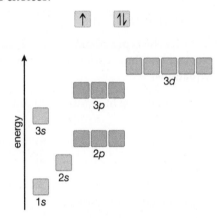

3.94 Construct an orbital diagram to show the electron configuration for a sodium *ion*. Add single electrons or a pair of electrons as needed to each orbital box until the diagram is complete.

Answer choices:

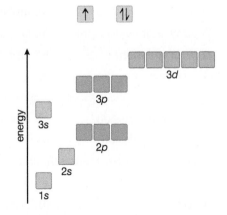

3.95 Construct an orbital diagram to show the electron configuration for a neutral atom of *fluorine*. Add single electrons or a pair of electrons as needed to each orbital box until the diagram is complete.

Answer choices:

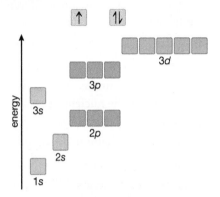

3.96 Construct an orbital diagram to show the electron configuration for a fluorine *ion*. Add single electrons or a pair of electrons as needed to each orbital box until the diagram is complete.

Answer choices:

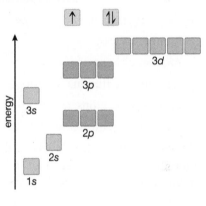

Chapter 4

4.1 Radioactivity

LO 1: **Define radioactivity and represent radioisotopes with correct atomic symbols.**

4.01 Boron-10 is an isotope used in boron neutron capture therapy (BNCT), an experimental treatment for some types of brain cancers. What is the correct atomic symbol for boron-10?

a) $^{10}_{5}\text{Bo}$ b) $^{10}_{5}\text{B}$

c) $^{5}_{10}\text{B}$ d) $^{10}_{10}\text{B}$

4.02 Myocardial perfusion imaging (MPI) is a medical test that shows how well the heart muscle is pumping blood. The procedure uses thallium-201 chloride and can detect coronary artery disease. What is the correct atomic symbol for the isotope thallium-201?

a) $^{81}_{201}\text{Tl}$ b) $^{201}_{120}\text{Tl}$

c) $^{201}_{81}\text{Tl}$ d) $^{120}_{201}\text{Tl}$

4.03 Radioactive metal atoms can be attached to antibodies to target and treat certain cancers. This approach, known as radioimmunotherapy, uses antibodies labeled with a radioactive isotope to deliver toxic radiation to a target cell. What is the correct symbol for the isotope of copper with a mass number of 67 used in this treatment? Consult the periodic table if needed.

a) $^{67}_{29}$Cu b) $^{67}_{38}$Cu

c) $^{67}_{29}$Co d) $^{29}_{67}$Cu

4.04 Determine the number of protons and the number of neutrons in the nucleus of each example. Consult the periodic table if needed.

a) nucleus of a sodium-25 isotope

number of protons = [?]

number of neutrons = [?]

b) nucleus of a gallium-67 isotope

number of protons = [?]

number of neutrons = [?]

4.05 Determine the number of protons and the number of neutrons in the nucleus of each example.

a) nucleus of a copper-65 isotope

number of protons = [?]

number of neutrons = [?]

b) nucleus of a fluorine-20 isotope

number of protons = [?]

number of neutrons = [?]

4.06 Write the appropriate symbols for the following isotopes by adding the correct atomic symbol, atomic number, and mass number in the boxes. The first letter of each element symbol is capitalized. Consult the periodic table if needed.

a) a nucleus of the phosphorus atom containing 18 neutrons

Input boxes: ⬛☐

b) a nucleus of element 19 containing 21 neutrons

Input boxes: ⬛☐

c) a rubidium-82 isotope used in PET scanning of a patient's heart

Input boxes: ⬛☐

4.07 Write the appropriate symbols for the following isotopes by adding the correct atomic symbol, atomic number, and mass number in the boxes. The first letter of each element symbol is capitalized. Consult the periodic table if needed.

a) a chromium isotope with mass number 51 used to diagnose intestinal disorders

Input boxes: ⬛☐

b) an isotope of iron with 33 neutrons used to diagnose anemia

Input boxes: ⬛☐

c) a hydrogen isotope with a mass number of 3 that can be used to measure the water content of a patient

Input boxes: ⬛☐

4.08 Which option correctly shows the atomic symbols of the three naturally-occurring isotopes of magnesium?

a) $^{24}_{12}$Ma $^{25}_{12}$Ma $^{26}_{12}$Ma

b) $^{24}_{12}$Mn $^{25}_{12}$Mn $^{26}_{12}$Mn

c) $^{12}_{24}$Mg $^{12}_{25}$Mg $^{12}_{26}$Mg

d) $^{24}_{12}$Mg $^{25}_{12}$Mg $^{26}_{12}$Mg

4.09 Enter the missing information in the table.

Medical Use	Atomic symbol	Atomic number	Mass number	Number of protons	Number of neutrons
Smoke detectors	$^{241}_{95}$Am				
Prostate cancer treatment	$^{103}_{46}$Pd				

4.2 Nuclear Reactions

LO 2: Identify the types of radioactivity and common nuclear reactions using balanced nuclear equations.

4.10 Match each type of emitted radiation with its mode of decay.

a) −1 charge b) no charge

c) +2 charge d) +1 charge

Target boxes: alpha emission, beta emission, gamma emission, positron emission

4.11 What type of nuclear process produces $^{0}_{+1}\beta$?

a) beta emission b) gamma emission

c) positron emission d) alpha emission

4.12 What type of nuclear process produces $^{4}_{2}$He?

a) gamma emission b) beta emission

c) positron emission d) alpha emission

4.13 What type of nuclear process emits $^{0}_{-1}\beta$?

a) beta emission b) alpha emission

c) positron emission d) gamma emission

4.14 What type of nuclear process produces $^{0}_{0}\gamma$?

a) positron emission b) alpha emission

c) gamma emission d) beta emission

4.15 Which is *not* a correct representation of a positron?

a) $^{0}_{+1}$e b) $\beta+$

c) $^{4}_{2}$He d) $^{0}_{+1}\beta$

4.16 Match equation with the type of nuclear decay it represents. One or more decay type may not be represented by the equations shown.

a) $^{14}_{6}C \rightarrow {}^{0}_{-1}\beta + {}^{14}_{7}N$

b) $^{56}_{25}Mn \rightarrow {}^{0}_{-1}\beta + {}^{56}_{26}Fe$

c) $^{122}_{53}I \rightarrow {}^{0}_{1}\beta + {}^{122}_{52}Te$

d) $^{212}_{84}Po \rightarrow {}^{4}_{2}\alpha + {}^{208}_{82}Pb$

Target boxes: alpha emission, positron emission, beta emission, gamma emission

4.17 Which statement is true about the balanced nuclear equation of a beta-emitting isotope?

a) The new nucleus contains one more proton.

b) The new nucleus contains one fewer proton.

c) The new nucleus contains two more protons.

d) The new nucleus contains two fewer protons.

e) The new nucleus contains the same number of protons.

4.18 Which statement is true about the nucleus of an atom undergoing alpha emission?

a) The nuclear mass decreases by two units.

b) The nuclear mass increases by two units.

c) The nuclear mass decreases by four units.

d) The nuclear mass increases by four units.

e) The nuclear mass remains the same.

4.19 Which statement about the nuclear mass of the starting material isotope undergoing positron emission is correct?

a) The nuclear mass increases by one unit.

b) The nuclear mass decreases by one unit.

c) The nuclear mass decreases by two units.

d) The nuclear mass increases by two units.

e) The nuclear mass remains the same.

4.20 Identify the nuclear process shown in each reaction.

A. $^{208}_{84}Po \rightarrow {}^{204}_{82}Pb + {}^{4}_{2}He$

   a) alpha emission

   b) beta emission

   c) positron emission

   d) gamma emission

B. $^{118}_{54}Xe \rightarrow {}^{118}_{53}I + {}^{0}_{+1}\beta$

   a) alpha emission

   b) beta emission

   c) positron emission

   d) gamma emission

4.21 Identify the nuclear process shown in each reaction.

A. $^{79}_{37}Rb \rightarrow {}^{79}_{36}Kr + {}^{0}_{+1}\beta$

   a) alpha emission

   b) beta emission

   c) positron emission

   d) gamma emission

B. $^{55}_{24}Cr \rightarrow {}^{55}_{25}Mn + {}^{0}_{-1}e$

   a) alpha emission

   b) beta emission

   c) positron emission

   d) gamma emission

4.22 Complete the following equations by entering the element symbol, atomic number, and mass number in the appropriate boxes. The first letter of an element symbol is capitalized.

a) $^{15}_{8}O \rightarrow \boxed{}\boxed{} + {}^{0}_{+1}\beta$

b) $^{35}_{16}S \rightarrow \boxed{}\boxed{} + {}^{0}_{-1}\beta$

c) $^{226}_{88}Ra \rightarrow \boxed{}\boxed{} + {}^{4}_{2}\alpha$

4.23 Complete the equation by entering the element symbol, atomic number, and mass number for the starting material isotope in the appropriate boxes. The first letter of an element symbol is capitalized.

$$\boxed{}\boxed{} \rightarrow {}^{210}_{83}Bi + {}^{0}_{-1}e$$

4.24 Complete the equation by entering the element symbol, atomic number, and mass number for the starting material isotope in the appropriate boxes. The first letter of an element symbol is capitalized.

$$\boxed{}\boxed{} \rightarrow {}^{234}_{90}Th + {}^{4}_{2}\alpha$$

4.25 Complete the equation by entering the element symbol, atomic number, and mass number for the starting material isotope in the appropriate boxes. The first letter of an element symbol is capitalized.

$$\boxed{}\boxed{} \rightarrow {}^{11}_{5}B + {}^{0}_{+1}e$$

4.26 Potassium–argon dating is used in geology and archeology to date rocks and minerals. The technique measures the radioactive decay of potassium-40 to argon-40 over time. Naturally occurring radioactive potassium-40 decays with a half-life of 1.25×10^9 years. Most potassium-40 nuclei decay to stable calcium-40 by beta decay, but a small fraction decay to argon-40 by positron emission.

A. Which equation shows the radioactive decay of potassium-40 to calcium-40 by beta decay?

   a) $^{40}_{19}K \rightarrow {}^{40}_{18}Ar + {}^{0}_{-1}\beta$

   b) $^{40}_{19}K \rightarrow {}^{40}_{20}Ca + {}^{0}_{+1}\beta$

   c) $^{40}_{19}P \rightarrow {}^{40}_{20}Ca + {}^{0}_{-1}\beta$

   d) $^{40}_{19}K \rightarrow {}^{40}_{20}Ca + {}^{0}_{-1}\beta$

B. Which equation shows the radioactive decay of potassium-40 to argon-40 by positron emission?

a) $^{40}_{19}K \rightarrow \ ^{40}_{20}Ca + \ ^{0}_{-1}\beta$

b) $^{40}_{19}K \rightarrow \ ^{40}_{18}Ar + \ ^{0}_{+1}\beta$

c) $^{40}_{19}K \rightarrow \ ^{40}_{18}Ar + \ ^{4}_{2}He$

d) $^{40}_{19}K \rightarrow \ ^{40}_{18}Ar + \ ^{0}_{-1}\beta$

4.3 Detecting and Measuring Radioactivity

LO 3: Describe how scientists detect and measure radiation and recognize the common units used in nuclear chemistry.

4.27 Which picture correctly shows the relative penetrating ability of the common forms of radiation?

a)

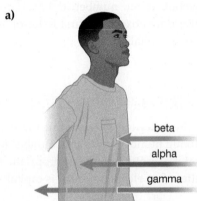

beta
alpha
gamma

b)

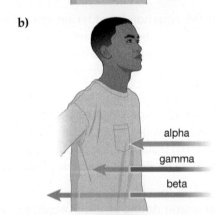

alpha
gamma
beta

c)

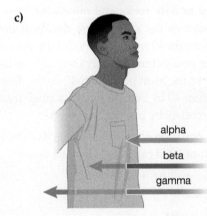

alpha
beta
gamma

d)

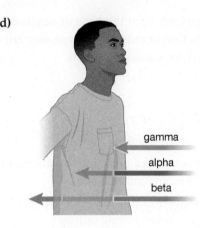

gamma
alpha
beta

4.28 Drag each type of radiation into the appropriate box to correctly indicate relative penetration.

Answer choices: beta, alpha, gamma

Target boxes:

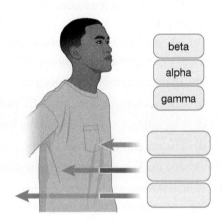

beta
alpha
gamma

4.29 Drag the symbol for each type of radiation into the appropriate box to correctly indicate relative penetration.

Answer choices: $^{0}_{-1}\beta$, $^{0}_{0}\gamma$, $^{4}_{2}\alpha$

Target boxes:

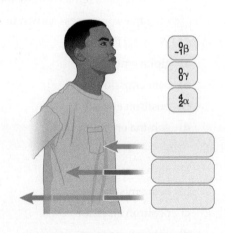

$^{0}_{-1}\beta$
$^{0}_{0}\gamma$
$^{4}_{2}\alpha$

4.30 Match each type of radiation to its penetrating ability in human tissue.

Answer choices: gamma radiation, beta particles, alpha particles

a) _____ : the lowest penetrating ability and can be stopped by skin

b) _____ : intermediate penetrating ability and can travel through the skin and moderately into body tissue

c) _____ : the greatest penetrating ability, and can travel deep into, or travel through the body

4.31 Which statement best describes how an effective dose of radiation is calculated?

a) An effective dose is calculated by multiplying the absorbed dose by a radiation-weighting factor (W_R).

b) An effective dose is calculated by multiplying the activity of the isotope in curies (Ci) by the time factor (t_e) of exposure.

c) An effective dose is calculated by adding the person's body mass to the product of the absorbed dose times the distance factor (D_e) from the radiation source.

d) An effective dose is calculated by dividing the absorbed dose by a radiation-weighting factor (W_R).

4.32 From the perspective of nuclear medicine, why is radiation often expressed in terms of rems instead of rads?

a) Rems are always the same as the patient's weight in kilograms.

b) Rems take into account the relative biological effect in addition to the quantity of radiation.

c) Rems come from natural sources and rads are from artificial sources.

d) Rems can be orally ingested but rads need to be injected by IV.

4.33 Use the information in each example to answer the questions.

a) If 1 Curie (Ci) is equal to 3.7×10^{10} becquerel (Bq), how many becquerel are in a 32 Curie sample of Y-90 used for cancer treatment? Express your answer in scientific notation with two significant figures and units of Bq.

b) If one Gray (Gy) is equal to 1×10^2 rad (D), how many Gray does 7.8×10^5 rad (D) correspond to? Express your answer in scientific notation with two significant figures and units of Gy.

4.34 *Background clinical information:* The diagnostic or therapeutic dosage of a radioactive substance given orally or intravenously is often given in millicuries (mCi). Since the emitter concentration is decreasing as it decays, it is important to determine the decay rate of the isotope solution per milliliter, so the dose can be calculated just before it is administered to the patient.

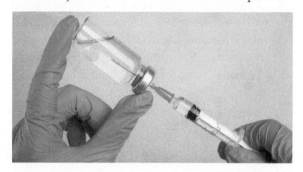

A physician treating a patient with thyroid dysfunction measures the activity of an iodine-131 containing solution as having a decay rate of 1.2×10^{-2} mCi per milliliter just before administering it. If the prescribed dose is 4.5×10^{-2} mCi, how many milliliters of solution should the patient receive? Enter your answer in standard decimal form with two significant figures and units of mL/dose.

4.35 Use the information in each example to answer the questions.

a) If one Rem (rem) equals one Roentgen (R) of gamma ray or X-ray in health effect, how many Rem will 1.5×10^{-3} Roentgen be? Express your answer in scientific notation with two significant figures and units of rem.

b) Given that one Roentgen (R) $= 0.96$ Rad (D) for tissue, determine the number of Rad (D) your answer in part (A) corresponds to. Express your answer in scientific notation with two significant figures and units of D.

4.36 A cancer patient with B-cell non-Hodgkin's lymphoma (NHL) has been prescribed a therapeutic dose of an anticancer drug carrying the beta emitting radionuclide Y-90.

a) If the patient is to receive a dose of Y-90 at 0.35 mCi per kg body weight, and weighs 72 kg, how many millicuries (mCi) will the patient receive? Enter your answer in standard notation with two significant figures and units of mCi.

b) Using your answer to part A, calculate the volume of drug that needs to be administered to the patient if the activity just before injection was measured to be 2.1 mCi/mL. Enter your answer in standard notation with two significant figures and units of mL/dose.

4.37 A sample of phosphorus-32 has an activity of 1.2 Ci. How many disintegrations occur in the phosphorus-32 sample in 30 seconds? 1 curie (Ci) $= 3.7 \times 10^{10}$ nuclei disintegrations/second.

a) 36   **b)** 1.1×10^{12}

c) 1.3×10^{12} **d)** 4.4×10^{10}

4.38 A patient getting a bone scan received an injected sample of technetium-99 with an activity of 0.025 Ci. How many disintegrations of the injected technetium-99 nuclei occur during the 120-minute procedure? 1 curie (Ci) $= 3.7 \times 10^{10}$ nuclei disintegrations/second.

a) 5.6×10^{10} **b)** 1.1×10^{11}

c) 5.0×10^{-9} **d)** 6.7×10^{12}

4.39 Use the given information to answer each of the questions.

a) If 3.7×10^{10} becquerel (Bq) is equal to 1 Curie (Ci), how many Curies does 8.5×10^{7} Bq correspond to? Express your answer in scientific notation with two significant figures and units of Ci.

b) The Roentgen (R) is a unit of exposure dose that measures X-rays or gamma rays in terms of the ions or electrons produced under certain conditions. If one Roentgen (R) corresponds to 0.96 Rad (D) for biological tissue, how many rads does 8.5 Roentgen correspond to? Express your answer in scientific notation with two significant figures and units of D.

4.40 Three common annual (per year) dose limits that apply to external exposure are: (1) deep dose to the whole body (5 rem or 0.05 Sv), (2) shallow dose to the skin or extremities (50 rem or 0.5 Sv), and (3) dose to the lens of the eye (15 rem or 0.15 Sv). Suppose a radiologist in the clinic is exposed to an estimated 2.0×10^{-5} Sv per hour to her arms while working with patients.

A. How many hours can the radiologist be exposed to this radiation each year before exceeding her dose limit? Enter your answer in scientific notation with two significant figures and units of h/yr in the space provided. _____

B. If the radiologist works 200 eight hour shifts a year, does she exceed her skin or extremities dose limit in this working environment?

a) Yes, she exceeds her annual dose limit under these working conditions.

b) No, she does not exceed her annual dose limit under these working conditions.

4.4 Half-life

LO 4: Calculate the amount of radioisotope remaining after one or more half-life.

4.41 Which statement best describes the half-life of a radioisotope?

a) the time of exposure required to cure one half of the cancer tumors in a clinical trial

b) the time it takes for one half of a radioactive sample to decay to one half its original weight

c) the time it takes for one half of the unstable nuclei in a radioactive sample to decay

d) the time it takes for the radioisotope to become an isotope with one half its atomic weight

4.42 Bismuth-213 decays through alpha emission with a half-life of 46 minutes. It is used to treat certain types of cancers using a method known as targeted alpha therapy (TAT).

Determine the number of half-lives in each case as whole number values.

a) 92 minutes   **b)** 276 minutes

4.43 Iodine-131 is a radioactive isotope used for the diagnosis and treatment of thyroid cancer. Given that I-131 has a half-life of 8 days, what fraction of the unstable nuclei in a I-131 sample will remain radioactive after 24 days? Enter your answer as a fraction, in the form of a/b, along with units of days.

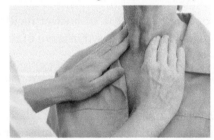

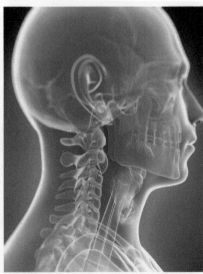

Text entry boxes: [_____]/[_____]

4.44 The iodine-131 isotope used for treatment of hyperthyroidism has a half-life of 8 days. How much of a given radioactive sample will remain after 32 days?

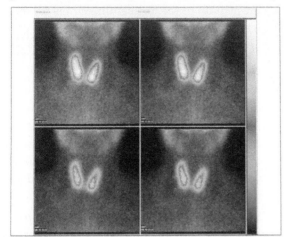

a) 8%   b) 24%   c) 20%

d) 12.5%   e) 4%   f) 0.25%

g) 15%   h) 6.25%

4.45 Sodium-24 is used as an isotope tracer to study blood flow and sodium uptake levels by different tissues in the body. If a sample containing sodium-24 has an activity of 6.0 mCi when administered to a patient, what is the activity of the sample after 30 hours? The half-life of sodium-24 is 15 hours. Express your answer in standard decimal notation with two significant figures and units of mCi.

4.46 Gold-198 is an isotope that decays through beta emission with a half-life of 2.7 days. It is used to treat prostate, cervical, and other forms of cancer in a method known as targeted brachytherapy. Determine the number of days in each case and answer using numeric values with two significant figures and units of days (d).

a) three half-lives   b) five half-lives

4.47 Sulfur-35 is a beta-emitting isotope used as a tracer in studies on the metabolism of sulfur-containing amino acids. If a sample containing sulfur-35 has an activity of 4.8×10^{-3} mCi, what is the activity of the sample after two half-lives? The half-life of sulfur-35 is 87.2 days. Express your answer in scientific notation with two significant figures and units of mCi.

4.48 Iron-59 has a half-life of 44.5 days. It is used as a tracer in the study of iron metabolism, and blood transfusion studies. If a medical test sample started with 2 mg of iron-59, which value most closely approximates the amount of iron-59 remaining after 1440 minutes?

a) 0.5 mg   b) 0.2 mg

c) 0.04 mg   d) 2 mg

4.49 The half-life of bromine-74 is 25 minutes. If a sample initially contains 45 mg of bromine-74, which value most closely approximates the amount remaining after a 48-hour period of time?

a) 1.9 mg   b) 9.4×10^{-34} mg

c) 4.5×10^{25} mg   d) 0.52 mg

4.50 The chromium-51 isotope is used for measuring blood volume to help diagnose congestive heart failure, hypertension, and kidney (renal) failure. If 2.5×10^{-6} Ci of Cr-51 is injected into a patient, which value most closely approximates the number of curies (Ci) remaining in the patient after a 2-hour procedure? The half-life of chromium-51 is 27.7 days.

a) 27.7 Ci   b) 9×10^{-8} Ci

c) 2.5×10^{-6} Ci   d) 0.5×10^{-6} Ci

4.51 The phosphorus-32 isotope is a beta emitting isotope used to treat certain types of cancer. If the half-life of this isotope is 14.3 days, how many days (d) will it take for the radiation level of a sample to decrease to one eighth of its original level?

a) 144 d   b) 1.79 d   c) 42.9 d   d) 0.0233 d

4.52 A piece of wood found during an archaeological dig at a prehistoric site has a carbon-14 activity of 5 counts per minute (cpm) on a Geiger counter compared to 40 cpm measured for new wood. Which value most closely approximates the age of the prehistoric wood found at the archaeological site? The half-life of carbon-14 is 5730 years.

a) 28,700 yr   b) 2.30×10^5 yr

c) 17,200 yr   d) 45,800 yr

4.53 Fluorine-18 decays through positron emission with a half-life of 110 minutes. It is used in positron emission tomography (PET) for bone scans, cancer imaging, and in metabolic studies. Determine the number of hours represented by six half-lives of fluorine-18. Express your answer as a whole number value with units of hours (h).

4.54 Technetium-99m (99mTc) is a gamma emitting isotope that is used in tens of millions of medical diagnostic procedures annually. The relatively short half-life of the isotope (6 hours) allows for rapid scanning while keeping total patient radiation exposure low. Which statement about technetium-99m is correct?

a) Over 90% of the radioactive technetium-99m in a sample will have decayed after 24 hours.

b) Nearly 25% of the technetium-99m in a radioactive sample will remain after 24 hours.

c) Over 90% of the radioactive technetium-99m in a sample will remain after 24 hours.

d) Nearly 25% of the radioactive technetium-99m in a sample will have decayed after 24 hours.

4.55 A patient undergoes a diagnostic imaging procedure for her thyroid that makes use of the iodine-123 isotope. The half-life of iodine-123 is 13 hours. If the patient receives 25 mg of I-123 at 9:00 a.m. Tuesday morning, how many mg remain active at 11:00 the following day? Express your answer in standard decimal form with two significant figures and units of mg.

4.5 Radioisotopes in Medicine

LO 5: Explain how nuclear chemistry is used in medicine.

4.56 Which imaging technique discussed in this chapter produces high-resolution images of internal organs using a computer to monitor the absorption of X-rays?

  a) confocal microscopy (CM)

  b) positron emission tomography (PET)

  c) computerized tomography (CT)

  d) magnetic resonance imaging (MRI)

4.57 Which imaging technique discussed in this chapter uses low-energy radio waves, not produced by nuclear reactions, to view internal organs?

  a) computerized tomography (CT)

  b) magnetic resonance imaging (MRI)

  c) confocal microscopy (CM)

  d) positron emission tomography (PET)

4.58 The radionuclides used for *diagnostic* procedures are often gamma emitters. Why do you think this is the case?

  a) Gamma emitting radionuclides are cheaper and have very long half-lives.

  b) Gamma emitting radionuclides don't penetrate tissue well, so don't cause damage.

  c) Gamma emitting radionuclides penetrate tissue well, so can be detected by imaging.

  d) Gamma emitting radionuclides are both highly stable and very effective at killing cancer tumors.

4.59 Which best explains the reason that radiation is used as a therapy to help shrink or kill cancer tumors in patients?

  a) The targeted radiation damages the genetic material (DNA) of the cancer cells, they begin to die, and the tumor gets smaller.

  b) The targeted radiation helps healthy cells around the tumor to reproduce faster and get stronger.

  c) The targeted radiation helps viral infections to start inside the tumor and produce more cell walls to surround and kill the tumor.

  d) The targeted radiation allows protons, neutrons, and electrons to all grow in number and then come together to form healthy cells.

4.60 A woman undergoing a breast imaging procedure known as Molecular Breast Imaging (MBI) receives 2.5 mL of a solution containing technetium-99m. If the activity of the technetium-99m is 8.4 mCi/mL, what dose does she receive?

  a) 0.048 mCi   b) 21 mCi

  c) 3.4 mCi   d) 0.30 mCi

4.61 A patient getting a PET scan needs to receive 15 mCi of fluorine-18 labeled fluorodeoxyglucose (FDG). If the sample vial contains FDG with an activity of 2.5 mCi/mL, how many milliliters need to be injected into the patient for the procedure? Enter your answer in standard decimal form with two significant figures and units of mL.

4.62 Selenium-75 is a gamma emitting isotope with a half-life of 120.4 days that is used as a tracer to study protein biochemistry. If a sample of cells receives 1.5 mL of a solution containing selenium-75 with an activity of 3.8 μCi/mL, how many microcuries (μCi) were added? Express your answer in standard decimal form with two significant figures and units of μCi.

4.63 A patient getting a diagnostic PET scan needs a 25 mCi dose of technetium-99m (Tc-99m). The vial containing the radioisotope in solution has an activity of 8.3 mCi/mL. What volume of solution must be given to the patient?

  a) 3.0 mL

  b) 2.1×10^2 mL

  c) 4.8×10^{-3} mL

  d) 0.33 mL

4.64 Mammograms are often used in routine scanning to check for breast cancer. If a typical mammogram delivers a dose of 0.030 rem, how many Sievert (Sv) does this correspond to? Express your answer in scientific notation with two significant figures and units of Sievert. 1 Sv = 100 rem.

  a) 3.0 Sv   b) 0.33 Sv

  c) 3.3×10^3 Sv   d) 3.0×10^{-4} Sv

4.65 Use the given information in each example to answer the questions.

    a) If a patient undergoing radiation treatment for prostate cancer receives 38 Gray (Gy) of gamma radiation, how many rad (D) does this correspond to? Express your answer in scientific notation with units of D to two significant figures. ($1 \text{ Gy} = 1 \times 10^2 \text{ D}$).

    b) A newborn baby will receive a bone scan using the gallium-67 isotope. If the prescribed dose is 7.1×10^{-2} millicuries per kilogram (mCi/kg), and the baby weighs 3.5 kg, how many mCi will the doctor administer to the baby? Express your answer in scientific notation with units of mCi to two significant figures. ($1 \text{ mCi} = 1 \times 10^{-3} \text{ Ci}$).

4.66 Use the information in each example to answer the questions.

    a) If a patient getting a lung scan using technetium-99m will receive 18 microcuries (μCi) radiation per kilogram (kg) body mass, how many microcuries will be given to the 62 kg patient? Express your answer in scientific notation with two significant figures and units of μCi.

    b) A 72.5 kg patient with hyperthyroidism has been prescribed a treatment involving iodine-131 at 4.0 microcuries (μCi) per kg body mass. How many millicuries (mCi) will the patient receive? Express your answer in scientific notation with two significant figures and units of millicuries mCi. (1000μCi $= 1$ mCi)

4.67 A patient undergoing myocardial (heart muscle) imaging needs a dose of 250 μCi/kg technetium-99m. How many millicuries (mCi) of technetium-99m should be given to a patient weighing 96 kg? Express your answer in standard decimal form with two significant figures and units of mCi.

4.68 The radionuclide strontium-89 is used to treat patients with painful bone metastasis. A doctor orders a patient dose to be 55 microcuries per kilogram (μCi/kg). If the radioactive concentration of the drug before injection of the solution is 1.5 millicuries per milliliter (mCi/mL), and the patient weighs 63 kg, how many milliliters (ml) of this solution should the doctor administer to the patient? Express your answer in standard notation with units of ml, to two significant figures. ($1 \text{ mCi} = 1 \times 10^3 \mu$Ci)

4.69 The average person in the United States receives an estimated 625 millirem/year dose of ionizing radiation. Of this value, medical radiation scans and nuclear medicine represents approximately 48% (300 mrem). Radon inhalation in our homes and workplaces has been estimated to be approximately 37% (228 mrem) of the total annual dose. Convert each of these values into units of Sievert. Express your answer in scientific notation with two significant figures and units of Sv. (1 Sv = 100 rem, 1000 mrem = 1 rem.)

    a) Convert 300 mrem medical radiation to Sievert (Sv).

    b) Convert 228 mrem inhaled radiation from radon gas to Sievert (Sv).

4.6 Nuclear Fission and Fusion

LO 6: Describe nuclear fission and fusion.

4.70 Which statement best describes nuclear fission?

    a) Heavy isotopes combine to form a larger nucleus and large amounts of energy.

    b) Light isotopes split into smaller fragments, releasing large amounts of energy.

    c) Light isotopes combine to form a larger nucleus and large amounts of energy.

    d) Heavy isotopes split into smaller fragments, releasing large amounts of energy.

4.71 Which statement best describes nuclear fusion?

    a) Heavy isotopes split into smaller fragments, releasing large amounts of energy.

    b) Light isotopes split into smaller fragments, releasing large amounts of energy.

    c) Light isotopes combine to form a larger nucleus and large amounts of energy.

    d) Heavy isotopes combine to form a larger nucleus and large amounts of energy.

4.72 Which statement best describes transmutation?

    a) a nuclear reaction that uses particles to bombard atoms to form new isotopes

    b) a nuclear reaction that uses heat to initiate the transfer of atoms between isotopes

    c) a nuclear reaction that requires the transition of product back to reactant

    d) a non-nuclear reaction that becomes a nuclear reaction over time

4.73 Construct a statement about fission and a statement about fusion by dragging the sentence fragments into the correct order within the box provided.

Answer choices: to form heavier nuclei, to form lighter nuclei, nuclear fission, splits heavy nuclei, nuclear fusion, joins light nuclei

Target boxes: 3 boxes arranged left-to-right for fission, 3 boxes arranged left-to-right for fusion

4.74 When uranium-235 undergoes nuclear fission, what reaction products help the chain reaction continue?

    a) positron   **b)** beta particle

    c) alpha particle   **d)** neutron

    e) gamma radiation

4.75 Which of these isotopes undergoes nuclear fission?

    a) $^{226}_{88}Ra$ **b)** $^{14}_{6}C$ **c)** $^{2}_{1}H$

    d) $^{235}_{92}U$ **e)** $^{34}_{14}Si$

4.76 Which of these isotopes undergoes nuclear fission?

    a) $^{32}_{15}P$ **b)** $^{232}_{90}Th$ **c)** $^{192}_{78}Pt$

    d) $^{84}_{35}Br$ **e)** $^{3}_{1}H$

4.77 Which of these isotopes undergoes nuclear fusion?

    a) $^{4}_{2}He$ **b)** $^{235}_{92}U$ **c)** $^{15}_{7}N$

    d) $^{14}_{6}C$ **e)** $^{3}_{1}H$

4.78 Which of these isotopes undergoes nuclear fusion?

    a) $^{2}_{1}H$ **b)** $^{90}_{39}Y$ **c)** $^{19}_{9}F$

    d) $^{131}_{53}I$ **e)** $^{57}_{27}Co$

4.79 Cesium-137 is a fission product of uranium-235 used in nuclear reactors. An exposure guideline lists the effective inhaled dose equivalent of radiation in terms of Sieverts per Becquerel. Your supervisor asks you to use the equation below to convert an inhaled Cs-137 dose of 8.8×10^{-9} (Sv/Bq) to rem/μCi. The formula for converting the units from Sieverts per Becquerel to rem per microcurie is: (Sv/Bq) $\times$ (3.7×10^{6}) = rem/μCi. Express your answer in scientific notation with units of rem/μCi with two significant figures in the spaces provided.

Chapter 5

5.1 Introduction to Bonding

LO 1: Define and describe ionic bonding.

5.01 Which pair of atoms is most likely to form an ionic bond with each other?

    a) K and I   **b)** K and Mg

    c) N and C   **d)** P and O

5.02 Which pair of atoms is most likely to form a covalent bond with each other?

    a) C and Ca   **b)** Ca and Cl

    c) Cl and Li   **d)** C and O

5.03 Determine if the following pairs of elements form ionic bonds or covalent bonds.

    Answer choices: potassium and chlorine, two fluorine atoms, sulfur and carbon

    Target boxes: ionic bonds, covalent bonds

5.04 Determine if the following pairs of elements form ionic bonds or covalent bonds.

    Answer choices: nitrogen and hydrogen, barium and sulfur, oxygen and hydrogen, calcium and fluorine

    Target boxes: ionic bonds, covalent bonds

5.05 Which compound is covalently bonded?

    a) Na_2S **b)** SrO

    c) H_2S **d)** RbI_2

5.06 Which compound is covalently bonded?

    a) CH_4 **b)** CaO

    c) MgI_2 **d)** KBr

5.07 Which compound is ionically bonded?

    a) H_2O **b)** LiF

    c) CCl_4 **d)** NH_3

5.08 Which compound is ionically bonded?

    a) Cl_2 **b)** N_2

    c) NO_2 **d)** $BeBr_2$

5.09 Identify each compound as covalent or ionic.

    Answer choices: C_2H_6, $MgCl_2$, MgO, CO_2, CsCl, CH_5N, BaS

    Target boxes: ionic compound, covalent compound

5.2 Ions

LO 2: Determine the charge on ions using the periodic table and the octet rule.

5.10 Which element is most likely to form an ion with a positive two (+2) charge?

    a) S   **b)** N   **c)** Rb   **d)** Ba

5.11 Which element is most likely to form an ion with a negative two (−2) charge?

    a) Br   **b)** Be   **c)** Se   **d)** Ar

5.12 **a)** What is the charge of the ion that forms in the scheme shown? Enter a numerical value in the box from 0 to 9 followed by a + or − sign to indicate the type of charge.

   b) How many electrons are contained in the ion formed in part A? Enter a numerical value in the box.

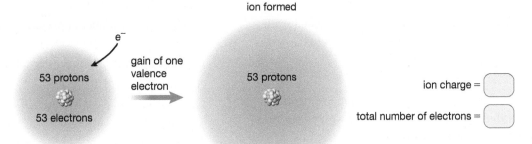

5.13 **a)** What is the charge of the ion that forms in the scheme shown? Enter a numerical value in the box from 0 to 9 followed by a + or − sign to indicate the type of charge.

   b) How many electrons are contained in the ion formed in part A? Enter a numerical value in the box.

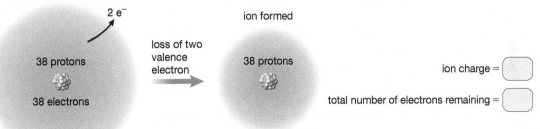

5.14 Identify the charge of the ions formed when elements from the following Groups react. Enter a numeric value in the box between 0 and 8 followed by a + or − sign to indicate the type of charge.

   a) Group 6A (16) _____

   b) Group 2A (2) _____

   c) Group 7A (17) _____

   d) Group 1A (1) _____

5.15 Drag the ions listed into the correct box to indicate if they are likely to form.

   Answer choices:
   Mg^+, Mg^{2+}, Mg^{2-}, Rb^+, Rb^-, S^{2-}, S^{2+}

   Target boxes: Yes, likely to form; No, unlikely to form

5.16 Consider each atom below and write the symbol for the predicted ion formed in each case. For example: Sr would be written as Sr^{2+} in the space provided.

   a) I _____

   b) K _____

   c) Cl _____

5.17 How many electrons are gained when these non-metals react to form negatively charged ions (anions)? Enter a number in the box below. Do not write a + or − sign after the number you input.

   a) sulfur _____

   b) iodine _____

   c) chlorine _____

   d) oxygen _____

5.18 How many electrons are lost when these metals react to form positively charged ions (cations)? Enter a number in the box below. Do not write a + or − sign after the number you input.

   a) barium _____

   b) potassium _____

   c) calcium _____

   d) sodium _____

5.19 Consider each atom and write the symbol for the predicted ion formed in each case. For example: Sr would be written as Sr^{2+} in the space provided.

a) Rb _____ b) N _____ c) Ca _____

5.20 Write the symbol for the predicted ion formed from each of these atoms. For example: Sr would be written as Sr^{2+} in the space provided.

a) S _____ b) Cs _____ c) Br _____

5.21 Write the symbol for the predicted ion formed from each of these atoms. For example: Sr would be written as Sr^{2+} in the space provided.

a) O _____ b) F _____ c) Mg _____

5.22 Match each ion with the noble gas that has the same number of electrons as the ion.

Answer choices:
Mg^{2+}, Cl^-, F^-, O^{2-}, Na^+, S^{2-}, Ca^{2+}, K^+

Target boxes: He, Ne, Ar

5.23 Match each ion with the noble gas that has the same number of electrons as the ion.

Answer choices: Ca^{2+}, N^{3-}, Be^{2+}, P^{3-}, Li^+, Al^{3+}

Target boxes: He, Ne, Ar

5.24 Determine the charge of the ion formed by each atom.

Answer choices: K , Ca, O, Cs, Na, F, S, I

Target boxes: 1^-, 2^+, 2^-, 1^+

5.25 What is the charge of the ion formed by each of the atoms?

Answer choices: Cl, Mg, Li, Be, Br, Sr, Se, Rb

Target boxes: 1^-, 2^+, 2^-, 1^+

5.26 Enter the element symbol and electric charge on each ion described here. For example, the magnesium ion is entered as Mg^{2+}.

a) 9 protons, 10 electrons _____

b) 34 protons, 36 electrons _____

c) 4 protons, 2 electrons _____

5.27 Enter the element symbol and electric charge on each ion described here. For example, the magnesium ion is entered as Mg^{2+}.

a) 19 protons, 18 electrons _____

b) 8 protons, 10 electrons _____

c) 16 protons, 18 electrons _____

5.28 Each of the following ions is important in biological systems. Indicate the total number of protons and total number of electrons for each ion by entering the numbers in the boxes.

a) Ca^{2+} Total number of protons _____

Total number of electrons _____

b) O^{2-} Total number of protons _____

Total number of electrons _____

c) K^+ Total number of protons _____

Total number of electrons _____

d) Cl^- Total number of protons _____

Total number of electrons _____

5.29 Drag the appropriate box to complete the table

Answer choices: S, Br

Answer choices: 2, 18, 19, 20, 36

Answer choices: 1^+, 2^+, 2^-

Symbol	Ion charge	Number of electrons in ion	Number of protons in ion
K	1^+	◯	◯
◯	◯	18	16
◯	1^-	◯	35
Ca	◯	18	◯
Li	◯	◯	3

5.30 Drag the appropriate box to complete the table.

Answer choices: Na, O, Cl

Answer choices: 7, 10, 11, 12

Answer choices: 1^-, 2^+

Symbol	Ion charge	Number of electrons in ion	Number of protons in ion
◯	2^-	◯	8
N	3^-	◯	◯
Mg	◯	10	◯
◯	1^+	10	◯
◯	◯	18	17

5.31 Each of the following ions is important in biological systems. Provide the total number of protons and total number of electrons for each ion by entering the numbers in the boxes.

a) Mg^{2+} Total number of protons _____

Total number of electrons _____

b) S^{2-} Total number of protons _____

Total number of electrons _____

c) Na^+ Total number of protons _____

Total number of electrons _____

d) I^- Total number of protons _____

Total number of electrons _____

5.32 Match the electron configuration of a neutral magnesium atom with the electron configuration of a magnesium ion.

Neutral atoms: $1s^2 2s^2 2p^6$, $1s^2 2s^2 2p^8 3s^2$, $1s^2 2s^2 2p^6 3s^2$

Ions: $1s^1 2s^2 2p^6 3s^4$, $1s^2 2s^2 2p^6$, $1s^2 2s^2 2p^8$

5.33 Match the electron configuration of a neutral oxygen atom with the electron configuration of an oxygen ion.

Neutral atoms: $1s^2 2s^2 2p^4$, $1s^1 2s^2 2p^6$, $1s^2 2s^2 2p^8$

Ions: $1s^2 2s^2 2p^8$, $1s^2 2s^2 2p^2$, $1s^2 2s^2 2p^6$

5.34 Write the complete atomic symbol for each atom or ion in the space provided. If a charge exists, enter the charge as a superscripted number followed by a $+$ or $-$ sign after the atomic symbol. For example, a specific isotope of calcium in the ionic form is written as $^{40}_{20}Ca^{2+}$.

a)
18 e⁻
15 p⁺
16 n

b)
8 e⁻
8 p⁺
8 n

c)
28 e⁻
30 p⁺
35 n

d)
23 e⁻
26 p⁺
28 n

Input boxes for: mass number, atomic number, and chemical symbol (with charge)

5.3 Ionic Compounds

LO 3: Write formulas for ionic compounds.

5.35 Select the appropriate words to complete the statement about ionic compounds.

Ionic bonding involves positively charged _____ combining with negatively charged _____ to form an ionic compound that is overall electrically _____.

Answer choices: neutral, protons, anions, cations, charged, electrons

5.36 More prescriptions are written for high blood pressure (hypertension) medications than almost any other health problem. Instead of taking prescription drugs, some people are successfully lowering their blood pressure by reducing their dietary sodium and increasing their potassium intake by eating a balanced diet that includes potassium rich foods such as bananas, sweet potatoes, beans, and squash.

a) How many protons and electrons are present in a neutral potassium atom? Enter a numeric value for the number of protons then a comma followed by a numeric value for the number of electrons. _____

b) Potassium ionizes to form a K^+ ion. How many electrons does this ion contain? Enter a numeric value. _____

c) What is the chemical formula for the ionic compound formed between potassium and chlorine? _____

5.37 Which is the correct formula for the ionic compound formed between strontium (Sr) and iodine (I)?

a) SrI **b)** SI_2

c) Sr_2I **d)** SrI_2

5.38 Which is the correct formula for the ionic compound formed between barium (Ba) and chlorine (Cl)?

a) BCl_2 **b)** Ba_2Cl_2

c) $BaCl_2$ **d)** $BaCI$

5.39 Write formulas for the ionic compound formed from the following pairs of elements. You do not need to write the charges of the ions in the formula. If more than one of the same ion is required for the formula, be sure to indicate that with a subscripted number (for example $CaCl_2$ indicates one Ca^{2+} combines with two Cl^- anions). You do not need to include subscripts of "1".

a) Li and Br _____

b) Mg and S _____

c) Na on O _____

5.40 Write formulas for the ionic compound formed from the O^{2-} ion and each of the metal cations below. You do not need to write the charges of the ions in the formula. If more than one of the same ion is required for the formula, be sure to indicate that with a subscripted number (for example $CaCl_2$ indicates one Ca^{2+} combines with two Cl^- anions). You do not need to include subscripts of "1".

a) Fe^{2+} and O^{2-} _____

b) Fe^{3+} and O^{2-} _____

c) Ca^{2+} and O^{2-} _____

5.41 Write formulas for the ionic compound formed from the O^{2-} ion and each of the metal cations below. You do not need to write the charges of the ions in the formula. If more than one of the same ion is required for the formula, be sure to indicate that with a subscripted number (for example $CaCl_2$ indicates one Ca^{2+} combines with two Cl^- anions). You do not need to include subscripts of "1".

a) K^+ and O^{2-} _____

b) Cu^{2+} and O^{2-} _____

c) Li^+ and O^{2-} _____

5.42 Write formulas for the ionic compound formed from the Ca^{2+} ion and each of the anions below. You do not need to write the charges of the ions in the formula. If more than one of the same ion is required for the formula, be sure to indicate that with a subscripted number (for example $CaCl_2$ indicates one Ca^{2+} combines with two Cl^- anions). You do not need to include subscripts of "1".

a) Ca^{2+} and Cl^- _____

b) Ca^{2+} and Br^- _____

c) Ca^{2+} and SO_4^{2-} _____

5.43 Write formulas for the ionic compound formed from the Al^{3+} ion and each of the anions below. You do not need to write the charges of the ions in the formula. If more than one of the same ion is required for the formula, be sure to indicate that with a subscripted number (for example $CaCl_2$ indicates one Ca^{2+} combines with two Cl^- anions). You do not need to include subscripts of "1".

a) Cl^- _____   b) O^{2-} _____

c) N^{3-} _____

5.44 Write formulas for the ionic compound formed from the two atoms listed below. You do not need to write the charges of the ions in the formula. If more than one of the same ion is required for the formula, be sure to indicate that with a subscripted number (for example $CaCl_2$ indicates one Ca^{2+} combines with two Cl^- anions). You do not need to include subscripts of "1".

a) barium and fluorine _____

b) potassium and oxygen _____

c) potassium and chlorine _____

5.45 Write formulas for the ionic compound formed from the following pairs of elements. You do not need to write the charges of the ions in the formula. If more than one of the same ion is required for the formula, be sure to indicate that with a subscripted number (for example $CaCl_2$ indicates one Ca^{2+} combines with two Cl^- anions). You do not need to include subscripts of "1".

a) Sr and I _____   b) K and S _____

c) Be and Br _____

5.46 Write formulas for the ionic compound formed from the following pairs of elements. You do not need to write the charges of the ions in the formula. If more than one of the same ion is required for the formula, be sure to indicate that with a subscripted number (for example $CaCl_2$ indicates one Ca^{2+} combines with two Cl^- anions). You do not need to include subscripts of "1".

a) Ca and Cl _____

b) Mg and O _____

c) K and Cl _____

5.47 Write formulas for the ionic compound formed from the following pairs of elements. You do not need to write the charges of the ions in the formula. If more than one of the same ion is required for the formula, be sure to indicate that with a subscripted number (for example $CaCl_2$ indicates one Ca^{2+} combines with two Cl^- anions). You do not need to include subscripts of "1".

a) Sr and Br _____

b) Cs and O _____

c) Li and S _____

5.48 Based on the provided formulas and your knowledge of ionic compounds, classify each as correct or incorrect.

Answer choices: $NaCl$, $MgCl_2$, KS, CaO, $SrCl_3$, Ca_2Br, $SrCl_2$, BaS_2

Target boxes: correct formula, incorrect formula

5.49 Determine the charge on the cation "X" in each of the following formulas?

Target boxes: 1+, 2+, 3 +

Answer choices: X_2O_3, XF_2, XO, X_3N

5.50 Determine the charge on the anion "Y" in each of the following formulas?

Answer choices: Mg_3Y_2, CaY_2, MgY, NaY

Target boxes: 1−, 2−, 3 −

5.4 Naming Ionic Compounds

LO 4: Write the name of ionic compounds from a given formula, and provide the formula when given the name of an ionic compound.

5.51 Write the ion symbol for the following ions. Charges should be superscripted and indicated by a number followed by either a + or − sign (Ba^{2+} for example). You do not need to include the number "1" in the superscript of an ion that has a charge of 1, but you do need to include the sign of the charge.

a) calcium ion _____

b) iron(III) ion _____

c) lithium ion _____

5.52 Write the ion symbol for the following ions. Charges should be superscripted and indicated by a number followed by either a plus (+) or minus (−) sign (Ba^{2+} for example). You do not need to include the number "1" in the superscript of an ion that has a charge of 1, but you do need to include the sign of the charge.

a) copper(II) ion _____

b) mercury(I) ion _____

c) cobalt(II) ion _____

5.53 Write the name of each for the following ions. Use only lowercase letters.

a) Br^- _____

b) O^{2-} _____

c) N^{3-} _____

5.54 Write the name of each for the following ions: Use only lowercase letters followed by Roman numerals in parentheses to indicate ion charge.

a) Pb^{4+} _____

b) Cd^{2+} _____

c) Sn^{4+} _____

5.55 Write the correct name for each of the formulas. Use all lowercase letters with a space between cations and anions.

a) KBr _____

b) $CaCl_2$ _____

c) NaBr _____

5.56 Write the correct name for each of the formulas. Use all lowercase letters with a space between cations and anions.

a) MgF_2 _____

b) BaS _____

c) LiF _____

5.57 Write the formulas for each of the ionic compounds. Be sure to use the subscript function when appropriate to indicate when more than one of the same ion is present in the formula. Do not include the number "1" in the subscript if there is only one of any particular ion in the formula.

a) potassium sulfide _____

b) cesium bromide _____

c) magnesium sulfide _____

5.58 Write the formulas for each of the ionic compounds. Be sure to use the subscript function when appropriate to indicate when more than one of the same ion is present in the formula. Do not include the number "1" in the subscript if there is only one of any particular ion in the formula.

a) potassium oxide _____

b) beryllium fluoride _____

c) magnesium bromide _____

5.59 Write the correct name for each of the formulas. Use all lowercase letters with a space between cations and anions. Use Roman numerals in parentheses to indicate the charge of transition metals.

a) PbO _____

b) $FeCl_2$ _____

c) Mn_2O_3 _____

5.60 Write the correct name for each of the ionic compounds. Use all lowercase letters with a space between cations and anions. Use Roman numerals in parentheses to indicate the charge of transition metals.

a) $CrBr_3$ _____

b) Na_2O _____

c) FeS _____

5.61 Write the correct name for each of the ionic compounds. Use all lowercase letters with a space between cations and anions. Use Roman numerals in parentheses to indicate the charge of transition metals.

a) CoF_2 _____

b) MgI_2 _____

c) CuBr _____

5.62 Write the formulas for each of the ionic compounds. Be sure to use the subscript function when appropriate to indicate when more than one of the same ion is present in the formula. Do not include the number "1" in the subscript if there is only one of any particular ion in the formula.

a) tin(IV) fluoride _____

b) copper(I) oxide _____

c) cobalt(III) nitride _____

5.63 Match the chemical name and chemical formula for each ionic compound. Not all chemical formulas match to one of the given chemical names.

Chemical formulas: Mg_2Cl, Ca_2F, Li_2O, Na_2S, LiO_2, BaO_2, PBr, CaF_2, KBr, BaO, $MgCl_2$, NaS_2.

Chemical names: calcium fluoride, magnesium chloride, sodium sulfide, lithium oxide, barium oxide, potassium bromide

5.64 Match the chemical name and chemical formula for each ionic compound. Not all chemical formulas match to one of the given chemical names.

Chemical formulas: BeO, NaF, CaO, K_2O, RbI, NaCl, CsI, CsI_2, RuI, SrF_2, BaO, $SrCl_2$.

Chemical names: calcium oxide, strontium chloride, sodium fluoride, cesium iodide, rubidium iodide, beryllium oxide

5.5 Polyatomic Ions

LO 5: Recognize the common polyatomic ions and write the name and formula of compounds with polyatomic ions.

5.65 Match the chemical formula for each polyatomic ion with its correct chemical name. Not all of the polyatomic ion formulas will be used.

Answer choices: $SO_4{}^{2-}$, $CO_3{}^{2-}$, $PO_4{}^{3-}$, $NH_4{}^+$, $CH_3CO_2{}^-$, OH^-.

Target boxes: phosphate, acetate, ammonium

5.66 Drag the chemical formula for each polyatomic ion into the appropriate boxes. Not all polyatomic ion chemical formulas will be used.

Answer choices: SO_4^{2-}, CO_3^{2-}, PO_4^{3-}, NH_4^+, $CH_3CO_2^-$, NO_3^-.

Target boxes: nitrate, sulfate, carbonate

5.67 Calcium oxalate is a primary component of kidney stones. What is the chemical formula for calcium oxalate? _____

5.68 Sodium nitrite is a chemical preservative commonly added to meat during curing and has long been a suspected carcinogen. What is the formula for sodium nitrite? _____

5.69 Potassium sulfate is widely used as a fertilizer to help increase crop yields. What is the formula for potassium sulfate? _____

5.70 Sodium cyanide is used to extract gold and other precious metals in the mining industry. Unfortunately, cyanide salts are some of the most rapidly acting of all known poisons and cause damage to the respiratory and nervous systems. What is the formula for sodium cyanide? _____

5.71 The compound $CaCO_3$ is a primary component of egg shells, sea shells, and coral reefs. What is the name of $CaCO_3$? Answers should be written in lowercase letters with a space between cations and anions. It may be helpful to refer back to a table of polyatomic ions when answering the question. _____

5.72 The compound $(NH_4)_3PO_4$ is a common ingredient of chemical fertilizers used to increase crop production. What is the name of $(NH_4)_3PO_4$? Answers should be written in lowercase letters with a space between cations and anions. It may be helpful to refer back to a table of polyatomic ions when answering the question. _____

5.73 The compound $(NH_4)_2SO_4$ is a fertilizer used to increase crop yields. What is the name of $(NH_4)_2SO_4$? Answers should be written in lowercase letters with a space between cations and anions. It may be helpful to refer back to a table of polyatomic ions when answering the question. _____

5.74 Write the correct name for each of the formulas containing polyatomic ions. Use all lowercase letters with a space between cations and anions. It may be helpful to refer back to a table of polyatomic ions when answering the question.

a) Na_2CO_3 _____

b) KNO_3 _____

c) $(NH_4)_3PO_4$ _____

5.75 Write the correct name for each of the formulas containing polyatomic ions. Use all lowercase letters with a space between cations and anions. It may be helpful to refer to a polyatomic ion table when answering this question.

a) $NaCH_3CO_2$ _____

b) KH_2PO_4 _____

c) $NaHCO_3$ _____

5.76 Write the correct name for each of the compound names containing polyatomic ions. Use all lowercase letters with a space between cations and anions. Use Roman numerals in parentheses ( ) to indicate the charge of transition metals. It may be helpful to refer to a polyatomic ion table when answering this question.

a) $Cu(NO_3)_2$ _____

b) $NiCl_2$ _____

c) $TiPO_4$ _____

5.77 Write the correct name for each of the compound names containing polyatomic ions. Use all lowercase letters with a space between cations and anions. Use Roman numerals in parentheses ( ) to indicate the charge of transition metals. It may be helpful to refer to a polyatomic ion table when answering this question.

a) $Mn(CH_3CO_2)_2$ _____

b) $ZnCO_3$ _____

c) $AgNO_3$ _____

5.78 Write formulas for the ionic compounds whose names are provided. Do not write the charges of the ions in the formula. If more than one of the same ion is in the formula, be sure to indicate that with a subscripted number (for example Na_2S indicates two Na^+ cations combine with one S^{2-} anion). Use parentheses ( ) around polyatomic ions if more than one polyatomic ion is needed in the formula. You do not need to include subscripts of "1". It may be helpful to refer to a polyatomic ion table when answering this question.

a) potassium sulfate _____

b) magnesium sulfate _____

c) calcium hydroxide _____

5.79 Write formulas for the ionic compound formed from the Ca^{2+} ion and each of these anions. Do not write the charges of the ions in the formula. If more than one of the same ion is in the formula, be sure to indicate that with a subscripted number (for example Na_2S indicates two Na^+ cations combine with one S^{2-} anion). Use parentheses ( )

around polyatomic ions if more than one polyatomic ion is needed in the formula. You do not need to include subscripts of "1". It may be helpful to refer to a polyatomic ion table when answering this question.

a) Ca^{2+} and S^{2-} _____

b) Ca^{2+} and NO_3^- _____

c) Ca^{2+} and PO_4^{3-} _____

5.80 Write formulas for these ionic compounds. Do not write the charges of the ions in the formula. If more than one of the same ion is in the formula, be sure to indicate that with a subscripted number (for example Na_2S indicates two Na^+ cations combine with one S^{2-} anion). Use parentheses ( ) around polyatomic ions if more than one polyatomic ion is needed in the formula. You do not need to include subscripts of "1". It may be helpful to refer to a polyatomic ion table when answering this question.

a) potassium cyanide _____

b) sodium nitrite _____

c) calcium oxalate _____

5.81 Write formulas for these ionic compounds. Do not write the charges of the ions in the formula. If more than one of the same ion is in the formula, be sure to indicate that with a subscripted number (for example Na_2S indicates two Na^+ cations combine with one S^{2-} anion). Use parentheses ( ) around polyatomic ions if more than one polyatomic ion is needed in the formula. You do not need to include subscripts of "1". It may be helpful to refer to a polyatomic ion table when answering this question.

a) iron(III) sulfate _____

b) copper(II) carbonate _____

c) cobalt(II) acetate _____

5.82 Write formulas for these ionic compounds. Do not write the charges of the ions in the formula. If more than one of the same ion is in the formula, be sure to indicate that with a subscripted number (for example Na_2S indicates two Na^+ cations combine with one S^{2-} anion). Use parentheses ( ) around polyatomic ions if more than one polyatomic ion is needed in the formula. You do not need to include subscripts of "1". It may be helpful to refer to a polyatomic ion table when answering this question.

a) nickel(II) oxalate _____

b) manganese(III) bromide _____

c) cadmium(II) hydroxide _____

Chapter 6

6.1 Introduction to Covalent Bonding

LO 1: Define and describe covalent bonding.

6.01 In a molecule composed of covalently bonded atoms, _____.

a) metal atoms are bonded to non-metal atoms

b) metal atoms are bonded to noble gas atoms

c) non-metal atoms are bonded to non-metal atoms through transfer of electrons

d) non-metal atoms are bonded to non-metal atoms through sharing of electrons

6.02 Which molecule contains two covalent bonds and two lone pairs?

a)

b)

c) H—C̈l̈:

d) S̈ H—S—H (with lone pairs)

6.03 Which molecule contains one covalent bond and three lone pairs?

a) H, B with H, H

b) H—C≡N:

c) H—B̈r̈:

d) :F̈—F̈:

6.04 Which element naturally occurs as a diatomic molecule.

a) helium

b) iodine

c) calcium

d) lithium

6.05 Which element naturally occurs as a diatomic molecule.

a) barium

b) boron

c) potassium

d) nitrogen

6.06 How many electrons are found in a single covalent bond?

a) one

b) two

c) four

d) six

e) eight

6.07 How many electrons are found in a covalent double bond?

a) two

b) four

c) six

d) eight

6.08 Six electrons shared between two elements represents what type of covalent bond?

a) ionic bond

b) single covalent bond

c) double covalent bond

d) triple covalent bond

6.09 Which elements form diatomic molecules?

a) phosphorous (P)   b) nitrogen (N)

c) fluorine (F)   d) neon (Ne)

e) sulfur (S)   f) lithium (Li)

g) hydrogen (H)

Target boxes: elements that exist naturally as diatomic molecules, elements that *do not* exist naturally as diatomic molecules

6.10 Which elements form diatomic molecules?

a) carbon (C)   b) boron (B)

c) chlorine (Cl)   d) oxygen (O)

e) silicon (Si)   f) sodium (Na)

g) iodine (I)

Target boxes: elements that exist naturally as diatomic molecules, elements that *do not* exist naturally as diatomic molecules

6.11 How many bonding electrons are found in each molecule? Enter a number in the box.

a) $\ddot{O}=\ddot{O}$ ☐

b)

$$H-\overset{\overset{H}{|}}{\underset{\underset{H}{|}}{C}}-\overset{\overset{H}{|}}{\underset{\underset{H}{|}}{C}}-\overset{..}{\underset{..}{O}}-H$$ ☐

6.12 How many lone pairs are found in each molecule? Enter a number in the box.

a) $\underset{H}{\overset{H}{\diagdown}}C=\ddot{O}$ ☐

b) $:\ddot{Br}-\overset{\overset{}{}}{\underset{\underset{:\ddot{Br}:}{|}}{P}}-\ddot{Br}:$ ☐

6.2 Covalent Bonding and the Periodic Table

LO 2: Compare and contrast covalent and ionic compounds.

6.13 How many bonds do the following atoms form to satisfy the octet rule and make an electrically neutral covalently-bonded molecule? Enter a number in each box.

a) hydrogen (H) ☐

b) carbon (C) ☐

c) fluorine (F) ☐

d) nitrogen (N) ☐

6.14 How many bonds do the following atoms form to satisfy the octet rule and make an electrically neutral covalently bonded molecule? Enter a number in each box.

a) oxygen (O) ☐

b) phosphorous (P) ☐

c) chlorine (Cl) ☐

d) sulfur (S) ☐

6.15 How many covalent bonds do elements in Group 7A typically form?

a) 0 covalent bonds; elements in Group 7A form ionic bonds only.

b) 1   c) 2   d) 3   e) 4

6.16 How many covalent bonds do elements in Group 5A typically form?

a) 0 covalent bonds; elements in Group 5A form ionic bonds only.

b) 1   c) 2   d) 3   e) 4

6.17 How many covalent bonds do elements in Group 6A typically form?

a) 0 covalent bonds. Elements in Group 6A form ionic bonds only.

b) 1   c) 2   d) 3   e) 4

6.18 How many covalent bonds do elements in Group 4A typically form?

a) 0 covalent bonds; elements in Group 4A form ionic bonds only.

b) 1   c) 2   d) 3   e) 4

6.19 Which element generally forms two covalent bonds?

a) carbon   b) nitrogen   c) helium

d) fluorine   e) oxygen

6.20 Which element generally forms one covalent bond?

a) silicon   b) neon   c) chlorine

d) carbon   e) oxygen

6.21 Which element generally forms four covalent bonds?

a) oxygen   b) carbon   c) bromine

d) nitrogen   e) sulfur

6.22 Which element generally forms three covalent bonds?

a) lithium   b) sulfur   c) iodine

d) nitrogen   e) carbon

6.23 Which compound is covalently bonded?

a) Na_2O b) CO_2

c) KCl d) CaO

6.24 Which compound is covalently bonded?

a) $NaCl$ b) $CaCl_2$

c) PCl_3 d) Na_2S

6.25 Which compound is *not* covalently bonded?

a) NH_3 b) I_2

c) BaI_2 d) CCl_4

6.26 Which answer correctly shows a covalent molecule formed with the element in row 2, Group 5A as the central atom?

a) $SrBr_2$ b) NH_3

c) PBr_3 d) HeB_3

6.27 Which answer correctly shows a covalent molecule formed with the element in row 3, Group 6A as the central atom?

a) SCl_2 b) SrO

c) CsB_2 d) Li_2S

6.28 How many covalent bonds and lone pairs does each element typically have? Enter the correct number in each box.

a) N ___ bond(s) ___ lone pair(s)
b) S ___ bond(s) ___ lone pair(s)

6.29 How many covalent bonds and lone pairs does each element typically have? Enter the correct number in each box.

a) P ___ bond(s) ___ lone pair(s)
b) C ___ bond(s) ___ lone pair(s)

6.30 How many covalent bonds and lone pairs does each element typically have? Enter the correct number in each box.

a) O ___ bond(s) ___ lone pair(s)
b) Br ___ bond(s) ___ lone pair(s)

6.31 Classify each compound according to the type of bond they contain.

a) K_2O b) H_2O c) $NaCl$

d) NH_3 e) H_2 f) BaS

g) Cl_2 h) $MgCl_2$

Target boxes: ionic, covalent

6.32 Classify each compound according to the type of bond they contain.

a) CaO b) CO_2 c) Na_2O

d) N_2 e) O_2 f) KBr

g) CH_3OH

Target boxes: ionic, covalent

6.33 How many total valence electrons are in each molecule? Enter a number in the box provided.

a)

b)

6.34 How many total valence electrons are in each molecule? Enter a number in the box provided.

a)
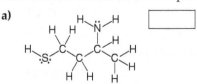

b)
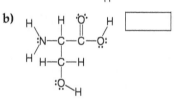

6.35 How many total valence electrons are in each molecule? Enter a number in the box provided.

a)
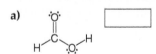

b)

6.3 Covalent Bonding and the Periodic Table

LO 3: Draw covalent compounds using Lewis structures.

6.36 Ethanoic acid (acetic acid) is involved in several metabolic processes in the body. How many non-bonding lone pairs of electrons are in this Lewis structure of acetic acid?

a) 0   b) 1   c) 2

d) 3   e) 4

6.37 Formic acid (methanoic acid) is found in the stings and bites of many ants and bees. The Lewis structure of formic acid is shown. How many total bonding electrons are in formic acid?

a) 10   b) 8   c) 6   d) 4

6.38 How many lone pairs of electrons are in the Lewis structure of ammonia (NH_3)?

a) 0   b) 1   c) 2

d) 3   e) 4

6.39 How many lone pairs of electrons are in the Lewis structure of water (H_2O)?

a) 0   b) 1   c) 2

d) 3   e) 4

6.40 How many lone pairs of electrons are in the Lewis structure of methane (CH_4)?

a) 0   b) 1   c) 2

d) 3   e) 4

6.41 Which molecule contains two single bonds, a double bond, and two lone pairs?

a) H—S̈—H

b) H₂C=CH₂ (depicted as H₂C=CH₂)

c) H—C≡N:

d) O=CH₂ (depicted as :Ö: above C with H—C—H)

6.42 Which molecule contains two double bonds and four lone pairs?

a)

b)

c) Ö=C=Ö:

d)

6.43 Which molecule contains eight single bonds, a double bond, and a triple bond?

a)

b)

c)

d)

6.44 Urea is an important molecule in the metabolism of nitrogen-containing compounds by animals and is the main nitrogen-containing substance in the urine of mammals. How many nonbonding lone pairs of electrons need to be added to complete this partial Lewis structure of urea?

a) 0   b) 1   c) 2

d) 3   e) 4

6.45 How many bonding electrons and non-bonding lone pairs are in this Lewis structure of the hydrogen cyanide molecule? Enter numbers in the boxes.

H··C⦂⦂⦂N:

Target boxes: number of bonding electrons, number of non-bonding lone pairs

6.46 Determine the total number of valence electrons in each molecule. Enter a number in the box.

a) I_2 [   ]

b) NBr_3 [   ]

c) C_2H_5Cl [   ]

6.47 Determine the total number of valence electrons in each molecule. Enter a number in the box.

a) SBr_2 [   ]

b) PCl_3 [   ]

c) C_2H_6N [   ]

6.48 Complete the Lewis structure for the compound by adding any missing double bonds or lone pairs of electrons on the molecule.

H—C—O—C—H (with H atoms on each carbon)

6.49 Glycerol is an important biological molecule found in many oils and fats. It is also used extensively in drug formulations. Fill in the lone pairs needed on the glycerol molecule to give each atom an octet (except hydrogen).

6.50 Pyruvic acid is an important molecule formed during the metabolism of glucose and helps supply energy to cells. Fill in the lone pairs needed on the pyruvic acid molecule to give each atom an octet (except hydrogen).

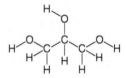

6.51 Draw the Lewis structure for each molecule, including lone pairs of electrons.

a) H_2S b) CH_2Cl_2

6.52 Draw the Lewis structure for each molecule, including lone pairs of electrons.

a) SiF_4 b) HOOH

6.53 Draw the Lewis structure for each molecule, including lone pairs of electrons.

a) HCCH

b) H_2CCH_2

c) H_3CCH_3

6.54 Cysteine is a naturally-occurring amino acid in the body and is found in a wide variety of foods. Complete this partial Lewis structure of cysteine by adding any missing double bonds or lone pairs of electrons on the molecule.

$$H-S-\overset{\overset{\displaystyle H}{|}}{C}-\overset{\overset{\displaystyle H}{|}}{\underset{\underset{\displaystyle N}{|}}{C}}-\overset{\overset{\displaystyle O}{||}}{C}-O-H$$

6.55 Alanine is a naturally-occurring amino acid in the body and is found in a wide variety of foods. Complete the partial Lewis structure of alanine by adding any missing double bonds or lone pairs of electrons on this molecule.

$$H-\overset{\overset{\displaystyle H}{|}}{C}-\overset{\overset{\displaystyle H}{|}}{\underset{\underset{\displaystyle N}{|}}{C}}-\overset{\overset{\displaystyle O}{||}}{C}-O-H$$

6.56 Oxalic acid is involved in metabolic processes and is also found in a variety of foods.

Complete the partial Lewis structure of oxalic acid by adding any missing double bonds or lone pairs of electrons on the molecule.

$$H-O-\overset{\overset{\displaystyle O}{||}}{C}-\overset{\underset{\displaystyle O}{}}{C}-O-H$$

6.57 Gamma-aminobutyric acid (GABA) is a signaling molecule involved in muscle control, vision, and in regulating anxiety. Complete the partial Lewis structure of GABA by adding any missing double bonds or lone pairs of electrons on the molecule.

6.58 Lactic acid is an important biological molecule involved with energy production in the body. Complete the partial Lewis structure of lactic acid by adding any missing double bonds or lone pairs of electrons on the molecule.

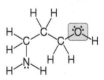

6.4 Predicting Shapes of Molecules

LO 4: Predict the shapes of covalent compounds using VSEPR theory.

6.59 The amino acid cysteine is a building block for proteins. Predict the bond angles around the indicated carbon atom in cysteine.

a) 90°   b) 109.5°

c) 120°   d) 180°

6.60 Predict the bond angles around the indicated carbon atom in the structure.

a) 90°   b) 109.5°

c) 120°   d) 180°

6.61 Predict the bond angles around the indicated carbon atom in the structure.

a) 90°   b) 109.5°

c) 120°   d) 180°

6.62 Predict the bond angles around the indicated carbon atom in the structure.

$$H-C\equiv C-\overset{\overset{\displaystyle H}{|}}{\underset{\underset{\displaystyle H}{|}}{C}}-H$$

a) 90°   b) 109.5°

c) 120°   d) 180°

6.63 Predict the molecular geometry around the indicated atom in the structure.

a) linear   b) bent

c) trigonal planar   d) pyramid

e) tetrahedral

6.64 Predict the molecular geometry around the indicated atom in the structure.

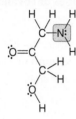

a) linear   b) bent

c) trigonal planar   d) pyramid

e) tetrahedral

6.65 Predict the molecular geometry around the indicated atom in the structure.

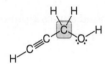

a) linear   b) bent

c) trigonal planar   d) pyramid

e) tetrahedral

6.66 Predict the molecular geometry around the indicated carbon atom in the structure.

a) linear   b) bent

c) trigonal planar   d) pyramid

e) tetrahedral

6.67 Predict the molecular geometry around the indicated carbon atom in the structure.

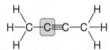

a) linear   b) bent

c) trigonal planar   d) pyramid

e) tetrahedral

6.68 Identify the bond angles for each structure by dragging the structures into the corresponding box.

a)   b)

c)   d)

e)

Target boxes: $109.5°, 120°, 180°$

6.69 Match each shape with the correct term describing the molecular geometry.

Answer choices: linear, pyramidal, square planar, trigonal planar, square pyramid, tetrahedral, octahedral, bent

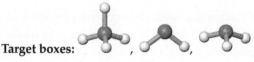

Target boxes:

6.70 Methane (CH_4) has the same shape as _____.

a) CH_2O b) SO_3 c) HCN

d) CO_2 e) HCCH   f) $MgSO_4$

g) H_2O h) CH_3Br

6.71 Drag the appropriate geometric term into the correct box.

Answer choices: linear, trigonal planar, tetrahedral, bent, pyramidal

Target boxes:

• A molecule has a central atom with three electron groups around it. All three are involved in bonding and there are no lone pairs on the central atom. What molecular geometry does the molecule have around this central atom?

• A molecule has a central atom with four electron groups around it. Three are involved in bonding and there is a lone pair. What molecular geometry does the molecule have around this central atom?

• A molecule has a central atom with four electron groups around it. All four are involved in bonding. What molecular geometry does the molecule have around this central atom.

6.72 Predict the shape around the bolded central atom by dragging the correct term into each box.

Answer choices: linear, trigonal planar, tetrahedral, bent, pyramidal

Target boxes: HCCH, H_2CCH_2, H_3CCH_3

6.73 Match each molecular shape with the correct formula. Not all formulas correspond to a geometric structure shown.

Answer choices: CH_2O, CH_3OH, CO_2, HCN, NH_3, $MgSO_4$, H_2O, CH_4

Target boxes:

6.74 Predict the shape of the following molecules and drag the correct term into each box.

Answer choices: linear, trigonal planar, tetrahedral, bent, pyramidal

Target boxes: PBr_3, CH_2Cl_2, H_2S, HCN

6.75 Hydroxylamine (H_2NOH) is a highly reactive substance that is used to introduce random mutations in DNA in order to study gene function.

a) Use the drawing tool to add all missing electrons to the hydroxylamine structure.

b) Select the *bonding angle* and *shape* around the indicated nitrogen atom in the structure.

Answer choices for bonding angle: $180°$, $120°$, $109.5°$, $90°$, $60°$

Answer choices for shape: linear, trigonal planar, bent, tetrahedral, pyramidal

6.76 Oxalic acid ($H_2C_2O_4$) is a sour tasting compound found in many plants. The ionic form of oxalic acid ($C_2O_4^{2-}$) is oxalate, which is a primary component of many kidney stones.

a) What is the shape around each indicated atom in the oxalic acid molecule?

Answer choices for O: linear, trigonal planar, bent, tetrahedral

Answer choices for C: bent, tetrahedral, linear, trigonal

b) What are the expected bond angles around each indicated atom in the oxalic acid molecule?

Answer choices for O: $180°$, $120°$, $109.5°$, $90°$

Answer choices for C: $180°$, $120°$, $109.5°$, $90°$

6.5 Naming Covalent Compounds

LO 5: Write the name of a binary covalent compound from a given formula and provide the formula when given the name of a covalent compound.

6.77 Sulfur hexafluoride is used as an electrical insulator and to manufacture semiconductors. It is also a potent greenhouse gas. What is the correct molecular formula for sulfur hexafluoride?

a) S_6F b) SF_5

c) SiF_6 d) SF_6

6.78 Selenium dioxide is used as a coloring agent in the glass industry. It is also used in the cosmetics, lubricant, and chemical industry. What is the correct molecular formula for selenium dioxide?

a) Se_2O b) SeO_2

c) S_2O d) SO_2

6.79 What is the correct formula for diboron tetrachloride?

a) B_2Cl_5 b) Bo_2Cl_4

c) B_2F_4 d) B_2Cl_4

6.80 Nitrogen trifluoride is used in the manufacture of semiconductors and liquid crystal display (LCD) panels. What is the correct molecular formula for nitrogen trifluoride?

a) NeF_3 b) N_3F

c) NF_3 d) NFl_3

6.81 The molecule NO is an important signaling molecule in the cardiovascular system where it increases blood flow and lowers blood pressure. What is the correct name for the NO molecule?

a) mononitrate oxide

b) nitrogen monoxide

c) neon oxide

d) oxygen mononitrogen

6.82 What is the correct name for the molecule N_2F_2?

a) difluoro dinitrogen

b) dinitrogen difluorine

c) dinitride difluoride

d) dinitrogen difluoride

6.83 What is the correct name for the molecule P_4O_6?

a) tetraphosphorus hexaoxide

b) hexaoxygen tetraphosphide

c) tetrapotassium hexaoxide

d) phosphorus oxide

6.84 Name each of the following molecular compounds. Use only lowercase letters and a single space between words.

a) N_2O ▭   b) PF_3 ▭

c) CCl_4 ▭   d) SO_2 ▭

6.85 Name each of the following molecular compounds. Use only lowercase letters and a single space between words.

a) CS_2 ▭   b) N_2S_3 ▭

c) BF_3 ▭   d) NO_2 ▭

6.86 Write the formula for each of the following molecular compounds. Use subscripts for numbers other than one. It may be helpful to refer to the periodic table to ensure you use the correct element symbol for atoms. There should be no spaces between letters or numbers in the formulas you write.

a) diphosphorus pentoxide ⬚

b) carbon tetrabromide ⬚

c) carbon monoxide ⬚

d) dihydrogen sulfide ⬚

6.87 Write the formula for each of the following molecular compounds. Use subscripts for numbers other than one. It may be helpful to refer to the periodic table to ensure you use the correct element symbol for atoms. There should be no spaces between letters or numbers in the formulas you write.

a) silicon dioxide ⬚

b) sulfur dichloride ⬚

c) dinitrogen trioxide ⬚

d) diphosphorus tetraiodide ⬚

6.6 Representing Molecules

LO 6: Recognize a variety of ways to represent covalent compounds.

6.88 What is the correct formula of this molecule?

a) C_2H_8O b) C_3H_8O c) C_3H_7O d) C_2H_9O

6.89 What is the correct formula of this molecule?

a) C_5H_{11} b) C_6H_{12} c) C_4H_{10} d) C_5H_{12}

6.90 What is the correct formula of the molecule shown?

a) C_6H_{10} b) C_5H_{10} c) C_5H_5 d) C_5H_{15}

6.91 Drag each structure into the box that correctly describes the molecule's representation.

a) $C_6H_{12}O_6$

b)

c)

e) C_4H_9N

d)

Target boxes: chemical formula, Lewis structure, 3D ball-and-stick

6.92 Glucose (also known as blood sugar) is a primary energy source for the body. How many hydrogen atoms are *not* shown on the skeletal structure of this cyclic glucose sugar molecule?

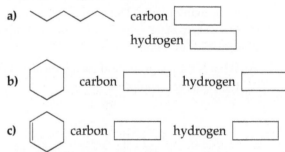

a) 5 missing hydrogen atoms

b) 6 missing hydrogen atoms

c) 7 missing hydrogen atoms

d) 8 missing hydrogen atoms

6.93 Indicate the number of carbon and hydrogen atoms in the following skeletal structures. Enter a number into each box provided.

a)   carbon ⬚
            hydrogen ⬚

b)   carbon ⬚   hydrogen ⬚

c)   carbon ⬚   hydrogen ⬚

Input boxes: number of carbon atoms, number of hydrogen atoms

6.94 Indicate the number of carbon and hydrogen atoms in each skeletal structure. Enter a number in each box.

a)   carbon ⬚
            hydrogen ⬚

b)   carbon ⬚
            hydrogen ⬚

Input boxes: number of carbon atoms, number of hydrogen atoms

6.95 Indicate the number of carbon and hydrogen atoms in each skeletal structure. Enter a number in each box.

a) 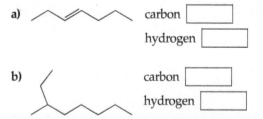   carbon ⬚
                           hydrogen ⬚

b) 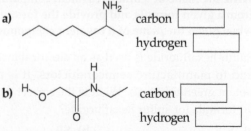   carbon ⬚
                           hydrogen ⬚

Input boxes: number of carbon atoms, number of hydrogen atoms

6.96 Indicate the number of carbon and hydrogen atoms in each skeletal structure. Enter a number in each box.

a)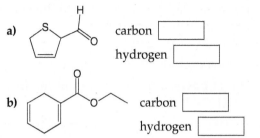

carbon ⬜

hydrogen ⬜

b)

carbon ⬜

hydrogen ⬜

Input boxes: number of carbon atoms, number of hydrogen atoms

6.97 Citric acid (top), found in many fruits, is a natural preservative and a key molecule in energy production in the body. Tartaric acid (bottom), found in many plants, is used in industrial baking, and is found in wine. Compare and contrast the similarities and differences between the two molecules. Draw out each molecule on a piece of paper, circle any common features they share. Add any missing hydrogen atoms and lone pairs not shown in the structures shown, then write the chemical formula for each by providing the missing numbers of carbon, hydrogen, and oxygen atoms.

citric acid

citric acid molecular formula = ⬜

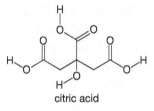

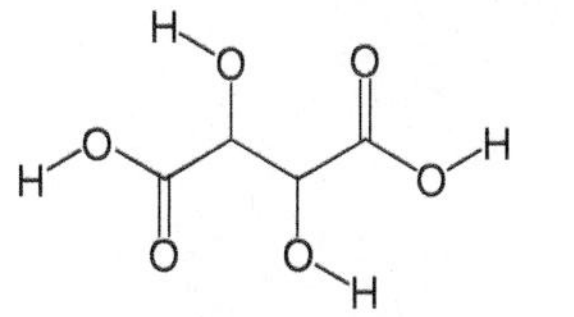

tartaric acid

tartaric acid molecular formula = ⬜

6.98 Ornithine is an amino acid involved in the urea cycle and is also a starting molecule in the production of cocaine. Eflornithine is a medication used to treat African sleeping sickness and is on the World Health Organization's List of Essential Medicines. Compare and contrast these two molecules then determine which statement is true.

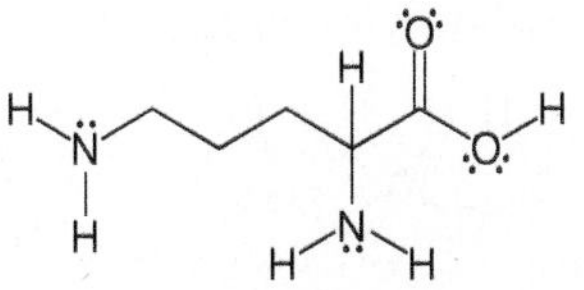

ornithine 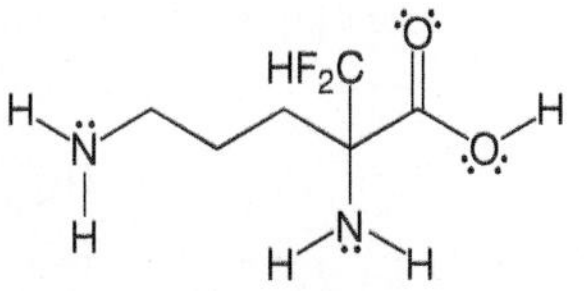   eflornithine

a) Ornithine has a greater number of hydrogen atoms and fewer carbon atoms than eflornithine.

b) The ornithine and eflornithine molecules have very different structures and biological functions.

c) Ornithine has one fewer carbon atom and the same number of hydrogen atoms as eflornithine.

d) Ornithine has fewer carbon atoms but a greater number of hydrogen atoms than eflornithine.

6.99 Examine the structure of the cholesterol-lowering drug, Zocor (simvastatin) and the carbon atoms indicated by the arrows. What are the molecular shapes around each indicated carbon atom?

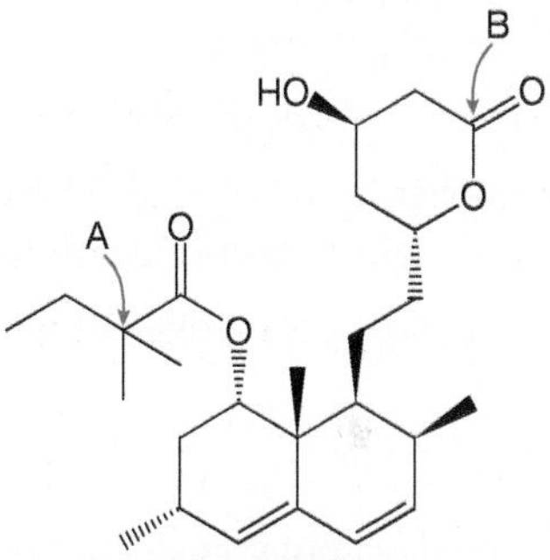

simvastatin

Answer choices: tetrahedral, pyramidal, trigonal planar, bent

Target boxes: geometry around carbon atom A, geometry around carbon atom B

6.100 Enalapril and Lisinopril are drugs used to treat hypertension (high blood pressure). They both work by inhibiting an enzyme that produces signaling molecules that cause the muscles of small arteries to constrict raising blood pressure. Compare and contrast the structures of these two drug molecules. Determine the total number of carbon atoms in each molecule.

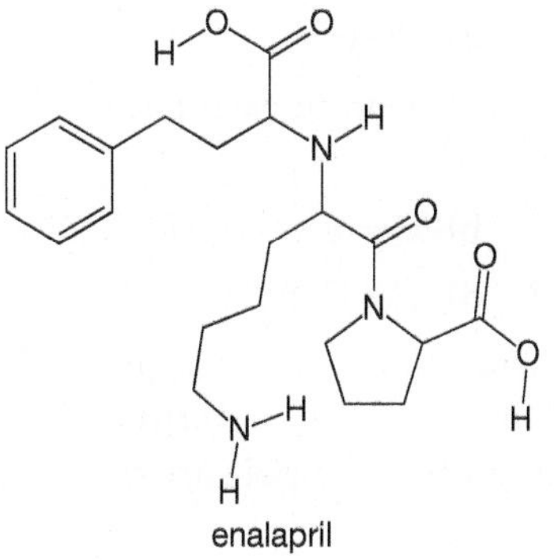

enalapril

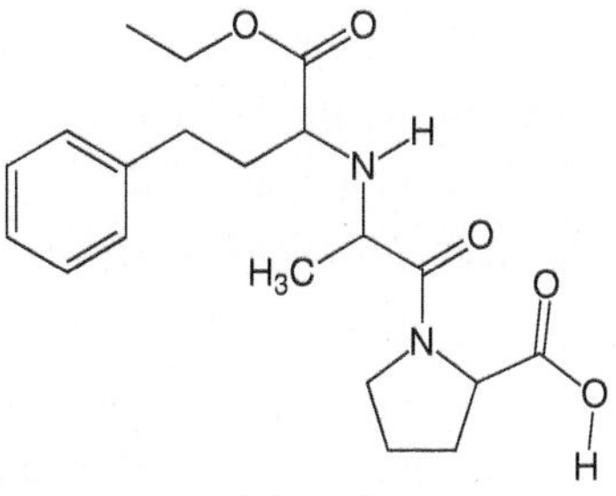

lisinopril

a) Enalapril has _____ total carbon atoms.

b) Lisinopril has _____ total carbon atom.

Chapter 7

7.1   Electronegativity & Bond Polarity

LO 1: Determine the polarity of a chemical bond using electronegativity values of atoms.

7.01 Which option correctly ranks the atoms listed from lowest electronegativity to highest electronegativity? It may be helpful to refer to the periodic table or electronegativity table (Figure 7.2).

a) N, P, Al, Mg, Na   b) Na, Mg, P, Al, N

c) Na, Mg, Al, P, N   d) Mg, Al, Na, P, N

7.02 Refer to the electronegativity table (Figure 7.2) and then order the elements from left-to-right by increasing electronegativity.

Answer choices: Be, K, Si, O, S

Target boxes: five boxes arranged left-to-right from lowest to highest electronegativity

7.03 Select the most polar covalent bond.

a) C—N   b) C—O

c) C—S   d) C—Br

7.04 Select the most polar covalent bond.

a) N—N   b) N—O

c) N—P   d) N—C

7.05 Select the most polar covalent bond.

a) O—H   b) H—N

c) C—H   d) H—Cl

7.06 Select the most polar covalent bond.

a) P—Cl   b) H—I

c) S—O   d) Si—Cl

7.07 Select the least polar covalent bond in the set.

a) C—Si   b) S—H

c) C—C   d) P—Br

7.08 Select the least polar covalent bond in the set.

a) S—P   b) B—H

c) S—Br   d) P—H

7.09 Select the more polar covalent bond in each pair. Refer to Figure 7.2.

a) P—O or S—O   b) C—N or C—H

c) C—O or C—N   d) H—Cl or H—O

7.10 Use the electronegativity table (Figure 7.2) to determine the appropriate direction of the dipole arrow for each bond. Drag the appropriate dipole arrow into each box.

Answer choices: dipole arrow pointing right, dipole arrow pointing left

Target boxes: N—H, C—N, P—O, C—O

7.11 Identify which of these bonds are polar. If a bond is polar, assign partial charges by dragging the appropriate partial charge symbols to the empty box above the bond. Identify nonpolar bonds with "not polar". Refer to Figure 7.2.

Answer choices: $\delta^+\delta^-$, $\delta^-\delta^+$, not polar

Target boxes: a box over each of the following: O—H, C—F, S—S, C—H

7.12 Dopamine is an important chemical messenger in our bodies made from the amino acid, tyrosine. Use the electronegativity table (Figure 7.2) to determine the polarity of each numbered bond and then arrange the numbered bonds in order of most polar to least polar from left to right.

Answer choices: 1, 2, 3

Target boxes: three boxes arranged left-to-right from most polar to least polar

7.13 Use the electronegativity table (Figure 7.2) to determine the appropriate direction of the dipole arrow for each bond. Drag the appropriate dipole direction arrow onto each box for this amino acid molecule, serine.

Answer choices: up arrow, down arrow, slanted up arrow, slanted down arrow

Target boxes: labeled A (H—N), B (C—O), C (N—C), D (O—H)

7.14 Use the electronegativity table (Figure 7.2) to determine the appropriate partial charge orientations for each bond indicated. Drag the appropriate partial charge orientation into each box shown for the molecule.

Answer choices:

Target boxes: labeled A (Cl—C), B (O—C), C (N—H)

7.2 Polarity of Molecules

LO 2: Predict whether a molecule is polar or nonpolar.

7.15 Classify the molecules as polar or nonpolar.

$$:\ddot{B}r—\overset{\displaystyle}{\underset{\displaystyle :\ddot{B}r:}{P}}—\ddot{B}r: \qquad \overset{H}{\underset{H}{}}C=\ddot{O}:$$

Answer choices: polar, nonpolar

7.16 Classify the molecules as polar or nonpolar.

Answer choices: polar, nonpolar

7.17 Select the polar molecule in the set.

a) :N≡N:

b)
$$:\ddot{B}r—\overset{\displaystyle :\ddot{B}r:}{\underset{\displaystyle :\ddot{B}r:}{C}}\cdots\ddot{B}r:$$

c) :B̈r—B̈r:

d)
$$H—\overset{\displaystyle :\ddot{C}l:}{\underset{\displaystyle :\ddot{C}l:}{C}}\cdots\ddot{C}l:$$

7.18 Select the polar molecule in the set.

a)
$$H_3C\overset{\displaystyle CH_3}{\underset{\displaystyle \overset{\displaystyle }{C}}{C}}=\overset{\displaystyle CH_3}{\underset{\displaystyle CH_3}{C}}$$

b) :F̈—F̈:

c)

d) H₂C—C≡C—CH₂
   H₃C   CH₃

7.19 Classify the molecules as polar or nonpolar.

Answer choices: polar, nonpolar

7.20 Select the *nonpolar* molecule in this set.

a)

b)

c)

d)

7.21 Classify the molecules as polar or nonpolar.

Answer choices: polar, nonpolar

7.22 Select the *nonpolar* molecule in this set.

a)   b)

c)   d)

7.23 Draw the following molecules on paper and determine if each is polar or nonpolar. Match each molecule to the explanation that describes why it is polar or nonpolar.

a) CF_4 b) PH_3

Answer choices: Polar because the charge is not distributed evenly across the molecule, Nonpolar because the charge is distributed evenly across the molecule

7.24 Draw the following molecules on paper and determine if each is polar or nonpolar. Match each molecule to the explanation that describes why it is polar or nonpolar.

a) $CHFCl_2$ b) $SiCl_4$ c) SH_2

Answer choices: Polar because the charge is not distributed evenly across the molecule, Nonpolar because the charge is distributed evenly across the molecule

7.25 Identify the *nonpolar* molecule.

a)

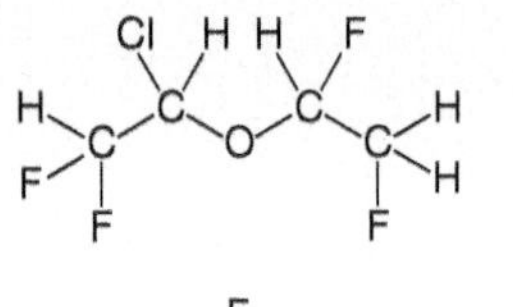

b)

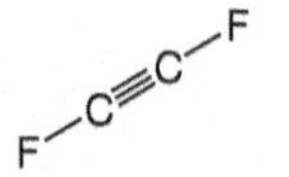

c)

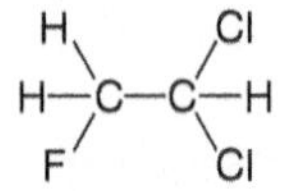

d)

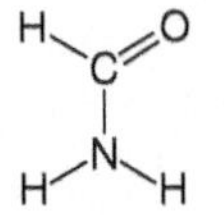

7.26 Draw the following molecules on paper and determine if each is polar or nonpolar.

Match each molecule to the explanation that describes why it is polar or nonpolar.

a) CS_2

b) HCCH

Answer choices: Polar because the charge is not distributed evenly across the molecule, Nonpolar because the charge is distributed evenly across the molecule

7.3 Polarity of Large Molecules

LO 3: Identify polar and nonpolar regions of large molecules.

7.27 Classify the molecules shown as polar or nonpolar.

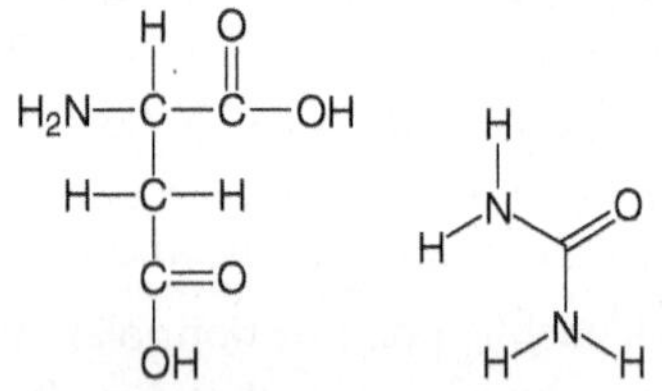

aspartic acid , urea

Answer choices: polar, nonpolar

7.28 Classify the molecules shown as polar or nonpolar.

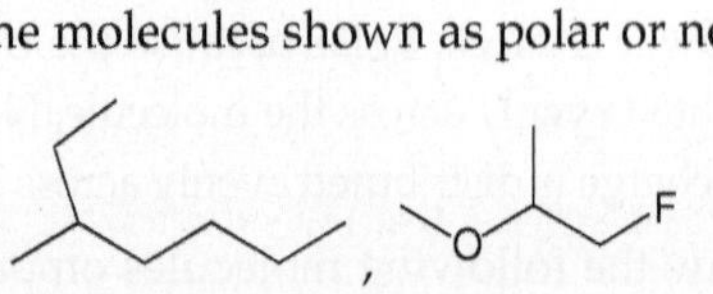

Answer choices: polar, nonpolar

7.29 Vitamin A is important for proper growth and development. It is also important to the immune system and for vision. Examine the structure of vitamin A and predict whether the molecule is polar, nonpolar, or a mixture of both.

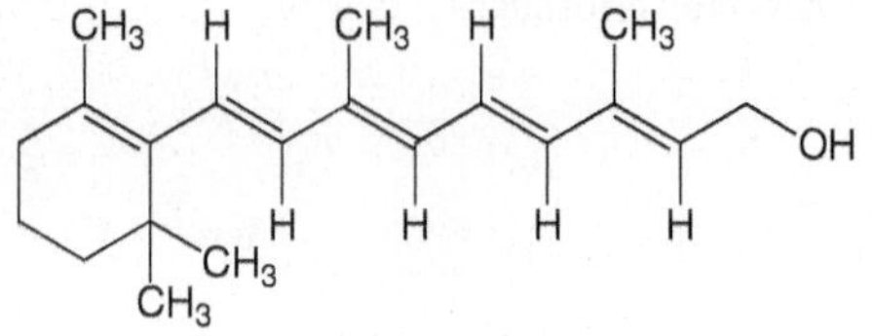

vitamin A

a) polar   b) nonpolar

c) mixture of polarity types

7.30 Compare these amino acid structures and select the answer that describes their polarities.

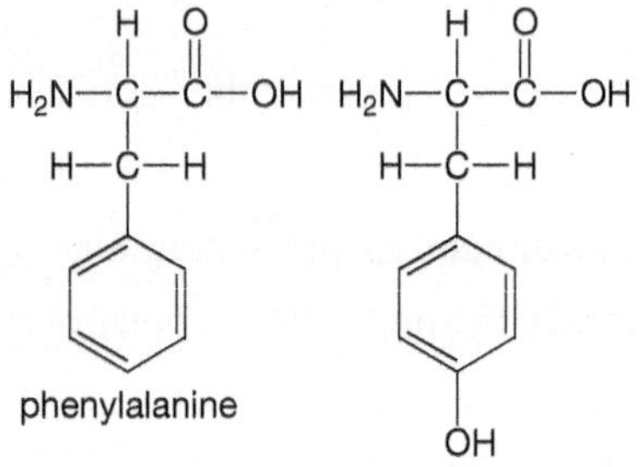

phenylalanine

tyrosine

a) Phenylalanine is more polar than tyrosine because it has fewer atoms.

b) Tyrosine is more polar because it contains an additional polar OH group that phenylalanine does not have.

c) There is no difference in molecular structure or polarity between the two.

d) There is no way to predict which amino acid is more polar without conducting an experiment.

7.31 Estradiol and estrone are two human sex hormones. Study their structures and select the description that explains how the highlighted regions impact the polarity of the molecules.

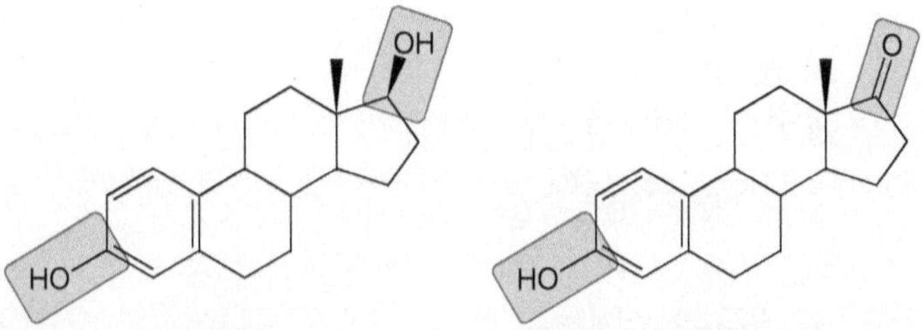

estradiol

estrone

a) The highlighted regions are nonpolar, so they contribute to the hormone molecules being completely nonpolar.

b) The highlighted regions are polar and create polar regions on the nonpolar carbon rings of the hormone molecules.

c) The highlighted regions are polar and the carbon rings of the hormones are also polar, so both molecules are completely polar.

d) The highlighted regions are ionic and contribute to the hormone molecules being ionic.

7.32 Testosterone and progesterone are both human sex hormones. Study their structures and select the best description of the highlighted regions.

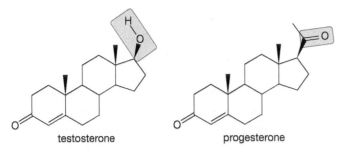

testosterone   progesterone

a) The highlighted regions are ionic and contribute to the hormone molecules being ionic.

b) The highlighted regions are both nonpolar and contribute to the hormone molecules being completely nonpolar.

c) The highlighted regions are polar and the rest of the structure of each hormone is also polar making the molecules completely polar.

d) The highlighted regions are both polar and create polar regions on the primarily nonpolar hormone molecules.

7.33 Amino acids differ from each other by their unique branching "R" groups. Study the branching "R" group of each amino acid and classify it as ionic, polar, or nonpolar.

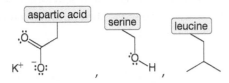

Answer choices: ionic, polar, nonpolar

7.34 Amino acids differ from each other by their unique branching "R" groups. Study the branching "R" group of each amino acid and classify it as ionic, polar, or nonpolar.

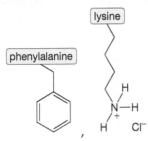

Answer choices: ionic, polar, nonpolar

7.35 Amino acids differ from each other by their unique branching "R" groups. Study the branching "R" group of each amino acid and classify it as ionic, polar, or nonpolar.

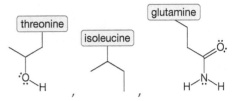

Answer choices: ionic, polar, nonpolar

7.36 Cyclobenzaprine (also known as Flexeril) is a medication used as a muscle relaxer to relieve skeletal muscle spasms. Examine the structure of cyclobenzaprine and determine if the majority of the molecule is polar, nonpolar, or approximately balanced (in terms of polar and nonpolar regions).

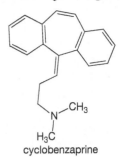

cyclobenzaprine

a) majority polar

b) majority nonpolar

c) approximately balanced

7.37 Farnesol is a naturally occurring building block for other molecules in the body. Examine the structure of farnesol and determine if the majority of the molecule is polar, nonpolar, or is approximately balanced (in terms of polar and nonpolar regions).

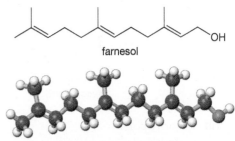

farnesol

ball and stick representation

a) majority polar

b) majority nonpolar

c) approximately balanced

7.38 Mannitol is a sweetener that is poorly absorbed from the intestines and often used as a sweetener in weight control or diabetic foods. Examine the structure of mannitol and determine if the majority of the molecule is polar, nonpolar, or is approximately balanced (in terms of polar and nonpolar regions).

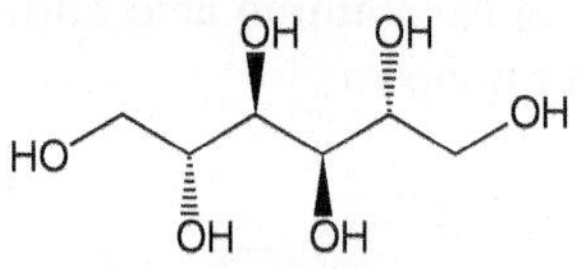

mannitol

a) majority polar

b) majority nonpolar

c) approximately balanced

7.39 Oleanolic acid is a naturally occurring molecule found in plants. Examine the structure of oleanolic acid and determine if the majority of the molecule is polar, nonpolar, or is approximately balanced (in terms of polar and nonpolar regions).

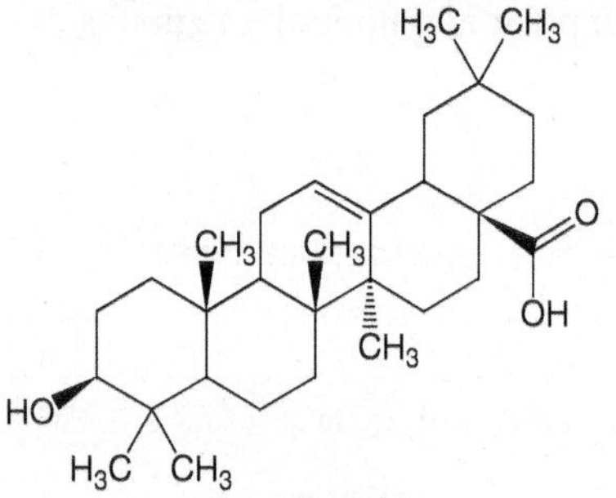

oleanolic acid

a) majority polar

b) majority nonpolar

c) approximately balanced

7.40 Gluconic acid is a naturally occurring molecule found in fruit and honey. Examine the structure of gluconic acid and determine whether the majority of the molecule is polar, nonpolar, or is approximately balanced (in terms of polar and nonpolar regions).

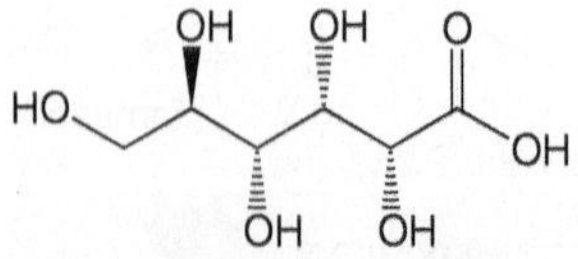

gluconic acid

a) majority polar

b) majority nonpolar

c) approximately balanced

7.41 Sucrose (also known as table sugar) is a naturally occurring sugar that is extracted and refined from either sugarcane or sugar beets. Examine the structure of sucrose and determine if the majority of the molecule is polar, nonpolar, or is approximately balanced (in terms of polar and nonpolar regions).

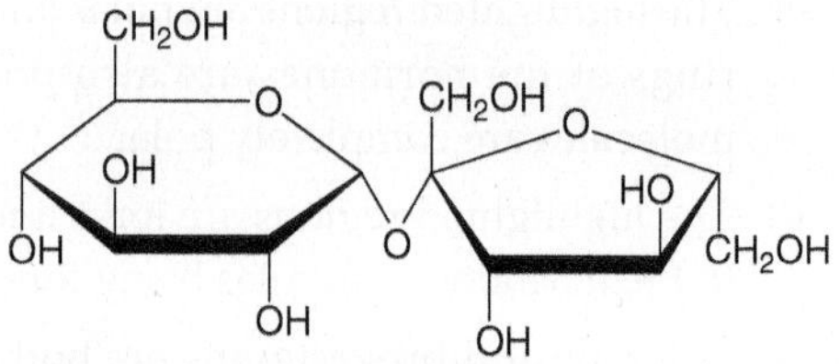

sucrose

a) majority polar

b) majority nonpolar

c) approximately balanced

7.42 Nystatin (also known as Mycostatin) is an antifungal medication used to treat yeast infections of the skin. Examine the structure of Nystatin and determine if the molecule overall is polar, nonpolar, or has both polar and nonpolar regions.

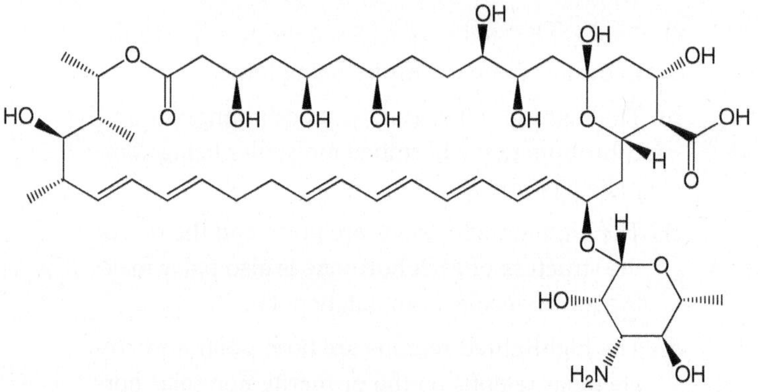

nystatin

a) polar

b) nonpolar

c) both polar and nonpolar regions

7.43 **A.** Compare these amino acid structures and match each comment to the appropriate molecule.

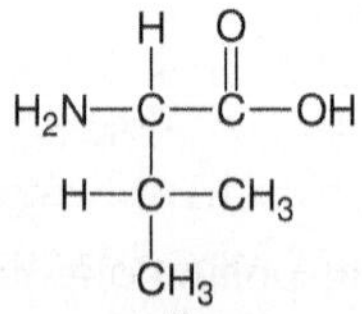

valine 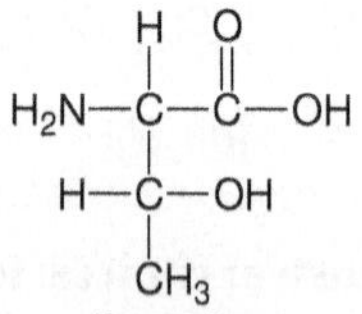 , threonine

Answer choices: contains an NH_2 group, contains a CO_2H group, contains an alcohol OH group, contains two CH_3 groups

B. Based on your answer from Part A, which amino acid would you expect to be more polar?

a) 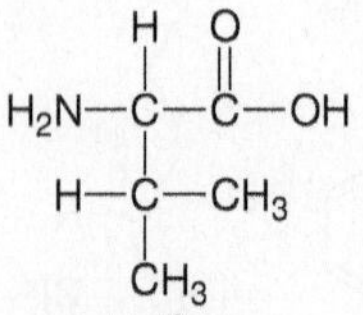
valine

b) 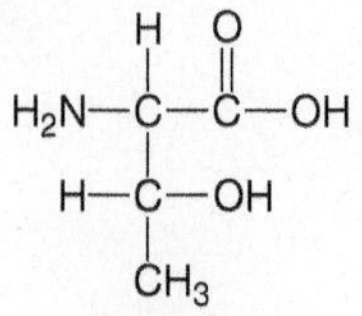
threonine

7.44 Daunorubicin (also known as daunomycin) is a chemotherapy drug used to treat certain types of cancer. Examine the structure of daunorubicin and determine if the molecule overall is polar, nonpolar, or a mixture of both.

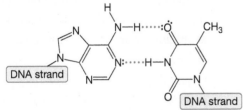

daunorubicin

a) polar

b) nonpolar

c) mixture of polarity types

7.4 Intermolecular Forces

LO 4: Recognize and describe the types of intermolecular forces.

7.45 Butane is a fuel commonly used in lighters. Two representations of the butane molecule (C_4H_{10}) are shown. Which intermolecular forces occur between butane molecules?

a) dispersion forces

b) dipole-dipole forces

c) hydrogen bonds

7.46 The "base pairing" in DNA directly impacts the structure and function of this all-important biomolecule. What type of intermolecular forces are shown by the dashed red lines between the A-T base pair shown below?

A-T base pairing in DNA

a) dispersion forces   b) dipole-dipole

c) hydrogen bonds   d) ionic bonds

7.47 Base pairing in DNA directly impacts the structure and function of this all-important biomolecule.

What type of intermolecular forces are shown by the dashed red lines between the G-C base pair?

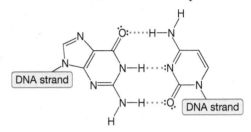

G-C base pairing in DNA

a) dispersion forces   b) dipole-dipole

c) hydrogen bonds   d) ionic bonds

7.48 Select the two types of intermolecular forces that the molecule shown can participate in with other identical molecules.

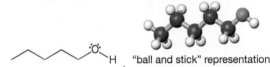

a) dispersion forces   b) dipole-dipole

c) hydrogen bonds   d) ionic bonds

7.49 Select the two types of intermolecular forces that the molecule shown can participate in with other identical molecules. In the ball and stick model, carbon is black, hydrogen is white, and oxygen is red.

"ball and stick" representation

a) dispersion forces   b) dipole-dipole

c) hydrogen bonds   d) ionic bonds

7.50 Select the three types of intermolecular forces that the molecule shown can participate in with other identical molecules.

a) dispersion forces   b) dipole-dipole

c) hydrogen bonds   d) ionic bonds

7.51 Urea is a nitrogen-containing molecule found in urine. What is the dominant intermolecular force that exists between urea and water?

urea , water

a) dispersion forces only

b) dipole-dipole forces

c) hydrogen bonds

7.52 Amino acids differ from each other by their unique branching "R" groups. Study the branching "R" group of the amino acid serine and choose the single most important type of intermolecular force that the side chain of serine experiences with water.

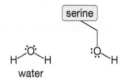

serine

water

a) dispersion forces

b) hydrogen bonds

c) dipole-dipole

d) ionic bonds

7.53 Amino acids differ from each other by their unique branching "R" groups. Study the branching "R" group of the amino acid asparagine and choose the single most important type of intermolecular force that the side chain of asparagine experiences with water.

asparagine

water

a) dispersion forces

b) hydrogen bonding

c) dipole-dipole

d) ionic bonding

7.54 Some vitamins are water soluble while others are fat soluble. Vitamin C is a water-soluble vitamin that is important to maintaining good health. Study the structure of vitamin C and choose the single most important type of intermolecular force vitamin C experiences with water.

water   vitamin C

a) dispersion forces

b) dipole-dipole

c) hydrogen bonding

d) ionic bonding

7.55 For proteins and enzymes to function properly in the cell, they typically adopt a specific folded structure stabilized by hydrogen bonds. Below is a diagram of a protein that has folded into a shape called

an alpha helix. Select the bonds that are hydrogen-bonding interactions.

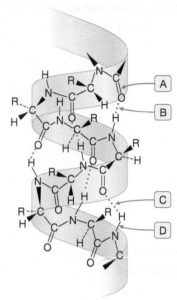

a protein alpha helix

Answer choices: A, B, C, D

7.56 For each compound shown, identify the major type of intermolecular forces experienced between molecules identical to itself.

a) NaOH   b) CH_4

c) NH_3 d) CaO

Answer choices: ionic bonds, dispersion forces only, dipole-dipole, hydrogen bonds

7.57 Estradiol is the primary female sex hormone and is essential for the development and maintenance of female reproductive tissues.

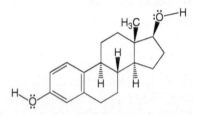

A. Based on your knowledge of polarity and intermolecular forces, would you describe this molecule as highly polar, somewhat polar, or nonpolar?

a) highly polar   b) somewhat polar

c) nonpolar

B. What intermolecular forces do you predict estradiol can have with water molecules?

a) dispersion forces

b) dipole-dipole

c) hydrogen bonds

d) ionic bonds

C. Do you predict that estradiol would be attracted to phospholipids such as the ones you learned about in this chapter? Select the most appropriate answer.

   a) Yes, because phospholipids contain only nonpolar regions, and the estradiol molecule is composed mostly of nonpolar regions.

   b) Yes, because phospholipids contain both polar and nonpolar regions like estradiol does.

   c) No. Phospholipids contain only polar and ionic regions, and the estradiol molecule is composed mostly of nonpolar regions.

   d) No. Phospholipids contain both polar and nonpolar regions and estradiol is only nonpolar.

7.58 What is the major type of intermolecular force experienced by each of the compounds when interacting with identical molecules?

   a) CH_3CN b) SiH_4

   c) CH_3Cl d) $CH_3CH_2CH_3$

   Answer choices: dispersion forces only, dipole-dipole, hydrogen bonding

7.59 What is the major type of intermolecular force experienced by each of the compounds when interacting with identical molecules?

   a) CO_2 b) PCl_3

   c) CHF_3 d) I_2

   Answer choices: dispersion forces only, dipole-dipole, hydrogen bonding

7.60 In 2010, the largest marine oil spill in history occurred during the BP Deep Horizon spill that released an estimated 210 million US gallons of oil into the Gulf of Mexico. In order to break up huge patches of oil, approximately 1,800,000 gallons of dispersant chemicals were then released by British Petroleum (BP).

Crude oil is a mixture of many different hydrocarbons with varying lengths, so let's consider a hydrocarbon chain that is 12 carbon atoms long to represent an oil molecule. Compare the structures of a dispersant molecule (Corexit 9500), an oil molecule, and a water molecule. Select the reason why the dispersant molecule might be effective at dispersing oil into water.

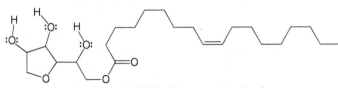

the "Corexit 9500" oil dispersant molecule

water   a 12-carbon long oil molecule

   a) The "oil dispersant" molecule contains ionic groups that help dissolve the oil into polyatomic ions and polar groups to better dissolve in water.

   b) The "oil dispersant" molecule contains a polar region that can hydrogen bond with water and a long non-polar chain that can share London dispersion forces with the oil.

   c) The "oil dispersant" molecule contains only nonpolar bonds that water and oil are attracted to which helps disperse oil into water.

   d) The "oil dispersant" molecule contains only polar bonds that water and oil are attracted to which helps disperse oil into water.

Chapter 8

8.1 Chemical Reactions and Equations

LO 1: Use chemical equations and coefficients to represent and balance chemical reactions.

8.1 Drag the missing terms from the menu to form a correct statement about chemical reactions.

In a chemical reaction, _____ are converted into _____ as the reaction proceeds in the forward direction.

Answer choices: catalysts, subscripts, enthalpy, products, coefficients, reactants, chemical equations

8.2 Diethylether ($C_4H_{10}O$) was the first widely used general anesthetic. It is produced from ethanol (C_2H_6O) in the reaction shown. Drag each substance in the chemical reaction into a box to identify it as a reactant or a product.

$$2C_2H_6O(l) \rightarrow C_4H_{10}O(l) + H_2O(l)$$

Answer choices: $2C_2H_6O(l)$, $C_4H_{10}O(l)$, $H_2O(l)$

Target boxes: one reactants box, one products box

8.3 A chemical equation is correctly balanced when

   a) the number of molecules of reactants equals the number of molecules of products.

   b) the number of protons in all reactants is equal to the number of neutrons in all products.

   c) the number of atoms of each element on both sides of the chemical equation is equal.

   d) the sum of the coefficients in front of all reactants equals the sum of the coefficients in front of all products.

8.4 Ozone (O_3) in Earth's upper atmosphere forms a protective layer that shields life on Earth from the sun's harmful solar radiation. Ozone is broken down in the upper atmosphere through chemical reactions such as the one shown here.

$$NO(g) + O_3(g) \rightarrow NO_2(g) + O_2(g)$$

Drag the atoms, as needed, into each box to create a visual representation of how many of each type of atom is present on both sides of the equation. Be sure the amounts of each substance match the balanced chemical equation.

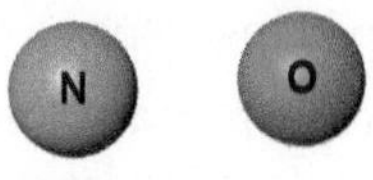

Answer choices: individual N atoms, individual O atoms

Target boxes: reactant, product

8.5 Ammonia (NH_3) is an important molecule in the global nitrogen cycle and is used in large quantities to produce agricultural fertilizers, pharmaceutical drugs, and other consumer items. Drag the compounds, as needed, into each box to create a visual representation of the reaction at the molecular level. Be sure the amounts of each compound match the balanced chemical equation.

$$3H_2(g) + 2N_2(g) \rightarrow 2NH_3(g)$$

Answer choices:

Target boxes: reactants, products

8.6 Sulfuric acid (H_2SO_4) in the atmosphere can produce acid rain. Most sulfuric acid produced and released into the atmosphere is a result of human activity such as the combustion of sulfur-containing fossil fuels in power plants. Drag the compounds, as needed, into each box to create a visual representation of this reaction at the molecular level. Be sure the amounts of each compound match the balanced chemical equation.

$$2SO_2(g) + O_2(g) + 2H_2O(g) \rightarrow 2H_2SO_4(aq)$$

Answer choices:

Target boxes: reactants, products

8.7 The formation of nitrogen dioxide (NO_2) is shown below. The gas nitrogen dioxide is an air pollutant that forms when fossil fuels such as gasoline, diesel, coal, and oil are burned. Extended exposure to elevated concentrations of NO_2 may contribute to the development of asthma and other respiratory issues.

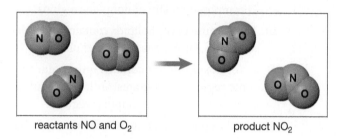

reactants NO and O_2 product NO_2

Write a complete balanced chemical equation for this reaction. Include the physical state abbreviation after each substance. All substances are gases.

_____ + _____ → _____

8.8 The reaction below shows the formation of acid rain.

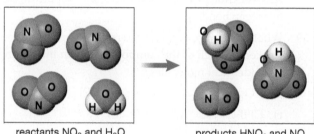

reactants NO_2 and H_2O products HNO_3 and NO

Write a complete balanced chemical equation for this reaction. Include the physical state abbreviation after each substance. All substances are gases.

_____ + _____ → _____

8.9 In the spaces provided, indicate the number of atoms of each element on each side of the following balanced chemical equation.

$$H_3PO_4(aq) + 3NH_4OH(aq) \rightarrow$$
$$(NH_4)_3PO_4(aq) + 3H_2O(l)$$

Number of H = ____   Number of H = ____

Number of N = ____   Number of N = ____

Number of O = ____   Number of O = ____

Number of P = ____   Number of P = ____

8.10 Ammonium bicarbonate (NH_4HCO_3) is used in the food industry as a raising agent for products such as cookies and crackers. Balance this reaction by adding coefficients.

$$\_\_CO_2(g) + \_\_NH_3(g) + \_\_H_2O(l) \rightarrow$$
$$\_\_NH_4HCO_3(aq)$$

8.11 Barium sulfate ($BaSO_4$) is used to produce common plastics such as polypropylene and polystyrene. Which reaction is a balanced chemical equation for the production of $BaSO_4$?

a) $Ba(NO_3)_2(aq) + 2Na_2SO_4(aq) \rightarrow$
$$3BaSO_4(s) + 4NaNO_3(aq)$$

b) $Ba(NO_3)_2(aq) + Na_2SO_4(aq) \rightarrow$
$$BaSO_4(s) + NaNO_3(aq)$$

c) $2Ba(NO_3)_2(aq) + Na_2SO_4(aq) \rightarrow$
$$2BaSO_4(s) + 2NaNO_3(aq)$$

d) $Ba(NO_3)_2(aq) + Na_2SO_4(aq) \rightarrow$
$$BaSO_4(s) + 2NaNO_3(aq)$$

8.12 Zinc metal (Zn) reacts with hydrochloric acid (HCl) to produce zinc chloride, which is used by law enforcement detectives for fingerprint identification. Balance the reaction by adding the necessary coefficients.

___$Zn(s)$ + ___$HCl(aq) \rightarrow$
$$\_\_\_ZnCl_2(aq) + \_\_\_H_2(g)$$

8.13 Iron(II) sulfate ($FeSO_4$) is an iron supplement given to people who have low iron in their blood. Sodium hydroxide (NaOH) is used for a wide range of applications including some in the paper industry. What is the coefficient in front of NaOH in the balanced chemical equation?

$NaOH(aq) + FeSO_4(aq) \rightarrow$
$$Na_2SO_4(aq) + Fe(OH)_2(s)$$

a) The coefficient in front of NaOH is 1.

b) The coefficient in front of NaOH is 2.

c) The coefficient in front of NaOH is 3.

d) The coefficient in front of NaOH is 5.

8.14 Iron metal (Fe) reacts with carbon dioxide (CO_2) in the air to form rust (Fe_2O_3) and carbon monoxide (CO). Balance this chemical equation by selecting the missing coefficients for this reaction.

____$Fe(s)$ + ____$CO_2(g) \rightarrow$
$$\_\_\_\_Fe_2O_3(s) + \_\_\_\_CO(g)$$

a) 2, 3, 2, 3   b) 2, 2, 1, 3

c) 6, 3, 3, 3   d) 2, 3, 1, 3

8.15 Ammonium nitrate (NH_4NO_3) is used in agriculture as a high-nitrogen fertilizer. The decomposition of ammonium nitrate can also produce "laughing gas," a common anesthetic in dentistry. Balance the reaction shown here by adding the necessary coefficients.

___$NH_4NO_3(s) \rightarrow$ ___$N_2O(g)$ + ___$H_2O(g)$

8.16 Fermentation is a complex biochemical process used in the wine and alcohol industry that converts the sugar glucose ($C_6H_{12}O_6$) to ethanol (C_2H_5OH) and carbon dioxide (CO_2). The unbalanced overall fermentation reaction is shown. Balance the reaction, and then identify the choice that correctly shows the coefficients in front of C_2H_5OH and CO_2.

$$C_6H_{12}O_6(aq) \rightarrow C_2H_5OH(aq) + CO_2(g)$$

a) $2C_2H_5OH$ and $3CO_2$

b) $3C_2H_5OH$ and $2CO_2$

c) $2C_2H_5OH$ and $2CO_2$

d) $2C_2H_5OH$ and $4CO_2$

8.2 Types of Reactions

LO 2: Identify combination, decomposition, replacement, and combustion chemical reactions.

8.17 Drag each chemical equation into the box that identifies its reaction type.

Answer choices: $SO_3(g) + H_2O(l) \rightarrow H_2SO_4(aq)$,
$H_2CO_3(aq) \rightarrow H_2O(l) + CO_2(g)$,
$2Na(s) + Cl_2(g) \rightarrow 2NaCl(s)$,
$HCl(aq) + NaOH(aq) \rightarrow NaCl(aq) + H_2O(l)$

Target boxes: double replacement reaction box, decomposition reaction box, single replacement reaction box, combination reaction box

8.18 Drag each chemical equation into the box that identifies its reaction type.

Answer choices: $A + 2B \rightarrow AB_2$,
$X + YZ_2 \rightarrow XYZ + Z$, $BD + AC \rightarrow AB + CD$,
$AC_2D \rightarrow AC + CD$

Target boxes: double replacement reaction box, decomposition reaction box, single replacement reaction box, combination reaction box

8.19 Drag each hypothetical chemical reaction into the box that identifies its reaction type.

Answer choices:

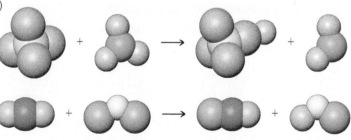

Target boxes: decomposition reaction box, single replacement reaction box, combination reaction box, double replacement reaction box

8.20 Drag each hypothetical chemical reaction into the box that identifies its reaction type.

Answer choices:

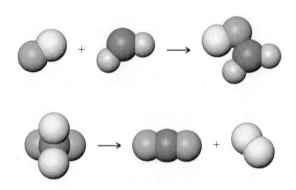

Target boxes: decomposition reaction box, single replacement reaction box, combination reaction box, double replacement reaction box

8.3 Oxidation-Reduction Reactions

LO 3: Analyze the outcomes of oxidation-reduction reactions.

8.21 Which reactant is oxidized, and which reactant is reduced in the reaction?

$$Cu^{2+}(aq) + Fe(s) \rightarrow Cu(s) + Fe^{2+}(aq)$$

a) $Cu(s)$ is oxidized and Fe^{2+} is reduced.
b) Cu^{2+} is oxidized and $Fe(s)$ is reduced.
c) $Fe(s)$ is reduced and Cu^{2+} is oxidized.
d) $Fe(s)$ is oxidized and Cu^{2+} is reduced.

8.22 Consider the reaction and identify the reactant that is oxidized and the reactant that is reduced.

$$Cu(s) + 2AgNO_3(aq) \rightarrow Cu(NO_3)_2(aq) + 2Ag(s)$$

a) Cu is oxidized and Ag is reduced.
b) Ag is oxidized and Cu is reduced.
c) O is oxidized and Ag is reduced.
d) N is oxidized and Cu is reduced.

8.23 Identify the reactant that gains electrons and the reactant that loses electrons in the reaction.

$$Pt^{2+}(aq) + Cu(s) \rightarrow Pt(s) + Cu^{2+}(aq)$$

a) $Pt(s)$ gains electrons and $Cu(s)$ loses electrons.
b) Pt^{2+} gains electrons and Cu^{2+} loses electrons.
c) Pt^{2+} gains electrons and $Cu(s)$ loses electrons.
d) $Cu(s)$ gains electrons and Pt^{2+} loses electrons.

8.24 Which material is oxidized, and which is reduced in the reaction?

$$Mn(s) + O_2(g) \rightarrow MnO_2(s)$$

a) Mn is reduced and O_2 is oxidized.
b) MnO_2 is reduced and O_2 is oxidized.
c) Mn is oxidized and O_2 is reduced.
d) Mn is oxidized and MnO_2 is reduced.

8.25 Which statement accurately describes this oxidation-reduction process?

$$Zn(s) + Cu^{2+}(aq) \rightarrow Zn^{2+}(aq) + Cu(s)$$

a) The Cu^{2+} ion loses two electrons through oxidation and the $Zn(s)$ gains two electrons through reduction.
b) The $Zn(s)$ loses two electrons through reduction and the Cu^{2+} gains two electrons through reduction.
c) The Cu^{2+} ion gains two electrons through reduction and the Zn^{2+} gains two electrons through oxidation.
d) The Cu^{2+} ion gains two electrons through reduction and the $Zn(s)$ loses two electrons through oxidation.

8.26 Which statement accurately describes the process shown?

$$Co^{2+} + 2e^- \rightarrow Co$$

a) The calcium ion with a charge of 2+ is reduced by the gain of two electrons.
b) The cobalt ion with a charge of 2+ is oxidized by the gain of two electrons.
c) The cobalt ion with a charge of 2+ is reduced by the gain of two electrons.
d) The cobalt ion with a charge of 2+ is reduced by the loss of two electrons.

8.27 Drag each chemical equation into a box to identify it as an oxidation reaction or a reduction reaction.

Answer choices: $Cu(s) \rightarrow Cu^{2+} + 2e^-$, $Li(s) \rightarrow Li^+ + 1e^-$, $Fe^{2+} \rightarrow Fe^{3+} + 1e^-$, $Ni^{2+} + 2e^- \rightarrow Ni(s)$, $2H^+ + 2e^- \rightarrow H_2(g)$, $Al^{3+} + 3e^- \rightarrow Al(s)$

Target boxes: oxidation box, reduction box

8.28 Drag each chemical reaction into a box to identify if the element in bold is oxidized or reduced.

Answer choices: $4\mathbf{Al}(s) + 3O_2(g) \rightarrow 2Al_2O_3(s)$, $\mathbf{Mg}(s) + 2HCl(aq) \rightarrow MgCl_2(aq) + H_2(g)$, $\mathbf{Cu}O(s) + H_2(g) \rightarrow Cu(s) + H_2O(g)$, $\mathbf{Br_2}(aq) + Zn(s) \rightarrow Zn^{+2}(aq) + 2Br^-(aq)$

Target boxes: reduction box, oxidation box

8.29 Determine whether the copper atom indicated by the bracket undergoes oxidation, reduction, combustion, or none of these as the reaction proceeds.

$$\overbrace{Cu(s)} + 4HNO_3(aq) \longrightarrow Cu(NO_3)_2(aq) + 2NO_2(g) + 2H_2O(l)$$

a) oxidation   b) reduction

c) combustion   d) none of these

8.30 Determine whether the copper atom indicated by the bracket undergoes oxidation, reduction, combustion, or none of these as the reaction proceeds.

$$3\overbrace{CuO(s)} + 2NH_3(g) \longrightarrow 3Cu(s) + N_2(g) + 3H_2O(g)$$

a) oxidation   b) reduction

c) combustion   d) none of these

8.31 A cardiac pacemaker is a small medical device placed in the chest to help control abnormal heart rhythms. The pacemaker uses low-energy electrical pulses from a battery to stimulate the heart to beat at a normal rate. The batteries used in pacemakers must be corrosion resistant and last up to 10 years. There are over 1,000,000 pacemakers in use today and most have a lithium-iodine battery. The battery reaction is shown. Which material is oxidized, and which is reduced in this reaction?

 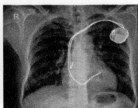

$$2Li(s) + I_2(s) \rightarrow 2LiI(aq)$$

a) Li is oxidized and LiI is reduced.

b) LiI is reduced and I_2 is oxidized.

c) I_2 is oxidized and Li is reduced.

d) Li is oxidized and I_2 is reduced.

8.32 Zinc metal is used to protect the metal hulls of ships and boats in salt water. A piece of zinc metal (called a sacrificial electrode) is connected by a wire to the ship's hull because the zinc metal corrodes in the salt water more readily than iron and the other metals the ship is made of. Consider the reaction shown and determine which material is oxidized and which is reduced.

$$Zn(s) + CuSO_4(aq) \rightarrow ZnSO_4(aq) + Cu(s)$$

a) Zn is oxidized and SO_4 is reduced.

b) Cu is oxidized and Zn is oxidized.

c) Zn is oxidized and Cu is reduced.

d) $CuSO_4$ is oxidized and $ZnSO_4$ is reduced.

8.4 The Mole

LO 4: Use Avogadro's number to calculate moles and particles.

8.33 How many golf balls are in one mole of golf balls? Enter a number in scientific notation.

8.34 How many golf balls are in two moles of golf balls? Enter a number in scientific notation.

8.35 How many soccer balls are in half a mole of soccer balls? Enter a number in scientific notation.

8.36 How many copper atoms are in two moles of copper metal?

a) $2 + 6.02 \times 10^{23}$ b) $6.02 \times 10^{23}/2$

c) 1.20×10^{24} d) 1.20×10^{23}

8.37 If there are 6.02×10^{23} molecules of CO_2 in a flask, how many moles of CO_2 are present?

a) 1 mol   b) 1.5 mol

c) 2 mol   d) 2.5 mol

8.38 How many atoms of oxygen (O) are in one mole of O_2 gas?

a) 1.00×10^{23} b) $6.02 \times 10^{23}/2$

c) 6.02×10^{23} d) $(6.02 \times 10^{23}) \times 2$

8.39 If there are 6.02×10^{23} atoms of oxygen (O) in a flask, how many O_2 molecules are present?

a) $6.02 \times 10^{23}/4$ b) $6.02 \times 10^{23}/2$

c) 6.02×10^{23} d) $(6.02 \times 10^{23}) \times 2$

8.40 A patient with an infection is prescribed the antibiotic drug amoxicillin. Which conversion factor can you use to convert the prescribed amount, which is 2.12×10^{-2} mol of amoxicillin, to the number of molecules?

amoxicillin

a) $\left[\dfrac{1 \text{ mol amoxicillin}}{6.02 \times 10^{23} \text{ molecule amoxicillin}}\right]$

b) $\left[\dfrac{1 \text{ molecule amoxicillin}}{6.02 \times 10^{23} \text{ moles amoxicillin}}\right]$

c) $\left[\dfrac{6.02 \times 10^{23} \text{ molecule amoxicillin}}{1 \text{ mol amoxicillin}}\right]$

d) $\left[\dfrac{6.02 \times 10^{23} \text{ moles amoxicillin}}{1 \text{ molecule amoxicillin}}\right]$

8.41 Carfentanil is a powerful drug in the opioid family that is estimated to be 10,000 times more potent than morphine. Many communities have seen an increase in the number of accidental overdoses of this drug by people addicted to heroin and other opioids. Which conversion factor can you use to convert 8.5×10^{22} molecules of carfentanil into moles of carfentanil?

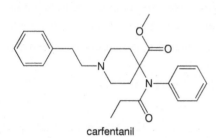

carfentanil

a) $\left[\dfrac{1 \text{ molecule carfentanil}}{6.02 \times 10^{23} \text{ mol carfentanil}} \right]$

b) $\left[\dfrac{6.02 \times 10^{23} \text{ molecule carfentanil}}{1 \text{ mol carfentanil}} \right]$

c) $\left[\dfrac{6.02 \times 10^{23} \text{ mol carfentanil}}{1 \text{ molecule carfentanil}} \right]$

d) $\left[\dfrac{1 \text{ mol carfentanil}}{6.02 \times 10^{23} \text{ molecule carfentanil}} \right]$

8.42 How many water molecules (H_2O) are in 2.50 moles of water?

a) 2.50 molecules H_2O

b) 1.51×10^{24} molecules H_2O

c) 4.15×10^{24} molecules H_2O

d) 4.52×10^{24} molecules H_2O

8.43 How many moles of sulfur does 8.50×10^{18} atoms of sulfur represent?

a) 1.41×10^{-5} mol sulfur

b) 8.50×10^{18} mol sulfur

c) 5.11×10^{42} mol sulfur

d) 7.08×10^4 mol sulfur

8.44 How many phosphate ions (PO_4^{3-}) are in 12.8 mol?

a) 2.13×10^{-23} phosphate ions

b) 7.71×10^{24} phosphate ions

c) 64 phosphate ions

d) 4.70×10^{22} phosphate ions

8.45 How many moles of methane (CH_4) are in each quantity? Express your answers in standard decimal form with three significant figures.

a) 8.49×10^{24} molecules of methane

b) 1.23×10^{22} molecules of methane

c) 5.95×10^{23} molecules of methane

8.46 How many water molecules (H_2O) are contained in each amount of moles? Express your answers in scientific notation with three significant figures.

a) 2.50 mol H_2O

b) 0.429 mol H_2O

c) 10.0 mol H_2O

8.5 Molar Mass and Mole Calculations

LO 5: Determine the molar mass for a substance and use the molar mass to convert between grams and moles.

8.47 Rank the following molecules in terms of increasing molar mass from smallest to largest. Estimate the molar mass of each molecule, and then drag them into the boxes so they are arranged left-to-right from smallest molar mass to largest molar mass.

Answer choices:

Target boxes: five boxes arranged left-to-right from smallest molar mass to largest molar mass

8.48 Drag the provided molecules into boxes so they are arranged left-to-right from smallest molar mass to largest molar mass.

Answer choices:

CH_3OH, HCl, CO, H_2O_2, CO_2

Target boxes: five boxes arranged left-to-right from smallest molar mass to largest molar mass

8.49 Which molecule has the *smallest* molar mass?

a) $C_6H_{12}O_6$　　　　b) $C_3H_7NO_2S$

c) $C_4H_{11}NO$　　　　d) CCl_4

8.50 Which molecule has the *largest* molar mass?

a) H_3PO_4　　　　b) H_2SO_4

c) CH_3CO_2H　　　　d) $C_3H_8O_3$

8.51 Which quantity has the greatest mass?

a) 1 mol of Na atoms　or　1 mol of Ne

b) 1 mol of N atoms　or　1 mol of N_2

c) 1 mol of He atoms　or　6.02×10^{23} H atoms

d) 2 mol of C atoms　or　1 mol of CO_2

8.52 Which quantity has the greatest mass?

a) 1 mol of Cu atoms　or　1 mol of Ne

b) 1 mol of O atoms　or　1 mol of O_2

c) 1 mol of C atoms　or　6.02×10^{23} S atoms

d) 1 mol of H_2O molecules　or　6.02×10^{23} O_2 molecules

8.53 Uric acid is a normal component of urine. Elevated blood concentrations of uric acid can lead to gout and have been associated with other medical conditions such as diabetes and the formation of kidney stones. How many moles of uric acid are in 281.7 g uric acid?

uric acid

uric acid: formula $= C_5H_4N_4O_3$, molar mass $= 168.11$ g/mol

a) 4.736×10^4 mol $C_5H_4N_4O_3$

b) 5.968×10^{-1} mol $C_5H_4N_4O_3$

c) 1.676 mol $C_5H_4N_4O_3$

d) 2.112×10^{-5} mol $C_5H_4N_4O_3$

8.54 How many grams are in 6.00 moles of each compound? Use the given molar masses and enter your answers in standard decimal form with three significant figures and units of grams.

a) $MgSO_4$. The molar mass of $MgSO_4$ is 120.37 g/mol.

b) $Al(OH)_3$. The molar mass of $Al(OH)_3$ is 78.01 g/mol.

c) C_3H_8. The molar mass of C_3H_8 is 44.09 g/mol.

d) NaOH. The molar mass of NaOH is 40.00 g/mol.

8.55 How many grams are in 0.500 moles of each compound? Use the given molar masses and enter your answers in standard decimal form with three significant figures and units of grams.

a) HCl _____ The molar mass of HCl is 36.46 g/mol

b) C_5H_{12} _____ The molar mass of C_5H_{12} is 72.15 g/mol

c) C_6H_6 _____ The molar mass of C_6H_6 is 78.11 g/mol

d) $CaBr_2$ _____ The molar mass of $CaBr_2$ is 199.89 g/mol

8.56 How many molecules are contained in each amount? Use the given molar masses and enter your answers in scientific notation with three significant figures and units of molecules.

a) 5.32 g CO_2 _____ The molar mass of CO_2 is 44.01 g/mol

b) 0.432 g CH_4 _____ The molar mass of CH_4 is 16.04 g/mol

c) 6.32 g H_2O _____ The molar mass of H_2O is 18.02 g/mol

d) 0.0231 g C_7H_{16} _____ The molar mass of C_7H_{16} is 100.21 g/mol

8.57 A bottle of acetaminophen contains 500 tablets, each of which has 200-mg of acetaminophen $(C_8H_9NO_2)$.

a) How many moles of acetaminophen $(C_8H_9NO_2)$ are in one 200-mg tablet? The molar mass of $C_8H_9NO_2$ is 151.16 g/mol. Enter your answer in scientific notation with three significant figures and units of mol.

b) How many molecules of acetaminophen $(C_8H_9NO_2)$ are in one 200-mg tablet? The molar mass of $C_8H_9NO_2$ is 151.16 g/mol. Enter your answer in scientific notation with three significant figures and units of molecules.

8.58 Estradiol, shown below, is a form of the female sex hormone estrogen. Estradiol is used in hormone replacement therapy to treat symptoms of menopause and may help reduce osteoporosis in postmenopausal women.

estradiol

molecular formula: $C_{18}H_{24}O_2$; molecular weight: 272.38 g/mol

Select the missing conversion factor needed to calculate the mass in grams of 3.88×10^{31} molecules of estradiol.

$$\left[\frac{3.88 \times 10^{31} \text{ molecules } C_{18}H_{24}O_2}{1} \right] \times$$

$$\left[\frac{1 \text{ mol } C_{18}H_{24}O_2}{6.02 \times 10^{23} \text{ molecules } C_{18}H_{24}O_2} \right] \times [?]$$

a) $\left[\dfrac{\text{mol } C_{18}H_{24}O_2}{272.38 \text{ g } C_{18}H_{24}O_2} \right]$

b) $\left[\dfrac{272.38 \text{ g } C_{18}H_{24}O_2}{\text{mol } C_{18}H_{24}O_2} \right]$

c) $\left[\dfrac{272.38 \text{ mol } C_{18}H_{24}O_2}{1 \text{ g } C_{18}H_{24}O_2} \right]$

d) $\left[\dfrac{1 \text{ g } C_{18}H_{24}O_2}{272.38 \text{ mol } C_{18}H_{24}O_2} \right]$

8.59 How many molecules of ethanol (CH_3CH_2OH) are in a glass of wine containing 19.5 g ethanol?

a) 8.98×10^2 molecules ethanol

b) 1.42×10^{24} molecules ethanol

c) 2.55×10^{23} molecules ethanol

d) 2.55 molecules ethanol

8.6 Calculations in Chemical Reactions

LO 6: **Calculate the amount of one substance in a reaction when given the amount of another substance in the reaction.**

8.60 Use the balanced chemical equation for the reaction that produces nitric acid in the atmosphere to answer the questions. Enter whole numbers without decimals.

$$3NO_2(g) + H_2O(g) \rightarrow 2HNO_3(g) + NO(g)$$

a) How many moles of H_2O are required to react completely with 6 moles of NO_2?

b) How many moles of nitric acid (HNO_3) are formed from 10 moles of H_2O and excess NO_2?

c) How many moles of nitric acid (HNO_3) are formed from 3 moles of NO_2 and excess H_2O?

8.61 Use the balanced **chemical** equation for the combination reaction that produces sodium chloride to answer the questions. Enter numeric values for each question.

$$2Na(s) + Cl_2(g) \rightarrow 2NaCl(s)$$

a) How many moles of Cl_2 are required to react completely with 4 moles of Na?

b) How many moles of NaCl are formed from 0.5 moles of Cl_2 and excess Na?

c) How many moles of NaCl are formed from 0.5 moles of Na and excess Cl_2?

8.62 Use the balanced chemical equation for the reaction that produces nitric acid in the atmosphere to answer the questions. The molar masses of each material in the reaction are listed under the balanced chemical equation. Enter your answers in standard form with two significant figures and units of grams.

$$3NO_2(g) + H_2O(g) \rightarrow 2HNO_3(g) + NO(g)$$
$$(40.01\,g/mol) \quad (18.02\,g/mol) \qquad (63.01\,g/mol) \quad (30.01\,g/mol)$$

a) How many grams of H_2O are required to react completely with 3.0 moles of NO_2?

b) How many grams of nitric acid (HNO_3) are formed from 0.30 moles of H_2O and excess NO_2?

c) How many grams of NO are formed from 0.60 moles of NO_2 and excess H_2O?

8.63 Use the balanced chemical equation for the combination reaction that produces sodium chloride to answer the questions. The molar masses of each material in the reaction are listed under the balanced equation.

$$2Na(s) + Cl_2(g) \rightarrow 2NaCl(s)$$
$$(22.99\,g/mol) \quad (70.90\,g/mol) \quad (58.44\,g/mol)$$

a) How many grams of Cl_2 are required to react completely with 8.0 moles of Na? Enter your answer in *scientific notation* to two significant figures and units of grams.

b) How many grams of NaCl are formed from 0.50 moles of Cl_2 and excess Na? Enter your answer in standard decimal notation to two significant figures and units of grams.

c) How many grams of NaCl are formed from 0.80 moles of Na and excess Cl_2? Enter your answer in standard decimal notation to two significant figures and units of grams.

8.64 Sulfur dioxide (SO_2) is produced by volcanic eruptions and in laboratories by the reaction between hydrogen sulfide (H_2S) and oxygen gas (O_2).

$$2H_2S(g) + 3O_2(g) \rightarrow 2SO_2(g) + 2H_2O(g)$$
$$34.08\ g/mol \quad 32.00\ g/mol \quad 64.07\ g/mol \quad 18.02\ g/mol$$

Which is the correct conversion sequence to calculate the number of grams of SO_2 that are produced when 7.85 g H_2S reacts with excess oxygen gas (O_2) according to the given balanced reaction.

a) $\left[\dfrac{7.85\ g\ H_2S}{1}\right] \times \left[\dfrac{34.08\ g\ H_2S}{1\ mol\ H_2S}\right] \times \left[\dfrac{2\ mol\ SO_2}{2\ mol\ H_2S}\right] \times \left[\dfrac{64.07\ g\ SO_2}{mol\ SO_2}\right]$

b) $\left[\dfrac{7.85\ g\ H_2S}{1}\right] \times \left[\dfrac{1\ mol\ H_2S}{34.08\ g\ H_2S}\right] \times \left[\dfrac{1\ mol\ SO_2}{2\ mol\ H_2S}\right] \times \left[\dfrac{64.067\ g\ SO_2}{mol\ SO_2}\right]$

c) $\left[\dfrac{7.85\ g\ H_2S}{1}\right] \times \left[\dfrac{1\ mol\ H_2S}{64.07\ g\ H_2S}\right] \times \left[\dfrac{2\ mol\ SO_2}{2\ mol\ H_2S}\right] \times \left[\dfrac{34.08\ g\ SO_2}{mol\ SO_2}\right]$

d) $\left[\dfrac{7.85\ g\ H_2S}{1}\right] \times \left[\dfrac{1\ mol\ H_2S}{34.08\ g\ H_2S}\right] \times \left[\dfrac{2\ mol\ SO_2}{2\ mol\ H_2S}\right] \times \left[\dfrac{64.07\ g\ SO_2}{mol\ SO_2}\right]$

8.65 Sulfur dioxide (SO_2) and nitrogen oxides (NOx) are released into the atmosphere when fossil fuels burn. These air pollutants react with water droplets and oxygen in the air, according to the following chemical reaction, to form acid rain, which has damaging ecological effects on lakes, forests, and streams.

$$SO_3(g) \quad + \quad H_2O(l) \quad \rightarrow \quad H_2SO_4(aq)$$
$$\text{80.07 g/mol} \qquad \text{18.02 g/mol} \qquad \text{98.08 g/mol}$$

Tree damage from acid rain, Grayson Highlands State Park, Virginia, USA

Which is the correct conversion sequence to calculate the number of grams of H_2SO_4 produced when 4.75×10^{13} g SO_2 reacts in the atmosphere with excess oxygen water (H_2O)?

a) $\left[\dfrac{4.75 \times 10^{13} \text{ g } SO_3}{1} \right] \times \left[\dfrac{1 \text{ mol } SO_3}{80.07 \text{ g } SO_3} \right] \times \left[\dfrac{1 \text{ mol } H_2O}{1 \text{ mol } SO_3} \right] \times \left[\dfrac{18.02 \text{ g } H_2O}{1 \text{ mol } H_2O} \right]$

b) $\left[\dfrac{4.75 \times 10^{13} \text{ g } SO_3}{1} \right] \times \left[\dfrac{1 \text{ mol } SO_3}{80.07 \text{ g } SO_3} \right] \times \left[\dfrac{4 \text{ mol } H_2SO_4}{3 \text{ mol } SO_3} \right] \times \left[\dfrac{98.08 \text{ g } H_2SO_4}{1 \text{ mol } H_2SO_4} \right]$

c) $\left[\dfrac{4.75 \times 10^{13} \text{ g } SO_3}{1} \right] \times \left[\dfrac{1 \text{ mol } SO_3}{80.07 \text{ g } SO_3} \right] \times \left[\dfrac{1 \text{ mol } H_2SO_4}{1 \text{ mol } SO_3} \right] \times \left[\dfrac{98.08 \text{ g } H_2SO_4}{1 \text{ mol } H_2SO_4} \right]$

d) $\left[\dfrac{80.07 \text{ g } SO_3}{1} \right] \times \left[\dfrac{1 \text{ mol } SO_3}{4.75 \times 10^{13} \text{ g } SO_3} \right] \times \left[\dfrac{1 \text{ mol } H_2SO_4}{1 \text{ mol } SO_3} \right] \times \left[\dfrac{98.08 \text{ g } H_2SO_4}{1 \text{ mol } H_2SO_4} \right]$

8.66 Sulfur dioxide (SO_2) and nitrogen oxides (NOx) are released into the atmosphere when fossil fuels burn. These air pollutants react with water droplets and oxygen in the air to form acid rain (H_2SO_4), which damages lakes, forests, and streams. As shown in the reaction below, H_2SO_4 can then react with $CaCO_3$ resulting in damage to buildings and art pieces such as statues that contain $CaCO_3$.

$$CaCO_3(s) \quad + \quad H_2SO_4(aq) \quad \rightarrow \quad CaSO_4(aq) \quad + \quad CO_2(g) \quad + \quad H_2O(l)$$
$$\text{100.09 g/mol} \qquad \text{98.08 g/mol} \qquad \text{136.14 g/mol} \qquad \text{44.01 g/mol} \qquad \text{18.02 g/mol}$$

Select the correct conversion sequence to calculate the number of grams of $CaCO_3$ that react with 2.25×10^8 g H_2SO_4.

a) $\left[\dfrac{2.25 \times 10^8 \text{ g } H_2SO_4}{1} \right] \times \left[\dfrac{1 \text{ mol } H_2SO_4}{98.08 \text{ g } H_2SO_4} \right] \times \left[\dfrac{1 \text{ mol } CaCO_3}{1 \text{ mol } H_2SO_4} \right] \times \left[\dfrac{100.09 \text{ g } CaCO_3}{1 \text{ mol } CaCO_3} \right]$

b) $\left[\dfrac{2.25 \times 10^8 \text{ g } CaCO_3}{1} \right] \times \left[\dfrac{1 \text{ mol } H_2SO_4}{98.08 \text{ g } CaCO_3} \right] \times \left[\dfrac{1 \text{ mol } CaCO_3}{1 \text{ mol } H_2SO_4} \right] \times \left[\dfrac{100.09 \text{ g } CaCO_3}{1 \text{ mol } CaCO_3} \right]$

c) $\left[\dfrac{2.25 \times 10^8 \text{ g } H_2SO_4}{1} \right] \times \left[\dfrac{98.08 \text{ g } H_2SO_4}{1 \text{ mol } H_2SO_4} \right] \times \left[\dfrac{1 \text{ mol } CaCO_3}{1 \text{ mol } H_2SO_4} \right] \times \left[\dfrac{100.09 \text{ g } CaCO_3}{1 \text{ mol } CaCO_3} \right]$

d) $\left[\dfrac{2.25 \times 10^8 \text{ g } H_2SO_4}{1} \right] \times \left[\dfrac{1 \text{ mol } H_2SO_4}{98.08 \text{ g } H_2SO_4} \right] \times \left[\dfrac{1 \text{ mol } CaCO_3}{1 \text{ mol } H_2SO_4} \right] \times \left[\dfrac{136.14 \text{ g } CaSO_4}{1 \text{ mol } CaCO_3} \right]$

8.67 A fuel for rocket engines contains a mixture of hydrogen peroxide (H_2O_2) and hydrazine (N_2H_4) and reacts as shown below.

$$N_2H_4(l) + 2H_2O_2(l) \rightarrow N_2(g) + 4H_2O(g)$$
$$32.05 \text{ g/mol} \quad 34.02 \text{ g/mol} \quad 28.01 \text{ g/mol} \quad 18.02 \text{ g/mol}$$

Select the missing conversion factor needed to calculate the mass of N_2H_4 in grams required to react completely with 4.50×10^{14} g of H_2O_2.

$$\left[\frac{4.50 \times 10^{14} \text{ g } H_2O_2}{1}\right] \times \left[\frac{1 \text{ mol } H_2O_2}{34.02 \text{ g/mol } H_2O_2}\right] \times \left[?\right] \times \left[\frac{32.05 \text{ g/mol } N_2H_4}{\text{mol } N_2H_4}\right] = \text{ g } N_2H_4$$

a) $\left[\dfrac{1 \text{ mol } N_2H_4}{2 \text{ mol } H_2O_2}\right]$
b) $\left[\dfrac{2 \text{ mol } H_2O_2}{1 \text{ mol } N_2H_4}\right]$
c) $\left[\dfrac{1 \text{ mol } N_2H_4}{4 \text{ mol } H_2O}\right]$
d) $\left[\dfrac{2 \text{ mol } N_2H_4}{1 \text{ mol } H_2O_2}\right]$

8.68 Calcium hydroxide ($Ca(OH)_2$) is used in the food industry, and also in water treatment. Calcium hydroxide reacts with acids such as phosphoric acid (H_3PO_4) to form calcium hydrogen phosphate ($CaHPO_4$) and water (H_2O).

$$Ca(OH)_2(aq) + H_3PO_4(aq) \rightarrow CaHPO_4(aq) + 2H_2O(l)$$
$$74.09 \text{ g/mol} \quad 97.99 \text{ g/mol} \quad 136.06 \text{ g/mol} \quad 18.02 \text{ g/mol}$$

Use the given molar masses to calculate how many grams of water (H_2O) can be produced if 2.55×10^5 grams of $Ca(OH)_2$ react according to the balanced chemical equation. For this calculation, you can assume there is more than enough H_3PO_4 to completely react with all of the $Ca(OH)_2$. Express your answer in scientific notation with three significant figures and units of grams.

8.69 Ammonium sulfate (($NH_4)_2SO_4$) is widely used as a fertilizer to increase crop yields. The global ammonium sulfate market size is in the billions of US dollars and is expected to increase with global population in the coming years.

$$H_2SO_4(aq) + 2NH_3(g) \rightarrow (NH_4)_2SO_4(aq)$$
$$98.08 \text{ g/mol} \quad 17.03 \text{ g/mol} \quad 132.14 \text{ g/mol}$$

Use the given molar masses and balanced chemical equation to determine the number of grams of ammonia (NH_3) needed to produce 7.50×10^8 grams ($NH_4)_2SO_4$. Express your answer in scientific notation with three significant figures and units of grams.

8.70 Barium sulfate ($BaSO_4$) is widely used in the medical field as a contrast agent during X-rays. It greatly improves visualization of the esophagus, stomach, and intestines on patient scans.

$$Na_2SO_4(aq) + BaCl_2(aq) \rightarrow BaSO_4(s) + 2NaCl(aq)$$
$$142.04 \text{ g/mol} \quad 208.23 \text{ g/mol} \quad 233.38 \text{ g/mol} \quad 58.44 \text{ g/mol}$$

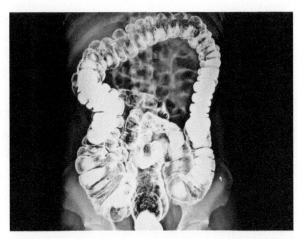

Use the given molar masses and balanced chemical equation to determine the number of grams of barium chloride ($BaCl_2$) needed to produce 275 grams $BaSO_4$. Express your answer in standard decimal form with three significant figures and units of grams.

8.7 Limiting Reactant

LO 7: Determine the limiting reactant and percent yield of a chemical reaction.

8.71 Dinitrogen monoxide (N_2O) is an anesthetic in medicine and also powers rockets.

$$2N_2(g) + O_2(g) \rightarrow 2N_2O(g)$$

A. Consider the given starting conditions shown and select the product mix that correctly shows the state of the system after reaction.

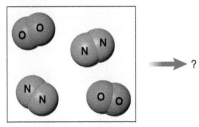

starting reaction conditions

a) Product mix A

b) Product mix B

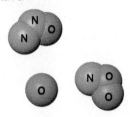

c) Product mix C

d) Product mix D

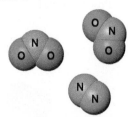

B. Write the chemical formulas for the limiting and excess reactants in the spaces provided.

Limiting reactant: _____

Excess reactant: _____

8.72 Methane (CH_4) is the main ingredient in natural gas and can react with oxygen (O_2) in the air to form the greenhouse gas carbon dioxide (CO_2) and water (H_2O).

$$CH_4(g) + 2O_2(g) \rightarrow CO_2(g) + 2H_2O(g)$$

A. Look at the given starting conditions shown and select the product mix that correctly shows the state of the system after reaction.

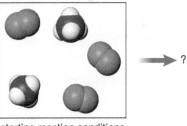

starting reaction conditions

a) Product mix A

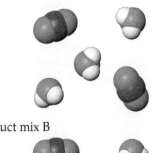

b) Product mix B

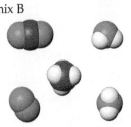

c) Product mix C

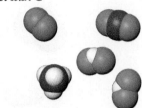

d) Product mix D

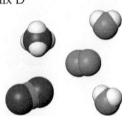

B. Write the chemical formulas for the limiting and excess reactants in the spaces provided.

Limiting reactant: _____

Excess reactant: _____

8.73 Welding torches use acetylene (C_2H_2) as a fuel. The heat released in the reaction, shown below, is used to weld metal together. The reaction also produces carbon dioxide (CO_2) and water (H_2O). If a welder has a cylinder that contains 325 g of acetylene (C_2H_2) and a cylinder that contains 875 g of oxygen gas (O_2), does the welder have enough oxygen to burn all of the acetylene fuel? Select the answer that explains your response.

$$2C_2H_2(g) + 5O_2(g) \rightarrow 4CO_2(g) + 2H_2O(g)$$

a) Yes, there is enough oxygen (O_2) in the cylinder to burn all of the acetylene fuel in the fuel cylinder.

b) Additional information is needed in order to solve this problem and answer the question.

c) No, there is not enough oxygen (O_2) in the cylinder to burn all of the acetylene fuel in the fuel cylinder.

d) No, more carbon dioxide (CO_2) is needed for the reaction to be complete.

8.74 Dinitrogen monoxide (N_2O) can react with oxygen gas (O_2) in the atmosphere to form nitrogen dioxide (NO_2), as shown in the following reaction. Calculate the theoretical yield in grams of NO_2 that can be produced if 1.75×10^5 grams N_2O reacts with 2.63×10^5 grams O_2.

$$2N_2O(g) + 3O_2(g) \rightarrow 4NO_2(g)$$

a) 7.56×10^5 g NO_2

b) 1.83×10^5 g NO_2

c) 1.64×10^4 g NO_2

d) 3.66×10^5 g NO_2

8.75 In addition to being an important cellular signaling molecule involved in a variety of physiological processes, nitrogen monoxide (NO) is an important intermediate in the chemical industry and also plays a role in air pollution formation.

$$4NH_3(g) + 5O_2(g) \rightarrow 4NO(g) + 6H_2O(g)$$
$$17.03 \text{ g/mol} \quad 32.00 \text{ g/mol} \quad 30.01 \text{ g/mol} \quad 18.02 \text{ g/mol}$$

a) Determine the theoretical yield of NO when 8.65×10^6 g NH_3 (g) reacts with 2.58×10^7 g O_2 (g). Express your answer in scientific notation with three significant figures and units of grams NO.

b) What is the chemical formula of the limiting reactant? Limiting reactant: _____

c) What is the chemical formula of the reactant in excess? Excess reactant: _____

8.76 Select the correct equation for percent yield.

a) percent yield $= \left[\dfrac{\text{theoretical yield}}{\text{actual yield}} \right] \times 100$

b) percent yield $= \left[\dfrac{\text{actual yield}}{\text{theoretical yield}} \right] \times 100$

c)
percent yield $= \left[\dfrac{\text{molar mass of product}}{\text{molar mass starting material}} \right] \times 100$

d) percent yield $= \left[\dfrac{\text{total grams products}}{\text{total grams reactants}} \right] \times 100$

8.77 A team of pharmaceutical chemists is working to produce a batch of the drug lisdexamfetamine (shown), which is used as a treatment for attention deficit hyperactivity disorder (ADHD).

lisdexamfetamine

The team isolates 8.57×10^5 grams of pure lisdexamfetamine from a process with a calculated theoretical yield of 2.13×10^6 grams. What is the percent yield? Express your answer in standard decimal form with three significant figures.

8.78 The ATP molecule (adenosine triphosphate) serves as a source of energy for many cellular processes. The cell produces ATP using the enzyme ATP synthase, which combines a phosphate group (PO_4) with the molecule ADP (adenosine diphosphate) in the simplified phosphorylation reaction shown.

$$\text{ADP} + \text{Phosphate} \rightarrow \text{ATP}$$
$$427.20 \text{ g/mol} \qquad\qquad 507.18 \text{ g/mol}$$

A biochemist in a laboratory wants to prepare ATP using the mechanism described above for her research on the enzyme ATP synthase. She combines 1.75 g of ADP with an excess of phosphate and enzyme and recovers 1.85 g ATP at the end of the experiment. What is her percent yield of ATP? Do not round intermediate results. Express your answer in standard decimal form with three significant figures.

Challenge and Application Problems

8.79 The molecule serotonin is a neurotransmitter that helps regulate mood, appetite, sleep, and memory. It is also involved in the digestion of the food.

serotonin $C_{10}H_{12}N_2O$

a) How many moles of hydrogen are contained in 1.00 mole of serotonin? Express your answer in standard notation with three significant figures. *Hint*: Consider the ratio of atoms in the molecular formula, which also represents the number of moles of each atom in each mole of serotonin.

b) How many moles of nitrogen are contained in 3.25 moles of serotonin? Express your answer in standard notation with three significant figures. *Hint*: Consider the ratio of atoms in the molecular formula, which also represents the number of moles of each atom in each mole of serotonin.

8.80 The carbon monoxide molecule (CO) is produced by incomplete combustion and released in automobile exhaust. The oxygen atom is shown as red, carbon as black.

a) Calculate the number of carbon monoxide molecules (CO) that can be assembled from 5.81×10^{25} carbon atoms if there are unlimited oxygen atoms available. Express your answer in scientific notation with three significant figures. *Hint*: Consider the ratio of carbon atoms to oxygen atoms in the CO molecule.

b) Calculate the number of moles of CO that the number of molecules in part (A) represents. Express your answer in standard decimal form with three significant figures.

8.81 Millions of kilograms of fertilizers are produced each year to support crop growth. One source of nitrogen in fertilizers is the nitrate ion (NO_3^-). Which amount contains the most nitrogen atoms?

a) $1.75 \text{ mol} (NH_4)NO_3$

b) $3.55 \times 10^{24} \ NO_3^-$ ions

c) $52.8 \text{ g Ca}(NO_3)_2$

d) 3.55 mol NaNO_3

8.82 The ammonia molecule (NH_3) is involved in the global nitrogen cycle.

$$H-\overset{..}{N}-H$$
$$|$$
$$H$$
ammonia

a) Calculate the number of NH_3 molecules in 3.68 mol of NH_3. Express your answer in scientific notation with three significant figures.

b) Calculate the number of hydrogen (H) atoms in 3.68 mol of NH_3. Express your answer in scientific notation with three significant figures. *Hint*: Note that there are three H atoms in each ammonia molecule.

8.83 The glycerol molecule ($C_3H_8O_3$) shown is an important building block for the lipids known as triglycerides. Oxygen atoms are shown as red, carbon as black, and hydrogen as white.

glycerol

a) Calculate the number of glycerol molecules that can be assembled from 8.24×10^{18} oxygen atoms if unlimited carbon and hydrogen atoms are available. Express your answer in scientific notation with three significant figures. *Hint*: There are three oxygen atoms in each glycerol molecule.

b) Convert the number of glycerol molecules in your answer in Part (A) to moles of glycerol. Express your answer in scientific notation with three significant figures.

8.84 The urea molecule (CH_4N_2O) shown is important for the metabolism of nitrogen-containing compounds by animals and is a main nitrogen-containing substance in the urine of mammals.

urea

a) Calculate the number of urea molecules in 63.8 mol of urea. Express your answer in scientific notation with three significant figures.

b) Calculate the number of nitrogen atoms (N) contained in 63.8 mol of urea. Express your answer in scientific notation with three significant figures. *Hint:* There are two N atoms in each urea molecule.

8.85 Elevated blood levels of the molecule TMAO (trimethylamine N-oxide) may be associated with an increased risk of heart attacks and strokes. The molecular formula of TMAO is $(CH_3)_3NO$ and its molar mass is 75.11 g/mol.

TMAO molecule $(CH_3)_3NO$

a) Calculate the number of TMAO molecules present in 95.45 g of TMAO. Express your answer in scientific notation with four significant figures.

b) How many hydrogen atoms (H) are contained in 95.45 g of TMAO? Express your answer in scientific notation with four significant figures. *Hint:* Make sure to determine the number of hydrogen atoms in the formula for TMAO.

8.86 Nitric oxide (NO) is an important cellular signaling molecule involved in a variety of processes in the body. Research into the functions of nitric oxide led to a Nobel Prize in 1998 for the scientists who identified its role as a cardiovascular signaling molecule.

nitric oxide (NO)

a) Calculate the moles of nitric oxide that can be produced with 8.75×10^{15} atoms of nitrogen and unlimited oxygen atoms. Express your answer in scientific notation with three significant figures.

b) Calculate the number of grams nitric oxide that can be produced with 8.75×10^{15} atoms of nitrogen and unlimited oxygen atoms. The molar mass of nitric oxide (NO) is 30.01 g/mol. Express your answer in scientific notation with three significant figures.

8.87 Drinking water is monitored for lead contamination for public health and safety. A reaction such as the one shown here, which forms a lead-containing solid, allows lead to be removed during water purification.

$$Pb(NO_3)_2(aq) + 2NaCl(aq) \rightarrow$$

331.21 g/mol   58.44 g/mol

$$PbCl_2(s) + 2NaNO_3(aq)$$

278.10 g/mol   84.99 g/mol

A chemist performs a small-scale water test by adding 2.87 g of NaCl to a water sample that has been found to contain 1.65 g of lead in the form of lead(II) nitrate $(Pb(NO_3)_2)$. How many grams of lead(II) chloride $(PbCl_2)$ solid can the reaction form? *Hint:* When considering the amounts of two or more starting materials, you need to determine the limiting reactant. Express your answer in standard decimal form with three significant figures.

Chapter 9

9.1 Energy

LO 1: Define energy and convert between energy units.

9.01 Determine if each situation is best described by potential energy or kinetic energy.

a)

b)

c)

d)

e)

Target boxes: potential energy, kinetic energy

9.02 Which is an example of potential energy?

a) chopping vegetables

b) riding a bicycle

c) washing the dishes

d) none of the above

9.03 An LED light is found to require 2.75 kcal during a test in the laboratory. Which value represents the same amount of energy? 1 kcal = 4.184 kJ.

a) 2.75 kJ

b) 4.184 kJ

c) 11.5 kJ

d) 0.657 kJ

9.04 A student interested in environmental studies conducts an experiment and determines that 725 J are needed for the test. How many calories does this represent? 1 cal = 4.184 J.

a) 3.03×10^3 cal

b) 5.77×10^{-3} cal

c) 173 cal

d) 3.30×10^{-4} cal

9.05 A researcher studying the thermal properties of materials adds 135 cal of energy to an experimental setup. How many joules does this represent? 1 cal = 4.184 J.

a) 1.77×10^{-3} J

b) 32.3 J

c) 3.10×10^{-2} J

d) 565 J

9.06 A bowl of rice and vegetables contains 375 Calories (kcal). How many kilojoules (kJ) are in this meal? 1 kcal = 4.184 kJ.

a) 1.57×10^6 kJ

b) 89.6 kJ

c) 1.11×10^{-2} kJ

d) 1.57×10^3 kJ

9.07 Nutritionists commonly use a value of 3500 food Calories (1 Cal = 1 kcal) as being equivalent to one pound (1 lb) of body fat. For example, if you eat 3500 Cal more than you need, you can gain one pound of weight and if you burn 3500 Cal more than you eat, then you can lose one pound of weight. Using this information, calculate how many kilojoules (kJ) are equivalent to one pound of body fat. Express your answer in scientific notation with two significant figures and units of kJ. 1 kcal = 4.184 kJ.

| kJ

9.08 If the amount of energy required to power the lights in a small home for 1.0 hour is 3.1×10^3 kJ, calculate the amount of energy in units of kcal needed to power these lights for 12 hours. 1 kcal = 4.184 kJ.

a) 8.9×10^3 kcal

b) 1.6×10^5 kcal

c) 7.4×10^2 kcal

d) 1.6×10^{-2} kcal

9.09 Solar powered lights and solar panel chargers are allowing a growing number of children and families to study and be productive after dark for the first time in communities without traditional electricity. If a child studies for 3 hours a night using a 1.5-Watt energy efficient LED bulb, how many kilojoules (kJ) of energy will she use during her study time each night? Express your answer with two significant figures. 1 W = 1 J/s and 1000 J = 1 kJ.

[ ] kJ

9.10 The development of Type II diabetes is strongly correlated with excess body weight and lack of physical exercise. Type II diabetes is largely preventable with thirty minutes of moderate exercise most days and a healthy diet. A typical snack of a large soft drink and bag of chips contains about 1.5×10^3 kJ. If a pound (lb) of body fat contains 3500 food Calories (kcal), how many snacks like this are equivalent to a pound of body fat? Express your answer in standard notation with two significant figures. 1 Cal = 1 kcal, and 1 kcal = 4.184 kJ.

[ ] snacks/lb

9.11 For dessert, you eat about one cup of ice cream that contains 1.3×10^3 kJ. If you burn 5.0 Cal/min, how many minutes would you need to walk to burn off the ice cream you ate? Express your answer in standard decimal form with two significant figures and units of min. 1 food Calorie (Cal) = 1 kcal, and 1 kcal = 4.184 kJ.

[ ] min

9.2 Energy Changes in Reactions

LO 1: Describe how energy is absorbed or released in a chemical reaction and classify chemical reactions as either endothermic or exothermic.

9.12 Refer to the table of bond energies. Identify the strongest bond in the set.

Bond	Bond Energies (kJ/mol)
H—H	436
H—C	410
H—O	460
C—O	350
C—N	300
O=O	499

a) C—N   b) H—O   c) H—C
d) O=O   e) C—O   f) H—H

9.13 Consider the table of bond energies. The formation of which bond releases the greatest amount of energy?

Bond	Bond Energies (kJ/mol)
H—H	436
H—C	410
H—O	460
C—O	350
C—N	300
O=O	499

a) C—O   b) C—N   c) H—C
d) H—H   e) H—O   f) O=O

9.14 Consider the table of bond energies. Which of these releases the least amount of energy when formed?

Bond	Bond Energies (kJ/mol)
H—H	436
H—C	410
H—O	460
C—O	350
C—N	300
O=O	499

a) C—N   b) H—O   c) H—C

d) O=O   e) C—O   f) H—H

9.15 Medical kits often contain instant cold packs that are used to help reduce swelling after an injury if ice is not available. Cold packs use an endothermic process that involves dissolving ammonium nitrate (NH_4NO_3) in water as shown. How many moles of NH_4NO_3 are required to absorb 182 kJ of heat? Express your answer in standard decimal form with two significant figures and units of moles.

$$NH_4NO_3(s) \rightarrow NH_4^+(aq) + NO_3^-(aq) \quad \Delta H = +26 \text{ kJ}$$

[ ] mol

9.16 Nitrogen monoxide (NO) is a signaling molecule that is involved in a number of biological processes. It can be produced in the laboratory and environment by the reaction of nitrogen gas (N_2) and oxygen gas (O_2) according to the reaction shown. What is the maximum number of moles of nitrogen monoxide that can be formed when 546 kJ of heat is provided to a mixture containing 3.00 moles of N_2 gas and 3.00 moles of O_2 gas? Express your answer in standard decimal form with three significant figures and units of moles.

$$N_2(g) + O_2(g) \rightarrow 2NO(g) \quad \Delta H = 182 \text{ kJ}$$

[ ] mol NO

9.17 How much heat is required to completely react two moles of carbon dioxide (CO_2) in the presence of excess water according to the reaction shown?

$$CO_2(g) + 2H_2O(l) \rightarrow CH_4(g) + 2O_2(g) \quad \Delta H = +890 \text{ kJ}$$

a) 88 kJ   b) 1780 kcal   c) 1780 kJ   d) 445 kJ

9.18 Hydrogen peroxide (H_2O_2) is commonly used as an antiseptic to sterilize wounds. It is stored in the dark because it is unstable and slowly decomposes in the presence of light. How much heat is released when one mole of hydrogen peroxide decomposes completely according to the reaction shown?

$$2H_2O_2(l) \rightarrow 2H_2O(l) + O_2(g) \quad \Delta H = -196 \text{ kJ}$$

a) 392 kJ   b) 2.88 kJ   c) 5.76 kJ   d) 98.0 kJ

9.19 The addition of bromine (Br_2) to benzene (C_6H_6) is an intermediary reaction used for preparing more complex molecules in the pharmaceutical industry. If the $\Delta H = +8$ kJ for the reaction, how many grams of benzene are required to have 3.15×10^2 kJ associated with the reaction? Is the reaction endothermic or exothermic? (The molar mass of benzene is 78.11 g/mol.)

a) 1.97×10^3 g C_6H_6; The reaction is endothermic.

b) 3.08×10^3 g C_6H_6; The reaction is endothermic.

c) 39.4 g C_6H_6; The reaction is endothermic.

d) 3.08×10^3 g C_6H_6; The reaction is exothermic.

9.20 Hydrogen fuel cells have been the subject of intense research due to their potential as an environmentally friendly energy source. The reaction between hydrogen gas (H_2) and oxygen gas (O_2) to produce water vapor has a $\Delta H = -242$ kJ/mol of H_2 fuel. How many kJ of heat are released if 355 g H_2 reacts? Hint: Convert the given number of g H_2 into mol H_2.

$$H_2(g) + \frac{1}{2}O_2(g) \rightarrow H_2O(g) + Cu(NO_3)_2(aq)$$

a) 4.25×10^4 kJ   b) 8.59×10^4 kJ   c) 0.682 kJ   d) 1.47 kJ

9.21 Carbohydrates such as glucose are major energy sources for our bodies. If your body requires 225 kcal of energy to walk for an hour, how many grams of glucose ($C_6H_{12}O_6$) are required for this walk based on the reaction shown? The molar mass of glucose ($C_6H_{12}O_6$) is 180.16 g/mol. Express your answer in standard decimal form with three significant figures and units of grams (g).

$$C_6H_{12}O_6(s) + 6O_2(g) \rightarrow 6CO_2(g) + 6H_2O(l) + 686 \text{ kcal}$$
glucose

$\boxed{}$ g

9.22 Ethanol (drinking alcohol) is metabolized in the body through the overall reaction shown. How many kilocalories of heat is produced when 5.75 g of ethanol react with excess oxygen (O_2) gas? The molar mass of ethanol (CH_3CH_2OH) is 46.07 g/mol.

$$CH_3CH_2OH(aq) + O_2(g) \rightarrow 2CO_2(g) + 3H_2O(l) + 327 \text{ kcal}$$
ethanol

a) 8.66×10^4 kcal **b)** 3.82×10^{-4} kcal **c)** 1.88×10^3 kcal **d)** 40.8 kcal

9.23 Photosynthesis is an endothermic process that involves the use of energy from the sun along with carbon dioxide (CO_2) and water (H_2O) to produce oxygen gas (O_2) and carbohydrates such as glucose ($C_6H_{12}O_6$). How much heat, in kilocalories, is needed to produce oxygen and 23.5 g of glucose? The molar mass of glucose ($C_6H_{12}O_6$) is 180.16 g/mol. Express your answer in scientific notation with three significant figures and units of kcal.

$$6CO_2(g) + 6H_2O(l) + 686 \text{ kcal} \rightarrow C_6H_{12}O_6(s) + 6O_2(g)$$
glucose

$\boxed{}$ kcal

9.24 How many grams of ethanol (drinking alcohol) produce 975 kilojoules of heat when reacted with excess oxygen (O_2) gas in the body according to the reaction shown? The molar mass of ethanol (CH_3CH_2OH) is 46.07 g/mol. Express your answer in standard decimal form with three significant figures and units of g. 1 kcal = 4.184 kJ

$$CH_3CH_2OH(aq) + O_2(g) \rightarrow 2CO_2(g) + 3H_2O(l) + 327 \text{ kcal}$$
ethanol

$\boxed{}$ g

9.25 Millions of tons of crop fertilizers are produced each year to help increase agricultural food production. Nitrogen dioxide (NO_2) is an important intermediate in the industrial synthesis of nitric acid which is then used to produce commonly used fertilizers. It can be produced by the combination of nitrogen gas and oxygen gas according to the endothermic reaction shown. What is the maximum number of *molecules* of NO_2 that can be formed when 475 kJ of energy are supplied to 3.0 moles of nitrogen gas in the presence of excess oxygen (O_2) gas?

$$N_2(g) + 2O_2(g) \rightarrow 2NO_2(g) \quad \Delta H = +68 \text{ kJ}$$

a) 1.8×10^{24} molecules $NO_2(g)$ **b)** 3.6×10^{24} molecules $NO_2(g)$

c) 6.0 molecules $NO_2(g)$ **d)** 1.0×10^{-23} molecules $NO_2(g)$

9.3 Energy Diagrams and Activation Energy

LO 3: Represent the energy of chemical reactions using energy diagrams.

9.26 Consider the reaction energy diagram. Which number on the graph represents the heat of reaction (enthalpy)?

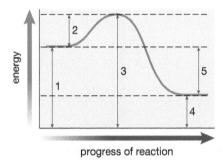

a) 1   **b)** 2   **c)** 3

d) 4   **e)** 5

9.27 Consider the reaction energy diagram. Which number on the graph represents the activation energy (E_a)?

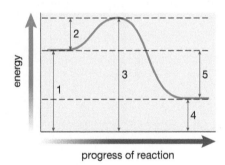

a) 1   **b)** 2   **c)** 3

d) 4   **e)** 5

9.28 Consider the reaction energy diagram below. Which number on the graph represents the energy of the products?.

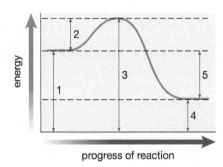

a) 1   **b)** 2   **c)** 3

d) 4   **e)** 5

9.29 Consider the reaction energy diagram. Which number on the graph represents the energy of the reactants?

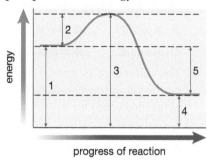

a) 1   **b)** 2   **c)** 3

d) 4   **e)** 5

9.30 Consider the reaction energy diagram. Which best characterizes the forward reaction?

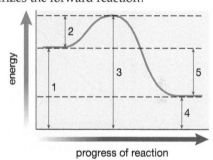

a) The reaction is endothermic

b) The reaction is catalytic

c) The reaction is thermoscopic

d) The reaction is exothermic

e) None of the above

9.31 Consider the two reactions illustrated on the energy diagram. In one reaction, compound A is converted to compound B. In a different reaction, compound A is converted to compound C.

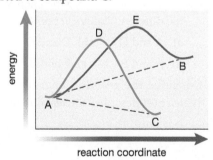

A. Identify each reaction as endothermic or exothermic.

Answer choices: Reaction A → B, Reaction A → C

Target boxes: endothermic, exothermic

B. Which reaction is the slower reaction? Which reaction is the faster reaction?

Answer choices: Reaction A → B, Reaction A → C

Target boxes: slower reaction, faster reaction

C. The difference in energy between which two points (on the curves shown) represents the heat of reaction (ΔH) for A $\rightarrow$ B?

a) A and D   b) D and C   c) A and C

d) A and E   e) E and B   f) A and B

D. The difference in energy between which two points (on the curves shown) represents the heat of reaction (ΔH) for A $\rightarrow$ C?

a) A and D   b) D and C   c) A and C

d) A and E   e) E and B   f) A and B

9.32 Consider the two reactions illustrated on the energy diagram. In one reaction, compound A is converted to compound B. In a different reaction, compound A is converted to compound C.

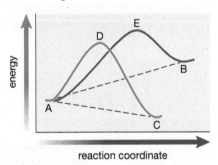

A. Which reaction forms products lower in energy?

a) Reaction A $\rightarrow$ B

b) Reaction A $\rightarrow$ C

c) Both reactions form products of equal energy

B. For reaction A $\rightarrow$ B, the energy of activation is the difference between points _____

a) A and D   b) D and C   c) A and C

d) A and E   e) E and B   f) A and B

C. For reaction A $\rightarrow$ C, the energy of activation is the difference between points _____

a) A and D   b) D and C   c) A and C

d) A and E   e) E and B   f) A and B

9.33 Consider the reaction energy diagram shown. Which best describes the reaction depicted?

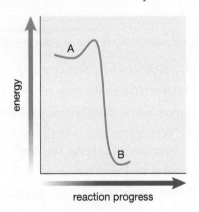

a) reaction with large E_a and small ΔH

b) highly endothermic reaction with large E_a

c) highly exothermic reaction with small E_a

9.34 Consider the reaction energy diagram shown. Which best describes the reaction depicted?

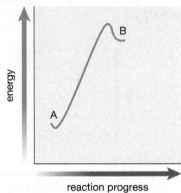

a) reaction with large E_a and small ΔH

b) highly endothermic reaction with large E_a

c) highly exothermic reaction with small E_a

9.35 Consider the reaction energy diagram shown. Which best describes the reaction depicted?

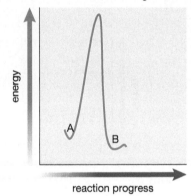

a) reaction with large E_a and small ΔH

b) highly endothermic reaction with large E_a

c) highly exothermic reaction with small E_a

9.4 Reaction Rates

LO 4: Predict the effect of concentration, temperature, and catalysts on the rate of a reaction.

9.36 Ozone (O_3) is a naturally occurring gas in the Earth's atmosphere that helps protect the Earth's surface from harmful ultraviolet (UV) rays from space. One of the many reactions that ozone undergoes is shown. Determine how each of the following changes affects the rate of this exothermic reaction.

$$NO(g) + O_3(g) \rightarrow NO_2(g) + O_2(g) + \text{heat}$$

a) removing some O_3

b) decreasing the temperature

c) adding a catalyst

d) adding some NO

Target boxes: reaction rate increases, reaction rate decreases, reaction rate does not change

9.37 Magnesium metal reacts with hydrochloric acid (HCl) to produce magnesium chloride $MgCl_2$ and hydrogen H_2 gas. Determine how each of the following changes affects the rate of this exothermic reaction.

$$Mg(s) + 2HCl(aq) \rightarrow MgCl_2(aq) + H_2(g) + heat$$

a) decreasing the concentration of Mg

b) increasing the concentration of HCl

c) increasing the temperature

d) decreasing the concentration of HCl

e) increasing the concentration of Mg

Target boxes: reaction rate decreases, reaction rate increases, reaction rate does not change, effect cannot be predicted

9.38 How do catalysts increase rates of reactions?

a) by decreasing the heat of reaction (ΔH)

b) by increasing the energy of the starting materials

c) by decreasing the energy of activation

d) by decreasing the energy of the products

e) by increasing the energy of activation

9.39 Which best describes the reason that perishable foods are often refrigerated?

a) Colder temperatures help speed up the production of enthalpy which protects the food from spoilage.

b) Colder temperatures reduce the ΔH for the reactions that lead to spoilage.

c) Colder temperatures cause endothermic reactions to have faster rates.

d) Colder temperatures help slow the rate of biochemical reactions that lead to spoilage.

9.40 Which statement about catalysts is true?

a) Catalysts are rapidly converted to exothermic products during reactions, therefore increasing reaction yield.

b) Catalysts are rapidly converted to endothermic reactants during chemical reactions, which increases reaction yield.

c) Catalysts convert endothermic reactions to exothermic reactions and are consumed in the alternate reaction pathways.

d) Catalysts are not consumed in reactions and can therefore be used again and again.

9.41 Which best describes a catalyst?

a) a substance that increases the rate of a reaction without being consumed in the reaction

b) a substance that increases the energy of the products

c) a substance that decreases the heat of reaction (DH)

d) a substance that is rapidly converted into products

e) a substance that increases the energy of activation (E_a) of a reaction

9.42 A scientist runs four exothermic chemical reactions side by side to compare observed reaction rates with previously calculated E_a values. Each reaction starts with the same concentration of starting materials and is run at the same temperature for the same period of time. Which activation energy value is most likely associated with the fastest observed reaction rate?

a) the reaction with a calculated E_a of 1.0×10^3 kcal

b) the reaction with a calculated E_a of 9.8×10^{-1} kcal

c) the reaction with a calculated E_a of 100 kcal

d) the reaction with a calculated E_a of 10 kcal

e) Reaction rate does not depend on the value of E_a.

9.43 Sort the items shown based on whether they are likely to be associated with a chemical reaction having a fast rate or a slow rate.

a) large negative DH, high reactant concentrations and small E_a

b) large E_a, large positive DH and low temperature

c) high temperature, a catalyst, and high reactant concentrations

Target boxes: associated with a fast reaction rate, associated with a slow reaction rate

9.44 The rate of a chemical reaction is determined by

a) calculating the limiting reactant

b) calculating the ratio of the product concentration to reactant concentration.

c) calculating the percent yield of the reaction

d) calculating the heat of reaction

e) calculating the amount of product formed in a unit of time

9.5 Equilibrium

LO 5: Describe the fundamental features of dynamic chemical equilibrium, write the expression for the equilibrium constant and predict the direction a reaction at equilibrium will shift when disturbed.

9.45 Consider the diagram for a chemical reaction. Is the equilibrium constant K for this reaction a large value or a small value?

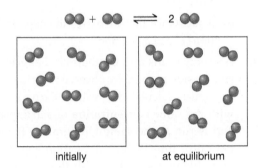

initially   at equilibrium

a) The K value for this reaction is a large value.

b) The K value for this reaction is a small value.

c) More information is needed in order to predict.

9.46 A scientist calculates equilibrium constants for three different reactions. Based on the numeric values shown, categorize each equilibrium mixture as containing mostly products, mostly reactants, or reactants in products in similar amounts.

a) $K = 1.2$

b) $K = 9.8 \times 10^{-32}$

c) $K = 2.5 \times 10^{26}$

Target boxes: mostly products, mostly reactants, products and reactants in similar amounts

9.47 Carbon monoxide reacts with oxygen to form carbon dioxide according to the reaction shown. What does the value of K indicate about this reaction at equilibrium?

$$2CO(g) + O_2(g) \rightleftharpoons 2CO_2(g) \quad K = 2 \times 10^{11}$$

a) The equilibrium mixture contains mostly reactants.

b) The equilibrium mixture contains twice as much product as reactant.

c) The equilibrium mixture contains mostly products.

d) The equilibrium mixture contains two thirds as much product as reactants.

e) The equilibrium mixture contains equal amounts of products and reactants.

9.48 Which of these equilibrium constants indicates a reaction that produces the smallest amount of product?

a) 9.71×10^{-16} b) 6.02×10^{23} c) 1.86×10^9

d) 1.00×10^{-10} e) 7.84

9.49 The reaction involving hydrogen gas combining with chlorine gas to form hydrogen chloride has an equilibrium constant $K = 1.3 \times 10^{34}$. What does the K value tell you about the concentrations of materials when the reaction is at equilibrium?

$$H_2(g) + Cl_2(g) \rightleftharpoons 2HCl(g) \quad K = 1.3 \times 10^{34}$$

a) The concentration of products is 1.3 times greater than the concentration of reactants.

b) The concentration of products is much greater than the concentration of reactants.

c) The concentration of products and reactants are obtained from the value of E_a, not the K value.

d) The concentration of reactants is much greater than the concentration of products.

e) Equilibrium cannot be reached with this value of K.

9.50 Consider the sample of molecules indicated by the colored circles that undergo a chemical reaction. The blue colored circles represent reaction starting materials. The red circles represent product molecules. Based on the figures shown, what is the *first* time point that indicates the chemical reaction has reached dynamic equilibrium?

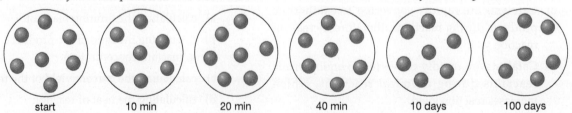

start   10 min   20 min   40 min   10 days   100 days

a) At the starting point, the reaction has already reached equilibrium.

b) By 10 minutes, the reaction has reached equilibrium.

c) By 20 minutes, the reaction has reached equilibrium.

d) By 40 minutes, the reaction has reached equilibrium.

e) By 10 days, the reaction has reached equilibrium.

f) By 100 days, the reaction has reached equilibrium.

9.51 Chemical reactions have a wide range of equilibrium constant values. Classify the reactions shown based on the relative amounts of products and reactants present at equilibrium.

a) $2H_2(g) + S_2(g) \rightleftarrows 2H_2S(g) \quad K = 1.1 \times 10^7$

b) $2NOBr(g) \rightleftarrows 2NO(g) + Br_2(g) \quad K = 2.0$

c) $Cl_2(g) + NO(g) \rightleftarrows 2NOCl(g) \quad K = 3.7 \times 10^8$

d) $3O_2(g) \rightleftarrows 2O_3(g) \quad K = 1.7 \times 10^{-56}$

Target boxes: mostly products, mostly reactants, both products and reactants in significant amounts

9.52 The hemoglobin protein in our red blood cells binds to oxygen (O_2) we breathe and helps distribute it throughout our bodies. Carbon monoxide (CO) binds to hemoglobin 140 times more strongly than oxygen gas. What does this indicate about the equilibrium constants for the two reactions of hemoglobin binding with carbon monoxide and oxygen?

a) The equilibrium constant for binding of carbon monoxide is smaller than it is for oxygen.

b) The equilibrium constant for binding CO is 140 times the reaction enthalpy of O_2.

c) The energy of activation for binding CO is 140 times equilibrium constant for binding O_2.

d) The ΔH for the binding of O_2 is $1/140^{th}$ the equilibrium constant for the binding of CO.

e) The equilibrium constant for binding of carbon monoxide is larger than it is for oxygen.

9.53 Which statement best describes dynamic chemical equilibrium?

a) The concentrations of the reactants and products become equalized.

b) The energy of activation for the forward and reverse reactions become equal.

c) The rate of the forward reaction is equal to the rate of the reverse reaction.

d) There are equal moles of the starting materials and products after a long period of time.

e) The DH values of the forward and reverse reactions become equal.

9.54 Which statement best describes dynamic chemical equilibrium?

a) Chemical equilibrium is reached when 100% of the starting materials have been converted to product and the reaction is complete.

b) Chemical equilibrium is reached when the chemical equation is correctly balanced by adding the appropriate coefficients in front of the reactants and products.

c) Chemical equilibrium is reached when the forward reaction is at its fastest rate.

d) Chemical equilibrium is reached when the concentrations of the reactants and products no longer change.

9.55 Methanol (CH_3OH) is an important industrial solvent and is a building block for larger medicinal and consumer products. It can be produced by reacting carbon monoxide (CO) with hydrogen gas (H_2) in the presence of a catalyst. For each of the following changes at equilibrium, determine if the equilibrium shifts in the direction of products, shifts in the direction of reactants, or does not change.

$$CO(g) + 2H_2(g) \rightleftarrows CH_3OH(g) + heat$$

a) remove some CH_3OH

b) increase the volume of the reaction container

c) decrease the temperature d) remove some H_2

Target boxes: equilibrium shifts in the direction of products, equilibrium shifts in the direction of reactants, equilibrium does not change

9.56 Nitrogen monoxide (NO) is an industrial by product that can react in the atmosphere to form a number of products that cause environmental damage. For each of the following changes at equilibrium, determine whether the equilibrium shifts in the direction of products, shifts in the direction of reactants, or does not change.

$$N_2(g) + O_2(g) \rightleftarrows 2NO(g)$$

a) increasing the pressure

b) removing some N_2 and O_2

c) increasing the volume d) removing some NO

Target boxes: equilibrium shifts in the direction of products, equilibrium shifts in the direction of reactants, equilibrium does not change

9.57 Calcium carbonate ($CaCO_3$) is a primary component of seashells and egg shells. It is used in large quantities in the construction industry as a building material and for the production of cement. Calcium carbonate also reacts with acids such as sulfuric acid (H_2SO_4). A geology student is conducting research and runs this reaction at the beach where the carbon dioxide produced can escape into the atmosphere. What will happen to the equilibrium if the student researcher adds additional H_2SO_4 to her initial reaction that had previously reached equilibrium?

a) The equilibrium does not change since the reaction is being run in the open atmosphere at the beach.

b) The equilibrium shifts to the left, producing more $CaCO_3$.

c) The equilibrium shifts to the left, producing more $CaSO_4$.

d) The equilibrium shifts to the right, producing more CO_2 that can then escape into the atmosphere.

9.58 Chlorine gas (Cl_2) released into the atmosphere from industrial processes can react with water vapor in the air to produce hydrochloric acid (HCl) contributing to "acid rain" (rainfall that atmospheric pollution has made sufficiently acidic to cause environmental harm). If the reaction shown here is at equilibrium, determine in what direction the equilibrium will shift when each of the following two changes occurs in two separate situations:

Situation 1, there is an increase in Cl_2.

Situation 2, there is a decrease in HCl.

$$2Cl_2(g) + 2H_2O(g) \rightleftharpoons 4HCl(g) + O_2(g)$$

a) Situation 1, shift left. Situation 2, shift right.

b) Situation 1 shift right. Situation 2, shift left.

c) Situation 1, shift right. Situation 2, shift right.

d) Situation 1, shift left. Situation 2, shift left.

9.59 Methanol (CH_3OH) is a small biodegradable molecule used to prepare commercial products including plastics, paints, adhesives, foams, and plywood. The large-scale synthesis of methanol combines carbon monoxide (CO) and hydrogen (H_2) gases. Based on the given equilibrium expression for the synthesis of methanol

(CH_3OH), which of the following represents the correct chemical equation for methanol synthesis?

Equilibrium expression: $K = \dfrac{[CH_3OH]}{[CO][H_2]^2}$

a) $CH_3OH(g) \rightleftharpoons CO(g) + 2H_2(g)$

b) $CO(g) + H_2(g) \rightleftharpoons 2CH_3OH(g)$

c) $2CO(g) + H_2(g) \rightleftharpoons CH_3OH(g)$

d) $CO(g) + 2H_2(g) \rightleftharpoons CH_3OH(g)$

9.60 The synthesis of methanol from carbon monoxide (CO) and hydrogen gas (H_2) is a combination reaction requiring one mole of CO and two moles of H_2 to produce each mole of CH_3OH. If the reaction shown here is at equilibrium, determine the direction the equilibrium will shift in two separate experiments:

Experiment 1, the pressure increases.

Experiment 2, some $CH_3OH(g)$ is removed.

$$CO(g) + 2H_2(g) \rightleftharpoons CH_3OH(g) + heat$$

a) Experiment 1, shift right. Experiment 2, shift right.

b) Experiment 1, shift left. Experiment 2, shift right.

c) Experiment 1, shift right. Experiment 2, shift left.

d) Experiment 1, shift left. Experiment 2, shift left.

9.61 Consider the sample of molecules indicated by the colored circles that undergo a chemical reaction. The blue colored circles represent reaction starting materials. The red circles represent product molecules. Based on the figures showing reaction time points, which statement is true?

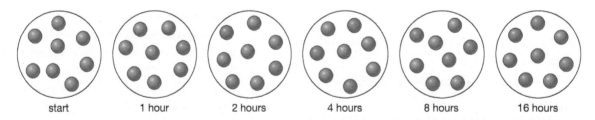

| start | 1 hour | 2 hours | 4 hours | 8 hours | 16 hours |

a) By 1 hour, the reaction has reached equilibrium.

b) By 2 hours, the reaction has reached equilibrium.

c) By 4 hours, the reaction has reached equilibrium.

d) By 8 hours, the reaction has reached equilibrium.

e) By 16 hours, the reaction has reached equilibrium.

f) By 16 hours, the reaction *might* have reached equilibrium, but additional time points are needed to determine this.

9.6 Calculating Equilibrium Constants

LO 6: Calculate equilibrium constants for reactions at equilibrium when given equilibrium concentrations of the reactants and products.

9.62 Carbon dioxide reacts with hydrogen gas to form carbon monoxide and water according to the equilibrium reaction shown. The equilibrium mixture in an

experiment was found to contain 0.45M CO_2, 0.048 M H_2, 0.37 M CO, and 0.38 M H_2O. Which is the correct value of K under these experimental conditions?

$$CO_2(g) + H_2(g) \rightleftharpoons CO(g) + H_2O(g)$$

a) 0.15   b) 1.5   c) 0.11

d) 6.5   e) 9.1

9.63 Nitrogen dioxide (NO_2) is a brown gas that contributes to the color of "smog" and air pollution often seen over cities around the world. Two molecules of nitrogen dioxide are able to combine to form dinitrogen tetroxide (N_2O_4) according to the equilibrium process shown. In a certain experiment, a scientist studying air quality determines the equilibrium concentration of NO_2 is 0.41 M and the equilibrium concentration of N_2O_4 is 0.97 M. What is the value of the equilibrium constant under these reaction conditions?

$$2NO_2(g) \rightleftharpoons N_2O_4(g)$$

a) 0.17   **b)** 2.4

c) 5.8   **d)** 0.42

9.64 Nitrogen monoxide reacts with hydrogen in an equilibrium reaction to form nitrogen and water as shown. The equilibrium mixture in an experiment was found to contain 0.021 M N_2, 0.141 M H_2O, 0.064 M NO and 0.014 M H_2. Which is the correct value of K under these experimental conditions?

$$2NO(g) + 2H_2(g) \rightleftharpoons N_2(g) + 2H_2O(g)$$

a) 1.9×10^{-3} **b)** 5.2×10^2

c) 3.3   **d)** 0.30

9.65 Ammonia (NH_3) is an important molecule found in the environment, our bodies, and is also used as a building block for commercial items such as fertilizers and pharmaceutical drugs. It can be formed in the laboratory by combining nitrogen gas and hydrogen gas according to the equilibrium reaction shown. What is the value of K in an experiment having the equilibrium concentrations measured as: $[H_2] = 0.39$ M, $[N_2] = 0.44$ M and $[NH_3] = 2.4$ M?

$$N_2(g) + 3H_2(g) \rightleftharpoons 2NH_3(g)$$

$K =$ ▢

9.66 A scientist studying alternative fuels conducts an experiment using the controlled combustion of ethanol (CH_3CH_2OH). In one experiment, she measures the equilibrium concentrations of the products and reactants to be as follows: $[CH_3CH_2OH] = 0.25$ M, $[O_2] = 0.15$ M, $[CO_2] = 0.89$ M and $[H_2O] = 1.0$ M. What is the value of K under these conditions?

$$CH_3CH_2OH(g) + 3O_2(g) \rightleftharpoons 2CO_2(g) + 3H_2O(g)$$

$K =$ ▢

9.67 Phosphorus pentachloride (PCl_5) is used as a raw material for the manufacture of a variety of commercial products, including in the pharmaceutical industry for the manufacture of penicillin and cephalosporin antibiotics. PCl_5 decomposes into PCl_3 and Cl_2 according to the equilibrium process shown. A researcher conducts an experiment and determines the equilibrium concentrations of $PCl_3 = 0.16$ M and $Cl_2 = 0.16$ M. If the equilibrium constant K for this experiment has a value of 8.1×10^{-2}, what is the equilibrium concentration of PCl_5 in units of molarity (M)? Express the concentration of PCl_5 at equilibrium in standard decimal form with two significant figures.

$$PCl_5(g) \rightleftharpoons PCl_3(g) + Cl_2(g)$$

$[PCl_5] =$ ▢ M

9.68 Carbon monoxide combines with hydrogen gas to form methane and water according to the equilibrium equation shown. In one experiment, equilibrium concentrations were determined to be as follows: $[H_2] = 0.22$ M, $[CH_4] = 1.9$ M and $[H_2O] = 1.7$ M. If the equilibrium constant K for this experiment is 7.6×10^2, calculate the equilibrium concentration of CO.

$$CO(g) + 3H_2(g) \rightleftharpoons CH_4(g) + H_2O(l)$$

a) 2.3×10^5 **b)** 0.40

c) 1.9×10^{-2} **d)** 2.5

9.69 Hydrogen iodide (HI) can be formed by the combination of hydrogen (H_2) and iodine (I_2). An environmental scientist studying this reaction obtained the following data for the reaction at equilibrium: $[H_2] = 6.1 \times 10^{-5}$ M and $[I_2] = 1.0 \times 10^{-3}$ M. If the equilibrium constant K for this experiment is 55, calculate the equilibrium concentration of HI.

$$H_2(g) + I_2(g) \rightleftharpoons 2HI(g) \quad K = 55$$

a) 1.8×10^{-3} **b)** 3.4×10^{-6}

c) 3.0×10^3 **d)** 1.1×10^{-3}

9.70 Two different molecules A and B bind to each other in a 1:1 ratio to form a complex that is being investigated as a possible cancer treatment. A solution that is initially 5.0×10^{-4} mol/L in molecule A and 5.0×10^{-4} mol/L in B is allowed to reach equilibrium. After reaching equilibrium, 1.0×10^{-4} mol/L of free A and 1.0×10^{-4} mol/L of free B remain unbound. Calculate the equilibrium constant K for this binding reaction. **Hint**: It might be helpful to make a chart showing initial concentration, final concentration, and change in concentration for A, B, and the AB complex. Express your answer in scientific notation with two significant figures.

$$A + B \rightleftharpoons AB$$

$K = \boxed{}$

Chapter 10

10.1 Properties of Gases

LO 10.1: **Apply the kinetic molecular theory to describe properties of gases.**

10.01 Which statement is correct?

a) Gases are less compressible than liquids but more compressible than solids because the distance between particles in gas is more than in solids but less than liquids.

b) Gases are less compressible than both liquids and solids because their molar masses are lower than the molar masses of compounds that are liquids and solids.

c) Gases are more compressible than liquids or solids because the distance between gas particles is much larger than for liquids and solids.

d) The compressibility of gases is similar to the compressibility of liquids and solids because phase changes can occur between all three phases.

10.02 In a lab experiment with a classmate, you observe that the pressure of the gas sample in a closed container increases when you increase the temperature. Which statement best describes the reason for your observation?

a) The attractive intermolecular forces between gas particles increases, resulting in an increase in force per unit area.

b) As the temperature increases, the force per unit area decreases, resulting in the higher observed pressure.

c) As the temperature increases, the concentration of gas particles in the container increases.

d) When the temperature is increased, the number and force of the collisions that the gas particles have against the walls of the container increases.

10.03 The force exerted on a surface per unit area is called _____.

a) density
b) intermolecular force
c) volume
d) pressure
e) kinetic energy

10.04 Select the correct statement about the distance between gas particles.

a) The distance between the particles is large relative to the size of the gas particles themselves.

b) The distance between the particles is fixed but the molecules move and are able to adopt the shape of the container.

c) The distance between the particles is small relative to the gas particles themselves.

d) The distance between the particles is defined as the force per unit area.

10.05 Which is *not* an assumption of the kinetic molecular theory of gases?

a) The attractive forces between gas particles are so small that they do not need to be considered.

b) There is very little space between gas particles.

c) Gas particles move faster with increasing temperature.

d) A single gas particle moves in a straight line until it collides with another particle or the wall of the container.

10.06 Select the measured value that represents a gas pressure.

a) 2.75 g/cm^3
b) 13.5 L
c) 273 K
d) 712 mmHg
e) 9.8 m/s^2

10.07 Three sealed containers (labeled 1, 2, 3) are each the same size, are at the same temperature, and contain the same type of gas. Rank the gas pressures in the containers from lowest to highest.

Answer choices:

a)

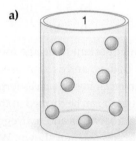

b)

c)

Target boxes: lowest pressure, intermediate pressure, highest pressure

10.08 A sample of gas is placed in a sealed, rigid container. Which of the following will increase when the temperature is increased? Select all that apply.

a) the pressure of the gas

b) the volume of the gas

c) the kinetic energy of the gas particles

d) the speed the gas particles are moving

e) the mass of gas in the container

10.09 A scientist measures the pressure of a gas sample to be 1.7 atm. Convert this pressure to units of mmHg. Express your answer in scientific notation with two significant figures and units of mmHg.

$$1 \text{ atm} = 760 \text{ mmHg}$$
$$= 760 \text{ torr}$$
$$= 101,325 \text{ Pa}$$
$$= 14.7 \text{ psi}$$
$$= 1.01325 \text{ bar}$$

pressure = [＿＿＿] mmHg

10.10 The pressure in a car tire is measured to be 35 psi. Convert this pressure to units of atm. Express your answer in standard decimal form with two significant figures and units of atm.

$$1 \text{ atm} = 760 \text{ mmHg}$$
$$= 760 \text{ torr}$$
$$= 101,325 \text{ Pa}$$
$$= 14.7 \text{ psi}$$
$$= 1.01325 \text{ bar}$$

pressure = [＿＿＿] atm

10.11 Blood pressure is generally measured in units of millimeters of mercury (mmHg). The readings are given in pairs as a fraction, with the upper (systolic) value first, and the lower (diastolic) value second. A nurse checks a patient known to have high blood pressure and finds his values to be 170/110. Convert both values to atmospheres.

$$1 \text{ atm} = 760 \text{ mmHg}$$
$$= 760 \text{ torr}$$
$$= 101,325 \text{ Pa}$$
$$= 14.7 \text{ psi}$$
$$= 1.01325 \text{ bar}$$

a) 0.14 atm/0.22 atm   b) 4.5 atm/6.9 atm

c) 0.22 atm/0.14 atm   d) 170 atm/110 atm

10.12 Scientists often express gas pressures in units of Pascal (Pa). A device records a pressure of 170 mmHg in an experiment. What is this value in units of Pa? Express your answer in scientific notation with two significant figures and units of Pa.

$$1 \text{ atm} = 760 \text{ mmHg}$$
$$= 760 \text{ torr}$$
$$= 101,325 \text{ Pa}$$
$$= 14.7 \text{ psi}$$
$$= 1.01325 \text{ bar}$$

pressure = [＿＿＿] Pa

10.13 Atmospheric pressure decreases as you ascend higher in elevation above sea level. Weather forecasters generally express atmospheric pressure in units of *bars* (bar), where 1 bar = 0.9869 atm. Denver Colorado is at an altitude of 1.65 km above sea level and has an average atmospheric pressure of 625 mmHg. What is the average atmospheric pressure in Denver Colorado expressed in units of bar?

$$1 \text{ atm} = 760 \text{ mmHg} \qquad 1 \text{ bar} = 0.9869 \text{ atm}$$
$$= 760 \text{ torr}$$
$$= 101,325 \text{ Pa}$$
$$= 14.7 \text{ psi}$$
$$= 1.01325 \text{ bar}$$

a) 4.81×10^5 bar   b) 0.833 bar

c) 1.23 bar   d) 0.811 bar

10.14 Atmospheric pressure is generally expressed in units of *bars* (bar) or *millibars* (mbar), where 1 bar = 0.9869 atm. Hurricane Katrina was an extremely destructive Category 5 hurricane that affected the Gulf Coast of the U.S. in August 2005. The hurricane killed more than 1000 people and caused more than $100 billion in damage. If the atmospheric pressure inside the eye of Hurricane Katrina was measured at 925 mbar, what is this pressure expressed in units of mmHg?

$$1 \text{ atm} = 760 \text{ mmHg} \qquad 1 \text{ bar} = 1000 \text{ mbar}$$
$$= 760 \text{ torr} \qquad\qquad 1 \text{ bar} = 0.9869 \text{ atm}$$
$$= 101,325 \text{ Pa}$$
$$= 14.7 \text{ psi}$$
$$= 1.01325 \text{ bar}$$

a) 6.94×10^5 mmHg   b) 712 mmHg

c) 1.44×10^{-3} mmHg   d) 694 mmHg

10.15 You and a friend are working on a lab experiment in your chemistry class. You are working with two sealed containers, each with the same volume (1.25 L), and both are at the same temperature (95 °C) and pressure (1.6 atm). One sealed container contains 2.75 g of helium (He) and the other contains 2.75 g of argon (Ar). Which conclusion about these two gas samples is correct?

a) The two flasks are at the same pressure since they are the same size, at the same temperature, and have the same number of grams of each gas inside.

b) The flask containing argon has a higher pressure than the flask containing helium.

c) The flask containing helium has a higher pressure than the flask containing argon.

d) The two flasks contain the same number of particles since they are the same size, at the same temperature, and have the same number of grams of each gas inside.

10.2 Gas Laws

LO 10.2: Use the gas laws to describe and calculate the relationship between volume, temperature, and pressure of a gas sample.

10.16 Classify each measured value as a temperature, pressure, or volume measurement.

Answer choices: 310 K, 2.4 atm, 16.8 mL, 675 mmHg, 63.5 C, 760 L

Target boxes: Temperature, Pressure, Volume

10.17 Consider the balloon shown. What would the balloon look like if the temperature increases while the pressure outside of the balloon and amount of gas remain constant?

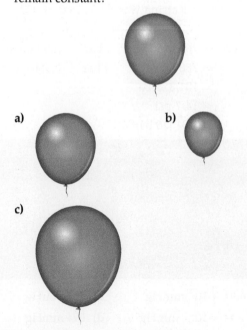

10.18 Consider the balloon shown. What would the balloon look like if the pressure outside of the balloon increased and the temperature and amount of gas remained constant?

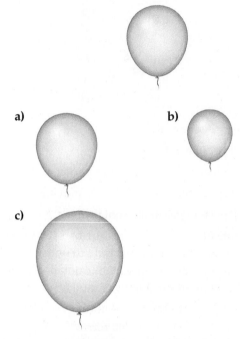

10.19 Consider the balloon shown. What would the balloon look like if the amount of gas inside the balloon did not change but both the pressure and the temperature (Kelvin) decreases by half?

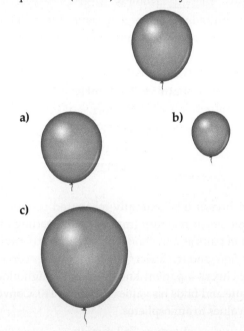

10.20 You and a friend pack groceries in your hometown (near sea level) for a camping trip in the mountains. When you get to the campsite the bag of chips you packed seems to have inflated and looks larger. If the initial volume of the air in the bag was 425 mL at 758 mmHg and the pressure at the campsite in the mountains is 595 mmHg, what is the final volume (in mL) of the bag? Express your answer in standard decimal form with three significant figures and units of mL.

volume = [   ] mL

10.21 A sample of oxygen gas (O_2) has a volume of 3.5 L at a pressure of 1.8 atm. What is the volume of the gas expressed in liters after the pressure is changed to 565 mmHg?

$$1 \text{ atm} = 760 \text{ mmHg}$$
$$= 760 \text{ torr}$$
$$= 101,325 \text{ Pa}$$
$$= 14.7 \text{ psi}$$
$$= 1.01325 \text{ bar}$$

a) 0.0112 L   b) 0.118 L

c) 8.47 L   d) 1.45 L

10.22 Chronic obstructive pulmonary disease (COPD) is a chronic inflammatory lung disease that causes obstructed airflow from the lungs making it difficult to breathe properly. In the hospital, a patient suffering from COPD takes a breath and his lungs expand from 3.3 L to 5.2 L in volume. If the initial pressure in his lungs is 748 mmHg, what is the pressure (in mmHg) inside the lungs before any additional air is inhaled? Express your answer in standard decimal form with three significant figures and units of mmHg.

pressure = [   ] mmHg

10.23 An athlete training for a skiing event exhales a volume of 2.3 L of air from her lungs into the cold mountain air, which is at −4.2 °C. If the air inside the athlete's lungs was initially at 35 °C, what volume (in L) does the exhaled air occupy at this colder outside temperature? The pressure and number of gas particles does not change.

a) −0.276 L   b) 0.50 L

c) 2.6 L   d) 2.0 L

e) 2.1 L

10.24 A hot air balloon has an initial volume of 775 L at 17 °C. What temperature must the air in a balloon be heated to if the desired final volume is 1320 L? Express your answer in standard decimal form with three significant figures and units of K.

temperature = [   ] K

10.25 Pressure cookers are used to cook food rapidly in a closed pot. When the contents of a pressure cooker are heated with a tight-fitting lid (constant volume), the pressure and the temperature increase. If the steam (water vapor) inside a pressure cooker is initially at 100 °C, and 0.975 atm, what is the final temperature (in °C) of the steam if the pressure is increased to 1.20 atm? Use an appropriate gas law to solve the problem taking care to convert temperatures to the appropriate units.

a) 186 °C   b) 123 °C

c) 0.00218 °C   d) 30.1 °C

e) 459 °C

10.26 An autoclave is a device used in laboratories and hospitals to sterilize materials. Autoclaves use a combination of water, pressure, and heat to create superheated steam that kills bacteria and other microorganisms. An autoclave containing steam at 100 °C and 0.982 atm pressure is heated to 265 °C. What is the final pressure inside the autoclave? Use an appropriate gas law to solve the problem taking care to convert temperature values to the appropriate units. Express your answer in standard decimal form with three significant figures and units of atm.

pressure = [   ] atm

10.27 A sample of nitrogen gas with a volume of 2.25 liters (L) and 1.85 atm pressure at 23 °C is allowed to expand to 3.50 L. What is the final pressure of the gas if the temperature remains at 23 °C and the number of moles in the sample does not change?

a) 1.19 atm   b) 2.88 atm

c) 0.841 atm   d) 4.26 atm

10.28 Trucks need to be careful to avoid tire blowouts when temperatures and pressures change during their trips. If a truck hauling goods in the summer has a tire pressure of 95.5 psi in the cool morning when the temperature is 12.0 °C, what is the tire pressure in pounds per square inch later in the afternoon when the temperature on the road surface is 42.0 °C?

a) 334 psi   b) 9.47×10^{-3} psi

c) 106 psi   d) 84.5 psi

10.29 A geyser is a spring that ejects heated water, steam, and other gases in volcanically active areas such as Yellowstone National Park in the United States. If 155 L of hot gas is ejected at 135 °C, what volume will the gas occupy at 105 °C?

a) 144 L

c) 167 L

b) 189 L

d) 121 L

10.30 A. A sample of gas has an initial pressure of 745 mmHg at a temperature of 295 K. What is the pressure if the temperature is increased to 415 K? Express your answer in scientific notation with three significant figures in units of mmHg.

pressure = [   ] mmHg

B. As temperature increased, did the pressure increase or decrease?

a) increase

b) decrease

10.31 A scuba diver's tank contains compressed air that allows her to breathe underwater. If a scuba tank contains 11.0 L of compressed air at 21 °C and contains the equivalent of 1150 L of air at 1.75 atm and 26 °C, what was the initial gas pressure in the scuba tank expressed in units of atmospheres (atm)?

a) 148 atm

c) 180. atm

b) 5.56×10^{-3} atm

d) 187 atm

10.32 A 7.5 L sample of nitrogen gas is stored at 25 °C and 2.0 atm. The sample is transferred to a smaller 3.0 L tank and the pressure is increased to 4.5 atm. What is the final temperature in kelvins? Express your answer in scientific notation with two significant figures and units of K.

temperature = [   ] K

10.33 The element radon (Rn) is a naturally occurring radioactive noble gas that generally exists in air at very low concentration. It occurs at higher concentrations in some types of soils, or in basements and crawl spaces under houses. High radon levels have been linked to an increased risk of lung cancer, so radon detectors are recommended for the basements of homes to monitor radon levels. In a laboratory experiment with a pure sample of radon, a scientist transfers a 0.255 L sample of the gas at 0.875 atm into a 0.125 L container with a new radon pressure 1.24 atm at a temperature of 28 °C. What was the initial temperature of the radon gas sample in Kelvin? Express your answer in scientific notation with three significant figures and units of K.

temperature = [   ] K

10.34 A 38 L sample of methane gas (CH_4) at 45 °C and 1.8 atm pressure is allowed to expand to 55 L and the temperature decreases to 28 °C. What is the new pressure of the methane gas sample?

a) 0.85 atm

b) 0.77 atm

c) 1.2 atm

d) 2.5 atm

10.35 A scientist studying greenhouse gases transfers a sample of pure CO_2 gas from a 0.435 L container with a pressure of 3.55 atm and a temperature of 138 °C to a larger container with a volume of 0.775 L and a pressure of 1.75 atm. What is the new temperature of the gas sample expressed in degrees Celsius?

a) 634 °C

b) 121 °C

c) 361 °C

d) 88 °C

10.3 Avogadro's Law

LO 10.3: **Apply Avogadro's law to describe the relationship between amount of gas and volume.**

10.36 Consider the balloon shown. What would the balloon look like if some gas leaks out of the balloon and the temperature and pressure outside of the balloon remain constant?

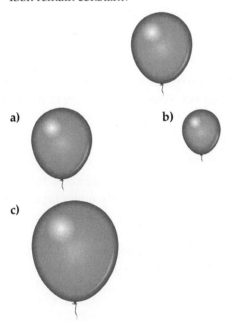

a)

b)

c)

10.37 A gas is placed in a sealed, rigid container. Select the items that will increase when more of the same gas is pumped into the container at constant temperature. Check all that apply.

a) the pressure of the gas inside the container

b) the number of gas particles inside the container

c) the number of collisions between the gas particles every minute

d) the atomic mass of each atom in the container

e) the mass of gas in the container

f) the volume of the sealed rigid container

10.38 How many liters does 2.5 mol of O_2 (g) occupy at STP?

a) 2.5 L   **b)** 0.018 L

c) 56 L   **d)** 9.0 L

e) 0.11 L

10.39 How many liters does 56.3 g of N_2 (g) occupy at STP? Under STP conditions, one mole of any gas occupies 22.4 L.

a) 112 L   **b)** 1.26×10^3 L

c) 70.4 L   **d)** 0.0897 L

e) 45.0 L

10.40 How many moles of helium gas are contained in 3.5 L at STP?

a) 2.4 mol   **b)** 0.42 mol

c) 2.1×10^2 mol   **d)** 4.7×10^{-3} mol

10.41 A bicycle tire that contains 0.21 mol of air in a volume of 1.8 L develops a leak that results in the volume decreasing to 0.65 L at constant temperature and pressure. How many moles of air are now in the deflated bicycle tire?

Express your answer in standard decimal form with two significant figures and units of mol.

moles of air = [　　　] mol

10.42 A party balloon containing 0.75 mol of helium (He) gas has a volume of 16.7 L. Calculate the new volume of the balloon if 0.21 mol of the helium gas escapes. The pressure and temperature are kept constant. Express your answer in standard decimal form with two significant figures and units of liters (L).

volume = [　　　] L

10.43 If 4.50 mol of oxygen gas (O_2) occupy 50.4 L, how many moles of oxygen gas would be in 92.6 L at the same temperature and pressure?

a) 8.27 mol O_2 **b)** 2.45 mol O_2

c) 42.2 mol O_2 **d)** 0.121 mol O_2

10.44 You and a friend are working on a lab experiment in your chemistry class. You are working with two sealed containers, each with the same volume of 4.5 L. Both containers are also at the same temperature (0 °C) and pressure (1 atm). One sealed container has 2.018 g of neon (Ne) and the other contains 8.380g of krypton (Kr). Which conclusion about these two gas samples is correct?

a) The pressures cannot be the same because the two containers are the same volume but have different numbers of grams of gas particles inside.

b) The flask containing krypton has the higher pressure than the flask containing neon since it contains a greater number of grams of gas.

c) The flask containing krypton contains more particles than the container with neon.

d) The two flasks contain different numbers of grams of gas but have the same number of particles.

10.4 The Ideal Gas Law

LO 10.4: Apply the Ideal Gas Law to determine P, V, T, or n of a gas when given three of the four variables.

10.45 Plants and algae use energy from the sun to convert carbon dioxide into sugars and release oxygen during photosynthesis. The oxygen gas produced during photosynthesis forms bubbles on aquatic plants. What is the volume of a bubble containing 1.4×10^{-6} mol of oxygen gas at 303 K and 1.04 atm pressure?

$$6CO_2 + 6H_2O \xrightarrow{\text{sunlight}} C_6H_{12}O_6 + 6O_2$$

a) 3.3×10^5 L   b) 3.0×10^4 L

c) 3.6×10^{-5} L   d) 3.3×10^{-5} L

10.46 What is the temperature of 3.25 mol of gas in a 43.5 L tank with a pressure of 2.65 atm? Express your answer in standard decimal form with three significant figures and units of Kelvin (K).

temperature = ☐ K

10.47 Hydrochloric acid reacts with sodium hydrogen carbonate as shown. A student in the chemistry lab studying this chemical reaction determines that 1.85 L of carbon dioxide (CO_2) gas is produced at 297 K and 0.974 atm in a particular experiment. How many moles (n) of CO_2 gas are produced in this experiment?

$$HCl(aq) + NaHCO_3(s) \rightarrow H_2O(l) + CO_2(g) + NaCl(aq)$$

a) 7.39×10^{-2} mol   b) 13.5 mol

c) 7.39×10^{-3} mol   d) 6.87×10^3 mol

e) 1.46×10^{-4} mol

10.48 A 12.5 L sample of oxygen gas (O_2) at 28 °C contains 1.42 mol. What is the pressure of this sample of oxygen gas?

a) 2.80 atm   b) 0.261 atm

c) 0.356 atm   d) 3.83 atm

10.49 The average total lung capacity for an adult woman is 4.2 L. How many moles (n) of gas are in the lungs of an average women when her lungs are full to capacity? Assume a pressure of 1.0 atm and a normal body temperature of 37 °C. Express your answer with two significant figures and units of mol.

$n =$ ☐ mol

10.50 A 16.5 L cylinder contains 48.5 g of CO_2 gas at 385 K. What is the pressure of this sample of carbon dioxide gas?

a) 92.9 atm   b) 0.474 atm

c) 2.11 atm   d) 0.0108 atm

10.51 A team of scientists working to understand climate change measures the pressure of a 5.15 mol gas sample to be 355 mmHg at −18 °C. What is the volume in liters (L) of this gas sample? Express your answer in standard decimal form with three significant figures and units of liters (L).

volume = ☐ L

10.52 A geologist is studying an unknown amount of hydrogen sulfide (H_2S) and determines it occupies 62.3 L at 0.988 atm and 296K. How many grams of H_2S gas are in this study sample? The molar mass of H_2S is 34.08 g/mol.

a) 2.53 g   b) 13.5 g

c) 5.10×10^4 g   d) 86.4 g

10.53 Magnesium metal reacts with hydrochloric acid as shown. In a lab experiment run at 19 °C and 0.887 atm, a scientist reacts 8.25 g of Mg with excess HCl and collects all of the hydrogen (H_2) gas produced. What volume (in L) of hydrogen gas does the scientist collect? The molar mass of Mg is 24.31 g/mol.

Express your answer in standard decimal form with three significant figures and units of liters (L).

$$Mg(s) + 2HCl(aq) \rightarrow MgCl_2(aq) + H_2(g)$$

volume = ☐ L

10.54 Oxygen gas is purchased in pressurized tanks and used in hospitals to treat patients with respiratory issues. What is the pressure (in units of atm) inside a 29.5-L tank of oxygen that contains 4.36 kg O_2 at room temperature (21 °C)? The molar mass of oxygen (O_2) is 32.00 g/mol. Express your answer in standard decimal form with three significant figures and units of atm.

pressure = ☐ atm

10.5 Dalton's Law of Partial Pressures

LO 10.5: Use Dalton's law to determine total and partial pressures of gas mixtures.

10.55 An environmental scientist studying changes in the gases in the atmosphere determines that a gas sample in an experimental container has the following partial pressures $P_{N_2} = 0.521$ atm, $P_{O_2} = 0.114$ atm, $P_{CO_2} = 0.103$ atm. What is the total pressure (in units of atm) inside the 15.5-L container at 17 °C? Express your answer in standard decimal form with three significant figures and units of atm.

P_{tot} = ☐ atm

10.56 Gas mixtures are often studied to better understand chemical reactions occurring in Earth's atmosphere. In an experiment, a scientist adds some carbon dioxide (CO_2) to a cylinder containing 1.3 atm of O_2 and 1.8 atm of N_2 to give a total pressure of 5.3 atm of gas. What is the partial pressure (in units of atm) of the added carbon dioxide? Express your answer in standard decimal form with two significant figures and units of atm.

P_{tot} = ☐ atm

10.57 The air pressure in a mountain town was measured to be 629 mmHg on a certain day. If a scientist collects an air sample and determines that N_2 represents 81.0 % of the air and O_2 represents 18.5 %, what are the partial pressures of these two gases in the sample?

a) 18.5 mmHg for O_2 and 81.0 mmHg for N_2

b) 116 mmHg for O_2 and 509 mmHg for N_2

c) 141 mmHg for O_2 and 616 mmHg for N_2

d) 509 mmHg for O_2 and 116 mmHg for N_2

e) 15.3 mmHg for O_2 and 67.0 mmHg for N_2

10.58 A balloon contains O_2 with a partial pressure of 475 mm Hg and CO_2 with a partial pressure of 155 mm Hg. If some N_2 gas is added to this mixture resulting in a final total pressure of 740 mm Hg, what is the partial pressure of each gas in the final mixture?

a) 475 mmHg for O_2, 155 mmHg for CO_2, and 740 mmHg for N_2

b) 1215 mmHg for O_2, 895 mmHg for CO_2, and 740 mmHg for N_2

c) 365 mmHg for O_2, 45 mmHg for CO_2, and 740 mmHg for N_2

d) 475 mmHg for O_2, 155 mmHg for CO_2, and 110 mmHg for N_2

10.59 An environmental scientist analyzes a sample of natural gas at 0.977 atm. He determines that the mixture contains 82% methane (CH_4), 7% ethane (CH_3CH_3), and 11% propane ($CH_3CH_2CH_3$). What are the partial pressures of each gas in this natural gas mixture?

a) 80.1 atm for methane, 6.84 atm for ethane, and 10.7 atm for propane

b) 0.820 atm for methane, 0.0700 atm for ethane, and 0.110 atm for propane

c) 0.801 atm for methane, 0.0684 atm for ethane, and 0.107 atm for propane

d) 0.0684 atm for methane, 0.801 atm for ethane, and 0.107 atm for propane

10.6 Phase Changes

LO 10.6: Describe the relationship between the strength of intermolecular forces and phase changes including boiling/melting points of substances.

10.60 The process by which water becomes ice is _____.

a) sublimation   b) melting

c) vaporization   d) freezing

10.61 The process by which water changes from the liquid phase to the gaseous phase is _____.

a) freezing   b) vaporization

c) sublimation   d) condensation

10.62 The process by which a substance undergoes a transition from the solid to the liquid state is _____.

a) vaporization   b) condensation

c) melting   d) deposition

10.63 Identify the compound in the set shown that has the highest boiling point.

a) He   b) H_2

c) CH_4 d) H_2O

10.64 Identify the compound in the set shown that has the highest boiling point.

a) CH_4

b) $CH_3CH_2NH_2$

c) CH_3CH_3

d) $CH_3CH_2CH_3$

10.65 Identify the compound in the set shown that has the highest boiling point.

a) CH_4

b) $CH_3CH_2CH_2CH_3$

c) $CH_3CH_2CH_3$

d) $CH_3CH_2CH_2CH_2CH_2CH_3$

10.7 Energy and Phase Changes

LO 10.7: Calculate energy quantities needed to undergo phase changes using heat of vaporization and heat of fusion values.

10.66 Identify the process that, when it occurs, releases energy to the surroundings.

a) melting

b) sublimation

c) evaporation

d) freezing

10.67 Identify the process that does not require the input of additional energy from the surrounding in order to occur.

a) condensation

b) evaporation

c) sublimation

d) melting

10.68 Determine whether heat is absorbed or released in each process. Drag the process into the appropriate bin.

Answer choices: condensing 25 g of steam, melting 4 g ice, evaporating 1 g water, freezing 13 g water

Target boxes: heat is absorbed, heat is released, unable to determine with given information

10.69 Which process requires the greatest amount of energy?

a) converting 35 grams of ice at 0 °C to 35 grams of liquid water at 0 °C

b) converting 35 of liquid water at 0 °C to 35 grams of liquid water at 100 °C

c) converting 35 grams of liquid water at 100 °C into 35 grams of water vapor at 100 °C

d) converting 35 of ice at −10 °C to 35 grams of ice at 0 °C

10.70 Which process releases the smallest amount of energy as it occurs?

a) converting 42 grams of liquid water at 0 °C to 42 grams of ice at 0 °C

b) converting 42 of water at 100 °C to 42 of water at 0 °C

c) converting 42 grams of water vapor at 100 °C into 42 grams of liquid water at 100 °C

d) converting 42 grams of ice at 0 °C to 42 grams of ice at −10 °C

10.71 Consider the heating curve of water shown. What physical state(s) is represented by the line segment indicated by the number 1?

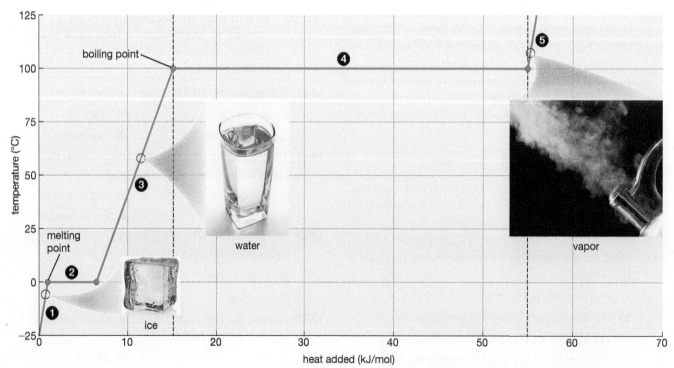

a) gas only   b) gas + liquid   c) liquid only   d) liquid + solid   e) solid only

10.72 Consider the heating curve of water shown. What physical state(s) is represented by the line segment 4?

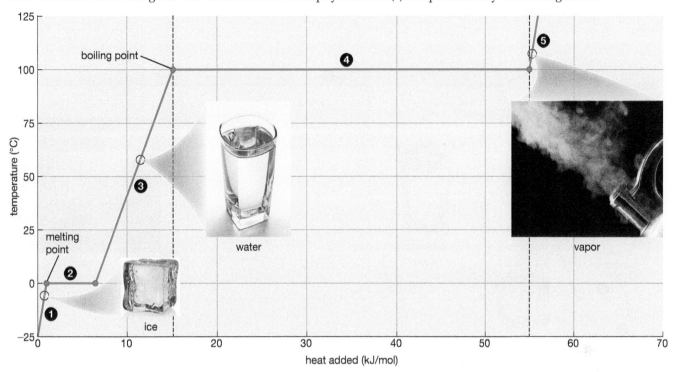

a) gas only   b) gas + liquid   c) liquid only   d) liquid + solid   e) solid only

10.73 Consider the heating curve of water shown. What physical state(s) is represented by the line segment labeled with the number 3?

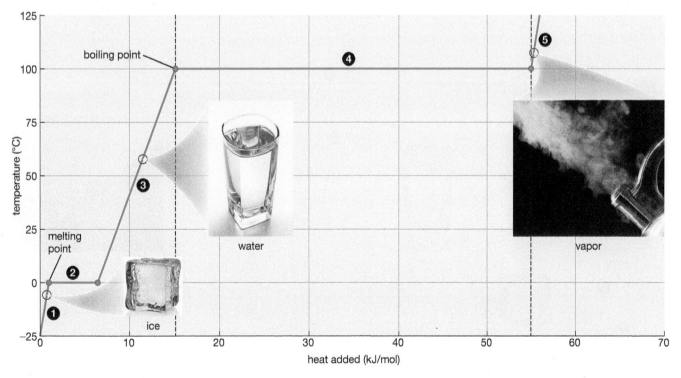

a) gas only   b) gas + liquid   c) liquid only   d) liquid + solid   e) solid only

10.74 Consider the heating curve of water shown below. What physical state(s) is represented by the line segment labeled with the number 2?

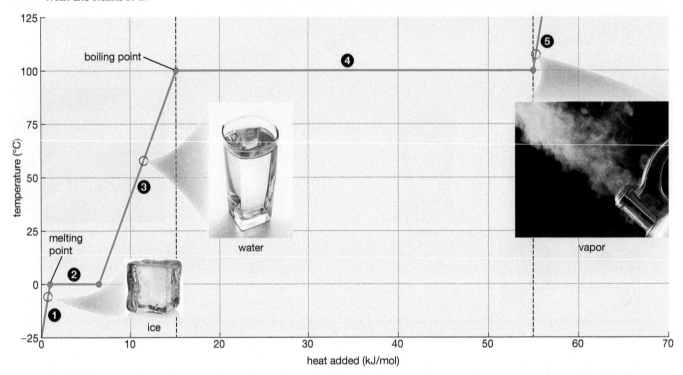

a) gas only   **b)** gas + liquid   **c)** liquid only   **d)** liquid + solid   **e)** solid only

10.75 Consider the heating curve of water shown here. What physical state(s) is represented by the line segment labeled with the number 5?

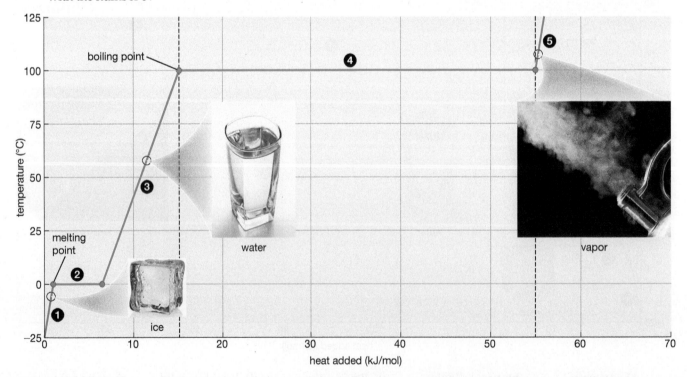

a) gas only   **b)** gas + liquid   **c)** liquid only   **d)** liquid + solid   **e)** solid only

10.76 How much energy in calories (cal) needs to be absorbed in order for 32 g of water to be vaporized?

Substance	Heat of Fusion cal/g (J/g)	Heat of Vaporization cal/g (J/g)
water (H_2O)	79.7 (333)	540 (2260)
ethanol (C_2H_6O)	26.1 (109)	200 (837)
butane (C_4H_{10})	19.2 (80.3)	92.5 (387)
ammonia (NH_3)	84.0 (351)	327 (1370)

Express your answer in scientific notation with two significant figures and units of cal.

energy = [   ] cal

10.77 How much energy in Joules (J) is released when 67 g of water freezes? The heat of fusion of water is 333 J/g. Express your answer in scientific notation with two significant figures and units of joules (J).

energy = [   ] J

10.78 How much energy in kilocalories (kcal) needs to be absorbed to melt a 4.52 kg block of frozen water (ice) that is at 0 °C? The heat of fusion of water is 79.7 cal/g. 1 kcal = 1000 cal, and 1 kg = 1000 g. Express your answer in scientific notation with three significant figures and units of kilocalories (kcal).

energy = [   ] kcal

10.79 How many joules (J) of energy are released when 8.75 mol of water in the gas phase (steam) at 100 °C condenses to liquid water at 100 °C?

Substance	Heat of Fusion cal/g (J/g)	Heat of Vaporization cal/g (J/g)
water (H_2O)	79.7 (333)	540 (2260)
ethanol (C_2H_6O)	26.1 (109)	200 (837)
butane (C_4H_{10})	19.2 (80.3)	92.5 (387)
ammonia (NH_3)	84.0 (351)	327 (1370)

a) 3.56×10^5 J b) 2.81×10^{-6} J
c) 1.98×10^4 J d) 8.51×10^4 J
e) 1.10×10^3 J

10.80 How many calories of energy are released to the environment when 14.2 L of water vapor at 100 °C and 0.971 atm are condensed to water vapor at 100 °C? The gas law constant R = 0.0821 (L)(atm)/(mol)(K) and the heat of vaporization of water is 540 cal/g.

a) 1.63×10^4 cal
b) 1.35×10^1 cal
c) 1.50×10^{-2} cal
d) 4.38×10^3 cal

Chapter 11

11.1 Liquids

LO 11.1: Describe the effects of intermolecular forces on the properties of liquids.

11.01 Which statement best describes viscosity?

a) the measure of a liquid's ability to vaporize below its boiling point

b) the measure of a solid's ability to rapidly melt, becoming a liquid at the critical transition temperature

c) the measure of a liquid's ability to conduct electricity

d) the measure of a liquid's resistance to flow

11.02 Which statement best describes the difference between evaporation and vaporization?

a) Vaporization occurs when liquid molecules escape into the gaseous state at temperatures lower than the boiling point. Evaporation is the escape of molecules from the liquid state into the gaseous state at the boiling point of the liquid.

b) Evaporation occurs when liquid molecules escape into the gaseous state at temperatures lower than the boiling point. Vaporization is the escape of molecules from the liquid state into the gaseous state at the boiling point of the liquid.

c) Evaporation occurs when liquid molecules escape into the gaseous state at temperatures lower than the boiling point. Vaporization is the reverse of evaporation and involves molecules in the gas state condensing into the liquid state.

d) Evaporation occurs when liquid molecules are in equilibrium with molecules in the gas state at the boiling point. Vaporization is the escape of molecules from the liquid state into the gaseous state below the boiling point of the liquid in an open container.

11.03 Your chemistry study group is taking turns trying to describe vapor pressure to each other. Which student provides the best description?

a) Your friend Jose says that vapor pressure is the pressure that must be applied to convert all of the vapor above a liquid back into the liquid state.

b) Your friend Minh says that vapor pressure is the pressure exerted by one mole of gas particles on the walls of a 22.4 L container (the molar volume) at standard temperature and pressure (STP).

c) Your friend Maria says that vapor pressure is the pressure exerted by the particles of vapor above a liquid.

d) Your friend Zola says that vapor pressure is the point at which the pressure of the vapor above a liquid in a sealed container is equal to the atmospheric pressure outside of the container.

11.04 Identify the statement that best describes the O—H bond.

a) The O—H bond is polar because oxygen is a significantly larger atom than hydrogen. The difference in atomic radius values between these two atoms places it in the polar covalent bond category.

b) The O—H bond is non-polar. The electronegativity difference between oxygen and hydrogen places it in the polar covalent bond category.

c) The O—H bond is polar because oxygen has more total electrons than hydrogen. The difference in the number of electrons between these two atoms places it in the polar covalent bond category.

d) The O—H bond is polar because oxygen is more electronegative than hydrogen. The difference in electronegativity values between these two atoms places it in the polar covalent bond category.

e) The O—H bond is polar because hydrogen is more electronegative than oxygen. The difference in electronegativity values between these two atoms places it in the polar covalent bond category.

11.05 Identify the statement that best describes a hydrogen bond.

a) an attraction between a hydrogen atom bonded to N, O, or C and an N, O, or C atom on another molecule or another region of the same molecule

b) an attraction between a hydrogen atom bonded to N, O, or F and an N, O, or F atom on another molecule or another region of the same molecule

c) the polar O—H bond in the water molecule

d) a covalent bond between hydrogen and oxygen or between hydrogen and carbon

e) an especially strong bond that is difficult to break between hydrogen and all non-metal atoms in Group 5A(15), 6A(16) and 7A(17) on the periodic table

11.06 Which statement best describes what occurs when solid LiBr dissolves in water?

a) The Li^+ cations are attracted to the partially negative hydrogen atoms of the water molecule.

b) The Li^+ anions are attracted to the partially positive oxygen atoms of the water molecule.

c) The Br^- anions are attracted to the partially positive hydrogen atoms of the water molecule.

d) The Br^- anions are attracted to the partially negative oxygen atoms of the water molecule.

11.07 Which statement best describes what happens when solid $MgCl_2$ dissolves in water?

a) The Mg^{2+} anions are attracted to the partially positive oxygen atoms of the water molecule.

b) The Cl^- cations are attracted to the partially positive oxygen atoms of the water molecule.

c) The Cl^- anions are attracted to the partially negative hydrogen atoms of the water molecule.

d) The Mg^{2+} cations are attracted to the partially negative oxygen atoms of the water molecule.

e) The Mg^{2+} cations are attracted to the partially positive hydrogen atoms of the water molecule.

11.08 The structures of three common organic molecules are listed below. Based on their structures and molar masses, arrange the molecules in order of increasing vapor pressure at room temperature (21 °C).

Answer choices:

$CH_3CH_2CH_2CH_3$
(butane)
,

$CH_2OHCH_2OHCH_2OH$
(propanetriol)
,

$CH_3CH_2CH_2CH_2OH$
(butanol)

Target boxes: lowest vapor pressure at room temperature, intermediate vapor pressure at room temperature, highest vapor pressure at room temperature

11.09 Predict which molecule has the highest vapor pressure at room temperature.

a) $CH_3CH_2CH_2CH_2CH_2CH_3$

b) $CH_3CH_2CH_2CH_2CH_2OH$

c) $CH_3CH_2CH_2CH_2CH_3$

d) $CH_3CH_2CH_2CH_2CH_2CH_2CH_3$

11.2 Solutions

LO 11.2: **Explain how solutions form based on the structure of the solute and solvent components.**

11.10 A solution is formed by dissolving a solute, , in water. A diagram of the aqueous solution is shown. Which best describes the solute in solution?

a) strong electrolyte   **b)** weak electrolyte

c) nonelectrolyte

11.11 A solution is formed by dissolving a solute, 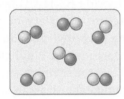, in water. A diagram of the aqueous solution is shown. Which best describes the solute in solution?

a) strong electrolyte   **b)** weak electrolyte

c) nonelectrolyte

11.12 A solution is formed by dissolving the solute, 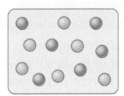, in water. A diagram of the aqueous solution is shown. Which best describes the solute in solution?

a) strong electrolyte   **b)** weak electrolyte

c) nonelectrolyte

11.13 Solutions are formed when the following solutes dissolve in water. Identify each solution as an electrolyte solution or a nonelectrolyte solution.

Answer choices:

$$KF(s) \xrightarrow{H_2O} K^+(aq) + F^-(aq),$$

$$C_3H_6O_3(s) \xrightarrow{H_2O} C_3H_6O_3(aq),$$

$$Mg(OH)_2(s) \xrightarrow{H_2O} Mg^{2+}(aq) + 2OH^-(aq),$$

$$C_5H_{10}O_5(s) \xrightarrow{H_2O} C_5H_{10}O_5(aq)$$

Target boxes: electrolyte solution, nonelectrolyte solution

11.14 Which of these molecules can hydrogen bond with liquid water (H_2O) molecules? (select any/all).

a)

b)

c)

d)

11.15 In a solution, the solvent _____.

a) must have opposite polarity as the solute

b) must not exceed the concentration of the solute

c) is the substance in the least amount

d) is the substance in the greatest amount

11.16 Predict which compound is most soluble in water.

a) H_2

b) HBr

c) He

d) CH_4

e) $CH_3CH_2CH_2CH_3$

11.17 A student in a laboratory prepares a solution by dissolving 1.575 g K_3PO_4 in 250 mL of pure H_2O. In this solution, H_2O is the _____.

a) solvent   **b)** solute

c) electrolyte   **d)** ionic compound

11.18 Identify the compound that does *not* dissolve well in water.

a) NH_3

b) CH_3CH_2OH

c) HCl

d) CH_3CH_3

e) KBr

11.19 Consider the information given about each solute. Determine whether aqueous solutions of each contain only ions, mostly molecules with some ions, or only molecules.

Answer choices:

Vitamin C	CaCl$_2$	Niacin
(a non-electrolyte)	(a strong electrolyte)	(a vitamin and weak electrolyte)

Target boxes: only ions, mostly molecules with some ions, only molecules

11.20 Consider the information given about each solute. Determine the type of intermolecular interactions that occur between solute and solvent in an aqueous solution. Drag each solute type into the correct bin.

Answer choices:

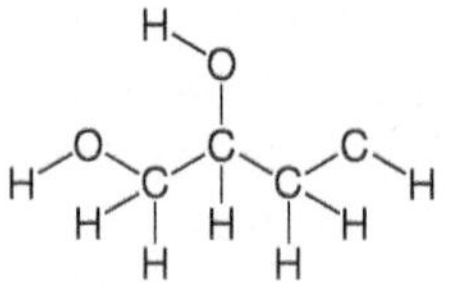

glycerol, used in the food industry, KCl, used in IV fluids for hospital patients;

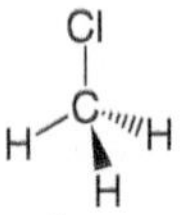

chloromethane, used as an industrial solvent

Target boxes: ion-dipole interactions, hydrogen bonding interactions, dipole-dipole interactions

11.21 For a chemistry laboratory experiment, you prepare a solution by dissolving 25.0 mL pure H_2O in 75.0 mL ethanol (CH_3CH_2OH). In this solution, H_2O is the _____.

a) ionic compound   b) solute

c) electrolyte   d) solvent

11.22 The compound $BaCl_2$ can be classified as a _____.

a) gas   b) nonelectrolyte

c) liquid   d) strong electrolyte

e) weak electrolyte

11.23 The compound propanol, can be classified as a _____.

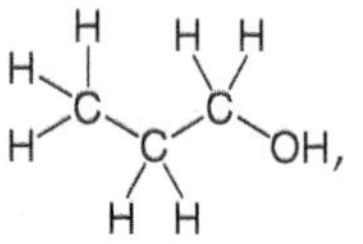

a) halogen   b) weak electrolyte

c) strong electrolyte   d) noble gas

e) nonelectrolyte

11.24 Identify the compound in the group that is a nonelectrolyte.

a) CsI   b) CS_2

c) $CaBr_2$ d) KOH

e) Na_2CO_3

11.3 Solutions in the Human Body and the Environment

LO 11.3: **Predict the solubility of a substance based on the polarity of molecules.**

11.25 Oil spills from the petroleum industry cause serious environmental damage. The 2010 Deepwater Horizon oil spill was a massive environmental disaster that released an estimated 210 million US gal

(780,000 m^3) of crude petroleum into the Gulf of Mexico. Oils are composed primarily of long hydrocarbon chains. Why do oils not dissolve in water, such as that in oceans, lakes, and rivers?

a) Oils are ionic and water is nonpolar.

b) Water is nonpolar and oils are polar.

c) Water is ionic and oils are polar.

d) Oils are nonpolar and water is polar.

11.26 Vinyl chloride (C_2H_3Cl) is used industrially to manufacture a variety of consumer products, including polyvinyl chloride (PVC) pipes and bottles. Unfortunately, vinyl chloride is sometimes released into the environment from industrial pollution. Examine the structure and predict whether it dissolves in lake water.

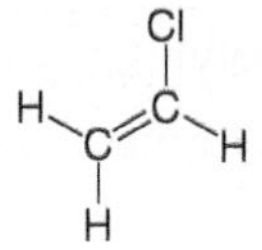

a) dissolves in lake water

b) does not dissolve in lake water

11.27 Water-soluble molecules and drugs are easily absorbed in the small intestines where plenty of water is present. These mostly polar molecules are also easily excreted in our urine. In contrast, drugs with a molecular structure that is mostly nonpolar are best absorbed when we eat them with oils or fats and are stored in the fat tissue in our bodies. Examine the molecular structures of the three molecules shown. Predict whether each will be primarily water-soluble or primarily fat-soluble.

Answer choices:

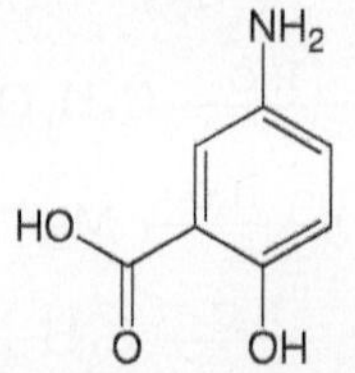

Mesalazine (5-aminosalicylic acid), a medication used to treat inflammatory bowel disease, including ulcerative colitis and Crohn's disease   ;

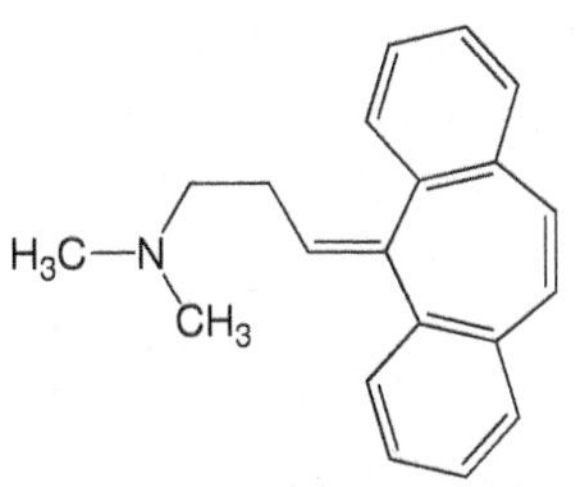

cyclobenzaprine (also known as Flexeril), a medication for muscle spasms   ;

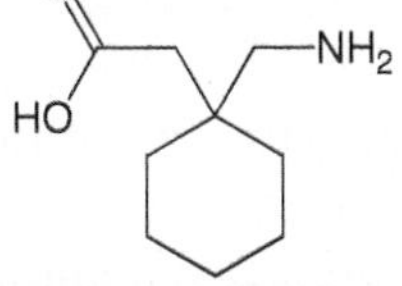

Gabapentin, used to treat seizures and neuropathic pain

Target boxes: water-soluble, fat-soluble

11.28 Water-soluble molecules and drugs are easily absorbed in the small intestines where plenty of water is present. These mostly polar molecules are also easily excreted in our urine. In contrast, drugs with a molecular structure that is mostly nonpolar are best absorbed when we eat them with oils or fats and are stored in the fat tissue in our bodies. Examine the molecular structures of the three molecules. Predict whether each will be primarily water-soluble or primarily fat-soluble.

Answer choices:

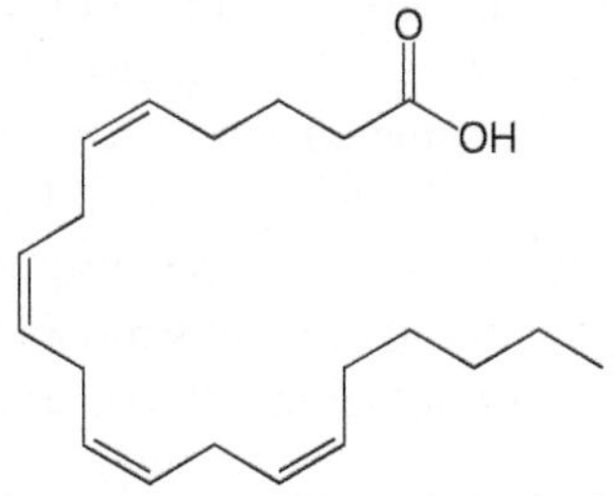

arachidonic acid, found in the brain, muscles, liver and cell membranes   ;

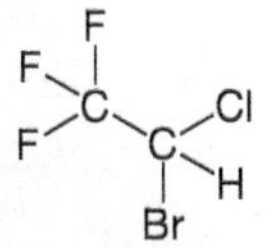

halothane, also known as Fluothane, a commonly used general anesthetic   ;

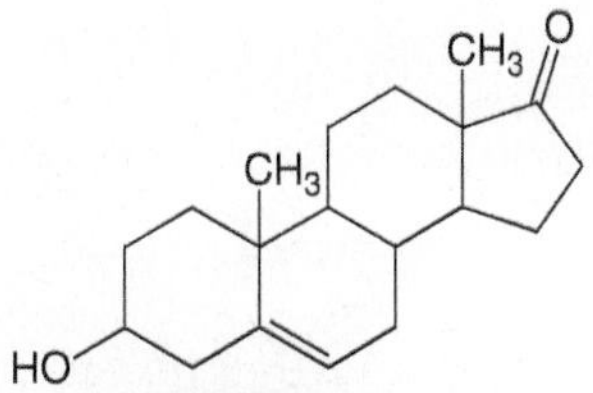

DHEA, also known as androstenolone, a steroid hormone

Target boxes: primarily water-soluble, primarily fat-soluble

11.29 Water-soluble molecules and drugs are easily absorbed in the small intestines where plenty of water is present. These mostly polar molecules are also easily excreted in our urine. In contrast, drugs with a molecular structure that is mostly nonpolar are best absorbed when we eat them with oils or fats and are stored in the fat tissue in our bodies. Examine the molecular structures of the three molecules. Predict whether each will be primarily water-soluble or primarily fat-soluble.

Answer choices:

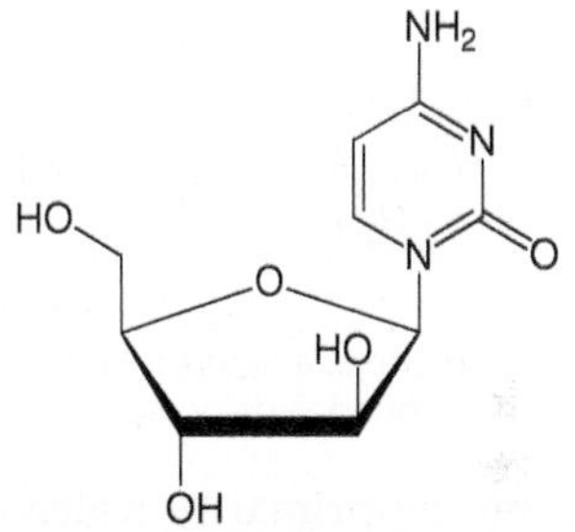

cytarabine, a chemotherapy medicine used to treat a variety of cancer types   ;

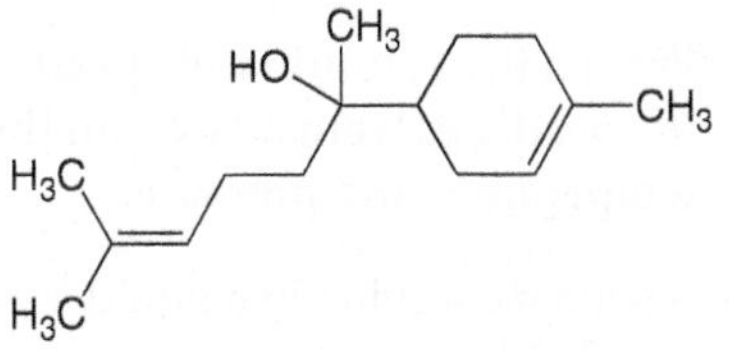

bisabolol, found in the essential oil of the *Chamomile* plant   ;

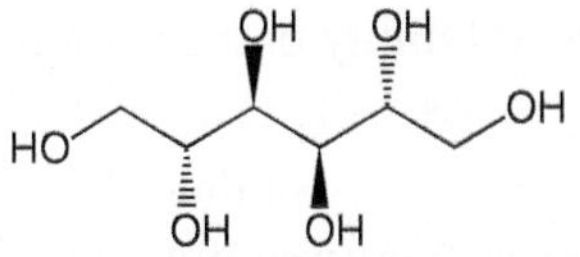

mannitol, a sugar alcohol used as an artificial sweetener and medication for glaucoma

Target boxes: primarily water-soluble, primarily fat-soluble

11.30 Water-soluble molecules and drugs are easily absorbed in the small intestines where plenty of water is present. These mostly polar molecules are also easily excreted in our urine. In contrast, drugs with a molecular structure that is mostly nonpolar are best absorbed when we eat them with oils or fats and are stored in the fat tissue in our bodies. Examine the molecular structures of the three molecules. Predict whether each will be primarily water-soluble or primarily fat-soluble.

Answer choices:

propofol, also known as Diprivan, used in anesthesia ;

niacin, an essential nutrient found in a variety of foods and taken as a dietary supplement ;

ornithine, a naturally occurring amino acid found in dairy, eggs, fish, and meat

Target boxes: primarily water-soluble, primarily fat-soluble

11.4 Factors Affecting Solubility

LO 11.4: **Predict the solubility of specific solutes in specific solvents based on the effects of temperature and pressure.**

11.31 For a solid dissolving in a liquid solvent, what is the common effect of increasing the temperature of the solution?

a) The solubility of the gas increases.

b) The solubility of the solid solute in the solution decreases.

c) The solubility of the solid solute in the solution remains the same, but the boiling point decreases.

d) The solubility of the solid solute in the solution remains the same but the freezing point increases.

e) The solubility of the solid solute in the solution increases.

11.32 Caffeine is a central nervous system stimulant that occurs naturally primarily in coffee beans and certain teas. Each day, billions of people rely on caffeine to help them wake up, and it is one the world's most widely consumed drugs. Caffeine functions by blocking the effects of adenosine, a neurotransmitter that relaxes the brain and makes you feel tired. Caffeine is a solid that is soluble in room temperature water at approximately 15 mg/mL. The solubility of caffeine in water is approximately 200 mg/mL at

80 °C, and 665 mg/mL in boiling water. Which statement best describes this solubility data?

caffeine

a) This data is in agreement with Henry's law which states that the solubility of a gas in a liquid is directly proportional to the partial pressure of the gas over the liquid.

b) The maximum solubility of caffeine in water is 200 mg/mL at any temperature.

c) Caffeine begins to recrystallize at a concentration of 15 mg/mL in water that is 80 °C.

d) Boiling water becomes supersaturated with caffeine at 200 mg/mL.

e) The solubility of caffeine in water increases dramatically with increasing temperature.

11.33 A biologist studying lake conditions found that for every 10 °C increase in water temperature there is a decrease of dissolved oxygen by about 1mg/L. She also determined that the average temperature in the lake has risen from 20 °C to 30 °C in the peak summer months during the last five years. Data she collected on the concentration of dissolved oxygen (O_2) gas shows a decrease from 9 mg/L to 8 mg/L during the same period of time. If fish in the lake require a minimum of 8 mg/mL dissolved oxygen to survive, what is a reasonable prediction the biologist can make about the fish population in the lake during the summer months in future years?

a) The increased temperature of the lake may be causing the concentration of dissolved oxygen to increase. If this trend continues into the future, the fish in the lake will find it increasingly difficult to survive.

b) The decreasing temperature of the lake may be causing the concentration of dissolved oxygen to increase. If this trend continues into the future, the fish in the lake will find it increasingly difficult to survive.

c) The increased temperature of the lake is probably unrelated to the increasing concentration of dissolved oxygen. There is not enough data to make a prediction about the probability of fish surviving in the lake in future years.

d) The increased temperature of the lake may be causing the concentration of dissolved oxygen to decrease. If this trend continues into the future, the fish in the lake will find it increasingly difficult to survive.

11.34 On a hot summer day, you make a glass of iced tea. Wanting to sweeten it, you add some sugar. After mixing thoroughly for a few minutes, you notice some undissolved sugar at the bottom of the glass. At this point, what is the state of the solution?

a) unsaturated

b) saturated

c) nonpolar

d) fat-soluble

11.35 Which statement best describes the solubility of a gas in a liquid solvent?

a) The solubility of a gas increases as the gas pressure above the liquid increases.

b) The solubility of a gas decreases as the gas pressure above the liquid increases.

c) The solubility of a gas increases as the temperature of the liquid increases.

d) The solubility of a gas depends only on liquid solvent polarity.

e) The solubility of a gas increases as the gas pressure above the liquid decreases.

11.36 Consider the diagram showing a mixture of gas and liquid in a sealed cylinder with rigid walls. The top can be moved up or down to change the volume of the cylinder. If the volume of the cylinder is reduced (at constant temperature) by pushing the top lower, what happens to the amount of gas that is dissolved in the liquid?

a) The amount of gas dissolved in the liquid also decreases.

b) The amount of gas dissolved in the liquid increases.

c) The amount of gas dissolved in the liquid remains the same, but the boiling point is decreased.

d) The amount of liquid evaporating into the gas phase increases.

11.37 You and your laboratory partner determine that the solubility of sodium chloride (NaCl) in pure water is 359 g/L at a certain temperature. How many grams of NaCl can be dissolved in 225 mL of pure water at this same temperature?

a) 8.08×10^4 g

b) 1.60 g

c) 80.8 g

d) 1.24×10^{-2} g

11.38 At sea level (where atmospheric pressure is 1 atm) an environmental scientist measures the solubility of oxygen (O_2) gas, from a sample of air, to be 8 mg O_2/L in water at 25 °C. The partial pressure of oxygen gas in air at sea level is 0.21 atm. Indicate whether each of the following changes would increase or decrease the solubility of oxygen gas in water.

Answer choices:

The air mixture is replaced with pure oxygen gas at the same temperature and pressure.,

The temperature of the water is increased at the same pressure.,

The same measurement is conducted at a high elevation mountain lake at the same temperature.,

The temperature of the water is decreased at the same pressure.

Target boxes: solubility increases, solubility decreases

11.39 The solubility of the ionic compound potassium phosphate (K_3PO_4) in water is 90 g/100 mL at 20 °C. A scientist adds 175 g of K_3PO_4 to 200 mL of water at this same temperature and mixes thoroughly for several minutes. Which of the following statements about this solution is true?

a) The solution contains a non-polar solute dissolved in a polar solvent.

b) The solution is supersaturated.

c) The solution is saturated.

d) The solution is unsaturated.

11.40 Barium sulfate ($BaSO_4$) is an ionic compound that is used to image the gastrointestinal (GI) tract of patients. The solubility of $BaSO_4$ in pure water is 0.285 mg/100 mL at 30 °C. A medical researcher tries to dissolve 0.171 mg in 50 mL water 30 °C. Which statement best describes this solution?

a) The solution is unsaturated and an additional 0.114 mg of $BaSO_4$ solid can dissolve before it becomes saturated.

b) The solution is saturated and there is approximately 0.0285 mg of undissolved $BaSO_4$ solid at the bottom of the solution container.

c) The solution is saturated and all of the $BaSO_4$ has dissolved at 30 °C.

d) The solution is unsaturated and an additional 0.143 mg of $BaSO_4$ solid can dissolve before it becomes saturated.

e) The solution is saturated and there is approximately 0.143 mg of undissolved $BaSO_4$ solid at the bottom of the solution container.

11.41 Refer to the solubility chart to determine whether each of the following solutions will be saturated or unsaturated based on the conditions described.

Substance	Solubility (g/100 g H_2O)	
	20 °C	50 °C
KCl	34.0	42.6
$NaNO_3$	88.0	114.0
$C_{12}H_{22}O_{11}$ (sugar)	203.9	260.4

Answer choices:

225 g of $NaNO_3$ is added to 200 g water at 50 °C and mixed thoroughly.

105 g of sugar is added to 50 g water at 20 °C and mixed thoroughly.

434 g of KCl is added to 1 kg of water at 50 °C and mixed thoroughly.

165 g of KCl is added to 500 g of water at 20 °C and mixed thoroughly.

Target boxes: saturated solution, unsaturated solution

11.42 For a chemistry project, you and your laboratory partner make a solution containing 351.54 g of sugar in 150 g H_2O at 50 °C. You then cool the solution to 20 °C. Use this information along with the information provided in the data table to determine how many grams of sugar remain in solution at 20 °C and how many grams of solid sugar precipitates out of solution as a solid after cooling.

Substance	Solubility (g/100 g H_2O)	
	20 °C	50 °C
$C_{12}H_{22}O_{11}$ (sugar)	203.9	260.4

a) Approximately 45.69 g remain in solution at 20 °C and approximately 305.85 g precipitates out of the solution as a solid.

b) All 351.54 g of the dissolved sugar remain in solution since it is only 90% saturated.

c) Approximately 275.3 g remain in solution at 20 °C and approximately 76.3 g precipitates out of the solution as a solid.

d) Approximately 305.85 g remain in solution at 20 °C and approximately 45.69 g precipitates out of the solution as a solid.

e) Approximately 203.9 g remain in solution at 20 °C and approximately 147.6 g precipitates out of the solution as a solid.

11.5 Solution Concentration and Dilution

LO 11.5: Calculate the concentration of solutions and use solution concentrations as a conversion factor.

11.43 Select the correct description of the mass/volume (m/v) percent.

a) grams of solute in 100 mL of solvent

b) grams of solute in 100 mL solution

c) grams of solvent in 100 mL of solution

d) grams of solvent in 100 g solution

e) moles of solute in 1 L of solution

11.44 Select the correct description of the volume/volume (v/v) percent.

a) the number of moles of solute dissolved in 1 L of solution

b) the number of milliliters of solution dissolved in 100 mL solute

c) the number of milligrams of solute dissolved in 100 mL solution

d) the number of milliliters of solute dissolved in 100 mL of solution

11.45 Select the correct description of molarity.

a) the number of moles of solute dissolved in 1 L of solvent

b) the number of grams of solute dissolved in 1 L solution

c) the number of moles of solute dissolved in 1 L of solution

d) the number of liters of solute dissolved in 1 mol of solvent

11.46 Which statement correctly describes what happens when a solution is diluted?

a) The amount of solvent does not change but the amount of solute increases.

b) The amount of solute decreases and the amount of solvent increases.

c) The amount of solute increases proportionally with the increased amount of solvent.

d) The amount of solute does not change but the amount of solvent increases.

e) The amount of solute remains the same but the amount of solvent decreases.

11.47 You drink hot tea by a fire on a cold evening. If you add 1.5 g of sugar in 250 mL of tea with sugar (the solution), what is the concentration of sugar expressed as % (m/v)? Express your answer in standard decimal form with two significant figures and units of % m/v.

concentration = ⬚ % (m/v)

11.48 Vinegar is a solution of acetic acid in water. If a 265 mL bottle of distilled vinegar contains 18.1 mL of acetic acid, what is the volume percent (v/v) of the vinegar solution? Express your answer in standard decimal form with three significant figures and units of % (v/v).

volume percent = ⬚ % (v/v)

11.49 A homogeneous aqueous solution containing an equal concentration of two dissolved substances is diluted in a laboratory. Consider the image of the initial solution, then identify the image that represents the diluted solution.

initial soultion   diluted soultion

Which of the following represents the diluted solution?

a)   b)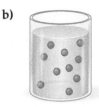

c)

11.50 Concentrating a solution is the opposite of diluting a solution. Select the statement that correctly describes a solution being concentrated.

a) The amount of solute increases proportionally with the decreased amount of solvent.

b) The amount of solute remains the same but the amount of solvent decreases.

c) The amount of solute decreases and the amount of solvent decreases.

d) The amount of solvent does not change but the amount of solute increases.

e) The amount of solute does not change but the amount of solvent increases.

11.51 What is the molarity of a 0.10 L solution containing 0.10 mol KBr? Try to answer this question using mental math or a pencil and paper instead of using a calculator.

molarity = ⬚ M

11.52 What is the molarity of a solution containing 58.44 g of sodium chloride (NaCl) dissolved in 0.500 L of solution? The molar mass of NaCl is 58.44 g/mol. Try to answer this question using mental math or a pencil and paper instead of using a calculator. Express your answer in standard decimal form with three significant figures and units of M.

molarity = ⬚ M

11.53 What volume (in L) of a 1.50 M KCl solution is needed to obtain 3.00 moles of KCl? Try to answer this question using mental math or a pencil and paper instead of using a calculator. Express your answer in standard decimal form with three significant figures and units of L.

volume = ⬚ L

11.54 Riboflavin (also known as vitamin B_2) is a vitamin used to produce energy and for overall health. It occurs in a variety of foods such as green vegetables, eggs, and meat. Riboflavin is also used as a dietary supplement to help prevent riboflavin deficiency. Calculate the mass/volume percent (m/v) of a 125 mL solution containing 1.5×10^{-3} g riboflavin in a nutrient solution given to a pregnant woman. Express your answer in scientific notation with two significant figures and units of % (m/v).

riboflavin (vitamin B_2)

mass/volume percent = [ ] % (m/v)

11.55 A scientist in a lab needs to determine the volume (mL) of a 12.5% (m/v) $MgCl_2$ solution that contains 4.85 g of $MgCl_2$. Which of the following is the correct value?

a) 38.8 mL
b) 2.58×10^{-2} mL
c) 0.606 mL
d) 1.65 mL

11.56 A person consumes 275 mL of an alcoholic drink that is 15.5% alcohol (ethanol) by volume. What volume of alcohol (in mL) did they consume from this drink? Express your answer in standard decimal form with three significant figures and units of mL.

volume = [ ] mL

11.57 A nurse in a cancer clinic prepares a medication from a 75 mL stock solution that is 25% (m/v). What is the concentration of the medication when the entire stock solution is added to an IV bag that will have a final volume of 550 mL?

concentration = [ ] % (m/v)

11.58 How many moles of NaCl are in 3.75 L of a 0.485 M solution? Express your answer in standard decimal form with three significant figures and units of mol.

number of moles = [ ] mol

11.59 15.0 mL of a 0.750 M solution of glucose is diluted to a final volume of 85.0 mL. What is the final concentration of the diluted glucose solution?

a) 4.25 M
b) 0.132 M
c) 956 M
d) 7.56 M

11.60 A 75% (v/v) solution of ethanol (CH_3CH_2OH) in water is used as a hand-sanitizing solution. How many milliliters of ethanol are in a 95 mL bottle of this alcohol solution? Express your answer in standard decimal form with two significant figures and units of mL.

volume = [ ] mL

11.61 An environmental scientist working with a potassium nitrate (KNO_3) solution dilutes 78.0 mL of a 0.275 M solution to a final volume of 345 mL. What is the resulting concentration in units of molarity (M)?

a) 1.22 M
b) 7.40×10^3 M
c) 16.1 M
d) 6.22×10^{-2} M

11.62 Scurvy is a disease that results from a lack of vitamin C (ascorbic acid). A hospital patient suffering from scurvy, severe dehydration, and malnutrition receives 175 mL of a solution that contains 1.5 % (m/v) vitamin C each day through his intravenous (IV) fluid. How many grams of vitamin C does he receive daily (g/d) from this solution?

a) 2.6 g/d
b) 0.38 g/d
c) 1.2×10^4 g/d
d) 8.6×10^{-5} g/d

11.63 What volume (in mL) of a 2.24 M KCl solution is required to make 875 mL of a diluted solution with a concentration of 0.315 M KCl?

a) 123 mL
b) 6.22×10^3 mL
c) 617 mL
d) 8.13×10^{-3} mL

11.64 Wastewater is water that has been used and must be treated before it can be used for drinking water, released into another body of water, or used for agriculture, industry, or recreational purposes. Wastewater treatment helps provide usable water for people around the world. A researcher in a wastewater treatment plant needs 2.85 moles of NaOH for an experiment. What volume (in liters) of a 1.15 M NaOH solution is needed to provide

2.85 moles of NaOH? Express your answer in standard decimal form with three significant figures and units of L.

volume = ☐ L

11.65 A student working at an environmental lab is asked to prepare an 8.5×10^{-3} M potassium phosphate (K_3PO_4) solution using 1.5 mL of a 0.25 M K_3PO_4 stock solution for ongoing work with soil analysis. What is the correct final volume of the solution that the student intern will prepare?

a) 2.3×10^{-2} mL   b) 5.1×10^{-2} mL

c) 3.2×10^{-3} mL   d) 44 mL

11.66 While working in a clinical laboratory, you make a solution by dissolving 8.25 g of potassium phosphate (K_3PO_4) in water to make a solution that has a volume of 275 mL. What is the molarity (M) of the solution? The molar mass of K_3PO_4 is 212.27 g/mol.

a) 95.6 M   b) 6.37×10^3 M

c) 1.07×10^{-2} M   d) 0.141 M

e) 1.41×10^{-4} M

11.67 Clinics and hospitals routinely analyze patient blood using a series of tests called a comprehensive metabolic panel. A total protein test is included in most blood panels and can help health care providers identify possible health issues if results are outside of the normal range of 60-80 g/L blood. Higher-than-normal values can indicate possible dehydration, chronic infections, and some kinds of cancer. Lower-than-normal values can indicate possible liver disease, malnutrition, internal bleeding, and other serious health concerns. If a child in the hospital has a total blood volume of 3.7 L and a total blood test indicates he has 165 grams of blood protein, what is his blood protein concentration expressed in g/dL? 10 dL = 1 L.

a) 4.5 g/dL   b) 4.4 g/dL

c) 45 g/dL   d) 0.022 g/dL

e) 0.22 g/dL

11.68 How many liters of a 1.50×10^{-3} M K_2SO_4 solution are needed to provide 2.75 g of K_2SO_4 for an experiment? The molar mass $K_2SO_4 = 174.01$ g/mol. Molarity(M) = mol/L.

a) 9.49×10^{-2} L   b) 1.39 L

c) 3.19×10^5 L   d) 10.5 L

e) 2.37×10^{-2} L

11.69 Healthy blood sugar (glucose) levels, measured approximately two hours after a meal, are commonly in the range of 140 milligrams per deciliter (mg/dL). If a patient has a total blood volume of 5.5 L and his blood glucose is measured to be 280 mg/dL, what is the total number of grams (g) of glucose in his body? There are ten deciliters in one liter and one thousand milligrams in one gram.

a) 1.5 g   b) 15 g

c) 1.5×10^8 g   d) 15,000 g

e) 0.15 g

11.70 Levels of the amino acid phenylalanine (Phe) in urine in excess of 30.0 mg/L can indicate a condition known as phenylketonuria (PKU disease). Although rare, the birth defect causing PKU disease, which if untreated, can lead to brain damage, intellectual disabilities, behavioral symptoms, or seizures. A clinician is discussing the status of an infant patient with a medical researcher. They need to convert the Phe concentration value expressed in mg/L to the corresponding value in units of molarity (M) in order to compare their patient's values with recently published data. What is the infant's phenylalanine level in M? The molar mass of phenylalanine is 165.19 g/mol. Express your answer in scientific notation with two significant figures and units of M.

phenylalanine level = ☐ M

11.71 The female sex hormone progesterone plays a critical role in human reproduction. If the blood concentration of progesterone in a woman on the day of ovulation (when the female egg is released from the ovary) was measured to be 6.5 nM (nanomolar), and her blood volume is 4.8 L, how many grams of progesterone are in her blood? The molar mass of progesterone is 314.46 g/mol. Remember, the prefix "nano" indicates 10^{-9}. Use the appropriate conversion factor(s) to solve the problem. Express your answer in scientific notation with two significant figures.

| | g progesterone

11.6 Colligative Properties

LO 11.6: Determine the effect of dissolved particles on the boiling point and freezing point of solutions.

11.72 Which statement best describes a volatile solute?

a) A volatile solute in one that dissociates into three or more ions when dissolved.

b) A volatile solute is one that does not readily escape into the vapor phase from the solution.

c) A volatile solute is one that lowers the freezing point of a solution as compared to the pure solvent.

d) A volatile solute is one that readily escapes the solution into the vapor phase.

11.73 Which statement best describes a nonvolatile solute?

a) A nonvolatile solute is one that does not dissolve well in aqueous solutions upon mixing.

b) A nonvolatile solute is one that readily escapes the solution into the vapor phase.

c) A nonvolatile solute is one that does not readily escape into the vapor phase from a liquid solution.

d) A nonvolatile solute is one that does not release heat when dissolved in water to form an aqueous solution.

11.74 Adding a solute to a solvent to prepare a solution changes several physical properties of the solvent. Consider the three glasses of water shown. Each contains the same volume. Colored dots indicate the presence of dissolved, nonvolatile solute particles that make up homogenous solutions. Identify the relative boiling points of each solution.

Answer choices:

Target boxes: lowest boiling point, intermediate boiling point, highest boiling point

11.75 When a solute is dissolved in a solvent to form a solution, the physical properties of the solution are different than those of the pure solvent. These colligative properties depend on the concentration of solute particles in the solution. Consider each example of a solute being dissolved in water to form an aqueous solution. Determine the number of moles released when one mole of each solute is dissolved in pure water.

Answer choices:

$$Ca(OH)_2(s) \xrightarrow{H_2O} Ca^{2+}(aq) + 2OH^-(aq),$$

$$C_3H_6O_3(s) \xrightarrow{H_2O} C_3H_6O_3(aq),$$

$$Na_2S(s) \xrightarrow{H_2O} 2Na^+(aq) + S^{2-}(aq)$$

Target boxes: produces 1 mole, produces 2 moles, produces 3 moles

11.76 Adding a solute to a solvent to prepare a solution changes several physical properties of the solvent. Consider the three glasses of water. Each contains the same volume. Colored dots indicate the presence of dissolved, nonvolatile solute particles that make up homogenous solutions. Identify the relative freezing points of each solution.

Answer choices:

Target boxes: lowest freezing point, intermediate freezing point, highest freezing point

11.77 When a solute is dissolved in a solvent to form a solution, the physical properties of the solution are different than those of the pure solvent. These colligative properties depend on the concentration of solute particles in the solution. Consider each example of a solute being dissolved in water to form an aqueous solution. Determine the number of moles released when one mole of each solute is dissolved in pure water.

Answer choices:

$$CsBr(s) \xrightarrow{H_2O} Cs^+(aq) + Br^-(aq),$$

$$K_2(SO_4)(s) \xrightarrow{H_2O} 2K^+(aq) + SO_4^{2-}(aq),$$

$$CH_3OH(l) \xrightarrow{H_2O} CH_3OH(l)$$

Target boxes: produces 1 mole, produces 2 moles, produces 3 moles

11.78 What is the boiling point of a solution prepared by dissolving 2.18 moles of glucose $C_6H_{12}O_6$, a non-volatile nonelectrolyte, in 1.00 kg of water? The boiling point of pure water (100 °C) is increased by 0.51 °C for every 1.0 mole of any nonvolatile solute dissolved per kilogram of water.)

a) 1.11 °C

b) 101.11 °C

c) −1.11 °C

d) 102.18 °C

e) 98.89 °C

11.79 What is the boiling point of a solution prepared by dissolving 4.75 moles of $MgCl_2$, a non-volatile strong electrolyte, in 1.00 kg of water? The boiling point of pure water (100 °C) is increased by 0.51 °C for every 1.0 mole of any nonvolatile solute dissolved per kilogram of water.)

a) 7.27 °C

b) 102.42 °C

c) 92.73 °C

d) 104.75 °C

e) 107.27 °C

11.80 A solvent that contains a nonvolatile solute has a higher boiling point than the pure solvent. The magnitude of boiling point elevation depends on the number of solute particles present. Consider each example of an aqueous solution then rank them in terms of boiling point. Recall that molarity (M) is the number of moles solute dissolved per liter solution.

Answer choices:

a 1.5 M solution of RbBr, a nonvolatile strong electrolyte,

a 2 M solution of $MgCl_2$, a nonvolatile strong electrolyte,

a 2 M solution of NaI, a nonvolatile strong electrolyte

Target boxes: lowest boiling point, intermediate boiling point, highest boiling point

11.81 A solvent that contains a nonvolatile solute has a higher boiling point than the pure solvent. The magnitude of boiling point elevation depends on the number of solute particles present. Consider each example of an aqueous solution then rank them in terms of boiling point. Recall that molarity (M) is the number of moles solute dissolved per liter solution. Drag each relative boiling point into the appropriate bin.

Answer choices:

a 0.10 M solution of KBr, a nonvolatile strong electrolyte,

a 0.15 M solution of BaS, a nonvolatile strong electrolyte,

a 0.15 M solution of $BaBr_2$, a nonvolatile strong electrolyte

Target boxes: lowest boiling point, intermediate boiling point, highest boiling point

11.82 What is the boiling point of a solution prepared by dissolving 2.18 moles of $Sr(NO_3)_2$, a non-volatile strong electrolyte, in 1.00 kg of water? Nitrate (NO_3^-) is a polyatomic ion with a charge of negative one. The boiling point of pure water (100 °C) is increased by 0.51 °C for every 1.0 mole of any nonvolatile solute dissolved per kilogram of water. Before attempting this problem, you may find it helpful to write out a balanced equation for $Sr(NO_3)_2$ dissolving in water to form ions in solution.

a) 103.34 °C

b) 96.66 °C

c) 102.18 °C

d) −3.34 °C

e) 101.11 °C

11.83 What is the boiling point of a solution prepared by dissolving 364.75 grams of LiBr(s), a non-volatile strong electrolyte, in 1.00 kg of water? The boiling point of pure water (100 °C) is increased by 0.51 °C for every 1.0 mole of any nonvolatile solute dissolved per kilogram of water. The molar mass of LiBr = 86.85 g/mol.

a) 102.14 °C

b) 95.72 °C

c) 104.28 °C

d) −4.28 °C

e) 464.75 °C

11.84 You are cleaning up the morning after a party at a cabin in the mountains and notice a bottle of alcohol that was left outside overnight did not freeze. The glass of water next to it did freeze. If the bottle contains 3.75 moles of ethanol (CH_3CH_2OH) in 1.00 kg of water, what is the freezing point of the alcohol solution? The freezing point of pure water, 0.0 °C, is decreased by 1.86 °C for every 1.0 mole of any nonvolatile solute dissolved per kilogram of water. Ethanol is a nonelectrolyte. Express your answer in standard decimal notation with three significant figures and units of °C.

freezing point = [   ] °C

11.85 Large amounts of sodium phosphate (Na_3PO_4) are used each year globally in a variety of industries. When dissolved in water, sodium phosphate dissociates into sodium cations and the polyatomic phosphate anion (PO_4^{3-}) to form a strong electrolyte solution. If a food scientist prepares a solution by dissolving 1.25 moles of Na_3PO_4 in 1.00 kg of water to conduct a food safety study, what is the freezing point of this solution? The freezing point of pure water, 0.0 °C, is decreased by 1.86 °C for every 1.0 mole of any nonvolatile solute dissolved per kilogram of water. Express your answer in standard decimal notation with three significant figures and units of °C.

freezing point = [   ] °C

11.86 Sodium sulfate (Na_2SO_4) is used in enormous quantities each year for the manufacture of detergents, paper production, and other applications. When dissolved in water, sodium sulfate dissociates into sodium cations and the polyatomic sulfate anion (SO_4^{2-}) to form a strong electrolyte solution. A production scientist running a test dissolves 242.87 g of Na_2SO_4 in 1.00 kg of water and determines the freezing point of the solution to confirm that it will not freeze during a new process being considered for the paper industry. What temperature should the scientist have calculated for the freezing point of this solution? The freezing point of pure water, 0.0 °C, is decreased by 1.86 °C for every 1.0 mole of any nonvolatile solute dissolved per kilogram of water. The molar mass of Na_2SO_4 is 142.04 g/mol. Express your answer in standard decimal notation with three significant figures and units of °C.

freezing point = ☐ °C

11.87 Lactose ($C_{12}H_{22}O_{11}$), also known as milk sugar, is a carbohydrate found in the milk of mammals. A student that is researching the effect of lactose on cell growth makes a solution containing 325.15 grams of lactose in 1.00 kg of water. What is the freezing point of this lactose solution? Lactose is a nonelectrolyte having a molar mass of 342.3 g/mol. The freezing point of pure water, 0.0 °C, is decreased by 1.86 °C for every 1.0 mole of any nonvolatile solute dissolved per kilogram of water. Express your answer in standard decimal notation with three significant figures and units of °C.

freezing point = ☐ °C

11.88 A construction worker suffering from low electrolyte levels is given 1.5 L of 0.45 % (m/v) NaCl, to help restore his blood concentration to the normal range. How many moles of particles are in this NaCl solution? (Sodium chloride is an ionic compound with a molar mass of 58.44 g/mol.)

a) 0.12 mol b) 0.23 mol
c) 2.3 × 10⁻⁴ mol d) 1.2 × 10⁻² mol
e) 5.8 × 10⁻² mol

11.89 Glucose ($C_6H_{12}O_6$), also called blood sugar, is your body's main energy source. Hypoglycemia is a condition in which your blood sugar level is significantly lower than normal. Hypoglycemia is commonly due to diabetes or malnutrition. Symptoms of hypoglycemia are often felt when blood sugar levels are 70 milligrams per deciliter (mg/dL) or lower. A hospital patient suffering from hypoglycemia is given an intravenous (IV) bolus of 1.2 L of 40.% (m/v) glucose, to treat his hypoglycemia. Glucose is a covalently bonded molecule that does not ionize in the IV solution. How many moles of dextrose (glucose) particles

are given to the patient in this treatment? The molar mass of glucose is 180.156 g/mol.

a) 2.7 × 10⁻³ mol b) 0.27 mol
c) 8.6 × 10⁴ mol d) 2.7 mol

11.7 Osmosis and Dialysis

LO 11.7: Describe the process of osmosis and how osmosis functions in the cell and is related to dialysis.

11.90 Which best describes a solution that has the same osmotic pressure as blood?

a) hypertonic b) isotonic
c) hemolytic d) hypotonic
e) creatonic

11.91 What is the term used to describe a solution that has an osmotic pressure that is less than blood?

a) hypertonic b) hemostatic
c) hemophilic d) hypotonic
e) isotonic

11.92 A solution that has an osmotic pressure greater than that of blood is _____.

a) hypotonic b) isotonic
c) hemoglobic d) hyperseptic
e) hypertonic

11.93 Red blood cells will burst when placed in which solution?

a) pure water b) 2.0 % (w/v) KCl
c) 1 % NaCl with 1% (w/v) glucose
d) 0.9% NaCl

11.94 The process of water molecules moving through a semipermeable membrane from a solution with a lower concentration of solute into a solution with a higher concentration of solute is _____.

a) dissociation b) desalination
c) concentration d) osmosis
e) emulsification

11.95 The pair of solutions listed in each box is separated from each other with a semipermeable membrane such as the one shown here and in Section 11.7. The pressure of the system is adjusted in each case such that movement of water across the membrane is from the solution listed first to the solution listed second as indicated by the arrow. Determine whether each situation represents osmosis or reverse osmosis.

Answer choices:

water

0.5 M NaCl to 0.2 M NaCl ,

water

0.1 M KBr to 0.8 KBr ,

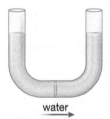

water

2% (m/v) MgCl₂ to 1% (m/v) MgCl₂ ,

water

1% (m/v) glucose to 8% (m/v) glucose

Target boxes: osmosis, reverse osmosis

11.96 The pair of solutions listed in each box is separated from each other with a semipermeable membrane such as the one shown below and in Section 11.7. The pressure of the system is adjusted in each case such that movement of water across the membrane is from the solution listed first to the solution listed second as indicated by the arrow. Determine whether each situation represents osmosis or reverse osmosis.

Answer choices:

water

12% (v/v) sucrose to 3% (m/v) sucrose ,

water

0.2 M K₃PO₄ to 0.6 M K₃PO₄ ,

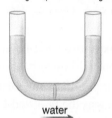

water

0.01 M Na₂S to 0.8 M Na₂S ,

water

15% (v/v) honey to 1% (v/v) honey

Target boxes: osmosis, reverse osmosis

Chapter 12

12.1 Defining Acids and Bases

LO 12.1: Identify and define acids, bases, and conjugate acid-base pairs.

12.01 When hydrogen bromide (HBr) dissolves in water it acts as a/an _____.

a) proton accepter   b) acid

c) source of hydroxide   d) base

12.02 When potassium hydroxide (KOH) dissolves in water it acts as a/an _____.

a) acid   b) source of H^+ ions

c) gas   d) base

12.03 Identify the compound that acts as a base when dissolved in water.

a) $CaCl_2$ b) H_2SO_4

c) $Ca(OH)_2$ d) $Ba(NO_3)_2$

12.04 Categorize the reactions as Brønsted-Lowry acids reacting with water or Brønsted-Lowry bases reacting with water.

$$HNO_3 + H_2O \rightleftharpoons H_3O^+ + NO_3^-$$
$$PO_4^{3-} + H_2O \rightleftharpoons HPO_4^{2-} + OH^-$$
$$H_2SO_4 + H_2O \rightleftharpoons H_3O^+ + HSO_4^-$$
$$CH_3NH_2 + H_2O \rightleftharpoons CH_3NH_3^+ + OH^-$$

Target boxes: Brønsted-Lowry acids reacting with water, Brønsted-Lowry bases reacting with water

12.05 Categorize the reactions as Brønsted-Lowry acids reacting with water or Brønsted-Lowry bases reacting with water.

$$HCO_3^- + H_2O \rightleftharpoons H_2CO_3 + OH^-$$
$$H_3PO_4 + H_2O \rightleftharpoons H_3O^+ + H_2PO_4^-$$
$$HI + H_2O \rightleftharpoons H_3O^+ + I^-$$
$$SO_4^{2-} + H_2O \rightleftharpoons HSO_4^- + OH^-$$

Target boxes: Brønsted-Lowry acids reacting with water, Brønsted-Lowry bases reacting with water

12.06 Which compound in the forward direction of this reaction acts as the Bronsted-Lowry base?

$$CO_3^{2-} + H_2O \rightleftharpoons HCO_3^- + OH^-$$

a) HCO_3^- b) H_2O c) OH^- d) CO_3^{2-}

12.07 Which compound in the forward direction of the reaction acts as the Bronsted-Lowry acid?

$$CN^- + H_2O \rightleftharpoons HCN + OH^-$$

a) OH^- b) H_2O c) CN^- d) HCN

12.08 Consider each dissociation reaction shown. Classify each compound as an acid, base, or neither.

$$NaNO_3 \rightarrow Na^+ + NO_3^-$$
$$H_2SO_4 \rightarrow H^+ + HSO_4^-$$
$$KBr \rightarrow K^+ + Br^-$$
$$Ca(OH)_2 \rightarrow Ca^{2+} + 2OH^-$$
$$HCl \rightarrow H^+ + Cl^-$$
$$LiOH \rightarrow Li^+ + OH^-$$

Target boxes: acid, base, neither

12.09 Consider each dissociation reaction shown. Classify each compound as an acid, base, or neither.

$$Mg(OH)_2 \rightarrow Mg^{2+} + 2OH^-$$
$$SrBr_2 \rightarrow Sr^{2+} + 2Br^-$$
$$H_3PO_4 \rightarrow H^+ + H_2PO_4^-$$
$$Ba(OH)_2 \rightarrow Ba^{2+} + 2OH^-$$
$$CaCl_2 \rightarrow Ca^{2+} + 2Cl^-$$
$$HI \rightarrow H^+ + I^-$$

Target boxes: acid, base, neither

12.10 The compound H_2S is produced in small amounts in the body and functions as a signaling molecule. Identify the conjugate base of H_2S.

a) H_3S^+ b) HS^- c) H_3S^- d) H_2SOH

12.11 The compound $HClO_4$ is used in the manufacture of liquid crystal displays (LCDs) and for the production of rocket fuel. Identify the conjugate base of $HClO_4$.

a) $H_2ClO_4^+$ b) ClO_3^-

c) ClO_4^+ d) ClO_4^-

12.12 Hydrogen carbonate (HCO_3^-) is a critical component in the pH buffering system in the human body and many aquatic habitats. Identify the conjugate acid of hydrogen carbonate (HCO_3^-).

a) H_2CO_3 b) CO_3^{2-}

c) $H_2CO_3^+$ d) HCO_2

12.13 Ethylamine ($CH_3CH_2NH_2$) is an organic molecule that is used as a building block for the production of a number of consumer products including herbicides and resins. Identify the conjugate acid of ethylamine?

ethylamine

a) $CH_3CH_2NH^+$ b) $CH_3CH_2NH_3^+$

c) $CH_3CH_2NH_3^-$ d) $CH_3NH_3^+$

12.14 Identify the conjugate acid of the HPO_4^{2-} ion.

a) PO_4^{3-} b) $H_2PO_4^+$

c) $H_2PO_4^-$ d) PO_4^-

12.2 Strengths of Acids and Bases

LO 12.2: Explain the difference between strong and weak acids and bases.

12.15 Which statement best describes a strong acid?

a) A strong acid is a substance that completely dissociates in water to form an aqueous solution of metal ions and hydroxide ions.

b) A strong acid is a substance that completely dissociates in water to form an aqueous solution of H^+ ions and its conjugate base.

c) A strong acid is a substance that only dissociates partially in water to form an aqueous solution of metal ions and hydroxide ions.

d) A strong acid is a substance that only ionizes slightly in water, forming only a small amount of H_3O^+ ions.

12.16 Which statement best describes a weak acid?

a) A weak acid is a substance that completely dissociates in water to form an aqueous solution of metal ions and hydroxide ions.

b) A weak acid is a substance that completely dissociates in water to form an aqueous solution of H^+ ions and its conjugate base.

c) A weak acid is a substance that only partially dissociates in water to form an aqueous solution of metal ions and hydroxide ions.

d) A weak acid is a substance that only ionizes slightly in water, forming only a small amount of H_3O^+ ions.

12.17 Three different compounds (HX, HQ, and AZ) are dissolved in separate containers of water to form three aqueous solutions. Classify each compound as a strong acid, weak acid, or not an acid.

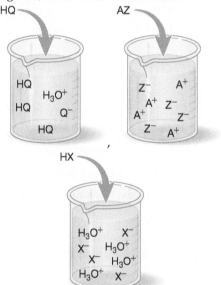

Target boxes: strong acid, weak acid, not an acid

12.18 Identify the strongest acid. Refer to the Table 12.1.

a) $H_2PO_4^-$ b) NaOH c) H_3PO_4 d) HF

12.19 Classify each chemical compound as a strong acid, weak acid, strong base, or weak base. Refer to Tables 12.1 and 12.2.

Answer choices: $Ba(OH)_2$, HBr, NH_3, CH_3COOH, KOH, HNO_3, NH_4^+

Target boxes: strong acid, weak acid, strong base, weak base

12.20 Identify the strongest acid. Refer to Table 12.1.

a) NH_4^+ b) H_2O c) H_3PO_4 d) H_2SO_4

12.21 Classify each compound as a strong acid, weak acid, strong base, or weak base. Refer to Tables 12.1 and 12.2.

Answer choices: CH_3NH_2, H_2CO_3, H_2SO_4, $Ca(OH)_2$, HI, LiOH, HCN

Target boxes: strong acid, weak acid, strong base, weak base

12.22 Identify the diprotic acid.

a) $Mg(OH)_2$ b) H_3PO_4

c) CH_3NH_2 d) H_2SO_4

12.23 Identify the diprotic acid.

a) CH_3OH b) H_2CO_3

c) H_2 d) $Ca(OH)_2$

12.24 Which is the triprotic acid?

a) NH_3 b) $Al(OH)_3$

c) H_3PO_4 d) H_2CO_3

12.25 Identify the strongest base. Refer to Table 12.2.

a) CH_3COO^- b) OH^-

c) NH_3 d) Br^-

12.26 Which of the compounds is correctly identified? Refer to Tables 12.1 and 12.2.

a) H_2CO_3, strong acid

b) $Mg(OH)_2$, weak base

c) CN^-, strong base

d) ClO_4^-, strong base

e) CH_3COOH, strong acid

12.27 Identify the strongest base in the set. Refer to Table 12.2.

a) OH^- b) HCO_3^-

c) H_3O^+ d) ClO_4^-

12.28 Sort these aqueous chemical reactions into those that favor reactants and those that favor products at equilibrium. Refer to Tables 12.1 and 12.2.

$$HNO_3 + H_2O \rightleftharpoons H_3O^+ + NO_3^-$$
$$HCO_3^- + H_2O \rightleftharpoons H_2CO_3 + OH^-$$
$$NH_4^+ + F^- \rightleftharpoons NH_3 + HF$$
$$HBr + H_2O \rightleftharpoons H_3O^+ + Br^-$$

Target boxes: products favored, reactants favored

12.29 Sort these aqueous chemical reactions into those that favor reactants and those that favor products at equilibrium. Refer to Tables 12.1 and 12.2.

$$CH_3COOH + H_2O \rightleftharpoons CH_3COO^- + H_3O^+$$
$$HCN + H_2O \rightleftharpoons CN^- + H_3O^+$$
$$H_3PO_4 + H_2O \rightleftharpoons H_3O^+ + H_2PO_4^-$$
$$H_2PO_4^- + OH^- \rightleftharpoons H_2O + HPO_4^{2-}$$

Target boxes: products favored, reactants favored

12.30 Sort these aqueous chemical reactions into those that favor reactants and those that favor products at equilibrium. Refer to Tables 12.1 and 12.2.

$$H_2CO_3 + H_2O \rightleftharpoons H_3O^+ + HCO_3^-$$
$$NH_4^+ + H_2O \rightleftharpoons H_3O^+ + NH_3$$
$$NH_3 + HSO_4^- \rightleftharpoons NH_4^+ + SO_4^{2-}$$
$$HCN + F^- \rightleftharpoons HF + CN^-$$

Target boxes: products favored, reactants favored

12.3 Acid Dissociation Constants

LO 12.3: **Write the acid dissociation constant expression (K_a) and relate it to acid strength.**

12.31 Which statement about equilibrium and acid dissociation constants is correct?

a) Equilibrium favors the formation of the weaker acid (the acid with the smaller K_a value).

b) Equilibrium favors the formation of the stronger acid (the acid with the smaller K_a value).

c) Equilibrium favors the formation of the weaker acid (the acid with the larger K_a value).

d) Equilibrium favors the formation of the stronger base (the base with the larger K_a value).

12.32 Hydrogen sulfide (H_2S) is produced in swamps and sewers from the microbial breakdown of organic material in the absence of oxygen gas. H_2S is also found in volcanic gases, natural gas, some sources of well water, and even the human body in small amounts as a signaling molecule. Which is the K_a expression for H_2S?

$$H_2S\,(aq) + H_2O(l) \rightleftharpoons H_3O^+(aq) + HS^-(aq)$$

a) $K_a = \dfrac{[H_3O^+][HS^-]}{[H_2S][H_2O]}$

b) $K_a = \dfrac{[H_2S][H_2O]}{[H_3O^+][HS^-]}$

c) $K_a = \dfrac{[H_3O^+][HS^-]}{[H_2S]}$

d) $K_a = \dfrac{[H_2S]}{[H_3O^+][HS^-]}$

12.33 When dissolved in water, phosphoric acid (H_3PO_4) dissociates to form the hydronium ion and the dihydrogen phosphate anion. The K_a of phosphoric acid is 7.5×10^{-3}. Which is the dissociation reaction and acid dissociation expression?

a) $H_3PO_4(aq) + H_2O(l) \rightleftharpoons H_3O^+(aq) + H_2PO_4^-(aq)$

$$K_a = \dfrac{[H_3PO_4]}{[H_3O^+][H_2PO_4^-]} = 7.5 \times 10^{-3}$$

b) $H_2PO_4^-(aq) + H_3O^+(aq) \rightleftharpoons H_3PO_4(aq) + H_2O(l)$

$$K_a = \dfrac{[H_3PO_4]}{[H_3O^+][H_2PO_4^-]} = 7.5 \times 10^{-3}$$

c) $H_3PO_4(aq) + H_2O(l) \rightleftharpoons H_3O^+(aq) + H_2PO_4^-(aq)$

$$K_a = \dfrac{[H_3O^+][H_2PO_4^-]}{[H_3PO_4][H_2O]} = 7.5 \times 10^{-3}$$

d) $H_3PO_4(aq) + H_2O(l) \rightleftharpoons H_3O^+(aq) + H_2PO_4^-(aq)$

$$K_a = \dfrac{[H_3O^+][H_2PO_4^-]}{[H_3PO_4]} = 7.5 \times 10^{-3}$$

12.34 Without referring to a reference table, identify the strongest acid in the set based on the given K_a values.

a) H_2S, $K_a = 9.1 \times 10^{-8}$

b) $H_2PO_4^-$, $K_a = 6.2 \times 10^{-8}$

c) H_2CO_3, $K_a = 4.3 \times 10^{-7}$

d) HCN, $K_a = 4.9 \times 10^{-10}$

12.35 Without referring to a reference table, identify the weakest acid in the set based on the given K_a values.

a) H_2CO_3, $K_a = 4.3 \times 10^{-7}$

b) H_3PO_4, $K_a = 7.5 \times 10^{-3}$

c) CH_3COOH, $K_a = 1.8 \times 10^{-5}$

d) $H_2PO_4^-$, $K_a = 6.2 \times 10^{-8}$

12.36 Formic acid is found in the venom of several ants and insects. The structure of formic acid (also known as methanoic acid) is shown below. Its K_a value is 1.8×10^{-4}. Based on this information, and without referring to a table, identify the true statement about formic acid.

formic acid
(methanoic acid)

a) Formic acid is a triprotic acid.

b) Formic acid is a strong acid.

c) Formic acid is a weak acid.

d) Formic acid is a diprotic acid.

12.37 Rank the K_a values left-to-right by increasing acid strength. The weakest acid should be placed farthest to the left on the scale.

Answer choices:

$K_a = 1.5 \times 10^{-5}$,

$K_a = 1.1 \times 10^{-3}$,

$K_a = 8.7 \times 10^{-9}$,

$K_a = 9.8 \times 10^{-7}$

Target boxes: four boxes placed left to right

12.38 Increasing levels of carbon dioxide (CO_2) in our atmosphere are contributing to ocean acidification. When carbon dioxide dissolves in water, carbonic acid (H_2CO_3) is formed, making our oceans become more acidic. If an environmental scientist measures the equilibrium concentration of HCO_3^- and H_3O^+ to each have a value of 1.5×10^{-6} M, what is the concentration of H_2CO_3 in solution in units of molarity (M)?

$$H_2CO_3(aq) + H_2O(l) \rightleftharpoons H_3O^+(aq) + HCO_3^-(aq)$$

a) 1.9×10^5 M

b) 4.3×10^{-7} M

c) 1.5×10^{-6} M

d) 5.3×10^{-6} M

12.39 Carbonic acid is a diprotic acid. Identify the K_a expression for the *second* dissociation of carbonic acid in water. To get you started, the equation for the *first* dissociation of carbonic acid is shown below.

$$H_2CO_3(aq) + H_2O(l) \leftrightharpoons H_3O^+(aq) + HCO_3^-(aq)$$

a) $K_a = \dfrac{[H_3O^+][HCO_3^-]}{[H_2CO_3]}$

b) $K_a = \dfrac{[HCO_3^-]}{[H_3O^+][CO_3^{2-}]}$

c) $K_a = \dfrac{[H_3O^+][CO_3^{2-}]}{[HCO_3^-][H_2O]}$

d) $K_a = \dfrac{[H_3O^+][CO_3^{2-}]}{[HCO_3^-]}$

12.4 Pure Water Ionization

LO 12.4: Use the water dissociation constant (K_w) and ion concentrations to determine if a solution is acidic, basic, or neutral.

12.40 Which statement about balance between hydroxide and hydronium ion concentrations is correct for aqueous solutions?

a) In acidic solutions, $[OH^-]$ is greater than $[H_3O^+]$.

b) In neutral solutions, $[H_3O^+] = [H_2O]$.

c) In acidic solutions, $[OH^-]$ is less than $[H_3O^+]$.

d) In acidic solutions, $[H_2O]$ is less than $[H_3O^+]$.

12.41 Which statement about balance between hydroxide and hydronium ion concentrations is correct for aqueous solutions?

a) In basic solutions, $[H_2O]$ is less than $[OH^-]$.

b) In basic solutions, $[OH^-]$ is greater than $[H_3O^+]$.

c) In basic solutions, $[OH^-]$ is less than $[H_3O^+]$.

d) In neutral solutions, $[OH^-] = [H_2O]$.

12.42 Which is the product of $[H_3O^+]$ and $[OH^-]$ for K_w?

a) 7.0

b) 1.0×10^{-7}

c) 1.0×10^{14}

d) 7.0×10^{-14}

e) 1.0×10^{-14}

12.43 During a chemistry lab experiment, your lab team determines that the $[OH^-]$ is 1×10^{-10}. What is the $[H_3O^+]$ in this solution? Express your answer in scientific notation with one significant figure and units of M.

☐ M

12.44 What is the concentration of hydroxide $[OH^-]$ in an aqueous solution that has a hydronium $[H_3O^+]$ concentration of 1×10^{-5}? Express your answer in scientific notation with one significant figure and units of M.

☐ M

12.45 What is the concentration of the hydronium ion $[H_3O^+]$ in an aqueous solution that has a hydroxide ion $[OH^-]$ concentration of 8.2×10^{-3}? Express your answer in scientific notation with two significant figures and units of M.

☐

12.46 A physician's assistant receives results from the clinical lab for the $[OH^-]$ and $[H_3O^+]$ values for samples from her patient. Categorize each solution as acidic or basic.

blood $[OH^-] = 3.3 \times 10^{-7}$ M

urine $[H_3O^+] = 5.7 \times 10^{-6}$ M

gastric fluid $[OH^-] = 3.1 \times 10^{-12}$ M

semen $[OH^-] = 7.9 \times 10^{-7}$ M

saliva $[H_3O^+] = 2.0 \times 10^{-7}$ M

Target boxes: acidic, basic

12.47 Categorize each of the following solutions as acidic, basic, or neutral.

$[OH^-] = 1.7 \times 10^{-6}$ M

$[H_3O^+] = 2.5 \times 10^{-4}$ M

$[H_3O^+] = 9.2 \times 10^{-9}$ M

$[OH^-] = 1.0 \times 10^{-7}$ M

$[OH^-] = 6.4 \times 10^{-11}$ M

Target boxes: acidic, basic, neutral

12.48 A chemistry student measures the $[OH]$ and $[H_3O^+]$ values for aqueous solutions of some household items. Categorize each solution as acidic, basic, or neutral.

baking soda $[OH^-] = 1.4 \times 10^{-8}$ M

coffee $[H_3O^+] = 6.4 \times 10^{-6}$ M

aspirin $[H_3O^+] = 3.6 \times 10^{-4}$ M

soap $[OH^-] = 1.2 \times 10^{-6}$ M

cleanser $[H_3O^+] = 5.7 \times 10^{-10}$ M

orange juice $[OH^-] = 2.8 \times 10^{-12}$ M

Target boxes: acidic, basic, neutral

12.49 Which description best characterizes an aqueous solution with $[OH^-] = 7.0$ M?

a) slightly acidic

b) strongly basic

c) strongly acidic

d) slightly basic

e) exactly neutral

12.50 Which description best characterizes an aqueous solution with $[H_3O^+] = 7.0 \times 10^{-7}$ M?

a) slightly basic   b) exactly neutral

c) strongly basic   d) slightly acidic

e) strongly acidic

12.51 A student in the chemistry lab dissolves 2.1×10^{-3} mol of NaOH in water to make 3.5 L of solution. What is the concentration of hydronium ion $[H_3O^+]$ in this aqueous solution? M = mol/L.

a) $[H_3O^+] = 1.7 \times 10^{-11}$ M

b) $[H_3O^+] = 4.8 \times 10^{-12}$ M

c) $[H_3O^+] = 6.0 \times 10^{10}$ M

d) $[H_3O^+] = 1.7 \times 10^{11}$ M

12.52 Acids in the stomach such as HCl help digest the food we eat. A medical student studying the role of hydrochloric acid digestion dissolved 2.25 g of HCl in 1.75 L of water to form an HCl solution. What is the concentration of hydroxide ion $[OH^-]$ in this aqueous solution? The molar mass of HCl is 36.46 g/mol and molarity M = mol/L. Hint: First calculate the concentration of the HCl solution in units of molarity (M).

a) $[OH^-] = 7.8 \times 10^{-15}$ M

b) $[OH^-] = 3.5 \times 10^{12}$ M

c) $[OH^-] = 1.1 \times 10^{-15}$ M

d) $[OH^-] = 2.8 \times 10^{-13}$ M

12.5 pH

LO 12.5: Calculate pH to report the acidity or basicity of a solution from 0-14.

12.53 You and your lab partner measure the pH of some lab samples as part of an experiment in your anatomy and physiology (A&P) class. Categorize each solution as acidic, basic, or neutral.

blood plasma pH = 7.5

urine pH = 5.8

phosphate buffered saline pH = 7.0

gastric fluid pH = 1.2

sweat pH = 5.6

Target boxes: acidic, basic, neutral

12.54 A student measures the concentrations of H_3O^+ and OH^- in four different aqueous solutions in the lab. Which set of concentrations indicates a neutral solution?

a) $[H_3O^+] = 2.7 \times 10^{-11}$ M,
   $[OH^-] = 3.7 \times 10^{-4}$ M

b) $[H_3O^+] = 1.0 \times 10^{-2}$ M,
   $[OH^-] = 1.0 \times 10^{-12}$ M

c) $[H_3O^+] = 1.0 \times 10^{-7}$ M,
   $[OH^-] = 1.0 \times 10^{-7}$ M

d) $[H_3O^+] = 7.0 \times 10^{-6}$ M,
   $[OH^-] = 1.0 \times 10^{-9}$ M

12.55 A lab technician analyzed patient samples for a clinical research study. Categorize each bodily fluid as acidic, basic, or neutral.

pancreatic fluid pH = 8.4

saliva pH = 6.6

cerebrospinal fluid pH = 7.3

tears pH = 7.4

bile pH = 8.0

Target boxes: acidic, basic, neutral

12.56 Which description best characterizes a sample of lake water with a pH of 6.3?

a) extremely basic   b) slightly acidic

c) extremely acidic   d) slightly basic

12.57 Which description best characterizes an aqueous solution with a pH of 12.7?

a) extremely basic   b) slightly acidic

c) slightly basic   d) extremely acidic

12.58 A team of undergraduate research students is studying a cell culture sample with a concentration of $[H_3O^+] = 8.3 \times 10^{-6}$ M. What is the pH of this cell culture solution?

a) 8.30   b) 5.08

c) 6.92   d) 0.919

e) −5.08

12.59 Diabetic ketoacidosis (DKA) is a serious and potentially life-threatening condition that can occur in people with diabetes. DKA develops when there isn't enough insulin in the body to allow sufficient blood sugar into cells for use as energy. As a result, the liver begins to rapidly break down fat for fuel resulting in the blood becoming too acidic (below the normal pH value of 7.4). What is the $[H_3O^+]$ concentration in a patient hospitalized with DKA whose blood pH is 7.21? Express your answer in scientific notation with two significant figures and units of M.

12.60 Urine tests are routinely performed in clinics and hospitals to help assess health conditions of patients. A nurse is tending to a hospital patient with kidney disease. The pH of the patient's urine is 3.85. What is the $[H_3O^+]$ concentration in this urine sample?

a) 1.4×10^{-4} M   **b)** 5.9×10^{-1} M

c) 7.1×10^3 M   **d)** -1.4×10^{-4} M

12.61 An environmental scientist studying forest soils prepares an aqueous solution with a pH of 5.75. What is the concentration of hydronium ion $[H_3O^+]$ in this solution?

a) 8.25 M   **b)** $1 \times 10^{5.57}$ M   **c)** 5.75×10^{-7} M

d) 1.8×10^{-6} M   **e)** 6.0×10^{-9} M

12.62 A river that has been contaminated with industrial waste is being monitored by a team of environmental scientists. On the day following the contamination event, the concentration of $[H_3O^+]$ was measured to be 2.5×10^{-9} M. What is the pH of the river water sample? Express your answer in decimal form with three significant figures.

12.63 What is the pH of a solution with a concentration of $[OH^-] = 1 \times 10^{-5}$?

a) 5.0   **b)** 9.0   **c)** −5.0   **d)** 1×10^{-9}

12.64 A clinical sample was found to have a pH of 8.24. What is the hydroxide $[OH^-]$ concentration of this solution? Express your answer in scientific notation with two significant figures.

12.6 Acid-Base Reactions

LO 12.6: Write balanced equations for neutralization reactions and recognize reactions of acids with bicarbonate and carbonate.

12.65 Lithium hydroxide (LiOH) is used in the production of lithium-ion batteries in the electronics industry. Sulfuric acid (H_2SO_4) is used in the production of a wide range of consumer products. Which equation for the complete neutralization of sulfuric acid with lithium hydroxide is correctly balanced?

a) $H_2SO_4(aq) + Li_2OH(aq) \rightarrow Li_2SO_4(aq) + 2H_2O(l)$

b) $2HSO_4(aq) + 2LiOH(aq) \rightarrow Li_2SO_4(aq) + 2H_2O(l)$

c) $2H_2SO_4(aq) + 2Li(OH)_2(aq) \rightarrow 2LiSO_4(aq) + 4H_2O(l)$

d) $H_2SO_4(aq) + 2LiOH(aq) \rightarrow Li_2SO_4(aq) + 2H_2O(l)$

12.66 Strontium hydroxide $Sr(OH)_2$ is used in the plastics industry. Phosphoric acid H_3PO_4 is used in a wide variety of products in the food and detergent industries. Which equation for the complete neutralization of phosphoric acid with strontium hydroxide is correctly balanced?

a) $3H_3PO_4(aq) + 2Sr(OH)_2(aq) \rightarrow Ca_3(PO_4)_3(aq) + 5H_2O(l)$

b) $2H_3PO_4(aq) + 3Sr(OH)_2(aq) \rightarrow Sr_3(PO_4)_2(aq) + 6H_2O(l)$

c) $4H_3PO_4(aq) + 6Sr(OH)_2(aq) \rightarrow 2Sr_3(PO_4)_3(aq) + 12H_2O(l)$

d) $3H_3PO_4(aq) + Sr(OH)_2(aq) \rightarrow SrH(PO_4)_2(aq) + 2H_2O(l)$

12.67 What is the net equation for the acid-base neutralization reaction between hydrobromic acid (HBr) and cesium hydroxide (CsOH)?

a) $HBr(aq) + CsOH(aq) \rightarrow CsBr(aq) + H_2O(l)$

b) $H^+(aq) + Br^-(aq) + Cs^+(aq) + OH^-(aq) \rightarrow Cs^+(aq) + Br^-(aq) + H_2O(l)$

c) $H^+(aq) + OH^-(aq) \rightarrow H_2O(l)$ **d)** $Cs^+(aq) + Br^-(aq) \rightarrow CsBr(aq)$

12.68 Identify the spectator ions in the reaction shown.

$$HNO_3(aq) + LiOH(aq) \rightarrow LiNO_3(aq) + H_2O(l)$$

a) H^+ (aq) and NO_3^- (aq)   **b)** Li^+ (aq) and H_2O (l)   **c)** H^+ (aq) and OH^- (aq)   **d)** Li^+ (aq) and NO_3^- (aq)

12.69 Which of the following is an example of an acid-base neutralization reaction?

a) $CH_3CH_2OH(aq) \rightarrow 2CO_2(g) + 3H_2O(l)$

b) $Ca(OH)_2(s) + 2HI(aq) \rightarrow CaI_2(aq) + 2H_2O(l)$

c) $Na_3PO_4(aq) + MgCl_2(aq) \rightarrow Mg_3(PO_4)_2(s) + NaCl(aq)$

d) $MgO(s) + CO_2(g) \rightarrow MgCO_3(s)$

12.70 Identify the reaction that is *not* an acid-base neutralization.

a) $BaCl_2(aq) + Na_2SO_4(aq) \rightarrow BaSO_4(s) + 2NaCl(aq)$

b) $Ba(OH)_2(s) + 2HBr(aq) \rightarrow BaBr_2(aq) + 2H_2O(l)$

c) $HCl(aq) + NaHCO_3(aq) \rightarrow NaCl(aq) + CO_2(g) + H_2O(l)$

d) $HNO_3(aq) + NaOH(aq) \rightarrow NaNO_3(aq) + H_2O(l)$

12.71 What are the products formed in a complete acid-base neutralization reaction between nitric acid (HNO_3) and potassium carbonate (K_2CO_3)?

$$2HNO_3(aq) + K_2CO_3(aq) \rightarrow \underline{\hspace{3cm}}$$

a) $2K^+(aq) + CO_3^{2-}(aq) + H^+(aq) + NO_3^-(aq) + H_2O(l)$

b) $2K^+(aq) + CO_3^{2-}(aq) + H^+(aq) + NO_3^-(aq)$

c) $KHCO_3 + KNO_3 + H_2O(l)$ **d)** $CO_2(g) + H_2O(l) + 2KNO_3(aq)$

12.7 Titration

LO 12.7: Calculate the molarity of an acid or base solution from titration measurements.

12.72 Which compound (in aqueous solution) would be most useful in determining the unknown molarity of an H_2SO_4 solution using titration measurements?

a) Na_2SO_4 **b)** HCl

c) NaCl   **d)** NaOH

12.73 A student conducting undergraduate research in the chemistry laboratory wants to determine the molarity of a $Mg(OH)_2$ solution she is studying. She has the following set of solutions in the laboratory that have known concentrations. Which would be most useful to use in a titration measurement to determine the concentration of her unknown $Mg(OH)_2$ solution?

a) NaOH (aq)   **b)** HBr (aq)

c) NaCl (aq)   **d)** $MgCl_2$ (aq)

12.74 Which best describes the titration end point of an acid using a base of known concentration?

　a) when the volume of OH^- added is equal to volume of H^+ present

　b) when the pH indicator phenolphthalein begins to form bubbles of CO_2

　c) when the moles of OH^- added is equal to moles of H^+ present

　d) when all of the NaOH in the burette has been added to the acid

　e) when all of the unknown acid in the burette has been added to the base

12.75 A researcher is planning a titration experiment. How many moles of HCl are required to completely neutralize a solution containing 1.85 moles of $Mg(OH)_2$? Hint: consider the mole ratio in the balanced neutralization reaction shown.

$$2HCl(aq) + Mg(OH)_2(aq) \rightarrow 2H_2O(l) + MgCl_2(aq)$$

　a) 1.85 moles 　　　　b) 2.00 moles

　c) 3.70 moles 　　　　d) 0.925 moles

12.76 A student working on his lab assignment for chemistry class is planning out a titration experiment. How many moles of $Ca(OH)_2$ are required to completely neutralize a solution containing 3.68 moles of H_2SO_4? Hint: consider the mole ratio in the balanced neutralization reaction shown.

$$H_2SO_4(aq) + Ca(OH)_2(aq) \rightarrow 2H_2O(l) + CaSO_4(aq)$$

　a) 2.00 moles 　　　　b) 7.36 moles

　c) 1.84 moles 　　　　d) 3.68 moles

12.77 A team of students is studying the environmental impact of magnesium hydroxide and phosphoric acid contamination on drinking water found in wells around agricultural fields. The group needs to perform a titration experiment and is working on their calculations. How many moles of $Mg(OH)_2$ are required to completely neutralize a solution containing 6.73×10^{-4} moles of H_3PO_4? You may find it helpful to refer to the mole ratio in the balanced equation shown.

$$2H_3PO_4(aq) + 3Mg(OH)_2(aq) \rightarrow Mg_3(PO_4)_2(aq) + 6H_2O(l)$$

　a) 1.01×10^{-3} moles $Mg(OH)_2$

　b) 1.35×10^{-3} moles $Mg(OH)_2$

　c) 3.37×10^{-4} moles $Mg(OH)_2$

　d) 4.49×10^{-4} moles $Mg(OH)_2$

　e) 2.02×10^{-3} moles $Mg(OH)_2$

12.78 What is the concentration of a sodium hydroxide solution if 25.5 mL of a 0.175 M HCl solution is required to completely neutralize 25.5 mL of the NaOH solution? Try to determine the answer without using a calculator if you can. Express your answer in standard decimal form with three significant figures and units of M.

$$HCl(aq) + NaOH(aq) \rightarrow NaCl(aq) + H_2O(l)$$

12.79 If 16.2 mL of a 0.125 M HNO_3 solution is required to completely neutralize 10.5 mL of a NaOH solution, what is the concentration of the NaOH?

$$HNO_3(aq) + NaOH(aq) \rightarrow NaNO_3(aq) + H_2O(l)$$

　a) 5.19 M 　　　　b) 193 M

　c) 12.3 M 　　　　d) 0.193 M

12.80 How many *liters* of a 1.50×10^{-3} M sodium hydroxide solution are required to completely neutralize 1.25 L of a 1.50×10^{-3} M HBr solution? Express your answer in standard decimal form with three significant figures and units of M.

$$HBr(aq) + NaOH(aq) \rightarrow NaBr(aq) + H_2O(l)$$

12.81 What is the molarity of a KOH solution if an 18.0 mL test sample is neutralized by 28.0 mL of a 0.350 M HCl solution?

$$HCl(aq) + KOH(aq) \rightarrow KCl(aq) + H_2O(l)$$

　a) $[KOH] = 6.3$ M

　b) $[KOH] = 0.544$ M

　c) $[KOH] = 544$ M

　d) $[KOH] = 5.44 \times 10^{-4}$ M

12.82 A plastics manufacturing facility is found to have illegally dumped phosphoric acid waste into a nearby lake. Environmental scientists conduct a titration to determine the concentration of the acid and find that a 50.0-mL sample of H_3PO_4 contaminated water requires 11.5 mL of 0.250-M NaOH for complete neutralization. What is the molarity of the phosphoric acid in the lake water? *Hint*: Pay special attention to the mole ratio in the balanced equation and note that H_3PO_4 is a triprotic acid.

$$H_3PO_4(aq) + 3NaOH(aq) \rightarrow Na_3PO_4(aq) + 3H_2O(l)$$

　a) $[H_3PO_4] = 1.92 \times 10^{-2}$ M

　b) $[H_3PO_4] = 5.75 \times 10^{-2}$ M

　c) $[H_3PO_4] = 52.1$ M

　d) $[H_3PO_4] = 1.92 \times 10^{-5}$ M

12.8 Buffers

LO 12.8: **Explain the role of the weak acid and conjugate base in a buffer and calculate the buffer's pH.**

12.83 What is the function of a buffer?

a) act as a strong base when a strong acid is added

b) maintain a neutral pH of 7

c) maintain the pH of a solution

d) indicate the end point of a titration reaction

e) act as a strong acid when a strong base is added

12.84 Which of the following represents the best aqueous buffer solution? Refer to Tables 12.1 and 12.2.

a) $0.5\ M\ NaCl(aq)$ and $0.5\ M\ NaBr(aq)$

b) $1.5\ M\ H_2PO_4^-(aq)$ and $1.5\ M\ HPO_4^{2-}(aq)$

c) $1.0\ M\ H_3PO_4(aq)$ and $1.0\ M\ H_2SO_4(aq)$

d) $0.5\ M\ NaOH(aq)$ and $0.5\ M\ H_2O(l)$

12.85 Which set of compounds would form a buffered aqueous solution and which would not? Refer to Tables 12.1 and 12.2.

KCl and HCl

HI and NaI

HF and NaF

KBr and KOH

Target boxes: buffer, not a buffer

12.86 Which set of compounds would form a buffered aqueous solution and which would not? Refer to Tables 12.1 and 12.2.

HCN and H_2O

HCO_3^- and CO_3^{2-}

HPO_4^{2-} and PO_4^{3-}

HBr and NaBr

acetic acid and sodium acetate

Target boxes: buffer, not a buffer

12.87 Equal concentrations of which of the following would make a good aqueous buffer system? Refer to Tables 12.1 and 12.2.

a) H_2SO_4 and CH_3OH

b) H_3PO_4 and NaH_2PO_4

c) HNO_3 and KNO_3

d) $NaCl$ and $NaBr$

12.88 What is the function of the CO_3^{2-} in an aqueous buffer of HCO_3^- and CO_3^{2-}?

Refer to Table 12.1.

a) The CO_3^{2-} is not necessary since it is the conjugate base of HCO_3^-.

b) The CO_3^{2-} neutralizes added H_2O.

c) The CO_3^{2-} neutralizes added base.

d) The CO_3^{2-} neutralizes added acid.

12.89 Hydrogen cyanide (HCN) occurs naturally at low levels in the pits of fruits such as cherries, apricots, apples, and bitter almonds. However, HCN is also quite toxic at elevated levels and has been used as a chemical weapon. Which statement describes a buffer containing HCN and its salt NaCN? Refer to Table 12.1.

a) The CN^- neutralizes added base.

b) The HCN neutralizes added base.

c) The HCN neutralizes added acid.

d) The HCN is a strong acid, so this is not a buffered system.

12.90 Consider the buffer solution shown. Drag the quantities below to build the reaction that takes place when the base NaOH is added to the buffer solution.

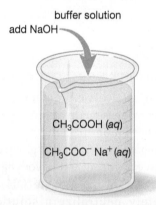

buffer solution
add NaOH

$CH_3COOH\ (aq)$

$CH_3COO^-\ Na^+\ (aq)$

$CH_3COOH(aq) + H_2O(l)$

$CH_3COO^-\ Na^+(aq) + HCl(aq)$

$CH_3COO^-\ Na^+(aq) + H_2O(l)$

$CH_3COOH(aq) + NaCl(aq)$

$CH_3COOH(aq) + NaOH(aq)$

$CH_3CO_3H(aq) + NaCl(aq)$

Target boxes:

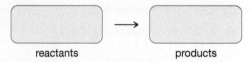

reactants   products

12.91 Consider the buffer solution shown. Drag the quantities below to build the reaction that takes place when the acid HCl is added to the buffer solution.

buffer solution

add HCl

HF (aq)

NaF (aq)

$NaF(aq) + H_2O(l)$

$HF(aq) + NaCl(aq)$

$HF(aq) + HCl(aq)$

$NaCl(aq) + H_2O(l)$

$HCl(aq) + NaF(aq)$

$HF(aq) + NaF(aq)$

Target boxes:

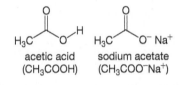

reactants   products

12.92 A medicinal chemist working in the laboratory prepares a buffer solution containing 0.75 M acetic acid (CH_3COOH) and 0.75 M sodium acetate ($CH_3COO^-Na^+$) for a study she is conducting on drug stability. The K_a of acetic acid is 1.8×10^{-5}. What is the pH of this buffer solution? Express your answer in standard decimal form with three significant figures.

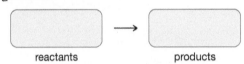

acetic acid   sodium acetate
(CH_3COOH)   ($CH_3COO^-Na^+$)

12.93 An oceanographer studying ocean acidification prepares a buffer in the laboratory. The solution contains 0.25 M sodium bicarbonate ($NaHCO_3$) and 0.25 M sodium carbonate (Na_2CO_3) for a study they are conducting on coral reef degradation. The overall buffer reaction is shown below and the K_a of bicarbonate HCO_3^- is 5.6×10^{-11}. What is the pH of this buffer solution? Express your answer in standard decimal form with four significant figures.

$$HCO_3^-(aq) + H_2O(l) \rightleftharpoons H_3O^+(aq) + CO_3^{2-}(aq)$$

12.94 A physician's assistant working in a clinical laboratory prepares a buffer containing 0.75 M hydrogen phosphate (HPO_4^{2-}) and 0.55 M phosphate (PO_4^{3-}) for an experiment on the stability of different metabolic enzymes. What is the pH of this buffer? The K_a of hydrogen phosphate (HPO_4^{2-}) is 2.2×10^{-13}.

$$HPO_4^{2-}(aq) + H_2O(l) \rightleftharpoons PO_4^{3-}(aq) + H_3O^+(aq)$$

a) $pH = -12.79$

b) $pH = 12.66$

c) $pH = 12.79$

d) $pH = 12.52$

Chapter 13

13.1 Organic Compounds

LO 1: Recognize the fundamental structural features of organic compounds and use appropriate representations to draw molecules.

13.01 Classify the following compounds as organic or inorganic.

Answer choices: $MgCl_2$, proteins, NaBr, lipids, carbohydrates, DNA

Target boxes: inorganic compounds, organic compounds

13.02 Select the correct Lewis dot structure of carbon.

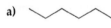

a)   b)

c)   d)

13.03 Classify each molecule according to its structure as a branched chain, ring, or straight-chain molecule.

Answer choices:

a)   b)

c)   d)

e)   f)

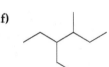

g)   h)

i.

Target boxes: branched chain, ring, or straight-chain

13.04 Identify which molecules contain the correct number of bonds and which do not.

Answer choices:

a)

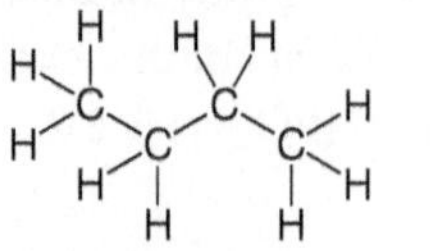

b)

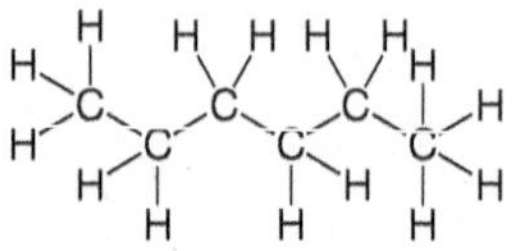

c)

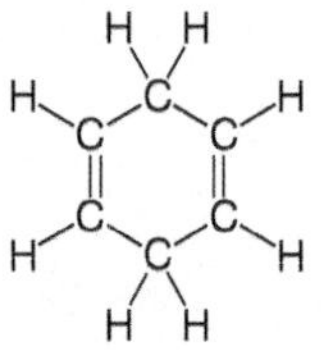

d)

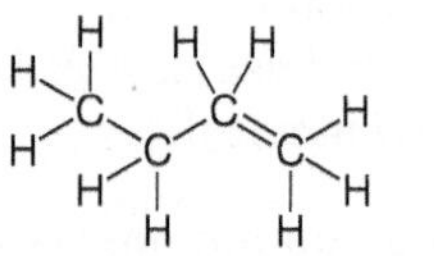

e)

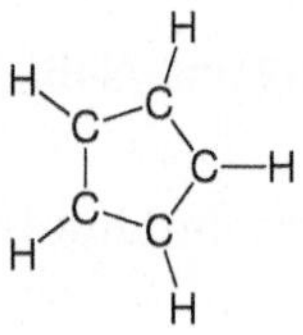

f)

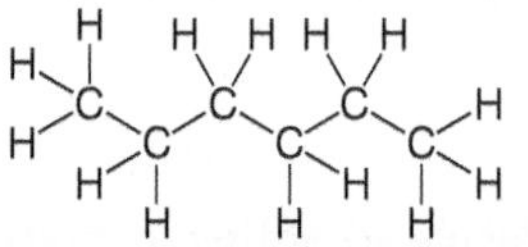

Target boxes: correct number of bonds, incorrect number of bonds

13.05 Select the correct bond angle for each example.

Answer choices: 109°, 102°, 108°, 190°, 120°, 180°

Target boxes:

a)

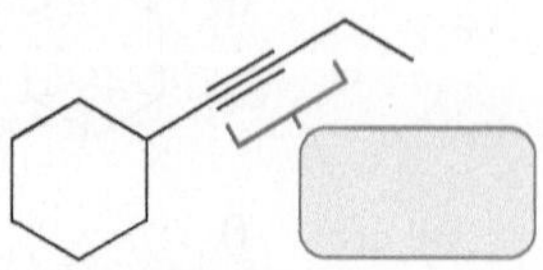

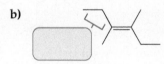

b)

c)

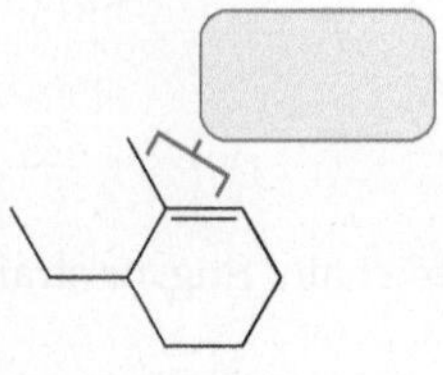

13.06 Determine the bond angles indicated by the letters A-C.

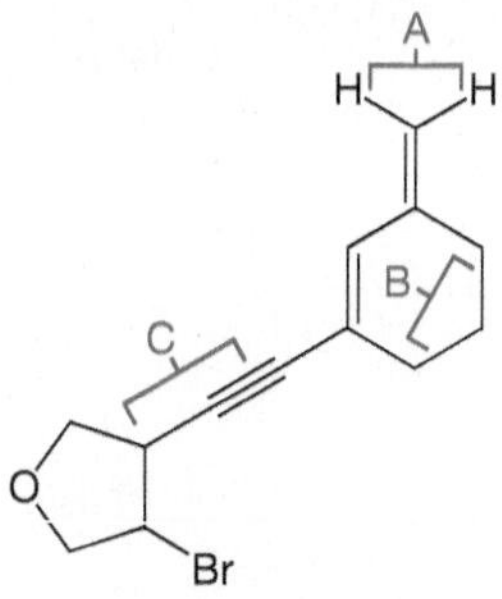

Answer choices: 102°, 120°, 108°, 180°, 109°, 190°

Target boxes: angle A, angle B, angle C

13.07 Terbinafine, also known as Lamisil, is an antifungal medication used to treat certain skin and nail infections, including ringworm, jock itch, and athlete's foot. Determine the geometry around each indicated carbon atom on the terbinafine molecule.

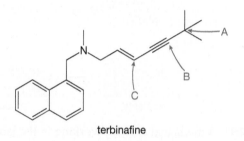

terbinafine

Answer choices: octahedral, tetrahedral, trigonal planar, linear

Target boxes: geometry about carbon A, geometry about carbon B, geometry about carbon C

13.08 Match each description with the appropriate heteroatom.

heteroatom: N, O, Cl

description:
- A heteroatom with six valence electrons, forms two bonds, and has two lone pairs of electrons
- A heteroatom with seven valence electrons, forms one bond, and has three lone pairs of electrons
- A heteroatom with five valence electrons, forms three bonds, and has one lone pair of electrons

13.09 Match each atom with the appropriate description.

atom: P, S, F

description:
- A heteroatom with six valence electrons, forms two bonds leaving two lone pairs of electrons
- A heteroatom with seven valence electrons, forms one bond leaving three lone pairs of electrons
- A heteroatom with five valence electrons, forms three bonds leaving one lone pair of electrons

13.10 Which set of molecules shows a Lewis structure, condensed structure, and skeletal structure of the same molecule?

a)

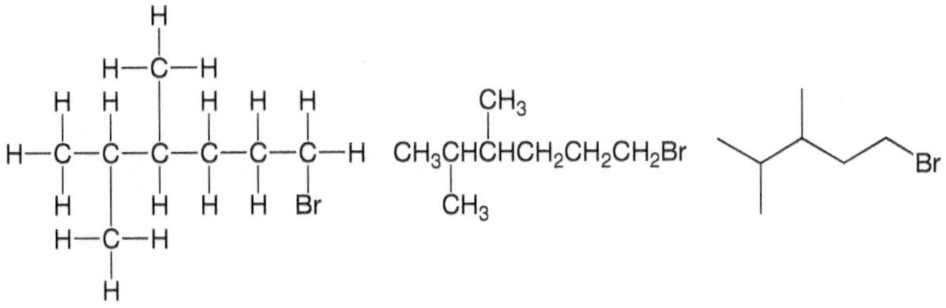

CH₃CHCHCH₂CH₂CH₂Br (CH₃ substituents)

b)

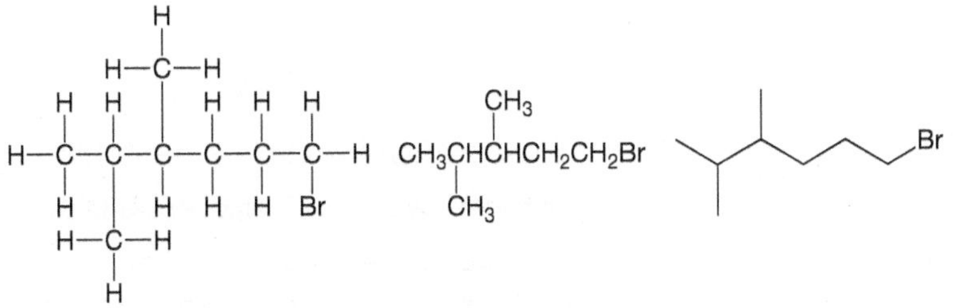

CH₃CHCHCH₂CH₂Br (CH₃ substituents)

c)

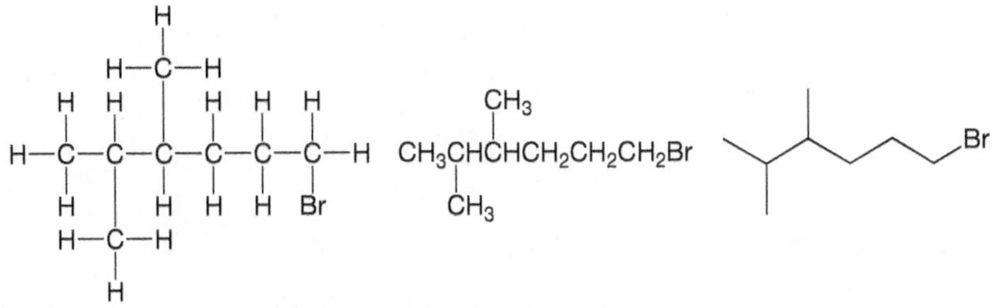

CH₃CHCHCH₂CH₂CH₂Br (CH₃ substituents)

d)

CH₃CHCHCH₂CH₂CH₂Br (CH₃ substituents)

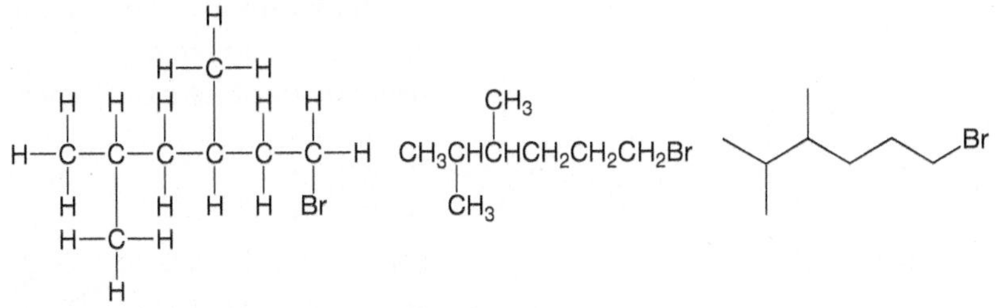

13.11 Select the condensed structure that matches this Lewis structure.

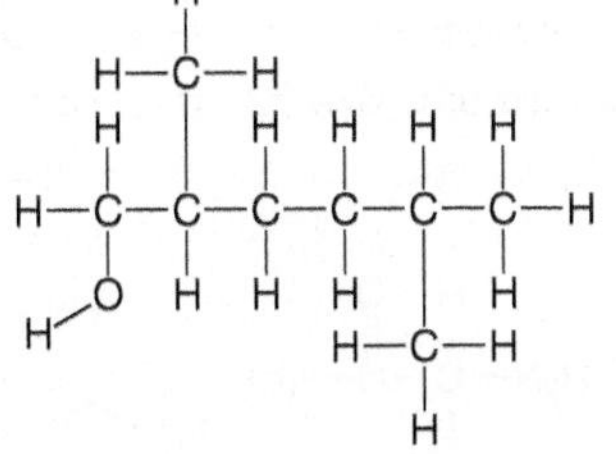

a)   CH₃
CH₂CHCH₂CH₂CH₂
OH   CH₃

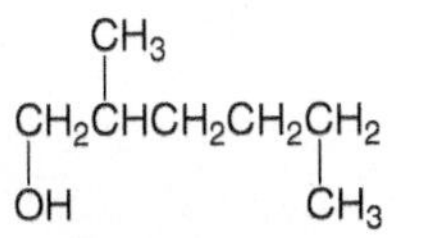

b)   CH₃
CH₂CHCH₂CH₂CHCH₃
OH   CH₃

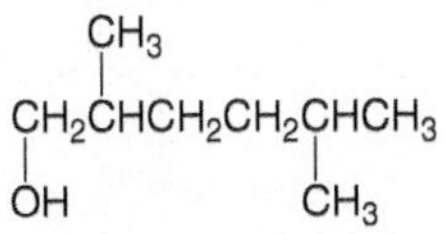

c)   CH₃
CH₂CH₂CHCH₂CHCH₃
OH   CH₃

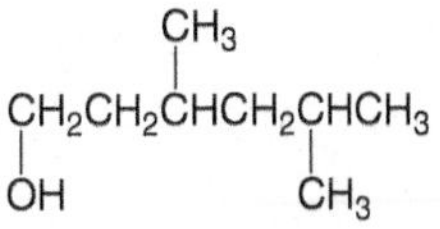

d)   CH₃
CH₂CHCH₂CH₂CHCH₃
CH₃   CH₃

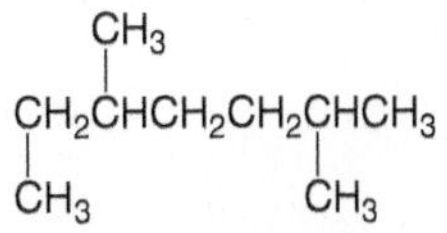

13.12 Select the skeletal structure that matches this Lewis structure.

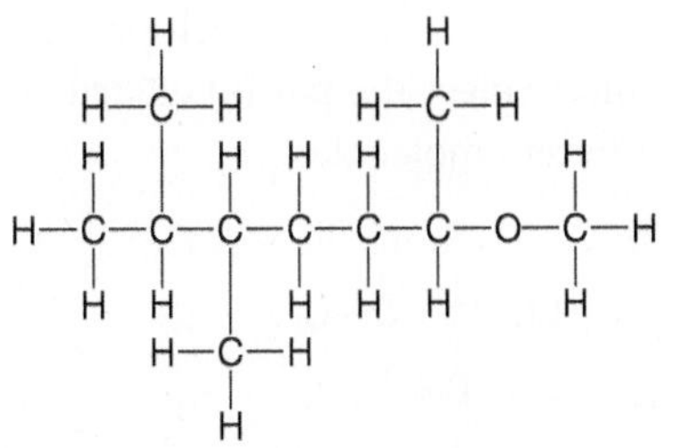

a)

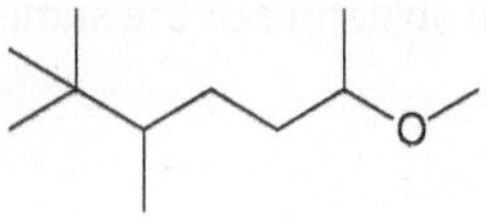

b)

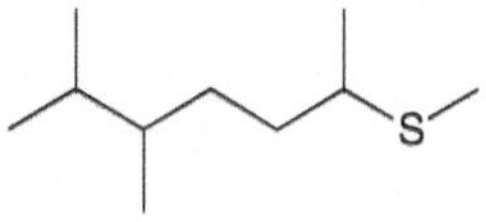

c)

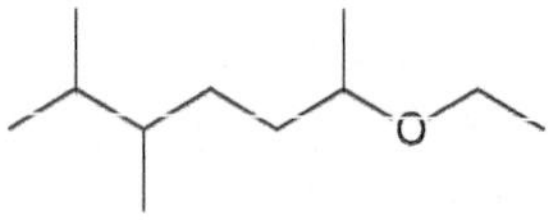

d)

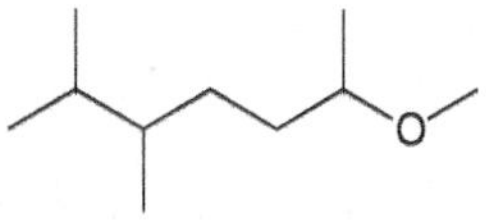

13.13 Identify the skeletal structure that matches the given Lewis structure.

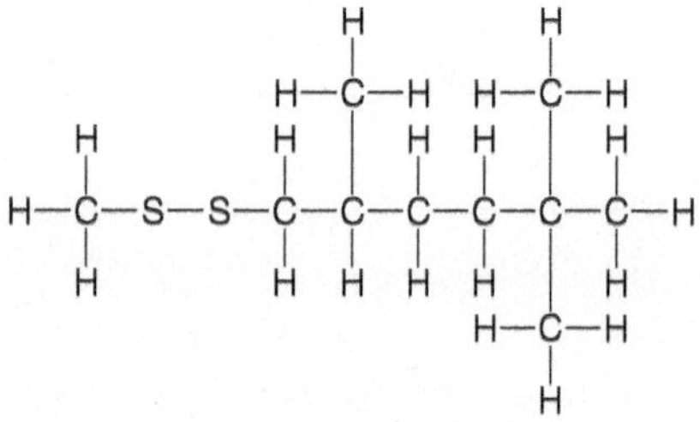

a)

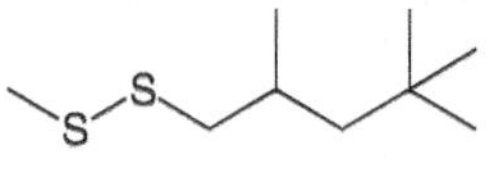

b)

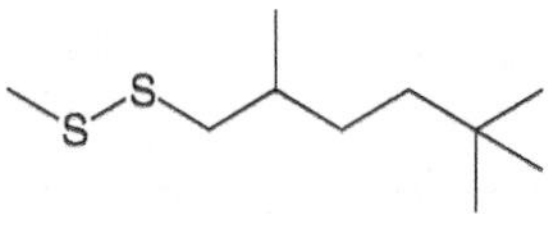

c)

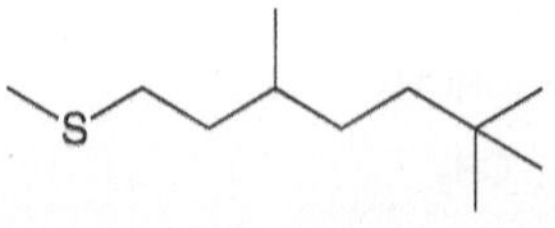

d)

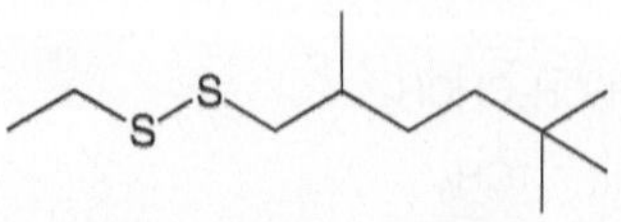

13.14 Amino acids are important building blocks for proteins and are involved in many important metabolic processes. Consider each pair of amino acid molecules. Select the pair(s) of structures that represent different molecules.

a)

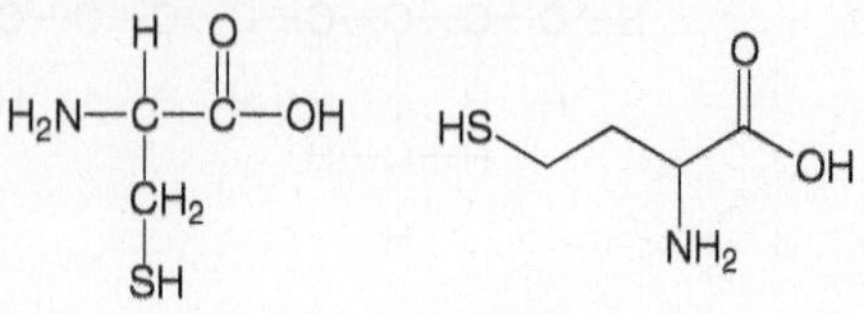

b)

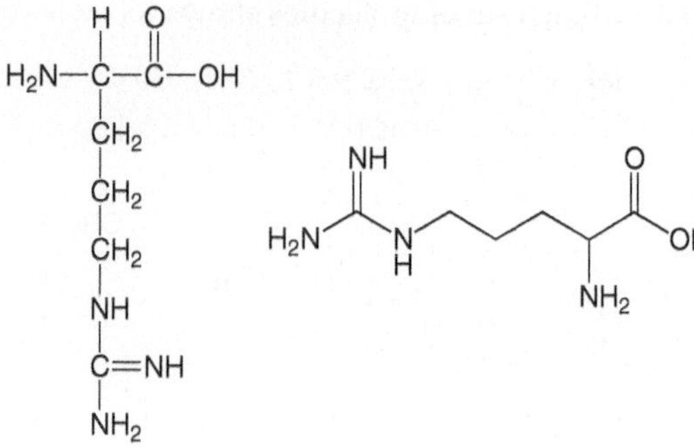

c)

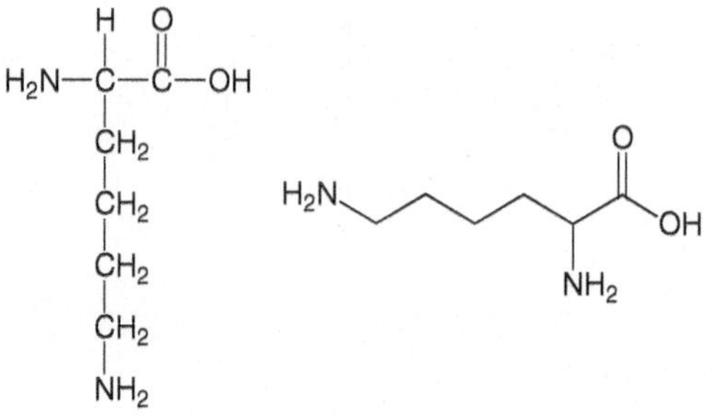

d)

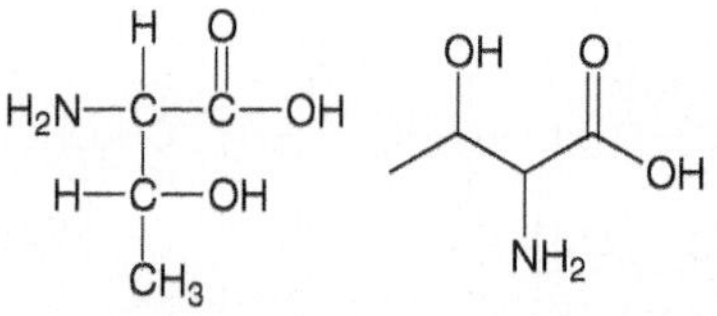

13.15 Amino acids are building blocks for proteins and are involved in many important metabolic processes. Consider each pair of amino acid molecules. Which pair(s) of structures represent different molecules?

a)

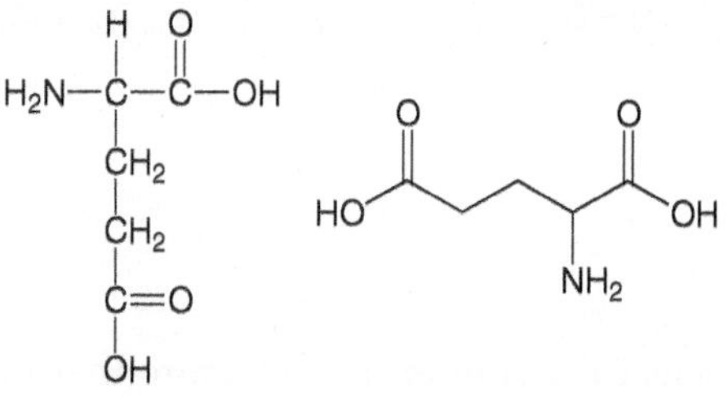

b)

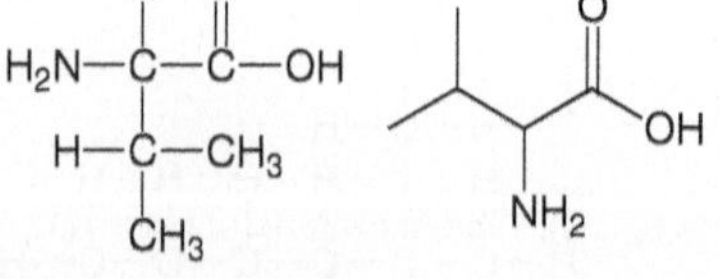

c)

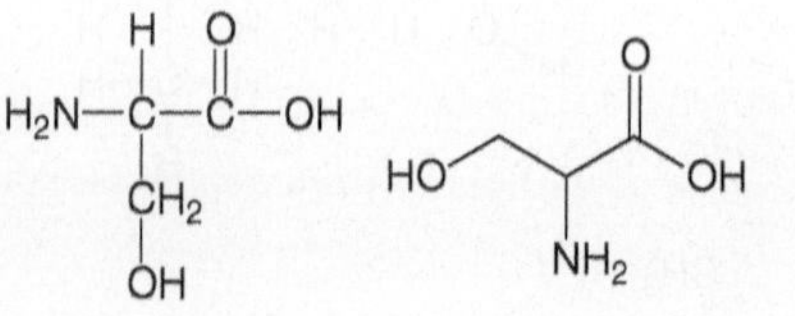

d)

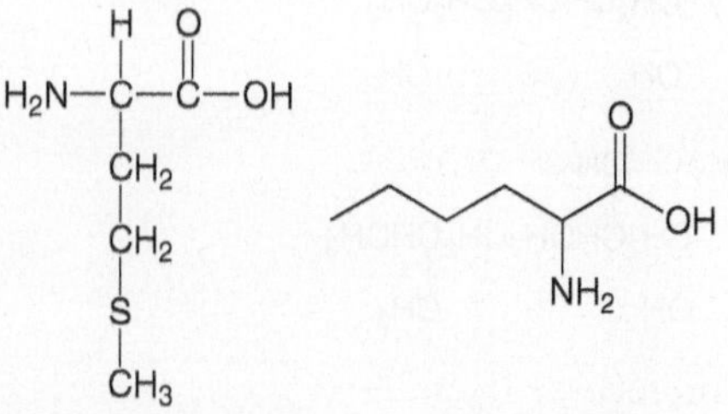

13.2 Alkanes and Cycloalkanes

LO 2: Identify and draw the first ten acyclic simple alkanes $(C_1\text{-}C_{10})$ and the first four cycloalkanes $(C_3\text{-}C_6)$.

13.16 Select the term that describes an organic molecule composed of an open chain with only carbon and hydrogen atoms connected only by single bonds.

  a) acyclic alkyne   **b)** cycloalkane

  c) acyclic alkene   **d)** cycloalkyne

  e) acyclic alkane

13.17 Determine the number of hydrogen atoms bonded to the indicated carbon atoms in the given molecule.

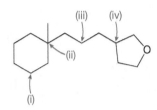

  Answer choices: 1, 2, 3, 4

  Target boxes: H on carbon (i), H on carbon (ii), H on carbon (iii), H on carbon (iv),

13.18 Which molecule does *not* have the molecular formula C_5H_{10}?

  a) 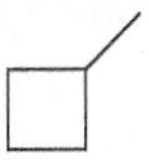   **b)**

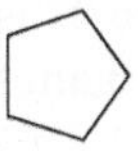

  c)    **d)**

13.19 Which molecule has the molecular formula C_6H_{14}?

  a) 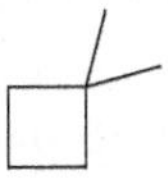   **b)**

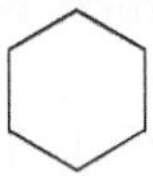

  c) 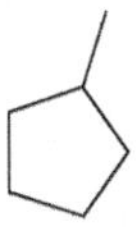   **d)**

13.20 Determine the molecular formula for each molecule.

  a)

   molecular formula = _____

  b)

   molecular formula = _____

  c)

   molecular formula = _____

  d)

   molecular formula = _____

13.21 Determine the molecular formula for each molecule.

  a)

   molecular formula = _____

  b)

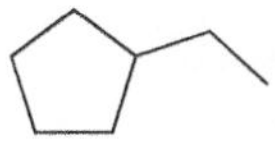

   molecular formula = _____

  c)

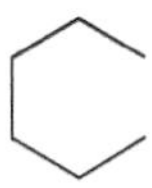

   molecular formula = _____

  d)

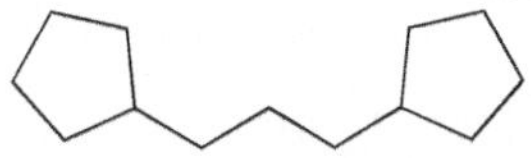

   molecular formula = _____

13.22 Complete the given balanced combustion reaction by determining the missing products that form when ethane is combusted. Drag the correct missing products into the appropriate boxes.

$$2C_2H_6(g) + 7O_2(g) \rightarrow 4\boxed{} + 6\boxed{} + \boxed{}$$
ethane

  Answer choices: $CH_4(g)$, $O_2(g)$, $H_2(g)$, $CO_2(g)$, ATP, energy, $N_2(g)$, $H_2O(g)$, $C_2O(g)$, $C_2(g)$

13.23 Identify the Lewis structure of the given skeletal structure.

  a)

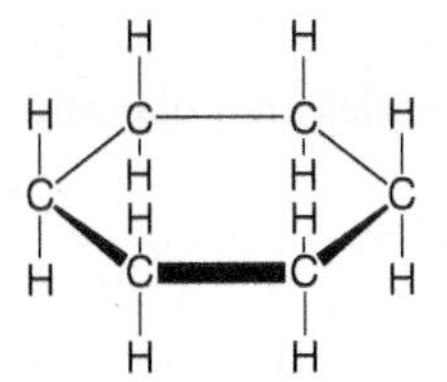

  b)

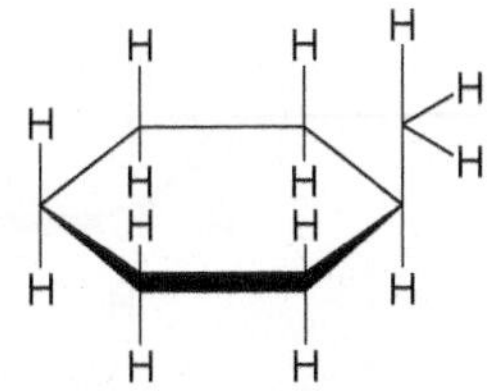

  c)

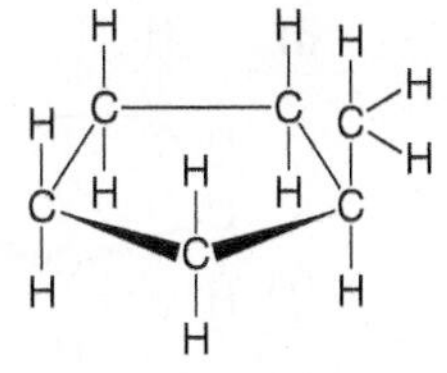

  d)

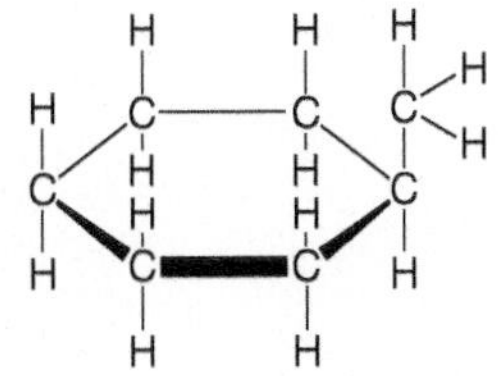

13.24 Identify the Lewis structure for the given molecule.

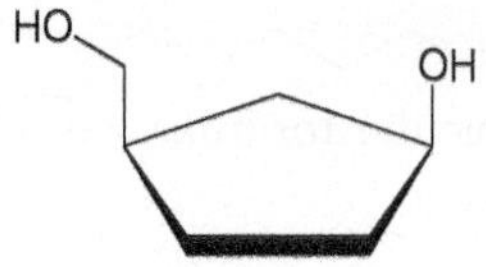

a)

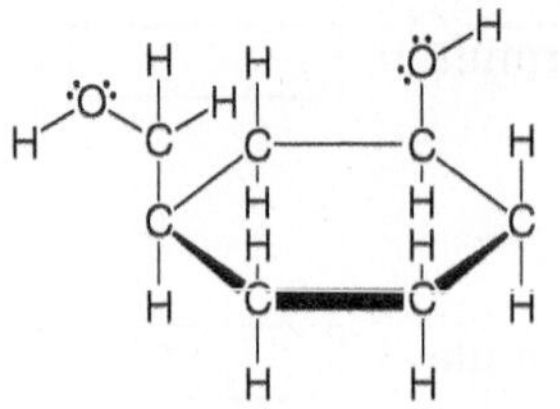

b)

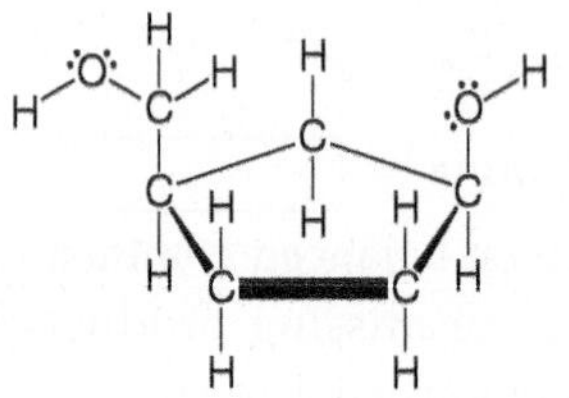

c)

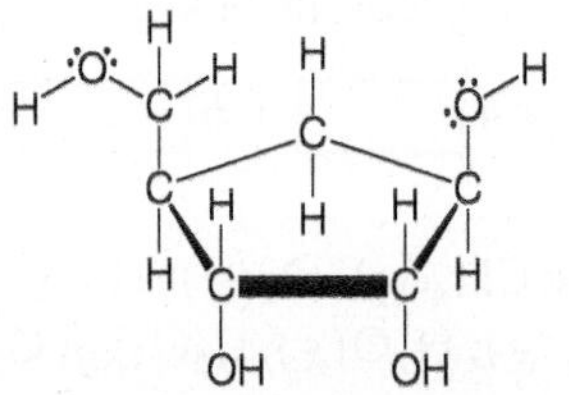

d)

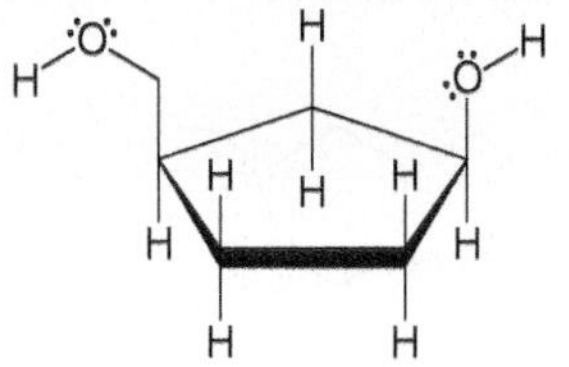

13.25 Determine which molecules are polar and which are non-polar.

Answer choices:

a)

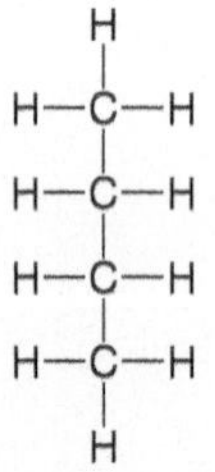

b)

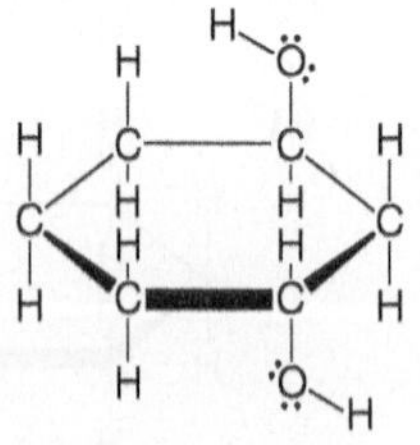

c)

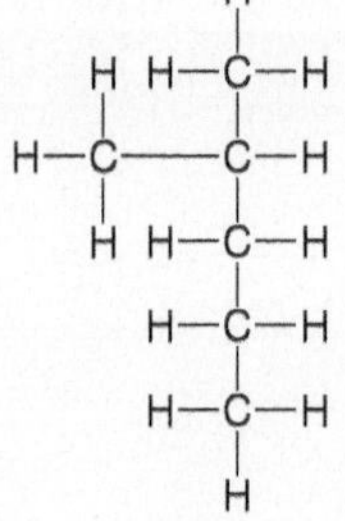

d)

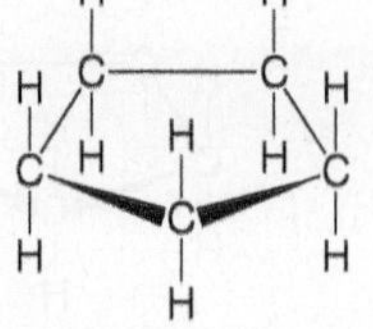

e)

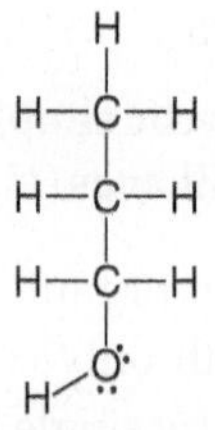

f)

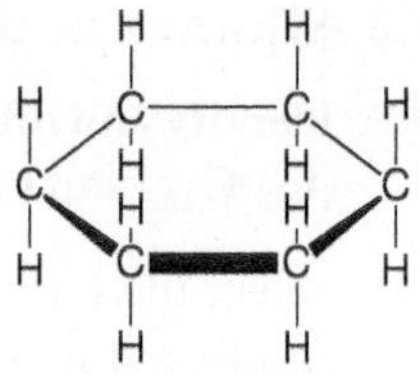

Target boxes: polar, non-polar

13.26 Determine which molecules are water soluble and which are insoluble in water.

Answer choices:

a)

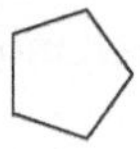

b)

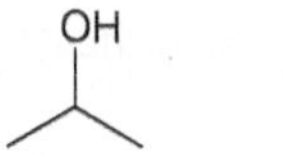

c)

d)

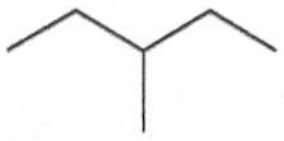

e)

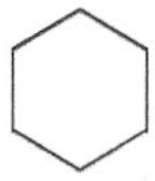

f)

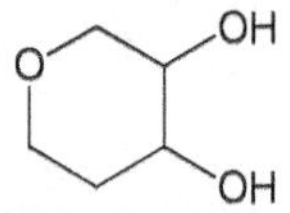

Target boxes: water soluble, insoluble in water

13.3 Branched Alkanes and Haloalkanes

LO 3: Recognize branching in alkanes and draw structural isomers for branched alkanes and haloalkanes.

13.27 Malaria is an infectious disease transmitted by mosquitoes. It causes symptoms including fever, tiredness, vomiting, headaches, seizures, coma, or death. The World Health Organization (WHO) estimates that there were over 400,000 deaths due to malaria in the year 2017 alone. Mefloquine, also known as lariam, is a medication used to help prevent and treat malaria. How many halogen atoms are on the mefloquine molecule?

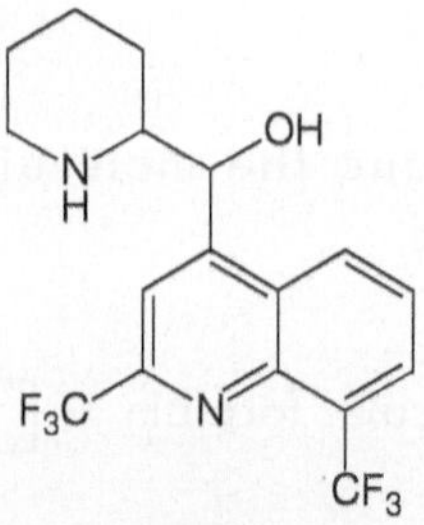

mefloquine

a) 0

b) 3

c) 6

d) unable to determine

13.28 Perfluorooctanoic acid (PFOA), also known as C8, is used in several industrial processes including the production of clothing, carpeting, upholstery, and non-stick coatings. Exposure to PFOA has been associated with an increased risk of cancer and other diseases. Consider the structure of the given PFOA molecule and determine the number of hydrogen atoms in the alkane chain of octanoic acid that have been replaced with fluorine atoms (green).

perfluorooctanoic acid (PFOA)

a) 8 b) 12 c) 14

d) 15 e) 17

13.29 Gabapentin, also known as Neurontin, is a medication used to help treat epilepsy, hot flashes, and restless leg syndrome. Identify the correct chemical formula of gabapentin.

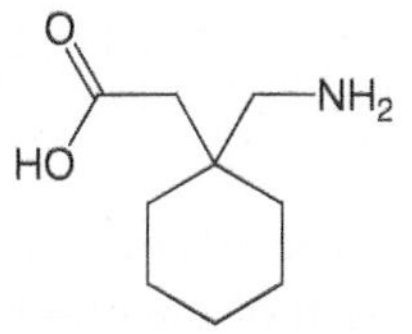

a) $C_8H_{17}NO_2$ b) $C_9H_{17}NO_2$

c) $C_9H_{19}NO_2$ d) $C_9H_{19}NO$

e) $CH_{17}NO_2$

13.30 Aspartic acid and glutamic acid are both essential amino acids in your diet. Use the structural diagrams to help determine which statement about the two amino acids is correct.

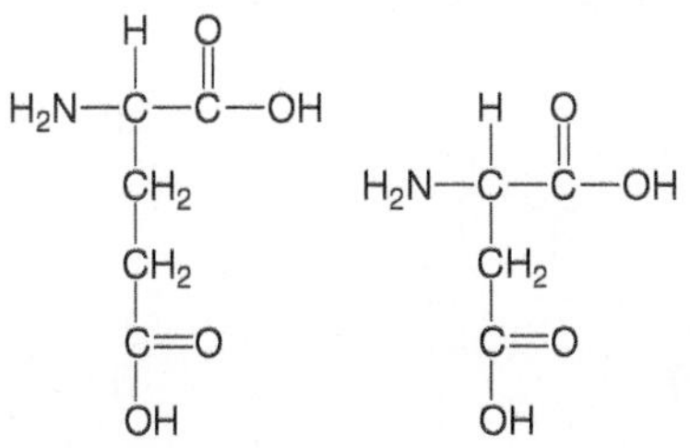

glutamic acid   aspartic acid

a) Glutamic acid and aspartic acid are structural isomers.

b) Glutamic acid and aspartic acid differ by one carbon and two hydrogen atoms.

c) Glutamic acid and aspartic acid differ by two carbon atoms and four hydrogen atoms.

d) Aspartic acid has one more branching group than glutamic acid.

e) Glutamic acid has two amino (NH_2) groups and aspartic acid only has one.

13.31 Identify the correct chemical formula of the branched haloalkane shown.

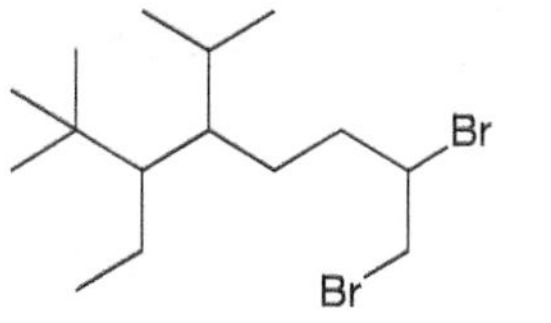

a) $C_{14}H_{30}Br_2$ b) $C_{15}H_{28}Br_2$

c) $C_{15}H_{30}Br_2$ d) $C_{15}H_{30}$

e) $C_{13}H_{28}Br_2$

13.32 Select the structural isomer of the given molecule.

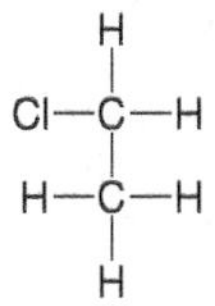

a) 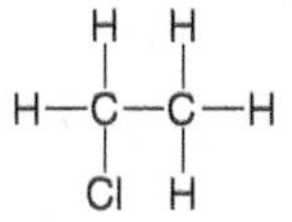 b)

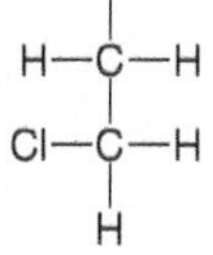

c) 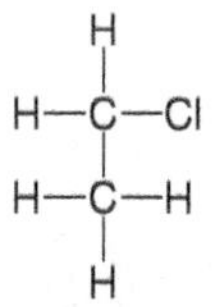 d)

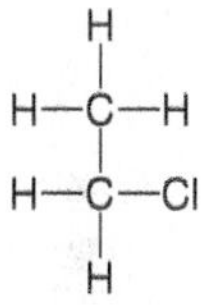

e) None. The molecules shown in (A), (B), (C), and (D) are the same molecule.

13.33 Which molecule is a structural isomer of the given molecule?

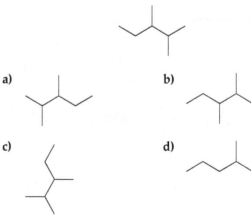

a) b)

c) d)

e)

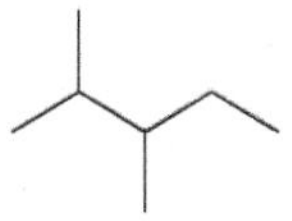

13.34 Alprazolam, also known as Xanax, is a medication commonly used to treat anxiety. Of the options shown, which is a structural isomer of alprazolam?

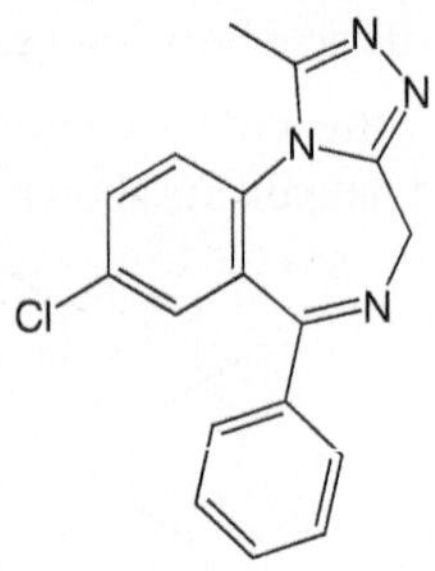

alprazolam

a)

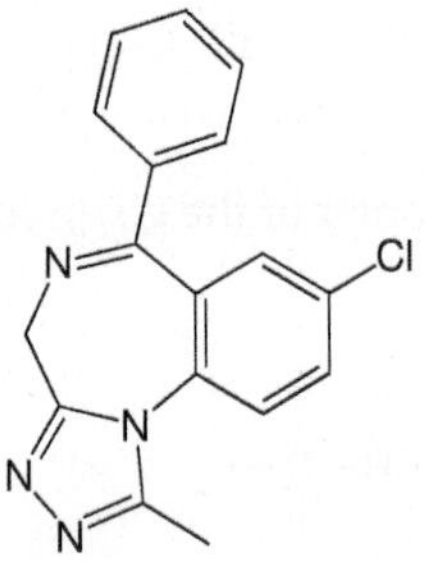

b)

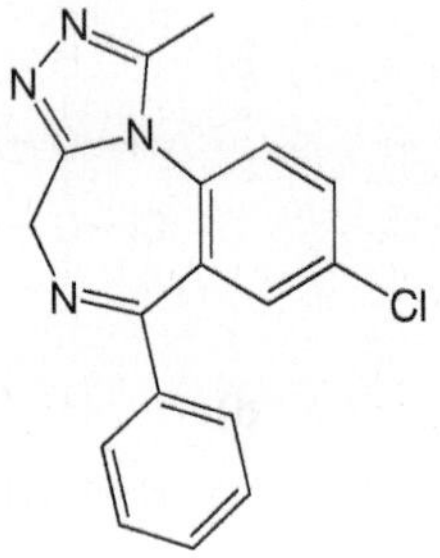

c)

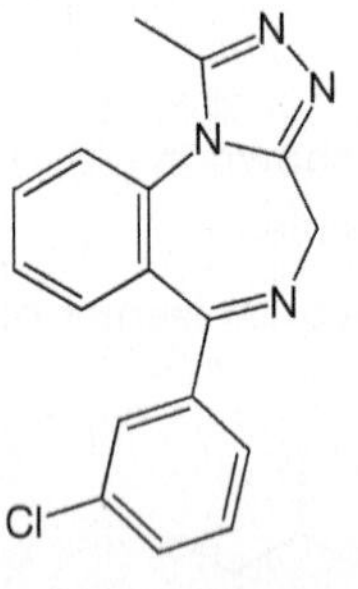

d)

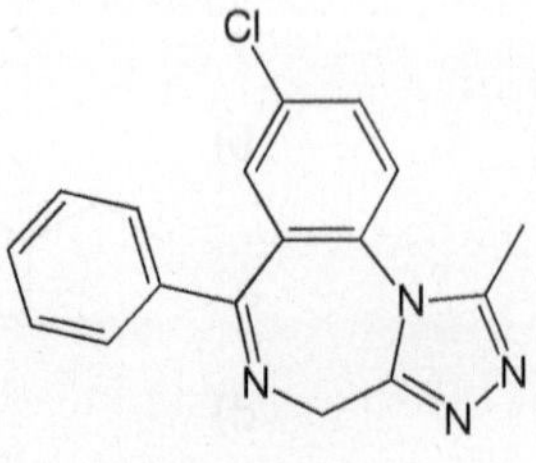

e)

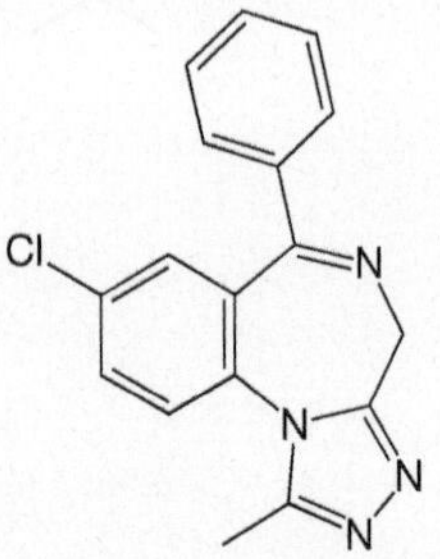

13.35 Select the structural isomer of the given molecule.

1-butanol

a)   OH

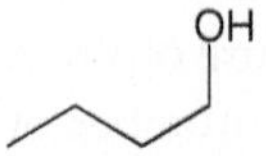

b)   OH

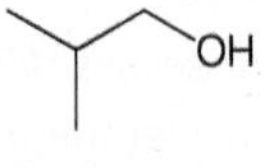

c)   OH

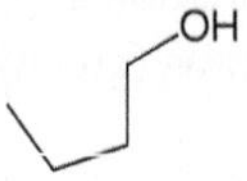

d) HO

13.36 Select the structural isomer of the given molecule.

1-bromopentane

a)   Br

b) Br

c) Br

d)   Br

e)   Br

13.37 Consider the given molecule then determine whether each of the other molecules is identical, a structural isomer, or not related to the molecule provided.

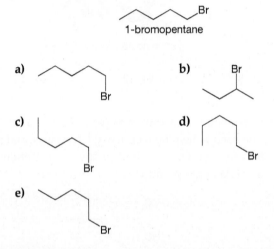

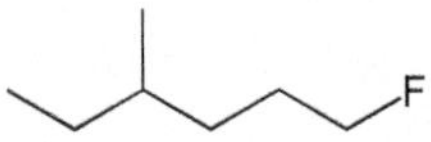

Answer choices:

a)   F

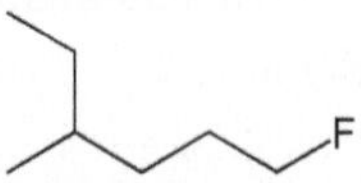

b) F

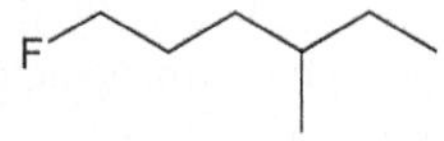

c)   F

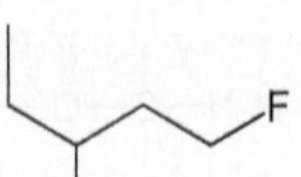

d)   F

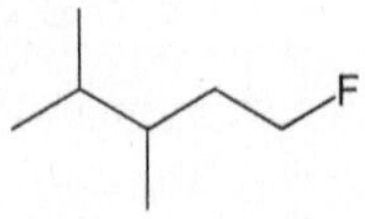

e) 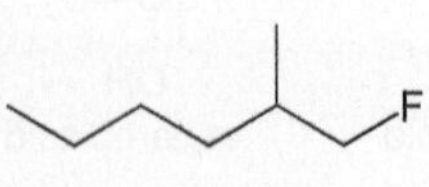   F

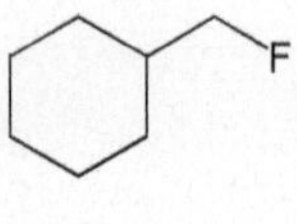

f)   F

g) F

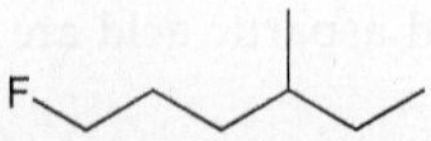

Target boxes: identical, structural isomer, not related

13.38 Bupropion, also known as Wellbutrin and Zyban, is a commonly prescribed antidepressant. It is also prescribed to help people quit smoking.

Examine the structure of bupropion, then consider the other molecules. Identify the structural isomer of bupropion.

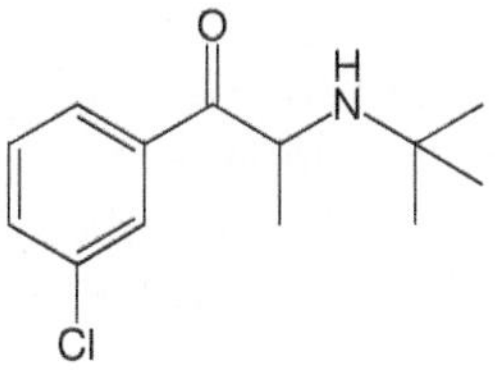

bupropion

Answer choices:

a)

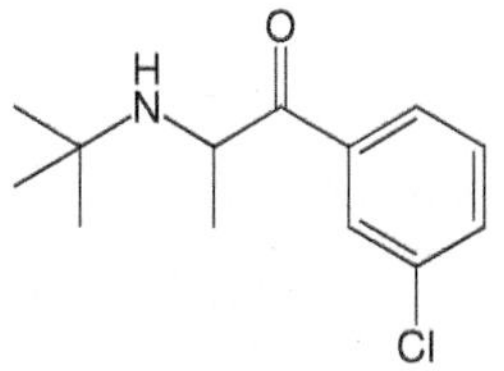

b)

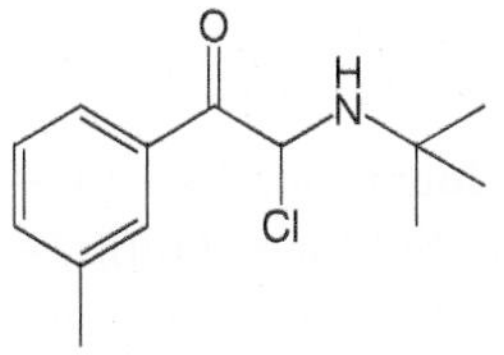

c)

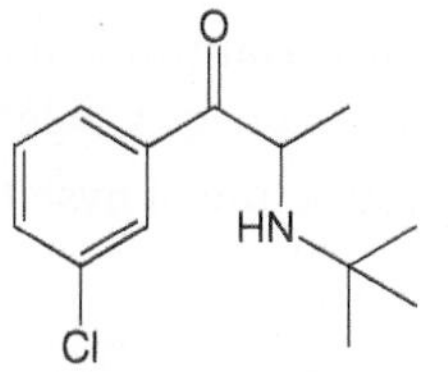

d)

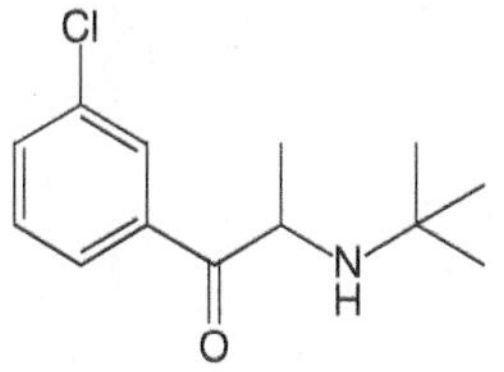

13.39 Drawing a structural isomer: Use the drawing tool to build the Lewis structure of an alcohol that represents a structural isomer of the given molecule. Be sure to include all atom labels and bonds present in the molecule. For this exercise, do not draw lone pairs of electrons on the oxygen atom that you add as part of the OH group.

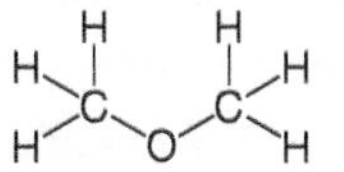

13.40 Drawing a structural isomer: Use the drawing tool to build the skeletal structure of a molecule that contains a five-membered cyclic alkane ring, which is a structural isomer of the given six-membered cycloalkane ring. Skeletal structures do not contain labels

on carbon atoms and hydrogen atoms bonded to carbon are also not shown.

13.4 Alkenes and Alkynes

LO 4: **Identify alkenes and alkynes and draw *cis-trans* isomers of alkenes.**

13.41 Pravastatin, also known as Pravachol or Selektine, is a drug commonly prescribed in combination with exercise, diet, and weight loss to help lower cholesterol and reduce the risk of cardiovascular disease. How many alkene groups are on the pravastatin molecule?

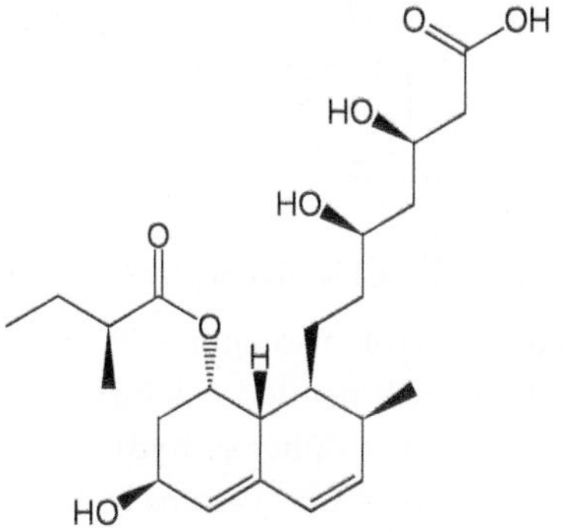

prevastatin

a) 0   b) 1   c) 2

d) 3   e) 4

13.42 Sort the given molecules into boxes for cis alkene, a trans alkene, or an alkyne.

Answer choices:

a)

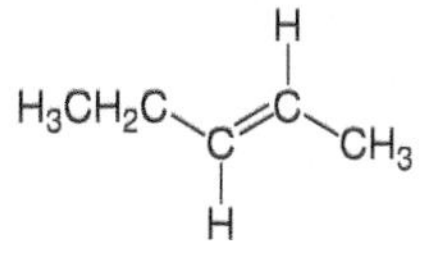

b)

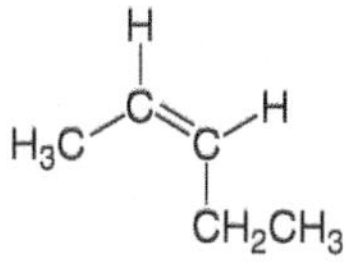

c)

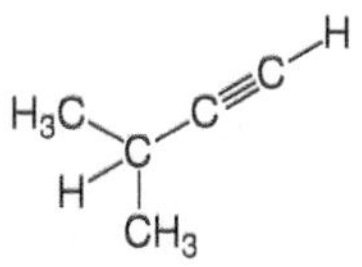

d)

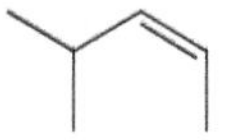

e)

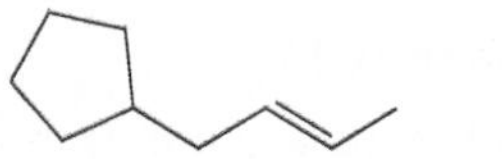

f)

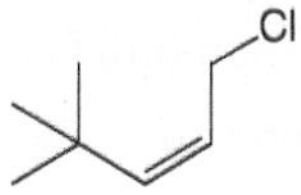

g)

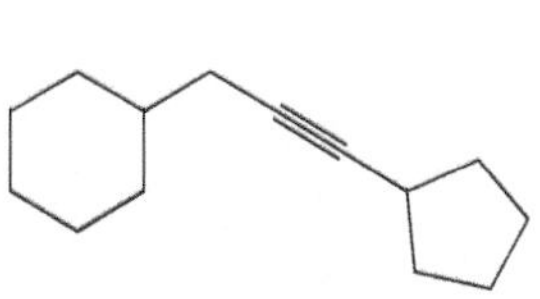

h)

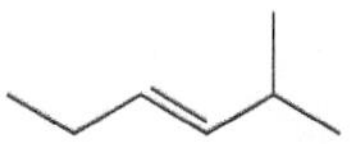

Target boxes: cis alkene, trans alkene, alkyne

13.43 Sort the given molecules into boxes for cis alkene, a trans alkene, or an alkyne.

Answer choices:

a)

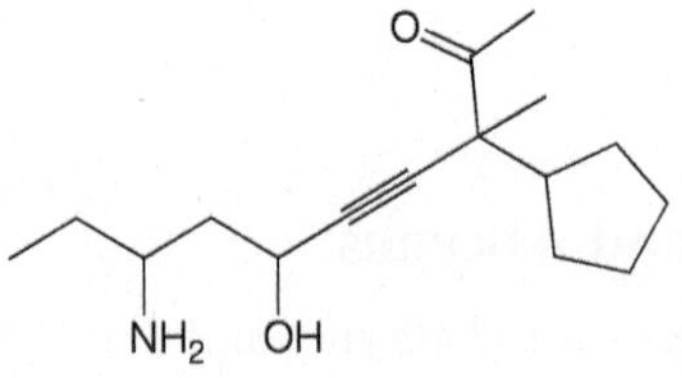

b)

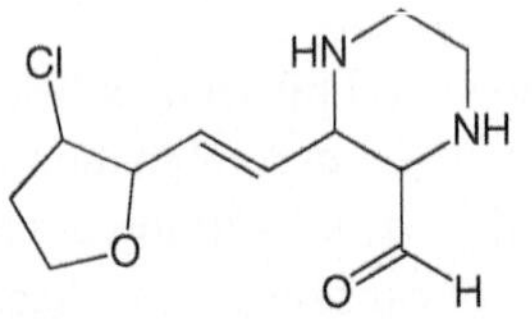

c)

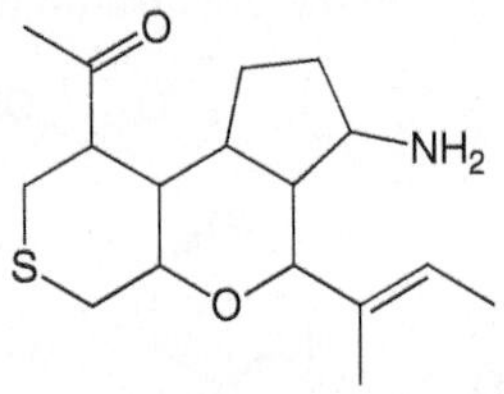

Target boxes: cis alkene, trans alkene, alkyne

13.44 Ergocalciferol, also known as vitamin D_2, helps the body absorb needed calcium and other minerals. Identify the number of hydrogen atoms bonded to the indicated carbon atoms in ergocalciferol.

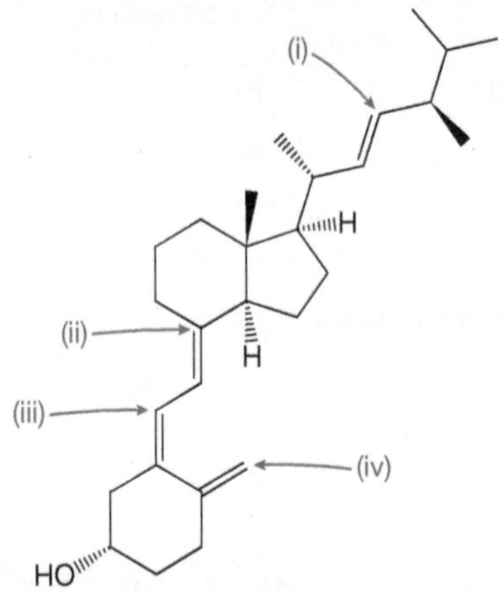

ergocalciferol

Answer choices: 0, 1, 2, 3, 4

Target boxes: H on carbon (i), H on carbon (ii), H on carbon (iii), H on carbon (iv)

13.45 Determine the bond angle around each indicated carbon.

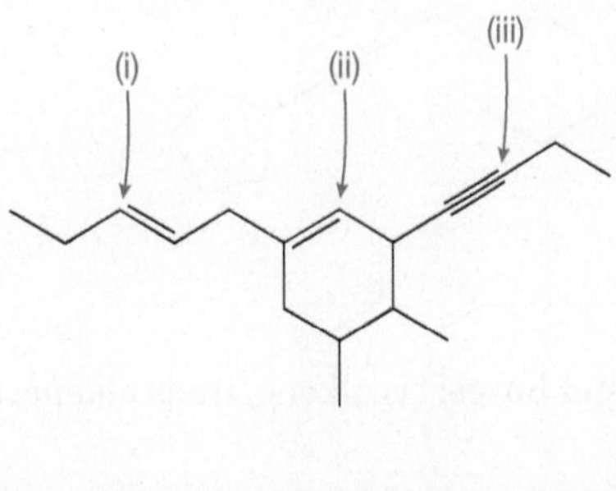

Answer choices: 190°, 180°, 120°, 102°, 109°, 90°, or 20°

Target boxes: bond angle at position (i), bond angle at position (ii), bond angle at position (iii)

13.46 Leukotriene B_4 (LTB4) is a molecule that participates in the body's inflammation response. Determine whether each carbon-carbon double bond in the leukotriene molecule is *cis* or *trans*.

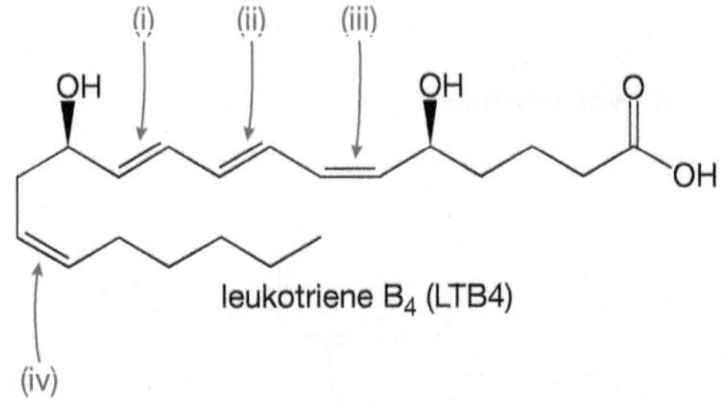

leukotriene B_4 (LTB4)

Answer choices: cis carbon-carbon double bond, trans carbon-carbon double bond

Target boxes: C=C double bond at (i), C=C double bond at (ii). C=C double bond at (iii), C=C double bond at (iv)

13.47 Nystatin, also known as Mycostatin, is an antifungal medication used to treat certain infections of the skin, mouth, vagina, and esophagus. Select the correct statement about the structure of nystatin.

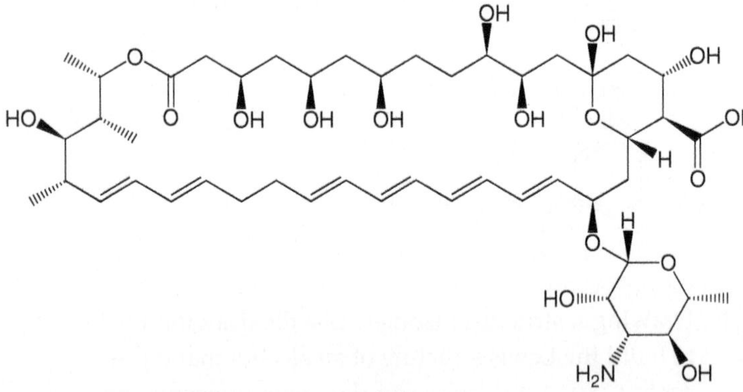

nystatin

a) There are six *cis* alkene groups on the nystatin molecule.

b) There are eight alkene groups on the nystatin molecule: six *trans* and two *cis*.

c) There are six *trans* alkene groups on the nystatin molecule.

d) There are eight alkene groups on the nystatin molecule: six *cis* and two *trans*.

e) There are four *trans* alkene groups on the nystatin molecule.

13.48 Determine the number of hydrogen atoms bonded to the indicated carbon atoms.

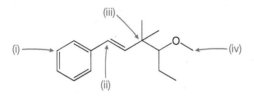

Answer choices: 0, 1, 2, 3, 4

Target boxes: H on carbon (i), H on carbon (ii), H on carbon (iii), H on carbon (iv)

13.49 Identify any molecule(s) that are *not* structural isomers with the formula C_4H_8.

Answer choices:

Target box: *not* a structural isomer of the others

13.50 Drawing the skeletal structure of a reaction product: Use the drawing tool to build the skeletal structure of the product formed by the given hydrogenation reaction. Recall that skeletal structures do not contain labels for carbon atoms.

H_2 + Pd or Pt

hydrogenation reaction

13.51 Drawing the skeletal structure of a reaction product: Use the drawing tool to build the skeletal structure of the product that forms during the given hydrogenation reaction. Recall that skeletal structures do not contain labels for carbon atoms.

H_2 + Pd or Pt

hydrogenation reaction

13.52 Drawing the skeletal structure of a reaction product: Use the drawing tool to build the skeletal structure of the product of the given halogenation reaction. Recall that skeletal structures do not contain labels for carbon atoms.

Cl_2

halogenation reaction

13.53 Drawing the skeletal structure of a reaction starting material: Use the drawing tool to build the *skeletal structure* of the starting material for the given halogenation reaction. Recall that skeletal structures do not contain labels for carbon atoms.

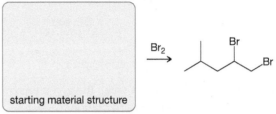

starting material structure

Br_2

halogenation reaction

13.54 Drawing the skeletal structure of a reaction product: Use the drawing tool to build the skeletal structure of the product of the given hydrohalogenation reaction. Recall that skeletal structures do not contain labels for carbon atoms.

HBr

halogenation reaction

13.55 Which product forms when the given unsymmetrical alkene undergoes a hydrohalogenation reaction?

HCl
⟶ [?]

a)   b)

c)   d)

13.56 Which product forms when the given unsymmetrical alkene undergoes a hydration reaction?

H_2O in acid
⟶ [?]

a)   b)

c)   d)

13.57 Drawing the skeletal structure of a reaction product: Use the drawing tool to build the skeletal structure for the product of the given hydration reaction. Recall that skeletal structures do not contain labels for carbon atoms. For this exercise, do not include lone pairs of electrons on oxygen.

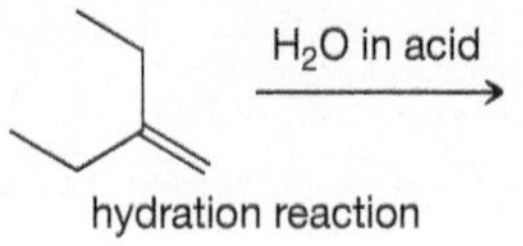

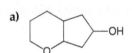

H₂O in acid

hydration reaction

13.58 Which product forms when the given unsymmetrical alkene undergoes a hydration reaction?

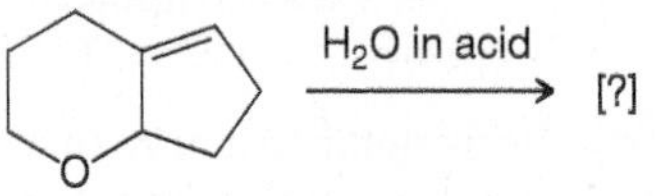

H₂O in acid
[?]

a)

b)

c)

d)

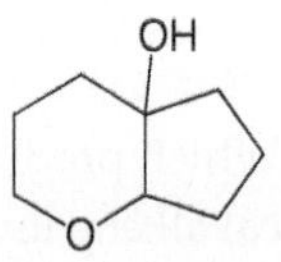

13.59 Sort the alkene reactants into categories based on those that produce the given alcohol as the major product of a hydration reaction and those that do not.

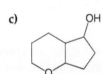

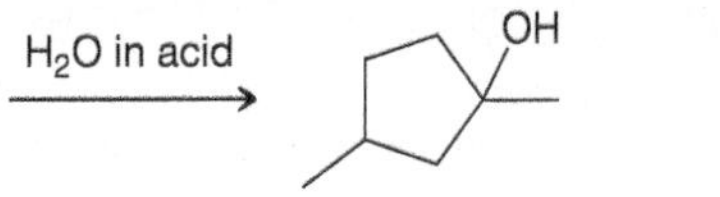

H₂O in acid

major alcohol product of the hydration reaction

Answer choices:

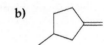

a)   b)

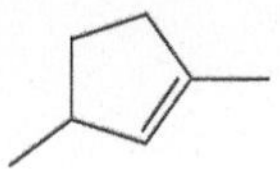

c) 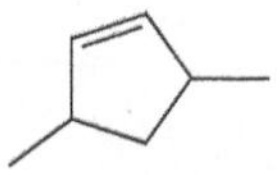   d)

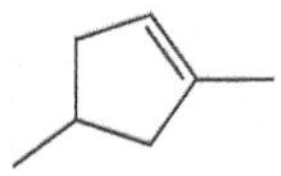

e)

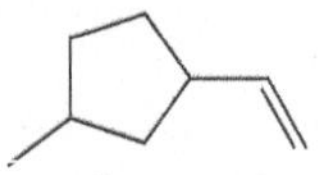

Target boxes:

- *does* produce the given alcohol as the major product of hydration

- *does not* produce the given alcohol as the major product of hydration

13.60 Select the monomer from which the given polymer was made. (Hint: It may be helpful to review the polymerization reaction summary diagram and the examples in Section 13.4.)

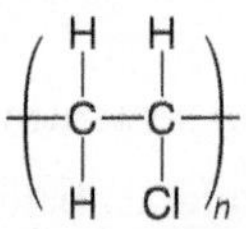

a) H   H
     C=C
    H   CH₂Cl

b) H   H
     C=C
    H   Cl

c) H   H
     C–C
    H   Cl

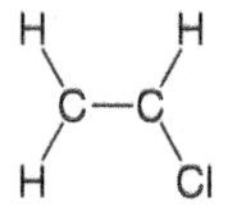

d) H   H
     C≡C
    H   Cl

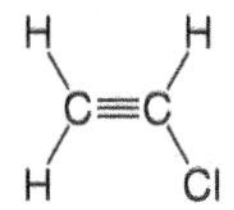

13.61 Select the option that includes the correct polymerization reaction starting material, product, and monomer unit within the polymer chain. (Hint: It may be helpful to review the polymerization reaction summary diagram and the examples in Section 13.4.)

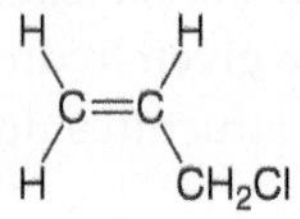

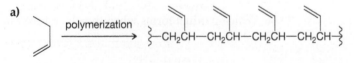

a)

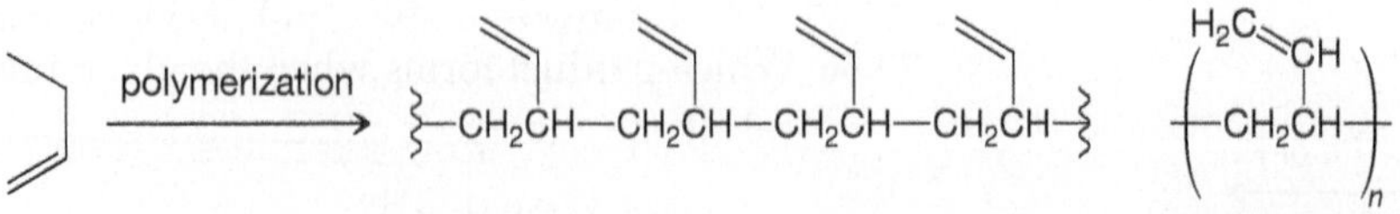

polymerization

{–CH₂CH–CH₂CH–CH₂CH–CH₂CH–}

H₂C=CH
(–CH₂CH–)ₙ

monomer unit repeated "*n*" times

b)

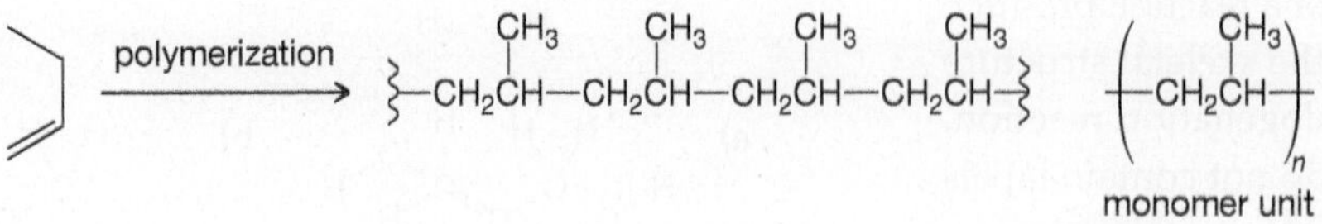

polymerization

        CH₃   CH₃   CH₃   CH₃
{–CH₂CH–CH₂CH–CH₂CH–CH₂CH–}

        CH₃
(–CH₂CH–)ₙ

monomer unit repeated "*n*" times

c)

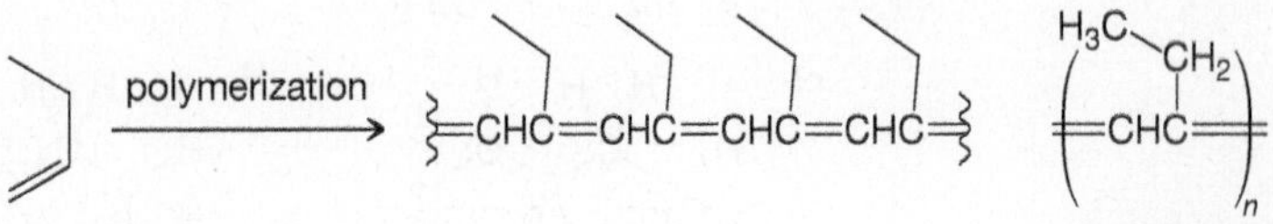

polymerization

{=CHC=CHC=CHC=CHC=}

H₃C   CH₂
(=CHC=)ₙ

monomer unit repeated "*n*" times

d)

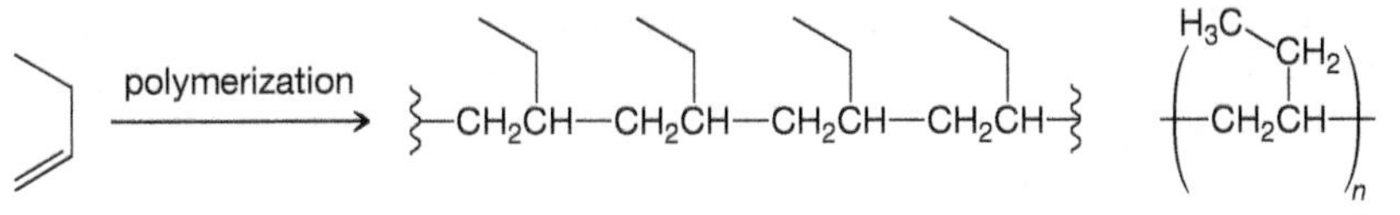

monomer unit
repeated "*n*" times

13.5 Aromatic Compounds

LO 5: Identify and draw aromatic compounds.

13.62 Tuberculosis (TB) is a bacterial infection that affects the lungs and is caused by mycobacterium tuberculosis (MTB). The World Health Organization (WHO) estimates that in 2018, as many as 25% of the world's population may be infected with tuberculosis. The medication 4-aminosalicylic acid (also known as para-aminosalicylic acid) is an antibiotic used with other anti-TB medications to help treat drug-resistant tuberculosis. Select the correct molecular formula of 4-aminosalicylic acid.

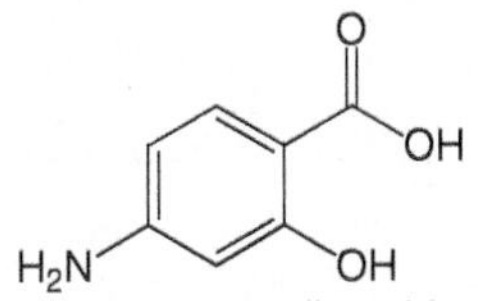

4-aminosalicylic acid

a) $C_7H_{10}NO_3$

b) $C_7H_7NO_3$

c) $C_7H_4NO_3$

d) $C_7H_{10}NO_2$

13.63 Efavirenz (EFV), also known as Sustiva, is a medication used to help treat and prevent HIV/AIDS. Which statement is true about the efavirenz molecule?

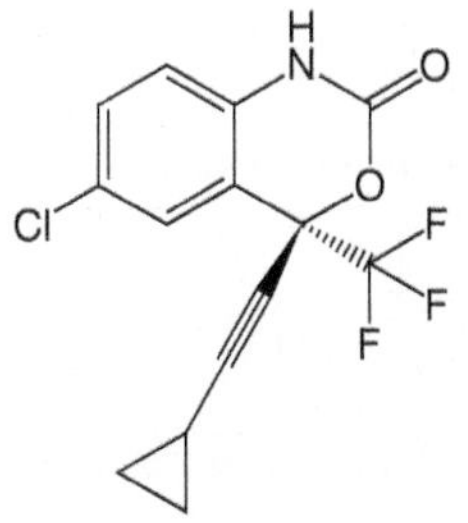

efavirenz

a) Efavirenz contains one aromatic ring, one alkyne group, one cyclopropane ring, and four halogen atoms.

b) Efavirenz contains two aromatic rings, one alkyne group, one cyclopropane ring, and four halogen atoms.

c) Efavirenz contains three aromatic rings, one alkyne group, and four halogen atoms.

d) Efavirenz contains two non-aromatic cyclohexane rings joined together, one alkyne group, one cyclopropane ring, and four halogen atoms.

13.64 Chlorambucil, also known as Leukeran is a chemotherapy drug used to help treat cancer patients suffering from chronic lymphocytic leukemia (CLL). Which statement is true about chlorambucil?

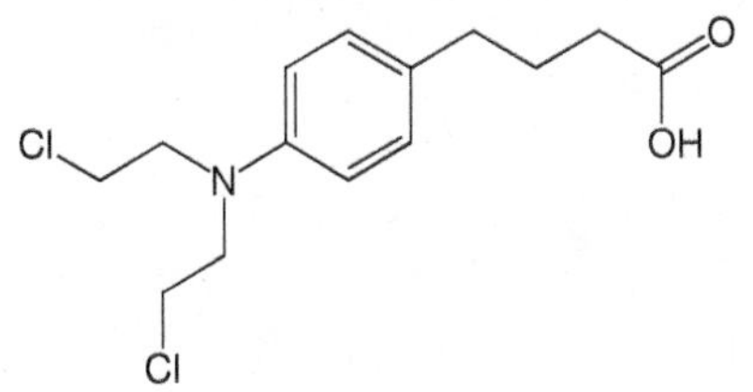

chlorambucil

a) Chlorambucil contains a mono-substituted benzene ring.

b) Chlorambucil contains a di-substituted benzene ring.

c) Chlorambucil contains a tri-substituted benzene ring.

d) Chlorambucil contains a di-substituted cyclohexane ring.

e) Chlorambucil is a polycyclic aromatic hydrocarbon (PAH).

13.65 Which statement about polycyclic aromatic hydrocarbons (PAHs) is true?

a) Polycyclic aromatic hydrocarbons (PAHs) are steroid building blocks.

b) Polycyclic aromatic hydrocarbons (PAHs) are enzyme precursors.

c) Polycyclic aromatic hydrocarbons (PAHs) are human carcinogens.

d) Polycyclic aromatic hydrocarbons (PAHs) are neurotransmitters.

13.66 Study the structure of each molecule and select the correct description for each.

Answer choices: mono-substituted aromatic, di-substituted aromatic, tri-substituted aromatic, not aromatic

Target boxes:

a)

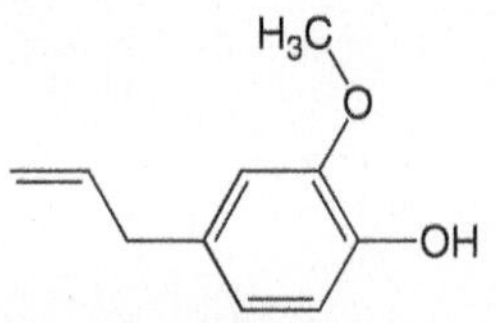

eugenol: found in essential oils
from cloves, nutmeg,
cinnamon, basil, and bay leaf

b)

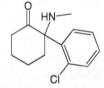

ketamine: pain medication
and used to start and maintain
anesthesia

c)

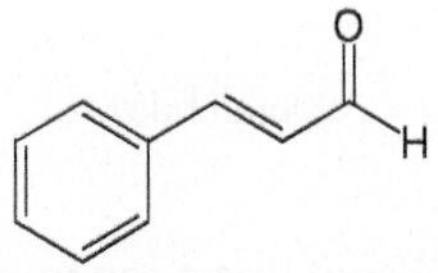

cinnamaldehyde: helps give
cinnamon its flavor and odor

d)

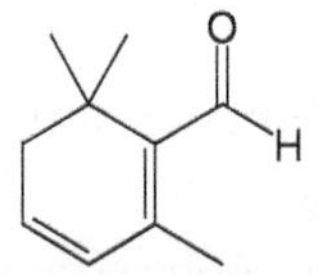

safranal: isolated from the
crocus flower and responsible
for the aroma of saffron

e)

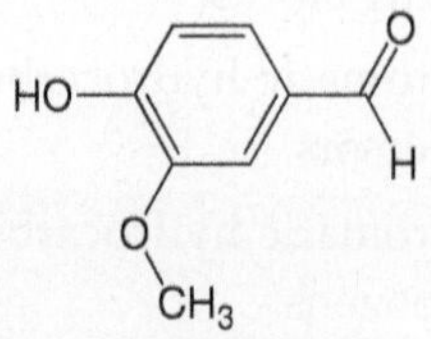

vanillin: from vanilla bean
extract and used in the food
industry as a flavor

Answer choices: mono-substituted aromatic, di-substituted aromatic, tri-substituted aromatic, not aromatic

Target boxes:

a)

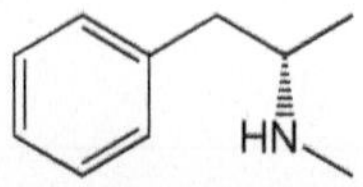

methamphetamine: stimulant
and addictive recreational drug

b)

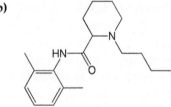

bupivacaine: nerve blocking
agent used for epidurals and
other surgeries

c)

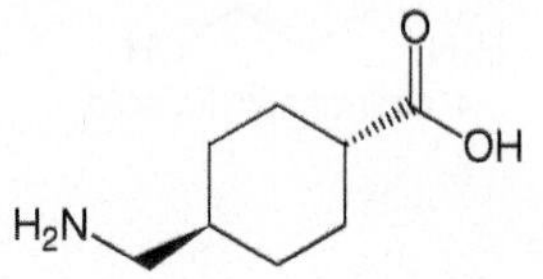

tranexamic acid: medication
used to treat or prevent blood
loss from trauma, surgery, and
post-partum bleeding

d)

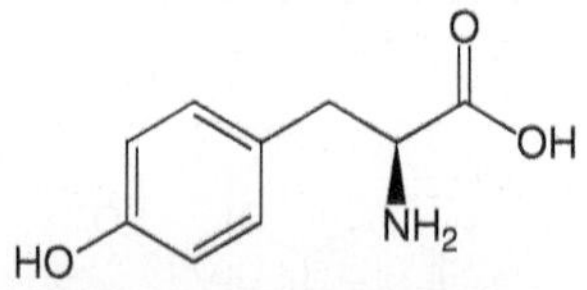

tyrosine: amino acid used by
cells for the biosynthesis of
proteins

e)

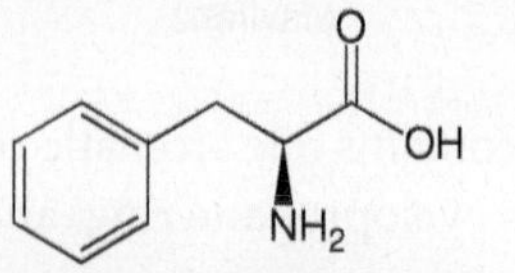

phenylalanine: essential amino
acid used by cells for the
biosynthesis of proteins

13.67 Study the structure of each molecule and select the
correct description for each.

13.68 Tamoxifen (TMX), also known as Nolvadex, is a medication used to help treat breast cancer. Determine the number of each type of atom in tamoxifen.

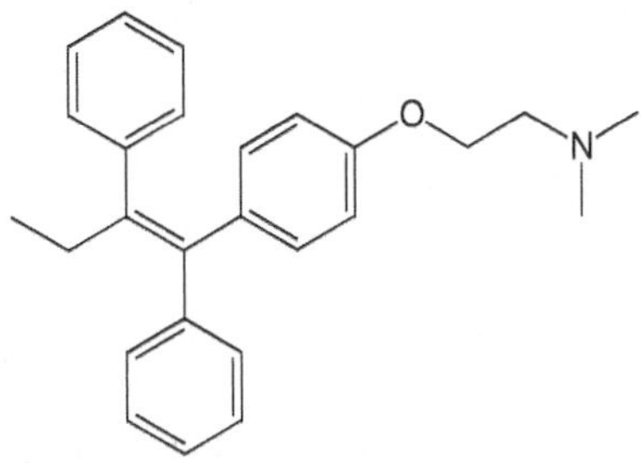

tamoxifen

Answer choices: 0, 1, 2, 3, 4, 22, 24, 26, 27, 29

Target boxes: carbon, hydrogen, nitrogen, oxygen

13.69 Consider the structures and functions of dopamine, methyldopa, and epinephrine (adrenaline) and then select the correct statement.

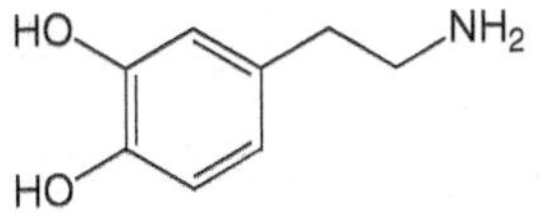

dopamine: hormone neurotransmitter involved in mood, learning, movement, pain processing, and other behavior and physical functions

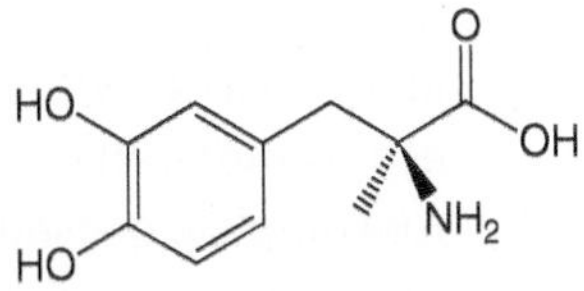

methyldopa: antihypertensive drug used to treat high blood pressure, especially during pregnancy

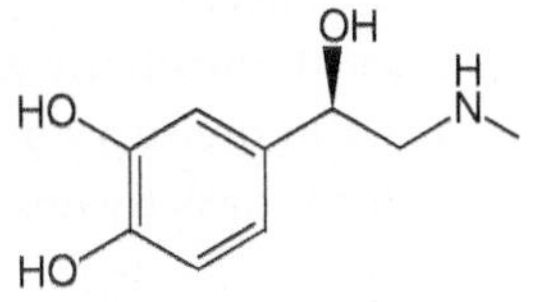

epinephrine (adrenaline): hormone neurotransmitter involved in the body's "fight-or-flight" response, and also used to treat anaphylaxis and cardiac arrest

a) All three molecules contain a branching group having a nitrogen atom and three carbons.

b) The formula of dopamine is $C_8H_{11}NO_2$, the formula for methyldopa is $C_{10}H_{13}NO_4$, and the formula for epinephrine (adrenaline) is $C_9H_{12}NO_3$.

c) All three molecules contain a tri-substituted aromatic benzene ring that has two hydroxyl (OH) groups in each case.

d) All three molecules are used to increase blood pressure and alertness in hospital patients.

13.70 The drugs aspirin, acetaminophen, and ibuprofen are three common over-the-counter non-steroidal anti-inflammatory drug (NSAID) medications used to help reduce pain, fever, and inflammation. Which statement about these three drugs is correct?

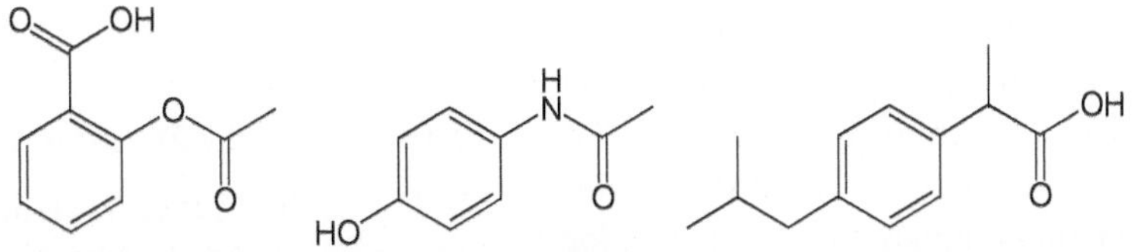

aspirin
(acetylsalicylic acid)

paracetamol
(acetaminophen)

ibuprofen

a) All three molecules contain a carboxylic acid (COOH) substituent group bonded to the aromatic benzene ring.

b) The formula for aspirin is $C_9H_8O_4$, the formula for paracetamol is $C_7H_7NO_2$, and the formula for ibuprofen is $C_{13}H_{18}O_2$.

c) All three drugs are steroidal anti-inflammatory drugs (SAID) medications used to help reduce pain, fever and inflammation.

d) All three molecules contain a di-substituted aromatic benzene ring and at least two oxygen atoms on the drug molecule.

13.71 Drag each molecule into the appropriate category.

Answer choices:

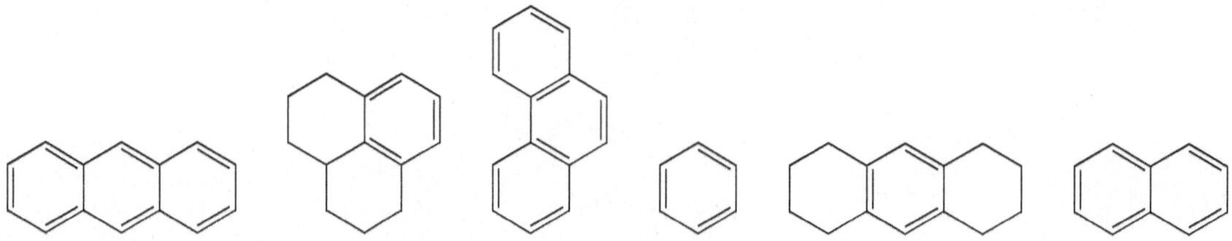

Target boxes: aromatic hydrocarbon, polycyclic aromatic hydrocarbon

13.72 Drag each molecule into the appropriate category.

Answer choices:

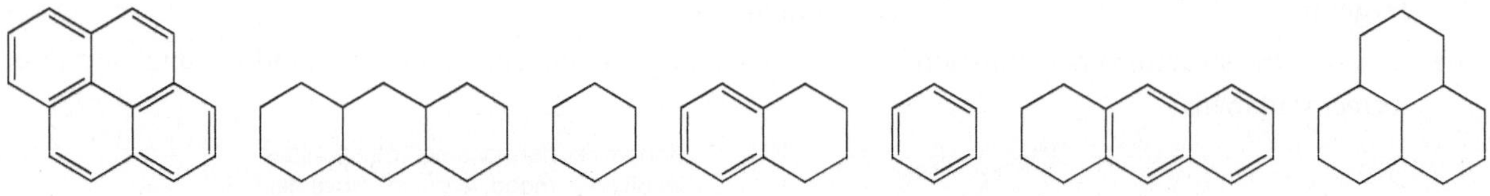

Target boxes: aromatic hydrocarbon, polycyclic aromatic hydrocarbon, not aromatic

---

13.73 Naproxen, also known as Naprosyn, is a non-steroidal anti-inflammatory drug (NSAID) used to treat pain, fever, and inflammation for a variety of conditions including rheumatoid arthritis, menstrual pain, tendinitis, and fever. Examine the structure of naproxen, then select the best description.

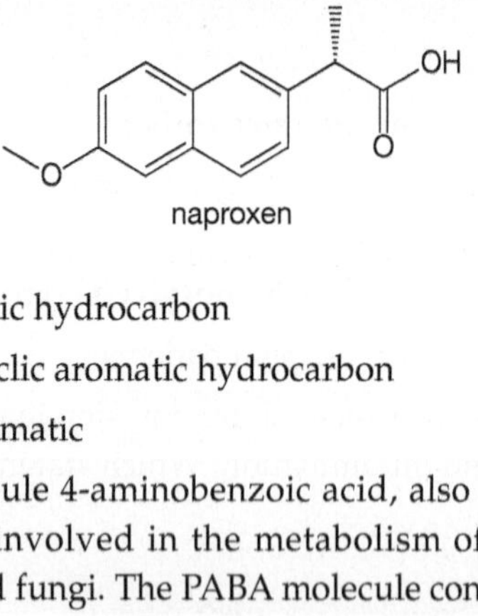

naproxen

a) aromatic hydrocarbon

b) polycyclic aromatic hydrocarbon

c) not aromatic

13.74 The molecule 4-aminobenzoic acid, also known as PABA, is involved in the metabolism of bacteria, plants, and fungi. The PABA molecule contains a di-substituted aromatic benzene ring with a carboxylic acid group (COOH) and an amino group (NH_2) attached as substituents. Identify the PABA molecule among the structures shown. (See Mastering for complete question and answer options.)

13.75 Gallic acid, also known as 3,4,5-trihydroxybenzoic acid, is a naturally occurring antioxidant found in several fruits and medicinal plants. It is also used as building block for other molecules and is being studied for a range of possible health-promoting effects. The gallic acid molecule contains an aromatic benzene ring with three hydroxyl (OH) groups and a carboxylic acid group (COOH)

attached as substituents. Identify the gallic acid molecule among the structures shown. (See Mastering for complete question and answer options.)

13.76 The molecule procaine, also known as Novocaine, is a local anesthetic and numbing agent commonly used in dentistry and for intramuscular injections. Which correctly describes procaine?

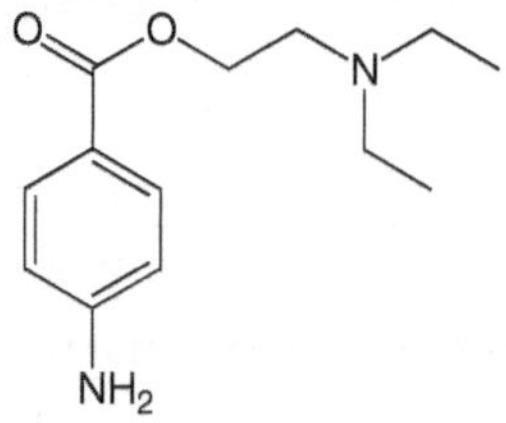

a) The aromatic ring in procaine is monosubstituted

b) The aromatic ring in procaine is disubstituted

c) The aromatic ring in procaine is tetrasubstituted

d) Procaine is not aromatic

13.6 Naming Organic Compounds

LO 6: **Use the IUPAC system for naming organic compounds to convert from structure to name and from name to structure for simple alkanes, alkenes, alkynes, and benzene compounds.**

13.77 Classify the structure of each molecule based on the name of the longest parent chain in each molecule.

Answer choices:

a)

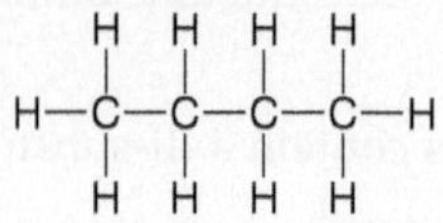

b)

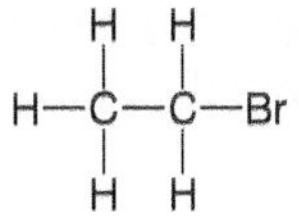

H—C—C—Br (with H H above, H H below)

c)

H—C—C—C—H (with H H H above, H H H below)

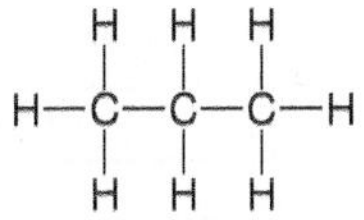

d)

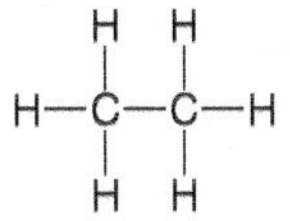

H—C—C—H (with H H above, H H below)

e)

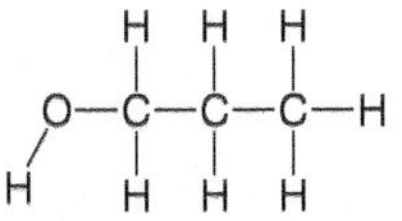

O—C—C—C—H (with H H H above on first, H H H H below)

f)

H—C—C—C—C—H (with H H Cl H above, H H H H below)

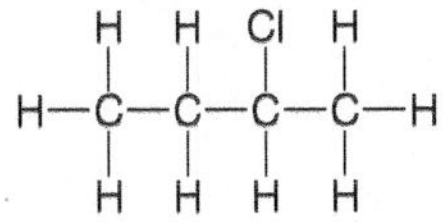

Target boxes: ethane parent chain, propane parent chain, butane parent chain

13.78 Select the molecule that has a butane parent chain.

a)

b)

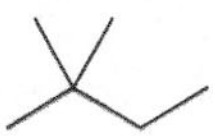

c)

d)

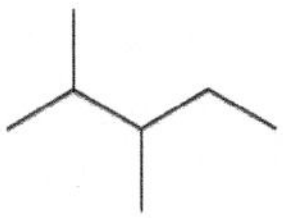

e)

13.79 Select the molecule that has a pentane parent.

a)

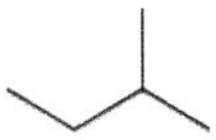

b)

c)

d)

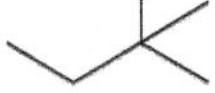

13.80 Sort the molecules by parent chain length. Drag each molecule into the correct category.

Answer choices:

a) $CH_3CH_2CH_2CH_2CH_3$

b) $CH_3CH_2CH(CH_3)_2$

c) $CH_3CH_2CH_3$

d) $CH_3CH_2CH_2CH_3$

e) $CH_3CH(CH_3)_2$

f) $CH_3C(CH_3)_3$

g) $CH_3CH_2CH(CH_3)CH_2CH_3$

Target boxes: propane parent chain, butane parent chain, pentane parent chain

13.81 Select the correct structure of 2,3-dimethylhexane.

a)

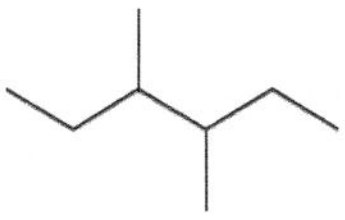

b)

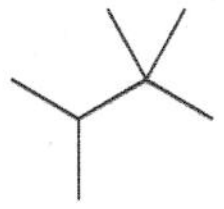

c)

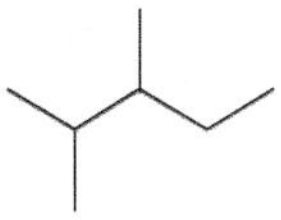

d)

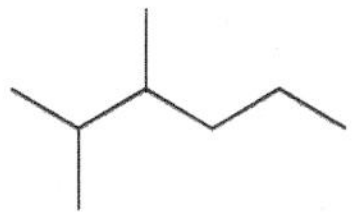

e)

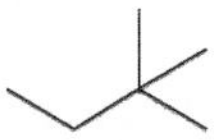

13.82 What is the correct name of this branched alkane?

a) 3-ethylheptane

b) 4-ethylhexane

c) 3-ethylhexane

d) 1,1-diethylbutane

13.83 What is the name of this branched haloalkane?

a) 3-bromo-4-methylpentane

b) 3-bromo-2-methylhexane

c) 2-methyl-3-bromopentane

d) 3-bromo-2-methylpentane

13.84 What is the name of this branched haloalkane?

a) 3-ethyl-2-fluorohexane

b) 4-ethyl-5-fluorohexane

c) 2-fluoro-3-ethylhexane

d) 3-ethyl-2-fluorohexanene

13.85 Which of the following figures represents the structure of 3,4-diethyloctane?

a)

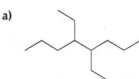

b)

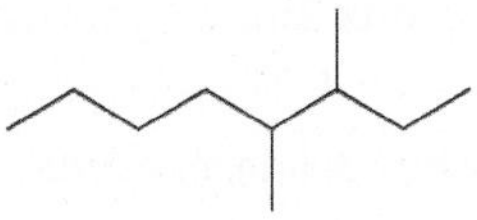

c)

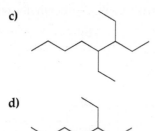

d)

13.86 Drawing *cis* and *trans* isomers: Use the drawing tool to build the *skeletal structure* of *trans*-2-hexene. Skeletal structures do not include hydrogen atoms that are bonded to carbon, and labels for carbon atoms are not included.

13.87 Drawing *cis* and *trans* isomers: Use the drawing tool to build the *skeletal structure* of *cis*-3-octene. Skeletal structures do not include hydrogen atoms that are bonded to carbon, and labels for carbon atoms are not included.

13.88 Drawing a cycloalkane: Use the drawing tool to build the *skeletal structure* of 1,4 dimethylcyclohexane. Skeletal structures do not include hydrogen atoms that are bonded to carbon, and labels for carbon atoms are not included.

13.89 Drawing an aromatic compound: Use the drawing tool to build the *skeletal structure* of 1,3 dimethylbenzene. Skeletal structures do not include hydrogen atoms that are bonded to carbon, and labels for carbon atoms are not included.

13.90 Drawing an alkene: Use the drawing tool to build the *skeletal structure* of 1,2 dimethylcyclohexene. Skeletal structures do not include hydrogen atoms that are bonded to carbon, and labels for carbon atoms are not included.

13.91 Drawing a branched haloalkene: Use the drawing tool to build the *skeletal structure* of 1-bromo-2-methylpentane. Skeletal structures do not include hydrogen atoms that are bonded to carbon or labels for carbon atoms.

13.92 Complete the name of the given molecule by dragging the missing fragment into the space provided.

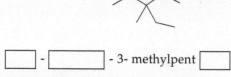

[   ]-[   ]- 3- methylpent [   ]

Answer choices for box 1: 1, 2, 3, 4, 5

Answer choices for box 2: methyl, ethyl, propyl, butyl, pentyl

Answer choices for box 3: ane, ene, yne

13.93 Complete the name of the given molecule by dragging the missing fragment into the space provided.

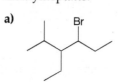

[   ]-[   ]-[   ]-[   ] heptane

Answer choices for boxes 1 and 3: 1, 2, 3, 4, 5, 6

Answer choices for boxes 2: and 4: methyl, ethyl, propyl, butyl, pent, hex, hept, oct

13.94 Select the correct structure of 4-bromo-3-ethyl-2-methylheptane.

a)   Br

b)

      Br

c)   Br

d)

      Br

13.95 Select the correct structure of 2-pentyne.

a)
H—C≡C—C—C—C—H

b)
H—C—C—C═C—C—H

c)
H—C—C—C═C—C—H

d)
H—C—C≡C—C—H

e)
H—C—C—C≡C—C—H

13.96 Select the correct structure of *trans*-2-pentene.

a) 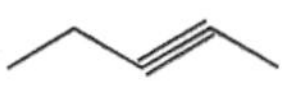   b)

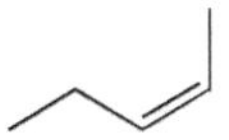

c) 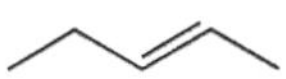 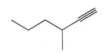   d)

13.97 What is the correct name of the given molecule?

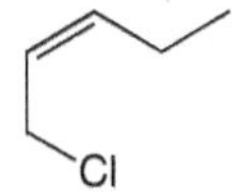

a) *cis*-1-chloropentene

b) *cis*-1-chloro-2-pentene

c) *cis*-5-chloro-3-pentene

d) *trans*-1-chloro-2-pentene

13.98 What is the correct name of the given molecule?

a) 4-methyl-5-hexyne

b) 3-methyl-1-hexene

c) 3-propyl-1-butyne

d) 3-methyl-1-hexyne

13.99 Select the correct name of the given molecule.

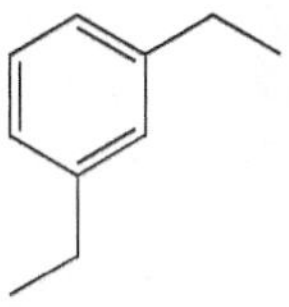

a) ethylbenzene

b) 1,3-diethylbenzene

c) 1,5-diethylbenzene

d) 1,3-diethylcyclohexane

13.100 Drawing a tri-substituted aromatic hydrocarbon: Use the drawing tool to build the *skeletal structure* of 1,3,5 triiodobenzene. Skeletal structures do not include hydrogen atoms that are bonded to carbon or labels for carbon atoms.

13.101 Which of the following figures represents the structure of 2-ethyl-3-methyl-1-pentene?

a)   b)

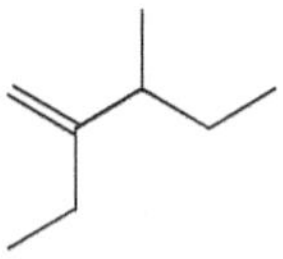

c) 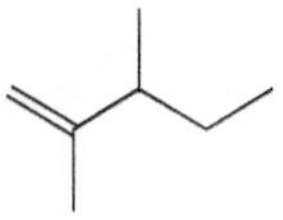   d)

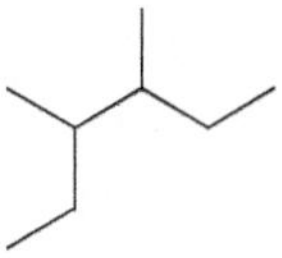

Chapter 14

14.1 Chemical Reactions and Equations

LO 14.1: Analyze the structural and physical properties of alcohols.

14.1 Complete the sentences.

A tertiary (3°) alcohol has _____ carbon atom(s) attached to the alcohol carbon.

A primary (1°) alcohol has _____ carbon atom(s) attached to the alcohol carbon.

A secondary (2°) alcohol has _____ carbon atom(s) attached to the alcohol carbon.

Answer choices: one, two, three, four

14.2 Classify each molecule as a primary (1°) alcohol, secondary (2°) alcohol, tertiary (3°) alcohol, or not an alcohol

Answer choices: $(CH_3)_2CHOH$, $(CH_3)_3COH$, CH_3CH_2OH

Target boxes: primary (1°) alcohol, secondary (2°) alcohol, tertiary (3°) alcohol, not an alcohol

---

14.3 Classify each molecule as a primary (1°) alcohol, secondary (2°) alcohol, tertiary (3°) alcohol, or not an alcohol.

a) 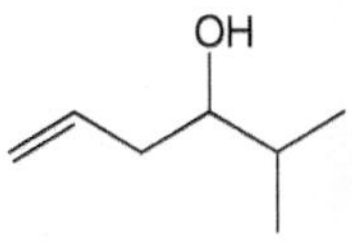   b) 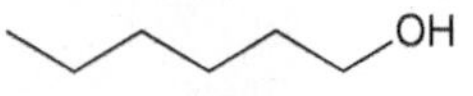   c) 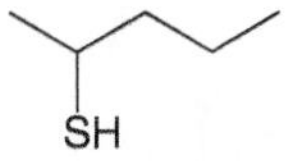   d) 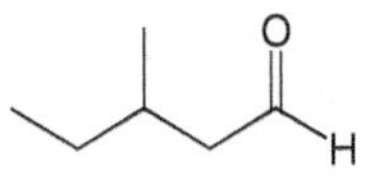   e)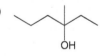

Target boxes: primary (1°) alcohol, secondary (2°) alcohol, tertiary (3°) alcohol, not an alcohol

14.4 Classify each molecule as a primary (1°) alcohol, secondary (2°) alcohol, tertiary (3°) alcohol, or not an alcohol.

a) 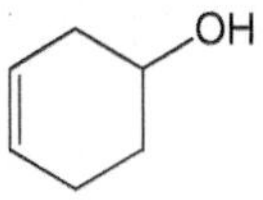   b) 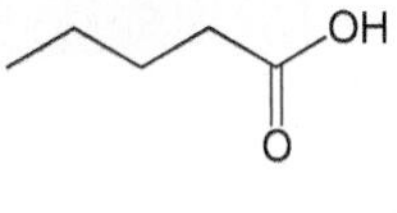   c) 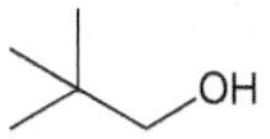   d) 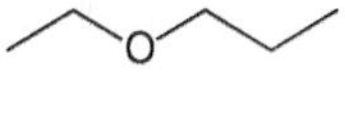   e)

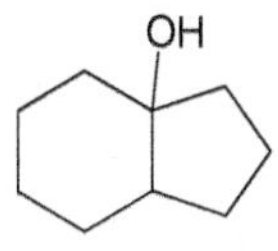

Target boxes: primary (1°) alcohol, secondary (2°) alcohol, tertiary (3°) alcohol, not an alcohol

14.5   Classify each molecule as a primary (1°) alcohol, secondary (2°) alcohol, tertiary (3°) alcohol, or not an alcohol.

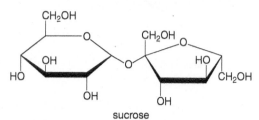

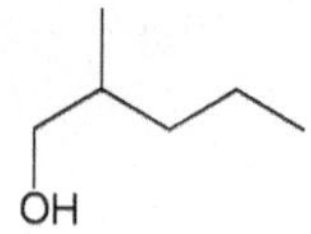

Target boxes: primary (1°) alcohol, secondary (2°) alcohol, tertiary (3°) alcohol, not an alcohol

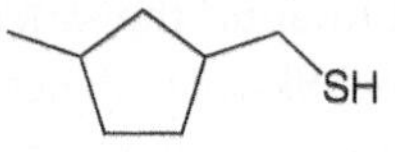

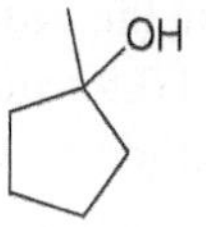

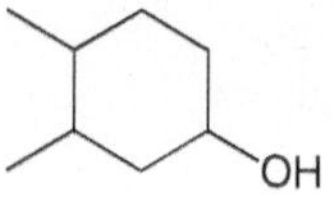

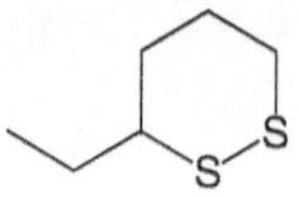

14.6   Sucrose (also known as table sugar) is a common sweetener in many foods. The sucrose molecule contains two sugar rings connected by a shared oxygen atom. Complete the following sentences.

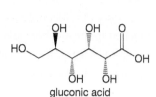

sucrose

Cakes and many other sweets contain the sugar sucrose.

A sucrose molecule has _____ primary (1°) alcohol groups.

A sucrose molecule has _____ secondary (2°) alcohol groups.

A sucrose molecule has _____ tertiary (3°) alcohol groups.

Answer choices: 0, 1, 2, 3, 4, 5

14.7   Gluconic acid occurs naturally in fruit and honey. It is also used to help treat chemical burns from hydrofluoric acid (HF) and is included in certain intravenous (IV) fluids given to patients in the hospital.

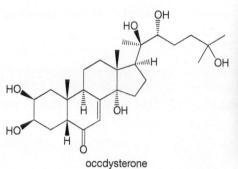

gluconic acid

hospital patient receiving IV fluids containing gluconic acid

A gluconic acid molecule has _____ primary (1°) alcohol groups. *Hint*: the OH portion of a carboxylic acid ($R-CO_2H$) group is not an alcohol group.

A gluconic molecule has _____ secondary (2°) alcohol groups.

A gluconic molecule has _____ tertiary (3°) alcohol groups.

Answer choices: 0, 1, 2, 3, 4, 5, 6

14.8   The hormone ecdysterone regulates molting (metamorphosis) in insects and other animals. How many tertiary (3°) alcohol groups are on the given ecdysterone molecule?

occdysterone

a katydid molting

a) 1   b) 2   c) 3   d) 6

14.9 Drawing a secondary alcohol: Use the drawing tool to add a hydroxyl (OH) group to the appropriate carbon (on the given partial molecule structure) to form a secondary (2°) alcohol. Do not add additional carbon atoms to the structure or lone pairs of electrons on the oxygen atom added as part of the OH group.

14.10 Drawing a primary alcohol: Use the drawing tool to add a hydroxyl (OH) group to the appropriate carbon (on the given partial molecule structure) to form a primary (1°) alcohol. Make sure your answer contains a new bond to the new OH group and a total of six carbon atoms. Do not add additional carbon atoms to the structure or lone pairs of electrons on the oxygen atom added as part of the OH group.

14.11 Drawing a tertiary alcohol: Use the drawing tool to add a hydroxyl (OH) group to the appropriate carbon (on the given partial molecule structure) to form a tertiary (3°) alcohol. Do not add additional carbon atoms to the structure or lone pairs of electrons on the oxygen atom added as part of the OH group.

14.12 Drawing a primary alcohol: Use the drawing tool to build the *skeletal structure* of a three-carbon primary (1°) alcohol. Do not draw hydrogen atoms that are bonded to carbon or lone pairs of electrons on the oxygen atom added as part of the OH group. Remember, skeletal structures do not contain labels for carbon atoms.

14.13 Drawing a secondary alcohol: Use the drawing tool to build the *skeletal structure* of a three-carbon secondary (2°) alcohol. Do not draw hydrogen atoms that are bonded to carbon or lone pairs of electrons on the oxygen atom added as part of the OH group. Remember, skeletal structures do not contain carbon atom labels.

14.14 Drawing a tertiary alcohol: Use the drawing tool to build the *skeletal structure* of a non-cyclic four-carbon tertiary (3°) alcohol. Do not draw hydrogen atoms that are bonded to carbon or lone pairs of electrons on the oxygen atom added as part of the OH group. Remember, skeletal structures do not contain carbon atom labels.

14.15 Identify the molecules that are able to participate in hydrogen bonding interactions with other identical molecules, and those that are not.

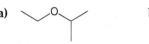

e)

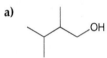

Target boxes: can hydrogen bond with identical molecules, cannot hydrogen bond with identical molecules

14.16 Which molecule is most soluble in water?

14.17 Arrange the molecules left-to-right in terms of increasing water solubility.

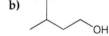

Target box: box with an arrow indicating increasing water solubility to the right

14.18 Which molecule has the highest boiling point?

14.19 Which molecule has the highest boiling point?

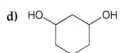

14.20 Xylitol is a sugar substitute used in food and chewing gum. How many atoms in the xylitol molecule are capable of forming hydrogen bonds with other molecules?

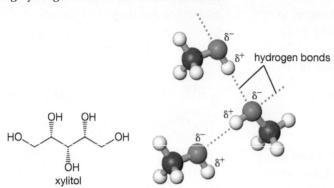

Recall that hydrogen bonding requires that a hydrogen atom is bonded to O, N, or F. This hydrogen atom can then form a hydrogen bond with an O, N, or F on another molecule as shown here for methanol molecules hydrogen bonding with themselves.

xylitol

a) three   b) four   c) five   d) ten

14.2 Ethers

LO 14.2: Analyze the structural and physical properties of ethers.

14.21 Identify the molecules as ethers or not ethers.

Answer choices:

a) Br

b)

c)

d)

e)

f)

Target boxes: ethers, not ethers

14.22 Which molecule is an ether?

a)   b)   c)   d)

14.23 Categorize each molecule as either an ether or an alcohol.

Answer choices:

a)   b)   c)

d)   e)   f)

Target boxes: ethers, alcohols

14.24 Which medication contains an ether?

a)

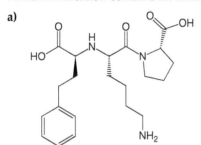

lisinopril, used to treat high
blood pressure and heart failure

b)

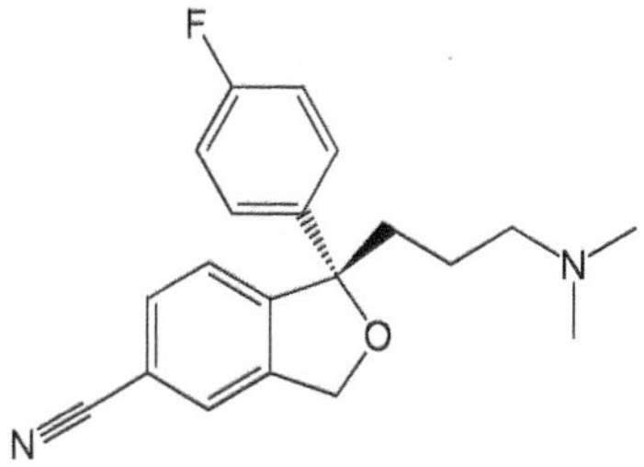

escitalopram, an antidepressant

c)

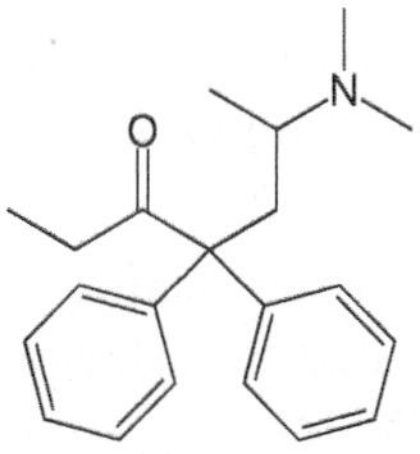

methadone, an opioid
for pain treatment

d)

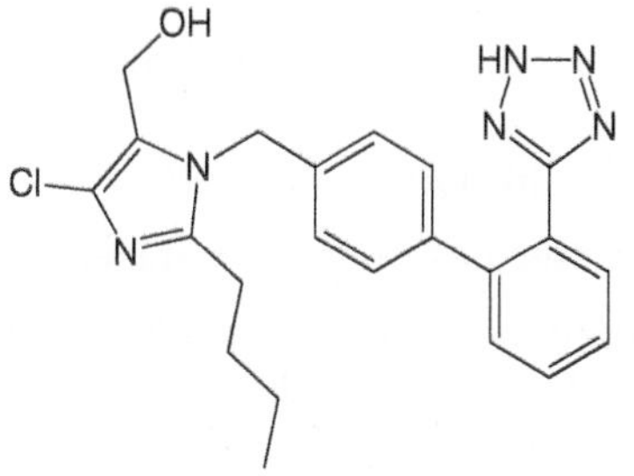

losartan, a treatment
for high blood pressure

14.25 Which molecule is *not* a cyclic ether?

a) 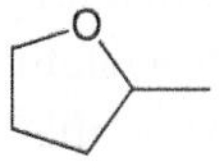   b) 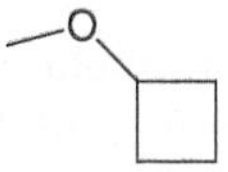   c) 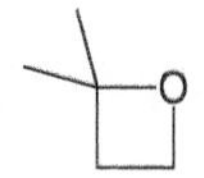   d)

14.26 Codeine is a commonly prescribed opiate drug used for pain management. On the given codeine molecule, which colored region(s) contains an ether group?

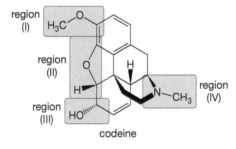

codeine

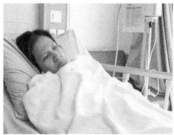

a) region I   b) region II   c) region III   d) region IV   e) regions I and II

14.27 Use the drawing tool to build the *skeletal structure* of a cyclic ether having only two carbon atoms. Do not draw hydrogen atoms that are bonded to carbon or lone pairs of electrons on the ether oxygen atom. Remember, skeletal structures do not contain labels for carbon atoms. Hint: could one of the carbon atoms in a cyclopropane ring be replaced by an oxygen atom?

14.28 A. Use the drawing tool to build the *skeletal structure* of a cyclic ether molecule with three carbon atoms. Do not draw hydrogen atoms that are bonded to carbon or lone pairs of electrons on the ether oxygen atom. B. Draw another cyclic ether molecule having only three carbon atoms that is different than the one you drew in (A). Your answer for (B) should be a constitutional isomer of your answer in (A). Recall that constitutional isomers are isomers that differ in the way the atoms are connected to each other. Remember, skeletal structures do not contain labeled carbon atoms. Hint: consider three- membered rings with an "R" group attached and also a four-membered ring.

14.29 Which molecule has the highest boiling point?

a) [structure: ether]

b) [structure: alkane]

c) [structure: alkane]

d) [structure: alcohol with OH]

14.30 What is the approximate bond angle between the two propyl groups in this molecule?

[structure with O]

approximate C–O–C bond angle = ?

a) 120°   b) 190°   c) 109°   d) 60°

14.31 Rank the molecules in order of increasing boiling point (bp).

a) [cyclohexane with O ether]   b) [cyclohexane with OH]

c) [cyclohexane with propyl]

Target boxes: lowest bp, intermediate bp, highest bp

14.3 Functional Groups Containing Sulfur

LO 14.3: Analyze the structural and physical properties of sulfur functional groups (thiols, thioethers).

14.32 Which molecule contains a thiol group?

a) [structure]
H₂N–C–C–OH with H, O, CH₂, CH₂, C=O, NH₂

b) [structure]
H₂N–C–C–OH with H, O, CH₂, CH₂, S, CH₃

c) [structure]
H₂N–C–C–OH with H, O, CH₂, indole ring, HN

d) [structure]
H₂N–C–C–OH with H, O, CH₂, SH

14.33 Which amino acid molecule contains a thioether (sulfide) group?

a) [structure]
H₂N–C–C–OH with H, O, CH₂, SH

b) [structure]
C–OH with O, HN ring (proline)

c) [structure]
H₂N–C–C–OH with H, O, CH₂, CH₂, S, CH₃

d) [structure]
H₂N–C–C–OH with H, O, CH₂, OH

14.34 In which ways are ethers and thioethers similar?

a) Both ethers and thioethers have carbon containing groups bonded to each side of an element from group 2A.

b) Both ethers and thioethers contain hydrogen atoms bonded directly to one side of an element from group 6A.

c) Both ethers and thioethers feature carbon-containing groups bonded to each side of an element from group 6A.

d) Both ethers and thioethers are capable of hydrogen bonding with other molecules identical to themselves.

14.35 The aleph molecule (also known as DOT) is a psychedelic hallucinogenic drug related structurally to amphetamine, a central nervous system stimulant. Which of the highlighted regions on this aleph molecule is a thioether group?

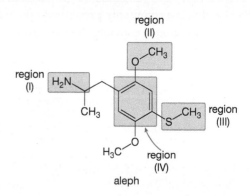

aleph

a) region (I)   b) region (II)

c) region (III)   d) region (IV)

14.36 Which molecule contains *both* a thiol and a thioether (sulfide) group?

a)

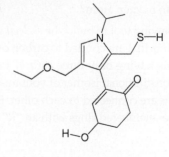

b)

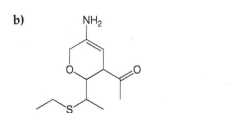

c)

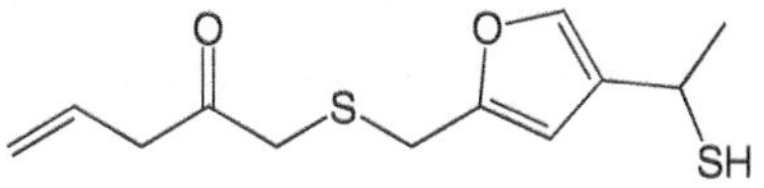

d)

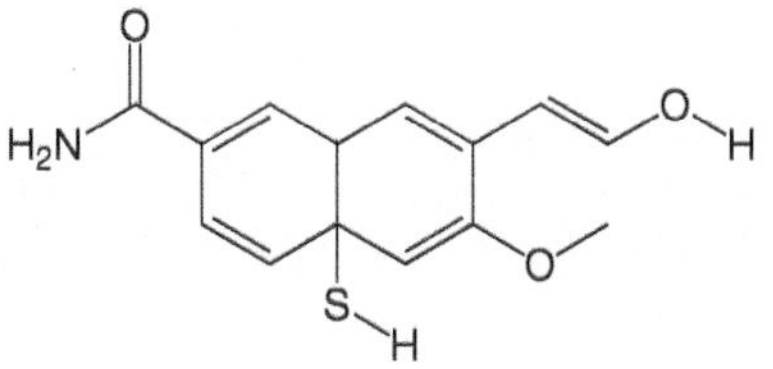

14.37 Which molecule contains *neither* a thiol group nor a thioether group?

a)

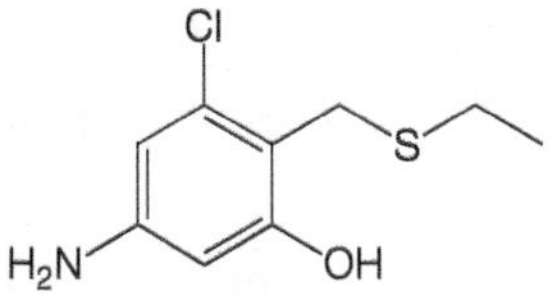

b)

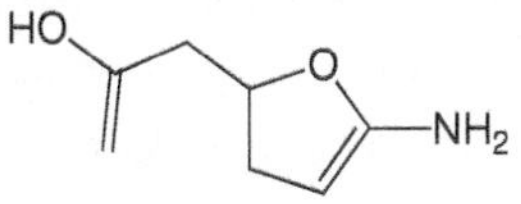

c)

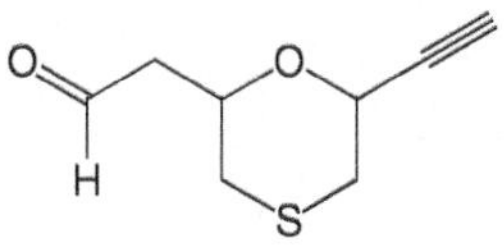

d)

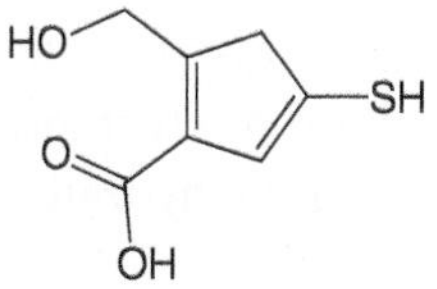

14.38 Classify each molecule as either an alcohol, ether, thiol, or thioether.

a)   **b)**

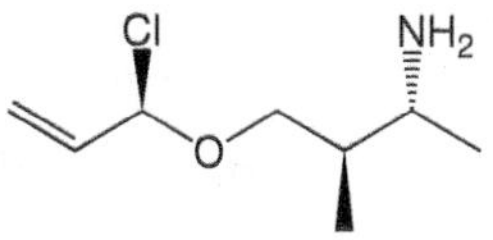

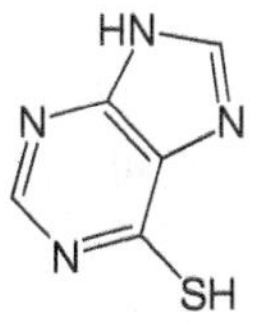

c)

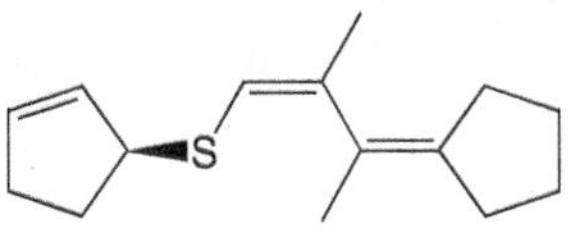

d)

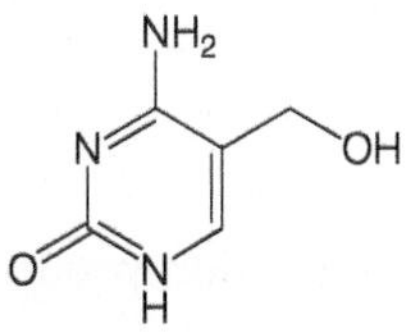

Target boxes: alcohol, ether, thiol, thioether

14.39 Identify the molecule in each pair that has the higher boiling point.

a)    SH   or   OH

b) 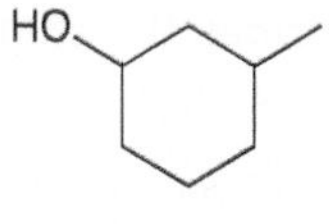   HO   or   HO

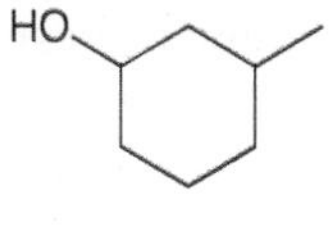

c) 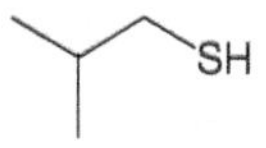   SH   or   OH

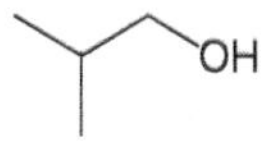

14.40 What is the approximate bond angle between the two butyl groups in the given molecule?

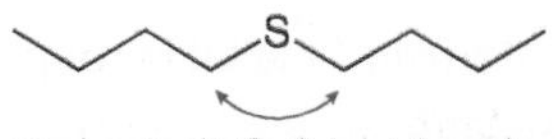

approximate C–S–C bond angle = ?

a) 60°   **b)** 109°
c) 120°   **d)** 180°

14.41 Identify which molecules are capable of hydrogen bonding with other identical molecules.

a) 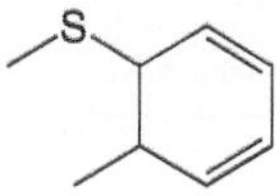   **b)**

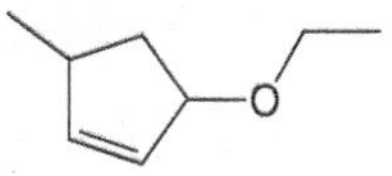

c) 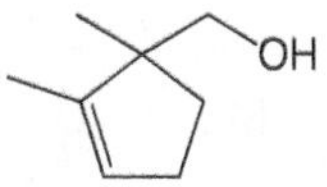   **d)**

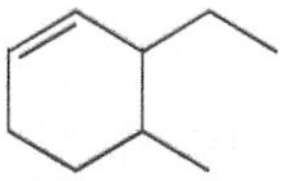

e)

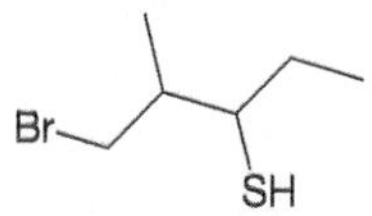

Target boxes: can hydrogen bond with other identical molecules, cannot hydrogen bond with other identical molecules

14.42 Arrange the molecules left to right in terms of increasing solubility in water.

a)    SH

b)    OH

c)

d) 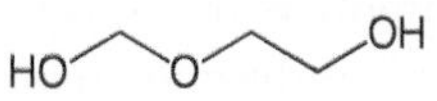   HO   O   OH

Target box: box with an arrow indicating increasing water solubility to the right

14.4 Reactions of Alcohols and Thiols

LO 4: Determine the products of the reactions of alcohols and thiols (dehydration of alcohols, and oxidation of thiols).

14.43 Which statement best describes the changes that occur in the reactant as it forms the alkene product?

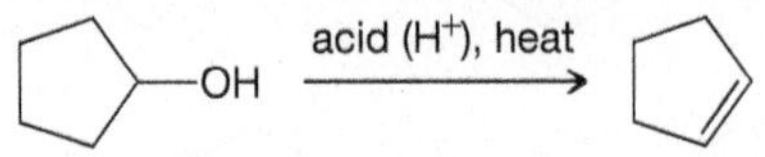

acid (H⁺), heat

a) The OH group is removed from the reactant.

b) The OH group in the reactant is replaced by an H atom.

c) Two H atoms are removed from the reactant.

d) An H atom and the OH group are removed from the reactant.

14.44 Categorize the major products that form when the given starting material undergoes oxidation or dehydration. Drag each product molecule into the correct reaction box. Hint: One or more of the possible product structures may not correspond to any of the product boxes.

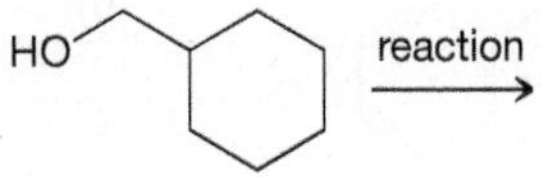

reaction

starting material

a) 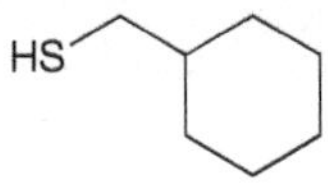 HS

b) 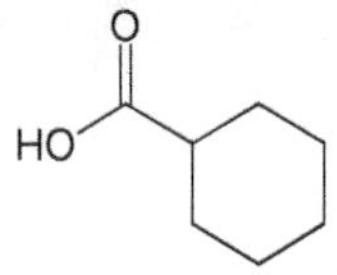 HO

c)

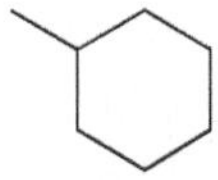

d)

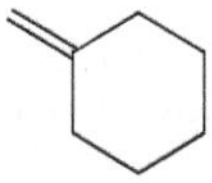

e)

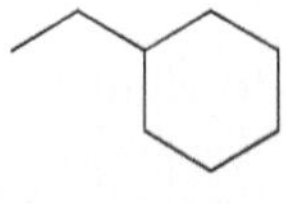

f)

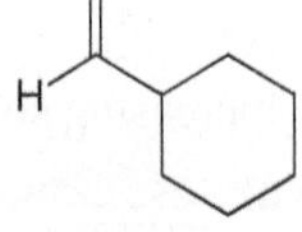

Target boxes: product after partial oxidation, product after complete oxidation, product after dehydration

14.45 Categorize the major products that form when the given starting material undergoes oxidation or dehydration. Drag each product molecule into the correct reaction box. Hint: One or more of the possible product structures may not correspond to any of the product boxes.

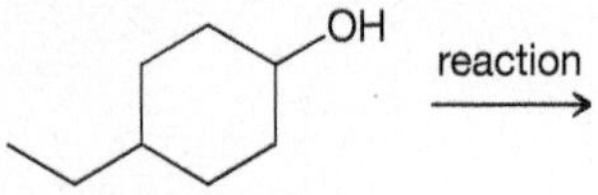

reaction

starting material

a)

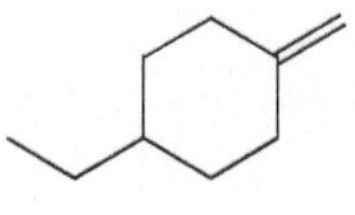

b)

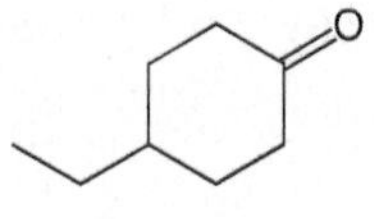

c)

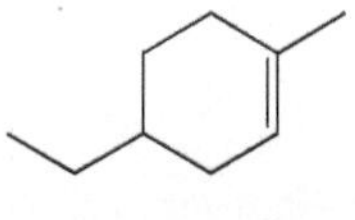

d)

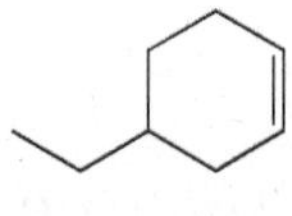

Target boxes: product after oxidation, product after dehydration

14.46 Categorize the major products that form when the given starting material undergoes oxidation or dehydration. Drag each product molecule into the correct reaction box. Hint: One or more of the possible product structures may not correspond to any of the product boxes.

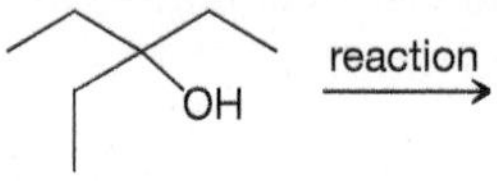

reaction

starting material

a)

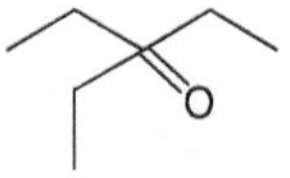

b)

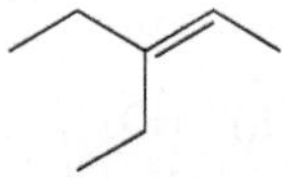

c)

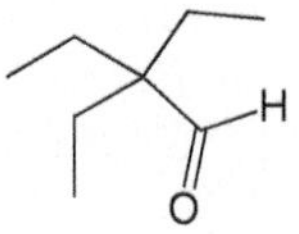

d)

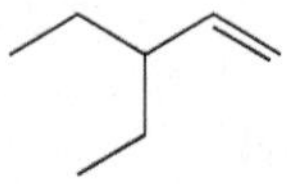

e) No reaction

Target boxes: product after oxidation, product after dehydration

14.47 Identify the major and minor product formed when the given alcohol undergoes a dehydration reaction.

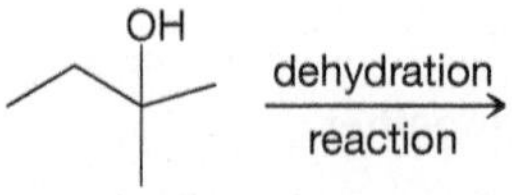

dehydration reaction

a)

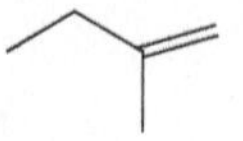

b)

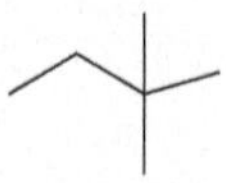

c) 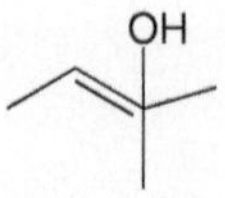 OH

d)

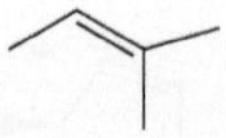

e) 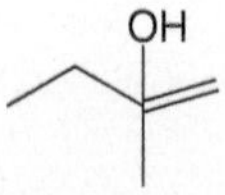 OH

Target boxes: major dehydration product, minor dehydration product

14.48 Identify the major and minor product formed when the given alcohol undergoes a dehydration reaction.

dehydration reaction

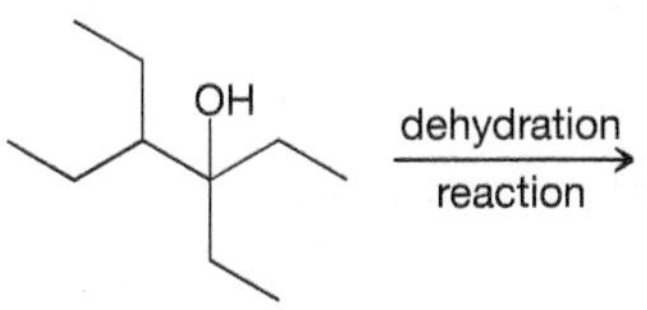

a)

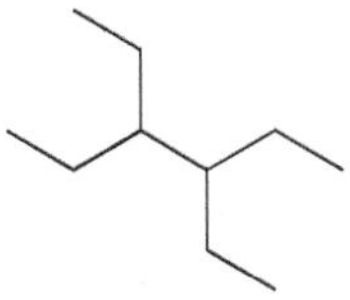

b)

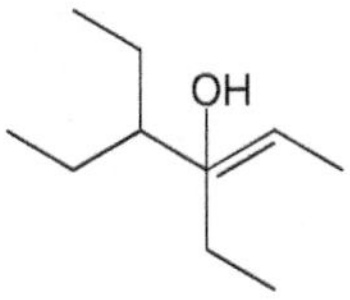

c)

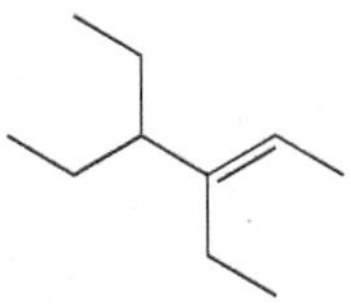

d)

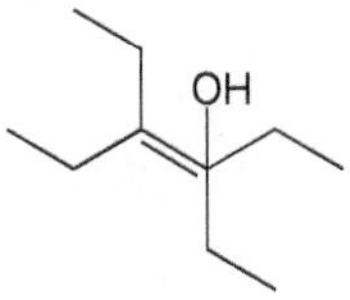

e)

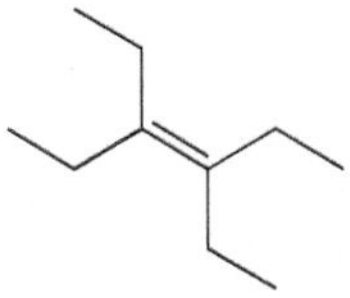

Target boxes: major dehydration product, minor dehydration product

14.49 Which alcohol produces this molecule as its major dehydration reaction product?

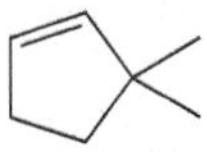

major dehydration product

a)

b)

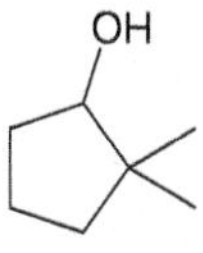

c)

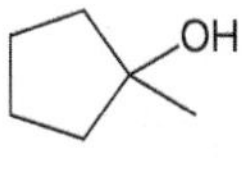

d)

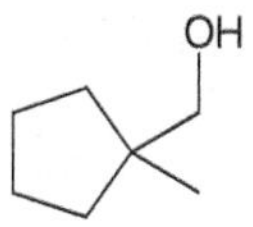

14.50 Which alcohol produces the given complete oxidation product?

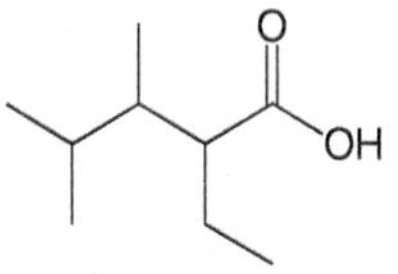

complete oxidation product

a)

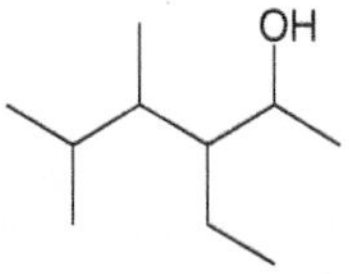

b)

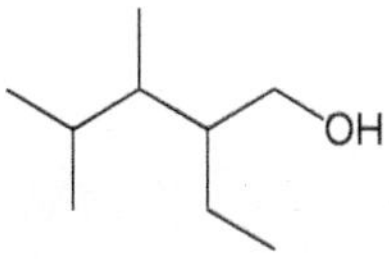

c)

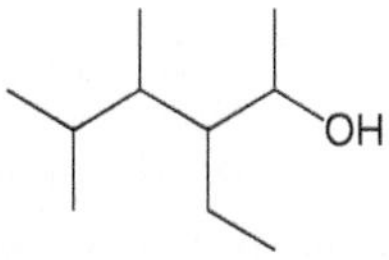

d)

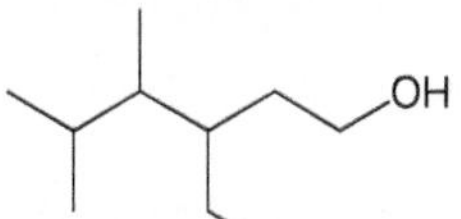

14.51 Use the drawing tool to build the *expanded structure* of the molecule produced during the complete oxidation of methanol (CH_3OH). Be sure to draw all atoms using atomic symbols (C, H, O) and all bonds connecting each atom. Do not include lone pairs of electrons for any atom.

14.52 Draw the *skeletal structure* of the organic molecule produced when the molecule below undergoes a dehydration reaction. Do not draw hydrogen atoms that are bonded to carbon or lone pairs of electrons on oxygen or sulfur atoms. Consider alcohol dehydration in this example and not alcohol oxidation. Remember, skeletal structures do not contain carbon atom labels.

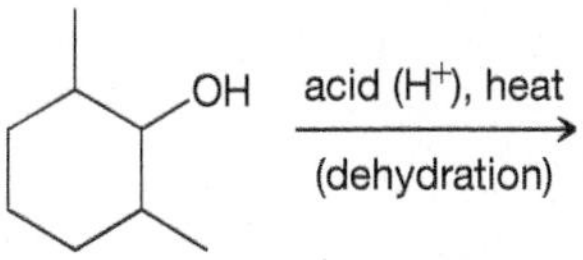

acid (H^+), heat (dehydration)

14.53 Oxytocin is a hormone released by the pituitary gland that acts as a neurotransmitter in the brain. Oxytocin plays a role in childbirth, the release of milk during nursing, and feelings of social bonding. Which of the highlighted regions in the oxytocin molecule contains the disulfide?

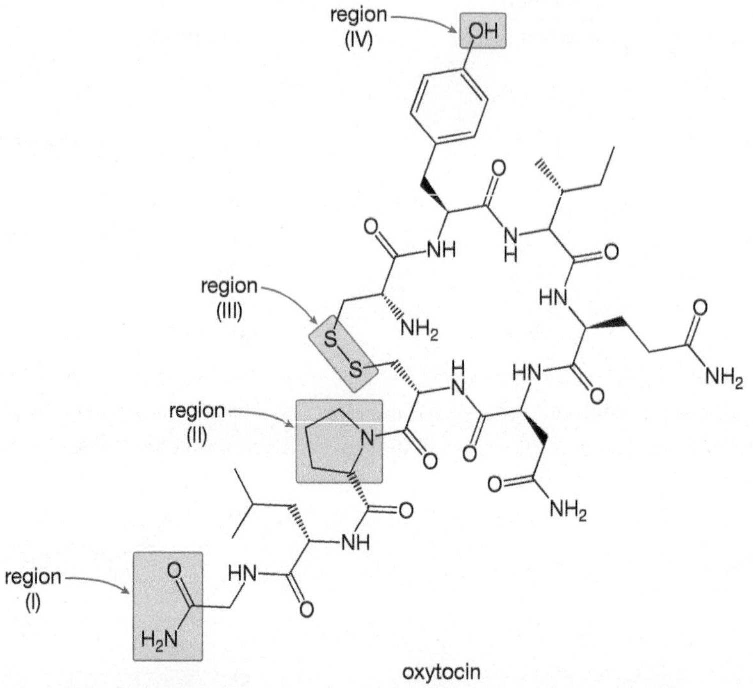

oxytocin

a) region (I)   **b)** region (II)   **c)** region (III)   **d)** region (IV)

14.54 Somatostatin is a peptide hormone that regulates other hormones including insulin. Examine the structure of the somatostatin molecule and determine which functional group it contains.

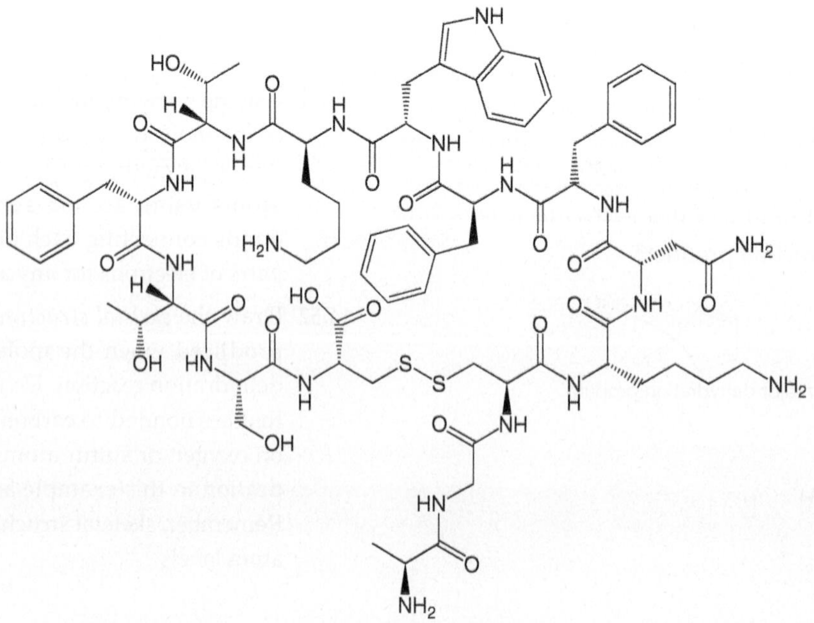

a) thiol   **b)** thioether   **c)** ether   **d)** disulfide

14.55 Coenzyme A is involved in a number of metabolic processes within the body. Which functional group is *not* found on the coenzyme A molecule?

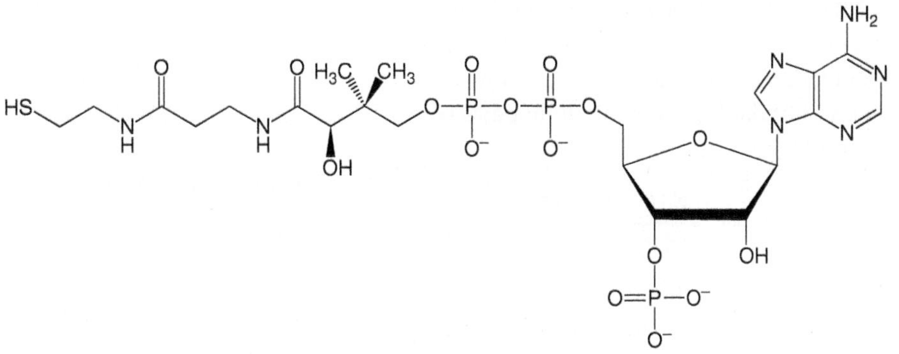

a) cyclic ether   b) alcohol   c) thiol   d) disulfide

14.56 Methane (CH_4) is one of the most common hydrocarbons on Earth and is an important greenhouse gas in the atmosphere. The biosynthesis of methane involves a reaction regulated by coenzyme M (2-mercaptoethyl sulfonic acid). Based on the reactions you have seen in this chapter, select the molecule produced when 2-mercaptoethyl sulfonic acid undergoes a thiol oxidation reaction.

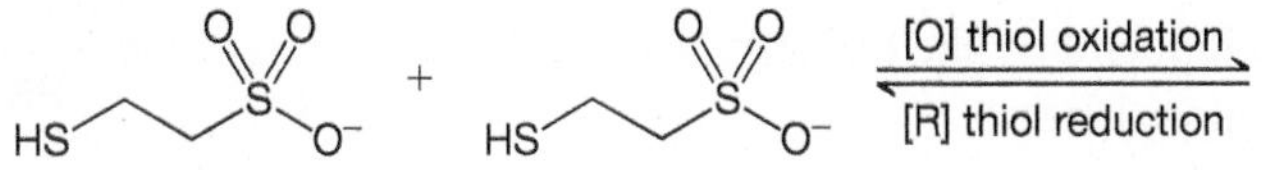

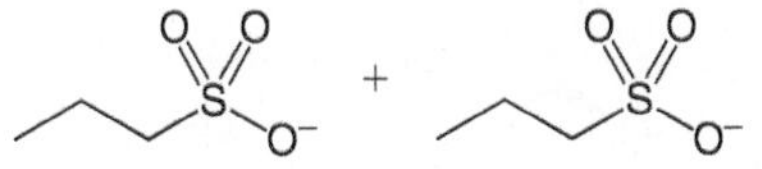

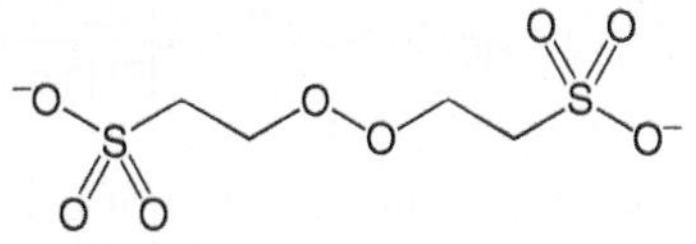

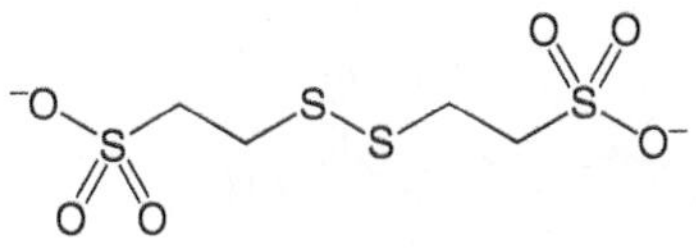

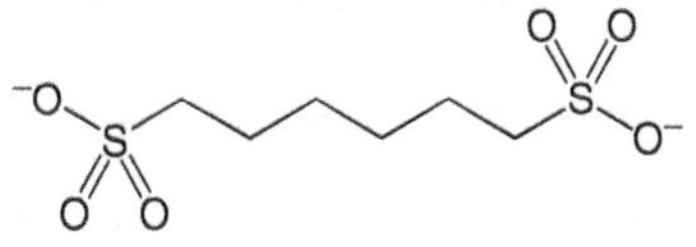

14.57 Which molecule is produced when coenzyme B is oxidized?

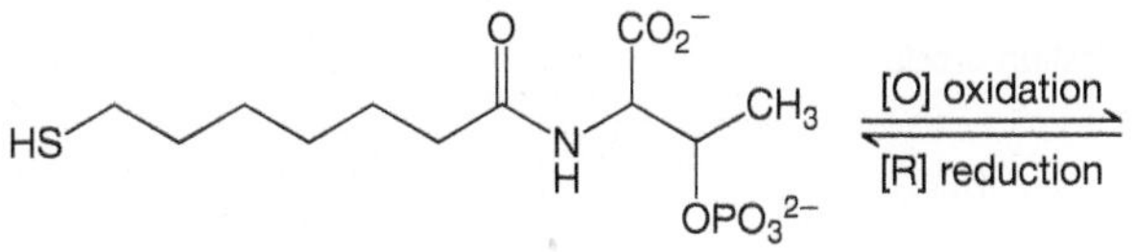

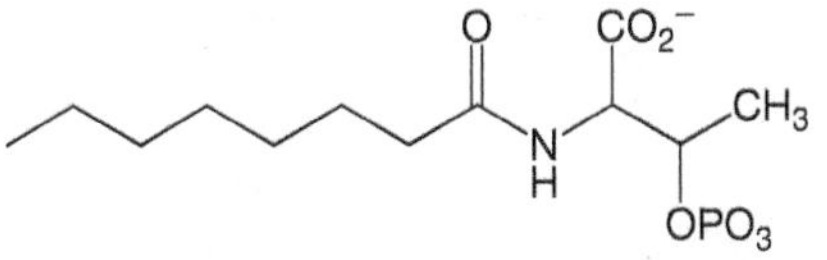

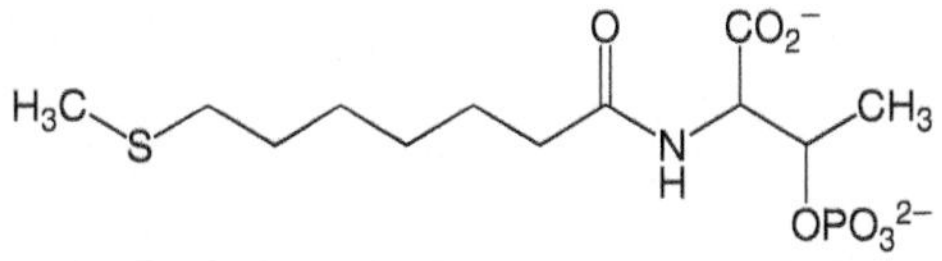

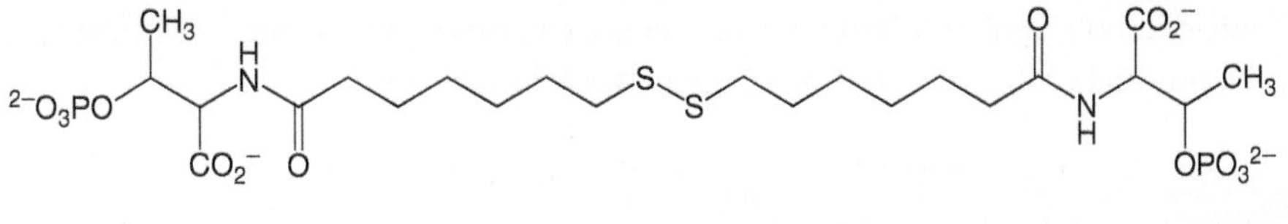

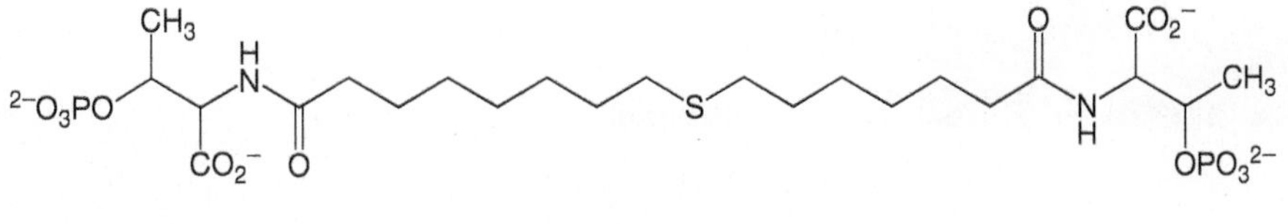

14.58 Methanethiol (CH_3SH) is a naturally occurring thiol found in some cheeses and nuts. Use the drawing tool to build the *expanded structure* of the molecule produced when methanethiol undergoes the given reaction. Remember, expanded structures show all atom labels and bonds. Do not draw lone pairs of electrons on sulfur.

$$CH_3SH \;+\; CH_3SH \;\underset{\text{[R] thiol reduction}}{\overset{\text{[O] thiol oxidation}}{\rightleftharpoons}}$$

14.59 Chemists use 2-mercaptoethanol (also known as β-mercaptoethanol, or BME) in biochemistry laboratories to help control the level of oxidation and reduction in protein samples. Use the drawing tool to build the *skeletal structure* of the molecule produced during thiol oxidation reaction of 2-mercaptoethanol. Do not draw hydrogen atoms that are bonded to carbon or lone pairs of electrons on oxygen or sulfur atoms. Only consider thiol oxidation in this example, and not alcohol oxidation. Remember, skeletal structures do not contain carbon atom labels.

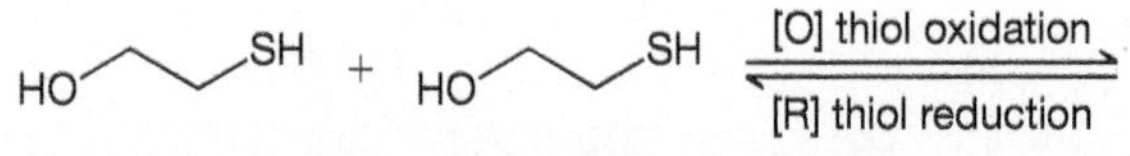

$$\text{HO}\diagdown\text{SH} \;+\; \text{HO}\diagdown\text{SH} \;\underset{\text{[R] thiol reduction}}{\overset{\text{[O] thiol oxidation}}{\rightleftharpoons}}$$

14.60 Which *two* alcohol molecules do not produce this alkene as a major dehydration reaction product?

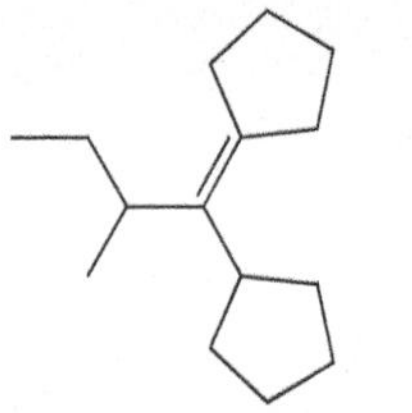

major dehydration product

(i)

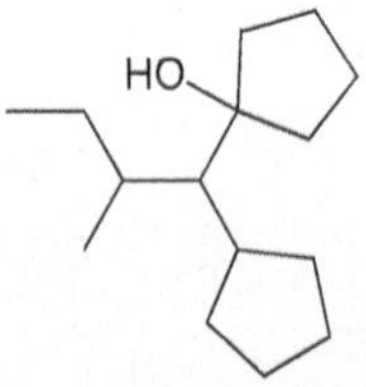

(ii)

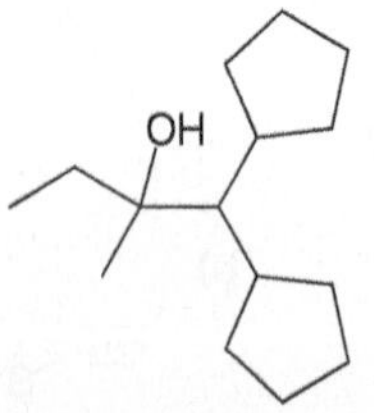

(iii)

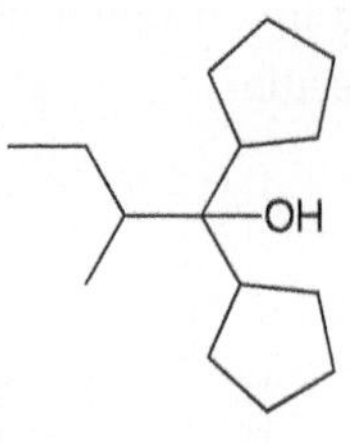

(iv)

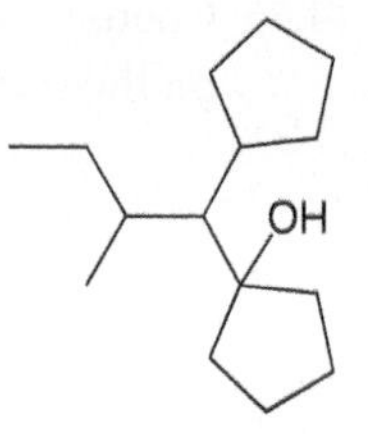

a) molecules (i) and (iv)

b) molecules (i) and (ii)

c) molecules (ii) and (iii)

d) molecules (ii) and (iv)

e) molecules (iii) and (iv)

14.61 Select the most likely oxidation product of this molecule. Hint: Carefully consider the structure and functional groups on the molecule.

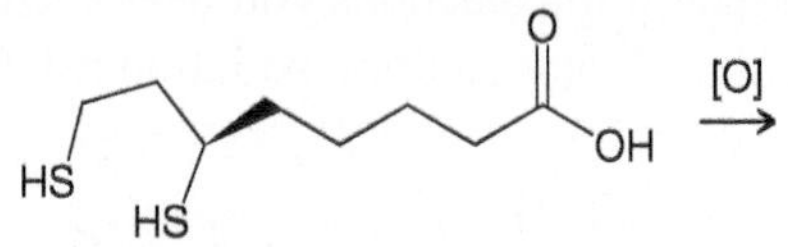

a)

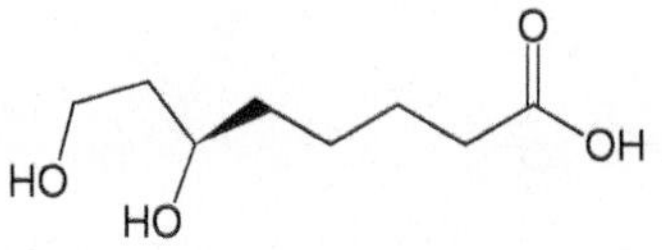

b)

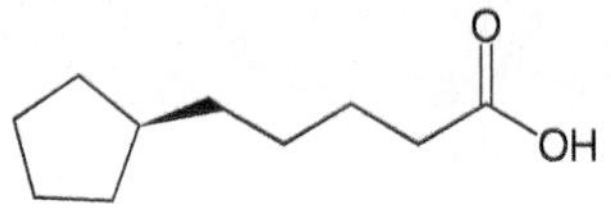

c)

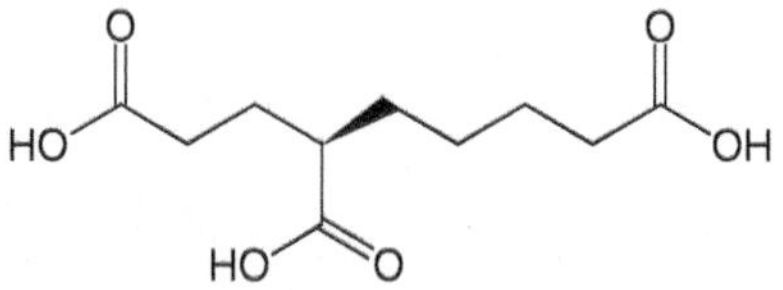

d)

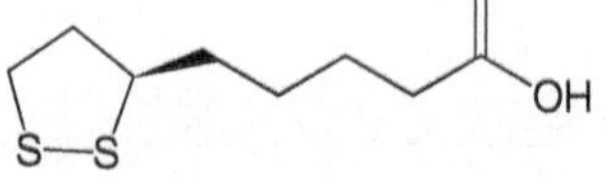

14.62 Bisabolol is a naturally occurring alcohol found in the chamomile plant. It is used as a fragrance in cosmetics. It may have anti-inflammatory, anti-microbial and anti-irritant properties. Categorize each structure as either a major product, minor product, or not a product of the dehydration of the bisabolol molecule.

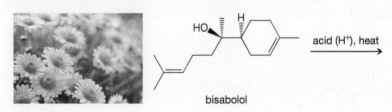

bisabolol

a)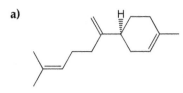

b)

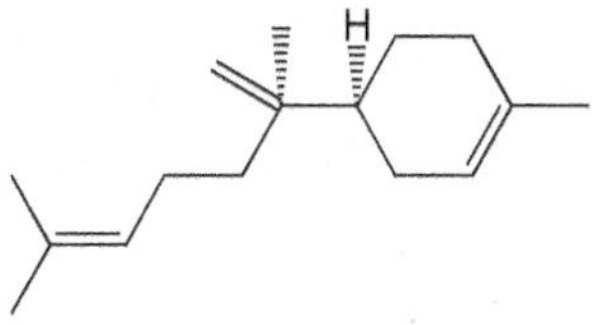

c)

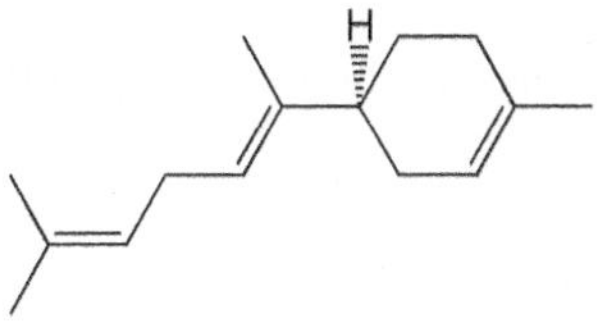

d)

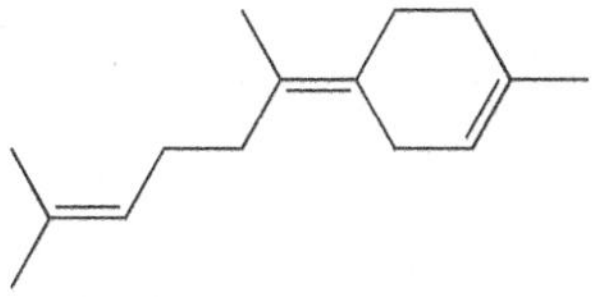

Target boxes: major product, minor product, not a product

14.5 Three-Dimensional Shape: Chiral Molecules

LO 14.5: Distinguish between chiral and achiral molecules.

14.63 Categorize the molecules as having a chiral center (chiral) or not having a chiral center (achiral).

a) 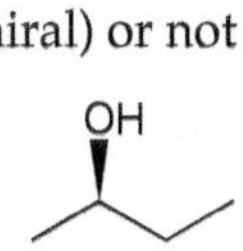 OH

b) 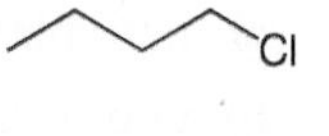 Cl

c) 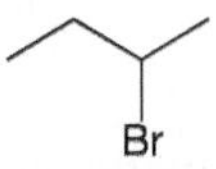 Br

d) 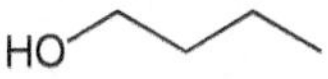 HO

Target boxes: chiral, achiral

14.64 Select the chiral molecule.

a) 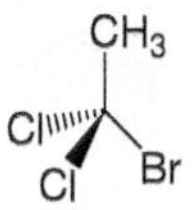 CH₃ Cl Cl Br

b) 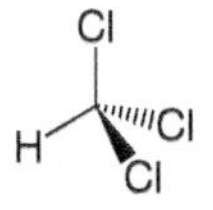 Cl H Cl Cl

c) 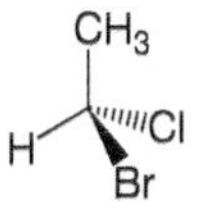 CH₃ H Cl Br

d) 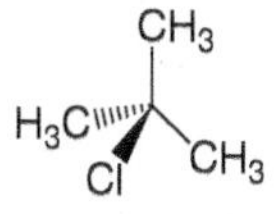 CH₃ H₃C Cl CH₃

14.65 Mannitol is a naturally occurring sugar alcohol found in fruits and vegetables. Which of the numbered carbon atoms on this mannitol molecule represents a chiral carbon center?

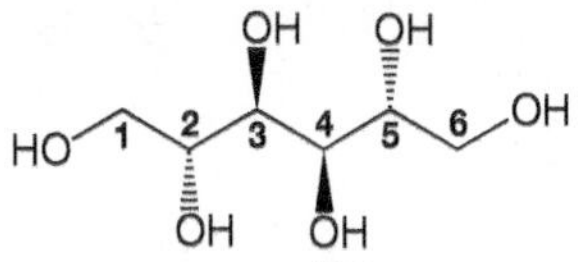

OH OH
HO 1 2 3 4 5 6 OH
OH OH
mannitol

a) all numbered carbon atoms (1-6)

b) carbon atoms 3 and 4

c) carbon atoms 2 and 5

d) carbon atoms 2, 3, 4, and 5

14.66 Dolutegravir (DTG), also known as Tivicay, is a medication used in combination with other drugs to help prevent and treat HIV/AIDS. How many chiral carbon centers does the dolutegravir molecule have?

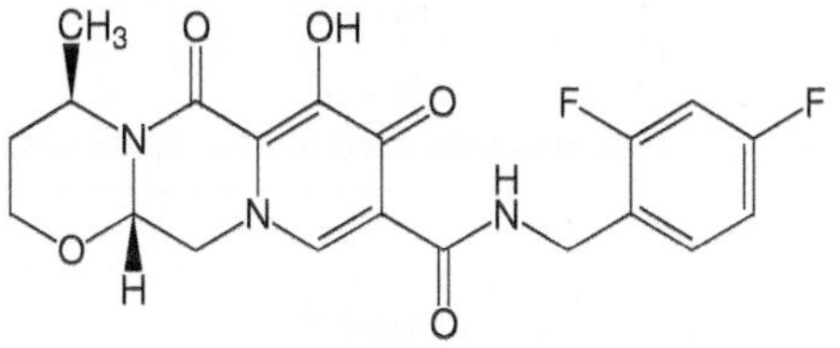

CH₃ O OH O F F N N H N O H dolutegravir (DTG)

a) one

b) two

c) three

d) four

14.67 Lidocaine is a drug commonly used to relieve pain and numb the skin. It is also used to treat irregular heartbeats known as arrhythmias. How many chiral carbon centers does the lidocaine molecule have?

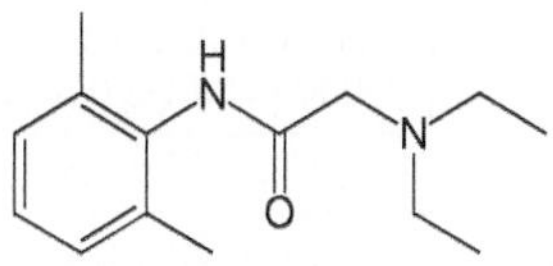

H N N O lidocaine

a) zero

b) one

c) two

d) three

14.68 Phytomenadione, also known as vitamin K1 or phylloquinone, is found in food and used as a dietary supplement. Which of the shaded areas on this phytomenadione molecule is a chiral carbon center?

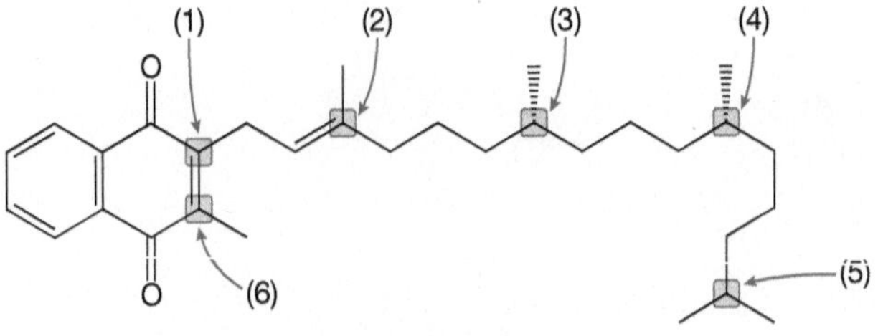

phytomenadione

a) regions (1), (2) and (6)

b) regions (2), (3) and (4)

c) regions (3), (4) and (5)

d) regions (3) and (4) only

e) regions (4) and (5) only

14.69 Which of the following molecules are *not* chiral?

cycloserine 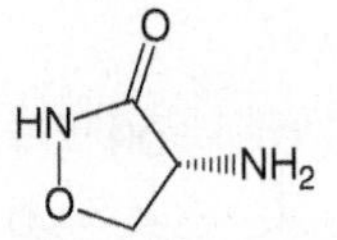
an antibiotic used to treat tuberculosis

paracetamol
(acetaminophen) 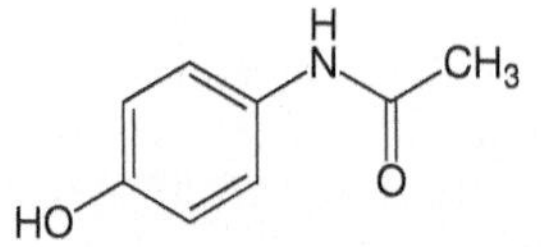
a medication used to treat pain and fever

nicotine 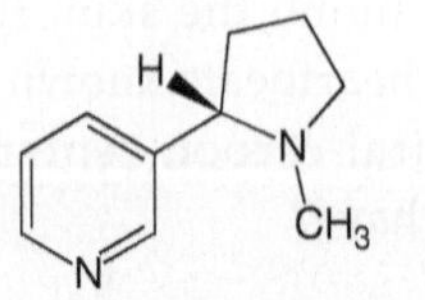
an addictive substance found in tobacco products

pyridoxine 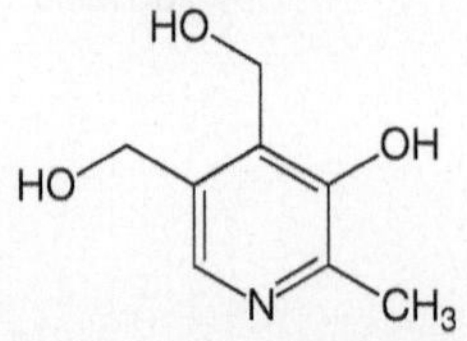
found in many foods and used as a dietary supplement to treat and prevent pyridoxine deficiency and anemia

a) nicotine and cycloserine

b) only paracetamol

c) only cycloserine

d) only nicotine

e) pyridoxine and paracetamol

14.70 Capecitabine, also known as Xeloda, is a chemotherapy medication used in the treatment of breast, gastric, and colorectal cancers. How many chiral carbon centers does the capecitabine molecule have?

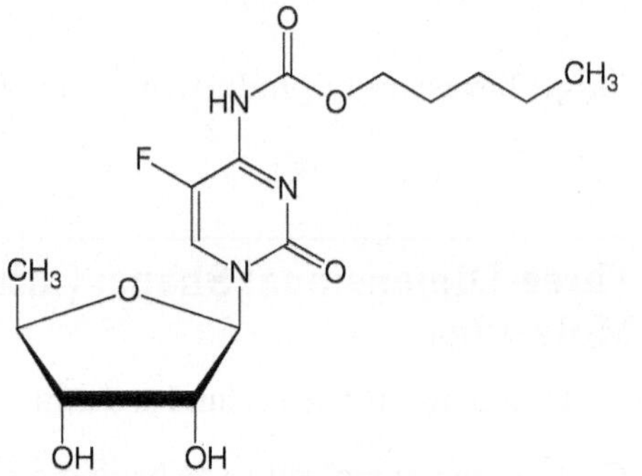

capecitabine

a) one chiral carbon center

b) two chiral carbon centers

c) three chiral carbon centers

d) four chiral carbon centers

14.71 Duloxetine, also known as Cymbalta, is a medication for depression and anxiety as well as managing pain.

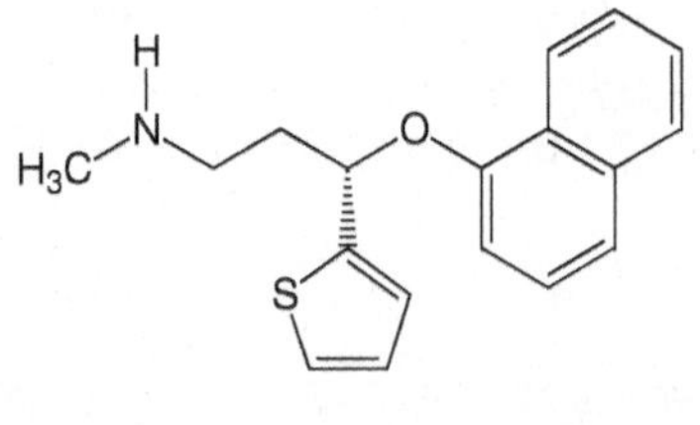

A. Identify the mirror image of duloxetine.

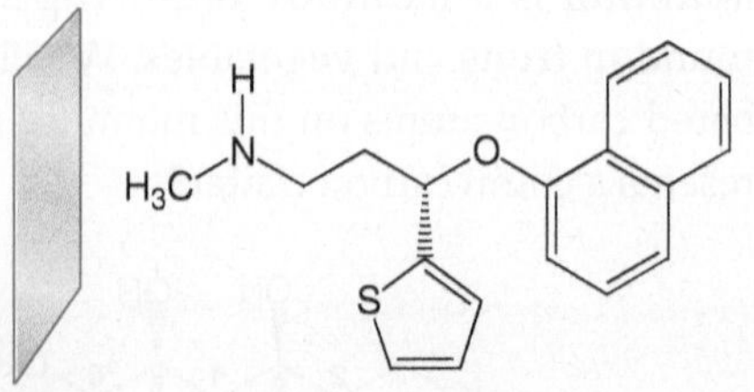

mirror

a)

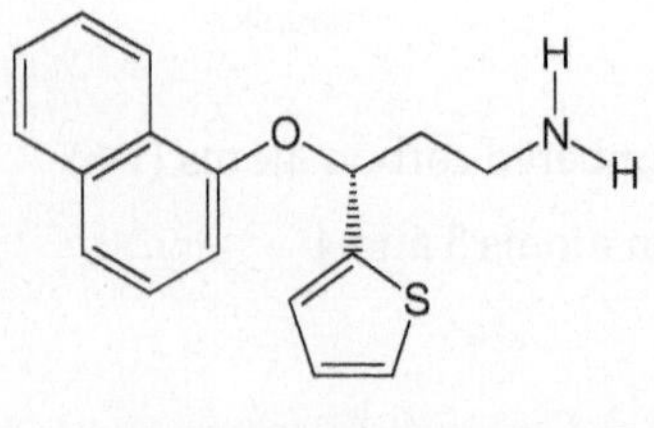

b)

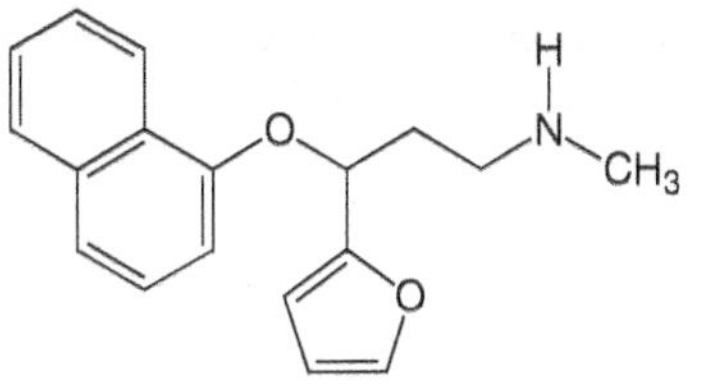

c)

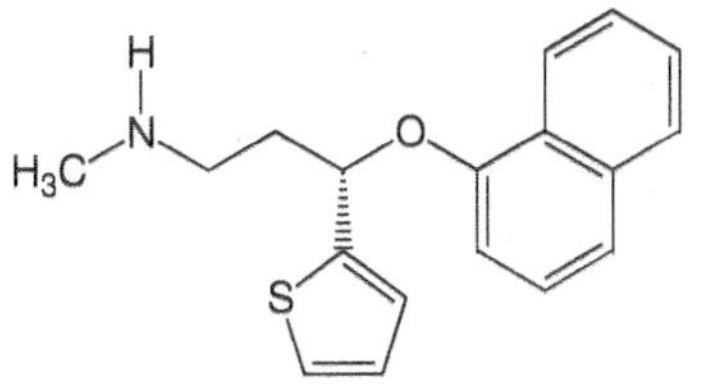

d)

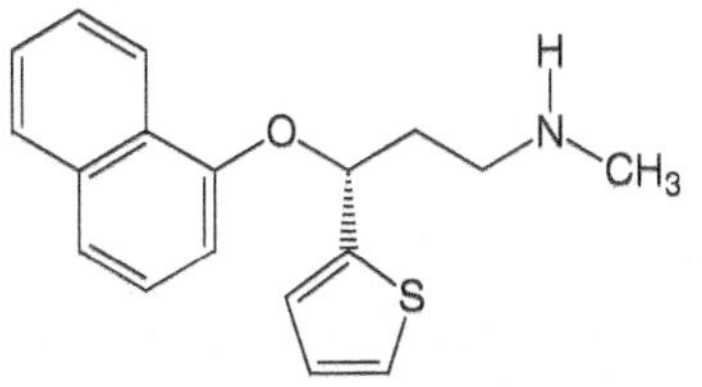

B. How are these two molecules related to each other, if at all?

    a) The two mirror-image molecules are identical to each other.

    b) The two mirror-image molecules are unrelated to each other.

    c) The two mirror-image molecules are enantiomers of each other.

    d) More information about the structure and function is needed to answer this question.

14.72 Ornithine is an amino acid that is generally not incorporated into proteins within the body. It does, however, play a key role in the urea cycle (a cycle of biochemical reactions that produces urea $(NH_2)_2 CO$ from ammonia (NH_3)).

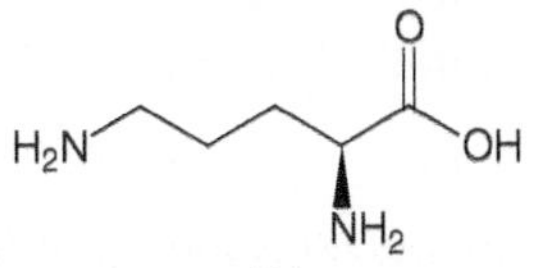

ornithine

A. Identify the mirror image of ornithine.

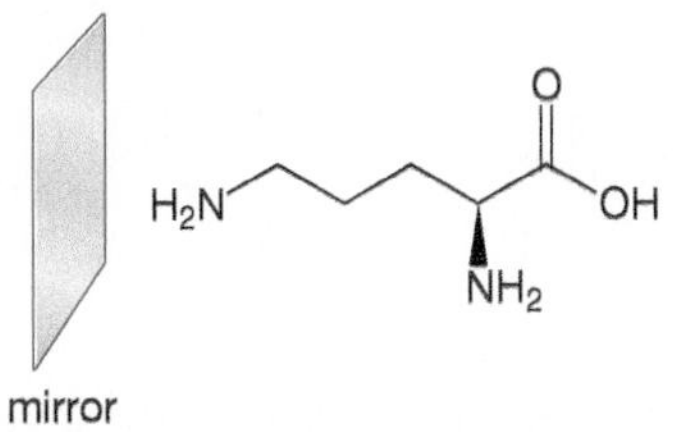

mirror

a)

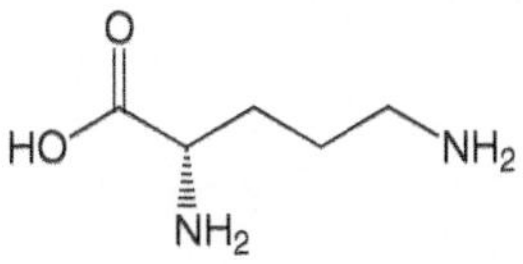

b)

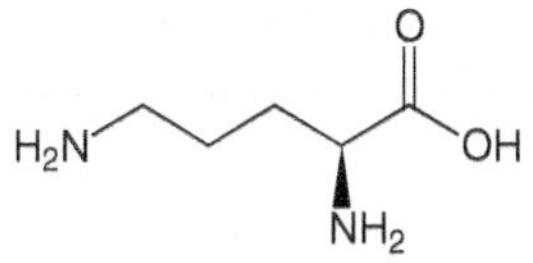

c)

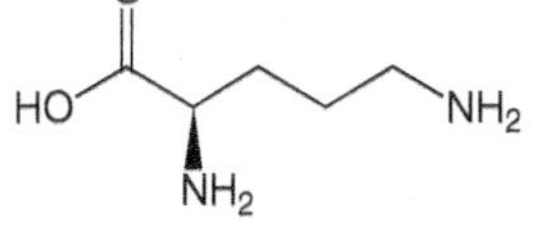

d)

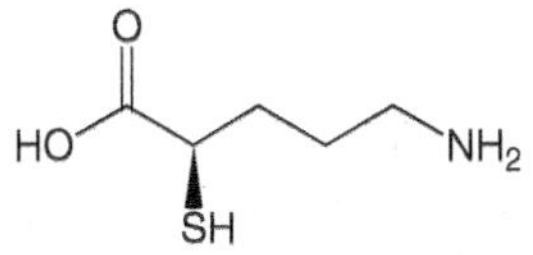

B. How are these two molecules related to each other, if at all?

    a) The two mirror-image molecules are enantiomers of each other.

    b) More information about the structure and function is needed to answer this question.

    c) The two mirror-image molecules are identical to each other.

    d) The two mirror-image molecules are unrelated to each other.

14.73 Fluphenazine, also known as Prolixin, is an antipsychotic medication used to treat schizophrenia. How many chiral carbon centers does the fluphenazine molecule have?

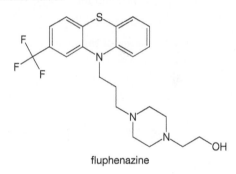

fluphenazine

a) zero   **b)** one   **c)** two   **d)** three

14.6 Naming Alcohols, Ethers, and Thiols

LO 14.6: Name alcohols, ethers, and thiols according to the IUPAC system.

14.74 Complete the name of the given molecule by dragging the missing fragments into the spaces provided.

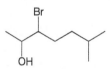

Answer choices 1: 1, 2, 3, 4, 5, 6

Answer choices 2: pent, hex, hept, non, dec

☐ -bromo-6-methyl-2- ☐ anol

14.75 Complete the name of the given molecule by dragging the missing fragments into the spaces provided.

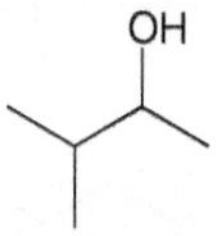

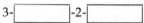

Answer choices: methyl, ethyl, propyl, butyl, pentyl, methanol, ethanol, propanol, butanol, pentanol

3-[   ]-2-[   ]

14.76 Select the correct name of the given molecule.

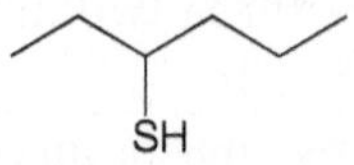

a) 4-hexanethiol   b) 3-pentanethiol

c) 3-hexanethiol   d) 4-thiohexane

14.77 Select the correct name for the given molecule.

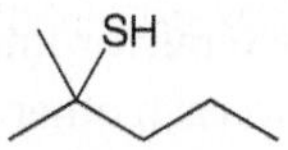

a) 2-methyl-2-pentanethiol

b) 2-methyl-1-pentanethiol

c) Isopropyl-1-butanethiol

d) 4-methyl-4-pentanethiol

14.78 Complete the name of the given molecule by dragging the missing fragments into the spaces provided.

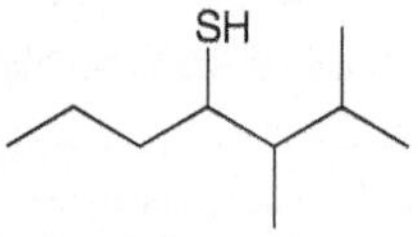

Answer choices 1: methyl, ethyl, propyl, isopropyl, dimethyl, diethyl

Answer choices 2: 2, 3, 4, 5, 6, 7

2,3-[   ]-[   ]-heptanethiol

14.79 Complete the name of the given molecule by dragging the missing fragments into the spaces provided.

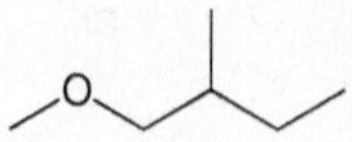

Answer choices 1: 1, 2, 3, 4

Answer choices 2: methyl, ethyl, propyl, methoxy, ethoxy, dimethyl

[   ]-[   ]-2-2-methylbutane

14.80 Select the correct structure of 2-methoxybutane.

a)

b)

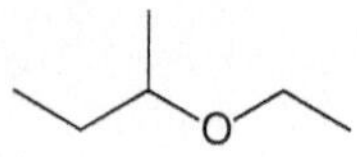

c)

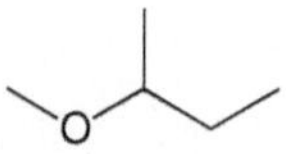

d)

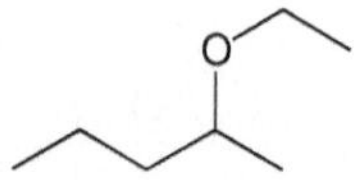

14.81 Select the molecule named 2-ethyl-1-pentanol?

a) HO

b) 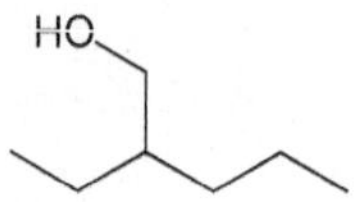 HO

c) 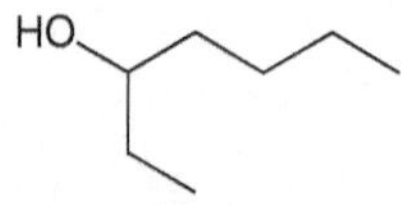 HO

d) 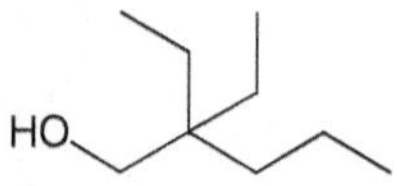 HO

14.82 Select the correct name for the molecule.

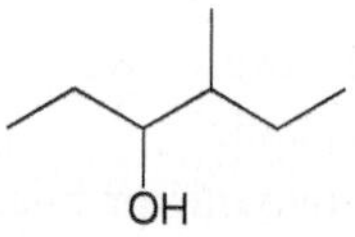

a) 4-methyl-3-hexanol

b) 2-ethyl-3-pentanol

c) 3-methyl-4-hexanol

d) 1,2-diethyl-1-propanol

14.83 Select the correct name for the molecule.

a) 1,2-diethyl-4-hydroxylcyclohexane

b) 1,2-diethyl-4-phenol

c) 3,4-diethylcyclohexanol

d) 1,2-diethyl-4-cyclohexanol

14.84 Which molecule is named 3,3,4-trimethyl-2-pentanol?

a) 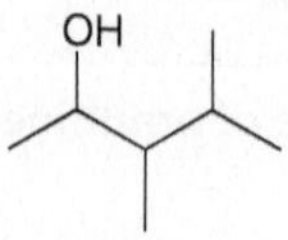 OH

b) 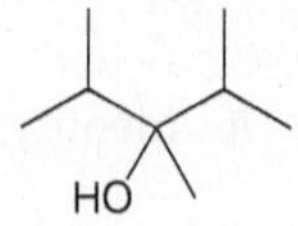 HO

c) 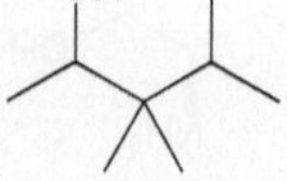 OH

d) 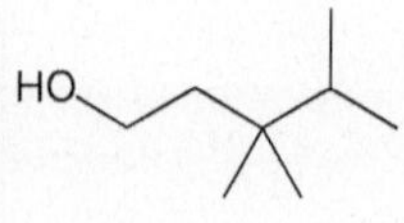 HO

14.85 Identify the structure with the given IUPAC name.

A. 1-bromo-2-ethyl-2-octanol

a)

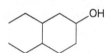

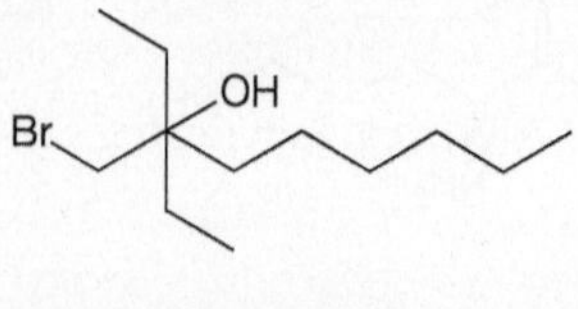

b)

c)

d)

B. 2-methylcyclopentanol

a)

b)

c)

d)

14.86 Select the correct IUPAC name for each molecule.

A.

a) 2-methyl-3-hexane
b) 2-methyl-3-hexanol
c) 5-methyl-4-pentanol
d) 1-methyl-3-hexanol

B.

a) 1,1-dimethyl-3-cyclohexanol
b) 3,3-dimethylcyclohexanol
c) dimethyl-3-cyclohexanol
d) 3,3-dimethylcyclopentanol

14.87 Select the correct name for the molecule.

a) 1-bromo-2-propyl-3-cyclohexanol
b) 3-bromo-2-propylphenol
c) 3-bromo-2-propylcyclohexanol
d) 3-bromo-2-ethylcyclopentanol

14.88 Complete the name of the given molecule by dragging the missing fragments into the spaces provided.

Answer choices 1: methyl, ethyl, propyl, butyl, pentyl, hexyl

Answer choices 2: 1, 2, 3, 4, 5, 6

Answer choices 3: butanethiol, butanedisulfide, pentanol, hexanol, hexanethiol, pentanthiol, hexaneoxide

3-

14.89 Use the drawing tool to draw the *skeletal structure* of dicyclohexyl ether. Do not draw hydrogen atoms that are bonded to carbon or lone pairs of electrons on the oxygen atom that you add as part of the ether group. Remember, skeletal structures do not include hydrogen atoms that are bonded to carbon. Labels for carbon atoms are also not included.

14.90 Use the drawing tool to build the *skeletal structure* of the ether 3-methoxyhexane. Do not draw hydrogen atoms that are bonded to carbon or lone pairs of electrons on the oxygen atom that you add as part of the ether group. Remember, skeletal structures do not include hydrogen atoms that are bonded to carbon. Labels for carbon atoms are also not included.

14.91 Use the drawing tool to build the *skeletal structure* of the alcohol 2-phenyl-3-hexanol. Do not draw hydrogen atoms that are bonded to carbon or lone pairs of electrons on the oxygen atom that you add as part of the alcohol group. Remember, skeletal structures do not include hydrogen atoms that are bonded to carbon. Labels for carbon atoms are also not included.

14.92 Use the drawing tool to build the *skeletal structure* of the thiol 3-methyl-2-pentanethiol. Do not draw hydrogen atoms that are bonded to carbon or lone pairs of electrons on the sulfur atom that you add as part of the thiol group. Remember, skeletal structures do not include hydrogen atoms that are bonded to carbon. Labels for carbon atoms are also not included.

14.93 Use the drawing tool to build the *skeletal structure* of the ether 2-ethoxydecane. Do not draw hydrogen atoms that are bonded to carbon or lone pairs of electrons on the oxygen atom in the ether group. Remember, skeletal structures do not include hydrogen atoms that are bonded to carbon, and labels for carbon atoms are not included.

Chapter 15

15.1 Structure of Aldehydes and Ketones

LO 1: Analyze the structural features of aldehydes and ketones.

15.01 Which figure shows a correctly drawn Lewis structure for a ketone?

a)
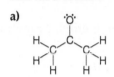

b)

c)
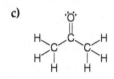

d)
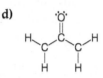

15.02 Sort the following molecules into those that contain a carbonyl group and those that do not.

Answer choices:

a)
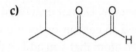

b)

c)
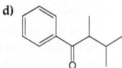

d)

e)

f)
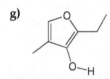

g)

h)

Target boxes: molecules that contain a carbonyl group, molecules that do *not* contain a carbonyl group

15.03 Sort the following molecules into those that contain a carbonyl group and those that do not.

Answer choices:

a)
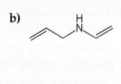

b)

c)

d)

e)

f)

g)
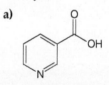

h)

Target boxes: molecules that contain a carbonyl group, molecules that do *not* contain a carbonyl group

15.04 Select the correct statement.

a) The carbonyl carbon atom in an aldehyde must be bonded with two carbon containing "R" groups.

b) A hydrogen atom must be bonded to the carbonyl carbon atom in an aldehyde.

c) A hydrogen atom must be bonded to the carbonyl carbon atom in a ketone.

d) Both aldehydes and ketones must have two carbon atoms bonded to the carbonyl group.

15.05 Which type of compound must have two carbon atoms bonded to the carbonyl carbon atom?

a) aldehyde

b) aldehydes and ketones

c) ketones

d) aldehydes and alkenes

e) alcohols and alkynes

f) neither aldehydes nor ketones

15.06 Which of the molecules shown contains an aldehyde?

a)

b)
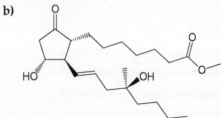

c)

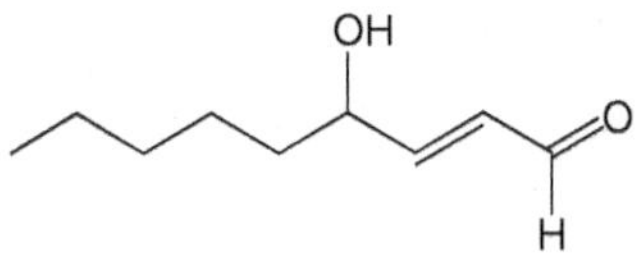

d)

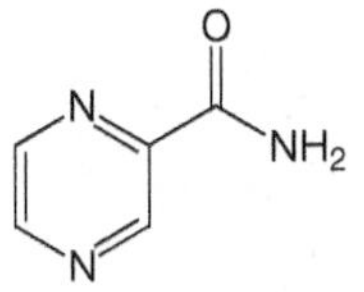

15.07 Select the molecule that contains a ketone.

a)

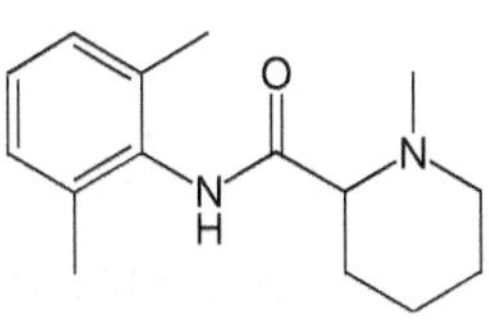

b)

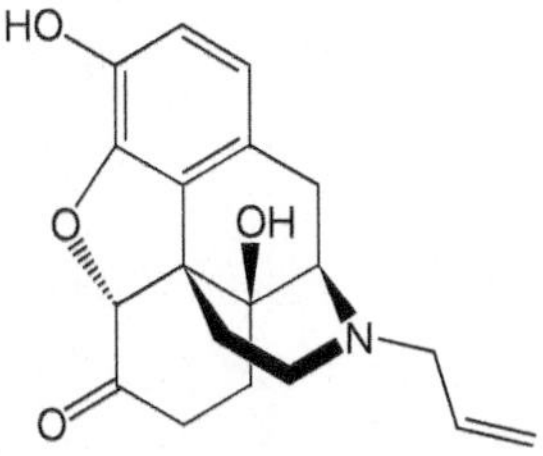

c)

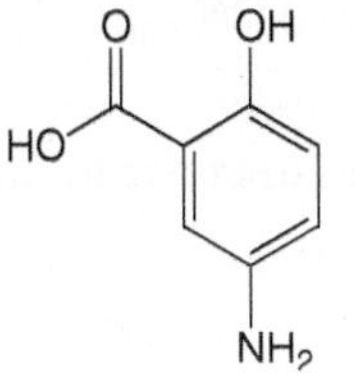

d)

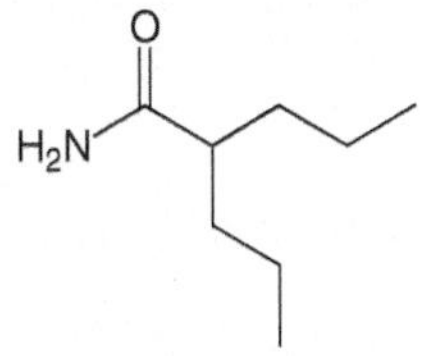

15.08 The molecule avobenzone, shown below, is used in a number of sunscreen products to help absorb ultraviolet (UV) rays that can burn human skin. Which statement about avobenzone is correct?

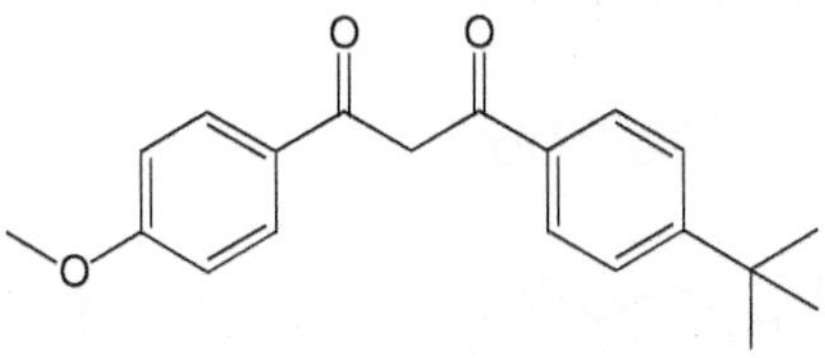

a) The avobenzone molecule contains an ether group, two aromatic benzene rings, and two aldehyde groups.

b) The avobenzone molecule contains an ether group, two cyclohexane rings, and two ketone groups.

c) The avobenzone molecule contains an alcohol group, two aromatic benzene rings, and two aldehyde groups.

d) The avobenzone molecule contains an ether group, two aromatic benzene rings, and two ketone groups.

15.09 Sort the molecules into boxes for aldehydes, ketones, or neither.

Answer choices:

a)

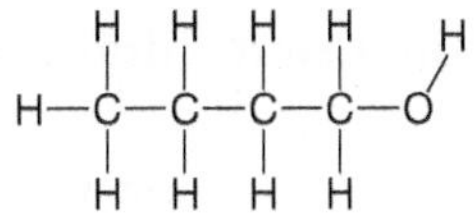

b)

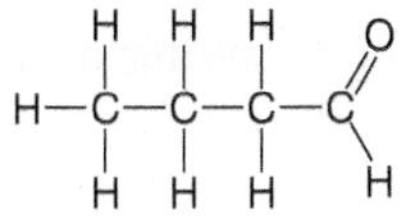

c)

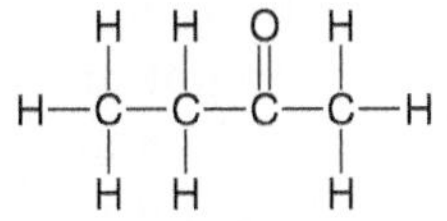

d)

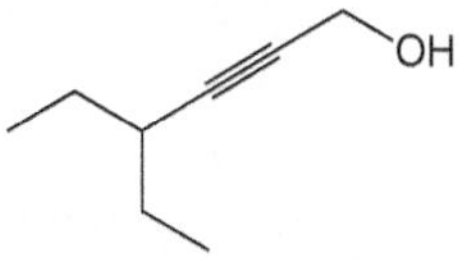

e)

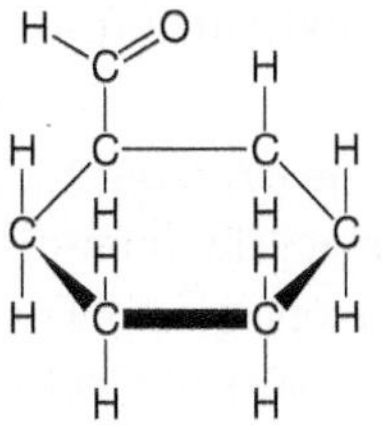

f)

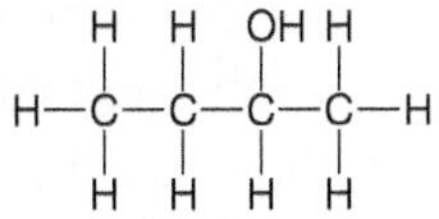

g)

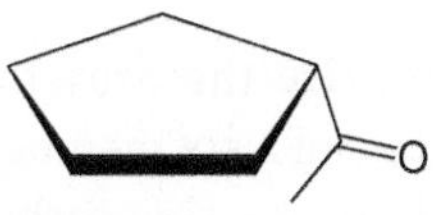

h)

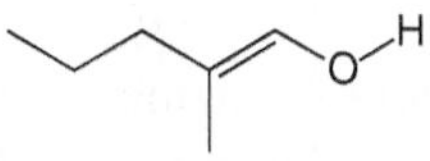

Target boxes: aldehyde, ketone, neither aldehyde nor ketone

15.10 Sort the molecules into boxes for aldehydes, ketones, or neither.

Answer choices:

a)

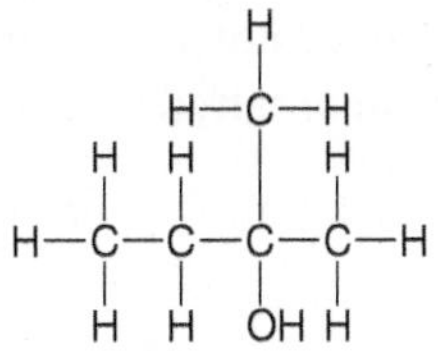

b)

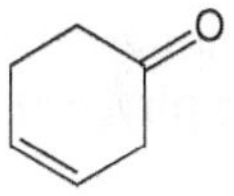

c)

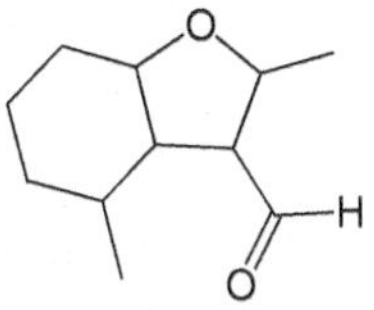

d)

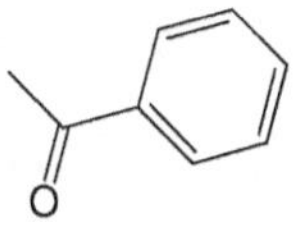

e)

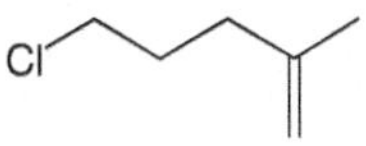

f)

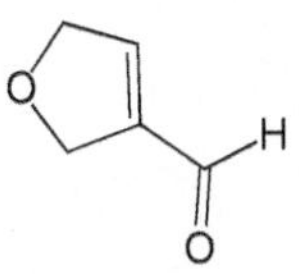

g)

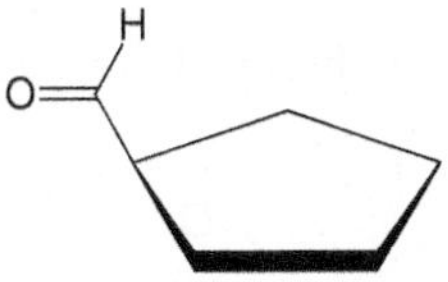

h)

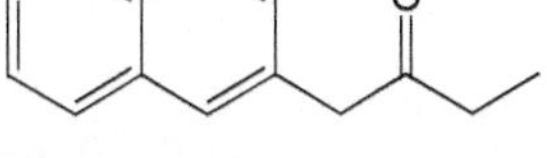

Target boxes: aldehyde, ketone, neither aldehyde nor ketone

15.11 Drawing an aldehyde: Use the drawing tool to build the *skeletal structure* of an acyclic (non-cyclic) three carbon alkane having an aldehyde group. For this exercise, do not draw the lone pairs of electrons on the oxygen atom but do include a bond and atom label for the hydrogen bonded with the carbonyl carbon atom in the aldehyde group.

15.12 Drawing an aldehyde: Use the drawing tool to build the *skeletal structure* of a five membered cyclic alkane (cyclopentane) having a single aldehyde group attached directly to one of the ring carbons. For this exercise, do not draw the lone pairs of electrons on the oxygen atom, but do include a bond and atom label for the hydrogen bonded with the carbonyl carbon atom in the aldehyde group.

15.13 Drawing a ketone: Use the drawing tool to build the *skeletal structure* of an acyclic (non-cyclic) three carbon alkane having a ketone group. For this exercise, do not draw the lone pairs of electrons on the oxygen atom.

15.14 Drawing an aldehyde: Use the drawing tool to build the *skeletal structure* of a six membered cyclic alkane (cyclohexane) having a ring carbon as part of a ketone group. For this exercise, do not draw the lone pairs of electrons on the oxygen atom.

15.2 Physical Properties Aldehydes and Ketones

LO 2: Compare the effects of intermolecular forces on the physical properties of aldehydes and ketones.

15.15 Select the molecule in each pair that has the higher *boiling point*.

A. or

B. or

C. or

15.16 Select the molecule in each pair that has the higher *boiling point*.

A. OH or

B. or

C. or

15.17 Select molecule in each pair that has the greater *solubility in water*.

A. or

B. or HO OH

C. or

15.18 Select molecule in each pair that has the greater *solubility in water*.

A. or

B. or

C. or HO OH

15.19 Distinguish polar molecules from non-polar molecules.

Answer choices:

a) H

b) OH

c)

d)

e)

f)

g) O O OH

h) HO OH

i) OH

Target boxes: polar molecules, non-polar molecules

15.20 Distinguish polar molecules from non-polar molecules.

Answer choices:

a) OH

b)

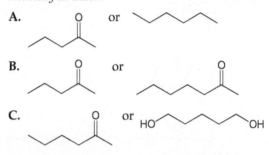
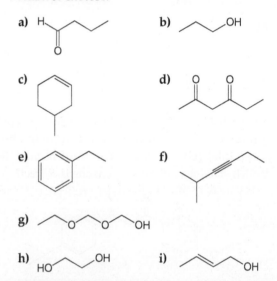

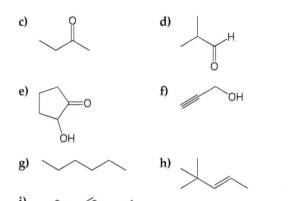

c) d)

e) f)

g) h)

i)

Target boxes: polar molecules, non-polar molecules

15.21 Distinguish molecules that are soluble in water from those that are not.

Answer choices:

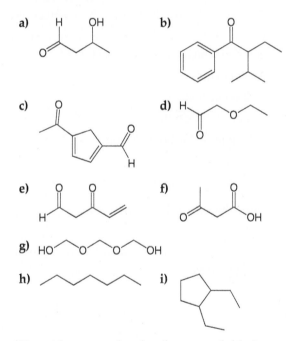

a) b)

c) d)

e) f)

g) HO O O OH

h) i)

Target boxes: molecules that are soluble in water, molecules that are not soluble in water (insoluble)

15.22 Distinguish molecules that are soluble in water from those that are not.

Answer choices:

a) b)

Cl

c) OH d)

e) f)

HO

g) HO O

h) HO H N

i)

Target boxes: molecules that are soluble in water, molecules that are *not* soluble in water (insoluble)

15.23 Which statement about hydrogen bonding is true?

   a) Hydrogen bonding occurs between aldehydes but not between ketones.

   b) Hydrogen bonding occurs between aldehydes and also between ketones.

   c) Hydrogen bonding occurs between ketones but not between aldehydes.

   d) Hydrogen bonding does not occur between aldehydes or between ketones.

15.24 Which statement about hydrogen bonding is true?

   a) Aldehydes and alcohols hydrogen bond with water, but ketones do not.

   b) Alcohols hydrogen bond with water, but aldehydes and ketones do not.

   c) Aldehydes, ketones, and alcohols all hydrogen bond with water.

   d) Ketones and alcohols hydrogen bond with water, but aldehydes do not.

15.25 Which statement about intermolecular dipole-dipole attractions is true?

   a) Dipole-dipole attractions occur between ketones but not aldehydes.

   b) Dipole-dipole attractions occur between aldehydes but not ketones.

   c) Dipole-dipole attractions do not occur between aldehydes or ketones.

   d) Dipole-dipole attractions occur between both aldehydes and between ketones.

15.26 Hydrogen bonding occurs between which combination of molecules?

   a) aldehyde–aldehyde   b) aldehyde–ketone

   c) ketone–ketone   d) all of these

   e) none of these

15.27 Hydrogen bonding occurs between which combination of molecules?

   a) aldehydes–water   b) ketones–water

   c) water–water   d) water–alcohols

   e) all of these

   f) both water-water and water-alcohols

15.28 In BioConnect 15.1, we learned about the health effect of formaldehyde. Select the correct Lewis structure of the formaldehyde molecule.

a)

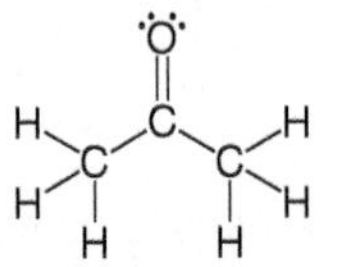

b)

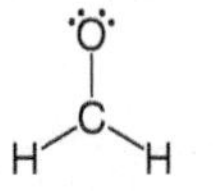

c)

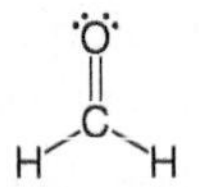

d)

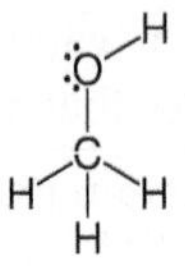

15.3 Reactions of Aldehydes and Ketones

LO 3: Predict the products of the oxidation and reduction of aldehydes and ketones.

15.29 Identify the correct statement(s).

a) The oxidation of tertiary (3°) alcohols produces ketones.

b) The reduction of aldehydes produces secondary (2°) alcohols.

c) The oxidation of secondary (2°) alcohols produces aldehydes.

d) The reduction of ketones produces secondary (2°) alcohols.

15.30 Identify the correct statement(s).

a) The oxidation of secondary (2°) alcohols produces carboxylic acids.

b) The reduction of aldehydes produces primary (1°) alcohols.

c) The oxidation of ketones produces carboxylic acids.

d) The reduction of ketones produces primary (1°) alcohols.

15.31 Identify the correct statement(s).

a) The oxidation of ketones produces secondary alcohols.

b) The reduction of aldehydes produces ketones.

c) The oxidation of aldehydes produces carboxylic acids.

d) The reduction of ketones produces tertiary alcohols.

15.32 Which of the following reactions represent oxidation and which represent reduction?

Answer choices:

carboxylic acid → aldehyde,

ketone → alcohol,

aldehyde → carboxylic acid,

alcohol → ketone,

aldehyde → alcohol

Target boxes: oxidation, reduction

15.33 Octanoic acid, also known as caprylic acid, is a naturally saturated eight-carbon fatty acid found in breast milk. Select the structure that is a potential starting material for the reaction shown.

a)

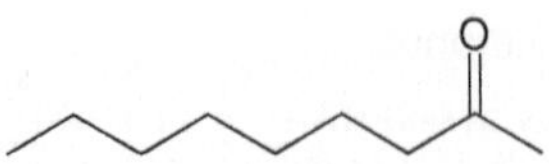

b)

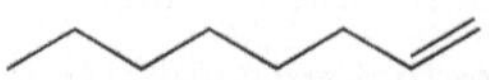

c)

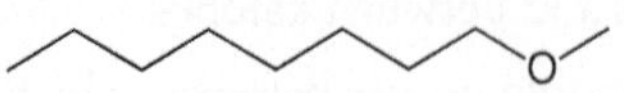

d)

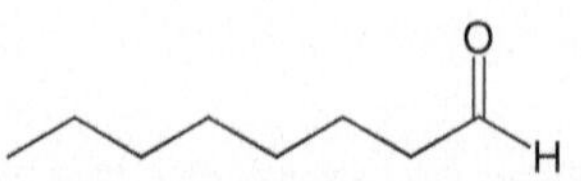

15.34 Oxidation of which molecule produces the carboxylic acid shown?

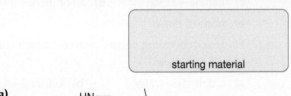

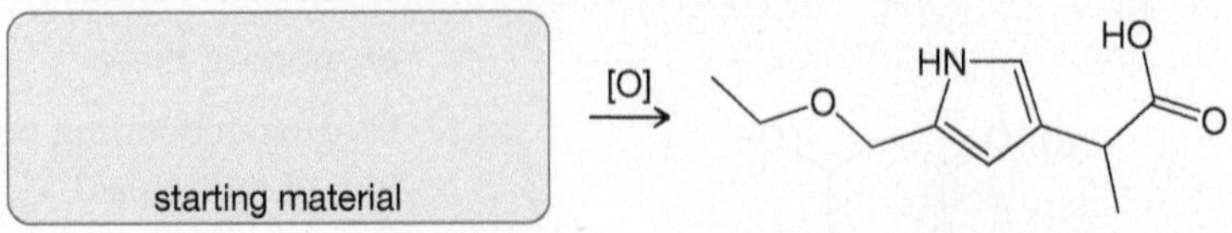

a)

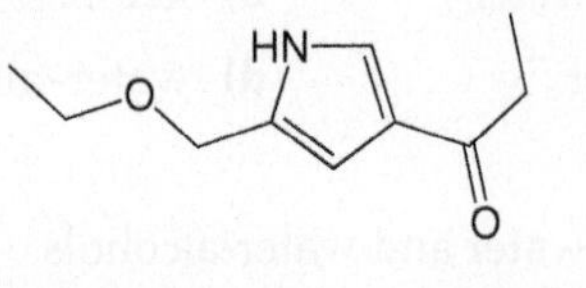

b)

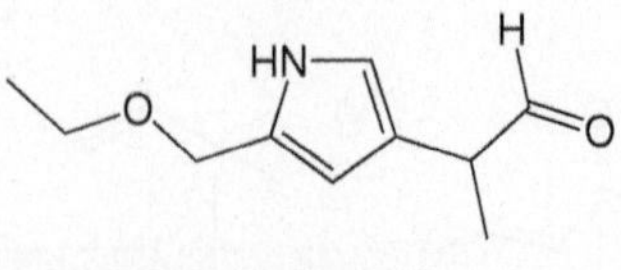

c)

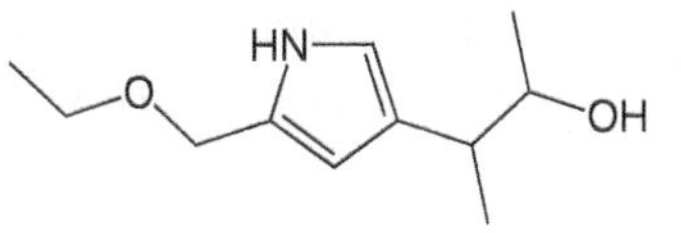

d)

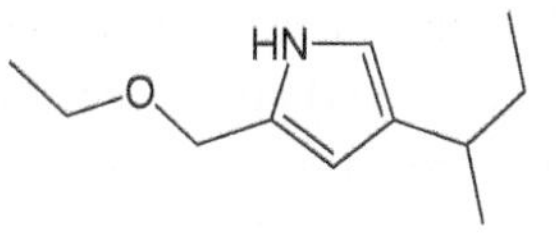

15.35 Drawing an oxidation product: Use the drawing tool to build the *skeletal structure* of the product formed when the molecule shown undergoes oxidation. For this exercise, do not draw the lone pairs of electrons on oxygen.

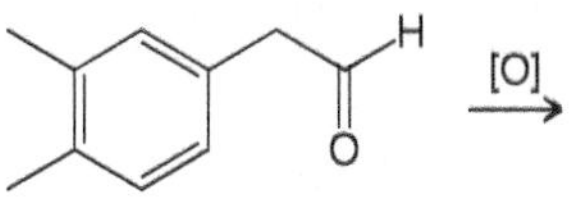

15.36 Drawing an oxidation product: Use the drawing tool to build the *skeletal structure* of the product formed when the molecule shown undergoes oxidation. For this exercise, do not draw the lone pairs of electrons on oxygen. It may be helpful to select the carbon chain tool (⁀⁀) along the left side of the drawing window and then click and drag as an efficient way to produce the six-carbon parent chain. Choose buttons from the Tools (for bonds), Atoms, and Advanced Template toolbars to build the skeletal structure.

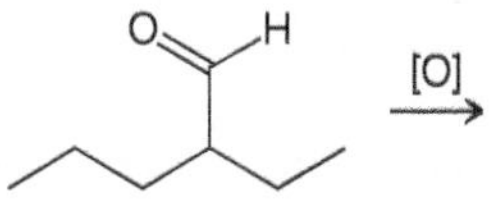

15.37 Which of the following describes the product of the proposed oxidation reaction shown.

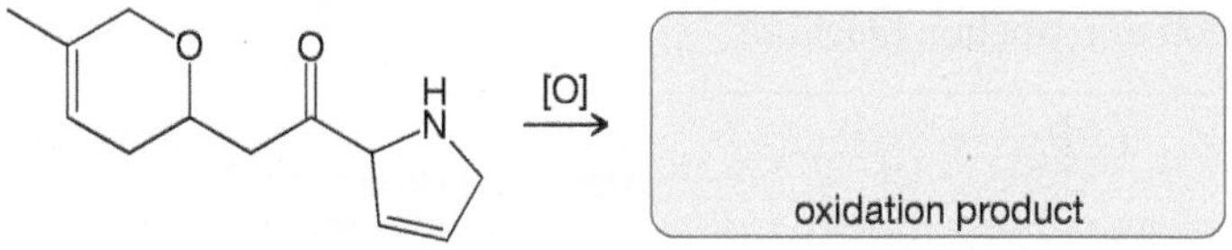

oxidation product

a) 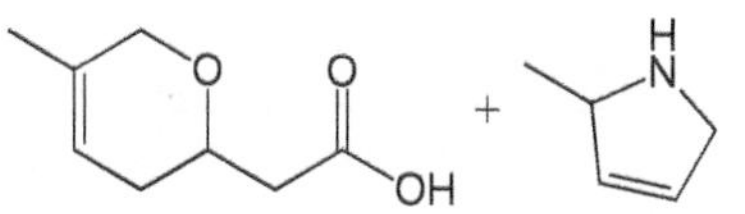 **b)** 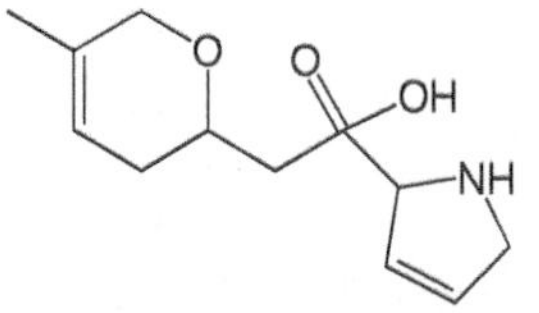 **c)** No reaction **d)**

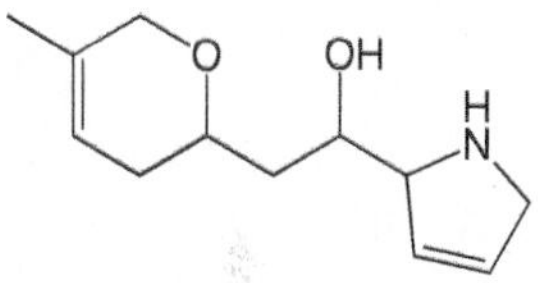

15.38 Drawing a reduction product: Use the drawing tool to build the *skeletal structure* of the product formed when the molecule shown undergoes reduction. For this exercise, do not draw the lone pairs of electrons on oxygen. It may be helpful to select a ring structure located at the bottom of the drawing window as an efficient way to build the structure of your predicted product. Choose buttons from the Tools (for bonds), Atoms, and Advanced Template toolbars to build the skeletal structure.

$$\xrightarrow[\text{H}_2(g) + \text{Pd}]{\text{[R]}}$$

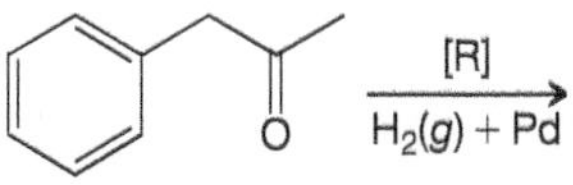

15.39 Malate dehydrogenase is an enzyme that uses NADH to reversibly catalyze the interconversion of malate and oxaloacetate depending on metabolic needs in the cell. When the reaction proceeds from left to right, as indicated by the bold arrow, is the reaction an oxidation or a reduction reaction?

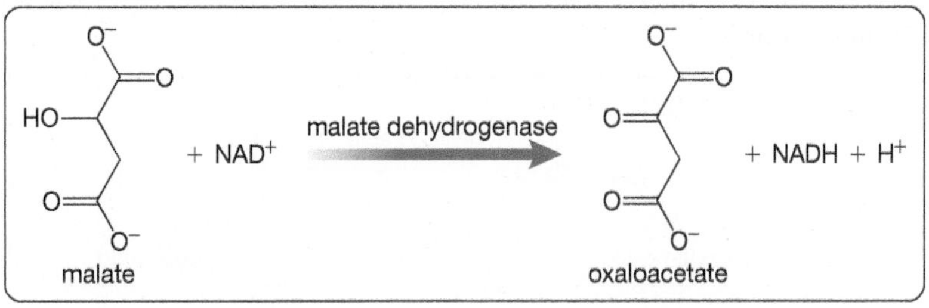

malate   + NAD$^+$ —— malate dehydrogenase ——→   oxaloacetate   + NADH + H$^+$

15.40 The enzyme 3-hydroxybutyrate dehydrogenase is involved in the synthesis and degradation of ketone bodies discussed in BioConnect 15.2. When the reaction proceeds from left to right as indicated by the bold arrow, is the reaction an oxidation or a reduction?

3-hydroxybutyrate   + NAD$^+$ [3-hydroxybutyrate dehydrogenase →]   acetoacetate   + NADH + H$^+$

Answer choices: oxidation, reduction

15.41 The enzyme alcohol dehydrogenase (ADH) belongs to the oxidoreductase family of enzymes and uses NADH to reversibly catalyze the conversion of alcohols and aldehydes. When the reaction proceeds from right to left, as indicated by the bold arrow, is the reaction an oxidation or a reduction reaction?

ethanol   + NAD$^+$ [← alcohol dehydrogenase]   ethanal   + NADH + H$^+$

15.42 Photosynthesis is the process by which green plants and other organisms capture and use energy from sunlight to drive the synthesis of carbohydrates from carbon dioxide (CO_2) and water (H_2O). Another process important in plant biology, *photorespiration*, consumes oxygen (O_2) and releases carbon dioxide (CO_2). One of the reactions involved in photorespiration is shown. When the reaction proceeds from left to right, as indicated by the bold arrow, is the reaction an oxidation or reduction reaction?

3-hydroxypyruvate   + NADH + H$^+$ [oxidoreductase enzyme →]   glycerate   + NAD$^+$

15.43 The enzyme lactate dehydrogenase (LDH) is involved in cellular metabolism, and it occurs in a variety of body tissues including blood cells and heart muscle. It is also released during tissue damage, so levels of LDH are also used in health care to detect tissue damage and disease. Lactate dehydrogenase uses NAD$^+$/NADH for the interconversion of lactic acid and pyruvic acid based on cellular needs. When the reaction proceeds from left to right, as indicated by the bold arrow, is the reaction an oxidation or a reduction?

lactic acid   + NAD$^+$ [lactate dehydrogenase →]   pyruvic acid   + NADH + H$^+$

15.44 Photosynthesis is the process by which green plants and other organisms capture and use energy from sunlight to drive the synthesis of carbohydrates from carbon dioxide (CO_2) and water (H_2O). Another process important in plant biology, *photorespiration*, consumes oxygen (O_2) and releases carbon dioxide (CO_2). As part of the photorespiration process, the enzyme glycolic acid oxidase (GOX) catalyzes the reversible interconversion of glyoxylic acid and glycolic acid. When the reaction proceeds from left to right, as indicated by the bold arrow, is the reaction an oxidation or reduction reaction?

glyoxylic acid   + H$_2$O$_2$ [glycolic acid oxidase →]   glycolic acid   + O$_2$

15.45 Oxalic acid $(C_2H_2O_4)$ is a naturally occurring di-carboxylic acid molecule produced in the liver. Oxalic acid also occurs in a variety of fruits and vegetables. When the reaction proceeds from left to right, as indicated by the bold arrow, is the reaction an oxidation or reduction reaction?

glyoxylic acid   oxalic acid

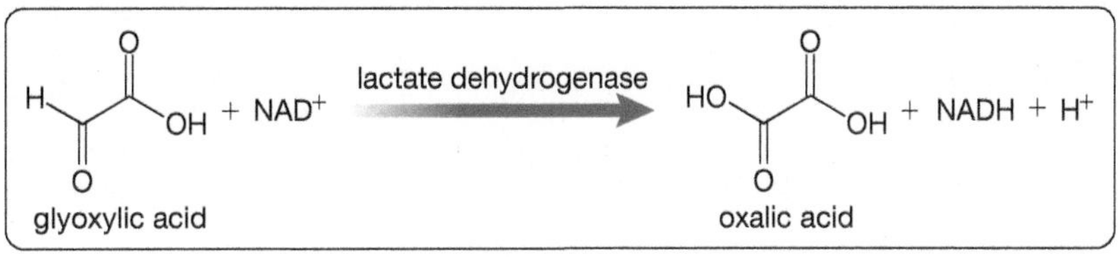

15.46 Glycerol 3-phosphate is produced during the metabolism of glucose (blood sugar). When the reaction proceeds from left to right, as indicated by the bold arrow, is the reaction an oxidation or reduction reaction?

glycerol-3-phosphate

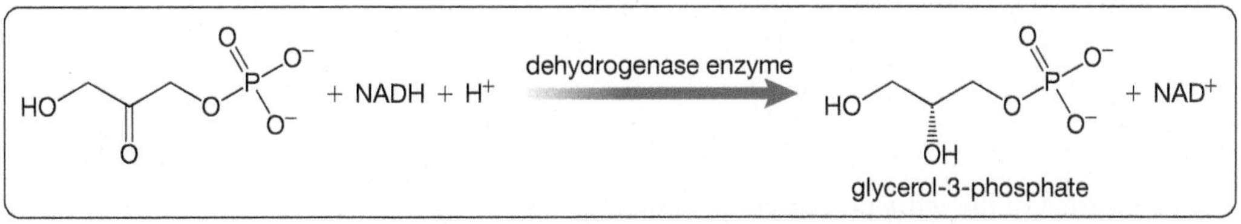

15.47 Methadone is used to help treat narcotic drug addiction by reducing cravings and withdrawal symptoms opiate addicts suffer. Choose the product formed when methadone is reduced.

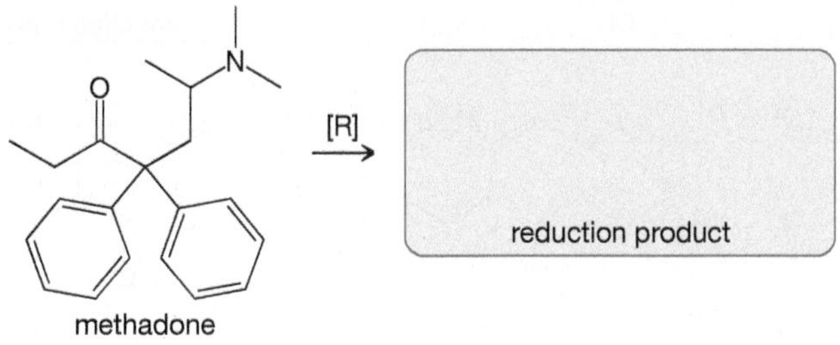

methadone   [R]   reduction product

a) 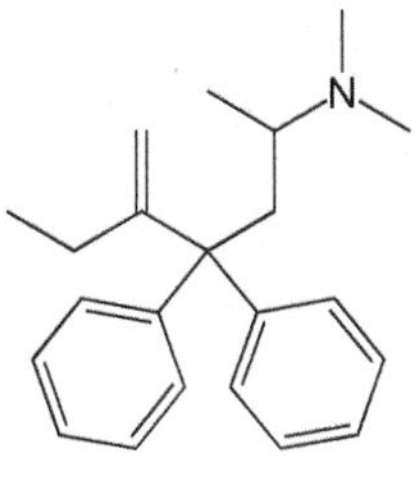   b) 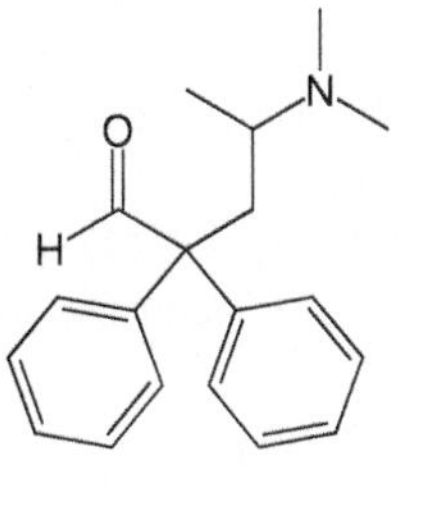   c) 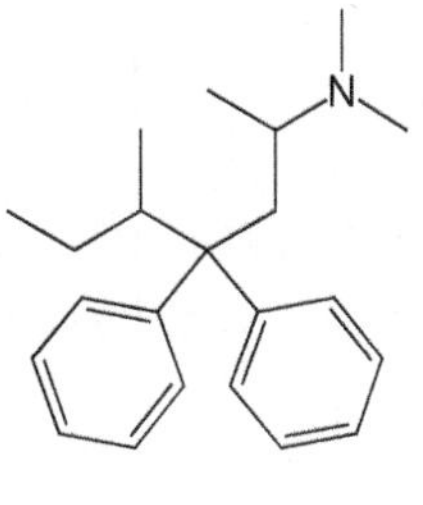   d)

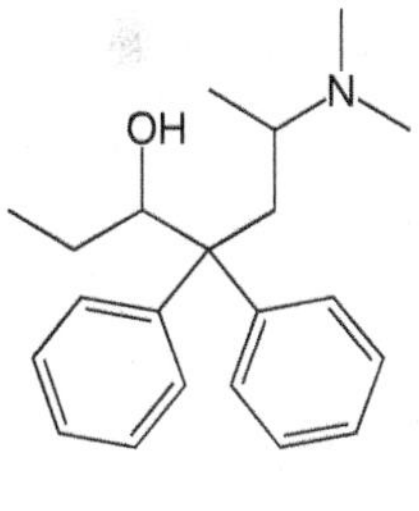

15.48 Amiodarone is a medication used to prevent and treat irregular heartbeats. Choose the product formed when amiodarone is reduced.

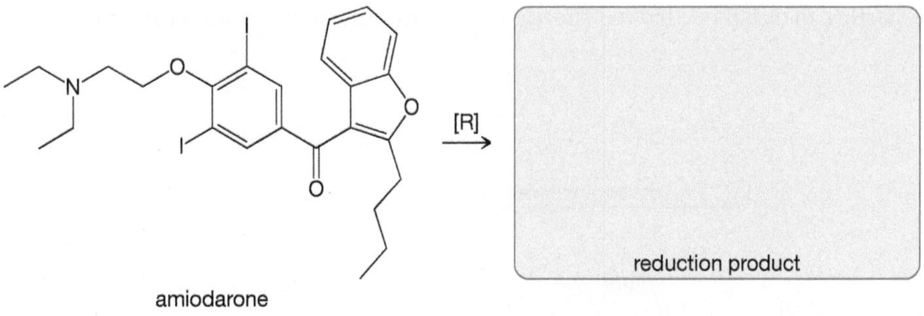

amiodarone   [R]   reduction product

a)

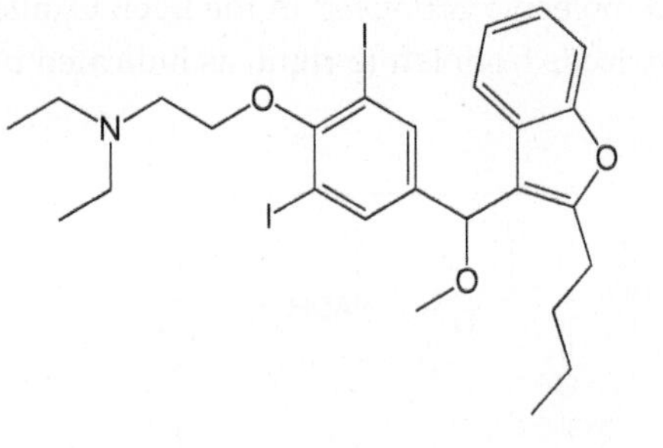

b)

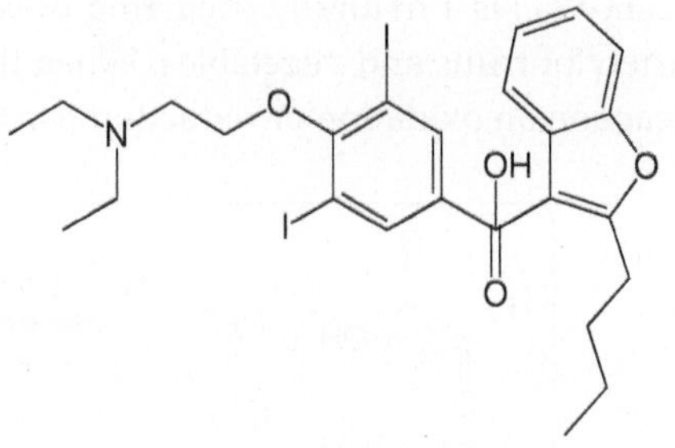

c)

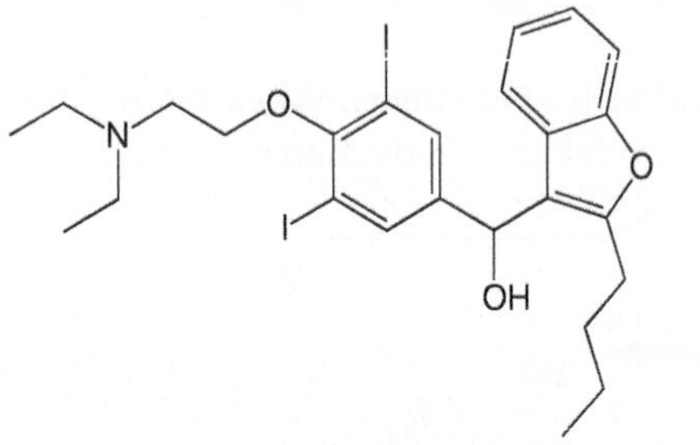

d)

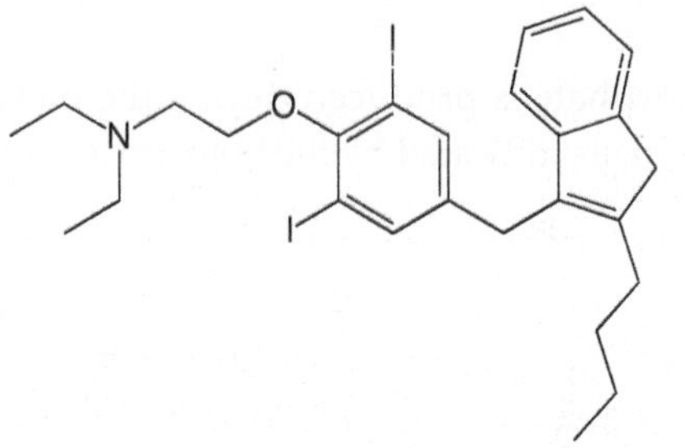

15.49 What is the product of the reduction reaction shown?

$$\xrightarrow[\text{H}_2(g) + \text{Pt}]{[R]}$$ reduction product

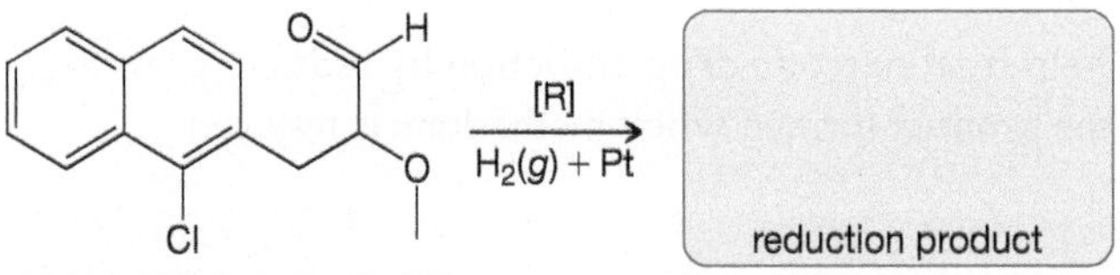

a) 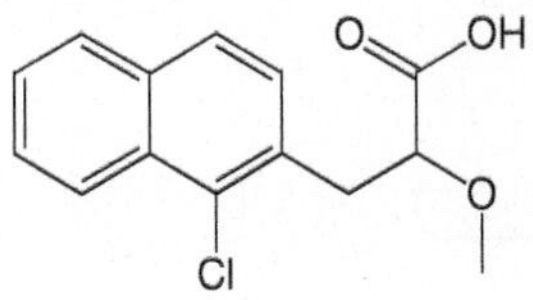   **b)** 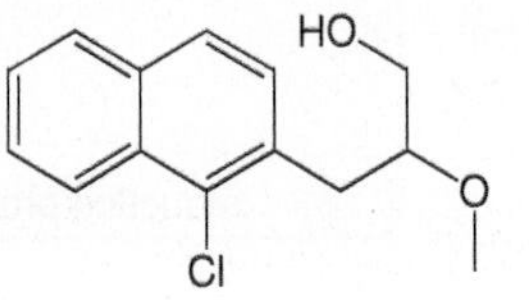   **c)** 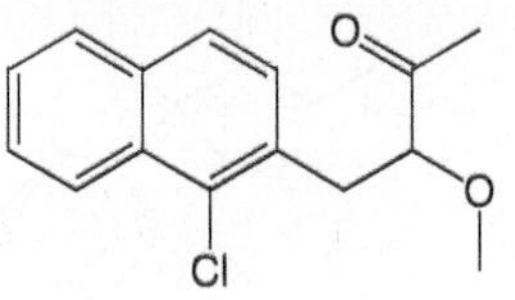   **d)**

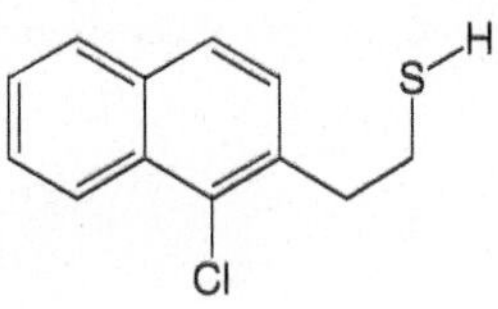

15.50 What is the product of the reduction reaction shown?

$$\xrightarrow[\text{H}_2(g) + \text{Pd}]{[R]}$$ reduction product

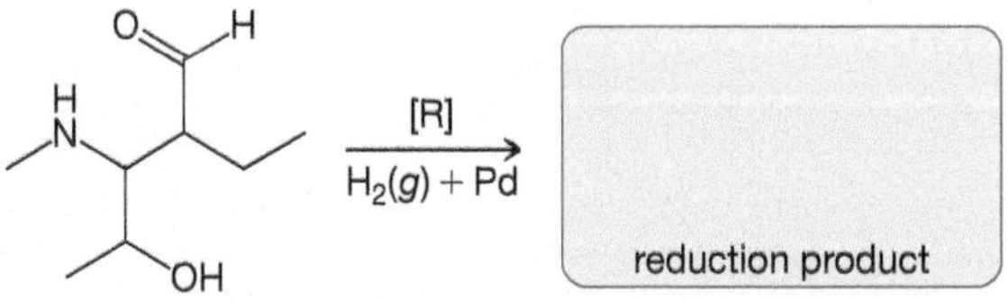

a) 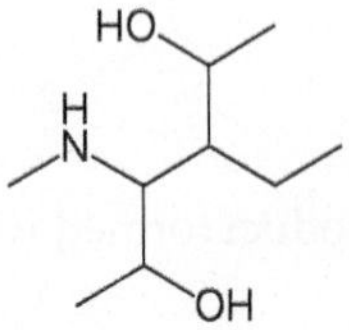   **b)** 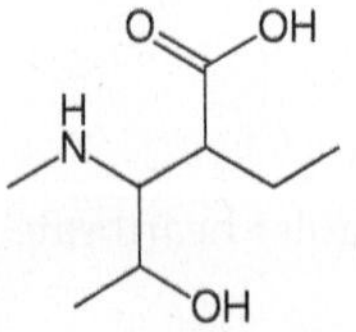   **c)** 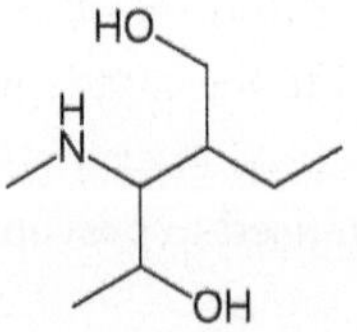   **d)**

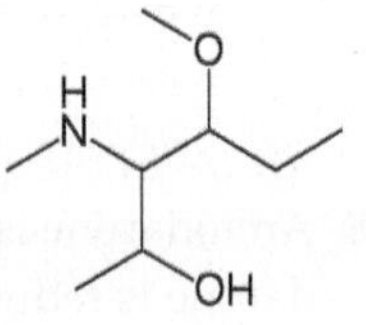

15.51 Predict the starting material needed to produce the reduction reaction product shown.

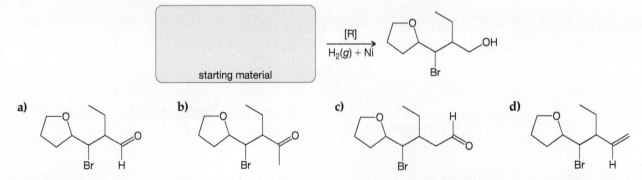

starting material $$\xrightarrow[\text{H}_2(g) + \text{Ni}]{[R]}$$

a)   **b)**   **c)**   **d)**

15.52 The drug metoprolol, shown below, is commonly prescribed to help treat high blood pressure, chest pain (angina), and heart failure. Predict the starting material needed to produce the reduction reaction product shown.

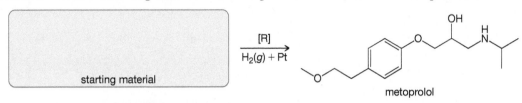

a)

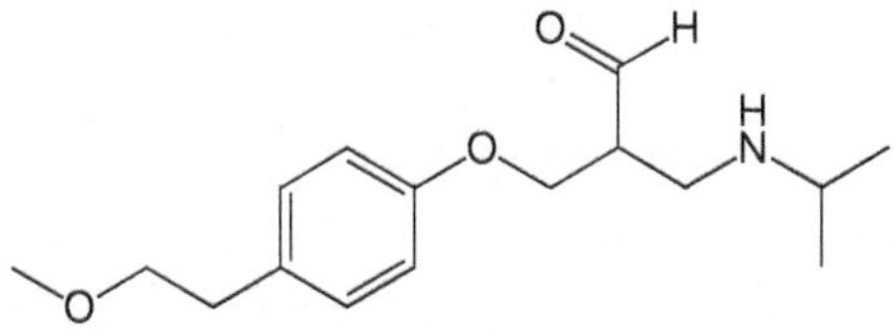

b)

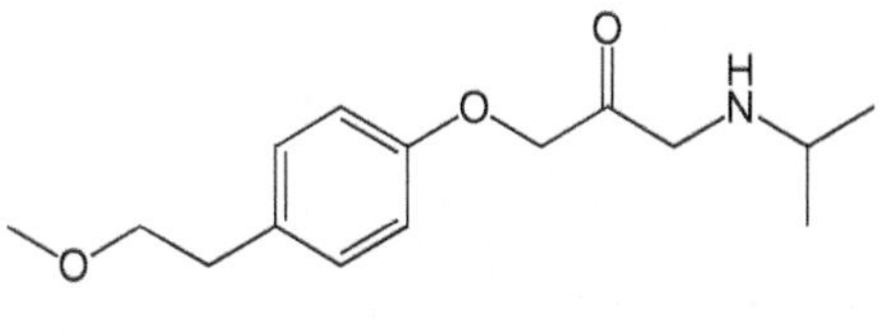

c)

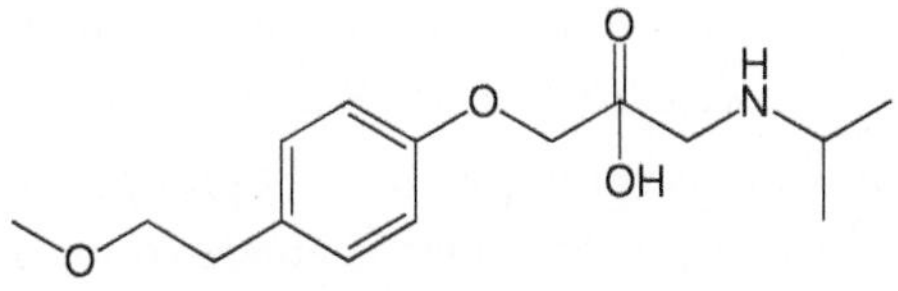

d)

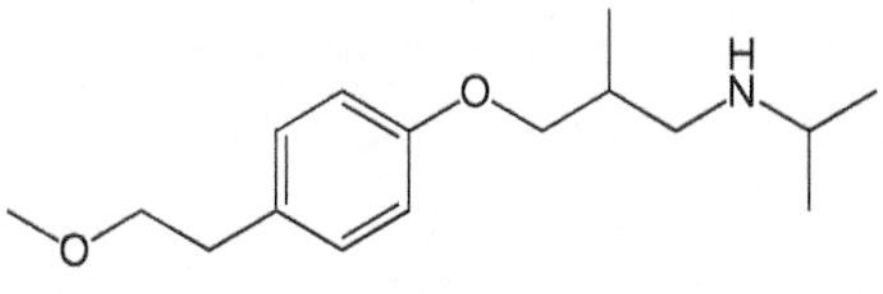

15.4 Forming Hemiacetals and Acetals

LO 4: Predict the products of addition of alcohols to aldehydes and ketones.

15.53 Which statement is correct?

a) A hemiacetal contains two —OH (hydroxyl) groups bonded to the same carbon atom whereas acetals contain an —OH (hydroxyl) group and an —OR group bonded to the same carbon atom.

b) A hemiacetal contains an —OH (hydroxyl) group and an —OR group bonded to the same carbon atom whereas acetals contain two —OR groups bonded to the same carbon.

c) A hemiacetal contains an —OR group and three —R groups bonded to the same carbon atom whereas acetals contain two —OR groups and two —R groups bonded to the same carbon.

d) A hemiacetal contains an —OH (hydroxyl) group and an acetone group bonded to the same carbon atom whereas acetals contain two acetone groups bonded to the same carbon.

15.54 Which figure depicts the structure of a hemiacetal?

a)

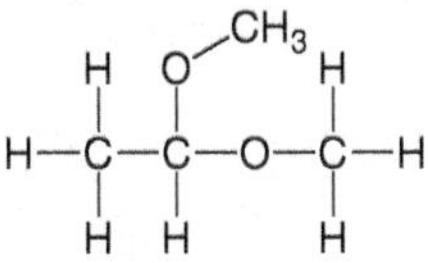

b)

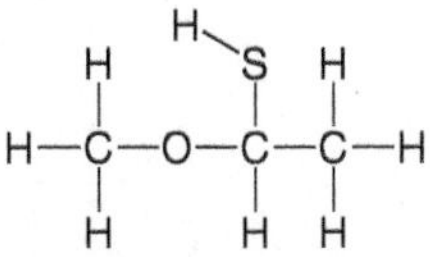

c)

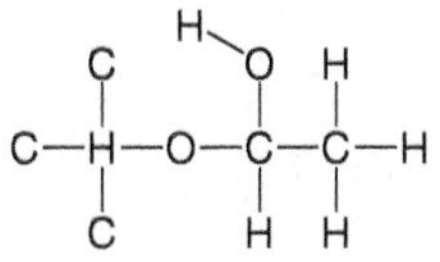

d)

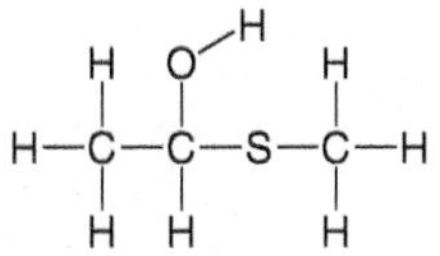

e)

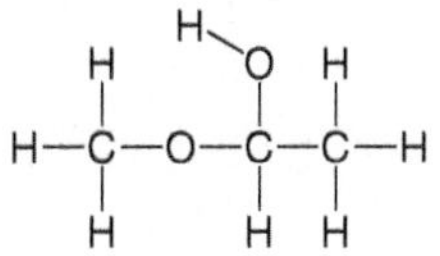

15.55 Which figure depicts the structure of a hemiacetal?

a)

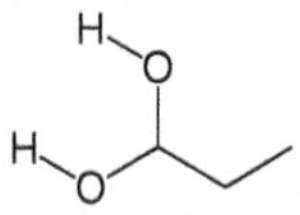

b)

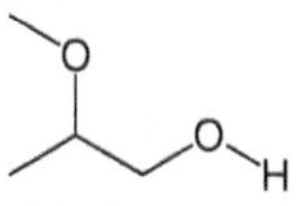

c)

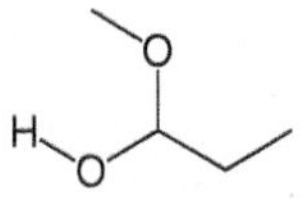

d)

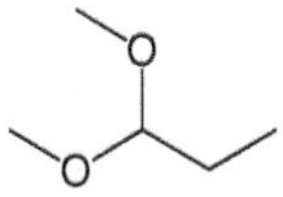

15.56 Which figure depicts the structure of a hemiacetal?

a)

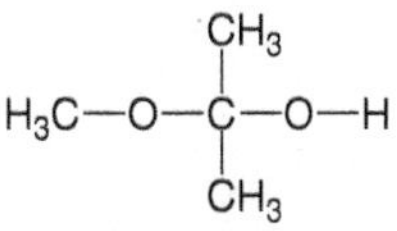

b)

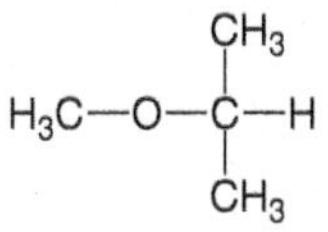

c)

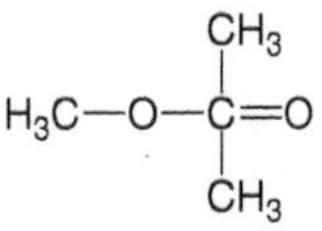

d)

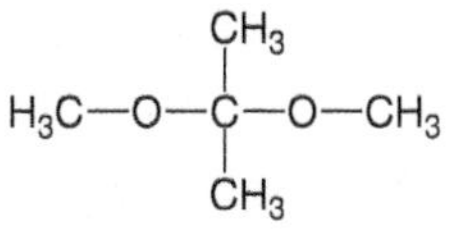

15.57 Which figure depicts the structure of an acetal?

a)

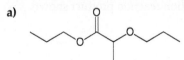

b)

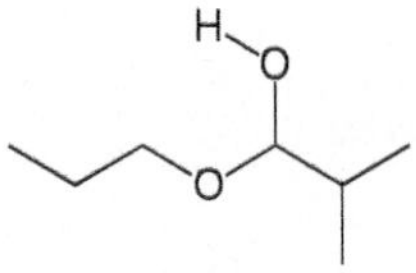

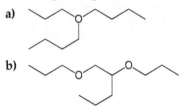

c)

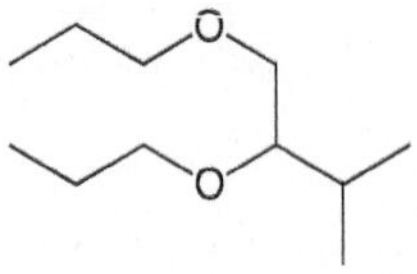

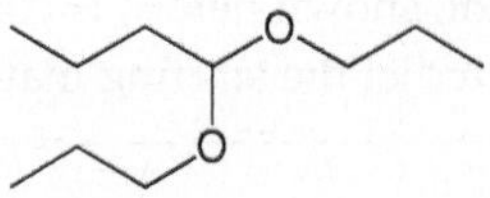

d)

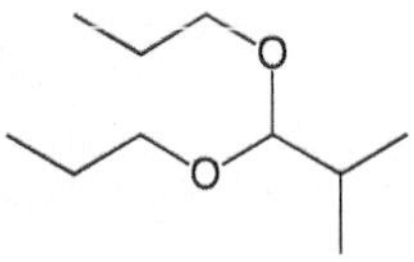

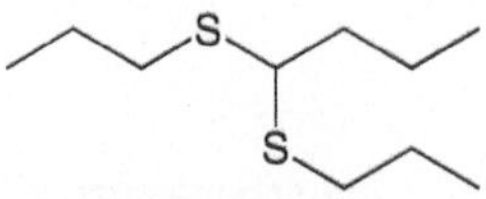

c)

d)

e)

15.58 Which figure depicts the structure of an acetal?

a)

b)

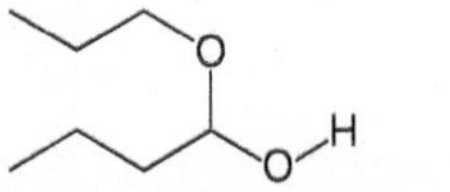

15.59 Choose the correct statement about acetal compounds.

a) Acetals contain two —OR groups bonded to the same carbon whereas ethers contain a sulfur atom bonded to two carbon-based R groups.

b) Acetals contain an —OH (hydroxyl) group and an —OR group bonded to the same carbon atom whereas ethers contain an oxygen atom bonded to two carbon-based R groups.

c) Acetals contain two —OR groups bonded to the same carbon whereas ethers contain an oxygen atom bonded to two carbon-based R groups.

d) Acetals contain two —OR groups bonded to the same carbon whereas ethers contain two —OR groups bonded to the same oxygen.

15.60 Which is the correct acetal compound produced in the reaction shown?

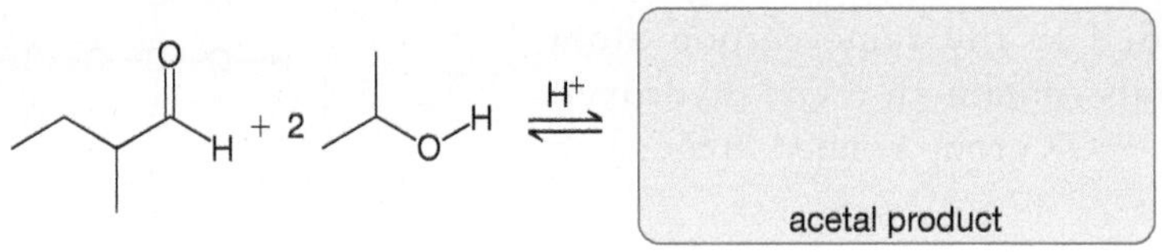

acetal product

a)

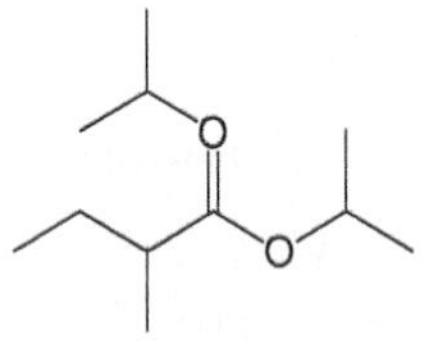

b)

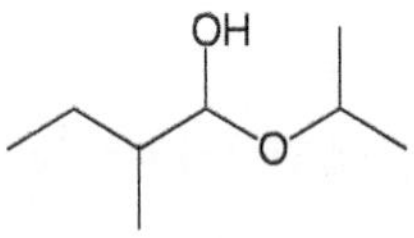

c)

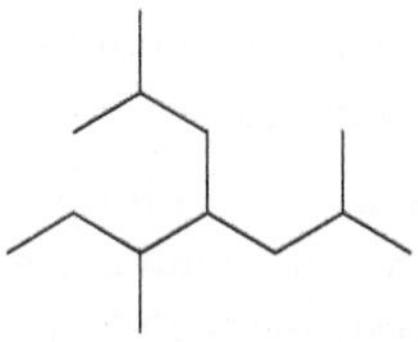

d)

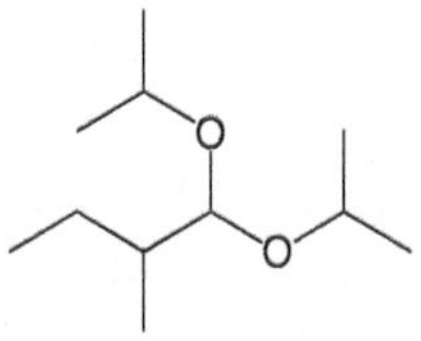

15.61 Identify the missing reactant needed to produce the hemiacetal product shown?

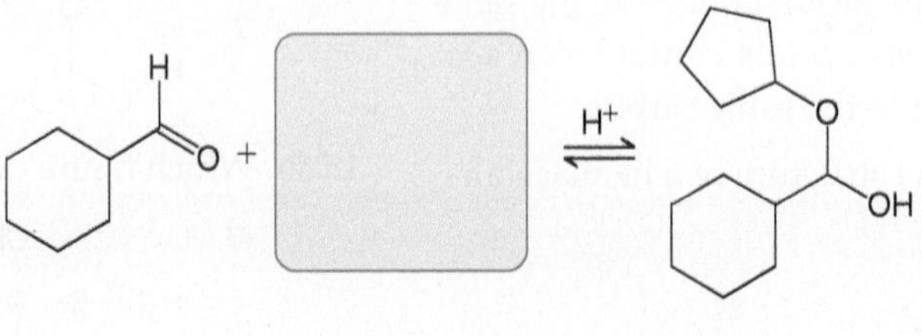

a)

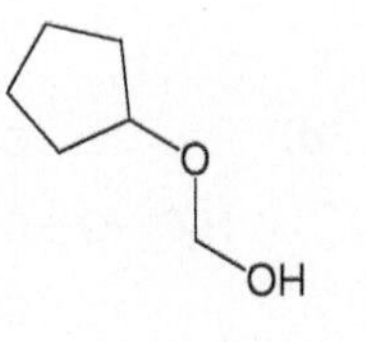

b)

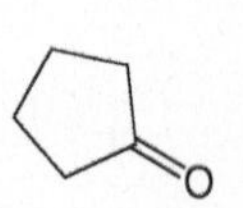

c)

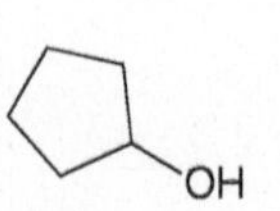

d)

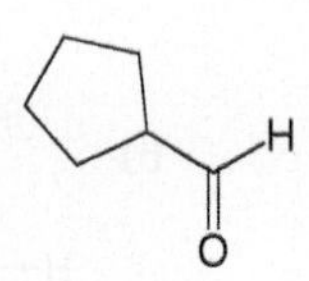

15.62 Drawing a hemiacetal: Use the drawing tool to complete the skeletal structure of the product formed when the two starting materials shown react to form a hemiacetal. Do not include lone pairs of electrons on oxygen, labels for carbon atoms, or show C—H bonds in your skeletal structure answer.

hemiacetal product

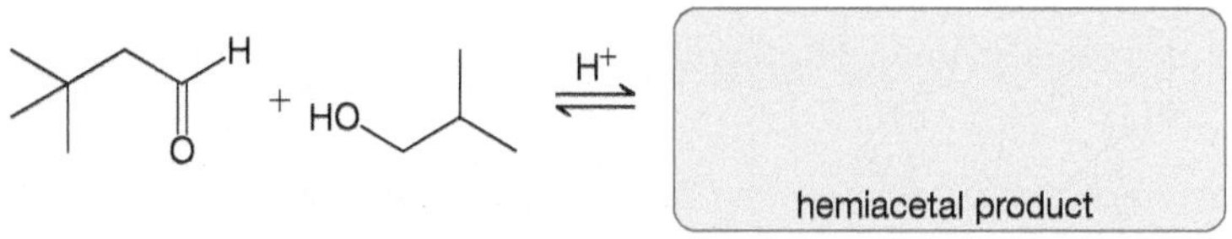

15.63 Drawing an acetal: Use the drawing tool to complete the skeletal structure of the product formed when the two starting materials shown react to form an acetal. Do not include lone pairs of electrons on oxygen, labels for carbon atoms, or show C—H bonds in your skeletal structure answer.

acetal product

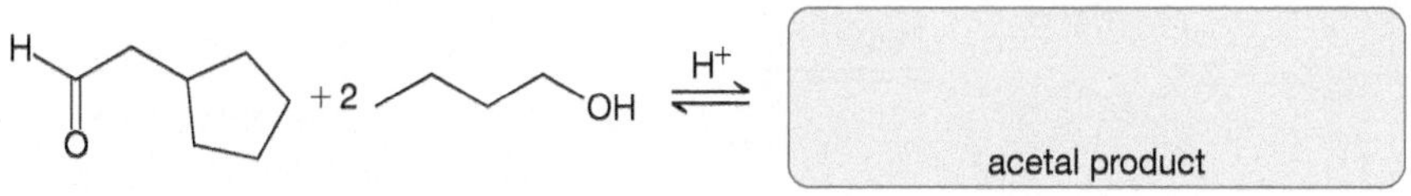

A partial structure of the acetal product is shown below.

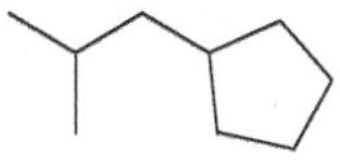

15.64 Which is the required starting material needed to produce the acetal product shown?

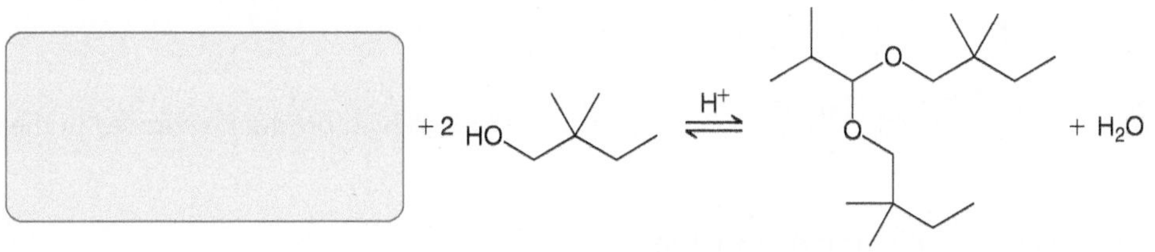

a) 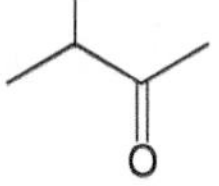 b) 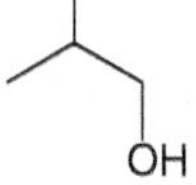 c) 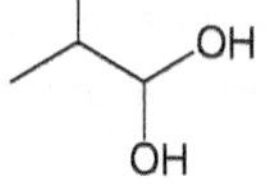 d)

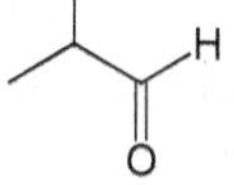

15.65 Which reaction conditions help form the hemiacetal product shown?

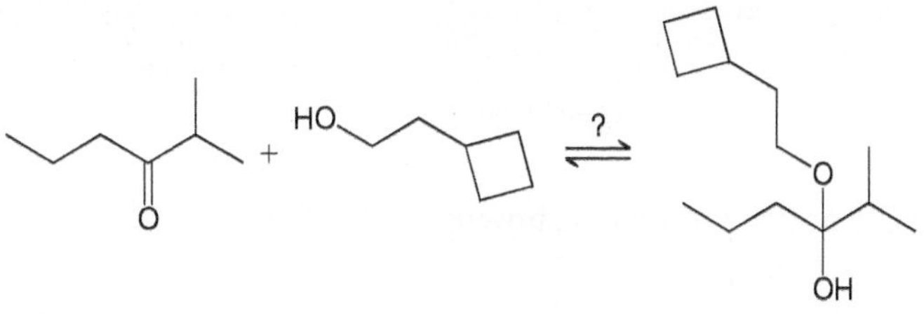

a) OH⁻   **b)** $H_2(g)$ + Ni, Pd or Pt   **c)** H⁺   **d)** Tollens' reagent (Ag^+) or $K_2Cr_2O_7$

15.66 Which combination of starting materials and reaction conditions are needed to produce the acetal product shown?

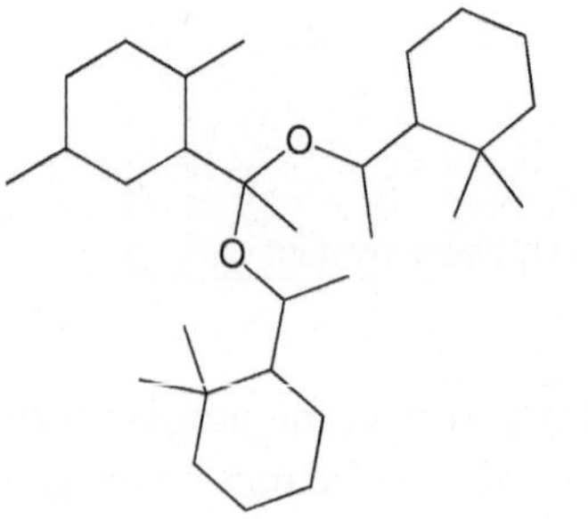

a)

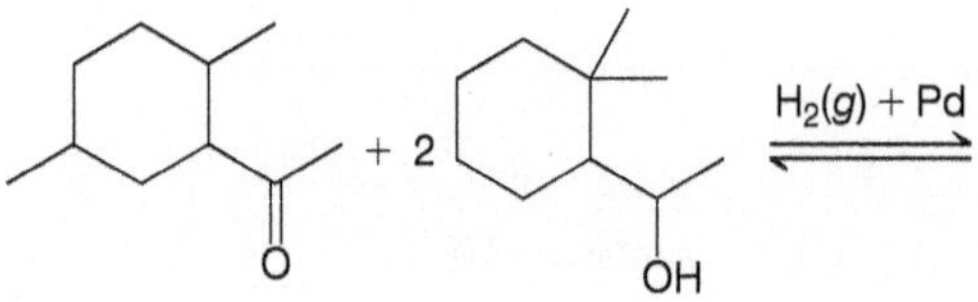

$H_2(g) + Pd$

b)

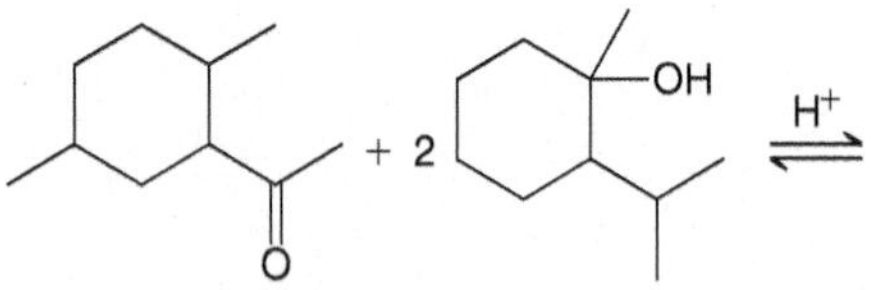

H^+

c)

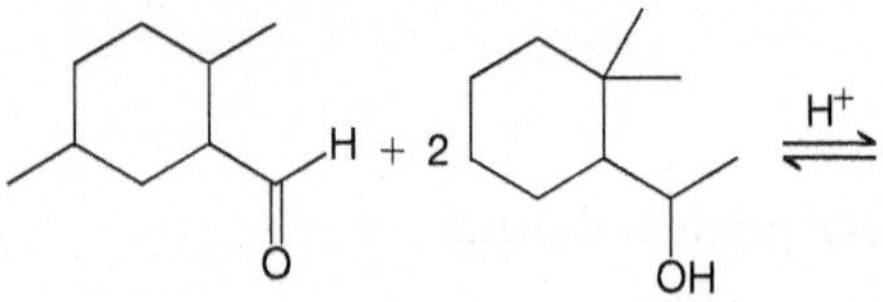

H^+

d)

H^+

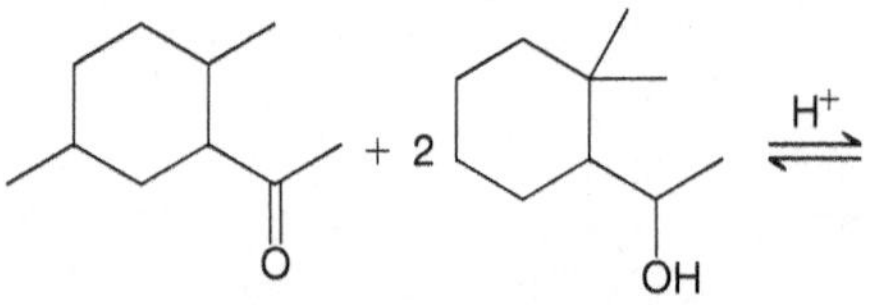

15.67 Drawing an acetal: Use the drawing tool to complete the skeletal structure of the product formed when the two starting materials shown react to form an acetal. Do not include lone pairs of electrons on oxygen, labels for carbon atoms, or show C—H bonds in your skeletal structure answer.

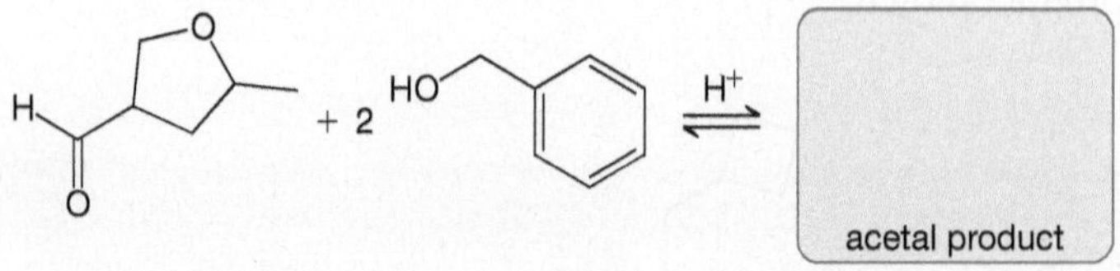

H^+ acetal product

A partial structure of the acetal product is shown below.

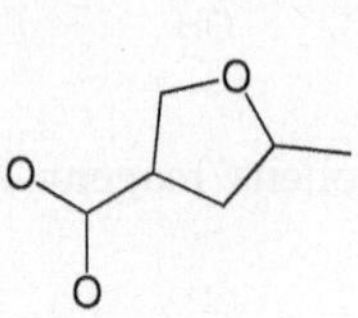

15.68 Which product is formed in the reaction shown?

H^+ product

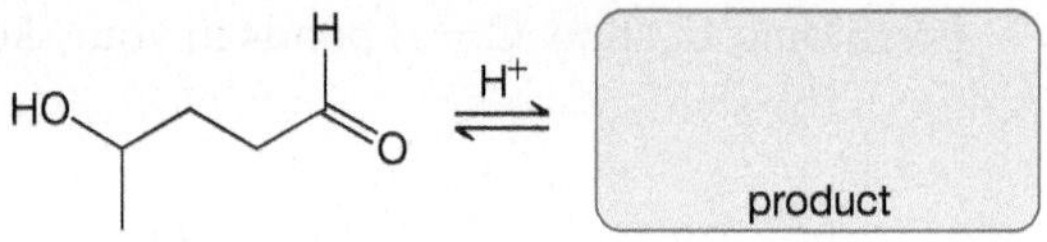

a)

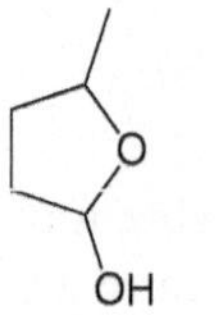

b)

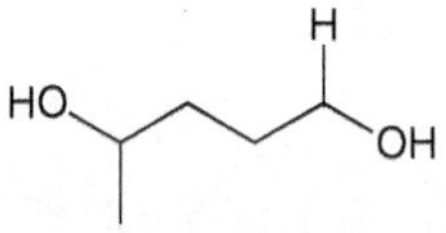

c)

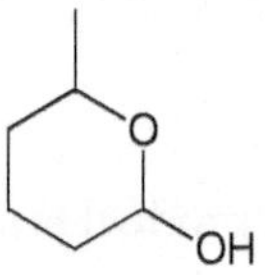

d)

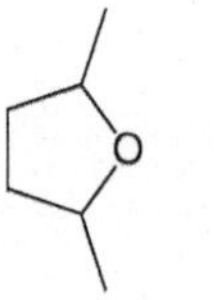

e)

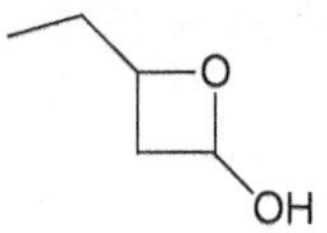

15.69 Which product is formed in the reaction shown?

H^+ product

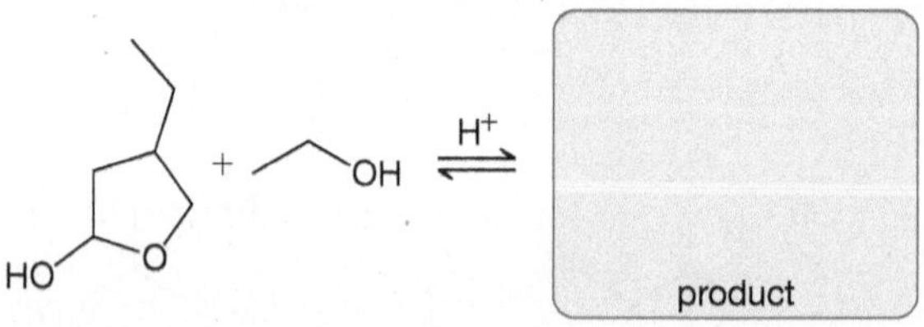

a)

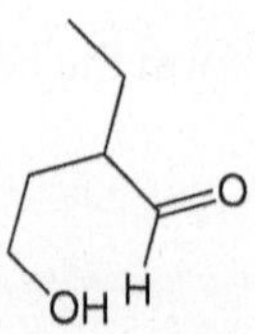

b)

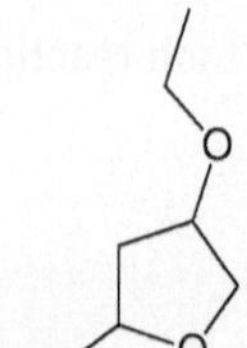

c)

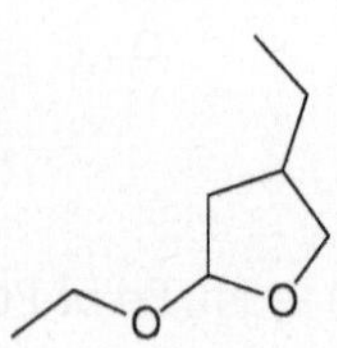

d)

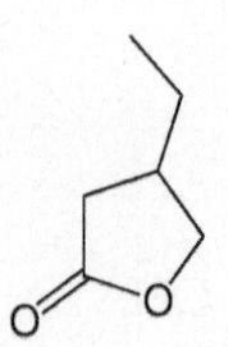

15.70 Carcinogens are substances that increase the risk of developing cancer. Aflatoxins are a class of carcinogens produced by certain molds that grow in soil, hay, grains, and decaying vegetation. The aflatoxin producing molds are often found in agricultural products that have been improperly stored. Aflatoxin B$_1$, shown below, is considered the most toxic aflatoxin and is correlated with increased risk of liver cancer in humans. Which product is formed when the ketone group of aflatoxin B$_1$ reacts to form an acetal compound according to the reaction shown?

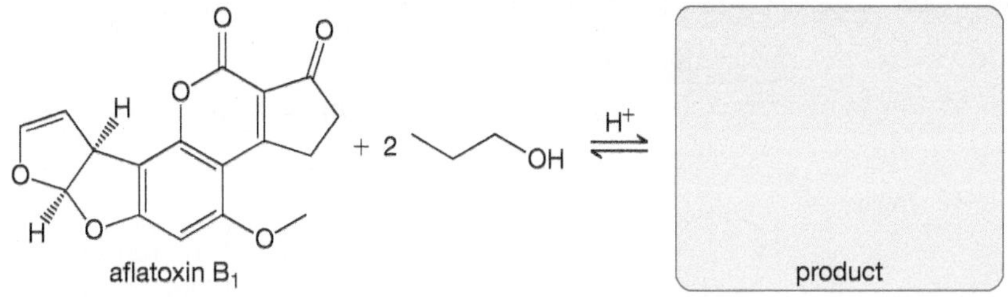

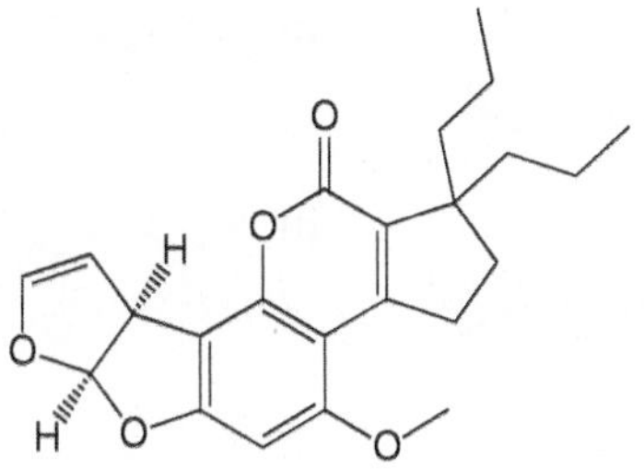

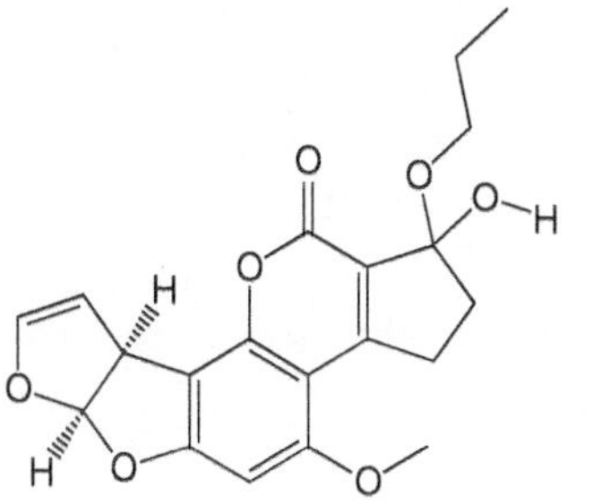

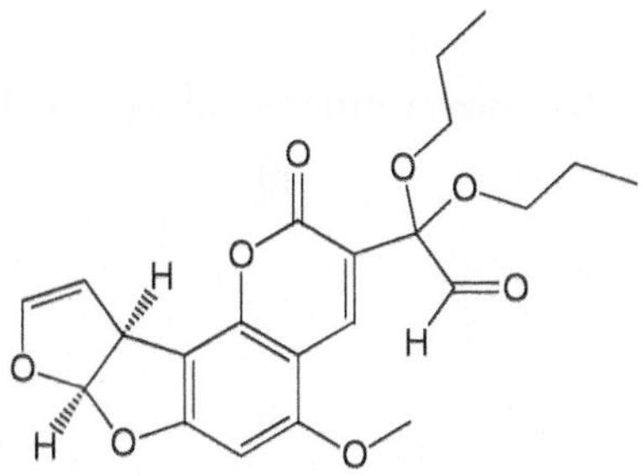

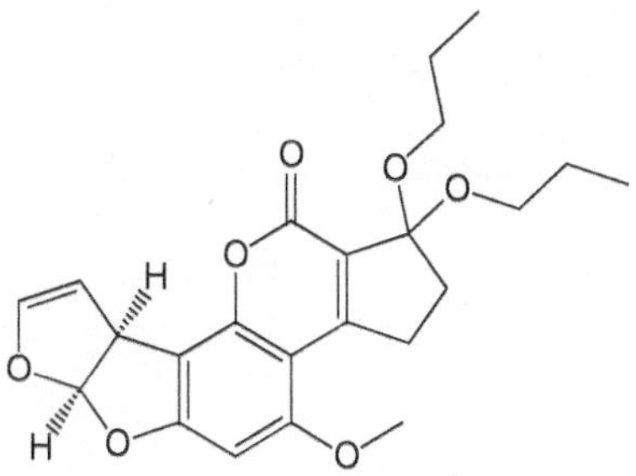

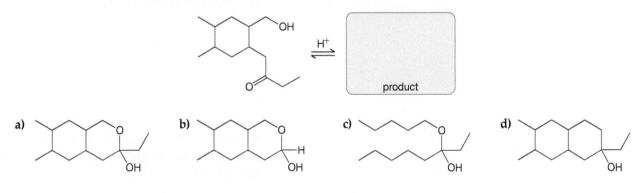

15.71 Which product is formed in the reaction shown?

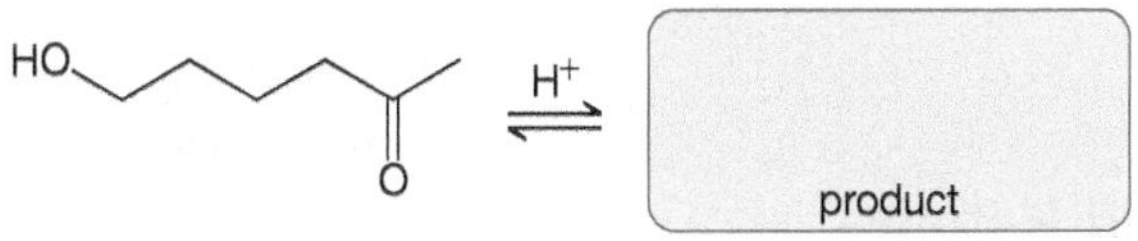

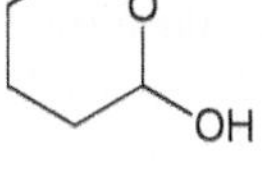

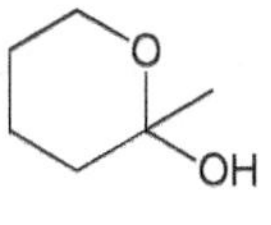

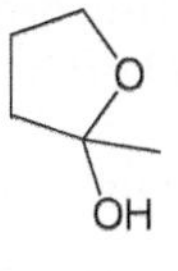

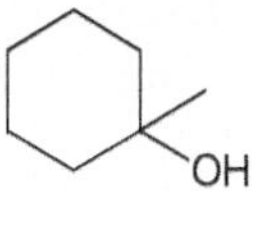

15.72 Which product is formed in the reaction shown when the starting material undergoes a hemiacetal ring closure reaction to form a second ring?

15.73 Predict the product for each reactant as it combines in a 1:1 ratio to form a cyclic acetal. Notice there are two hydroxyl (—Oh) groups in the starting materials.

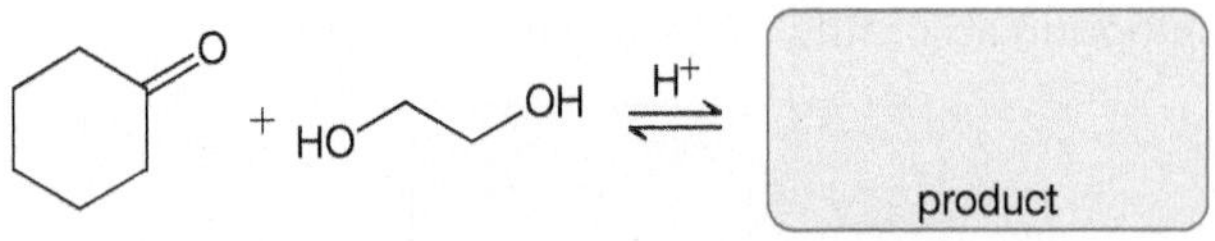

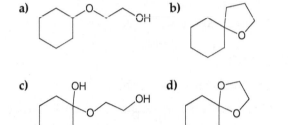

a) 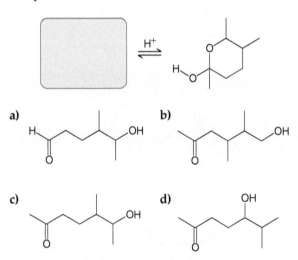 **b)**

c) **d)**

15.74 What starting material is needed to form the reaction product shown?

a) **b)**

c) **d)**

15.5 Naming Aldehydes and Ketones

LO 5: Use the IUPAC system for naming organic compounds for aldehydes and ketones.

15.75 Which of the following is a hexanal molecule?

a)

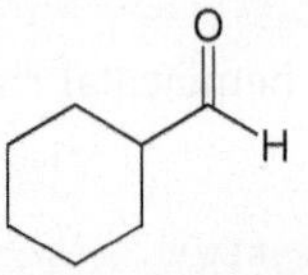

b) 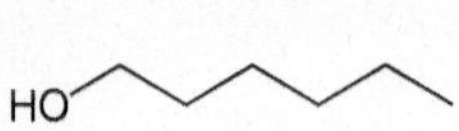 HO

c)

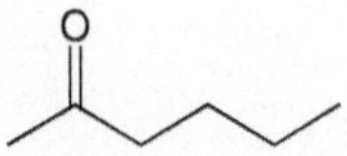

d)

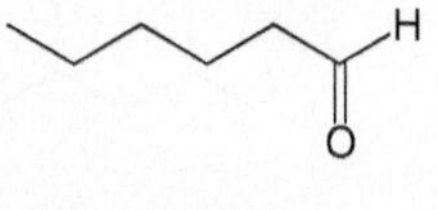

15.76 Which of the following is a 3-octanone molecule?

a) 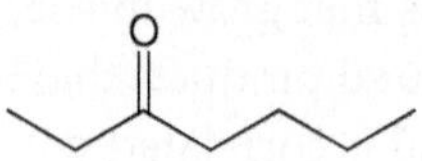 **b)**

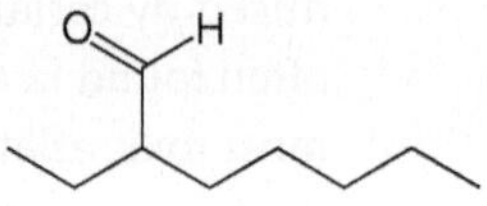

c) 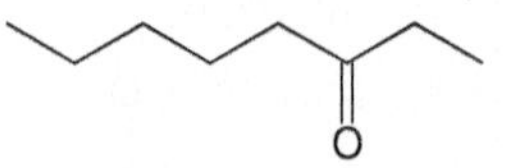 **d)**

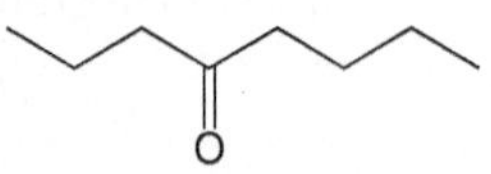

e)

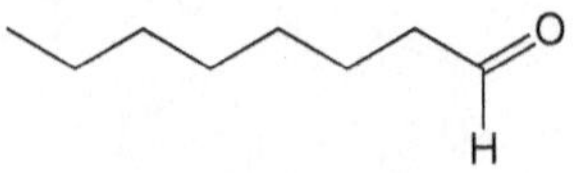

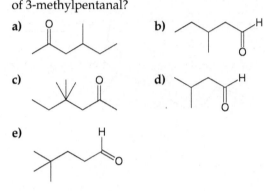

15.77 Which of the following depicts the correct structure of 3-methylpentanal?

a) **b)**

c) **d)**

e)

15.78 Which is the correct structure of 2-propylhexanal?

a) **b)**

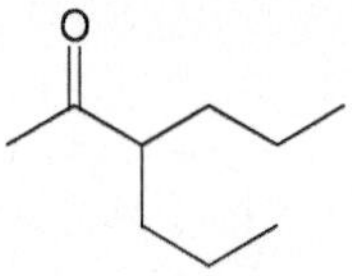

c) **d)**

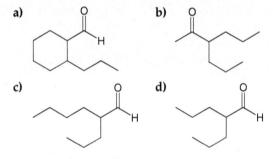

15.79 Draw the *skeletal structure* of 3-methylcyclopentanone. Your skeletal structure should not contain labels, carbon atoms, show hydrogen atoms, or show lone pairs of electrons on the oxygen atom.

15.80 What is the name for the molecule shown?

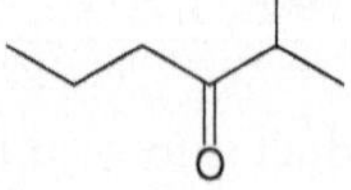

a) methyl-3-hexanone
b) 5-methyl-4-hexanone
c) 2-methyl-3-hexanone
d) 1,1-dimethyl-2-pentanone

15.81 Drawing an aldehyde: Use the drawing tool to build the *skeletal structure* of 2,3-dimethylpentanal. For this exercise, do not draw the lone pairs of electrons on the oxygen atom, but do include a bond and atom label for the hydrogen in the aldehyde group.

15.82 Draw the *skeletal structure* of 5-methyl-2-hexanone. Your skeletal structure should not contain labels on carbon atom bonds, labels on hydrogen atoms, or lone pairs of electrons on the oxygen atom.

15.83 Drag the answer choices into the spaces provided to complete the name of the molecule shown below.

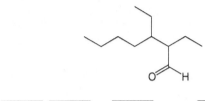

[   ] , [   ] -di [   ] heptan [   ]

Answer choices: 1   2   3   4   5   6

Answer choices: methyl   ethyl   propyl   butyl   pentyl   hexyl

Answer choices: -ol   -e   -al   -one

15.84 Which of the following depicts the structure of 4-ethyl-3-methylhexanal?

a)

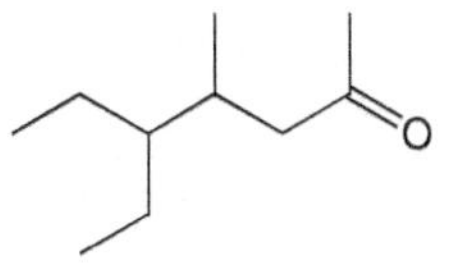

b)

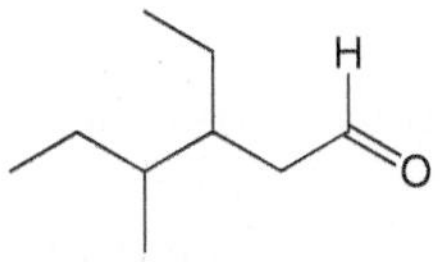

c)

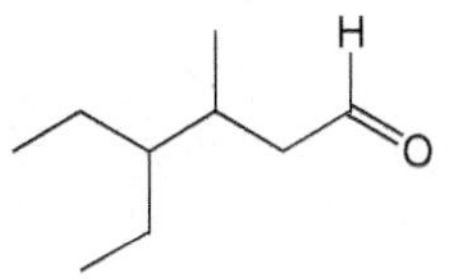

d)

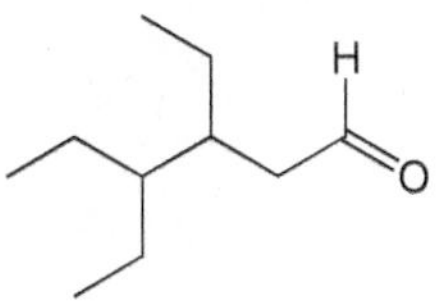

15.85 What is the name of the molecule illustrated here?

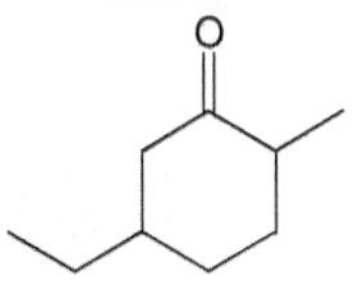

a) 1-ethyl-4-methyl-3-cyclohexanone
b) 5-ethyl-2-methylcyclohexanone
c) 1-ketone-2-methyl-5-ethylcyclohexane
d) 5-ethyl-2-methylhexanone

15.86 What is the name of the molecule illustrated here?

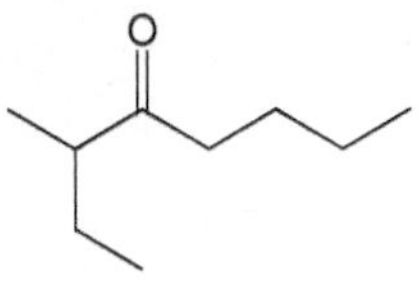

a) 2-ethyl-3-heptanone
b) 6-ethyl-5-heptanone
c) 3-methyl-4-octanal
d) 3-methyl-4-octanone

15.87 Drag the answer choices into the spaces provided to complete the name of the molecule shown below.

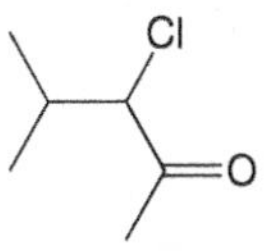

[   ] -chloro- [   ] -methyl [   ] - [   ] anone

Answer choices: 1   2   3   4   5   6

Answer choices: meth   eth   prop   but   pent   hex

Chapter 16

16.1 Introduction to Carbohydrates

LO 1: Identify the three major types of carbohydrates.

16.01 Select the functional groups found on all monosaccharides.

a) aldehyde
b) ketone
c) carboxylic acid
d) alcohol

16.02 Use the simplified representations of individual monosaccharide units to assemble block diagrams of the following disaccharide molecules. Drag the appropriate monosaccharide units into place on each side of the oxygen atom. It might be helpful to look up the disaccharide structures.

A.

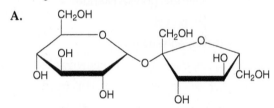

Sucrose is a disaccharide.

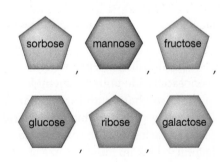

Target boxes:

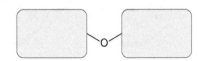

B.

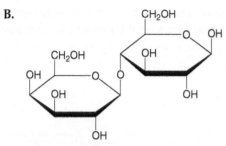

Lactose is a disaccharide.

Answer choices:

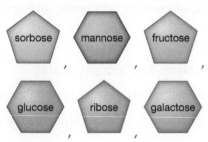

Target boxes:

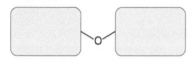

Maltose is a disaccharide.

Answer choices:

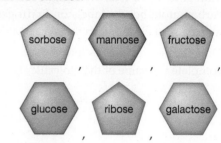

Target boxes:

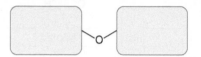

B.

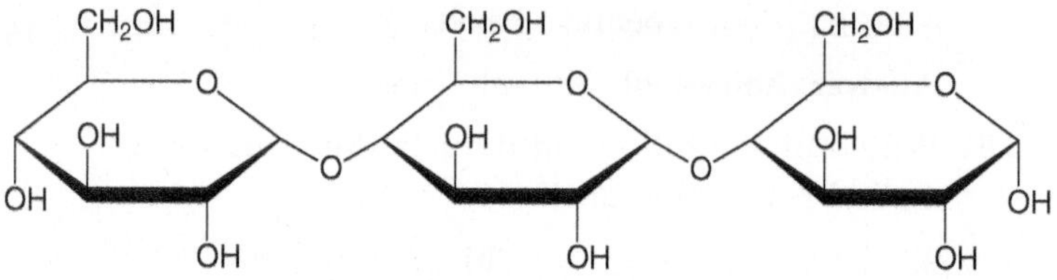

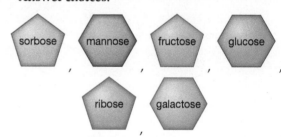

Maltotriose is a trisaccharide.

16.03 A carbohydrate that produces two monosaccharides when it is hydrolyzed is a _____. A carbohydrate that produces three or more monosaccharides after complete hydrolysis is a _____.

  a) dialcohol, polyalcohol

  b) disaccharide, polysaccharide

  c) diether, polyether

  d) disugar, polysugar

16.04 Which sugar is commonly known as blood sugar?

  a) sucrose   **b)** fructose

  c) glucose   **d)** lactose

16.05 Which organ in the body produces insulin?

  a) liver   **b)** kidney

  c) brain   **d)** pancreas

16.06 Use the simplified representations of individual monosaccharide units to assemble block diagrams of the disaccharide and trisaccharide molecules. Drag the appropriate monosaccharide units into place on each side of the oxygen atoms. It might be helpful to look up the structures of the molecules.

A.

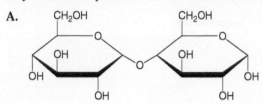

Answer choices:

Target boxes:

C.

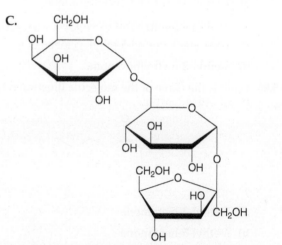

Raffinose is a trisaccharide found in vegetables, beans, and whole grains.

Answer choices:

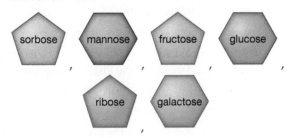

Target boxes:

16.07 What role does insulin play if blood sugar gets too high following a high-sugar meal or snack?

   a) Insulin helps further increase blood sugar to trigger a pH response.

   b) Insulin helps cells take up glucose from the blood.

   c) Insulin decreases skin temperature to facilitate heat conservation.

   d) Insulin triggers the production of sucrose, which increases blood flow.

16.08 Which test is commonly used to analyze long-term blood sugar control?

   a) ABO blood test

   b) WBC blood test

   c) LFT blood test

   d) HbA1c blood test

16.09 Which statement answers both of the following questions: What reactants are needed for the production of carbohydrates in photosynthesis? What reactants are used for carbohydrate metabolism during cellular respiration?

   a) Sunlight, carbon monoxide, and hydroxide produce carbohydrates in photosynthesis. Sugars such as glucose along with oxygen gas produce energy, carbon dioxide, and water during metabolic respiration of carbohydrates.

   b) Sunlight, carbon dioxide, and water produce carbohydrates in photosynthesis. Sugars such as glucose along with hydrogen gas produce energy, ozone, and water during metabolic respiration of carbohydrates.

   c) Sunlight, nitrogen dioxide, and water produce carbohydrates in photosynthesis. Sugars such as ethanol along with oxygen gas produce energy, carbon monoxide, and water during metabolic respiration of carbohydrates.

   d) Sunlight, carbon dioxide, and water produce carbohydrates in photosynthesis. Sugars such as glucose along with oxygen gas produce energy, carbon dioxide and water during metabolic respiration of carbohydrates.

16.2 Monosaccharides

LO 2: **Recognize and draw the major structural features of monosaccharides.**

16.10 Which term describes this monosaccharide?

$$
\begin{array}{c}
CH_2OH \\
\Vert O \\
H \!-\!\!\!-\! OH \\
CH_2OH
\end{array}
$$

   a) aldohexose   **b)** ketotetrose

   c) D-hemiacetal   **d)** ketopentose

16.11 Which term describes this monosaccharide?

$$
\begin{array}{c}
O\!\diagup\!\!H \\
H \!-\!\!\!-\! OH \\
HO \!-\!\!\!-\! H \\
CH_2OH
\end{array}
$$

   a) L-aldotetrose   **b)** D-ketotetrose

   c) L-aldopentose   **d)** D-aldotetrose

16.12 Which term describes this monosaccharide?

$$
\begin{array}{c}
CH_2OH \\
\Vert O \\
HO \!-\!\!\!-\! H \\
HO \!-\!\!\!-\! H \\
H \!-\!\!\!-\! OH \\
CH_2OH
\end{array}
$$

   a) D-ketopentose   **b)** L-ketohexose

   c) D-ketohexose   **d)** L-ketopentose

16.13 Which term describes this monosaccharide?

$$
\begin{array}{c}
H\!\diagup\!\!O \\
H \!-\!\!\!-\! OH \\
HO \!-\!\!\!-\! H \\
H \!-\!\!\!-\! OH \\
CH_2OH
\end{array}
$$

   a) L-aldopentose   **b)** D-aldopentose

   c) L-aldotetrose   **d)** D-ketopentose

16.14 Complete the Fischer projection of D-glucose by dragging the missing OH groups into a correct location on the structure. It might be helpful to refer back to the structure of D-glucose shown in the chapter.

Answer choices: OH , OH , OH , OH

Target boxes:

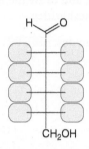

16.15 Complete the Fischer projection of D-fructose by dragging the missing OH groups and the ketone group into correct locations on the structure. It might be helpful to refer back to the structure of D-fructose shown in the chapter.

Answer choices: OH , OH , OH , =O

Target boxes:

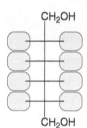

16.16 Identify all ketotetroses in the set of structures shown. Check *all* that apply.

a) 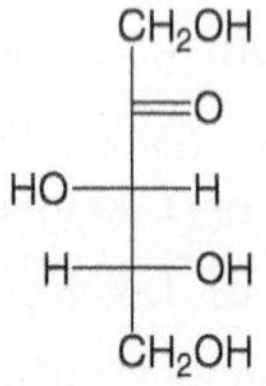
```
    CH₂OH
    |
    =O
    |
HO——H
    |
H——OH
    |
    CH₂OH
```

b) 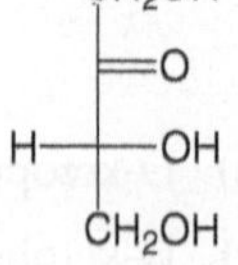
```
    CH₂OH
    |
    =O
    |
H——OH
    |
    CH₂OH
```

c) 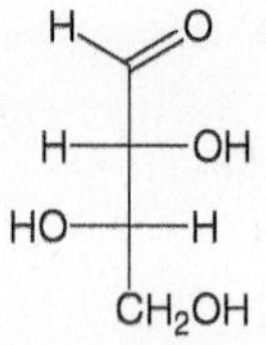
```
H   O
 \\ //
    |
H——OH
    |
HO——H
    |
    CH₂OH
```

d) 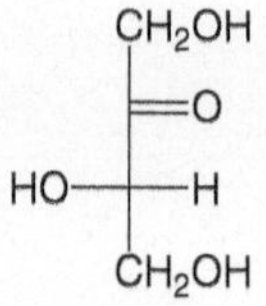
```
    CH₂OH
    |
    =O
    |
HO——H
    |
    CH₂OH
```

e) 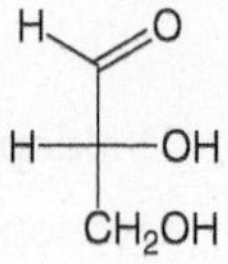
```
H   O
 \\ //
    |
H——OH
    |
    CH₂OH
```

f) 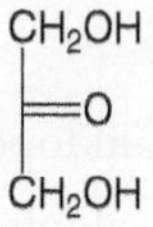
```
    CH₂OH
    |
    =O
    |
    CH₂OH
```

16.17 Which chiral center always determines whether a monosaccharide is D or L?

a) the carbonyl carbon in the Fischer projection

b) the chiral carbon next down the chain from the carbonyl group in the Fischer projection

c) the chiral carbon farthest from the carbonyl group in the Fischer projection

d) the carbon in the CH₂ group farthest from the carbonyl group in the Fischer projection

16.18 How many chiral centers does each monosaccharide contain?

A. 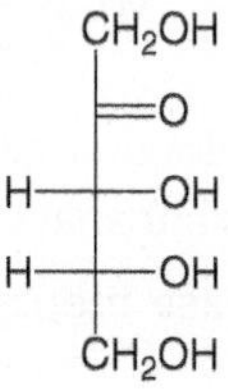
```
    CH₂OH
    |
    =O
    |
H——OH
    |
H——OH
    |
    CH₂OH
```

a) 2   b) 3   c) 4   d) 5

B. 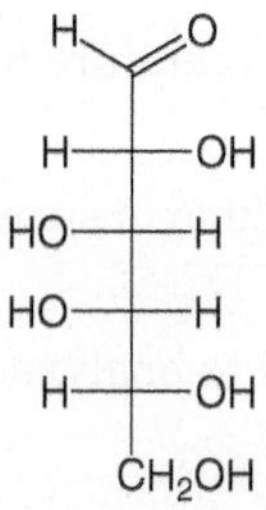
```
H   O
 \\ //
    |
H——OH
    |
HO——H
    |
HO——H
    |
H——OH
    |
    CH₂OH
```

a) 3   b) 4   c) 5   d) 6

C. 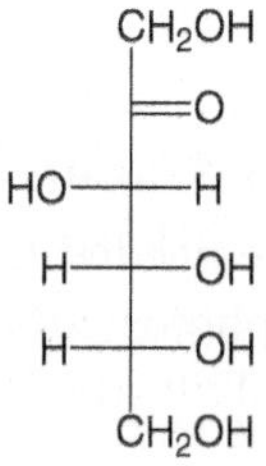
```
    CH₂OH
    |
    =O
    |
HO——H
    |
H——OH
    |
H——OH
    |
    CH₂OH
```

a) 3   b) 4   c) 5   d) 6

D. 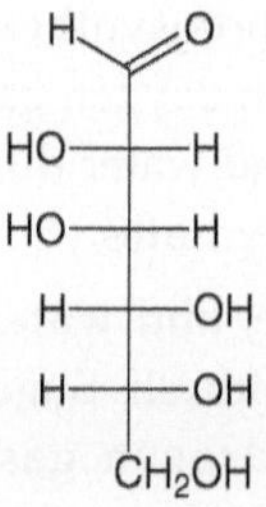
```
H   O
 \\ //
    |
HO——H
    |
HO——H
    |
H——OH
    |
H——OH
    |
    CH₂OH
```

a) 3   b) 4   c) 5   d) 6

16.19 How many chiral centers does each monosaccharide contain?

A.

H—C=O
H——OH
H——OH
H——OH
CH₂OH

a) 2   b) 3   c) 4   d) 5

B.

CH₂OH
=O
H——OH
CH₂OH

a) 1   b) 2   c) 3   d) 4

C.

H—C=O
HO——H
CH₂OH

a) 0   b) 1   c) 2   d) 3

D.

CH₂OH
=O
H——OH
HO——H
H——OH
CH₂OH

a) 3   b) 4   c) 5   d) 6

16.20 Use the fragments to build Fischer projections of two *different* 2-ketopentose isomers. For each molecule, drag the pieces into position. Hint: Each should have OH groups in alternating orientations along the chains at the sites of the chiral carbons. By convention, carbon #1 is located at the top of each Fischer projection.

Answer choices: H—C=O , CH₂OH , C=O , C=C , HO—C—H , H—C—OH , CH₂OH

Target boxes:

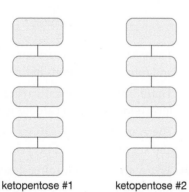

ketopentose #1   ketopentose #2

16.3 Cyclic monosaccharides

LO 3: Draw the cyclic forms of monosaccharides and classify as α and β anomers.

16.21 Which statement best describes an anomeric carbon?

a) The anomeric carbon is farthest down the chain from the most oxidized carbon atom in the Fischer projection. It becomes a chiral center when a monosaccharide forms a cyclic hemiacetal.

b) The anomeric carbon is the carbon with the first OH group pointing left (L) in the Fischer projection before hemiacetal formation. It becomes a chiral center when a monosaccharide forms a cyclic hemiacetal.

c) The anomeric carbon is the carbon with the carboxyl (CO_2H) group branching from it before hemiacetal formation. It becomes a tertiary alcohol when a monosaccharide forms a cyclic hemiacetal.

d) The anomeric carbon was the carbonyl carbon before hemiacetal formation. It becomes a chiral center when a monosaccharide forms a cyclic hemiacetal.

16.22 Which process establishes an equilibration between the alpha (α) and beta (β) anomers of a cyclic monosaccharide?

a) chirality formation   b) mutarotation

c) double hydration   d) inversion

16.23 What functional groups are required to be part of a molecule so that it can undergo an intramolecular cyclization reaction to form a cyclic hemiacetal? Drag the name of all of the groups needed into the box shown.

Answer choices: carboxyl, cyclohexyl, hydroxyl, thiol, ether, carbonyl

Target box: functional groups required on the same molecule in order for it to form a cyclic hemiacetal

16.24 Classify the compounds into each category.

Answer choices:

Target boxes: acetal, hemiacetal, aldehyde

16.25 Complete the Haworth structure of α-D-glucose by dragging the missing OH groups into the correct locations and orientations around the ring. You may find it helpful to refer back to the structure of D-fructose shown before you complete this problem. Leaving a box empty indicates a hydrogen (H) at that position.

Answer choices: OH , OH , OH , OH

Target boxes:

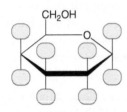

16.26 Which statement best describes the process of mutarotation?

a) In aqueous solution, only six-membered monosaccharide rings can open and close in a reversible process giving rise to the acyclic (open chain) form and the two cyclic forms (α and β) all in equilibrium.

b) In aqueous solution, monosaccharide rings can open and close in a reversible process giving rise to the acyclic (open chain) form and the two cyclic forms (aldo and keto) all in equilibrium.

c) In aqueous solution, monosaccharide rings can open and close in a reversible process giving rise to the acyclic (open chain) form and the two cyclic forms (D and L) all in equilibrium.

d) In aqueous solution, monosaccharide rings can open and close in a reversible process giving rise to the acyclic (open chain) form and the two cyclic forms (α and β) all in equilibrium.

16.27 Consider the Haworth structure of β-D-altrose shown, then complete the structure for the product of β-D-altrose mutarotation by dragging the missing OH groups into the correct locations and orientations around the ring.

CH₂OH

β-D-altrose

Answer choices: OH , OH , OH , OH

Target boxes:

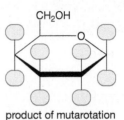

product of mutarotation

16.28 Kanamycin A is an antibiotic used to treat severe bacterial infections such as tuberculosis (TB) and is a World Health Organization (WHO) essential medicine. Determine the designation for the highlighted anomeric carbon in the kanamycin A molecule.

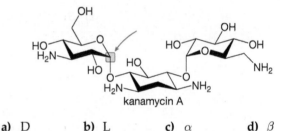

kanamycin A

a) D   b) L   c) α   d) β

16.29 Sorbose is a rare monosaccharide that occurs naturally in the L-form instead of the D-form like most other naturally occurring sugars. Sorbose is used for the commercial production of tens of millions of kilograms of vitamin C annually in the United States. The Fischer projection of the open chain form and the Haworth projection of one of the cyclic forms of L-sorbose are shown. How many chiral carbons are present in each form?

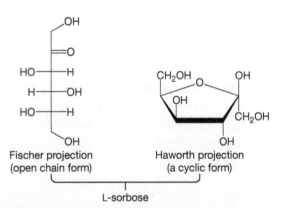

Fischer projection   Haworth projection
(open chain form)   (a cyclic form)

L-sorbose

a) There are five chiral carbons in open chain form and four chiral carbons in the cyclic form.

b) There are three chiral carbons in open chain form and four chiral carbons in cyclic form.

c) There are five chiral carbons in open chain form and six chiral carbons in cyclic form.

d) There are three chiral carbons in open chain form and three chiral carbons in cyclic form.

16.30 Complete the structures of the two anomers resulting from cyclic ring formation by dragging the missing H and OH into the correct positions to form the alpha (α) and beta (β) anomers of D-glucose.

Answer choices: H , OH , H , OH

Target boxes:

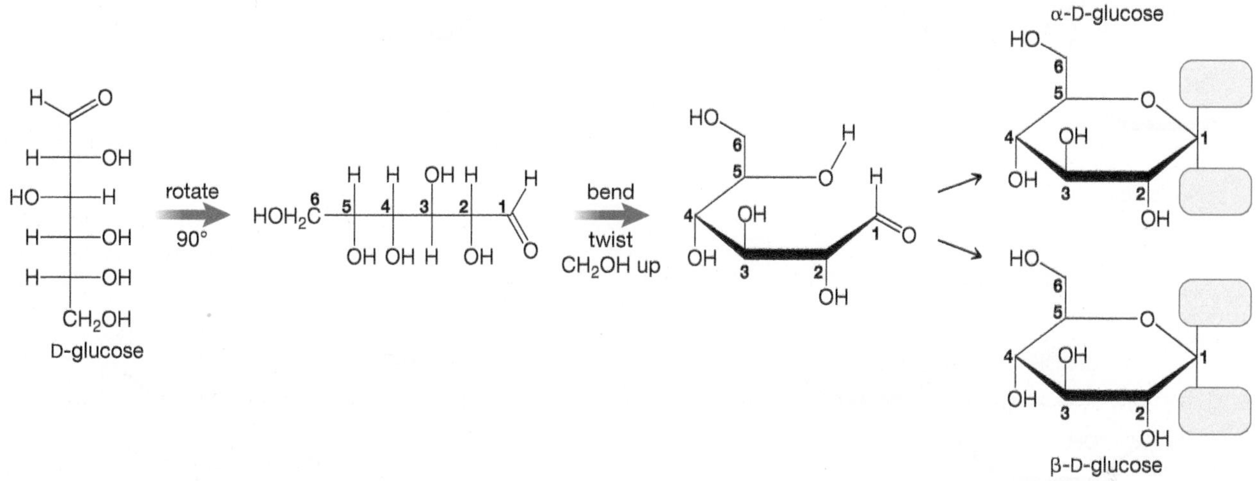

16.4 Reactions of monosaccharides

LO 4: Predict and draw the oxidation and reduction products of monosaccharides.

16.31 What type of molecule is produced by the reduction of aldoses with hydrogen gas and a transition metal catalyst?

a) aldonic acids

b) cyclic hemiacetals

c) alditols

d) aldoketoses

16.32 What do you see when a reducing sugar sample tests positive in a Benedict's test?

a) A color change from red to blue is observed as the oxidation reaction takes place.

b) The formation of bubbles is observed and the reaction releases heat as the reaction takes place.

c) A color change from blue to red is observed as the hydrogenation reaction takes place.

d) A color change from blue to red is observed as the oxidation reaction takes place.

16.33 Which type of sugar produces a positive Benedict's test result?

a) oxidizing sugars

b) alditols

c) reducing sugars

d) sugar acids

16.34 Which statement best describes the reaction of ketoses with Benedict's reagent?

a) The ketone carbonyl group becomes oxidized in basic conditions to form a carboxylic acid which then reacts with Benedict's reagent.

b) The CH_2OH group next to the ketone carbonyl group rearranges in basic conditions to form an aldose which then reacts with Benedict's reagent.

c) Ketones do not react with Benedict's reagent unless they are part of an α $(1 \rightarrow 4)$-glycosidic linkage with a sugar alcohol.

d) The CH_2OH group farthest down the chain from the most oxidized carbon atom is the one that reacts with Benedict's reagent.

16.35 Drawing a monosaccharide reaction product: Erythrose is involved in metabolic processes and photosynthesis in plants. Complete the drawing of the product formed when D-erythrose is reacted with Cu^{2+} under basic conditions (OH^-) and heat by adding the appropriate bonds and atoms. Do not add lone pairs of electrons to the structure.

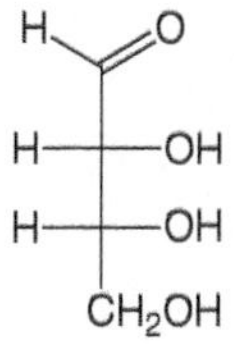

16.36 Lactose, commonly called milk sugar, is a disaccharide and reacts with Benedict's reagent as a reducing sugar. Use the figure to predict the product that forms when lactose reacts with Benedict's reagent.

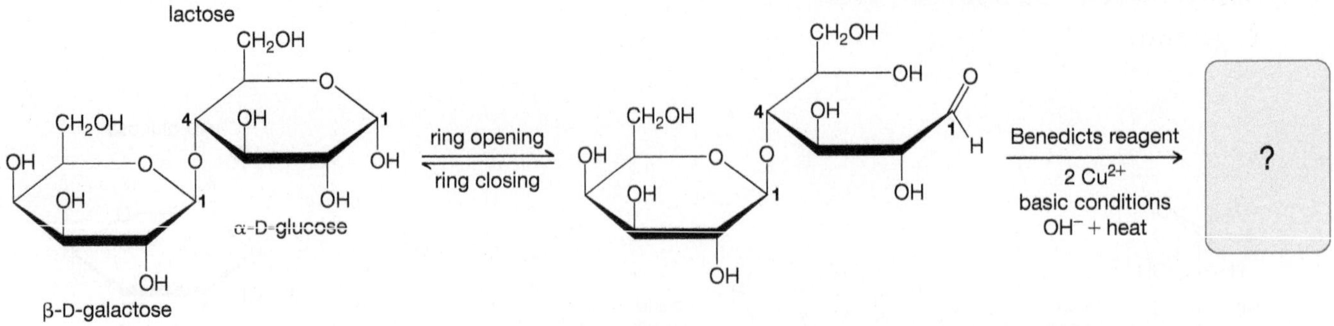

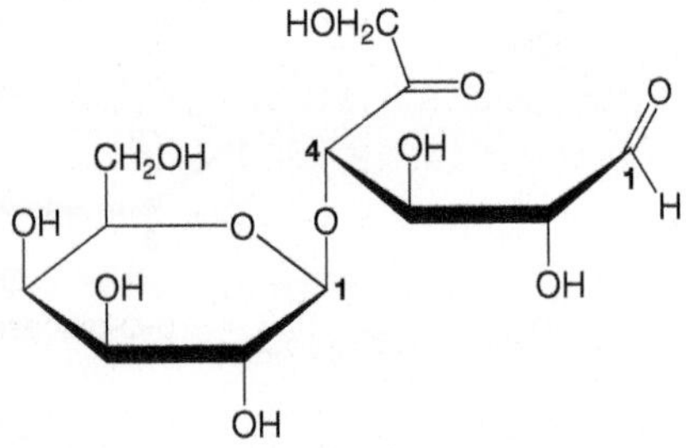

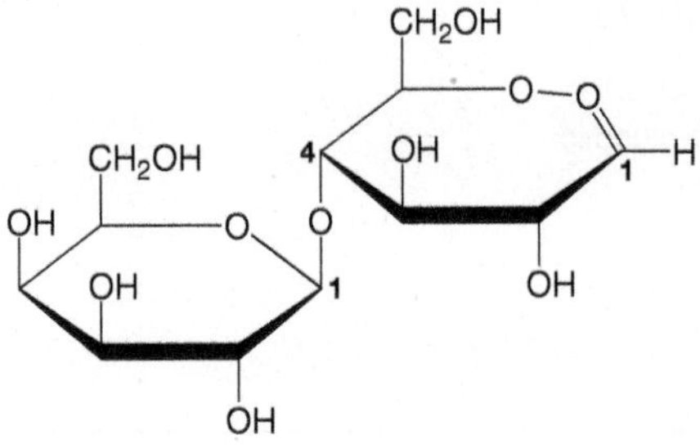

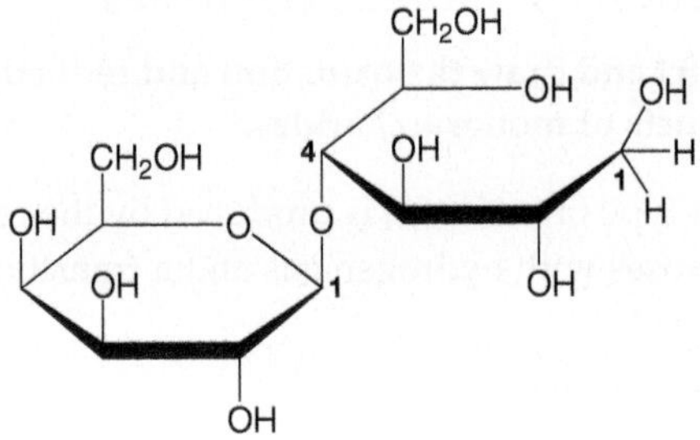

16.37 Mannitol is a sugar alcohol used to decrease pressure in the eyes of people suffering from glaucoma. It is also used as a sweetener in diabetic and weight loss foods because it is not metabolized by humans. Mannitol is produced by the hydrogenation of fructose or enzymatic reduction by mannitol dehydrogenase. Use this reaction to predict the structure of mannitol.

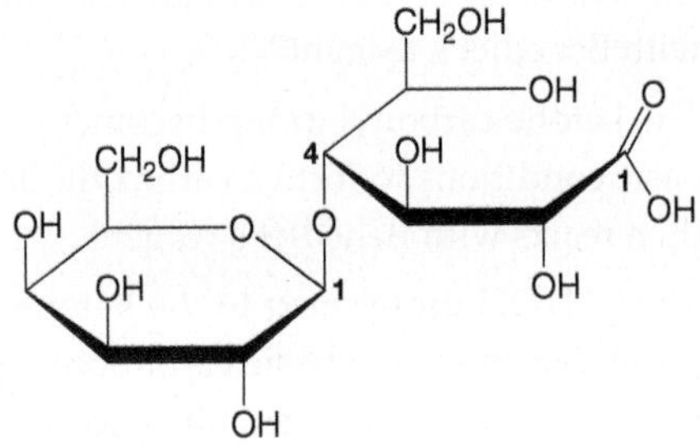

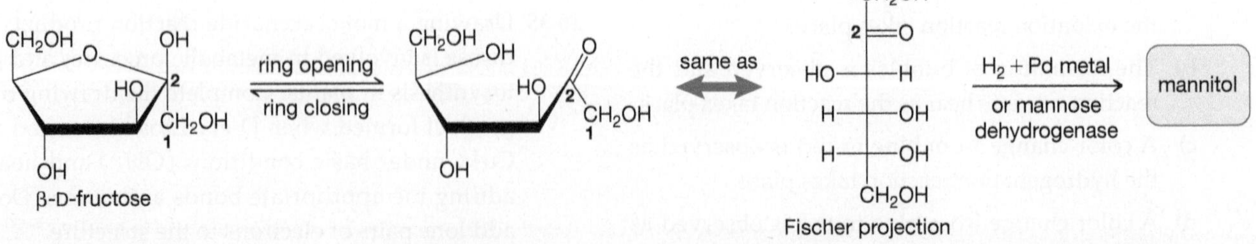

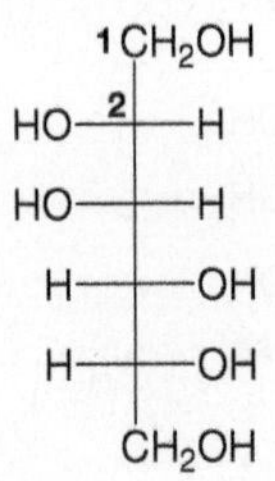

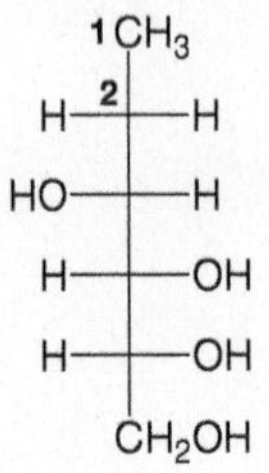

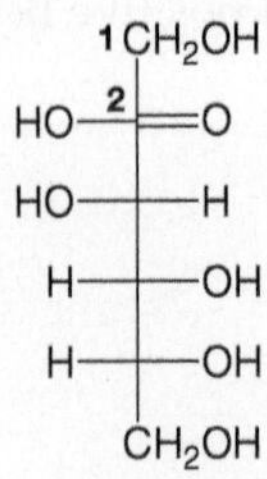

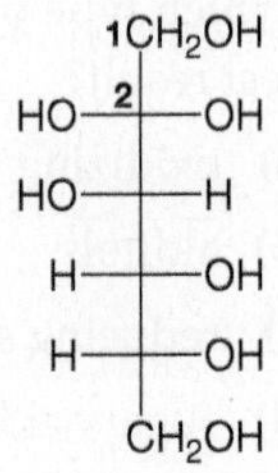

16.38 Drawing a monosaccharide reaction product: Arabinose is found in nature as a component of pectin, a structural polysaccharide in cell walls of plants. Complete the drawing of the product formed when D-arabinose reacts with H_2 gas and Pd metal. Do not add lone pairs of electrons to the structure.

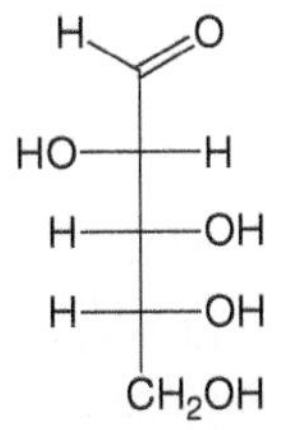

H C=O
HO——H
H——OH
H——OH
CH_2OH
D-arabinose

16.39 Lyxose is found in the cell membranes of some bacteria. Complete the drawing of the product formed when D-lyxose is reduced to a sugar alcohol. Do not add lone pairs of electrons to the structure.

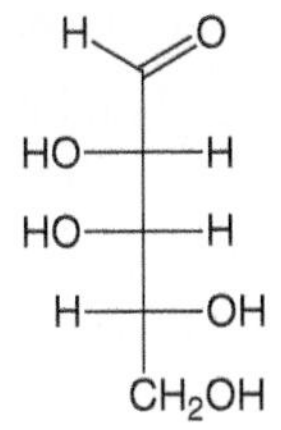

H C=O
HO——H
HO——H
H——OH
CH_2OH
D-lyxose

16.40 Raffinose is a trisaccharide found in beans of legumes. It is fermented in the gut and used as an energy source for gut bacteria. Treatment of raffinose with the enzyme invertase (β-fructosidase) produces fructose and melibiose. Treatment of raffinose with α-galactosidase produces sucrose and galactose. Examine the diagram below and identify the missing molecules.

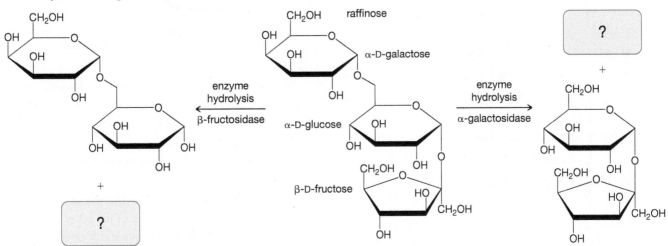

Target boxes: indicated by boxes with [?]
Answer choices: galactose, fructose, glucose, sucrose

16.5 Disaccharides

LO 5: Recognize and draw the major structural features of disaccharides.

16.41 Which term describes the C—O bond that joins two monosaccharides together in a disaccharide?

   a) hemiacetal linkage   **b)** anomeric linkage

   c) glycosidic linkage   **d)** saccharide linkage

16.42 Which statement describes the hydrolysis of a disaccharide. Select all correct answers.

   a) An acetal is formed.

   b) Two monosaccharides are formed.

   c) Two molecules of water are added to the disaccharide.

   d) A glycosidic linkage is broken.

   e) The ring oxygen atom in each sugar unit is converted to a water molecule.

16.43 The glycosidic bond connecting the two monosaccharides in a disaccharide is a(n) _____.

   a) aldehyde

   b) hemiacetal

   c) ketone

   d) acetal

   e) alcohol

16.44 Which statement best describes a disaccharide that has an α $(1 \rightarrow 3)$ glycosidic linkage?

a) The glycosidic bond is pointing down on the ring linked at C3 and up at C1.

b) Both monosaccharides have two connections with each other, one at C1 and another at C3.

c) The glycosidic bond connects C1 and C3 on the same ring and is pointing down.

d) The glycosidic bond links C1 of one ring to C3 of the other and is pointing downward on the ring linked at C1.

16.45 What type of glycosidic linkage is found in this disaccharide?

a) $\beta(1 \rightarrow 4)$ glycosidic linkage

b) α $(1 \rightarrow 4)$ glycosidic linkage

c) β $(1 \rightarrow 2)$ glycosidic linkage

d) α $(1 \rightarrow 2)$ glycosidic linkage

e) β $(1 \rightarrow 6)$ glycosidic linkage

f) α $(1 \rightarrow 6)$ glycosidic linkage

g) β $(1 \rightarrow 5)$ glycosidic linkage

h) α $(1 \rightarrow 5)$ glycosidic linkage

16.46 Not all glycosidic linkages join two or more monosaccharide units. In fact, many glycosidic linkages found in nature and pharmaceuticals connect a monosaccharide to another non-carbohydrate. The molecule salicin is produced by willow and poplar trees and is chemically related to aspirin. When salicin is consumed, the glycosidic linkage is broken down and the two parts of the molecule (glucose and salicyl

alcohol) are metabolized separately. What type of glycosidic linkage is present in the salicin molecule?

salicin

a) α b) L   c) β d) D

16.47 Which statement best describes the formation of the disaccharide lactose?

lactose

β-D-galactose α-D-glucose

a) The hemiacetal of one monosaccharide reacts with the hemiacetal of the other monosaccharide and a water molecule is formed.

b) The acetal of one monosaccharide reacts with the hemiacetal of the other monosaccharide and a water molecule is formed.

c) The glycosidic bond of one monosaccharide reacts with the OH group of the other monosaccharide and a water molecule is formed.

d) The anomeric carbon atoms of the two monosaccharides become directly linked to each other and a water molecule is formed.

e) The hemiacetal of one monosaccharide reacts with an OH group on another monosaccharide to form an acetal and a water molecule.

16.48 Glucosamine is an amino sugar found in the exoskeleton of insects and crustaceans. In the structure of glucosamine, the OH group on C_2 of glucose is replaced with an amino group (NH_2). Chitobiose is a dimer of β $(1 \rightarrow 4)$-linked glucosamine units that can be separated by enzymatic or chemical hydrolysis. What is the structure of starting material, chitobiose?

β-D-glucosamine

a)

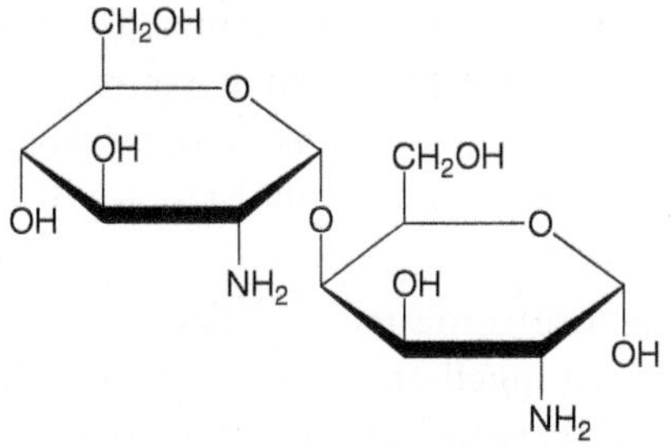

b)

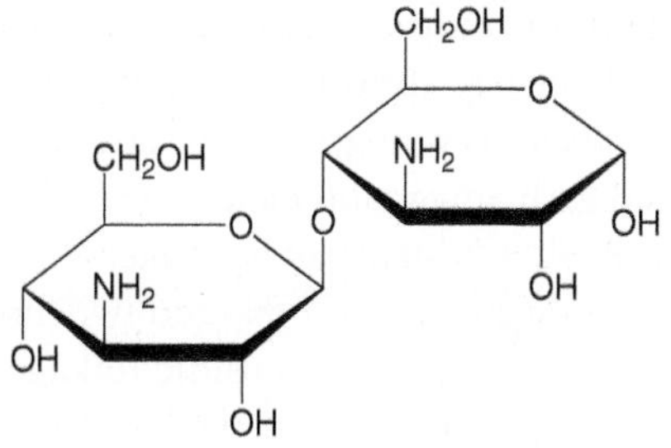

c)

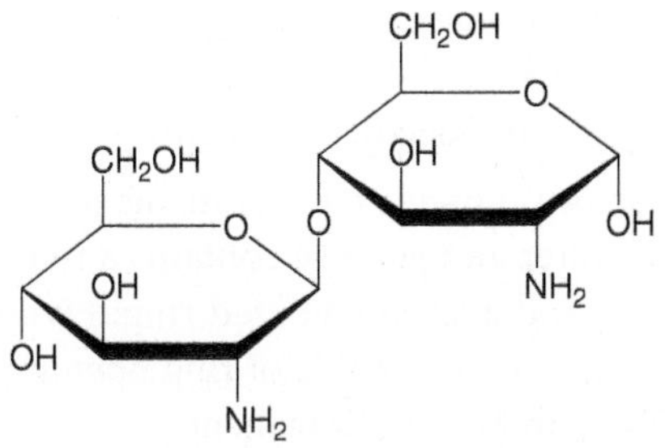

d)

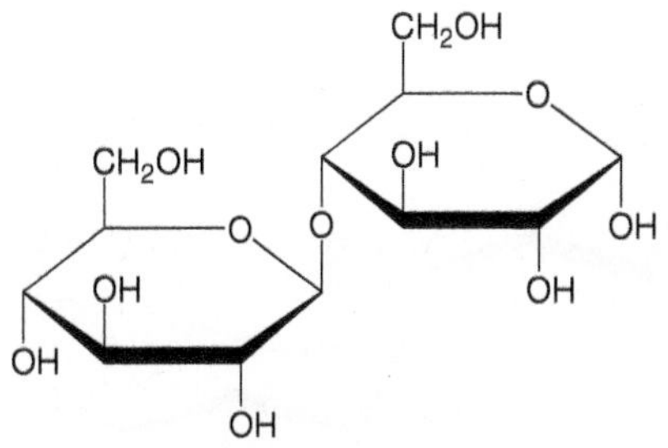

16.49 In addition to Fischer and Haworth projections, carbohydrates and carbohydrate-containing molecules are sometimes drawn in open-chain and cyclic forms using wedges and dashes to show stereochemistry. For example, the disaccharide xylobiose contains two xylose monomers connected by a β-1,4-glycosidic linkage as shown. Identify the correct products formed by the hydrolysis of the disaccharide xylobiose.

xylose acyclic form

xylose cyclic form

$+ \ H_2O$ $\xrightarrow{\text{chemical or enzyme hydrolysis}}$? + ?

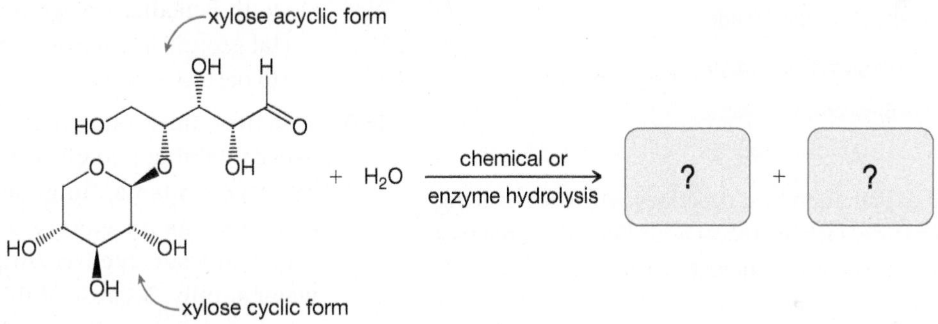

a)

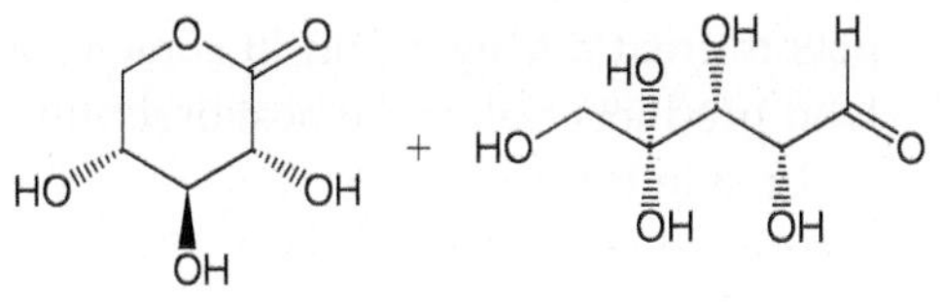

b)

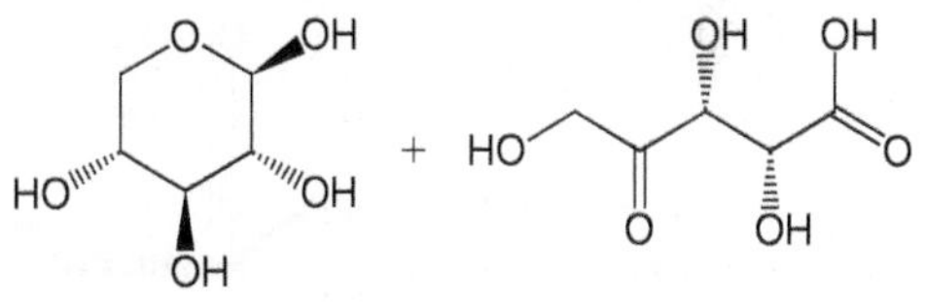

c)

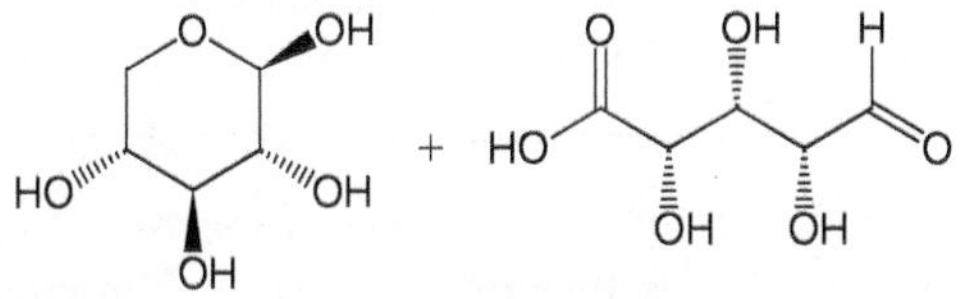

d)

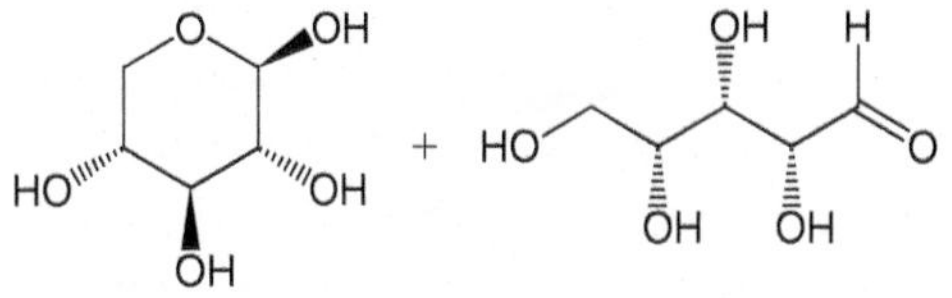

16.50 Lactulose is a non-absorbable disaccharide composed of galactose and fructose. It is designated by the World Health Organization (WHO) as an essential medicine for the treatment of hepatic encephalopathy (loss of brain function that occurs when liver damage prevents toxins from being properly filtered out of the blood) and chronic constipation. What is the correct designation for the glycosidic linkage in lactulose?

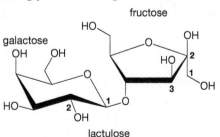

fructose

galactose

lactulose

a) α (1→4)-glycosidic linkage   b) α (1→5)-glycosidic linkage   c) β (1→5)-glycosidic linkage   d) β (1→4)-glycosidic linkage

16.51 Amygdalin is naturally occurring in many plants and seeds such as apricot, apple, peach, and plum. It is classified as a cyanogenic glycoside because when digested each amygdalin molecule contains a nitrile group ($R-C\equiv N$) that can be broken down into the toxic cyanide anion ($-C\equiv N$) and two molecules of glucose. What type of glycosidic linkage joins the two glucose molecules together in the amygdalin molecule?

amygdalin

a) α (1 → 4)-glycosidic linkage

b) α (1 → 6)-glycosidic linkage

c) β (1 → 6)-glycosidic linkage

d) β (1 → 4)-glycosidic linkage

16.52 Which explanation best describes why the reducing disaccharide, lactose, reacts with Benedict's reagent but the disaccharide, sucrose, does not?

a) Lactose contains two galactose units joined together, each of which can react with Benedict's reagent. Sucrose contains fructose, which is a ketose that cannot react with Benedict's reagent.

b) Lactose contains two identical glucose units joined together. Sucrose is a disaccharide containing a glucose and a fructose joined together. Disaccharides containing identical sugar units cannot ring open to form aldehydes and cannot react with Benedict's reagent.

c) Lactose contains two six-membered rings joined together and sucrose contains a five-membered ring and a six-membered ring. Five-membered rings are not capable of ring opening and reacting with Benedict's reagent.

d) Lactose contains a glycosidic linkage that leaves the anomeric carbon (C_1) of one monosaccharide unit free as a hemiacetal capable of ringing open to form an aldehyde that reacts with Benedict's reagent. There are no hemiacetal groups in sucrose to allow the same process to occur.

16.53 Trehalose (also known as mycose) is a disaccharide containing two glucose units that is produced by insects, plants, fungi, and bacteria. Trehalose can serve as an energy source and also helps organisms survive freezing temperatures or low water supply. Because of the water retention properties of trehalose, it is used in artificial tear products to treat dry eyes and in some cosmetics and food products. Select the best description of mutarotation in trehalose?

trehalose

a) The glycosidic linkage in trehalose involves C_1 of each glucose unit. As a result, ring opening and mutarotation is more difficult in trehalose than in monosaccharides or disaccharides that are not connected by C_1-C_1 linkages.

b) The glycosidic linkage in trehalose involves C_1 of each glucose unit. As a result, ring opening and mutarotation is especially easy in trehalose as compared to monosaccharides or disaccharides that are not connected by C_1—C_1 linkages.

c) Trehalose contains two glucose units connected by C_1—C_1 linkages. As a result, ring opening and mutarotation is especially important in trehalose which converts the D form to the L form of each sugar unit

16.6 Polysaccharides

LO 6: Recognize and draw the major structural features of polysaccharides.

16.54 Which term describes a carbohydrate that contains four or more monosaccharides joined together?

a) quaternary saccharide

b) multisaccharide

c) polysaccharide

d) polysugar

16.55 Match the name of each polysaccharide with the most appropriate function.

Answer choices: cellulose, glycogen, starch

Target boxes: polysaccharide in animals used for glucose storage, polysaccharide in plants used for structural support, polysaccharide in plants used for glucose storage

16.56 Which statement best describes cellulose?

a) Cellulose is an unbranched polysaccharide composed of repeating glucose units joined by β (1 → 4)-glycosidic linkages.

b) Cellulose is a branched polysaccharide composed of repeating glucose units joined by β (1 → 4)-glycosidic linkages.

c) Cellulose is an unbranched polysaccharide composed of repeating galactose units joined by β (1 → 4)-glycosidic linkages.

d) Cellulose is an unbranched trisaccharide composed of repeating glucose units joined by β (1 → 4)-glycosidic linkages.

16.57 Tomatine is a naturally occurring glycoalkaloid found in the stems and leaves of tomato plants. Tomatine is believed to have natural fungicidal, antimicrobial, and insecticidal properties and possibly some anticancer qualities. How many monosaccharide units are contained in a single molecule of tomatine?

a) There are four monosaccharide units per tomatine molecule.

b) There are five monosaccharide units per tomatine molecule.

c) There are seven monosaccharide units per tomatine molecule.

d) There is one monosaccharide unit per tomatine molecule.

16.58 Digoxin is a medicine used to treat heart failure and certain types of irregular heartbeats by affecting the levels of sodium (Na^+) and potassium (K^+) ions in heart muscle cells. What type of linkage connects the non-sugar portion of the drug to the sugar containing portion? How many monosaccharide units are contained in a single molecule of digoxin?

a) The linkage between the sugar and non-sugar portion of the drug is an alpha (α) linkage. There is only one monosaccharide unit per digoxin molecule.

b) The linkage between the sugar and non-sugar portion of the drug is a beta (β) linkage. There is only one monosaccharide unit per digoxin molecule.

c) The linkage between the sugar and non-sugar portion of the drug is beta (β) linkage. There are three monosaccharide units per digoxin molecule.

d) The linkage between the sugar and non-sugar portion of the drug is (D) linkage. There are three monosaccharide units per digoxin molecule.

16.59 Hyaluronic acid is a naturally occurring polysaccharide found in connective tissue, neural tissue, and fluids of the eyes and joints. It is administered by mouth or injection to treat osteoarthritis and other joint disorders. Hyaluronic acid contains "n" repeating units of two different monosaccharide molecules paired together by two different types of alternating glycosidic linkages. Examine the structure and determine which carbon atoms (by number) on each monosaccharide ring are used to form the different glycosidic linkages in hyaluronic acid.

a) Carbon # 1 and carbon # 3 are used in one monosaccharide unit.

Carbon # 1 and carbon # 2 are used in the other monosaccharide unit.

b) Carbon # 1 and carbon # 3 are used in one monosaccharide unit.

Carbon # 1 and carbon # 4 are used in the other monosaccharide unit

c) Carbon # 3 and carbon # 4 are used in one monosaccharide unit.

Carbon # 4 and carbon # 3 are used in the other monosaccharide unit.

d) Carbon # 2 and carbon # 4 are used in one r monosaccharide unit.

Carbon # 2 and carbon # 5 are used in the other monosaccharide unit.

16.60 Which statement correctly describes important similarities and differences between cellulose and amylopectin (each of which contain $(1 \rightarrow 4)$-glycosidic linkages)? It might be helpful to review the presentation of cellulose and amylopectin in the chapter.

a) Cellulose and amylopectin are both highly abundant polysaccharides that contain repeating units of glucose joined with $(1 \rightarrow 4)$-glycosidic linkages. The specific geometry of the linkages is different, however. Amylopectin contains α $(1 \rightarrow 4)$-glycosidic linkages, but cellulose contains β $(1 \rightarrow 4)$-glycosidic linkages. Fortunately, humans are able to digest both of these polysaccharides as energy sources.

b) Cellulose and amylopectin are both highly abundant polysaccharides that contain repeating units of glucose joined with $(1 \rightarrow 4)$-glycosidic linkages. The specific geometry of the linkages is different, however. Cellulose contains α $(1 \rightarrow 4)$-glycosidic linkages, but amylopectin contains β $(1 \rightarrow 4)$-glycosidic linkages, which humans cannot digest.

c) Cellulose and amylopectin are both highly abundant polysaccharides that contain repeating units of glucose joined with $(1 \rightarrow 4)$-glycosidic linkages. The specific geometry of the linkages is different, however. Amylopectin contains α $(1 \rightarrow 4)$-glycosidic linkages, but cellulose contains β $(1 \rightarrow 4)$-glycosidic linkages, which humans cannot digest.

16.61 Which statement correctly describes similarities and differences between amylopectin and glycogen? It might be helpful to review the presentation of amylopectin and glycogen in the chapter.

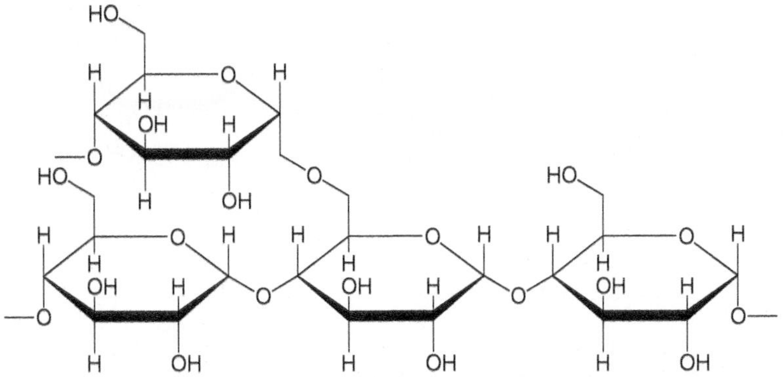

amylopectin

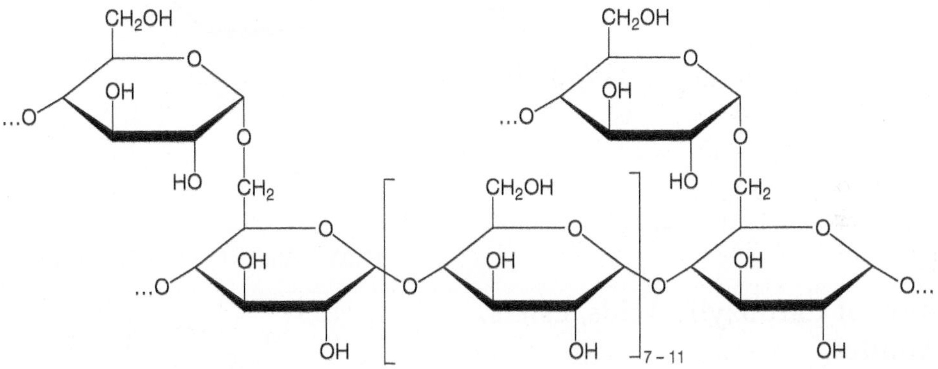

glycogen

a) Amylopectin and glycogen are both glucose-based polysaccharides containing both β $(1 \rightarrow 4)$-glycosidic linkages and β $(1 \rightarrow 6)$-branch points. Amylopectin is found in animals and glycogen is found in plants. Glycogen accounts for approximately 80% of starch, whereas amylopectin is stored in the liver and muscles. Glycogen is more branched and can be much larger than amylopectin.

b) Amylopectin and glycogen are both glucose-based polysaccharides containing α $(1 \rightarrow 4)$-glycosidic linkages and α $(1 \rightarrow 6)$-branch points. Amylopectin is found in plants and glycogen is found in animals. Amylopectin accounts for approximately 80% of starch, whereas glycogen is stored in the liver and muscles. Glycogen is more branched and can be much larger than amylopectin.

c) Amylopectin and glycogen are both glucose-based polysaccharides containing α $(1 \rightarrow 6)$-glycosidic linkages and α $(1 \rightarrow 4)$-branch points. Amylopectin is found in both plants and animals whereas glycogen is found in animals only. Amylopectin accounts for approximately 80% of starch, whereas glycogen is stored in the blood. Glycogen is less branched and is much larger than amylopectin.

16.62 Chondroitin sulfate A is a polysaccharide found in tendons and cartilage. It contains "n" repeating pairs of two different monosaccharide derivatives. What are the structures of the two repeating monosaccharide derivatives in the repeating pairs within chondroiton-6-sulfate?

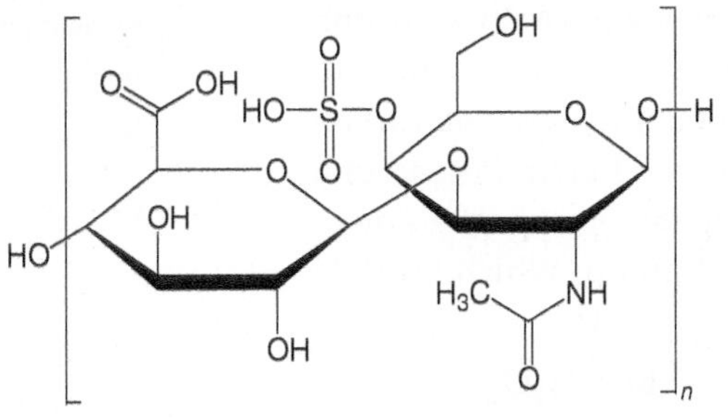

a)

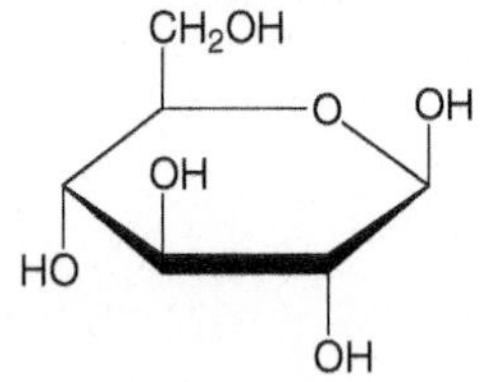

and

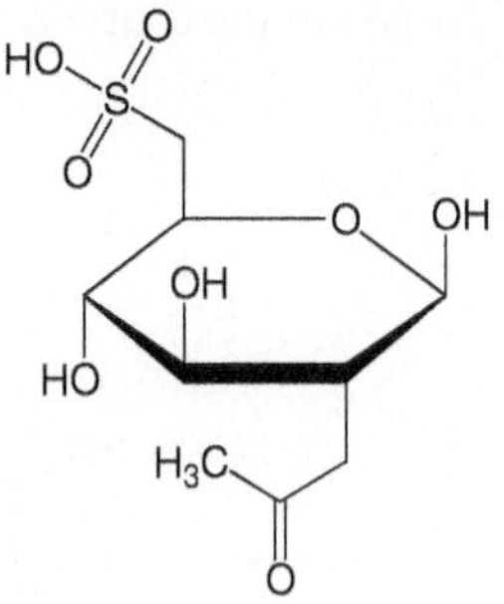

b)

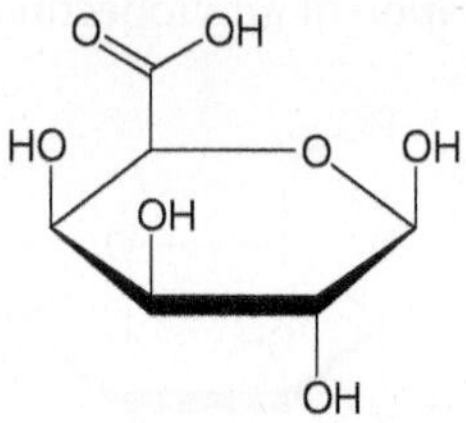

and

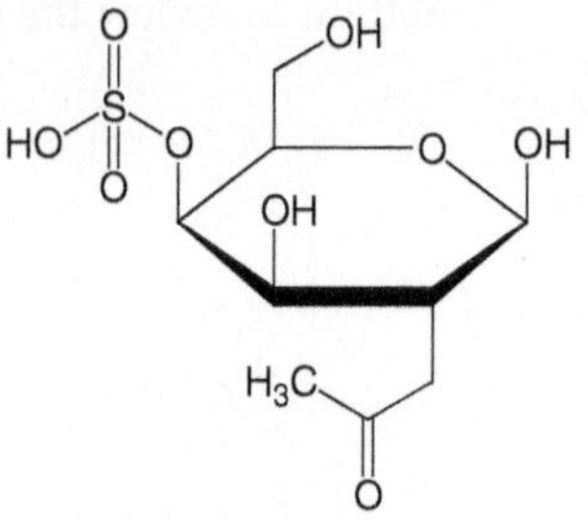

c)

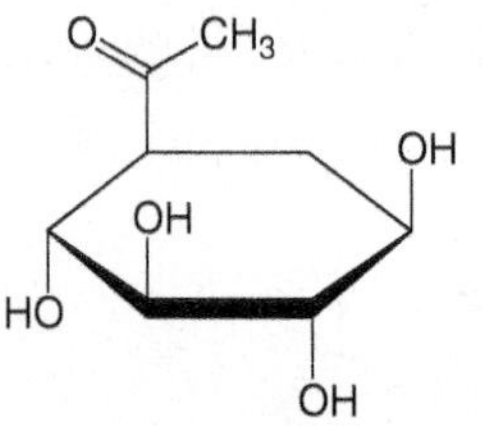

and

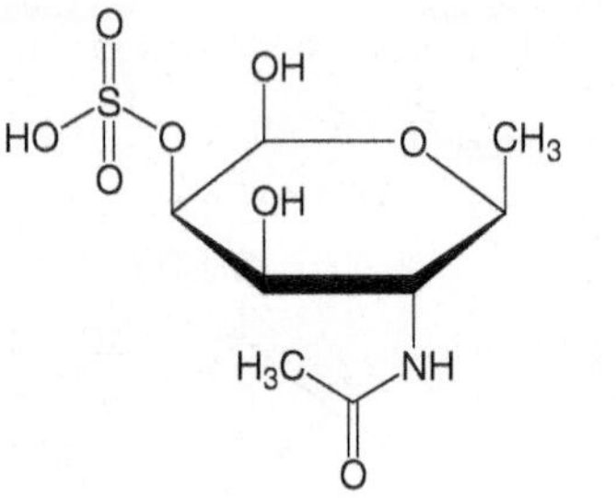

d)

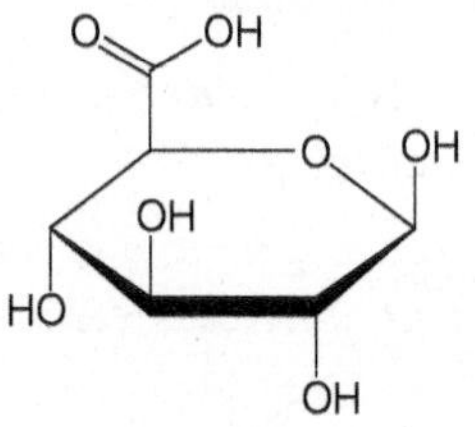

and

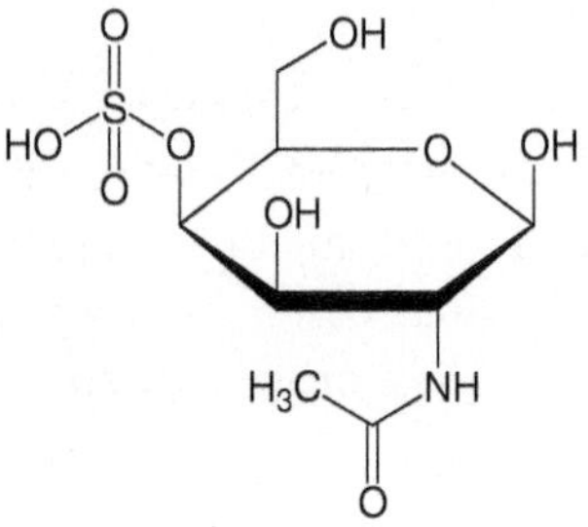

Chapter 17

17.1 Structure of Carboxylic Acids, Esters, and Amides

LO 1: Analyze the structural features of carbonyl-containing compounds: carboxylic acids, esters, and amides.

17.01 Which structure is a correctly drawn carboxylic acid?

a)

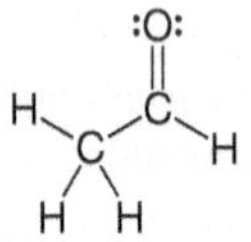

b)

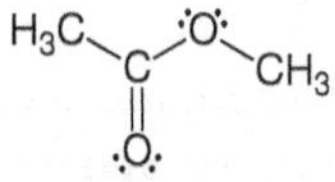

c)

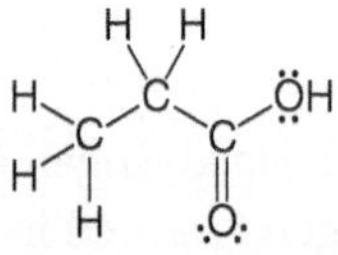

d)

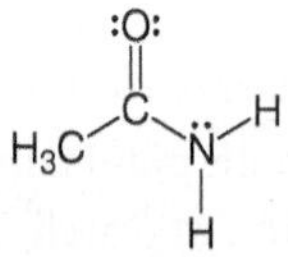

e)

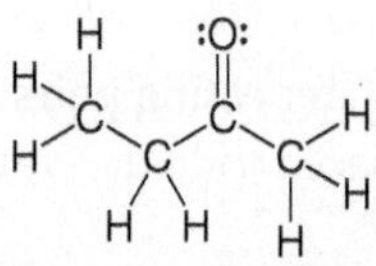

17.02 Methanoic acid (formic acid) is a naturally occurring acid found in stinging red ant venom. It is the simplest carboxylic acid, containing only one carbon atom. Methanoic acid has an H atom instead of a carbon-containing R group on the opposite side of the carbonyl from the OH group. Which formula correctly identifies methanoic acid?

a) CH_3OH

b) CH_2O_2

c) $C_2H_4O_2$

d) CH_2O

17.03 Which structure is a correctly drawn ester?

a)

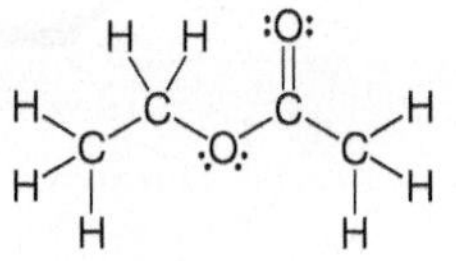

b)

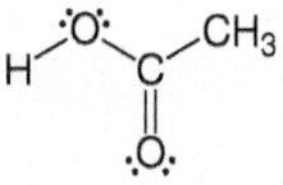

c)

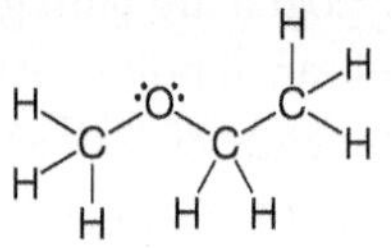

d)

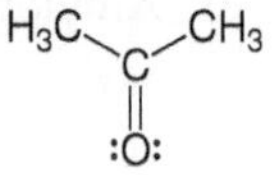

17.04 Which of the following is *not* a correctly drawn amide?

a)

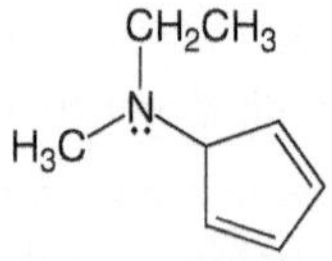

b)

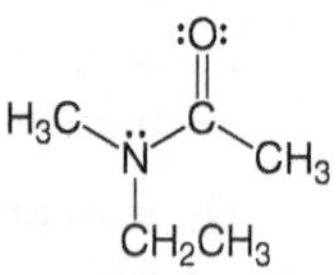

c)

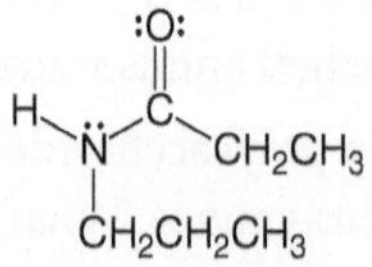

d)

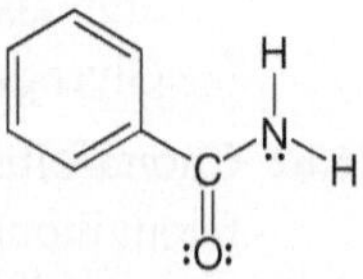

17.05 Sort the following molecules into a group that contains a carboxylic acid group and a group that does *not* contain a carboxylic acid group.

Answer choices:

a)

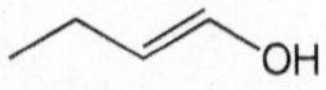

b)

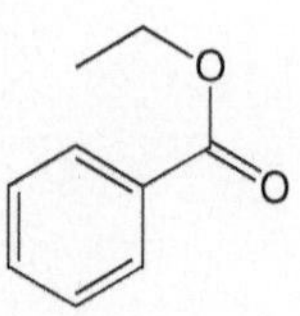

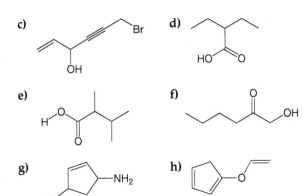

c) d)

e) f)

g) h)

Target choices: contains a carboxylic acid group, does not contain a carboxylic acid group

17.06 Sort the following molecules into a group that contains an ester group and a group that does *not* contain an ester group.

Answer choices:

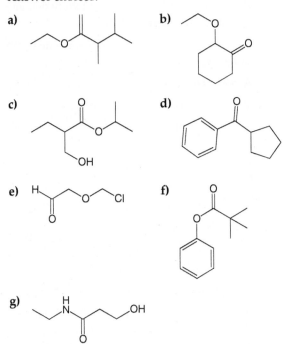

a) b)

c) d)

e) f)

g)

Target boxes: contains an ester group, does not contain an ester group

17.07 Sort the following molecules into a group that contains an amide group and a group that does *not* contain an amide group.

Answer choices:

a) 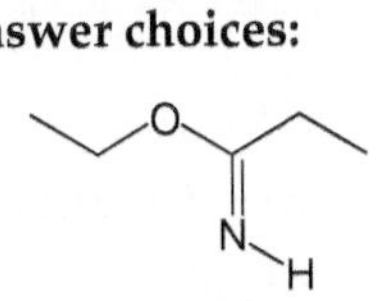 b)

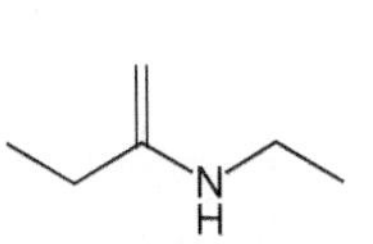

c) 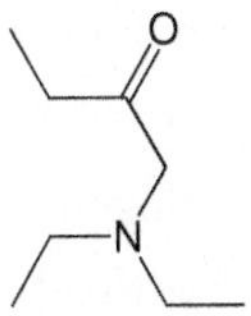 d)

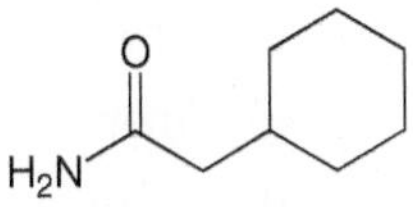

e) 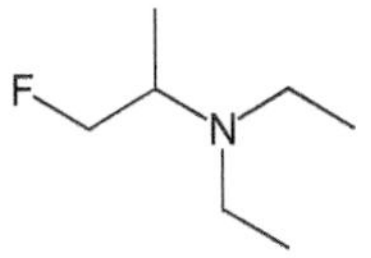 f)

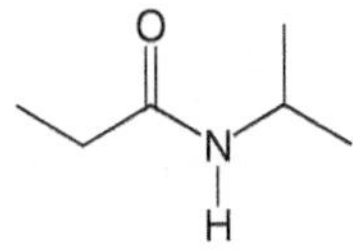

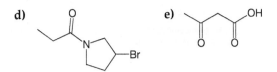

g) 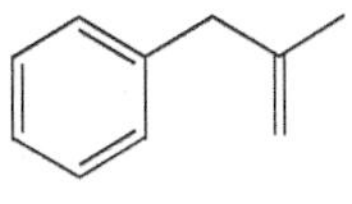 h)

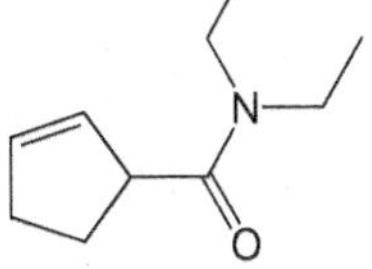

Target boxes: contains an amide group, does not contain an amide group

17.08 Sort the following molecules into the appropriate category.

Answer choices:

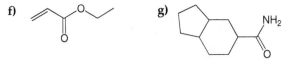

a) 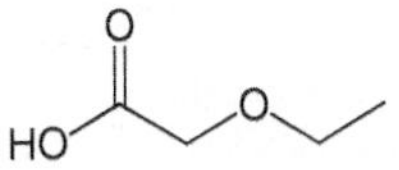 b)

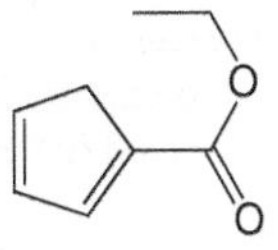

c)

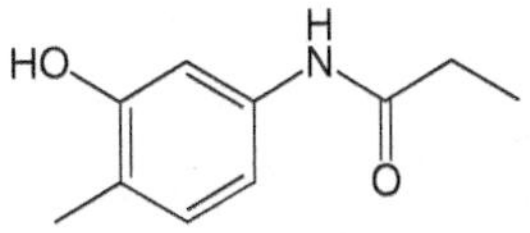

d) e)

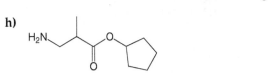

f) g)

h)

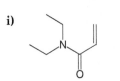

i)

Target boxes: amide, ester, carboxylic acid

17.09 Drawing an amide: Use the drawing tool to build the *skeletal structure* of an acyclic (non-cyclic) three carbon primary amide. For this exercise, do not draw the lone pairs of electrons on oxygen or nitrogen, but do include any hydrogen atoms bonded to nitrogen.

17.10 Drawing an ester: Use the drawing tool to build the *skeletal structure* of an acyclic (non-cyclic) ester having an ethyl ($-CH_2CH_3$) bonded to the carbonyl group and an ethyl bonded to oxygen as the OR′ group. The molecule should have a total of five carbon atoms. For this exercise, do not draw the lone pairs of electrons on oxygen.

17.11 Sort the following molecules into the appropriate category.

Answer choices:

a)

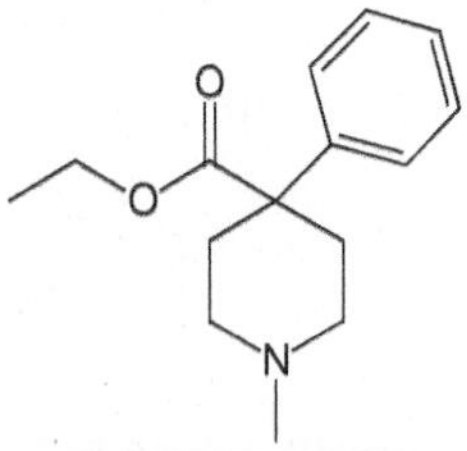

pethidine (Demerol): a
synthetic opioid pain killer

b)

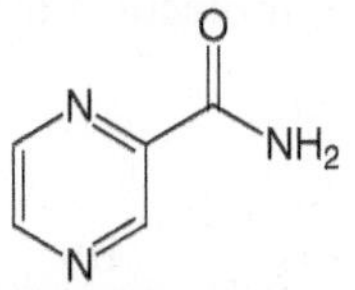

pyrazinamide (Rifater): a medication
used to help treat tuberculosis (TB)

c)

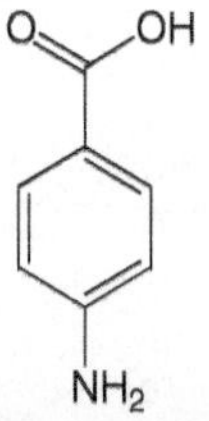

4-aminobenzoate:
involved in metabolism

d)

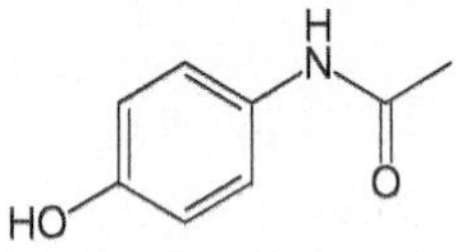

bupivacaine (Marcaine):
used to numb an area of
the body during surgery,
childbirth, and dental
procedures

e)

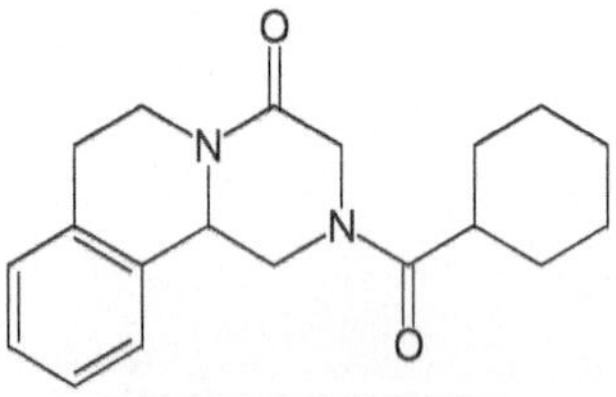

praziquantel (Biltricide): a
medication used to treat
parasitic worm infections

Target boxes: ester, amide, carboxylic acid

17.12 Sort the following molecules into the appropriate category.

a)

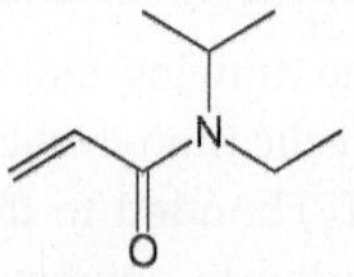

b)

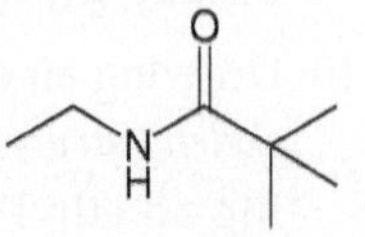

c) H₂N

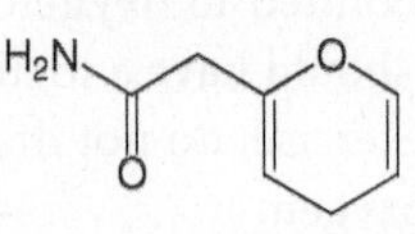

d) Br

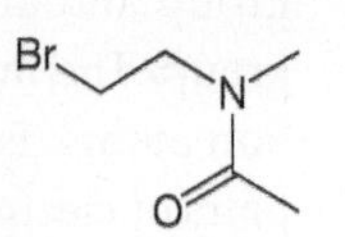

e)

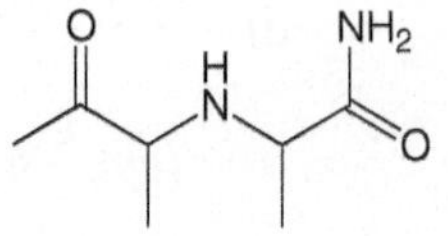

f)

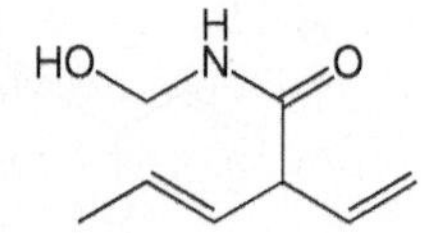

Target boxes: primary (1°) amide, secondary (2°) amide, tertiary (3°) amide

17.13 Which statement about amides is true?

a) Primary (1°) amides contain one H atom on N and have two C—N bonds.

b) Tertiary (3°) amides contain three H atoms and three C—N bonds.

c) Primary (1°) amides contain one C—N bond and one H atom on N.

d) Secondary (2°) amides contain one H atom on N and two C—N bonds.

e) Tertiary (3°) amides contain three N atoms and no C—N bonds.

f) Secondary (2°) amides contain two N atoms and two H atoms on each N.

17.14 Sort the following molecules into the appropriate category.

Answer choices:

a) **b)**

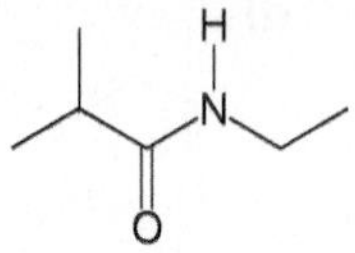

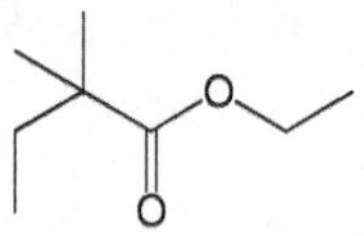

c) 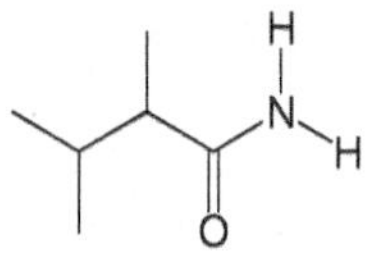 **d)**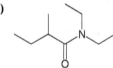

Target boxes: primary (1°) amide, secondary (2°) amide, tertiary (3°) amide, ester

17.15 Zolpidem, also known as Ambien, is a sedative commonly used to help people that have difficulty sleeping (insomnia). Which groups are found on the zolpidem molecule? Select all that apply.

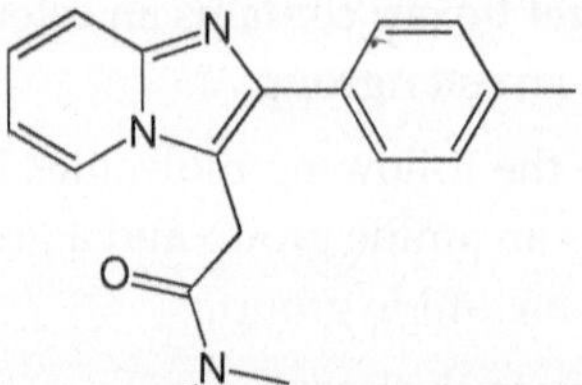

zolpidem

a) ester   b) primary (1°) amide

c) carboxylic acid   d) alkyne

e) secondary (2°) amide   f) aromatic ring

g) ether   h) tertiary (3°) amide

i) cyclohexane ring   j) halogen

k) thioether   l) hydroxyl

17.16 Levothyroxine is a medication used to help treat thyroid hormone deficiency. Which groups are found on the Levothyroxine molecule? Select all that apply.

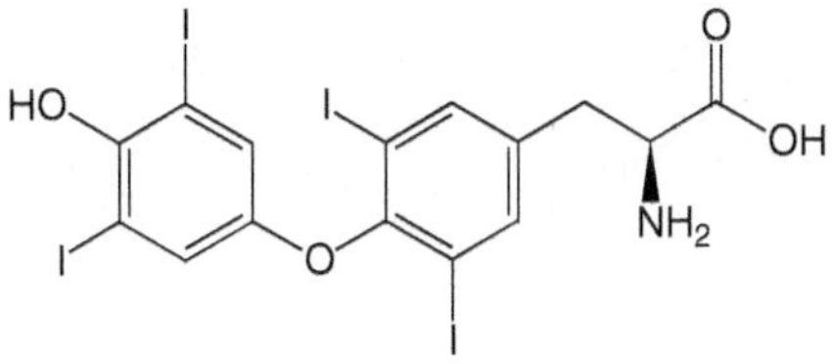

levothyroxine

a) amide

b) ester

c) carboxylic acid

d) thiol

e) hydroxyl

f) alkyne

g) ether

h) halogen

i) cyclohexane ring

j) aromatic ring

17.17 Lisinopril is a commonly prescribed medication used to help treat high blood pressure and heart failure. Which groups are found on the lisinopril molecule? Select all that apply.

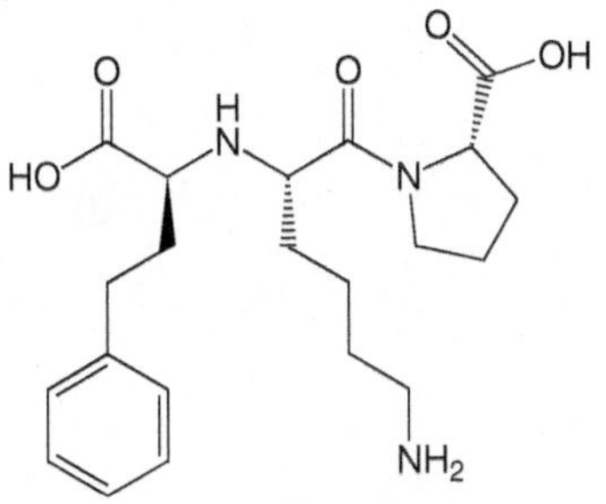

lisinopril

a) halogen

b) aromatic ring

c) ester

d) alkyne

e) carboxylic acid

f) ether

g) amide

17.18 Cefotaxime is an antibiotic used to treat bacterial infections including meningitis, pneumonia, sepsis, gonorrhea, and urinary tract infections. Which groups are present on the cefotaxime molecule? Select all that apply.

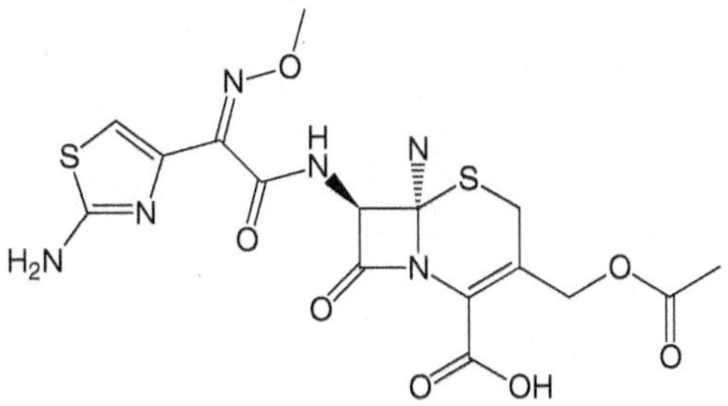

cefotaxime

a) ester

b) carboxylic acid

c) thiol

d) alkyne

e) thioether

f) alkene

g) halogen

h) amide

17.2 Physical Properties

LO 2: **Analyze the effect of intermolecular forces on the physical properties of carboxylic acids, esters, and amides.**

17.19 Identify the molecule in each pair with the higher boiling point.

A. 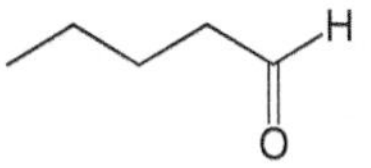 or

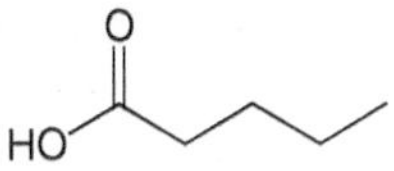

B. 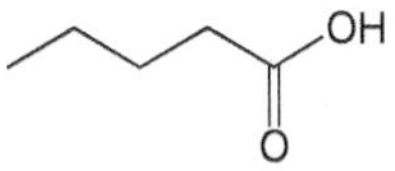 or

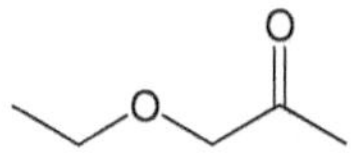

C. 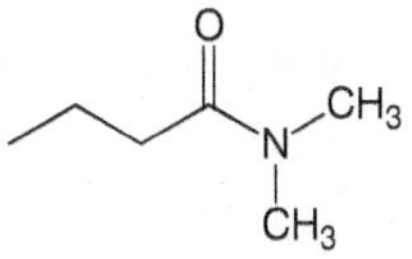 or

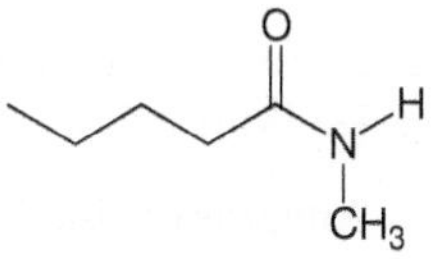

17.20 Identify the molecule in each pair with the higher boiling point.

A. 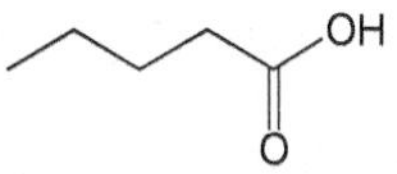 or

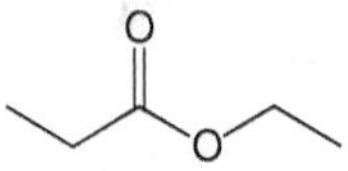

B. 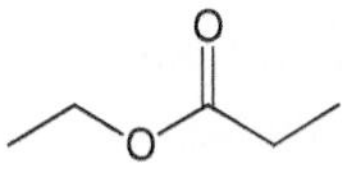 or

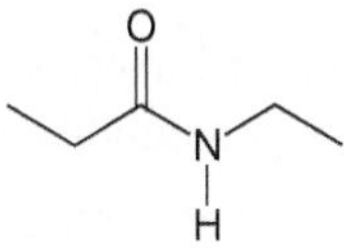

C. 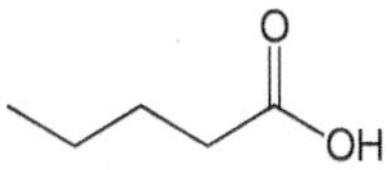 or

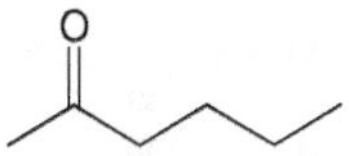

17.21 Identify the molecule in each pair with the greatest solubility in water.

A. 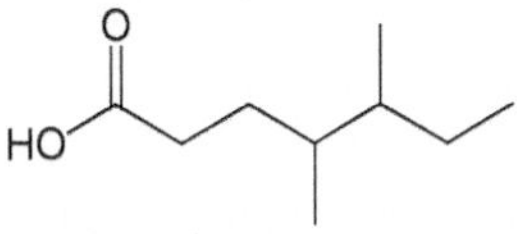 or

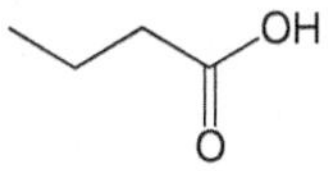

B. 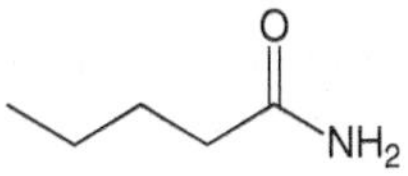 or

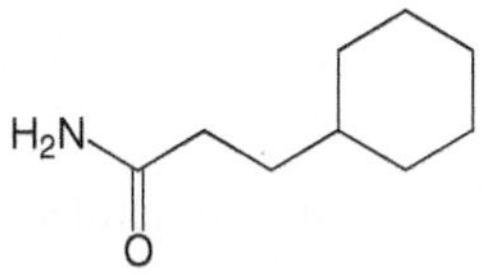

C. 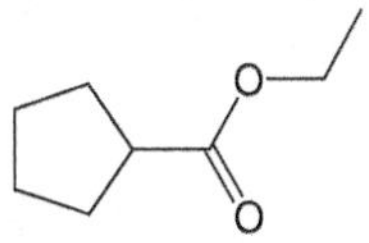 or

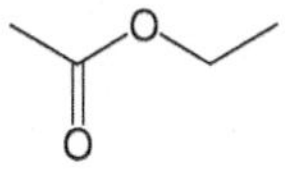

17.22 Identify the molecule in each pair with the greatest solubility in water.

A.  or

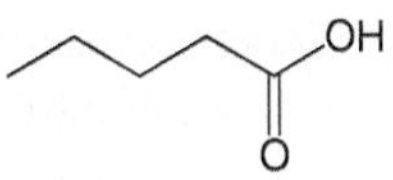

B. 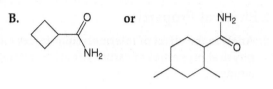 or

C. ![structure] or ![structure with OH]

D. ![structure] or ![structure]

17.23 Arrange the molecules in order of increasing water solubility.

Answer choices:

a) ![structure]   b) ![HO structure]

c) ![structure]

Target boxes: lowest water solubility, intermediate water solubility, highest water solubility

17.24 Arrange the molecules in order of increasing water solubility

Answer choices:

a) ![structure]   b) ![structure]

c) ![structure]

Target boxes: lowest water solubility, intermediate water solubility, highest water solubility

17.25 Arrange the molecules in order of increasing water solubility.

Answer choices:

a) ![structure]   b) ![H structure OH]

c) ![structure OH]

Target boxes: lowest water solubility, intermediate water solubility, highest water solubility

17.26 Which of the amide molecules shown are able to hydrogen bond with another identical molecule?

Answer choices:

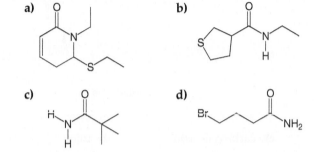

Target boxes: *can* form hydrogen bonds with other identical molecules, *cannot* form hydrogen bonds with other identical molecules

17.27 Which of the amide molecules shown are able to hydrogen bond with another identical molecule?

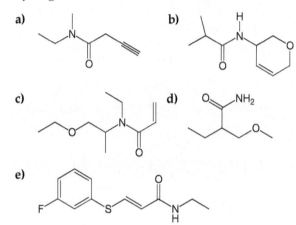

Target boxes: *can* form hydrogen bonds with other identical molecules, *cannot* form hydrogen bonds with other identical molecules

17.28 Which of the molecules shown are soluble in water?

Answer choices:

a) ![structure]   b) ![structure OH]

c) ![structure OH]   d) ![structure NH₂]

e) ![structure OH]

f) ![HO structure N-H]

Target boxes: soluble in water, not soluble (insoluble) in water

17.29 Which of the molecules shown are soluble in water?

Answer choices:

a)

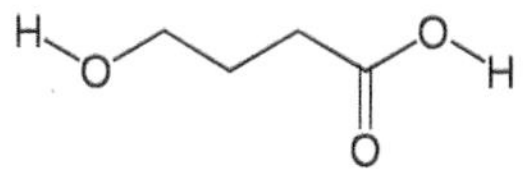

b)

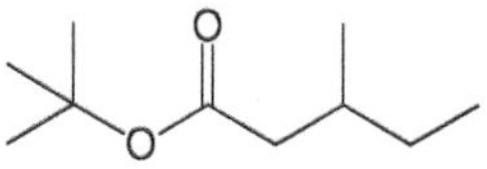

c)

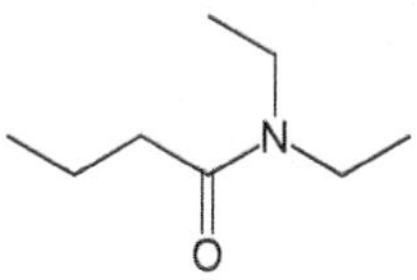

d)

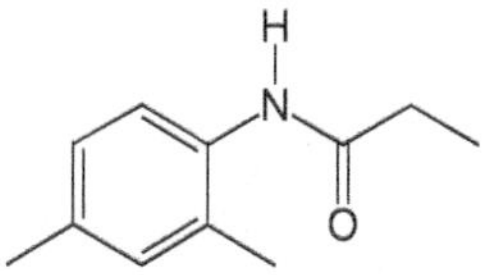

e)

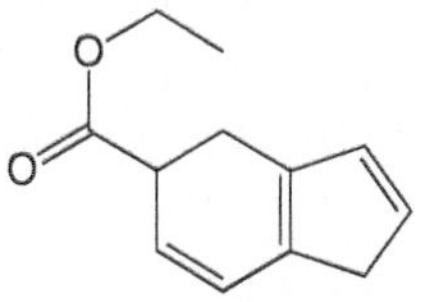

f)

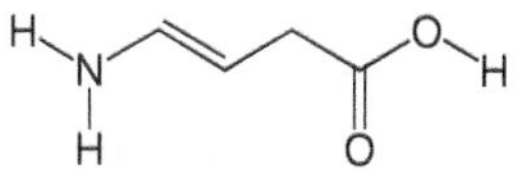

g)

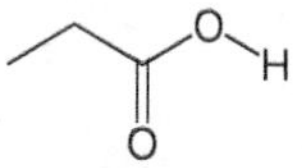

Target boxes: soluble in water, not soluble (insoluble) in water

17.30 Which diagram correctly shows an ester hydrogen bonding with water?

a)

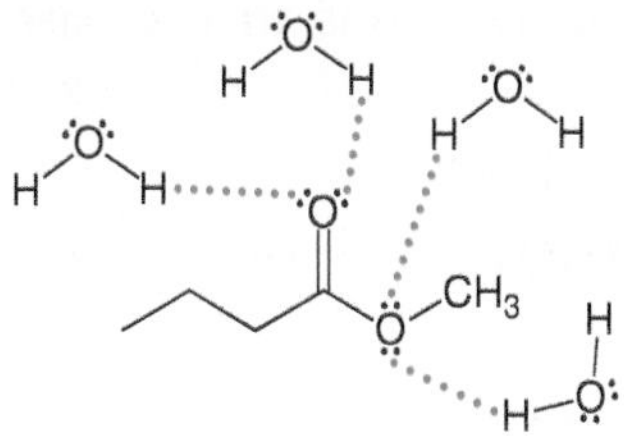

b)

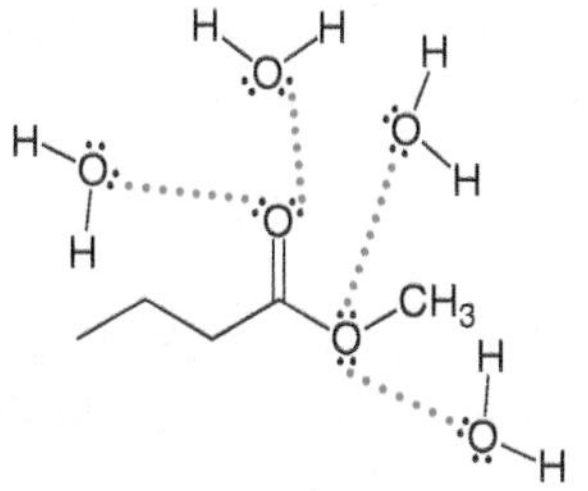

c)

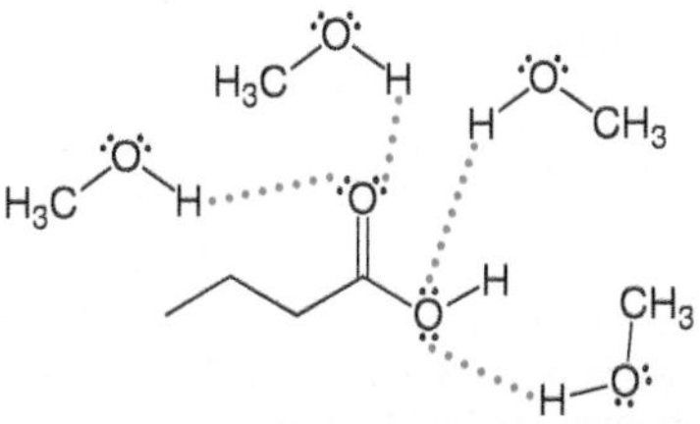

d)

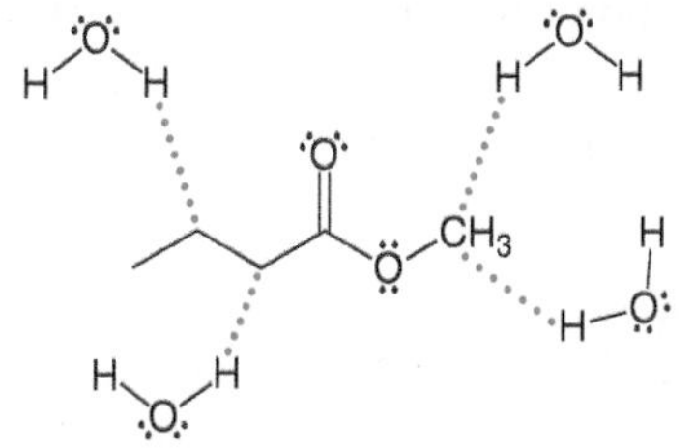

17.3 The Acidic Properties of Carboxylic Acids

LO 3: Evaluate reactions of carboxylic acids with bases.

17.31 Which phrase best describes this molecule?

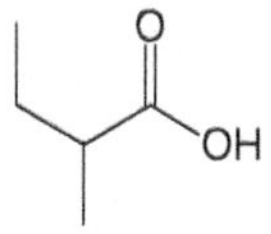

a) weak base
b) strong base
c) weak acid
d) strong acid

17.32 Which of the following diagrams of a molecule is a correctly drawn carboxylate *salt*?

a)

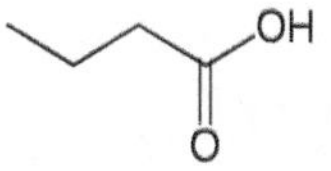

b)

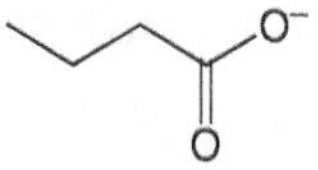

c)

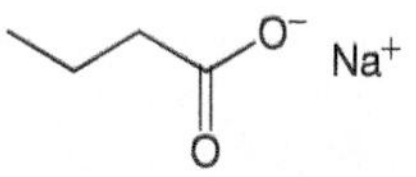

d)

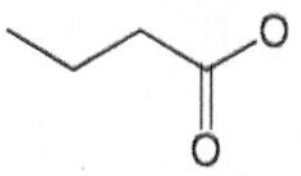

17.33 When a carboxylic acid is dissolved in water, equilibrium favors_____.

a) the starting material carboxylic acid

b) formation of the carboxylate anion

c) the starting material carboxylic acid and carboxylate anion product equally

d) neither the starting material carboxylic acid nor the carboxylate anion product

17.34 The acid dissociation constant (K_a) for the carboxylic acid depicted below is 10^{-5}. Which molecule(s) is favored at equilibrium?

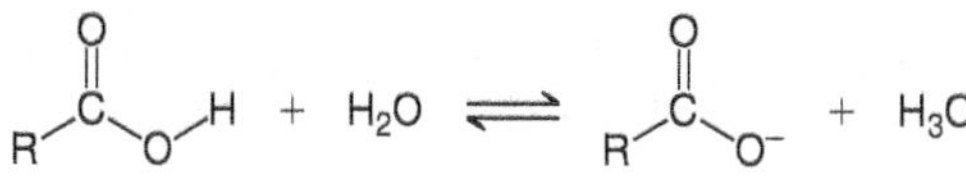

$$R-C(=O)-O-H + H_2O \rightleftharpoons R-C(=O)-O^- + H_3O^+$$

a) Both $R-C(=O)-O-H$ and $R-C(=O)-O^-$ are equally favored at equilibrium.

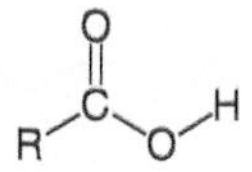

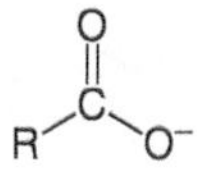

b) Neither $R-C(=O)-O-H$ nor $R-C(=O)-O^-$ is favored at equilibrium.

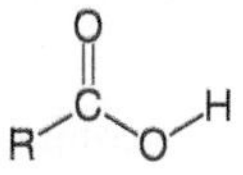

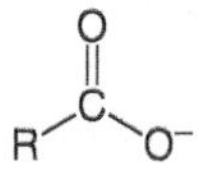

c) 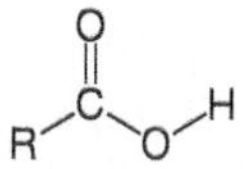 $R-C(=O)-O-H$ is favored.   d) 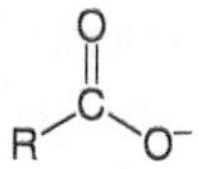 $R-C(=O)-O^-$ is favored.

17.35 Which reaction correctly shows a carboxylic acid reacting with KOH?

a)

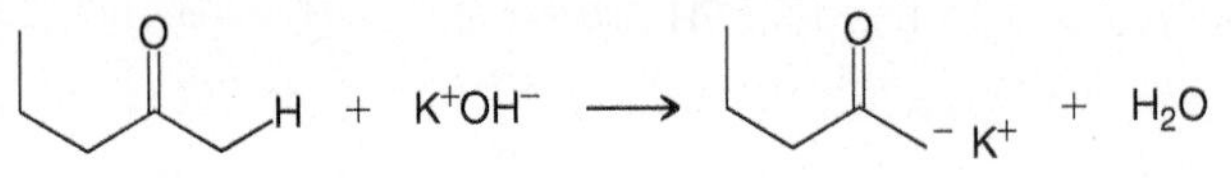

b)

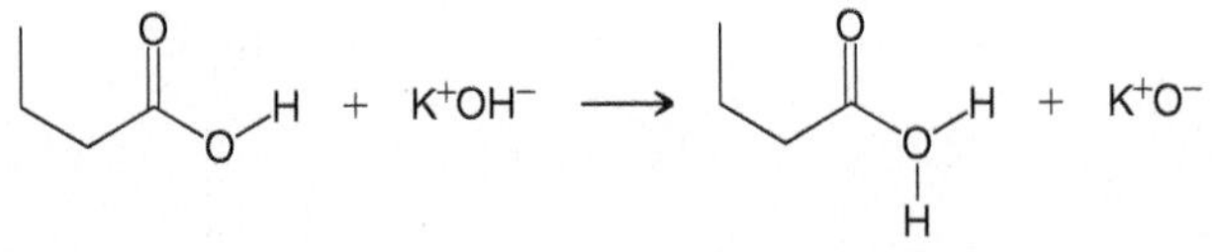

c)

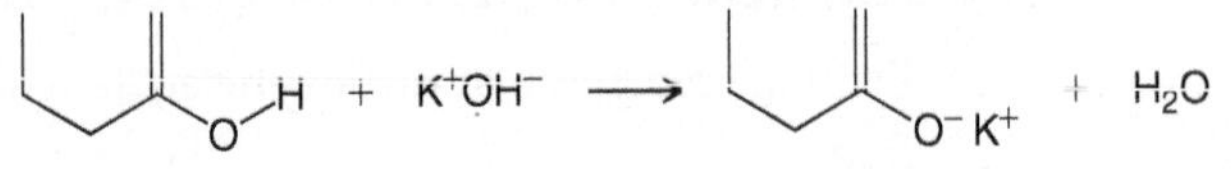

d)

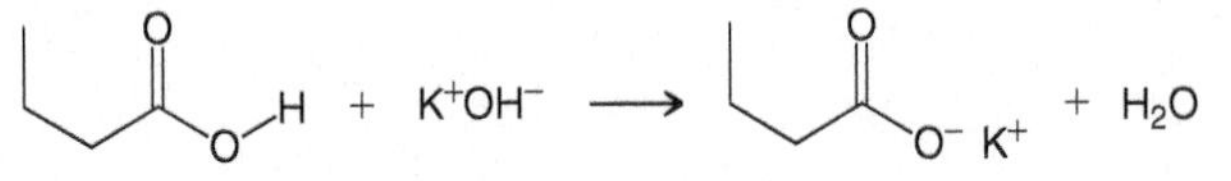

17.36 Construct a reaction that forms a carboxylate salt by dragging the appropriate pieces into the shaded boxes.

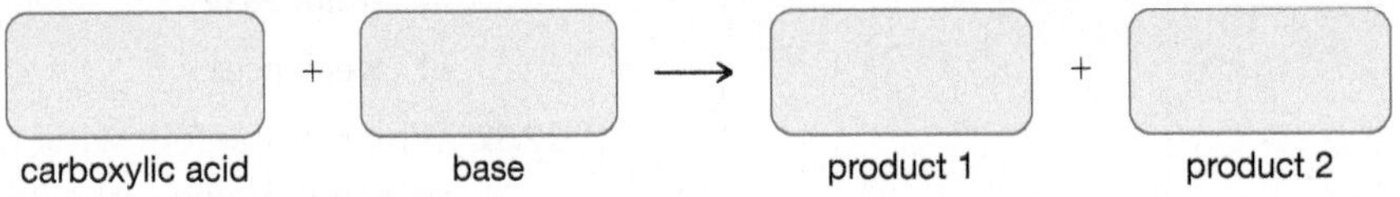

| carboxylic acid | base | product 1 | product 2 |

Answer choices:

a)

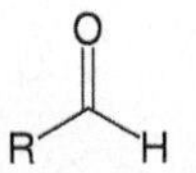

b) H_3O^+

c)

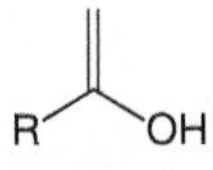

d) HCl

e)

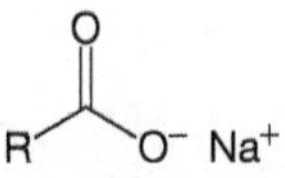

f)

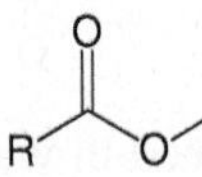

g) H_2O

h)

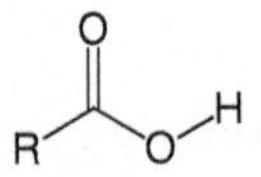

i) $Na^+ OH^-$

j)

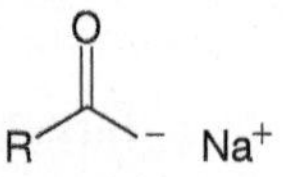

Target boxes: carboxylic acid, base, product 1, product 2

17.37 Identify the soap molecule.

a)

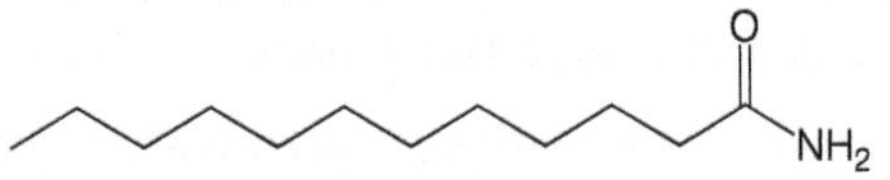

b)

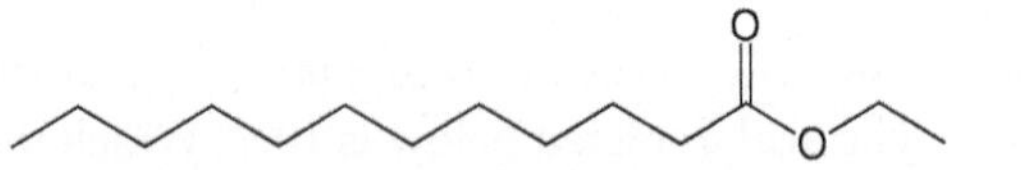

c)

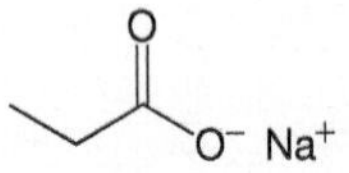

d)

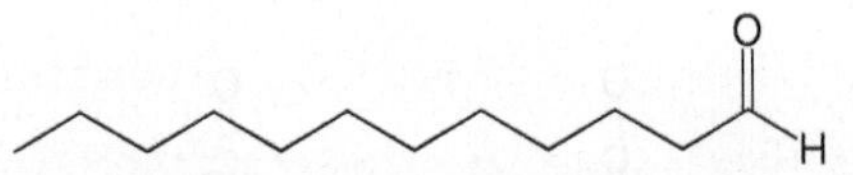

e)

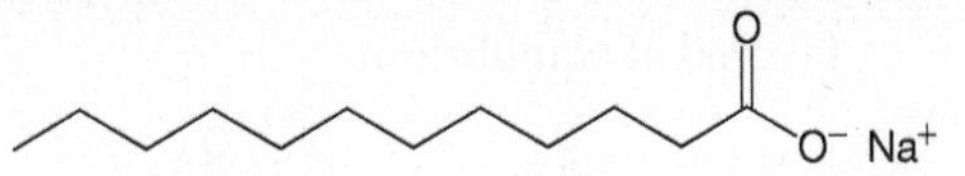

17.38 Which set of molecules is a conjugate acid-base pair?

a) HCl and NaOH

b) H_2O and CH_3OH

c) CH_3CO_2H and $CH_3CO_2^-$

d) CO_2 and CO_3^-

17.39 Which set of molecules is an acid-base conjugate pair?

a) HNO_3 and H_2SO_4

b) H_2O and H_2O_2

c) H_2SO_4 and H_3PO_4

d) HCO_2H and HCO_2^-

17.40 When a carboxylic acid reacts with sodium hydroxide to form a carboxylate salt, what other product is formed?

a) HCl

b) H_2O

c) CO_2

d) OH^-

17.41 Match the structure of each molecule shown with the appropriate description.

Answer choices:

a)

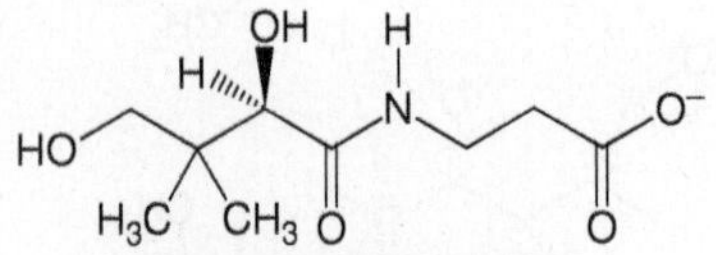

vitamin B_5: an essential human nutrient found in both plants and animals

b)

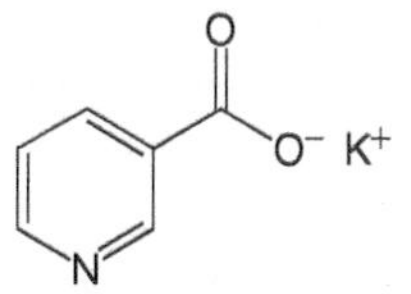

niacin: an essential
human nutrient found in
both plants and animals

c)

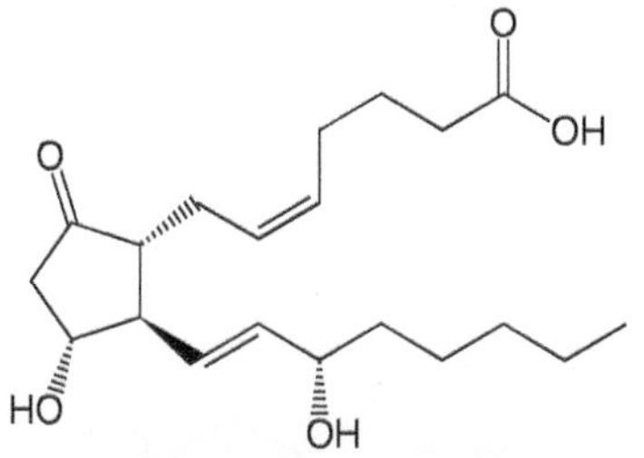

prostaglandin E₂: a naturally
occurring molecule important to
the labor and birthing process

Target boxes: carboxylic acid, carboxylate anion, carboxylate salt

17.42 Lactic acid is produced in your body during metabolism and exercise. What is the product of the reaction shown?

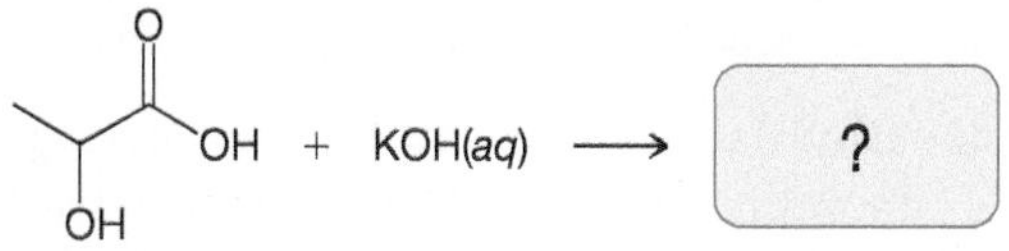

lactic acid

a)

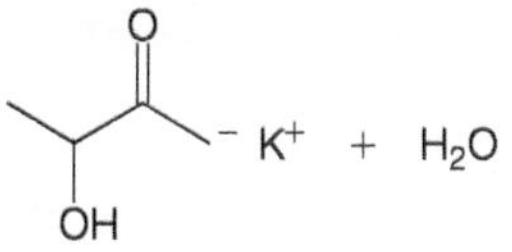

b)

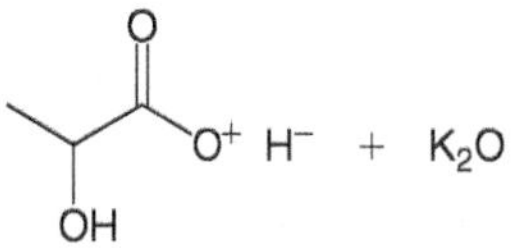

c)

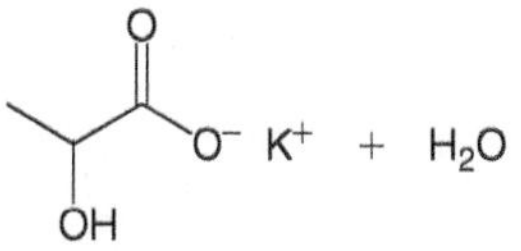

d)

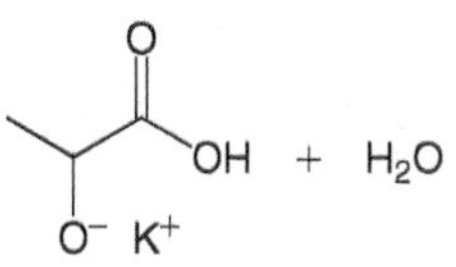

17.43 Methotrexate (MTX) is a medicine used to treat a number of cancers and autoimmune diseases including rheumatoid arthritis, psoriasis, and Crohn's disease. Which statement about the methotrexate molecule is correct?

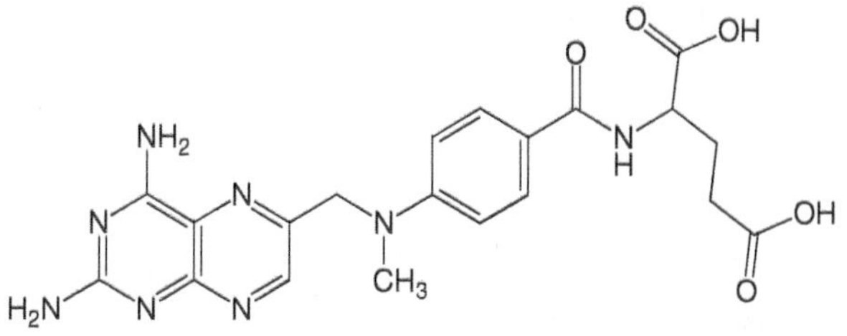

methotrexate (MTX)

a) Methotrexate has two acidic hydrogens and one amide group.

b) Methotrexate has six acidic hydrogens and two amide groups.

c) Methotrexate has three acidic hydrogens and four amide groups.

d) Methotrexate has two acidic hydrogens and three amide groups.

17.44 EDTA is a chemical that binds tightly to metals and minerals such as lead, mercury, chromium, copper, calcium, and iron. It is used as a medication to treat lead poisoning. EDTA is also used for reducing calcium levels in people suffering from hypercalcemia, often a result of overactive parathyroid glands. Which statement about the methotrexate molecule is correct?

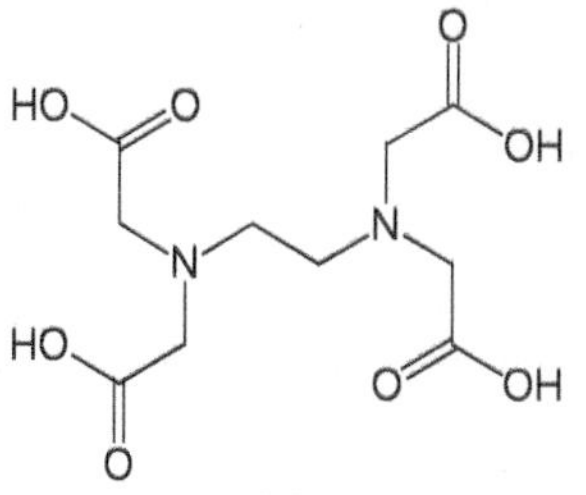

EDTA

a) EDTA has four acidic hydrogens and two amide groups.

b) EDTA has four acidic hydrogens and four ester groups.

c) EDTA has no acidic hydrogens and four amide groups.

d) EDTA has four acidic hydrogens and no amide groups.

17.4 Reactions of Carboxylic Acids, Esters, and Amides

LO 4: **Analyze reactions of carboxylic acids, esters, and amides.**

17.45 In the following reaction, identify the missing product?

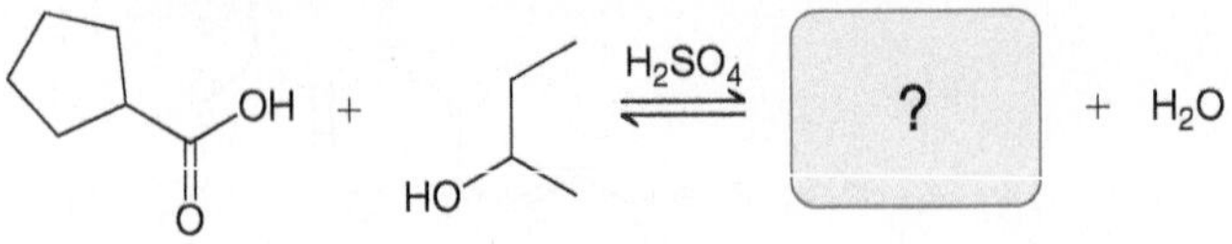

a)

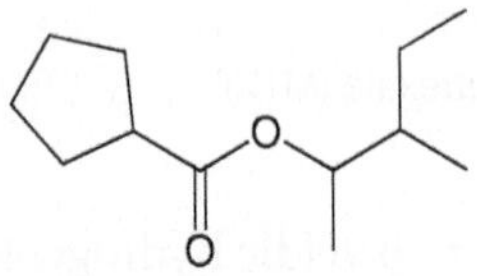

b)

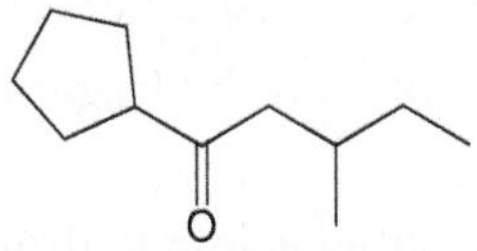

c)

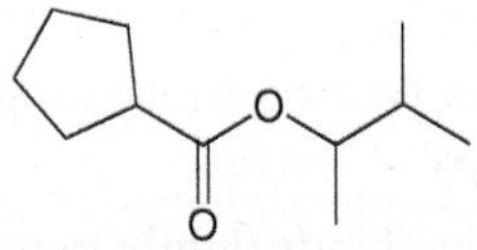

d)

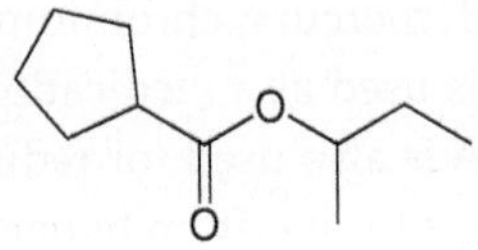

17.46 In the following reaction, identify the missing starting materials.

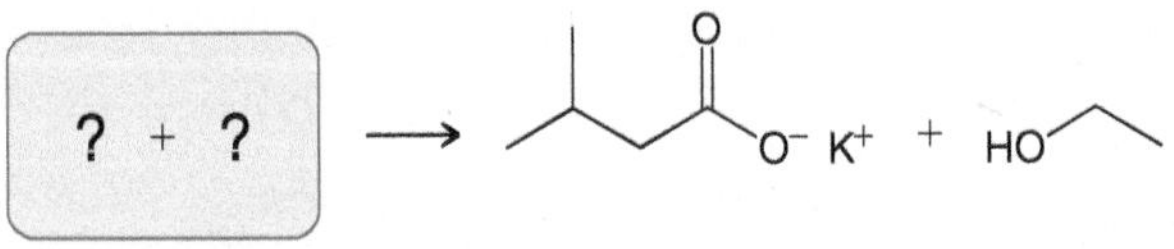

a)

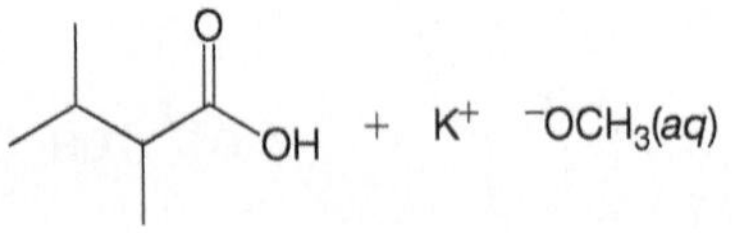

b)

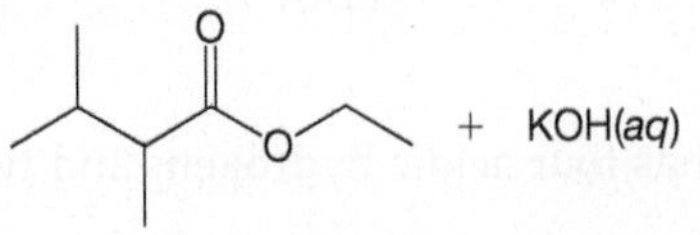

c)

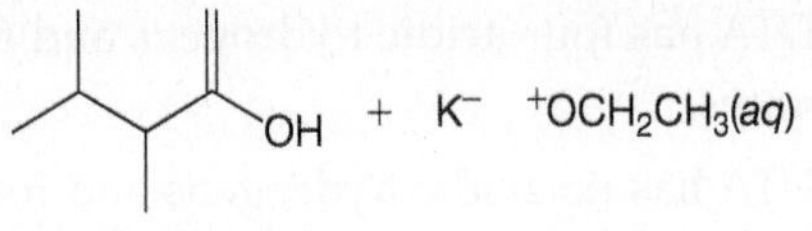

d)

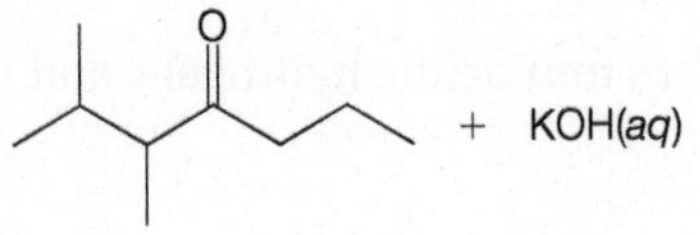

17.47 Benzyl benzoate, also known as Scabanca, is an insect repellent and medication used to treat lice. Identify the products of the reaction shown?

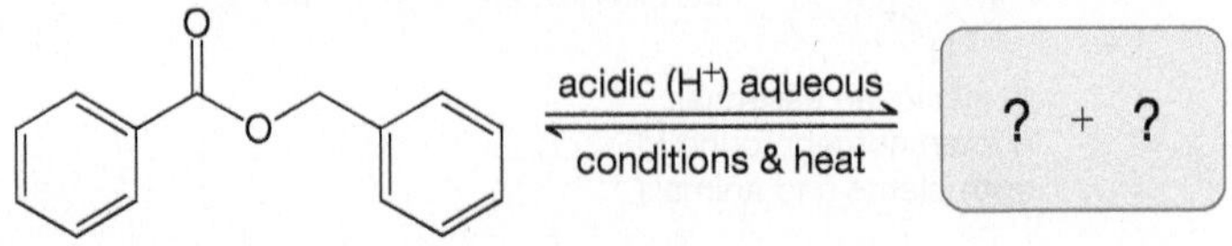

a)

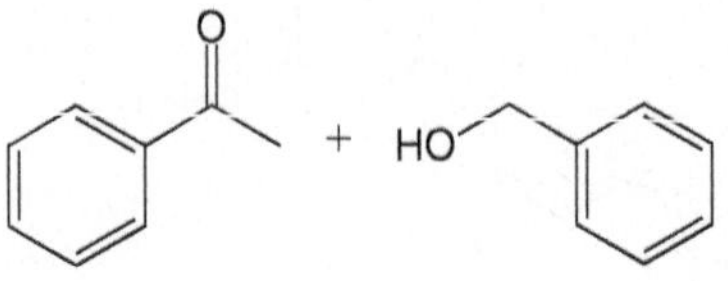

b)

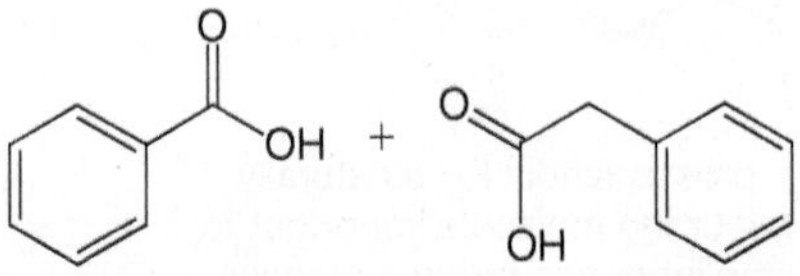

c)

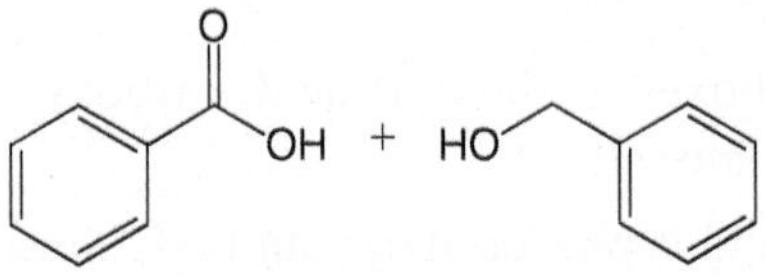

d)

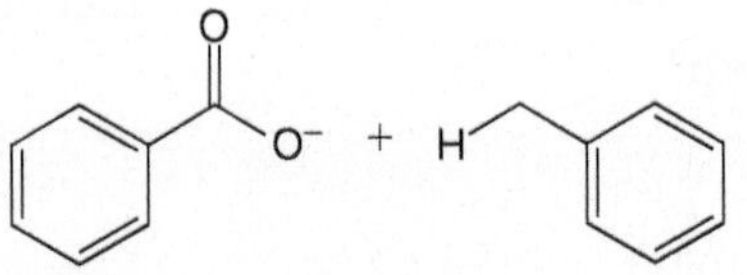

17.48 Ethyl lactate is a naturally occurring substance found in a variety of foods such as fruits, chicken, and wine. It is also used industrially in pharmaceutical preparations, food additives, and fragrances. Identify the products formed when ethyl lactate undergoes this ester hydrolysis reaction.

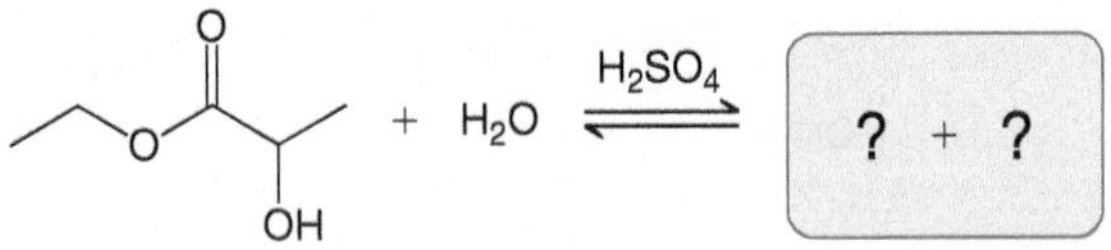

a)

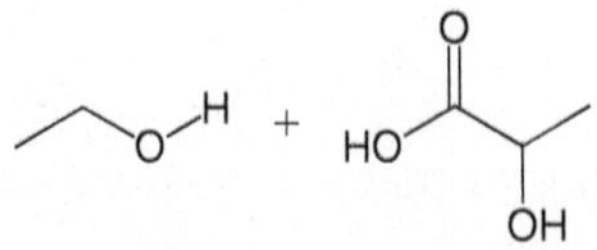

b)

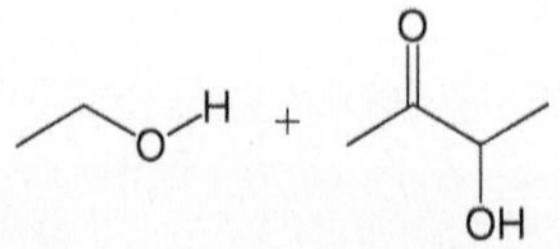

c)

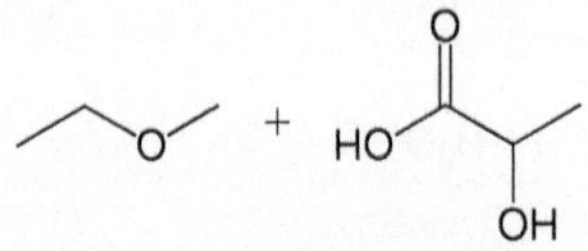

d)

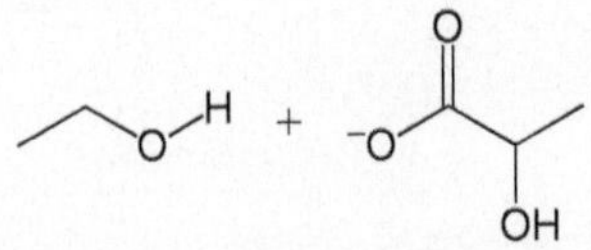

17.49 2-ethylhexyl salicylate, also known as octyl salicylate, is used in sunscreens and cosmetics to help absorb ultraviolet (UVB) rays that damage skin. Which reaction conditions are needed for an ester hydrolysis reaction of 2-ethylhexyl salicylate under basic conditions?

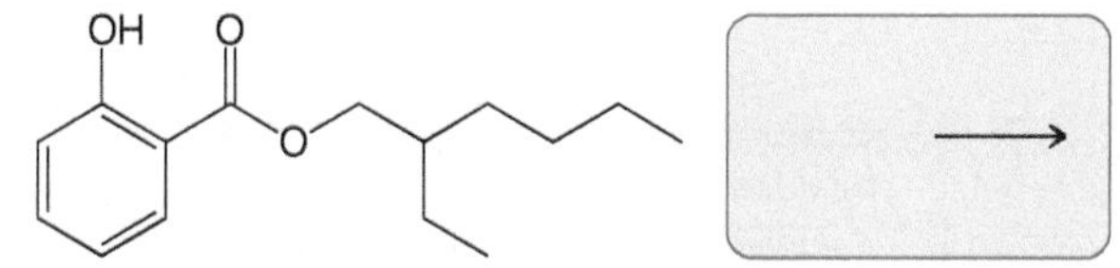

a) $H_2O + H_2SO_4$ **b)** $CH_3OH + H_2SO_4$ **c)** $H_2O + NaOH$ **d)** $H_2O_2 + NH_3$

17.50 Pethidine, also known as meperidine or Demerol, is a synthetic opioid used for pain management. Stomach acids can hydrolyze pethidine and reduce the concentration of the medication in the body over time. What products are formed in this reaction of pethidine?

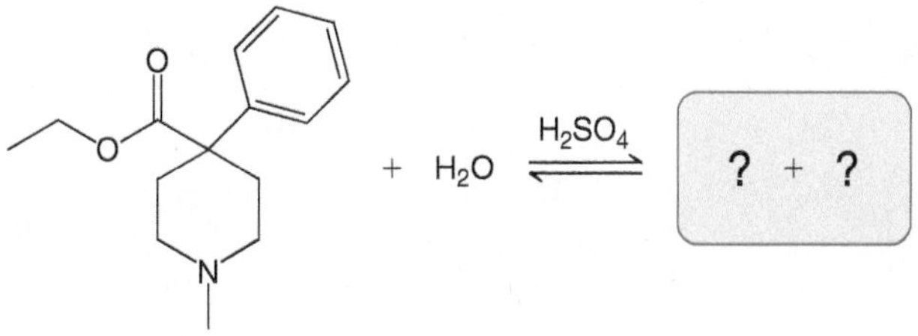

a)

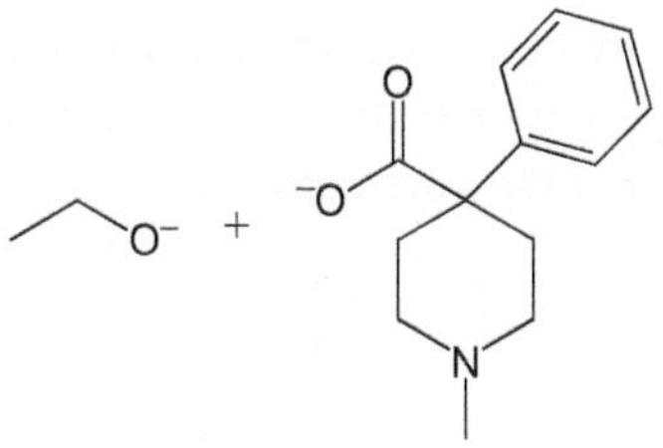

b)

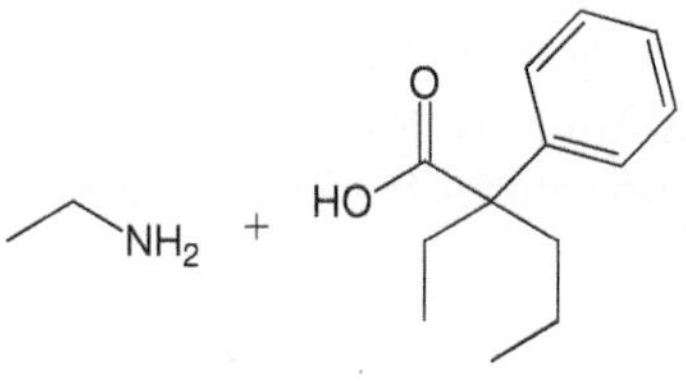

c)

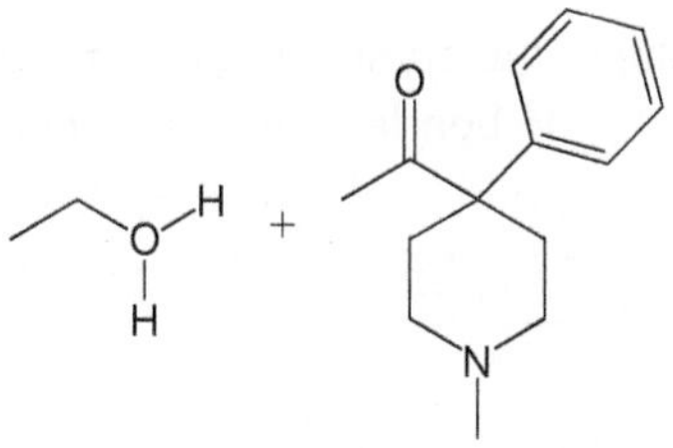

d)

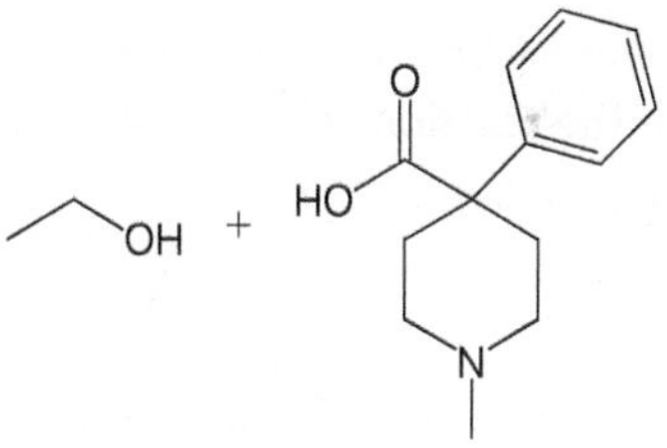

17.51 Homosalate is used in sunscreens to help protect the skin from harmful ultraviolet (UV) rays. What starting materials are needed to produce the homosalate molecule in an ester formation reaction?

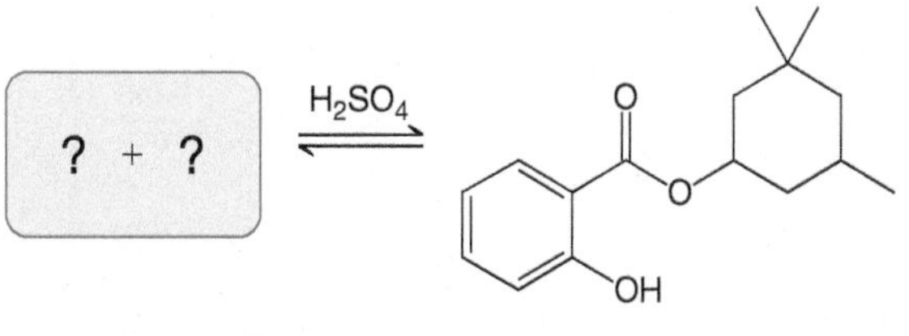

a)

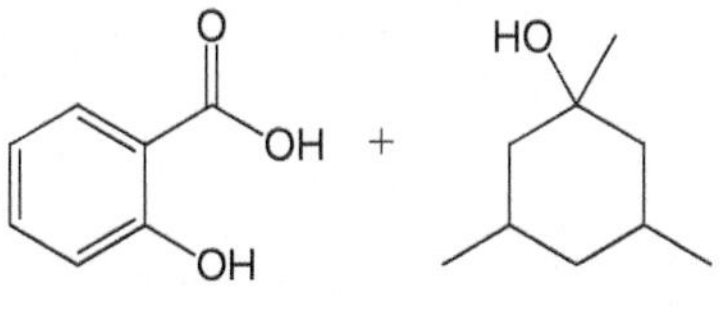

b)

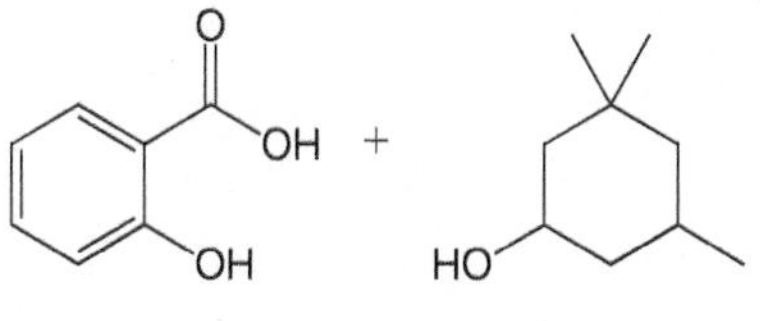

c)

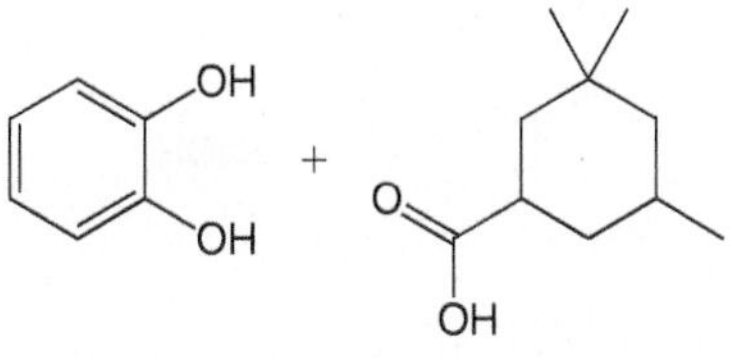

d)

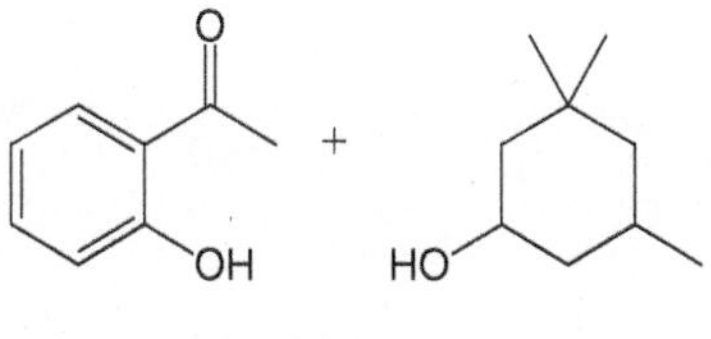

17.52 Diloxanide is a medication used to treat amoebic dysentery, an infection that causes abdominal pain, diarrhea, or bloody diarrhea which may result in anemia due to loss of blood. Identify the reactants needed to produce diloxanide by an esterification reaction under acidic conditions.

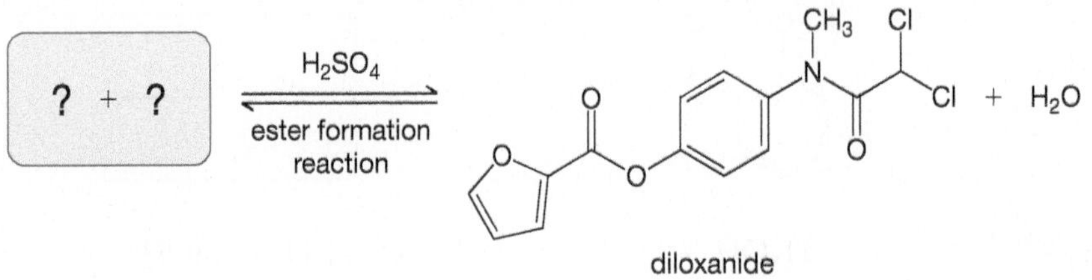

diloxanide

a)

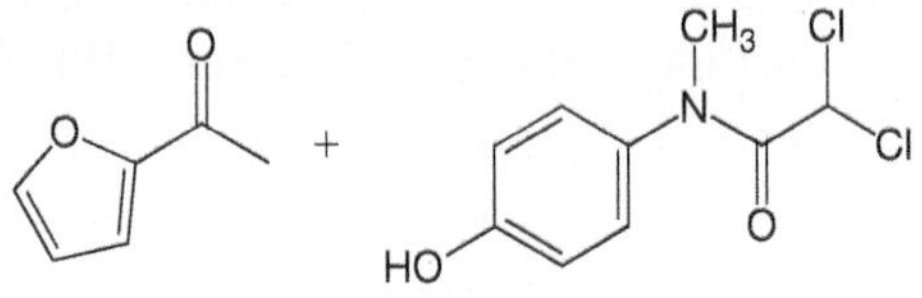

b)

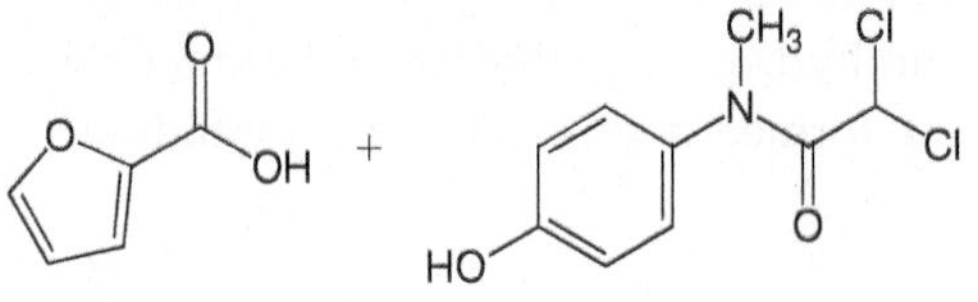

c)

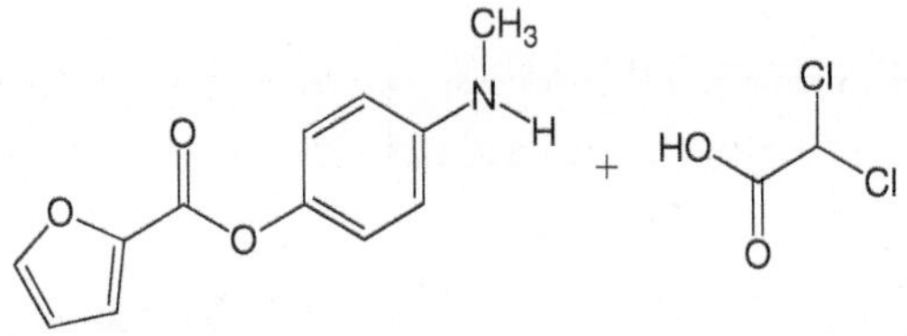

d)

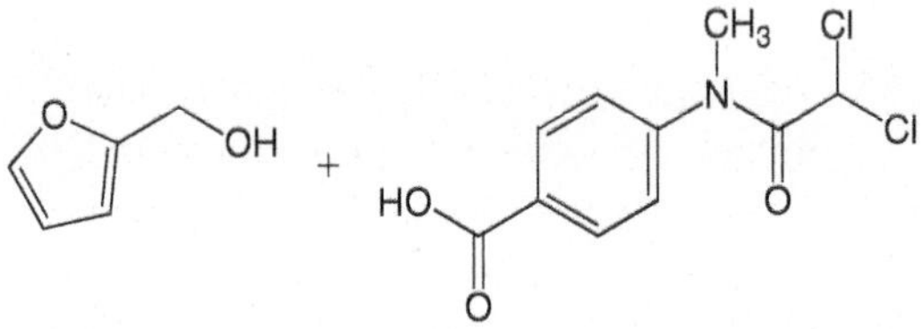

17.53 Drawing the *skeletal structure* of a reaction product: Draw the skeletal structure of the missing ester hydrolysis reaction product. Your skeletal structure should not show C—H bonds, lone pairs of electrons on oxygen atom(s), or labels on carbon atoms. Hydrogen atoms bonded to oxygen should be shown if they are present.

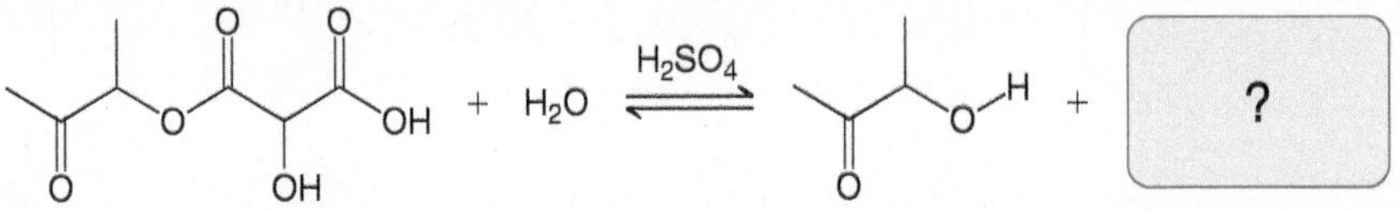

17.54 Drawing the *skeletal structure* of a reaction product: Draw the skeletal structure of the missing organic molecule product formed in the reaction shown. Your skeletal structure should not show C—H bonds, lone pairs of electrons on oxygen atom(s), or labels on carbon atoms. Hydrogen atoms bonded to oxygen should be shown if they are present.

organic molecule product

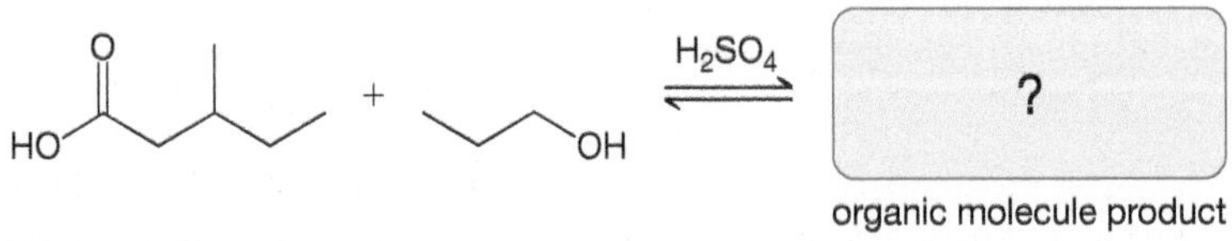

17.55 Identify the products formed in the reaction.

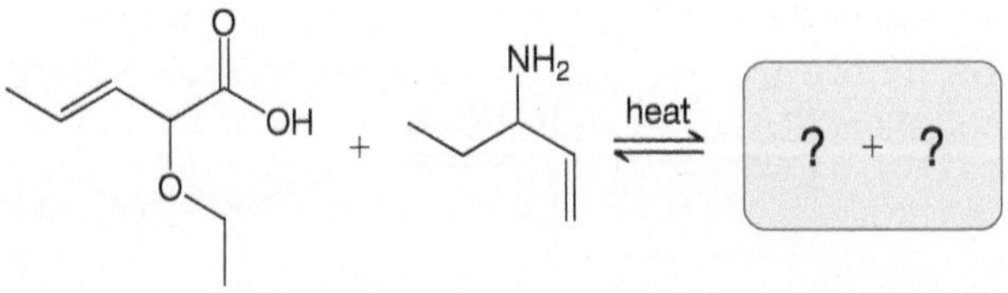

a)

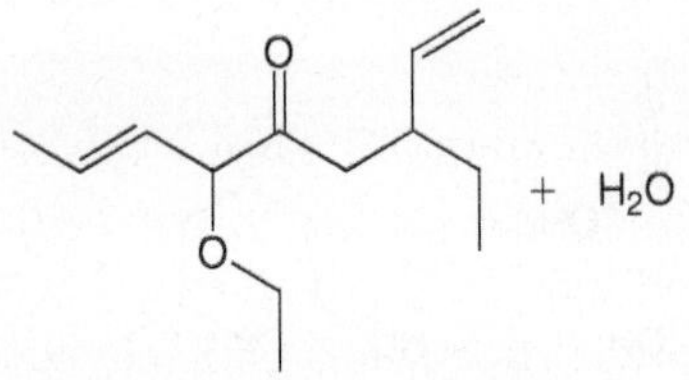

+ H_2O

b)

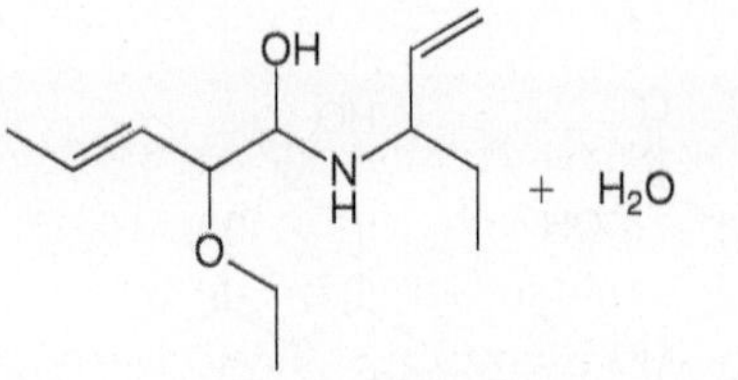

+ H_2O

c)

+ H_2O

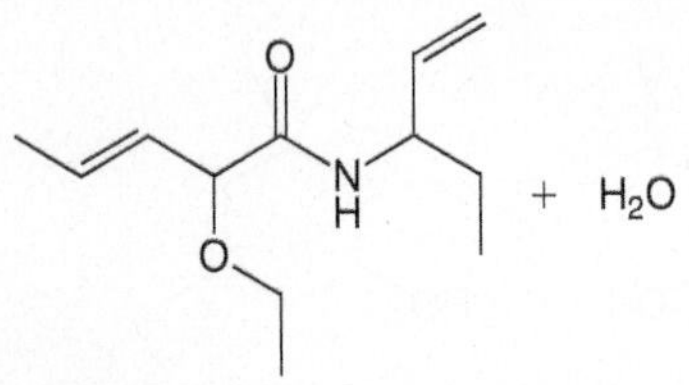

d)

+ NaOH

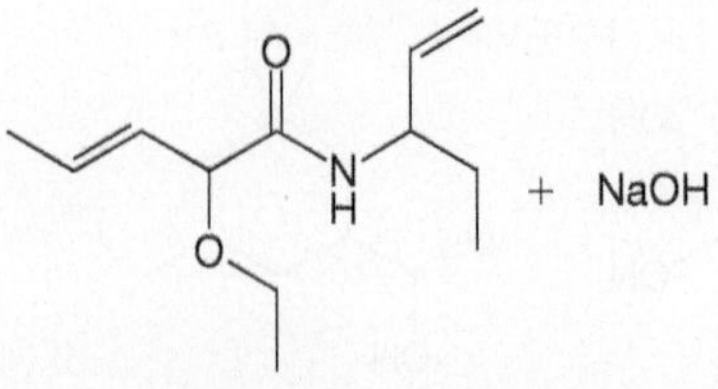

17.56 Pantothenic acid (Vit B$_5$) is an essential nutrient found in a variety of foods and is involved in metabolism. It is also taken as a vitamin supplement. Stomach acids can hydrolyze pantothenic acid over time and reduce the concentration of the vitamin in the body. Identify the products formed when pantothenic acid is hydrolyzed according to this reaction.

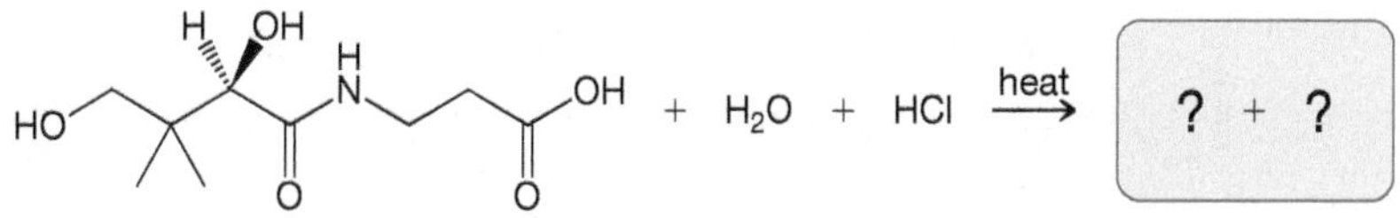

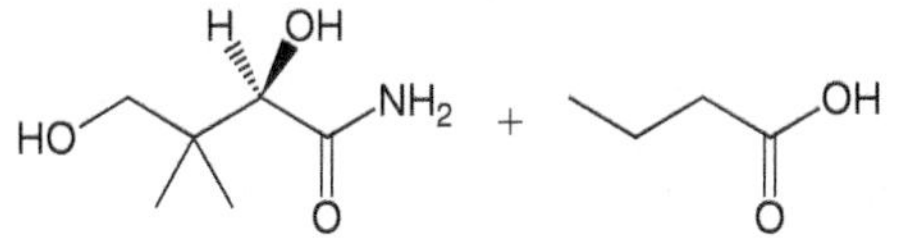

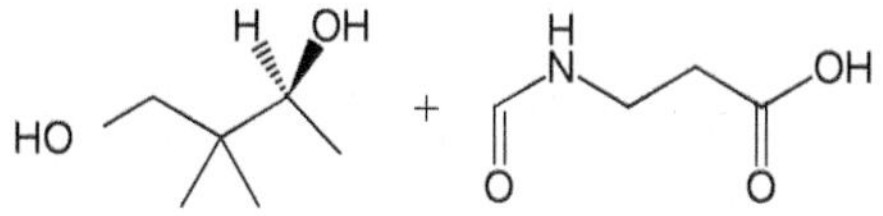

17.57 Nicotinamide (NAM), also known as niacinamide, is a form of vitamin B$_3$ found in certain foods. It is also used as a dietary supplement to prevent niacin deficiency (pellagra). As a cream, it is used to treat acne. Identify the starting materials needed to produce nicotinamide using an amide formation reaction?

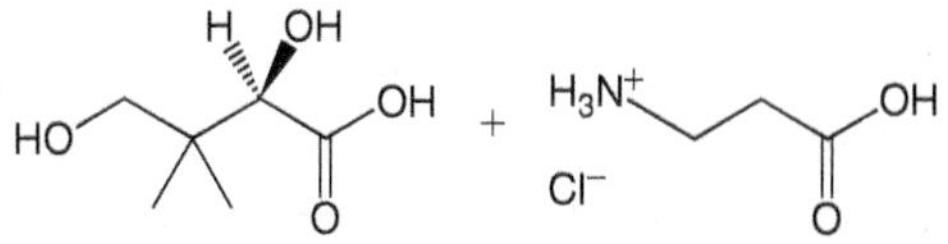

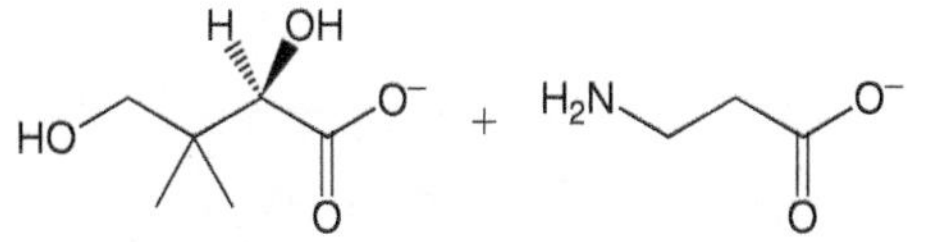

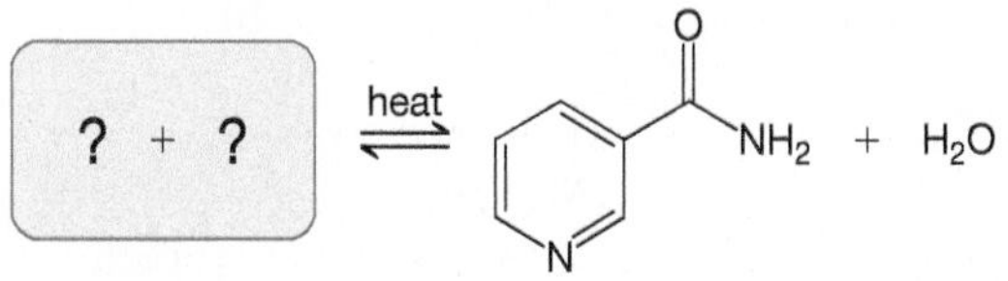

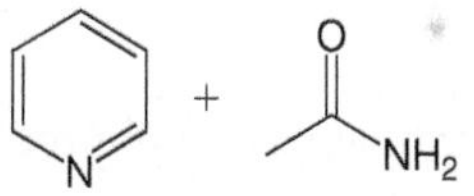

17.58 Drawing the *skeletal structure* of a reaction starting material: Paracetamol, also known as acetaminophen, is a commonly used pain reliever. Acids in the stomach can hydrolyze paracetamol and reduce the concentration of the medication in the body over time. Draw the skeletal structure of the paracetamol starting material that is missing from the amide hydrolysis reaction performed under acidic conditions. Your skeletal structure should not show C—H bonds, lone pairs of electrons on oxygen or nitrogen, or labels on carbon atoms. Hydrogen atoms bonded to oxygen and nitrogen should be shown if they are present.

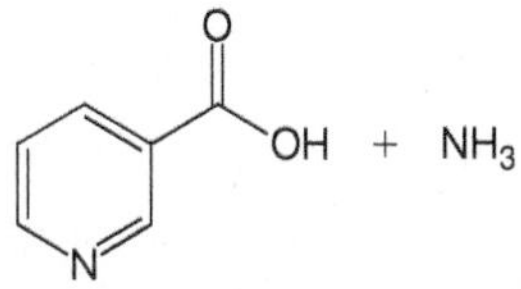

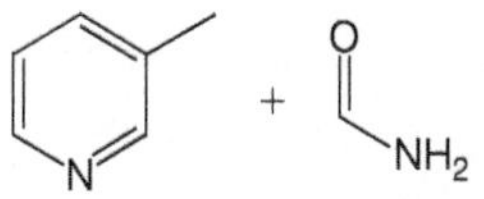

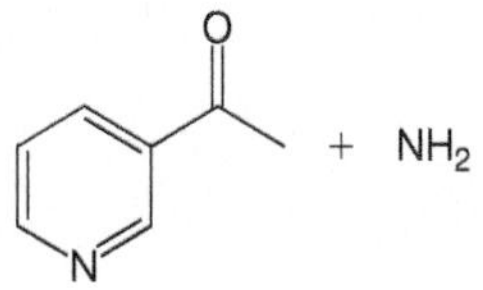

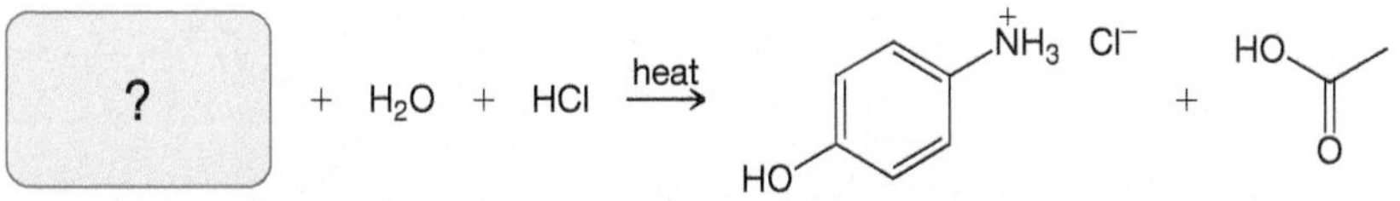

17.59 Drawing the *skeletal structure* of a reaction starting material: DEET (diethyltoluamide) is the active ingredient in many insect repellents. Draw the skeletal structure of the DEET starting material that is missing from the amide hydrolysis reaction performed under basic conditions. Your skeletal structure should not show C—H bonds, lone pairs of electrons on oxygen or nitrogen, or labels on carbon atoms. Hydrogen atoms bonded to oxygen and nitrogen should be shown if they are present.

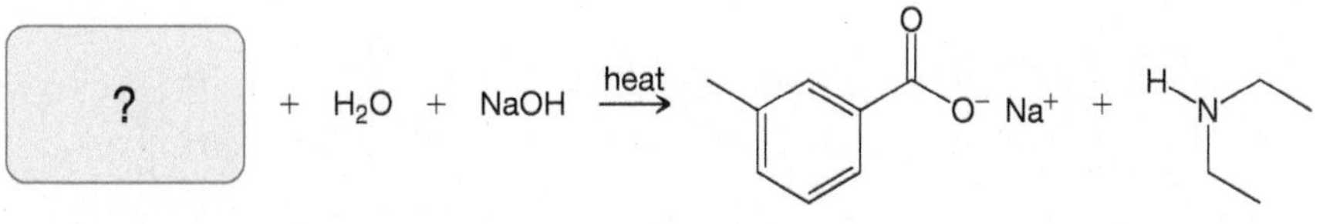

17.60 Which reaction conditions are needed for the amide hydrolysis reaction shown?

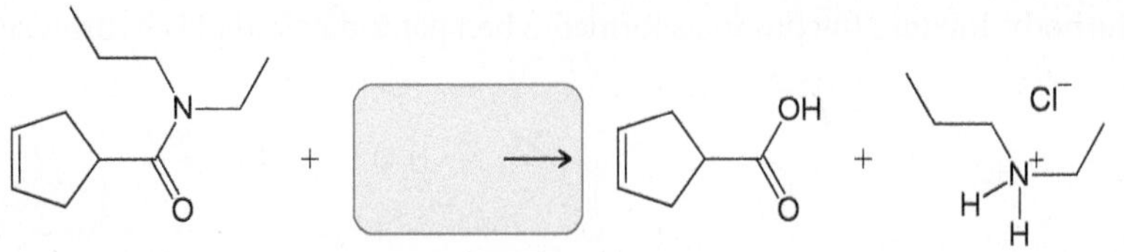

a) H_2O + NaOH + heat   **b)** CH_3OH + heat   **c)** H_2O + HCl + heat   **d)** NH_2Cl + heat

17.61 Metoclopramide is a medication used to treat heartburn and other conditions. Identify the products formed when metoclopramide undergoes amide hydrolysis under basic conditions.

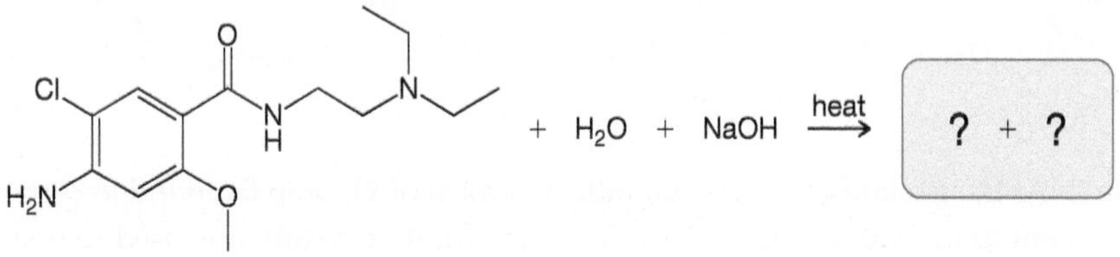

+ H_2O + NaOH $\xrightarrow{\text{heat}}$? + ?

a)

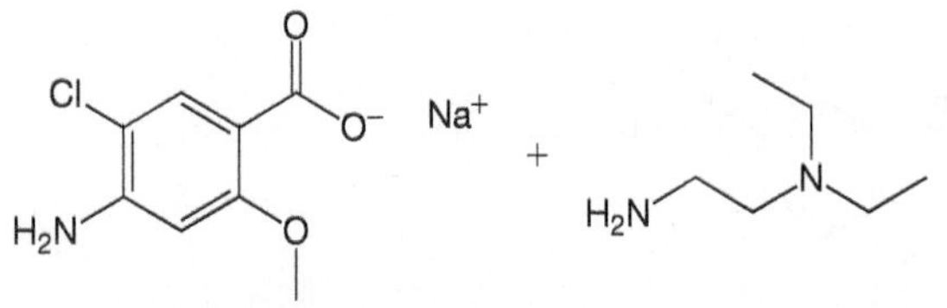

b)

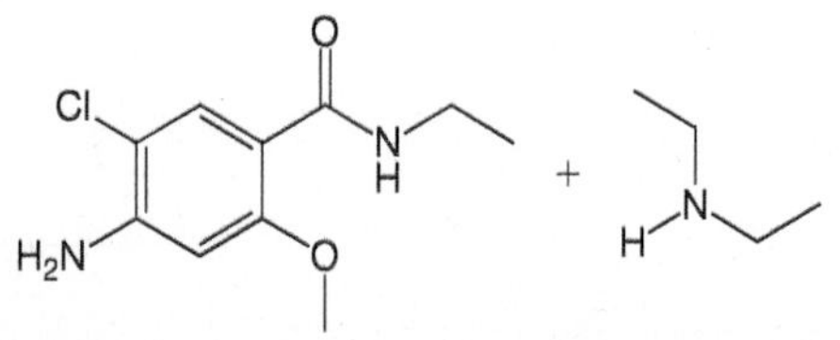

c)

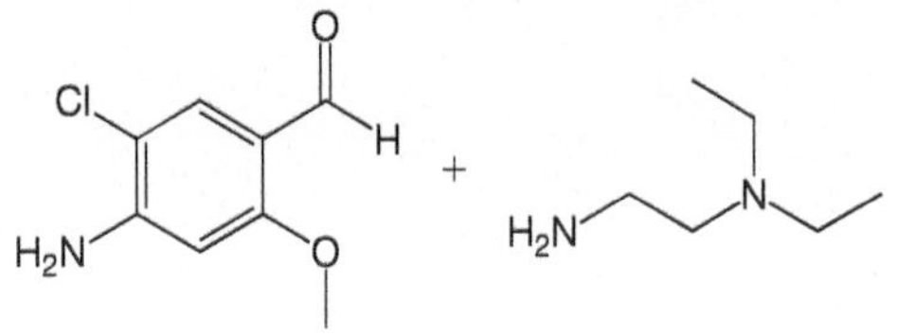

d)

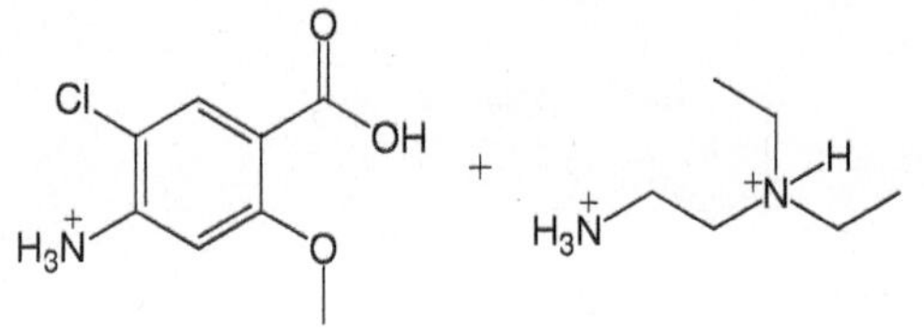

17.62 Identify the missing amine needed to produce the amide shown below?

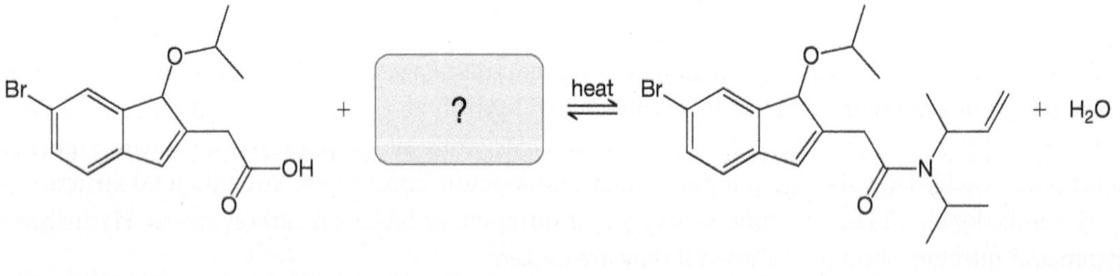

+ ? $\xrightarrow{\text{heat}}$ + H_2O

a) 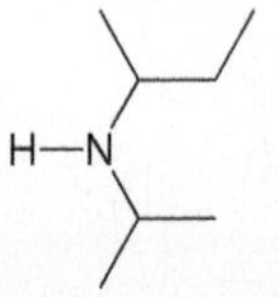   **b)** 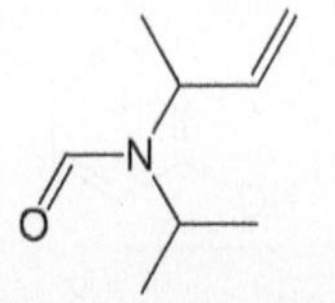   **c)** 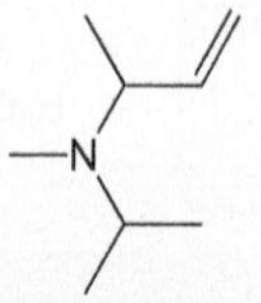   **d)**

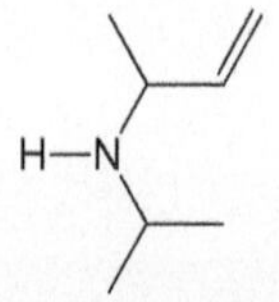

17.63 Drawing the *skeletal structure* of a reaction starting material: Draw the skeletal structure of the amide starting material that is missing from the amide hydrolysis reaction performed under acidic conditions. Your skeletal structure should not show C—H bonds, lone pairs of electrons on oxygen or nitrogen, or labels on carbon atoms. Hydrogen atoms bonded to oxygen and nitrogen should be shown if they are present.

 + H_2O + HCl $\xrightarrow{\text{heat}}$

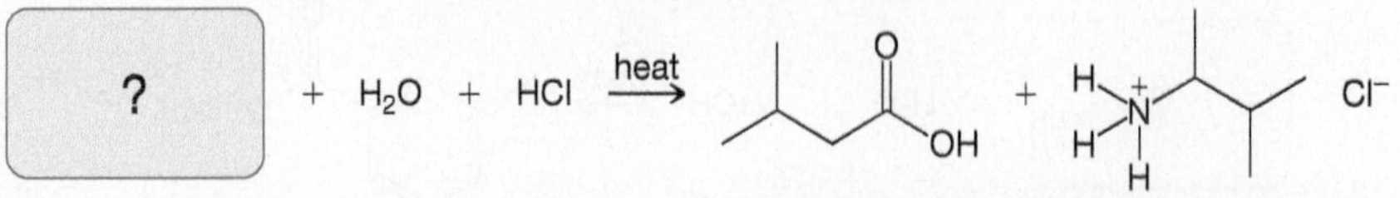

17.64 Dasatinib, also known as Sprycel, is used to help treat leukemia. Identify the products formed when dasatinib is hydrolyzed in the reaction shown below.

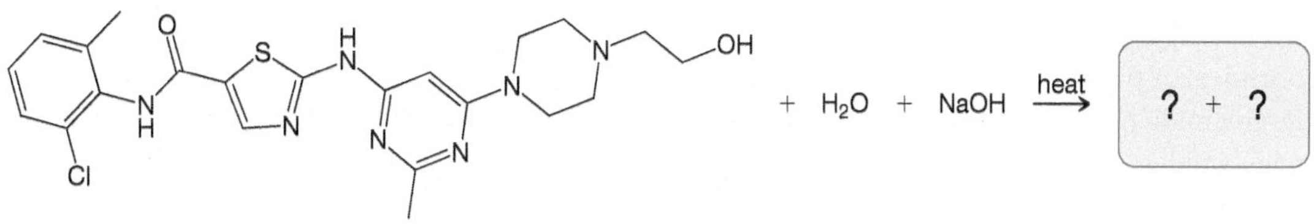

a)

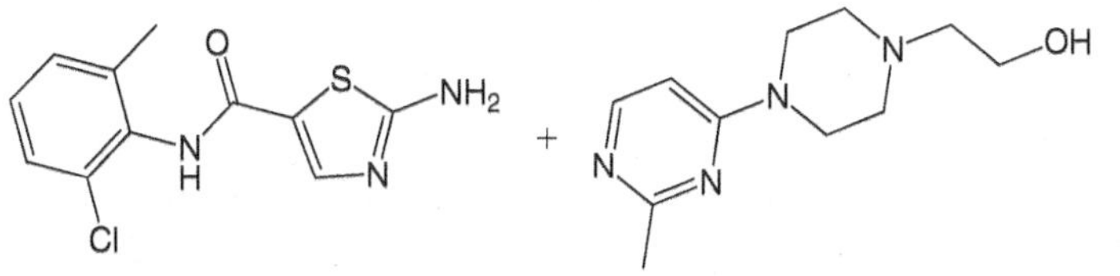

b)

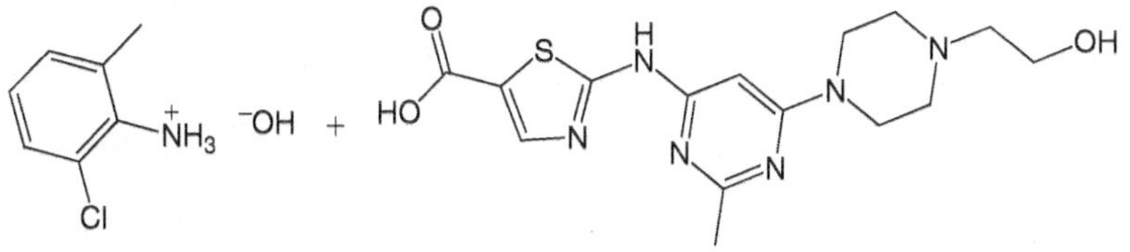

c)

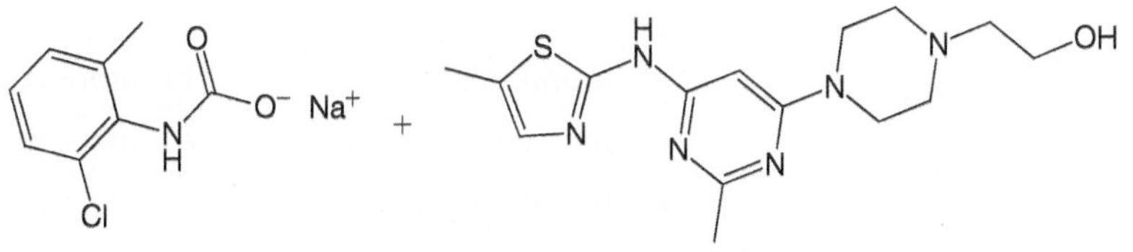

d)

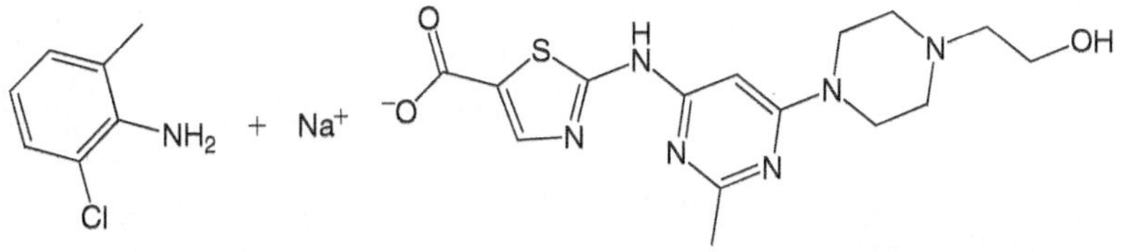

17.65 Drawing the skeletal structure of a cyclic ester reaction product: Cyclic esters (called lactones) form when a carboxylic acid and an alcohol group on the same molecule come together in a ring closure reaction. The result is an ester functional group having an oxygen atom within the ring and a carbonyl group next to the ring oxygen. Draw the *skeletal structure* of the cyclic ester formed in the reaction shown. Your skeletal structure should not show C—H bonds, lone pairs of electrons on oxygen, or labels on carbon atoms.

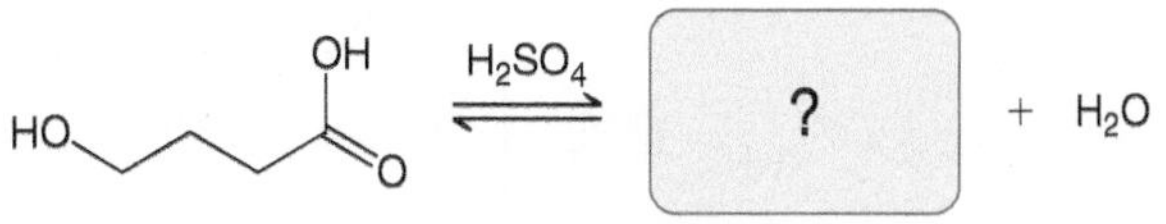

17.66 Drawing the skeletal structure of a cyclic amide reaction product: Cyclic amides (called lactams) form when a carboxylic acid and an amine group on the same molecule come together in a ring closure reaction. The result is an amide functional group having a nitrogen atom within the ring and a carbonyl group next to the ring nitrogen. Draw the *skeletal structure* of the cyclic amide formed in the reaction shown. Your skeletal structure should not show C—H bonds, lone pairs of electrons on oxygen or nitrogen, or labels on carbon atoms. Hydrogen atoms bonded to oxygen and nitrogen should be shown if they are present.

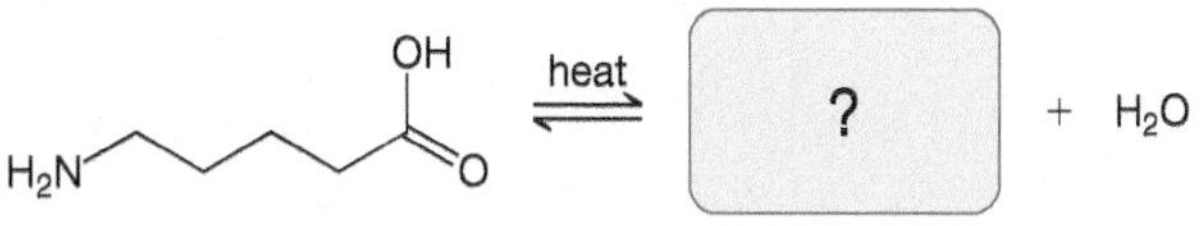

17.67 Amoxicillin is a member of the β-lactam antibiotic family and is used to treat bacterial infections. Cyclic amides (called lactams) contain the amide functional group having a nitrogen atom within a ring and a carbonyl group next to the ring nitrogen. They undergo amide hydrolysis reations, as do non-cyclic (acyclic) amides. The result is a ring-opening reaction to form an open chain structure. Part of the chemical structure of amoxicillin is shown. What is the product formed in the amide hydrolysis ring opening reaction of this molecule?

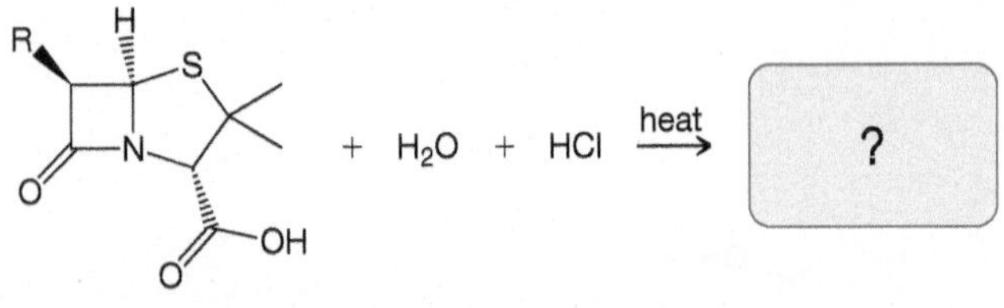

a)

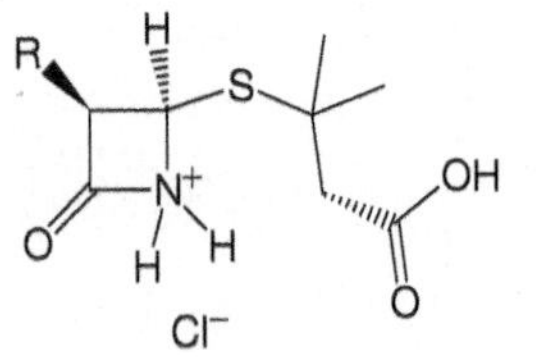

b)

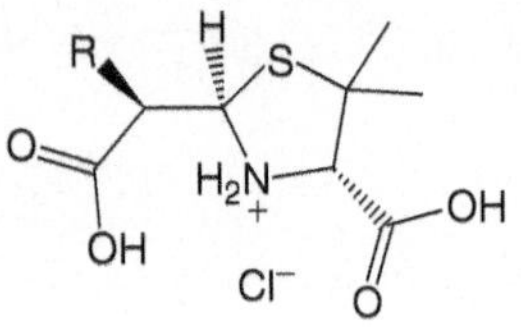

c)

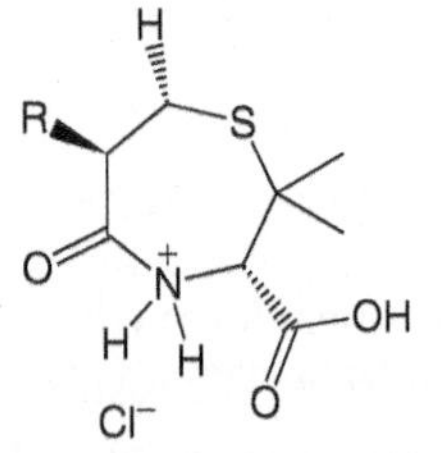

d)

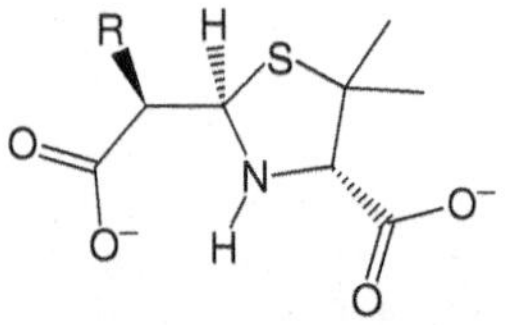

17.5 Ester and Amide Polymers

LO 5: Analyze the defining structural features of polyesters and polyamides.

17.68 Long-chain molecules made of many repeating units are called _____.

a) polydrons
b) multimers
c) polycythemics
d) polyunits
e) polymers

17.69 Identify the type of polymer shown.

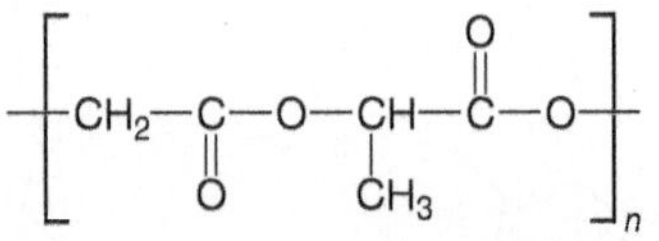

a) polyalkane   b) polypeptide
c) polyamide   d) polyester

17.70 Small molecules that constitute the repeating unit in polymers are called _____.

a) monomolecules   b) monocytes
c) mononucleosomes   d) monomers
e) unit molecules

17.71 Identify the type of polymer shown.

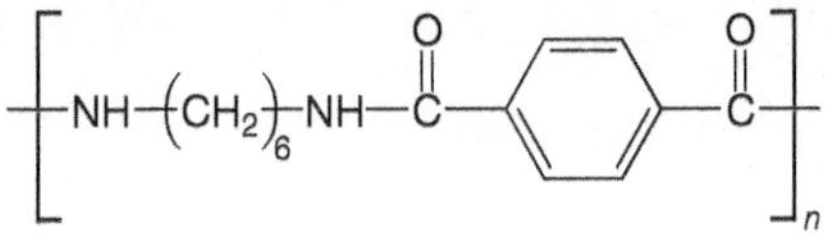

a) polyester   b) polyamine
c) polyamide   d) polyalkyne

17.72 Identify the missing product formed in the polymerization reaction shown below.

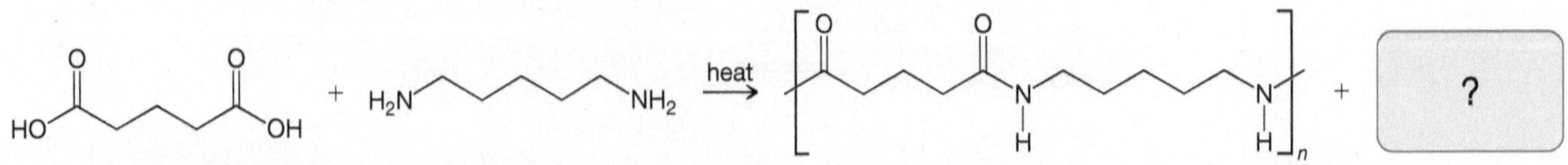

a) NH_3 b) H_2O c) H—O—N—H   d) C=O

17.73 Identify the type of polymer shown in the diagram.

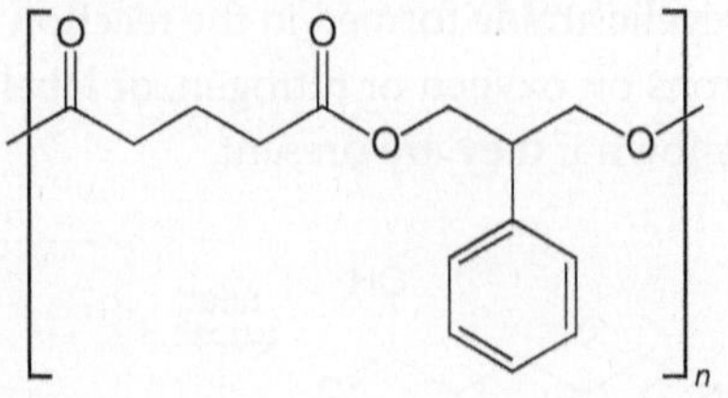

a) polyamide   b) polyester   c) polycyclohexane   d) polyalcohol

17.74 Identify the type of polymer shown in the following diagram.

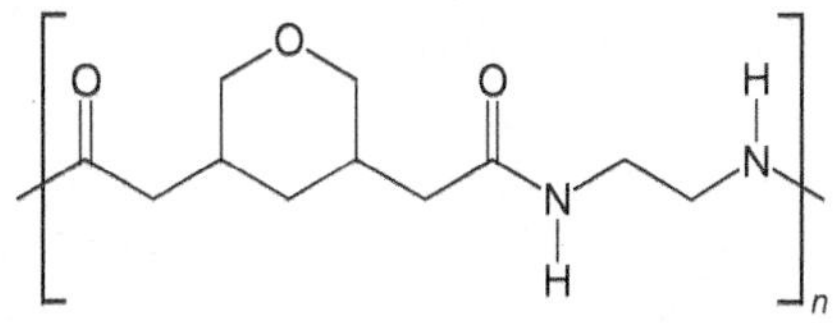

a) polybenzone   **b)** polyamide   **c)** polyketone   **d)** polyester

17.75 Consider the diagram of the formation of a polyester from monomer units that consist of a dicarboxylic acid and a dialcohol. Identify the structures of the monomers, indicated by the square and triangle, that are needed to produce this specific polymer structure.

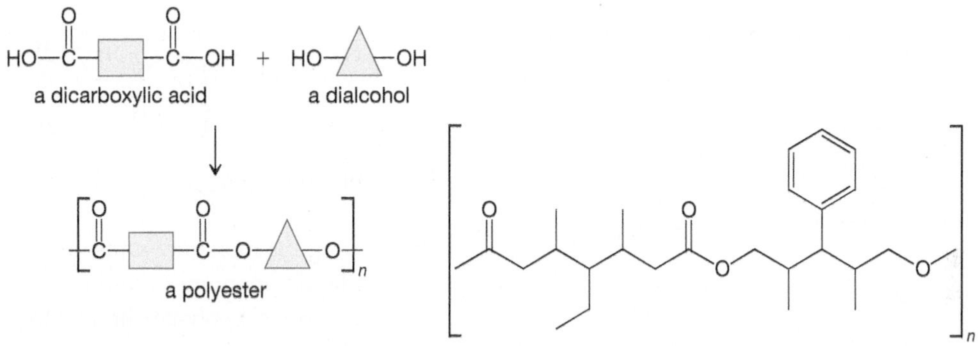

a)

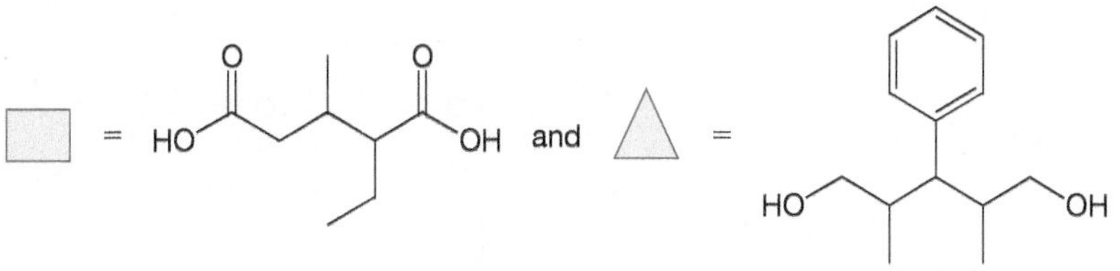

b)

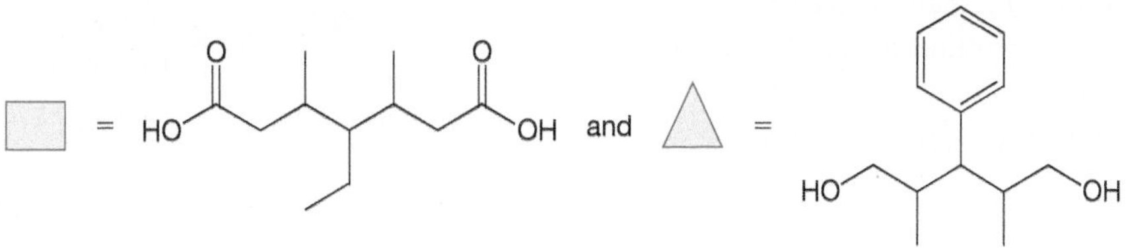

c)

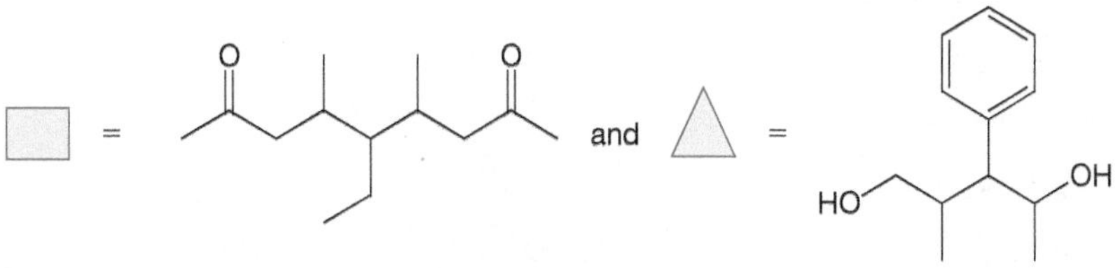

d)

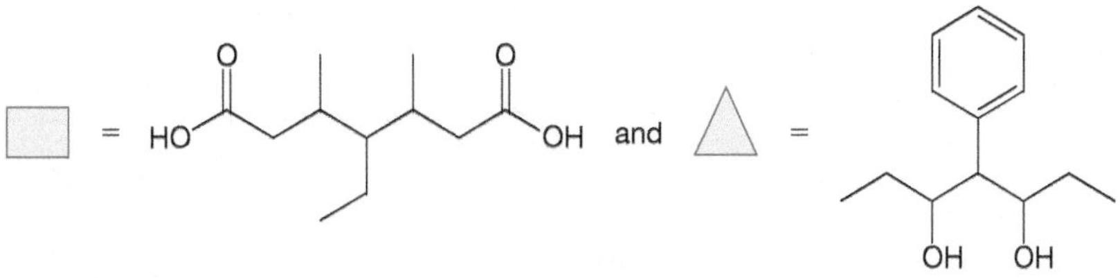

17.76 By some estimates, as many as a million plastic bottles are bought around the world every minute. Many of these are made of the polyester polyethylene naphthalate (PEN). Identify the monomers needed to make the PEN polymer.

PEN

a)

+ HO

b)

+

c)

+ HO OH

d)

+

17.77 Drag the monomer units into the correct positions to identify monomer 1 and monomer 2 that are needed to form this polymer. Be sure to position the appropriate monomer units under the polymer in a way that they match the orientation of the illustrated polymer.

?

monomer 1

?

monomer 2

Answer choices for monomer (1):

a)

b)

c)

d)

Answer choices for monomer (2):

a)

b)

c) d)

e)

17.78 Drag the monomer units into the correct positions to identify monomer 1 and monomer 2 that are needed to form this polymer. Be sure to position the appropriate monomer units under the polymer in a way that they match the orientation of the illustrated polymer.

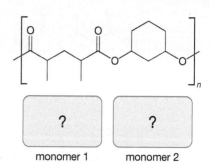

?

monomer 1

?

monomer 2

Answer choices for monomer (1):

a)

HO OH

b)

c)

HO OH

d)

e)

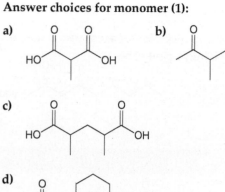

Answer choices for monomer (2):

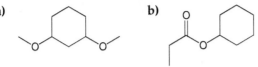

a)   b)

c)   d)

e)

17.6 Naming Carboxylic Acids and Esters

LO 6: **Apply the IUPAC naming system to carboxylic acids, esters, and amides.**

17.79 Drag the missing fragments into the spaces to complete the name of this carboxylic acid molecule.

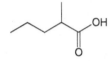

☐ - methyl ☐ anoic acid

Answer choices for leftmost box 1: 1, 2, 3, 4, 5, 6

Answer choices for rightmost box 2: meth, eth, prop, but, pent, hex

17.80 Complete the name of this ester molecule by dragging the missing fragments into the spaces provided.

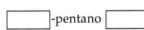

☐ -pentano ☐

Answer choices for leftmost box 1: methyl, ethyl, propyl, butyl, pentyl, hexyl

Answer choices for rightmost box 2: ic acid, ne, ate, yne

17.81 Drag the missing fragments into the spaces to complete the name of this amide molecule.

N-☐ pentano ☐

Answer choices for leftmost box 1: methyl, ethyl, propyl, butyl, pentyl, hexyl

Answer choices for rightmost box 2: oate, one, oic, amide, ene, amine

17.82 Drawing a carboxylic acid: Draw the *skeletal structure* of propanoic acid, an alkane-based carboxylic acid having a total of three carbon atoms. Your skeletal structure should not show C—H bonds, lone pairs of electrons on oxygen, or labels on carbon atoms. Hydrogen atom(s) bonded to oxygen should be shown if present on the molecule.

17.83 Drawing an ester: Draw the *skeletal structure* of ethyl benzoate. Hint: this is an ester composed of a benzene ring as the R group bonded to the carbonyl carbon, and a two-carbon OR′ alkane group. Your skeletal structure should not show C—H bonds, lone pairs of electrons on oxygen, or labels on carbon atoms.

17.84 Drawing an amide: Draw the *skeletal structure* of octanamide. Hint: this is a non-branched straight chain alkane-based primary amide having a total of eight carbon atoms. Your skeletal structure should not show C—H bonds, lone pairs of electrons on oxygen or nitrogen, or labels on carbon atoms. Hydrogen atom(s) bonded to nitrogen should be shown if present on the molecule.

17.85 Drag the missing fragments into the spaces to complete the name of this carboxylic acid.

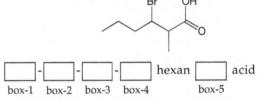

☐-☐-☐-☐ hexan ☐ acid

box-1   box-2   box-3   box-4   box-5

Answer choices for boxes, left-to-right:

a) 1, 2, 3, 4, 5, 6

b) boron, bromine, bromo, barium, beryllium

c) methyl, ethyl, propyl, butyl, pentyl, hexyl

d) oate, one, oic, al, ene, yl

17.86 Drag the missing fragments into the spaces to complete the name of this ester molecule.

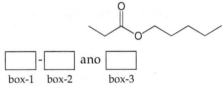

☐-☐ ano ☐

box-1   box-2   box-3

Answer choices for boxes, left-to-right:

a) methyl, ethyl, propyl, butyl, pentyl, hexyl

b) meth, eth, prop, but, pent, hex

c) ic acid, ne, ate, yne

17.87 Which of the following molecules is 4-methylhexanoic acid?

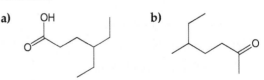

a)   b)

c) 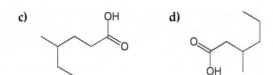   **d)**

17.88 Which of the following molecules is octyl ethanoate?

a)

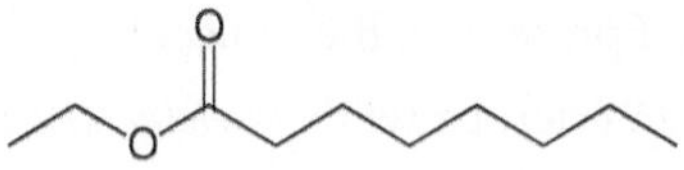

b)

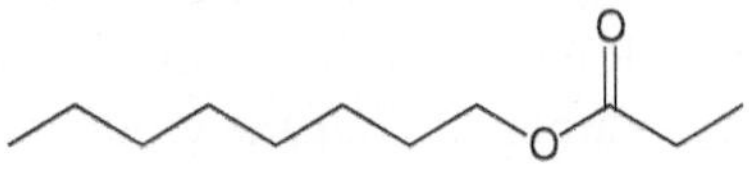

c)

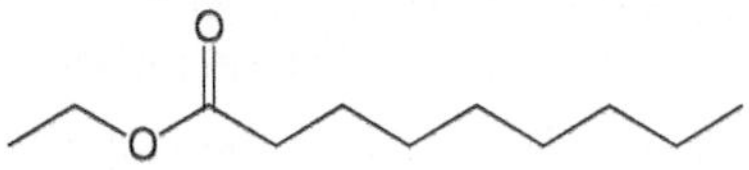

d)

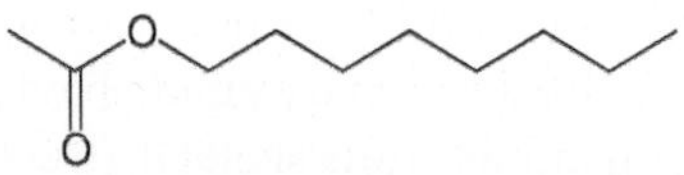

17.89 Drawing a carboxylic acid: Draw the *skeletal structure* of 3-hydroxy-pentanoic acid. Your skeletal structure should not show C—H bonds, lone pairs of electrons on oxygen, or labels on carbon atoms. Hydrogen atom(s) bonded to oxygen should be shown if present on the molecule.

17.90 Drawing an ester: Draw the *skeletal structure* of pentyl ethanoate. Your skeletal structure should not show C—H bonds, lone pairs of electrons on oxygen, or labels on carbon atoms.

17.91 Drawing an amide: Draw the *skeletal structure* of N,N-dimethylbutanamide. Your skeletal structure should not show C—H bonds, lone pairs of electrons on oxygen or nitrogen, or labels on carbon atoms.

17.92 Which is the correct name for this molecule?

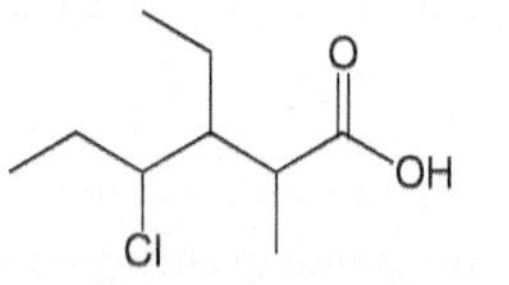

a) 4-chloro-3-ethyl-2-methylhexanoic acid
b) 2-methyl-3-ethyl-4-chlorohexanoic acid
c) 4-chloro-3-ethyl-2-methylhexanoate
d) 3-chloro-4-ethyl-5-methylhexanoic acid

17.93 Which is the correct name of this molecule?

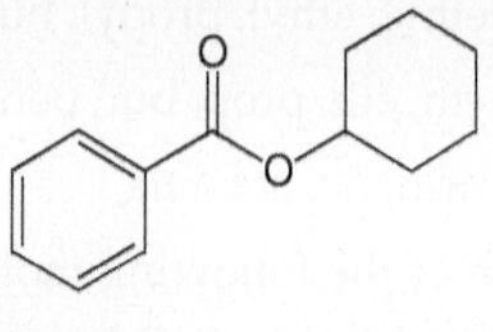

a) cyclopentyl benzoate
b) benzyl cyclohexanoate
c) cyclohexyl benzoate
d) benzylester cyclohexane

17.94 Which of the following molecules is 5-fluoro-2-propylpentanoic acid?

a)

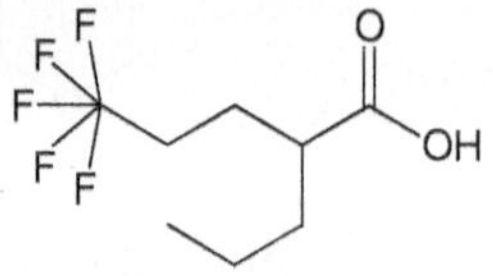

b)

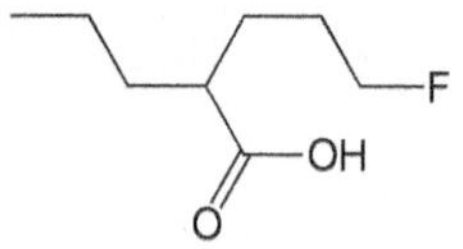

c) 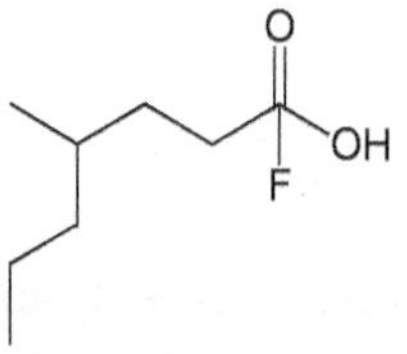   **d)**

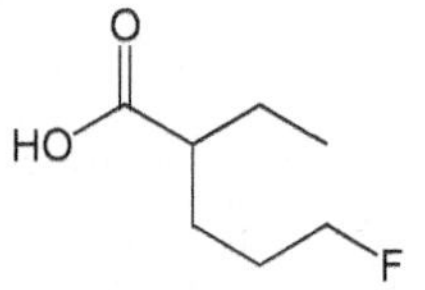

17.95 Which of the following molecules is methyl-3-methylbutanoate?

a) 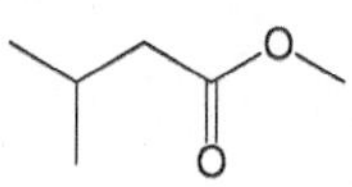   **b)**

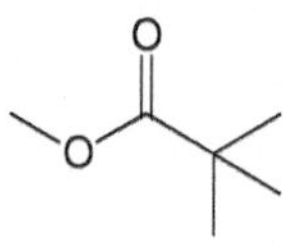

c) 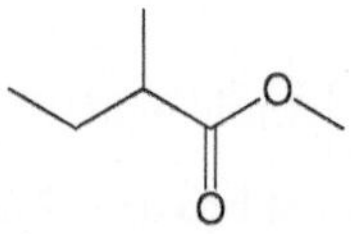   **d)**

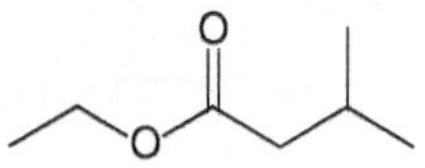

Chapter 18

18.1 Lipids and Fatty Acids

LO 1: Classify fatty acids and describe how double bonds impact fatty acid melting points.

18.01 Which type of lipid is shown in the diagram?

a) sphingolipid   b) wax
c) steroid   d) triacylglycerol

18.02 Which type of lipid is shown in the diagram?

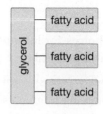

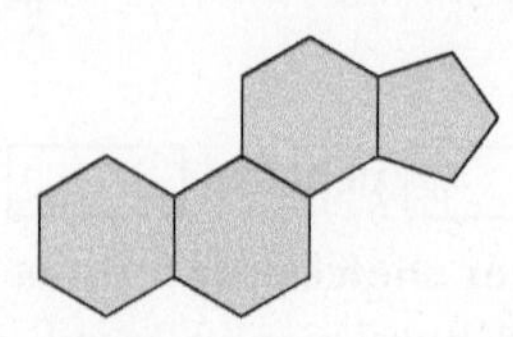

a) wax   b) steroid
c) triacylglycerol   d) sphingolipid

18.03 Which type of lipid is shown in the diagram?

a) triacylglycerol   b) fatty acid

c) wax   d) steroid

18.04 Which type of lipid is shown in the diagram

a) wax   b) steroid

c) triacylglycerol   d) glycerophospholipid

18.05 Vaccenic acid is a naturally occurring molecule found in human milk and dairy products such as milk, yogurt, and butter. Identify all the characteristic features of vaccenic acid.

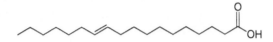

a) wax   b) ester

c) steroid   d) has formula $C_{17}H_{32}O_2$

e) cis fatty acid   f) has formula $C_{18}H_{32}O_2$

g) ketone   h) has formula $C_{18}H_{34}O_2$

i) omega-3 fatty acid   j) trans fatty acid

k) triacylglyceride

18.06 Which molecular formula is from a saturated fatty acid?

a) $C_{16}H_{30}O_2$ b) $C_4H_8O_2$

c) $C_{16}H_{32}O_2$ d) $C_{14}H_{30}O_2$

18.07 Identify the characteristics of saturated fatty acids.

Answer choices: ester, amide, C=C double, steroid, cis alkene, carboxylic acid, trans alkene, C—C single bonds, short carbon chain, primary amine

Target box: characteristics of saturated fatty acids

18.08 Classify each fatty acid as either saturated, *cis* unsaturated, or *trans* unsaturated.

Answer choices:

a) Oleic acid is found in olives, pecans, and sunflowers.

b) Lauric acid is found in coconut.

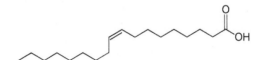

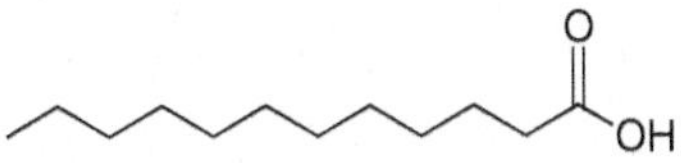

c) Elaidic acid is found in the durian fruit.

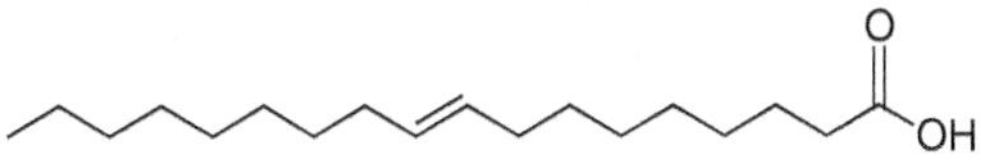

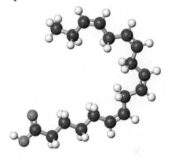

Target boxes: *cis* unsaturated fatty acid, saturated fatty acid, *trans* unsaturated fatty acid

18.09 Classify each fatty acid as either saturated, *cis* unsaturated, or *trans* unsaturated.

Answer choices:

a) Stearidonic acid is found in the seeds of the seed oils of hemp and blackcurrant.

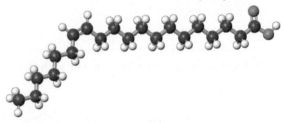

b) Paullinic acid is found in a variety of plants.

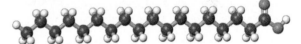

c) Stearic acid is found in animal fat.

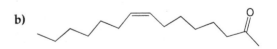

Target boxes: *cis* unsaturated fatty acid, saturated fatty acid, *trans* unsaturated fatty acid

18.10 Identify each molecule as a fatty acid or not a fatty acid.

Answer choices:

a)

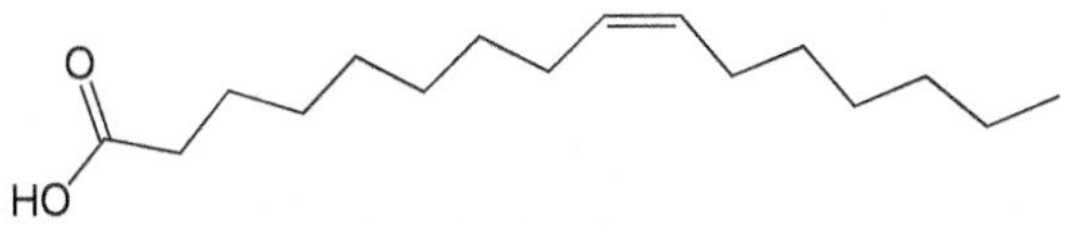

b)

c)

d)

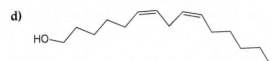

HO

e) HO

OH

OH

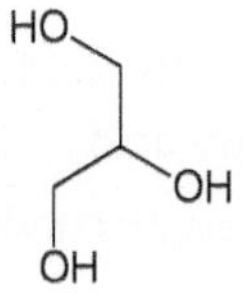

f)

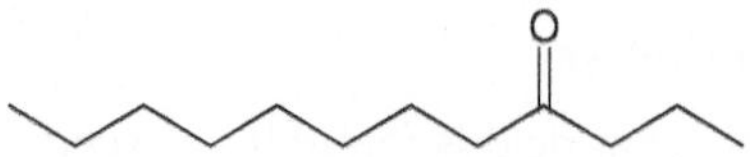

g)

HO

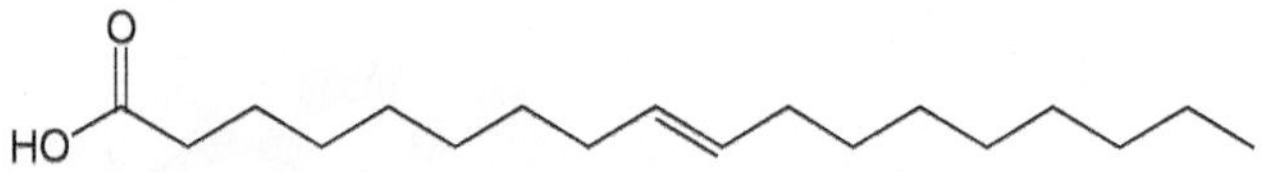

Target boxes: fatty acid, not a fatty acid

18.11 The fatty acids shown are found in certain fish oils. Which statement is correct?

A.

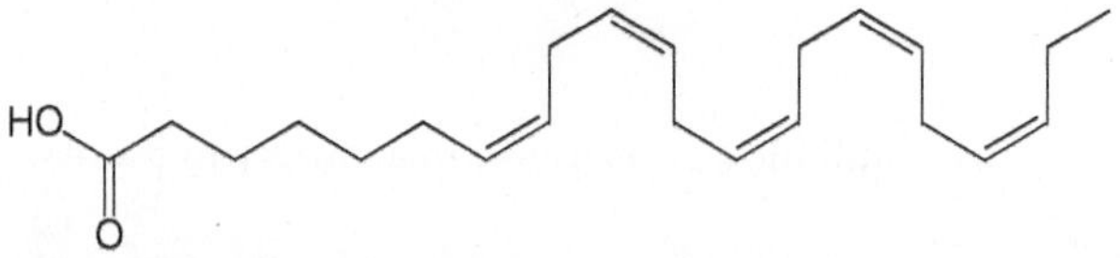

HO

a) There are five *trans* double bonds.

b) There are three *trans* double bonds and two cis double bonds.

c) There are two *trans* double bonds and three cis double bonds.

d) There are five *cis* double bonds.

B. O

HO

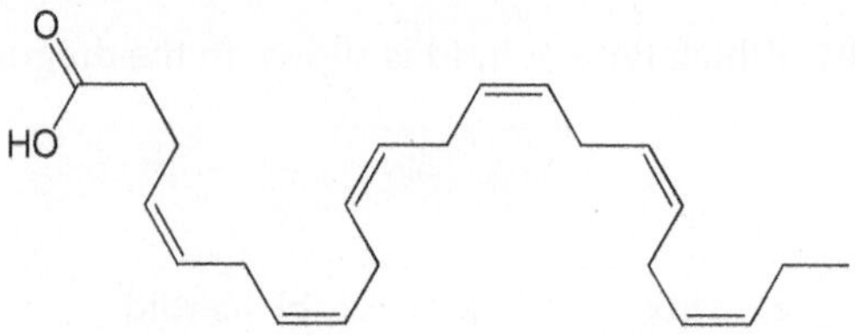

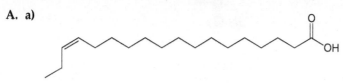

a) There are six *cis* double bonds.

b) There are three *cis* double bonds and three *trans* double bonds.

c) There are two *cis* double bonds and three *trans* double bonds.

d) There are five *cis* double bonds and one *trans* double bond.

18.12 Identify the molecule in each pair with the *lower* melting point.

A. a)

O

OH

b)

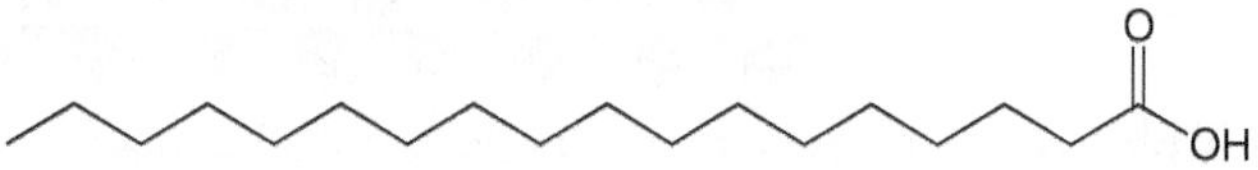

O

OH

B. a)

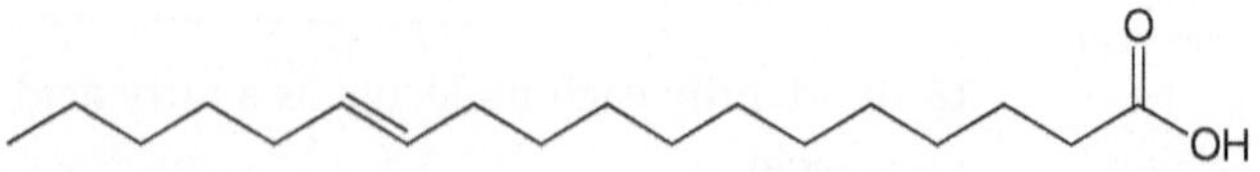

O

OH

b)

O

OH

C. a)

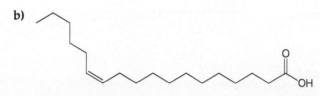

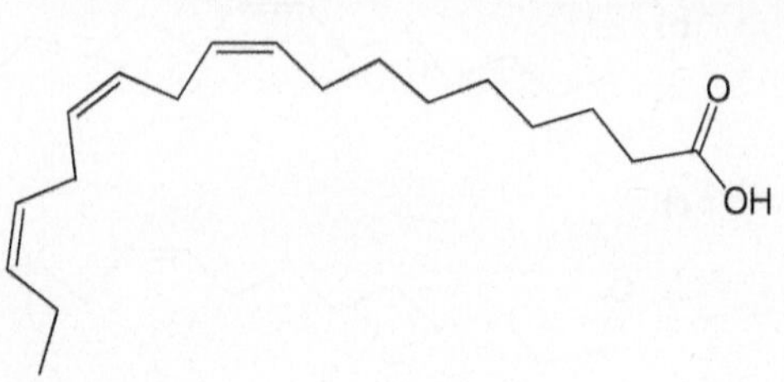

O

OH

b)

OH

O

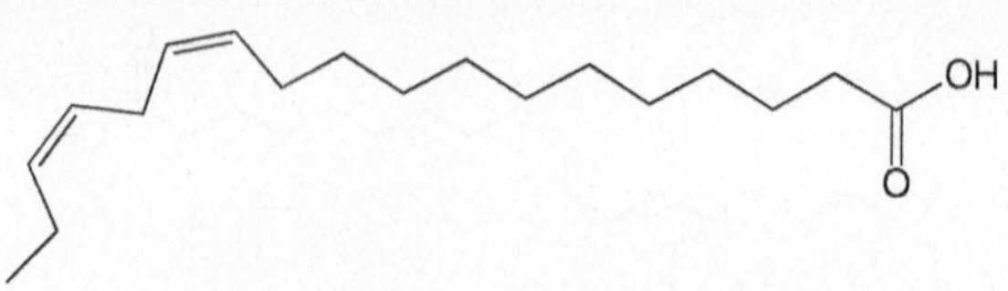

18.13 Identify the molecule in each pair with the *lower* melting point.

A. a)   b)

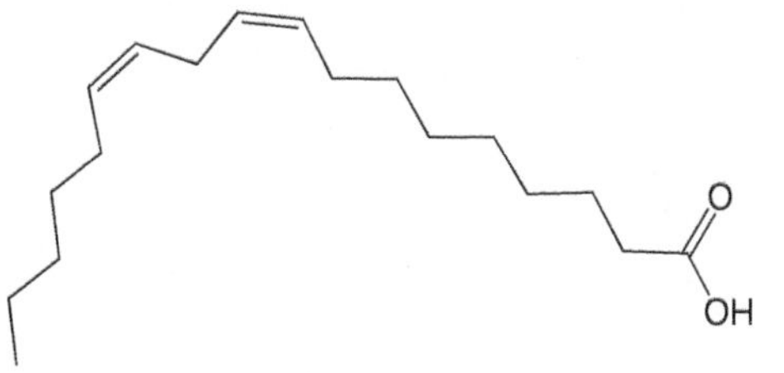

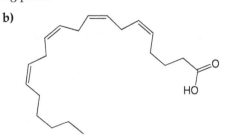

B. a) 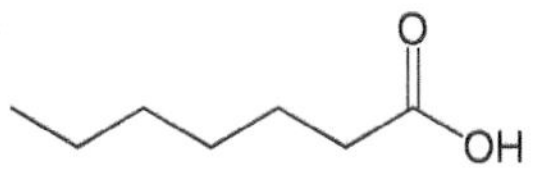   b)

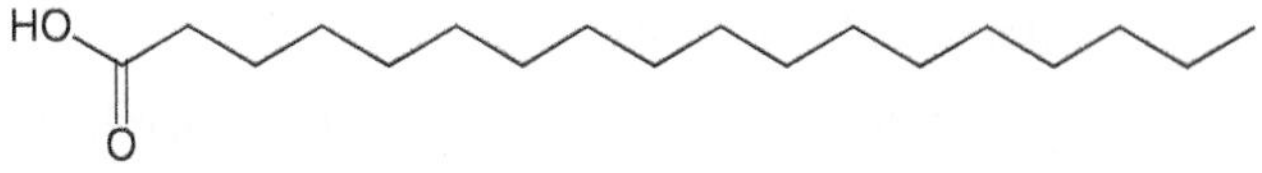

C. a) 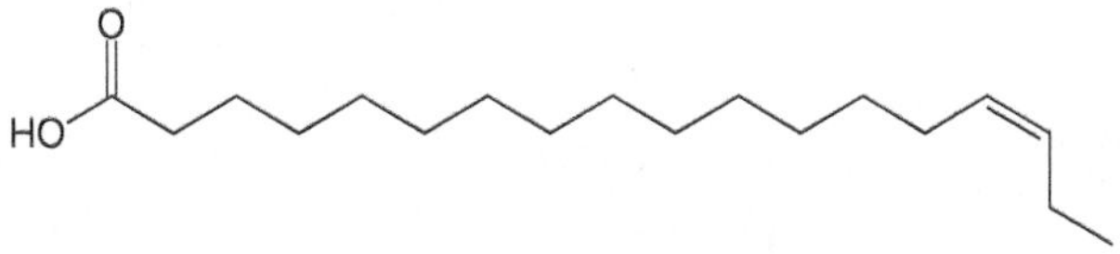   b)

18.14 Drawing a fatty acid: Use the drawing tool to build the *skeletal structure* of a saturated fatty acid with a total of 12 carbon atoms. Do not show C—H bonds, the lone pair of electrons on oxygen, or labels on carbon atoms. Hydrogen atom(s) bonded to oxygen should be shown if present on the molecule.

18.15 Drawing an omega-3 fatty acid: Use the drawing tool to build the *skeletal structure* of linolenic acid, an omega-3 fatty acid found in corn. The formula of linolenic acid is $C_{18}H_{30}O_2$. There are three *cis* double bonds on the linolenic acid molecule, located between C_3 and C_4, C_6 and C_7, and C_9 and C_{10}, as numbered counting inward from the CH_3 (omega) end of the molecule. Do not show C—H bonds, the lone pair of electrons on oxygen, or labels on carbon atoms. Hydrogen atom(s) bonded to oxygen should be shown if present on the molecule.

18.16 Both omega-3 and omega-6 fatty acids are important components in cell membranes and serve as building blocks to create an array of other molecules that regulate blood pressure, inflammation, brain development, and many other essential functions. Which molecule is an omega-6 fatty acid?

a)

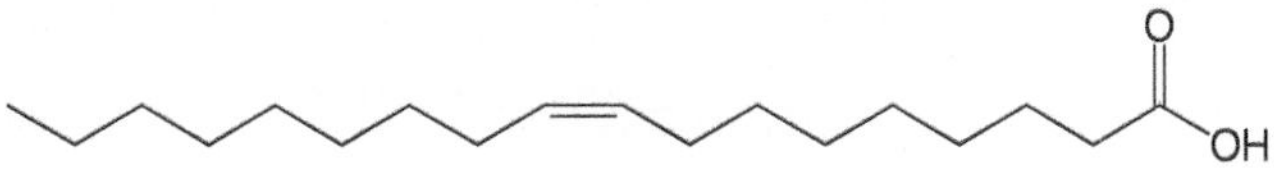

b)

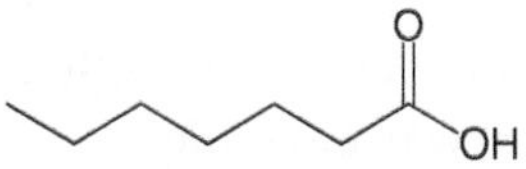

c)

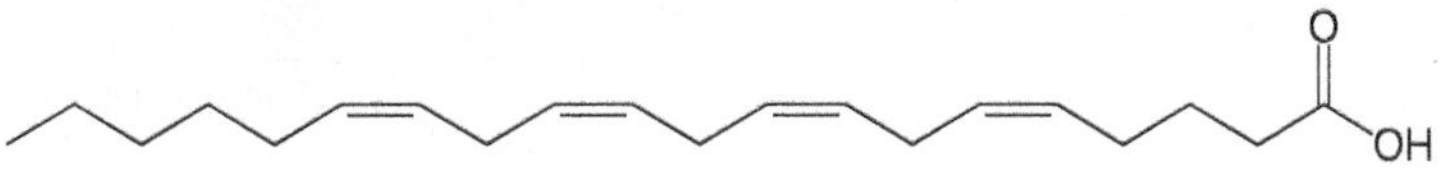

d)

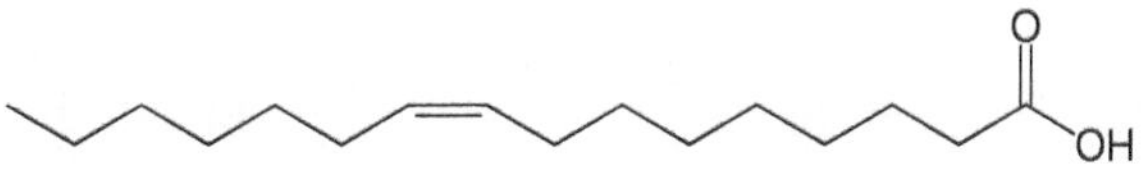

18.2 Waxes

LO 2: **Recognize and draw the structure of waxes including the carboxylic acid and alcohol portions of wax molecules.**

18.17 Which is a primary biological function of waxes?

a) Waxes help animals break down the protein we eat.

b) Waxes help plants increase their absorption of sunlight.

c) Waxes help protect plants from water loss and damage due to pests.

d) Waxes help our bodies synthesize omega-3 and omega-6 fatty acids.

18.18 What other product is formed when a fatty acid and a long chain alcohol react to form a wax?

a) H_2 b) CH_3OH

c) CO_2 d) H_2O

e) NH_3

18.19 Which molecule is a wax?

a)

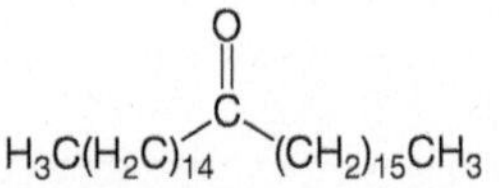

$H_3C(H_2C)_{14}$ — C(=O) — $(CH_2)_{15}CH_3$

b)

$H_3C(H_2C)_{14}$ — C(=O) — $O(CH_2)_{15}CH_3$

c)

$H_3C(H_2C)_{14}$ — CH(OH) — $(CH_2)_{15}CH_3$

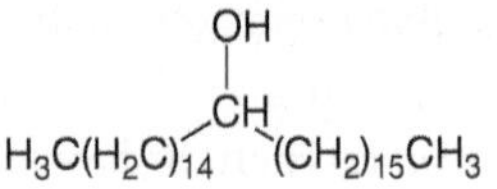

d)

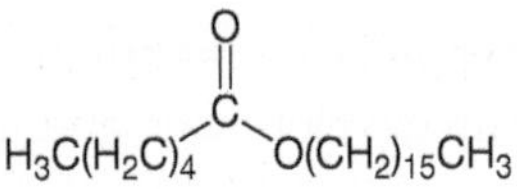

$H_3C(H_2C)_4$ — C(=O) — $O(CH_2)_{15}CH_3$

e)

$H_3C(H_2C)_{14}$ — C(=O) — $O(CH_2)_4CH_3$

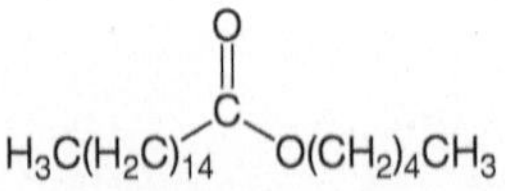

18.20 Which molecule is a wax?

a)

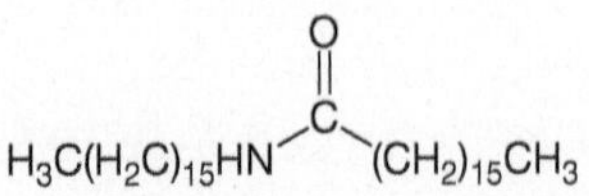

$H_3C(H_2C)_{15}HN$ — C(=O) — $(CH_2)_{15}CH_3$

b)

$H_3C(H_2C)_{24}$ — C(=O) — H

c)

$H_3C(H_2C)_{15}$ — O — $(CH_2)_{15}CH_3$

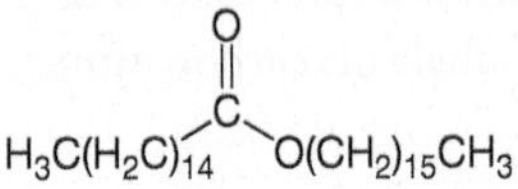

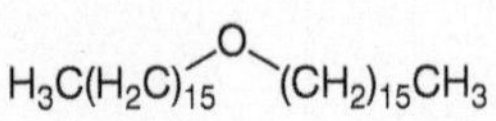

d)

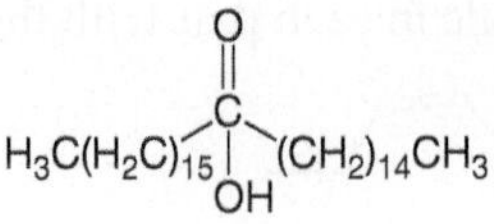

$H_3C(H_2C)_{15}$ — C(=O) — $(CH_2)_{14}CH_3$, with OH

e)

$H_3C(H_2C)_{29}O$ — C(=O) — $(CH_2)_{14}CH_3$

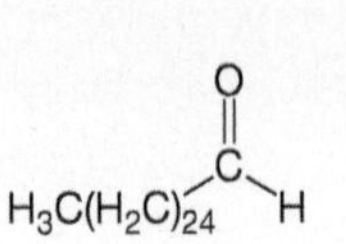

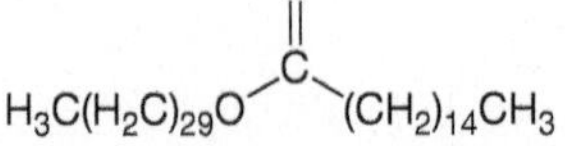

18.21 Myricyl palmitate is a primary component of beeswax. Which solvent is myricyl palmitate most soluble in?

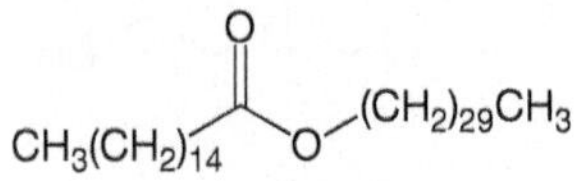

$CH_3(CH_2)_{14}$ — C(=O) — O — $(CH_2)_{29}CH_3$

myricyl palmitate
(wax molecule)

a) CH_3OH

b) H_2O

c) CH_3CH_2OH

d) $CH_3(CH_2)_6CO_2CH_2CH_3$

18.22 Which molecule is made from a fatty acid with 18 total carbons and a long chain alcohol with a total of 18 carbon atoms?

a)

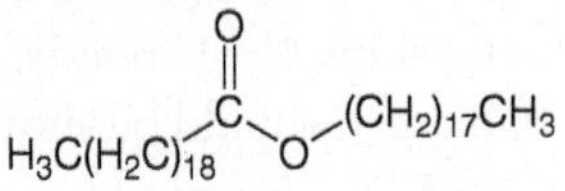

$H_3C(H_2C)_{18}$ — C(=O) — O — $(CH_2)_{17}CH_3$

b)

$H_3C(H_2C)_{18}$ — C(=O) — O — $(CH_2)_{18}CH_3$

c)

$H_3C(H_2C)_{18}$ — C(=O) — $(CH_2)_{17}CH_3$

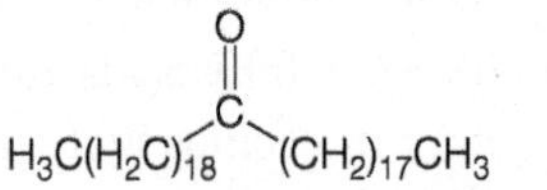

d)

$H_3C(H_2C)_{16}$ — C(=O) — O — $(CH_2)_{17}CH_3$

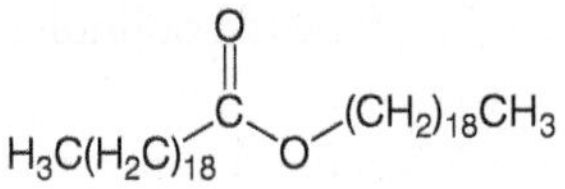

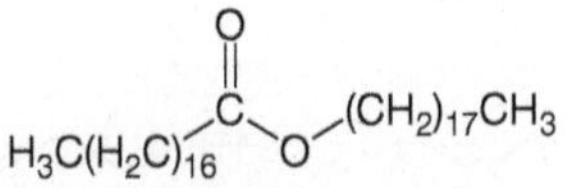

18.23 Which number indicates the site of the new bond formed when a fatty acid reacts with a long chain alcohol to form this wax molecule?

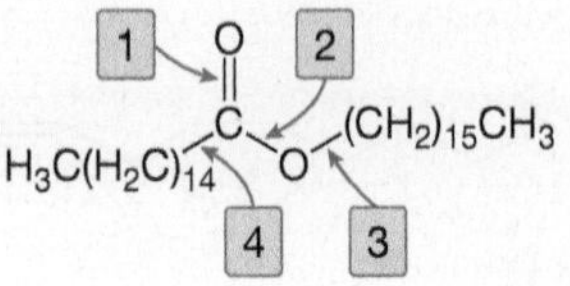

$H_3C(H_2C)_{14}$ — C(=O) — O — $(CH_2)_{15}CH_3$ (with sites 1, 2, 3, 4 labeled)

a) Site 1 b) Site 2

c) Site 3 d) Site 4

18.24 What are the two starting materials needed to form this wax molecule?

$$H_3C(H_2C)_{24} - \overset{\overset{\displaystyle O}{\|}}{C} - O - (CH_2)_{29}CH_3$$

a) $CH_3(CH_2)_{23}COOH + CH_3(CH_2)_{29}CH_2{-}OH$

b) $CH_3(CH_2)_{22}COOH + CH_3(CH_2)_{22}CH_2{-}OH$

c) $CH_3(CH_2)_{24}COOH + CH_3(CH_2)_{28}CH_2{-}OH$

d) $CH_3(CH_2)_{28}COOH + CH_3(CH_2)_{24}CH_2{-}OH$

18.25 Drawing a wax: Use the drawing tool to build the *skeletal structure* of the wax formed between myristic acid $CH_3(CH_2)_{12}CO_2H$ and cetyl alcohol $CH_3(CH_2)_{15}OH$. Do not show C—H bonds, the lone pair of electrons on oxygen, or labels on carbon atoms. Hydrogen atom(s) bonded to oxygen should be shown if present on the molecule.

18.26 Drawing a wax: Use the drawing tool to build the *skeletal structure* of the wax formed between palmitic acid $CH_3(CH_2)_{14}CO_2H$ and the alcohol $CH_3(CH_2)_{13}OH$. Do not show C—H bonds, the lone pair of electrons on oxygen, or labels on carbon atoms. Hydrogen atom(s) bonded to oxygen should be shown if present on the molecule.

18.27 Drawing a wax: The jojoba plant produces a wax that is widely used in personal care products and cosmetics. The wax contains eicosenoic acid $CH_3(CH_2)_7 CH{=}CH(CH_2)_9 CO_2H$ and the alcohol $CH_3(CH_2)_7 CH{=}CH(CH_2)_8 OH$. Use the drawing tool to build the *skeletal structure* of the wax formed between these two molecules. Be sure that your drawing clearly shows the *cis* geometry in the carbon-carbon double bond found in the fatty acid and the long chain alcohol. Do not show C—H bonds, the lone pair of electrons on oxygen, or labels on carbon atoms. Hydrogen atom(s) bonded to oxygen should be shown if present on the molecule.

18.28 In Chapter 17, we learned about the formation and hydrolysis of esters. What products are formed when the wax below is hydrolyzed?

$$H_3C(H_2C)_{10} - \overset{\overset{\displaystyle O}{\|}}{C} - O - (CH_2)_{13}CH_3 \ + \ H_2O \ \xrightleftharpoons{\text{acid (H}^+\text{)}} \ \boxed{?}$$

a) $CH_3(CH_2)_{10}OH + CH_3(CH_2)_{13}CH_2{-}OH$

b) $CH_3(CH_2)_{10}COO^-Na^+ + CH_3(CH_2)_{13}CH_2{-}OH$

c) $CH_3(CH_2)_{10}COOH + CH_3(CH_2)_{12}CH_2{-}OH$

d) $CH_3(CH_2)_{10}COOH + CH_3(CH_2)_{13}COOH$

18.3 Triacylglycerols

LO 3: **Draw the structure of triacylglycerols and predict the hydrolysis products of triacylglycerols.**

18.29 What are the components of a triacylglycerol?

a) three fatty acids connected to glycerol with ester bonds

b) two fatty acids and a long-chain alcohol connected to glycerol with ester bonds

c) three long-chain alcohols connected to three fatty acids

d) one long-chain alcohol connected to three fatty acids with carboxylic acid bonds

e) three glycerol molecules connected to three fatty acids with ester bonds

18.30 A triacylglycerol may contain _____. Select all that apply.

a) ketone

b) saturated fatty acid

c) halogen

d) *cis* unsaturated fatty acid

e) short chain carboxylic acid

f) steroid

g) *trans* unsaturated fatty acid

h) polycyclic hydrocarbon

i) polyunsaturated fatty acid

j) polycyclic aromatic hydrocarbon

18.31 Which molecule is a triacylglycerol?

a)

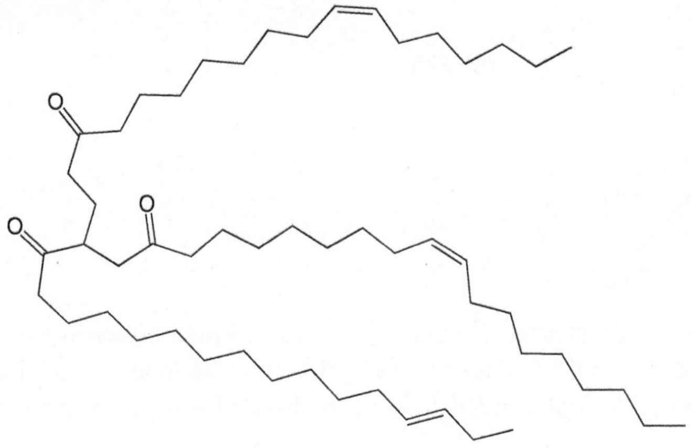

b)

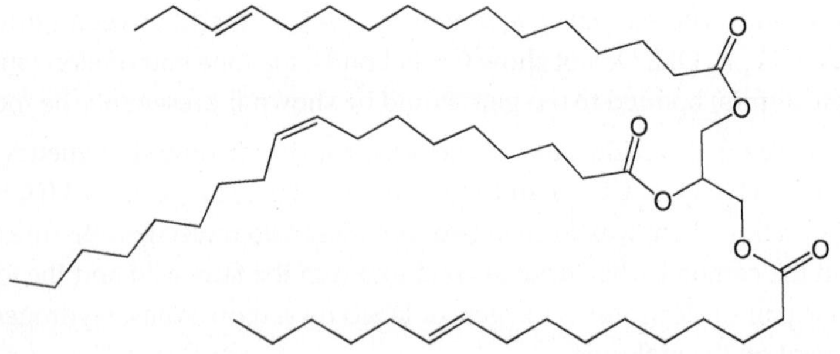

c)

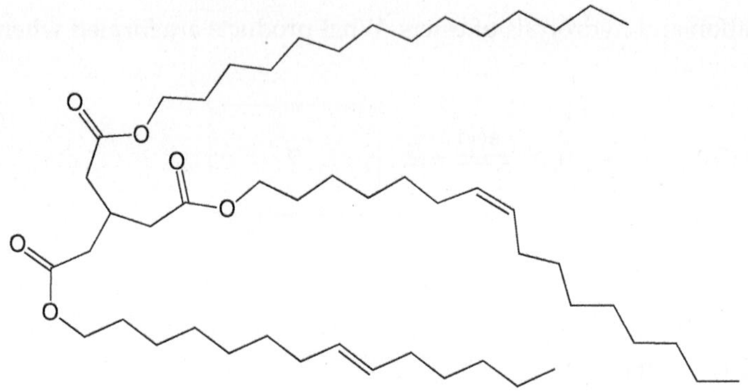

d)

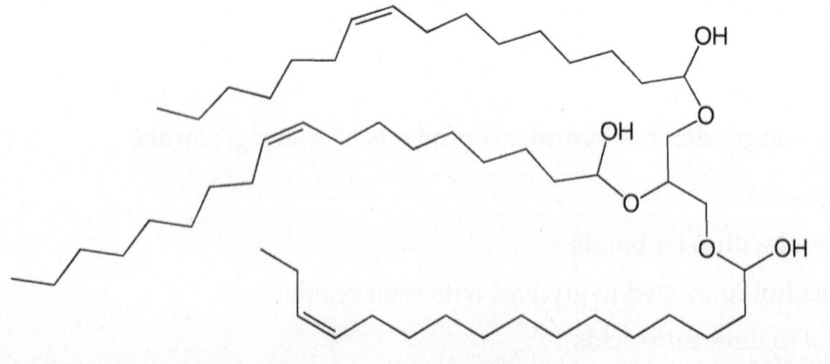

18.32 Which of these mixed triacylglycerols contains two *cis* poly unsaturated fatty acids and a saturated fatty acid?

a)

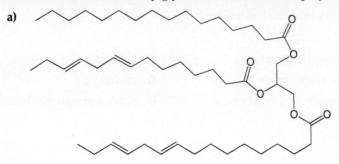

b)

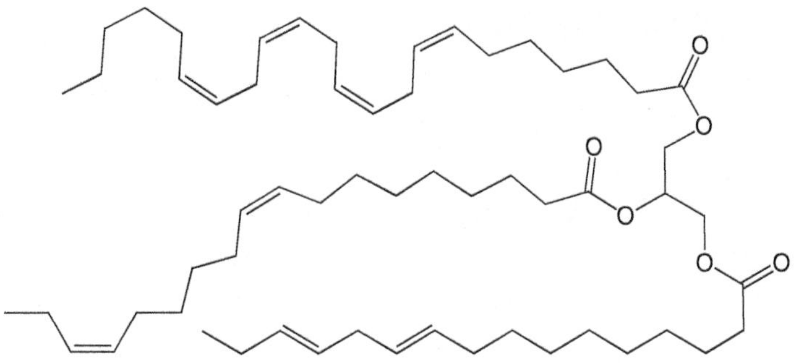

c)

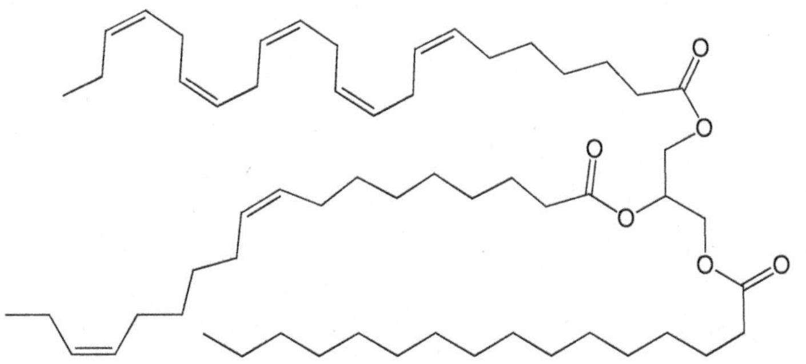

d)

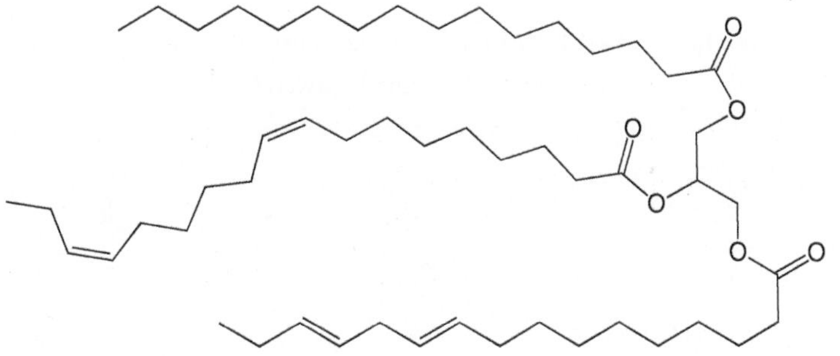

18.33 Which mixed triacylglycerol contains a saturated fatty acid, a *cis* unsaturated fatty acid and a *trans* unsaturated fatty acid?

a)

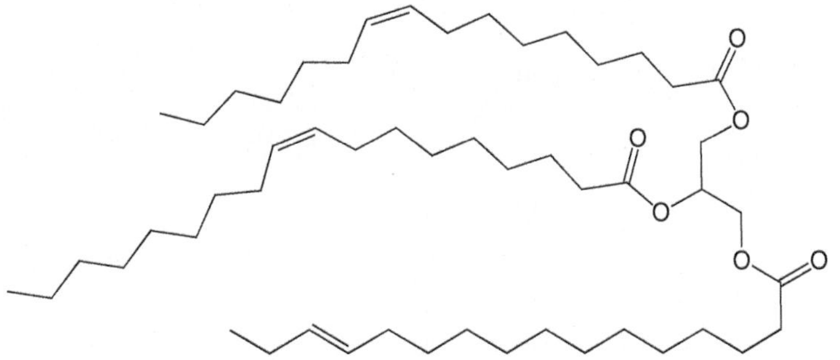

b)

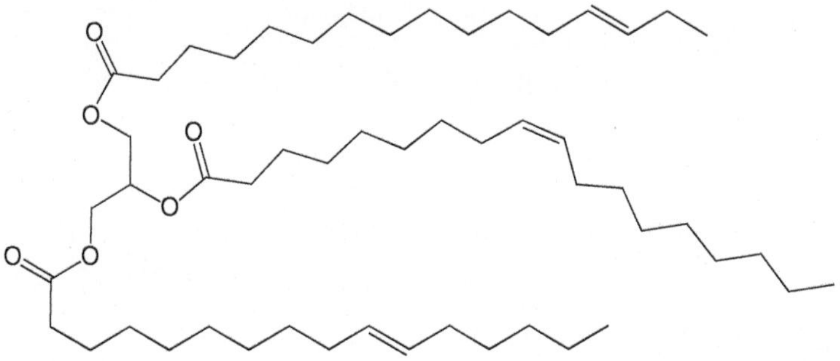

c)

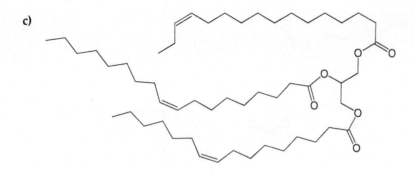

d)

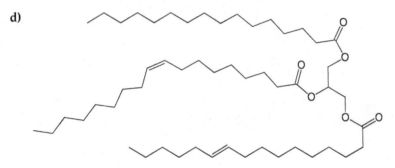

18.34 Identify the missing starting material needed for the triacylglycerol formation reaction shown.

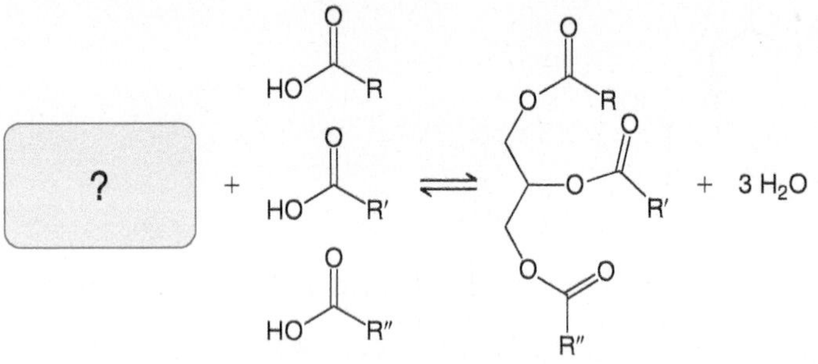

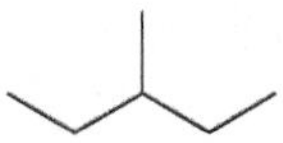

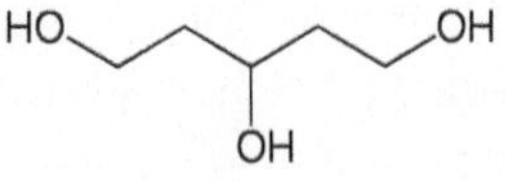

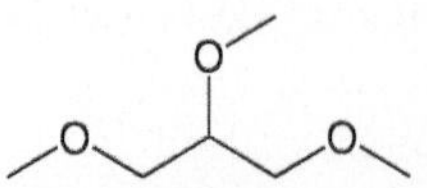

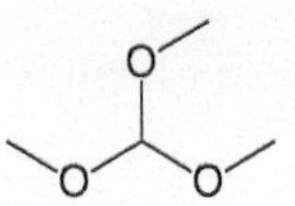

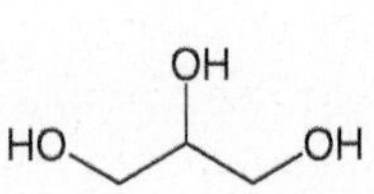

18.35 What are the starting materials needed to form the triacylglycerol shown?

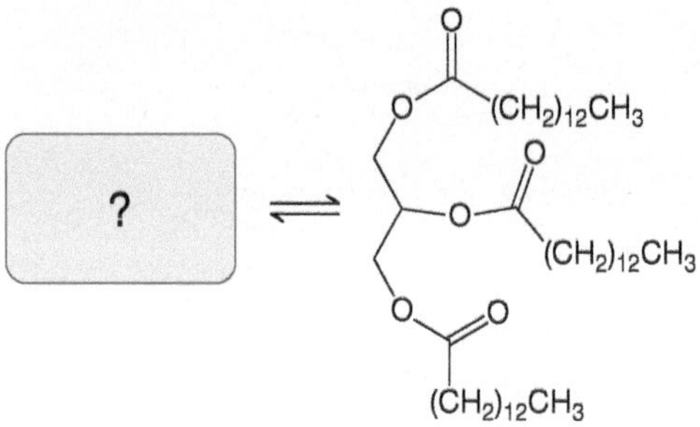

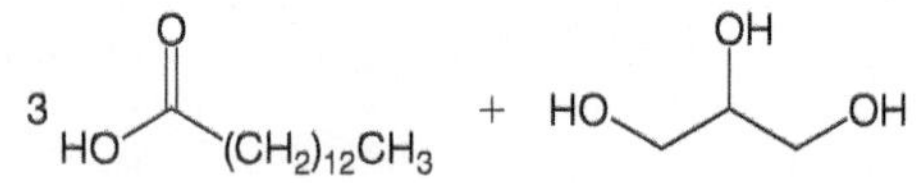

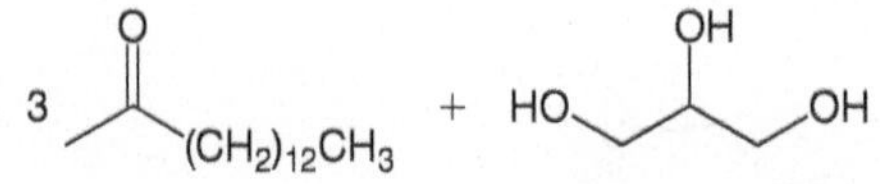

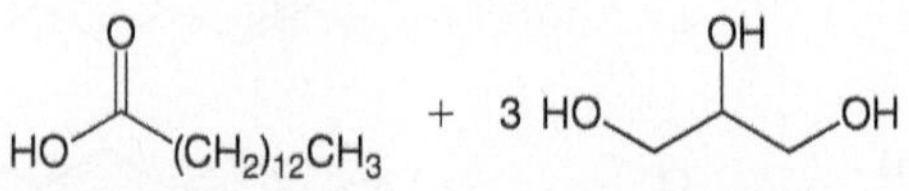

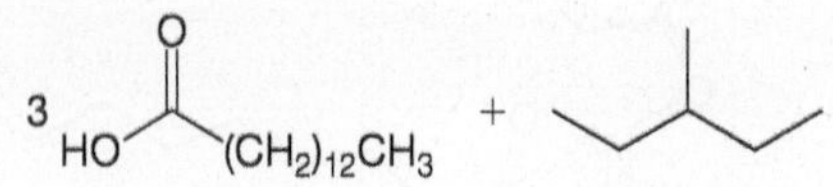

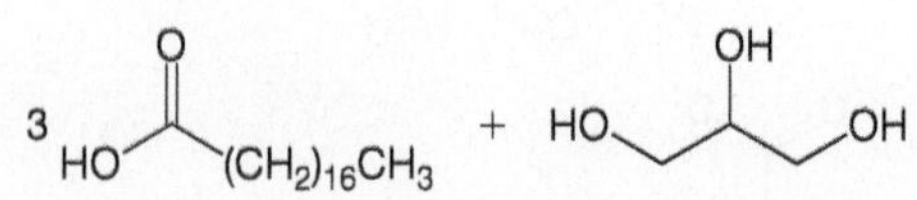

18.36 What are the products formed in the reaction?

+ 3 H₂O $\xrightarrow[\text{enzyme}]{\text{lipase}}$?

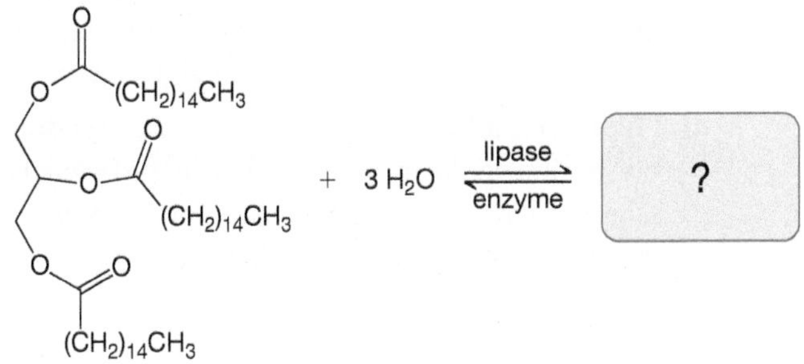

a)

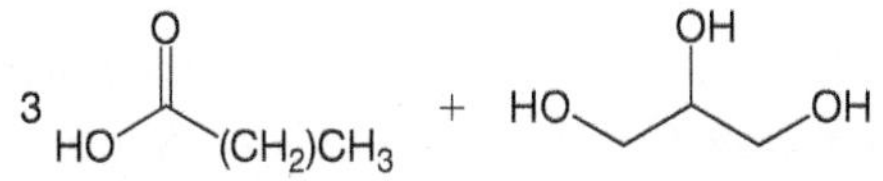

b)

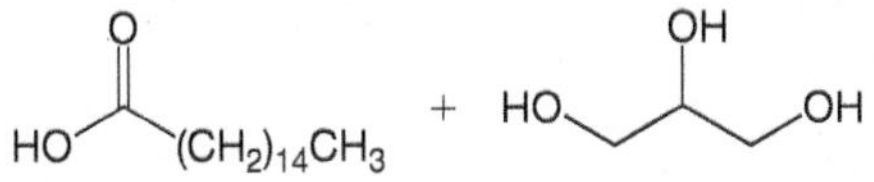

c)

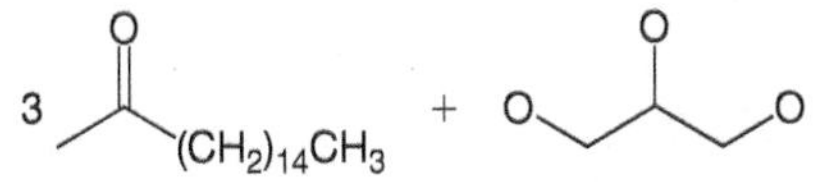

d)

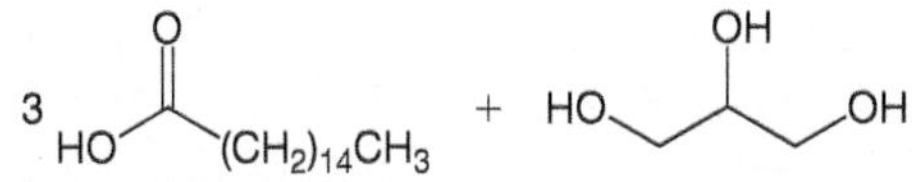

e)

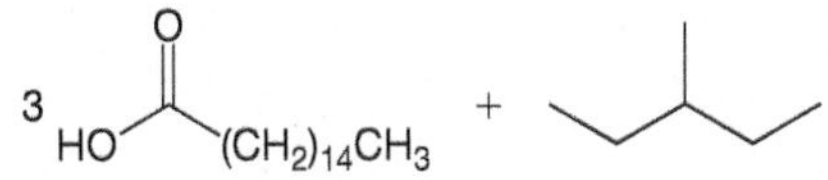

18.37 What are the products formed in the reaction?

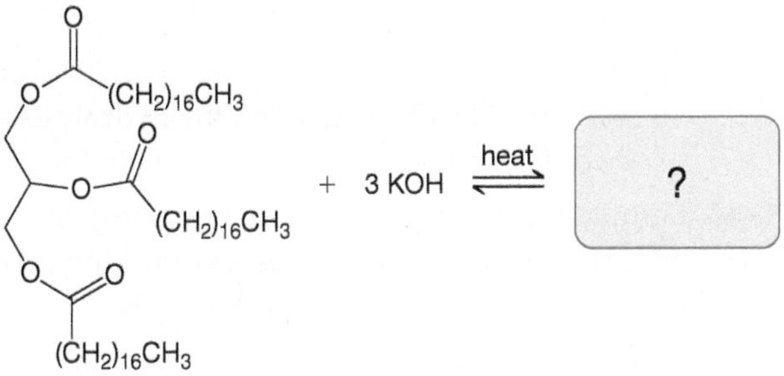

+ 3 KOH $\xrightarrow{\text{heat}}$?

a)

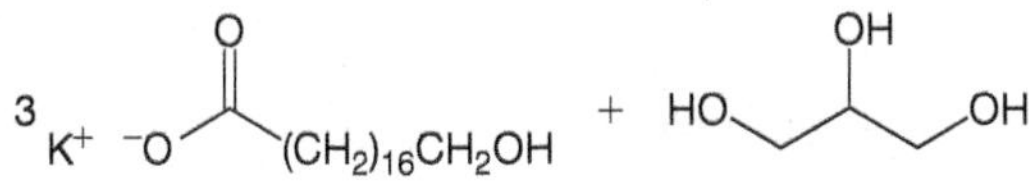

b)

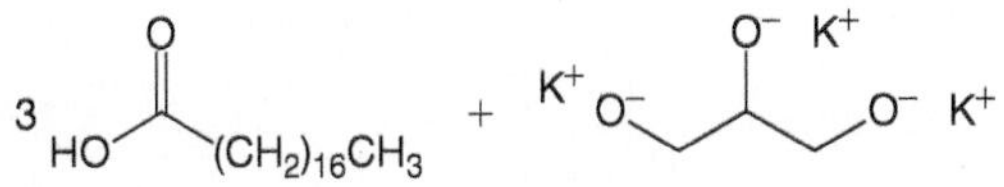

c)

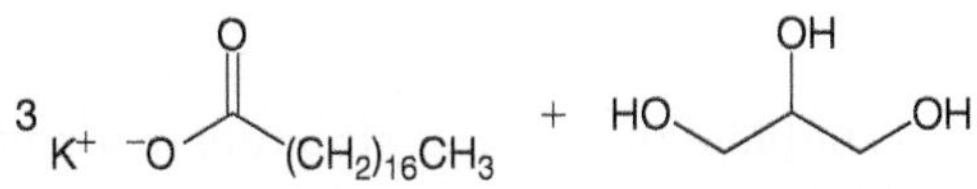

d)

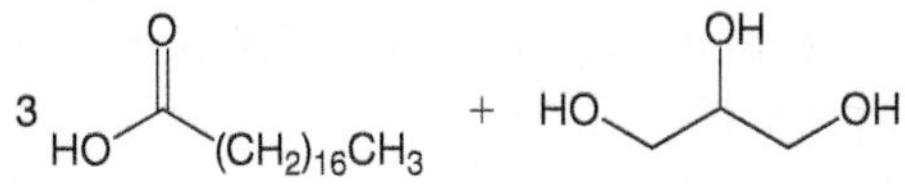

e) + 3 HO⟋⟍OH

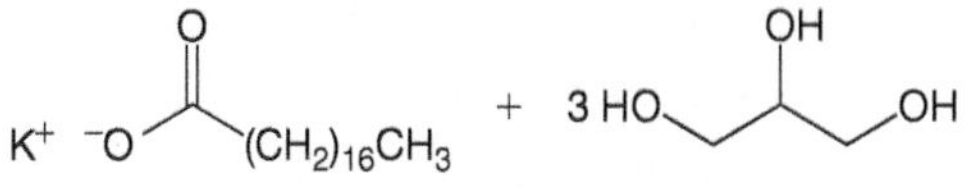

18.38 What products are formed in this reaction?

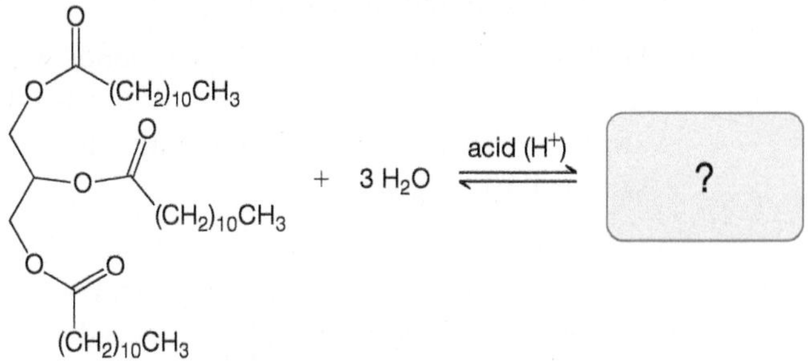

+ 3 H₂O $\xrightleftharpoons{\text{acid (H}^+\text{)}}$?

a)

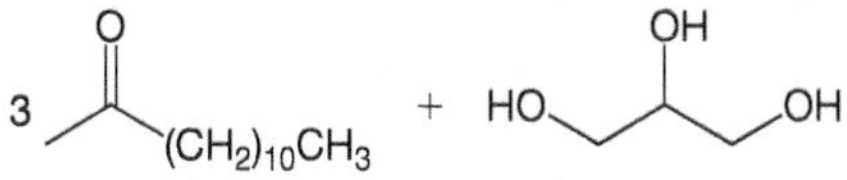

b)

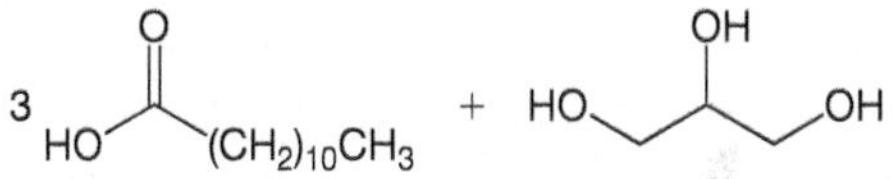

c)

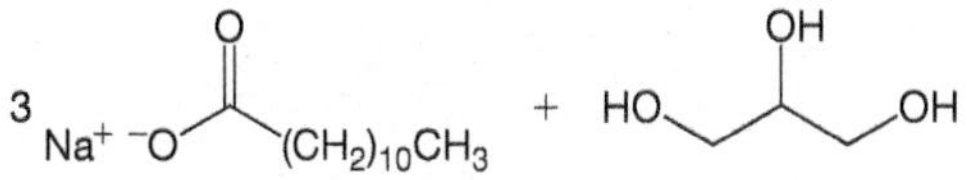

d)

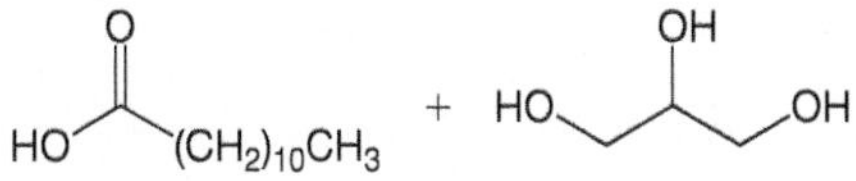

e)

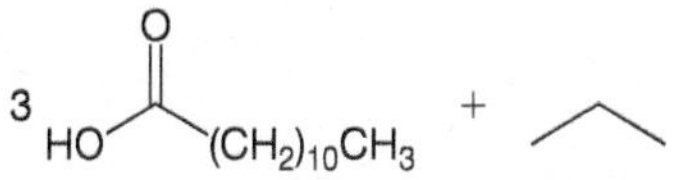

18.39 Drawing a triacylglycerol: Use the drawing tool to build the *skeletal structure* of the triacylglycerol formed from three molecules of myristic acid $(CH_3\text{—}(CH_2)_{12}\text{—COOH})$. Do not show C—H bonds, the lone pair of electrons on oxygen, or labels on carbon atoms. Hydrogen atom(s) bonded to oxygen should be shown if present on the molecule.

18.40 Drawing a triacylglycerol: Use the drawing tool to build the *skeletal structure* of the triacylglycerol formed from two molecules of palmitic acid $(CH_3\text{—}(CH_2)_{14}\text{—COOH})$, and one molecule of oleic acid $(CH_3\text{—}(CH_2)_7\text{—CH}=CH\text{—}(CH_2)_7\text{—COOH})$. Place the oleic acid, which has its C=C double bond in the *cis* geometry, as the fatty acid in the middle of the three in the triacylglycerol. Do not show C—H bonds, the lone pair of electrons on oxygen, or labels on carbon atoms. Hydrogen atom(s) bonded to oxygen should be shown if present on the molecule.

18.41 Which statement about the chemical modification of triacylglycerols is true?

a) Hydrolysis releases one or more of the fatty acids from a triacylglycerol, whereas hydrogenation adds H atoms to carbon-carbon double bonds to form saturated triacylglycerols.

b) Hydrolysis forms one or more ester bonds with fatty acids, whereas hydrogenation adds H atoms to carbon-carbon double bonds to form saturated triacylglycerols.

c) Hydrolysis releases one or more of the fatty acids from a triacylglycerol, whereas hydrogenation removes H atoms from saturated triacylglycerols to form unsaturated triacylglycerols.

d) Hydrolysis adds H atoms to carbon-carbon double bonds to form saturated triacylglycerols, whereas hydrogenation releases one or more of the fatty acids from a triacylglycerol.

18.42 Drawing a hydrogenation reaction product: Use the drawing tool to build the *skeletal structure* of the product formed during *complete* hydrogenation of the triacylglycerol shown. Do not show C—H bonds, the lone pair of electrons on oxygen, or labels on carbon atoms. Hydrogen atom(s) bonded to oxygen should be shown if present on the molecule.

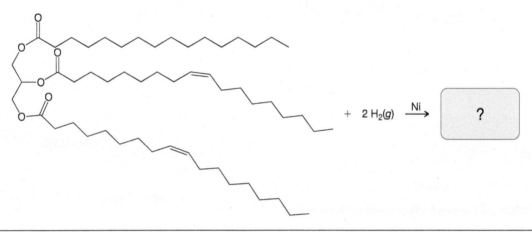

18.4 Phospholipids

LO 4: Identify the two common types of phospholipids and describe the role of phosphoacylglycerols in cell membrane structure.

18.43 The World Health Organization (WHO) estimates that there are 1.3 to 4.0 million cases of cholera a year, resulting in 21,000–143,000 deaths. Cholera is often transmitted by contaminated drinking water and if left untreated, cholera can kill within hours due to rapid dehydration. How does the cholera bacterium *Vibrio cholerae* cause severe diarrhea?

a) The cholera bacterium triggers rapid, life-threatening diarrhea by disrupting the function of the cell membranes lining the intestines.

b) The cholera bacterium triggers rapid, life-threatening diarrhea by triggering an autoimmune response that damages the small intestine and colon.

c) The cholera bacterium triggers rapid, life-threatening diarrhea by disrupting the myelin sheath that protects the walls of the intestines.

d) The cholera bacterium triggers rapid, life-threatening diarrhea by triggering the hydrolysis and shedding of triacylglycerides stored in the liver.

18.44 Complete the general structure of a phosphoacylglycerol by dragging pieces of text into the correct shaded regions on the template structure.

Answer choices: amino alcohol, steroid, fatty acid, ketone, glycerol, wax, NO_3, H^+, PO_4, SO_4, OH, CH_3OH

Target boxes:

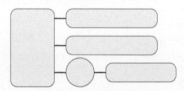

18.45 Complete the general structure of a sphingolipid, specifically, sphingomyelin by dragging pieces of text into the correct shaded regions on the template structure.

Answer choices: glucose, glycerol, fatty acid, steroid, amino alcohol, sphingosine, H_2O, SO_4, OH, PO_4, H^+, NO_3

Target boxes:

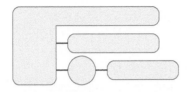

18.46 Identify the specific type of lipid depicted by each of the following block diagrams.

A.

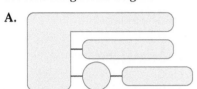

B.

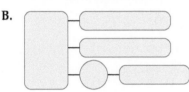

C.

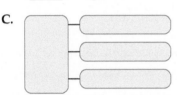

Answer choices: wax, triacylglycerol, steroid, phosphoacylglycerol, fatty acid, sphingomyelin, trisaccharide

Target boxes: lipid depicted in (A), lipid depicted in (B), lipid depicted in (C)

18.47 Classify this lipid.

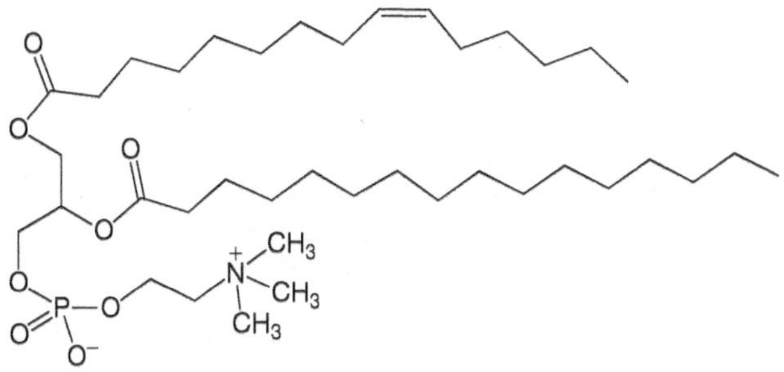

a) triacylglycerol   b) glycolipid
c) steroid   d) wax
e) phosphoacylglycerol   f) fatty acid
g) sphingomyelin   h) disaccharide

18.48 Classify this lipid.

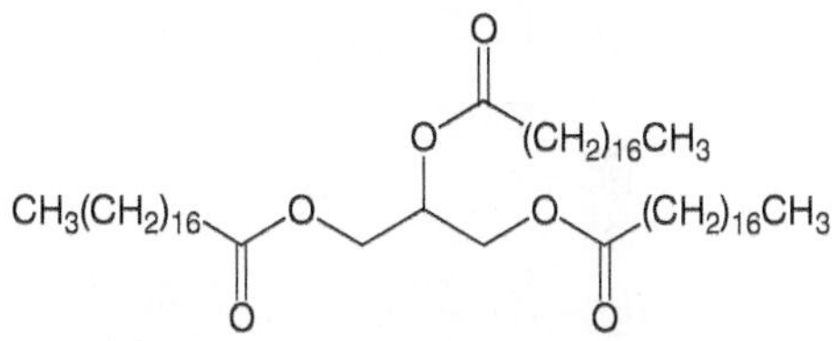

a) triacylglycerol   b) glycolipid
c) steroid   d) wax
e) phosphoacylglycerol   f) fatty acid
g) sphingomyelin   h) disaccharide

18.49 Classify this lipid.

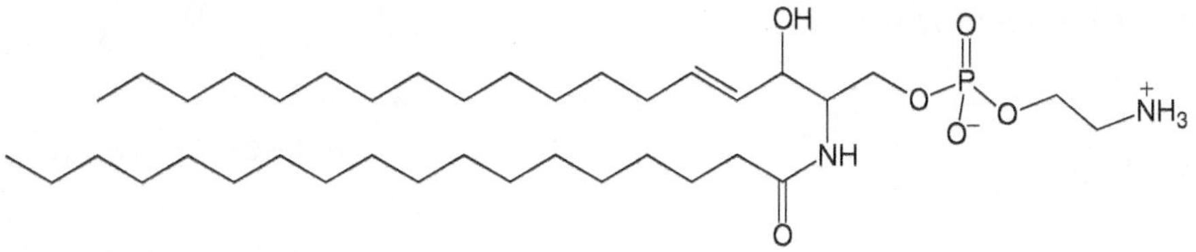

a) triacylglycerol   b) glycolipid   c) steroid   d) wax
e) phosphoacylglycerol   f) fatty acid   g) sphingomyelin   h) disaccharide>

18.50 Which lipid contains two fatty acids having 16 carbons atoms each and the amino alcohol serine?

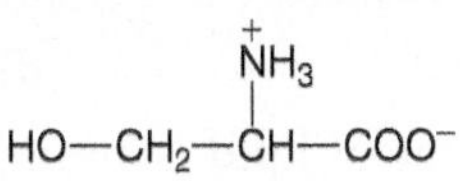

amino alcohol serine

a)

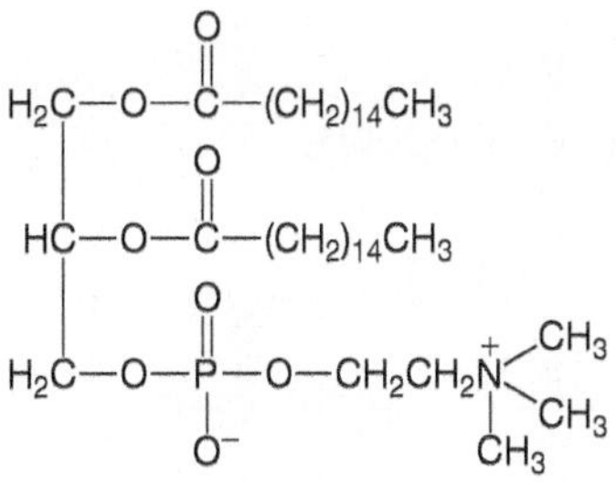

b)

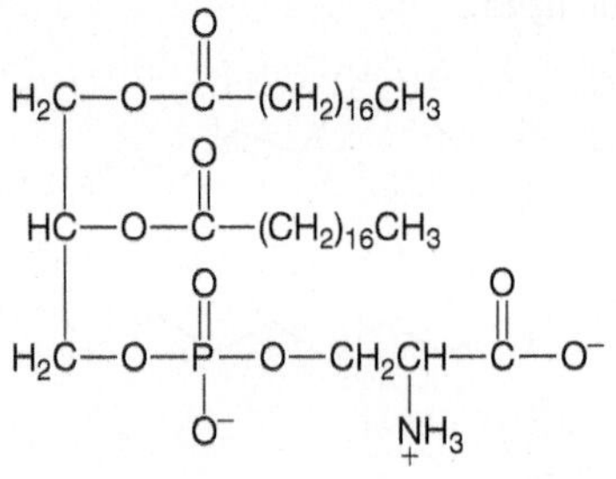

c)

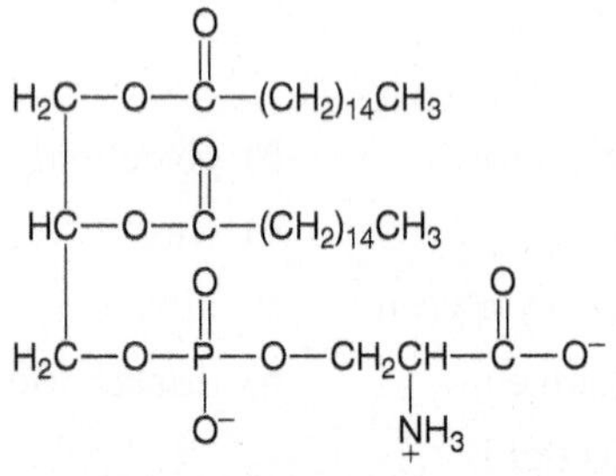

d)

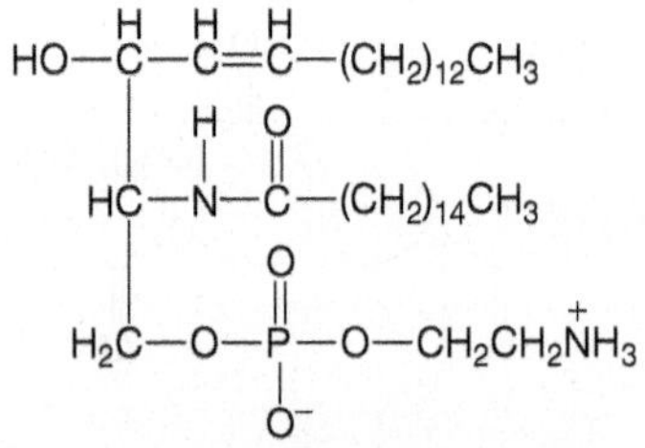

18.51 Which lipid contains sphingosine?

a)

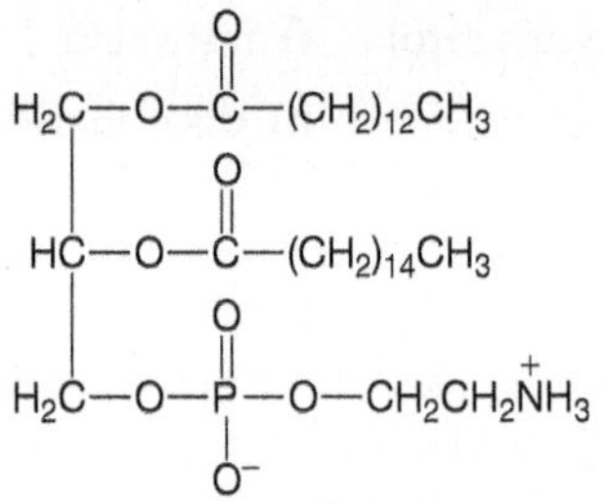

b)

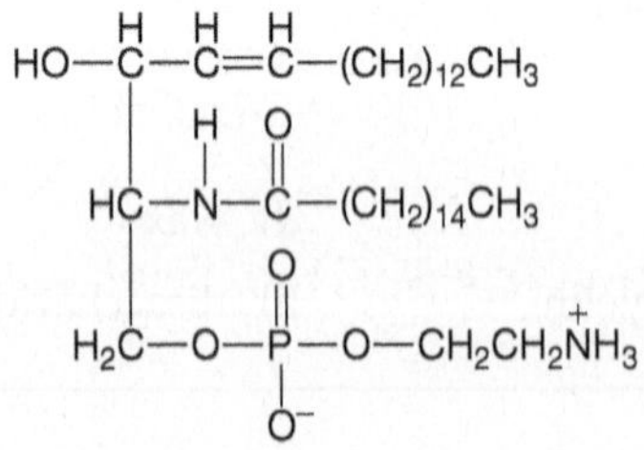

c)

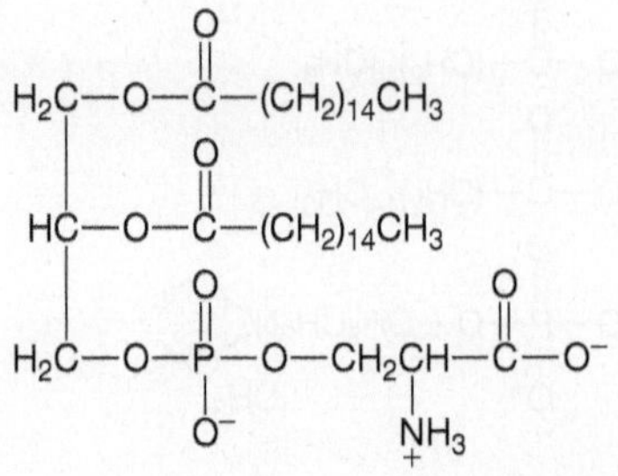

d)

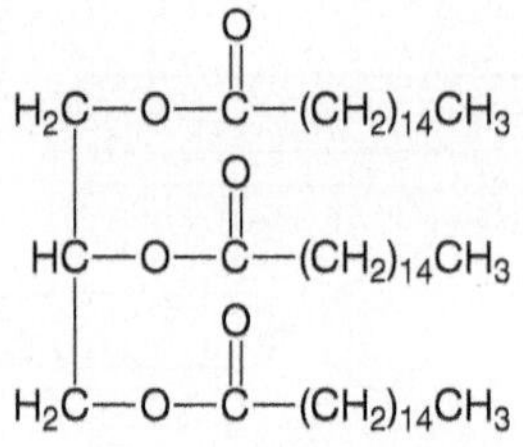

18.52 Select all molecules that are *not* a phosphoacylglycerol.

a)

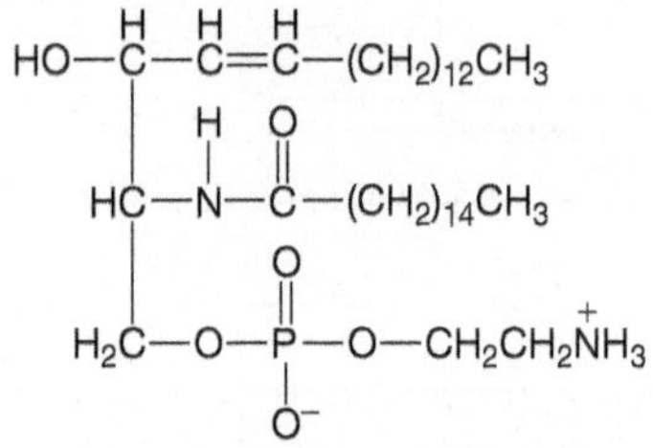

b)

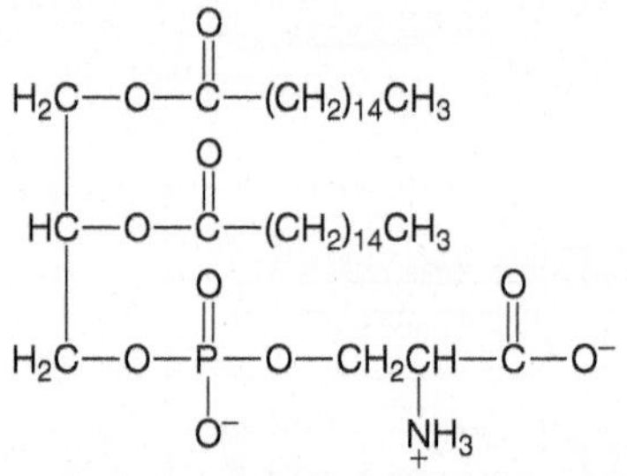

c)

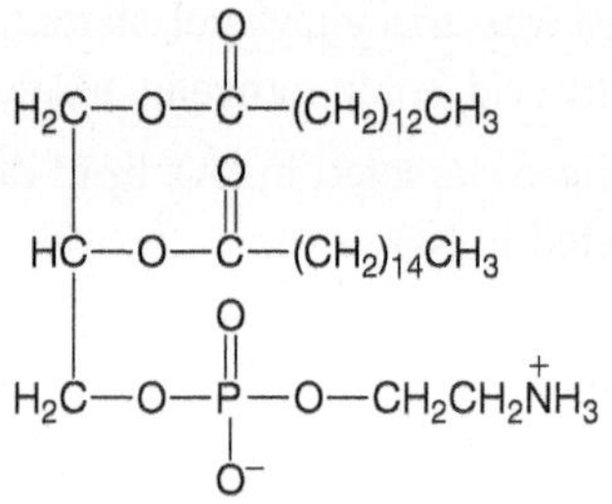

d)

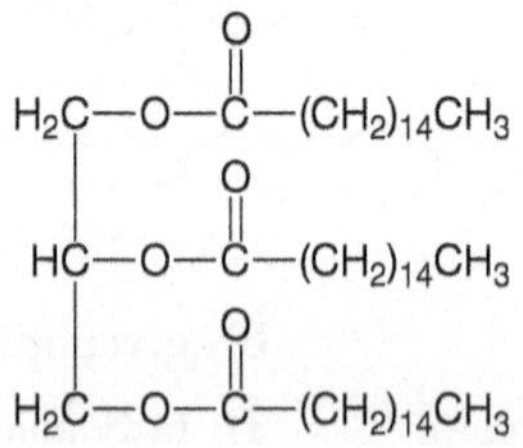

18.53 Select the names of all molecules that are *not* an amino alcohol commonly found in phosphoacylglycerols.

a) ethanolamine   **b)** histamine

c) choline   **d)** serine

18.54 Which type of lipid is an important component of the protective coating surrounding nerve cells?

a) phosphoacylglycerols   **b)** waxes

c) steroids   **d)** sphingomyelins

e) triacylglycerols

18.55 Gaucher's disease is an inherited lipid storage disorder that affects many of the body's organs and tissues. Lipid storage diseases are caused by genetic deficiencies in one or more of the enzymes needed to decompose certain complex lipids such as glycolipids (sugars attached to lipids). As a result, glycolipids such as glucocerebroside accumulate, damaging the liver and spleen. The fatty substances also can build up in bone tissue, weakening the bone and increasing the risk of fractures. The disease can also affect cognitive ability, cause blindness, and lead to premature death. What building block is found in the molecular structure of glucocerebroside?

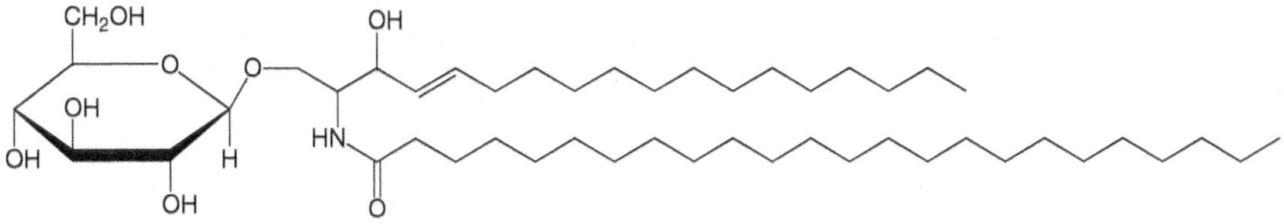

glucocerebroside

a) phosphoacylglycerol   b) wax   c) steroid

d) polysaccharide   e) sphingosine

18.5 Steroids and Hormones

LO 5: Recognize the general structure of steroids and steroid hormones and be familiar with several examples of each.

18.56 Which statement describes a primary role that lipoproteins play in the body?

a) directly increase red blood cell count   b) help transport cholesterol in the body

c) increase the metabolic turnover of cellulose   d) directly increase white blood cell count

e) convert fructose to glucose for cellular respiration

18.57 What medical condition is the synthetic steroid digoxin primarily used for?

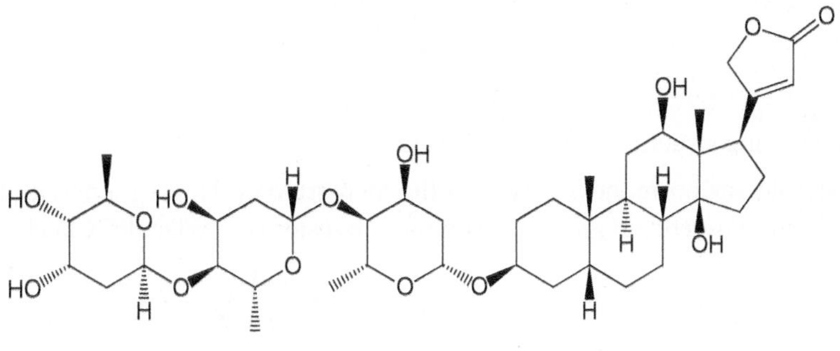

a) depression   b) heart disease   c) increasing fertility

d) allergies   e) insomnia   f) birth control

18.58 Prednisone is a medication used to treat asthma, allergies, and autoimmune disorders such as rheumatoid arthritis. What class of molecule does prednisone belong to?

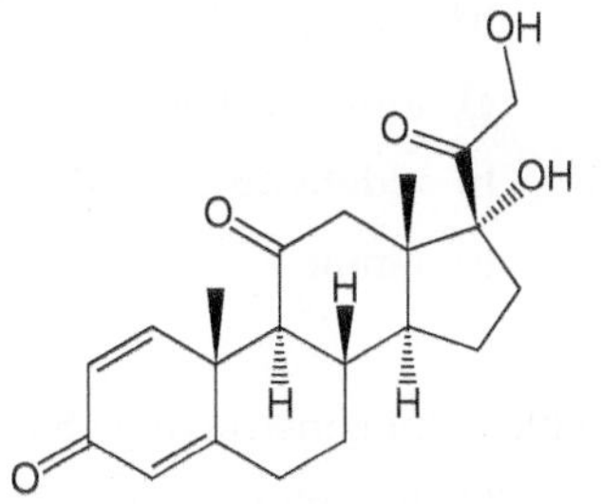

a) carbohydrate   b) wax   c) steroid

d) triacylglycerol   e) phosphoacylglycerol

18.59 Identify the region that best identifies the steroid skeleton on the digoxin molecule.

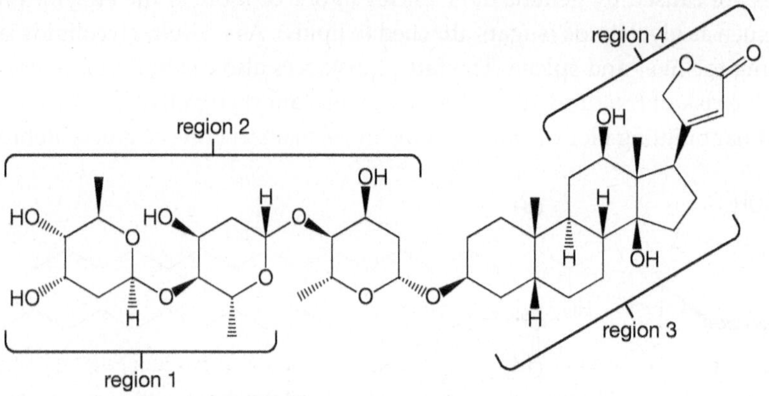

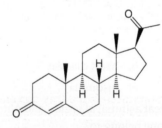

a) Region 1   **b)** Region 2   **c)** Region 3   **d)** Region 4

18.60 Categorize these structures as having a steroid ring structure or not having a steroid ring structure. Keep in mind that molecules can flip and rotate without changing their structure or identity.

Answer choices:

a)
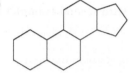

b)

c)

d)
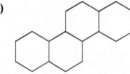

e)
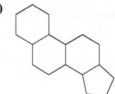

f)
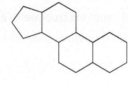

Target boxes: steroid ring structure, *not* a steroid ring structure

18.61 Progesterone is steroid sex hormone involved in the menstrual cycle, pregnancy, and development of the embryo during pregnancy. What functional groups are on the progesterone molecule? Check all that apply.

a) ester   **b)** alkene   **c)** secondary alcohol

d) tertiary alcohol   **e)** aromatic benzene ring   **f)** carboxylic acid

g) ether   **h)** aldehyde   **i)** alkyne

j) ketone   **k)** amine   **l)** thiol

m) primary alcohol

18.62 Which molecule is used as a building block for constructing steroidal hormones in the body?

a) fatty acids   **b)** triacylglycerols   **c)** vitamin C

d) cholesterol   **e)** sphingosine

18.63 Although both men and women both have the steroid hormones estradiol and testosterone, estradiol is often referred to as the primary female sex hormone. Testosterone is often called the primary male sex hormone. The reaction shown illustrates how testosterone is converted to estradiol in the body. Which statement best describes the chemical changes that take place in this reaction?

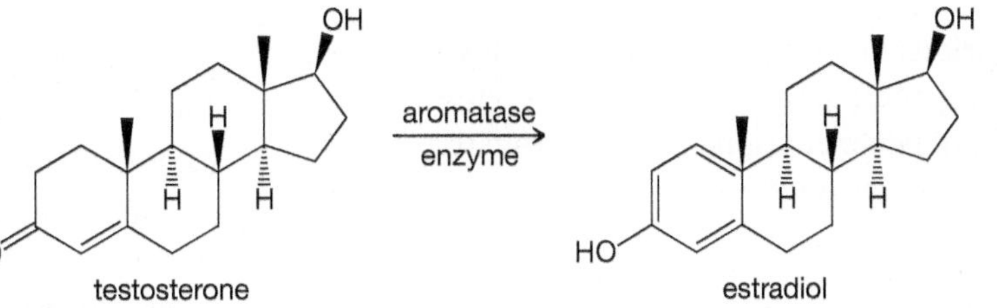

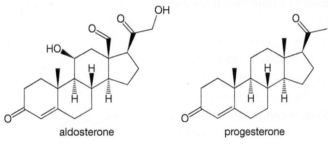

testosterone   estradiol

a) During the reaction, a hydroxyl (OH) group in estradiol is converted to a ketone group in testosterone. An aromatic benzene ring in estradiol is converted to a cyclohexene and a methyl (CH_3) group is added during the reaction.

b) During the reaction, the ketone carbonyl group in testosterone is converted to a hydroxyl (OH) group in estradiol. An aromatic benzene ring is also produced in estradiol during the reaction.

c) During the reaction, the ketone carbonyl group in testosterone is converted to a hydroxyl (OH) group in estradiol. A methyl (CH_3) group on testosterone is also removed and an aromatic benzene ring is produced in estradiol during the reaction.

d) During the reaction, an aromatic benzene ring is produced in estradiol. A methyl (CH_3) group is also removed from testosterone during the conversion of testosterone to estradiol.

18.64 Aldosterone is a steroid hormone that is involved in regulating blood pressure and maintaining sodium (Na^+) and potassium (K^+) levels in the kidney, colon, sweat glands, and colon. Progesterone is steroid sex hormone involved in the menstrual cycle, pregnancy, and development of the embryo during pregnancy. What functional groups does aldosterone have that are *not* found on progesterone? *Hint*: from the list provided, you should identify three groups.

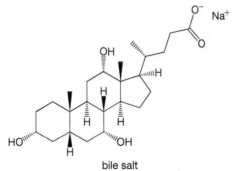

aldosterone   progesterone

a) amine	**b)** primary alcohol	**c)** alkyne	**d)** secondary alcohol
e) alkene	**f)** ether	**g)** thiol	**h)** aldehyde
i) ester	**j)** ketone	**k)** carboxylic acid	**l)** tertiary alcohol
m) amide			

18.65 Bile salts like the one shown below are produced in the liver and are involved in cholesterol metabolism and assisting with absorption of fat-soluble vitamins. What functional groups are on the bile salt molecule shown? Check all that apply.

bile salt

a) alkyne	**b)** tertiary alcohol	**c)** amine	**d)** secondary alcohol **e)** alkene
f) aromatic benzene ring		**g)** thiol	**h)** ether **i)** aldehyde
j) ester	**k)** ketone	**l)** carboxylate anion	**m)** primary alcohol

18.66 Hydrocortisone and betamethasone are corticosteroids that are used to treat conditions such as arthritis, severe allergies, blood disorders, and immune system disorders. These drugs act by helping to decrease your immune system's response to various diseases and reduce symptoms such as swelling and allergic-type reactions. How is the structure of betamethasone different from the structure of hydrocortisone?

hydrocortisone   betamethasone

a) Hydrocortisone has one less hydrogen atom and one more carbon atom than betamethasone.

b) Betamethasone has a fluorine atom, an additional methyl group, and an additional alkene group that hydrocortisone does not have.

c) Betamethasone has an aromatic benzene ring, a fluorine, and a methyl group that hydrocortisone does not have.

d) Hydrocortisone has a fluorine atom, a methyl group, and an additional alkene group that betamethasone does not have.

18.67 Prednisone and betamethasone are both corticosteroids that are used to treat conditions such as skin diseases, arthritis, severe allergies, and immune system disorders by decreasing the immune system's response and reducing inflammation. Which best describes the structural differences between betamethasone and prednisone?

prednisone   betamethasone

a) Betamethasone has a CH_3 methyl group that prednisone does not. Betamethasone also has a secondary alcohol instead of the ketone carbonyl ($C=O$) found on prednisone.

b) Prednisone has a fluorine atom and a CH_3 methyl group that betamethasone does not. Prednisone also has a secondary alcohol instead of the ketone carbonyl ($C=O$) found on betamethasone.

c) Prednisone has ketone group at the ring position where betamethasone has a tertiary alcohol. Prednisone is also missing a fluorine atom that is present on betamethasone.

d) Betamethasone has a fluorine atom and a CH_3 methyl group that prednisone does not. Betamethasone also has a secondary alcohol instead of the ketone carbonyl ($C=O$) found on prednisone.

18.68 Fluticasone is a corticosteroid used to reduce symptoms of asthma such as wheezing and shortness of breath. Prednisone is a corticosteroid used to treat conditions such as arthritis, breathing problems, severe allergies, skin diseases, and immune system disorders. These drugs act by helping decrease your immune system's response to various diseases and reducing symptoms such as swelling and allergic-type reactions. Which statement best describes the structural differences between these two steroids?

prednisone   fluticasone

a) Fluticasone has three fluorine atoms, one sulfur atom, and an additional methyl group that are not on prednisone. Fluticasone also has a secondary alcohol at the ring position that prednisone has a ketone carbonyl.

b) Prednisone has three fluorine atoms, one sulfur atom, and an additional methyl group that are not on fluticasone. Prednisone also has a secondary alcohol at the ring position that fluticasone has a ketone carbonyl, and is missing the primary alcohol found on fluticasone.

c) Prednisone is missing two fluorine atoms and a methyl group that are found on fluticasone. In addition, prednisone has a carboxylic acid group that is not found on fluticasone.

d) Fluticasone has three fluorine atoms, one sulfur atom, and an additional methyl group that are not on prednisone. Fluticasone also has a secondary alcohol at the ring position that prednisone has a ketone carbonyl and is missing the primary alcohol found on prednisone.

18.69 Drawing a steroid ring system: Use the drawing tool to build a skeletal structure of the basic four ring steroid ring skeleton shown at the beginning of Section 18.5. Do not show C—H bonds or labels on carbon atoms.

18.6 Prostaglandins and Leukotrienes

LO 6: Apply the IUPAC naming system to carboxylic acids, esters, and amides.

18.70 Asthma is a lung disease that constricts the airways making it difficult to breathe. Which class of molecule is involved in the asthmatic response?

a) steroids   **b)** leukotrienes

c) NSAIDs   **d)** phosphoglandins

18.71 Both prostaglandin E_2 (PGE_2), also known as alprostadil, and prostaglandin F_2 ($PGF_{2\alpha}$), also known as carboprost, are naturally occurring prostaglandins used medically to help induce labor, reduce bleeding after delivery, and treat babies with congenital heart defects. Which statement best describes the structural similarities and differences between these two prostaglandins?

PGE$_2$ PGF$_{2a}$

a) PGF_{2a} has three hydroxyl groups and two alkene groups. PGE_2 has two hydroxyl groups, two alkene groups, and an aldehyde group. Both prostaglandin molecules contain a five-membered ring, a carboxylic acid group, and a total of 20 carbon atoms.

b) PGF_{2a} has a ketone group in the five-membered ring and PGE_2 has a secondary alcohol group at this same position on the five-membered ring. Both prostaglandin molecules contain a five-membered ring, a carboxylic acid group, and a total of 20 carbon atoms.

c) PGE_2 has a ketone group on the five-membered ring and PGF_{2a} has a secondary alcohol group at this same position on the five-membered ring. Both prostaglandin molecules contain a five membered ring, a carboxylic acid group, and a total of 20 carbon atoms

d) PGE_2 has two hydroxyl groups and three alkene groups. PGF_{2a} has three hydroxyl groups, and two alkene groups. Both prostaglandin molecules contain a five-membered ring, a carboxylic acid group, and a total of 20 carbon atoms.

18.72 Leukotrienes are synthesized in several steps from what molecule?

a) prostaglandin E_1 (PGE_1)

b) eicosanoid

c) arachidonic acid

d) cortisol

e) NSAID

18.73 Leukotriene D4 (LTD4) is a leukotriene that induces the contraction of smooth muscle, resulting in bronchoconstriction and vasoconstriction. The drug Montelukast inhibits the enzymes involved with the synthesis of the leukotriene LTD_4, helping reverse the constricted airways associated with an asthma attack. Which functional group is *not* found on the LTD4 molecule?

a) cis alkene   **b)** carboxylic acid

c) amide   **d)** tertiary alcohol

e) 1° amine   **f)** trans alkene

18.74 Prostaglandin E_1 (PGE_1), also known as alprostadil, is a naturally occurring prostaglandin which is used as a medication to help treat babies with congenital heart defects until surgery can be carried out. Prostaglandin F_2 (PGF_{2a}), also known as carboprost, is a naturally occurring prostaglandin used medically to help induce labor. Which statement best describes the structural similarities and differences between these two prostaglandins?

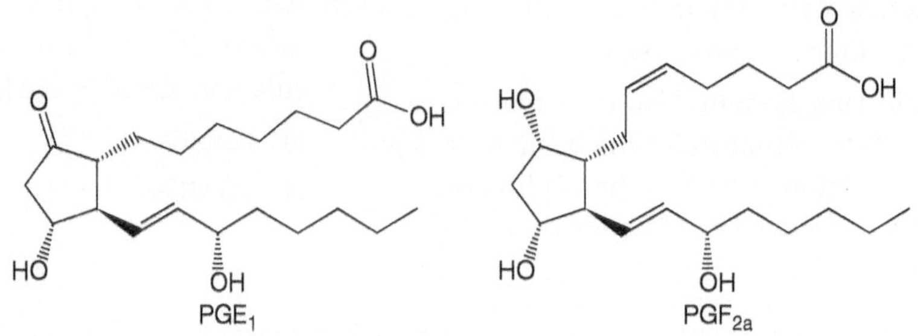

PGE₁ PGF₂ₐ

a) PGF_{2a} has three hydroxyl groups and two alkene groups. PGE_1 has two hydroxyl groups, one alkene group, and a ketone. Both prostaglandin molecules contain a five-membered ring, a carboxylic acid group, and a total of 20 carbon atoms.

b) PGE_1 has three hydroxyl groups and two alkene groups. PGF_{2a} has two hydroxyl groups, one alkene group, and a ketone. Both prostaglandin molecules contain a five-membered ring, a carboxylic acid group, and a total of 20 carbon atoms.

c) PGF_{2a} has three hydroxyl groups and two alkene groups. PGE_1 has two hydroxyl groups, one alkene group, and a ketone. Both prostaglandin molecules contain a five-membered ring, a carboxylic acid group, and a total of 21 carbon atoms.

d) PGF_{2a} has four hydroxyl groups and two alkene groups. PGE_1 has three hydroxyl groups, one alkene group, and a ketone. Both prostaglandin molecules contain a five-membered ring, a carboxylic acid group, and a total of 20 carbon atoms.

18.75 Asthma is a chronic disease of the lungs that causes airways to get inflamed and narrow, making breathing difficult. Leukotriene C4 (LTC_4) stimulates the secretion of mucus from cells in the bronchus, which in turn reduces the lung function of patients with bronchial asthma. Which statement most accurately describes the functional groups on the LTC_4 molecule?

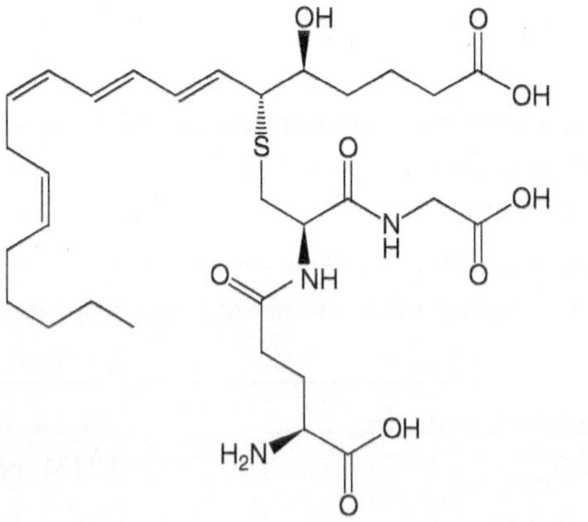

a) LTC_4 contains four alkenes, one hydroxyl, three carboxylic acids, one amide, two amines, and one thioether group.

b) LTC_4 contains four alkenes, one hydroxyl, three carboxylic acids, two amides, one amine, and one thioether group.

c) LTC_4 contains four alkenes, one hydroxyl, three carboxylic acids, two amides, one amine, and one thiol group.

d) LTC_4 contains four alkenes, one hydroxyl, three carboxylic acids, three amines, two ketones, and one thioether group.

18.76 Prostaglandin I2 (PGI$_2$), also known as prostacyclin, is a member of the eicosanoid family of lipid molecules. It functions as a vasodilator and also inhibits blood clotting in the body. Which statement most accurately describes the features of the PGI$_2$ molecule?

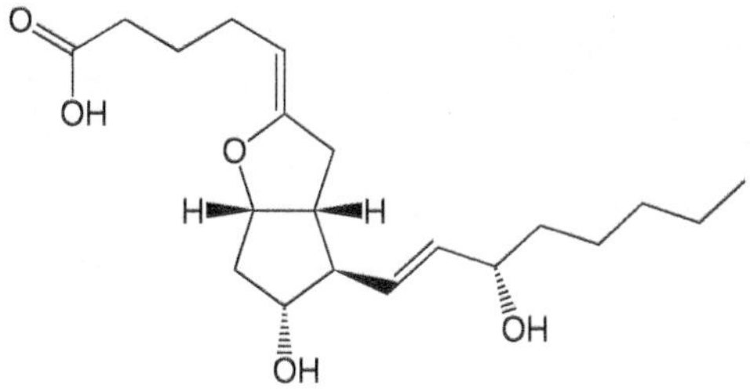

a) PGI$_2$ contains a total of 20 carbon atoms. The molecule contains two alkenes, two secondary alcohols, a cyclic ether, a ketone, and a primary alcohol group.

b) PGI$_2$ contains a total of 20 carbon atoms. The molecule contains two alkenes, two tertiary alcohols, a cyclic ether, and a carboxylic acid group.

c) PGI$_2$ contains a total of 22 carbon atoms. The molecule contains two alkenes, two secondary alcohols, a cyclic ether, and a carboxylic acid group.

d) PGI$_2$ contains a total of 20 carbon atoms. The molecule contains two alkenes, two secondary alcohols, a cyclic ether, and a carboxylic acid group.

18.77 Leukotriene B4 (LTB$_4$) is involved in the body's inflammation response. A scientist studying LTB$_4$ is interested in oxidation pathways and performs an alcohol oxidation reaction on the molecule. Predict the product formed when LTB$_4$ undergoes the complete alcohol oxidation reaction shown.

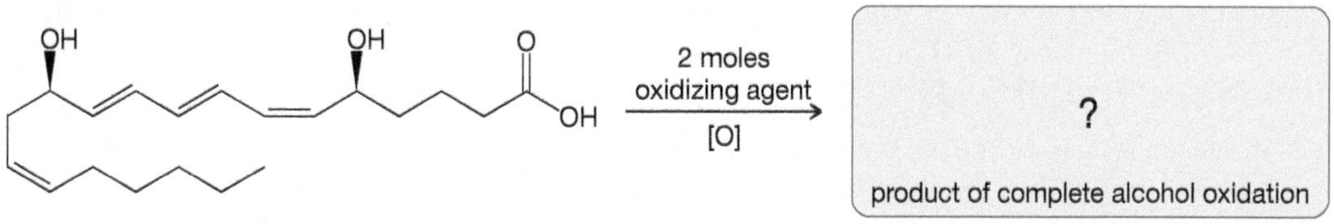

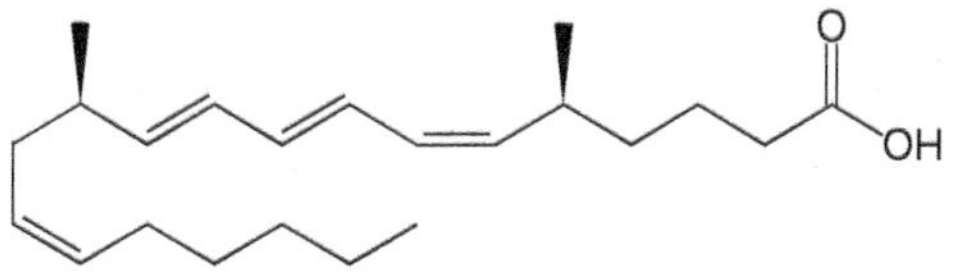

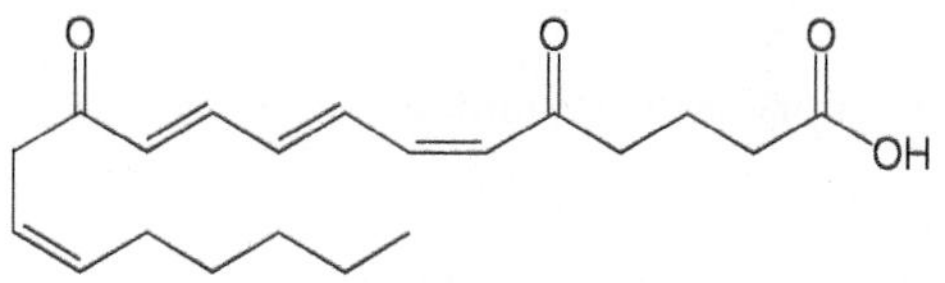

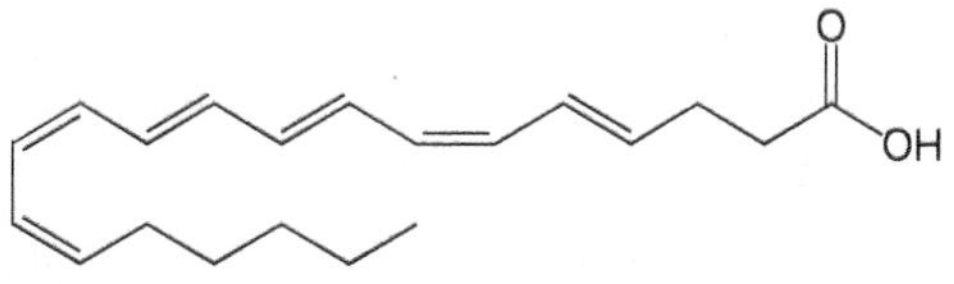

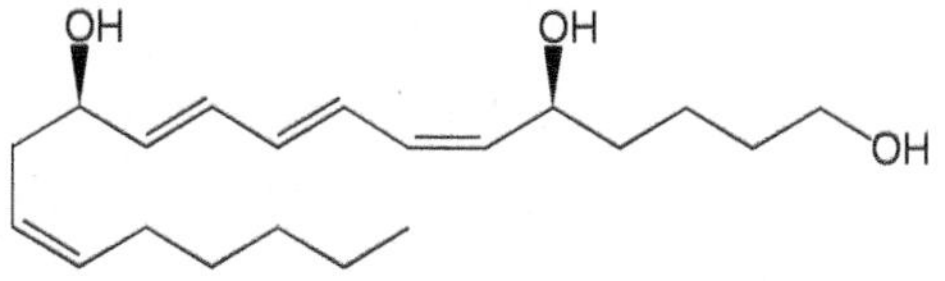

Chapter 19

19.1 Structure of Amines

LO 1: Identify amines and classify them as 1°, 2°, or 3°.

19.01 Match each structure with the appropriate classification.

Answer choices:

a)   **b)**

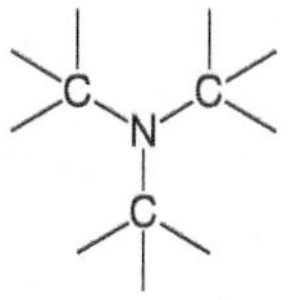

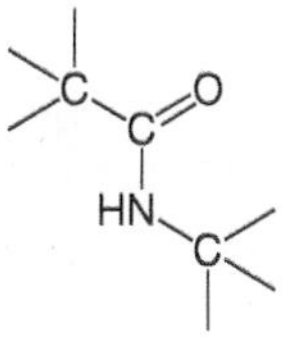

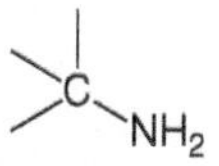

Target boxes:
- a primary (1°) amine
- a secondary (2°) amine
- a tertiary (3°) amine
- a primary (1°) amide
- a secondary (2°) amide
- a tertiary (3°) amide

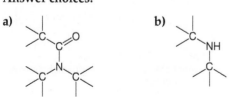

19.02 The drug MDMA, also known as ecstasy, is a psychoactive drug used recreationally to alter the senses and achieve a feeling of increased energy, empathy, and pleasure. What type of amine is MDMA? Select the appropriate term to complete the sentence.

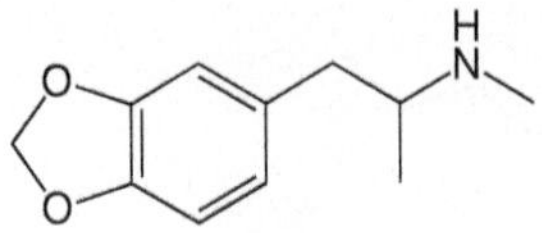

MDMA
(ecstasy)

The drug MDMA is a _____ amine.

a) primary

b) secondary

c) tertiary

d) quaternary

19.03 Ketamine is a medication used for starting and maintaining anesthesia. It is also used for the sedation of patients in intensive care and for the treatment of chronic pain and depression. What type of amine is found on the ketamine molecule?

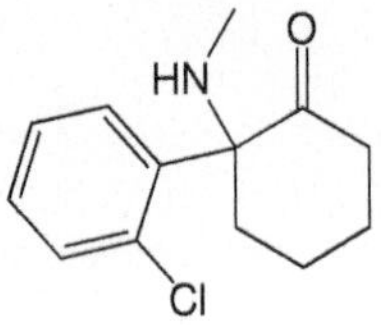

a) a primary (1°) amine

b) a secondary (2°) amine

c) a tertiary (3°) amine

d) a secondary (2°) amide

e) a tertiary (3°) amide

19.04 Meperidine, also known as Demerol, is a narcotic used to treat moderate to severe pain. What two functional groups are present on the meperidine molecule?

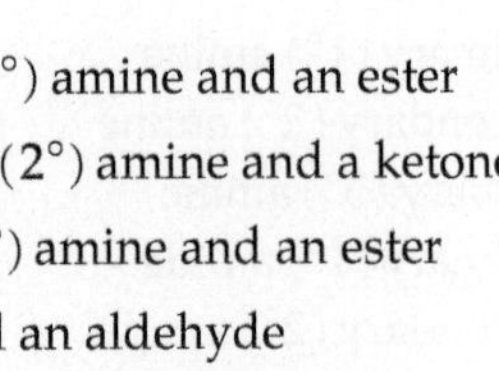

a) a primary (1°) amine and an ester

b) a secondary (2°) amine and a ketone

c) a tertiary (3°) amine and an ester

d) a purine and an aldehyde

e) a tertiary (3°) amide and an ester

19.05 Sort the following amines into the appropriate category.

Answer choices:

a)

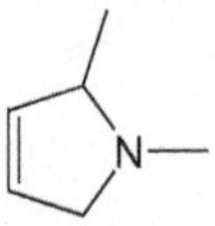

b)

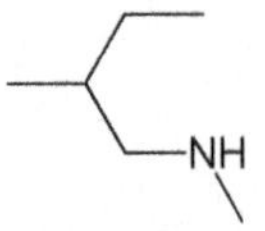

c)

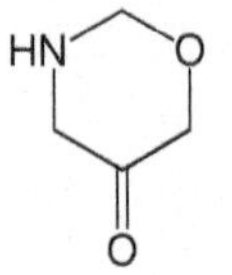

d)

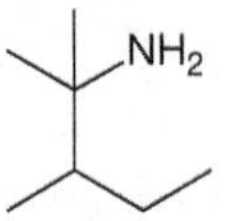

e)

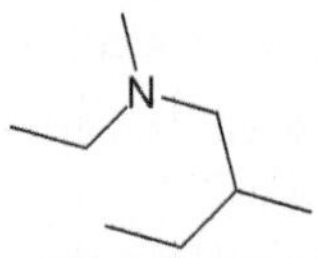

f)

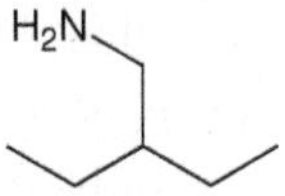

Target boxes: primary (1°) amide, secondary (2°) amide, tertiary (3°) amide

19.06 Classify the following amines.

Answer choices:

a)

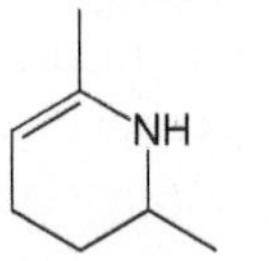

b)

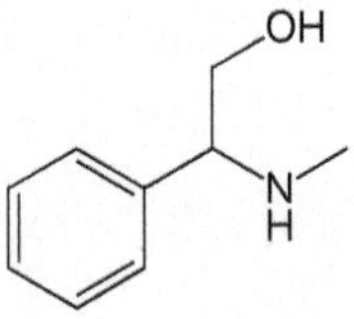

c)

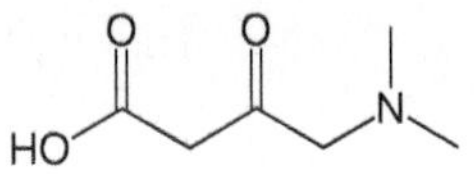

d)

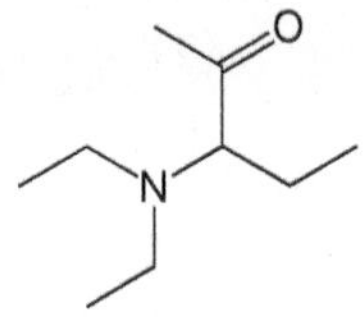

e)

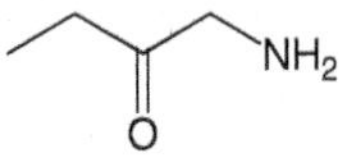

f)

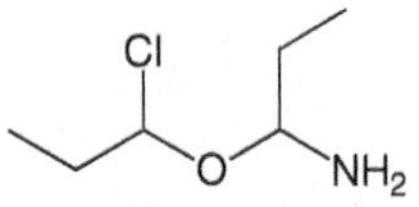

Target boxes: primary (1°) amide, secondary (2°) amide, tertiary (3°) amide

19.07 Amphetamine (sold under the brand name in Adderall) is used in the treatment of attention deficit hyperactivity disorder (ADHD) and for sleep disorders. It is also used recreationally to enhance cognitive and athletic performance. Methamphetamine is also used for attention deficit hyperactivity disorder and obesity. Both drugs are central nervous system (CNS) stimulants, have nearly identical structures, are abused recreationally, and are addictive. Which statement is true about amphetamine and methamphetamine?

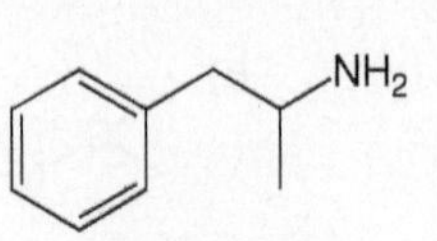

amphetamine
(Adderall)

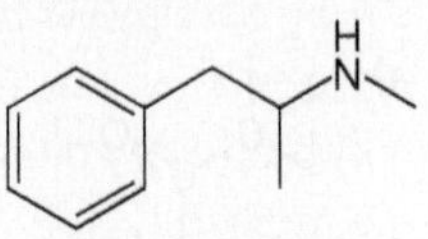

methamphetamine

a) Amphetamine is a secondary (2°) amine and methamphetamine is tertiary (3°) amine.

b) Amphetamine is a primary (1°) amide and methamphetamine is a secondary (2°) amide.

c) Amphetamine is a secondary (2°) amine and methamphetamine is a primary (1°) amine.

d) Amphetamine is a primary (1°) amine and methamphetamine is a secondary (2°) amine.

19.08 Complete each sentence by entering 0, 1, 2, 3, or 4 in each blank to create a correct statement.

a) 1° amines have _____ H atoms bonded to the nitrogen.

b) 2° amines have _____ C atoms (or alkyl groups) bonded to the nitrogen.

c) 3° amines have _____ H atoms bonded to the nitrogen.

19.09 The molecule sphingosine is a component of the myelin sheath, a coating that surrounds and protects nerve cells in your body. Select all the characteristic features in the sphingosine molecule.

sphingosine

a) ester   **b)** amide

c) ketone   **d)** aldehyde

e) primary alcohol   **f)** secondary alcohol

g) tertiary alcohol   **h)** primary amine

i) secondary amine   **j)** tertiary amine

k) alkene   **l)** alkyne

19.10 Drawing an amine: Use the drawing tool to build the *skeletal structure* of an acyclic (non-cyclic) tertiary (3°) amine having a total of three carbon atoms. Your skeletal structure should not show C—H bonds, the lone pair of electrons on nitrogen, or labels on carbon atoms. Hydrogen atom(s) bonded to nitrogen should be shown if present on the molecule.

19.11 Drawing an amine: Use the drawing tool to build the *skeletal structure* of an acyclic (non-cyclic) secondary (2°) amine having a total of three carbon atoms. Your skeletal structure should not show C—H bonds, the lone pair of electrons on nitrogen, or labels on carbon atoms. Hydrogen atom(s) bonded to nitrogen should be shown if present on the molecule.

19.12 Drawing an amine: Use the drawing tool to build the *skeletal structure* of an acyclic (non-cyclic) primary (1°) amine having a total of three carbon atoms. Your skeletal structure should not show C—H bonds, the lone pair of electrons on nitrogen, or labels on carbon atoms. Hydrogen atom(s) bonded to nitrogen should be shown if present on the molecule.

19.13 Heroin is an addictive opioid pain killer and recreational drug used to create a "high" and sense of well-being. Naloxone, sold under the brand name Narcan, is a medication used to block the effects of opioids and treat opioid overdoses. Which statement is true about heroin and naloxone?

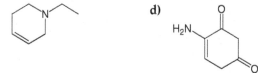

heroin   naloxone

a) Heroin is a heterocyclic tertiary (3°) amine and naloxone is a heterocyclic secondary (2°) amine.

b) Heroin is a heterocyclic tertiary (3°) amine and naloxone is a heterocyclic tertiary (3°) amine.

c) Heroin is a heterocyclic primary (1°) amine and naloxone is a heterocyclic primary (1°) amine.

d) Heroin is a heterocyclic primary (1°) amide and naloxone is a heterocyclic primary (1°) amide.

19.14 Classify each of the following molecules.

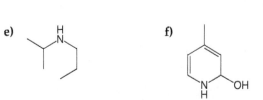

Target boxes: heterocyclic amine, non-heterocyclic amine, neither

19.15 Tryptophan is an amino acid used to make proteins in cells. It is an essential amino acid, meaning that we must obtain this amino acid from our food given that we cannot synthesize it. Serotonin is a neurotransmitter that is involved in memory as well as feelings of reward and happiness. Which description is true about tryptophan and serotonin?

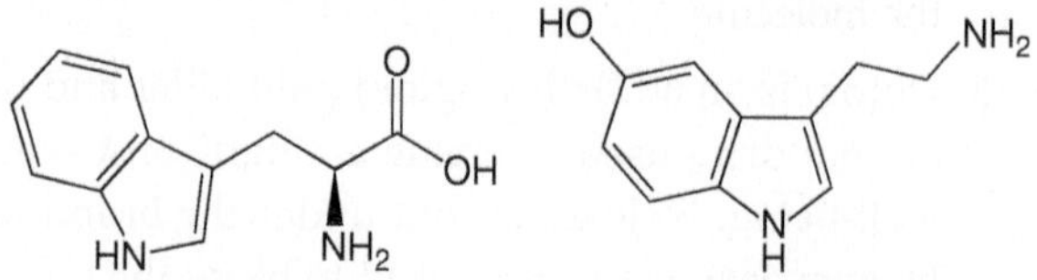

tryptophan   serotonin

a) Both tryptophan and serotonin are heterocyclic amines that also contain a primary amine group. In addition, tryptophan contains a carboxylic acid group, whereas serotonin contains a hydroxyl group.

b) Tryptophan is a heterocyclic amine, but serotonin is not. In addition, tryptophan contains a primary amide group and a hydroxyl group, whereas serotonin contains a hydroxyl group.

c) Serotonin is a heterocyclic amine, but tryptophan is not. In addition, tryptophan contains a primary amine and a carboxylic acid group, whereas serotonin contains a primary amine and a hydroxyl group.

d) Both tryptophan and serotonin are heterocyclic amines. In addition, tryptophan contains a secondary amide group and a carboxylic acid group, whereas serotonin contains a primary amine and a hydroxyl group.

19.2 Physical Properties of Amines

LO 2: Describe how intermolecular forces affect boiling points and water solubility of amines.

19.16 Determine if each diagram correctly shows hydrogen bonding between the two amines.

a)

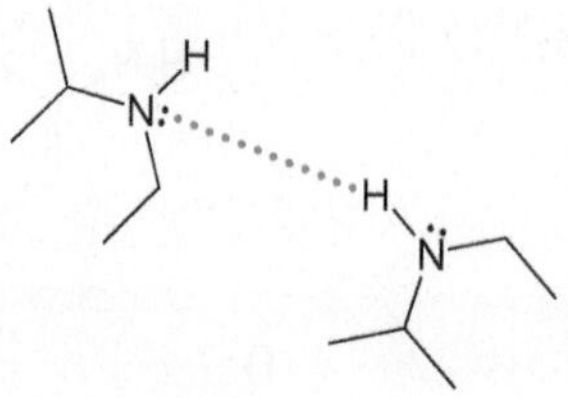

b)

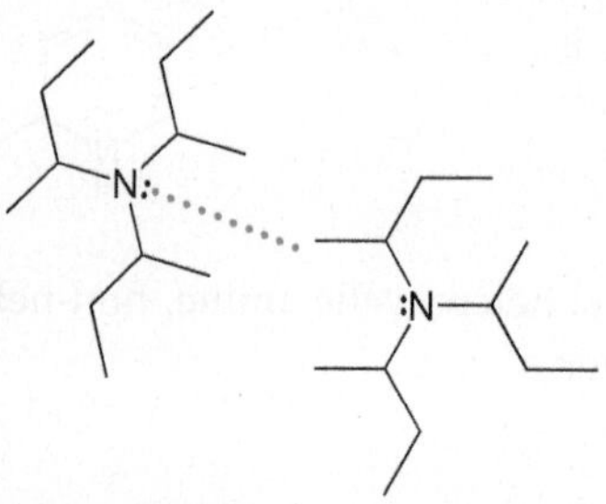

Radio buttons for: correct, incorrect

19.17 Determine if each diagram correctly shows hydrogen bonding between the two amines.

a)

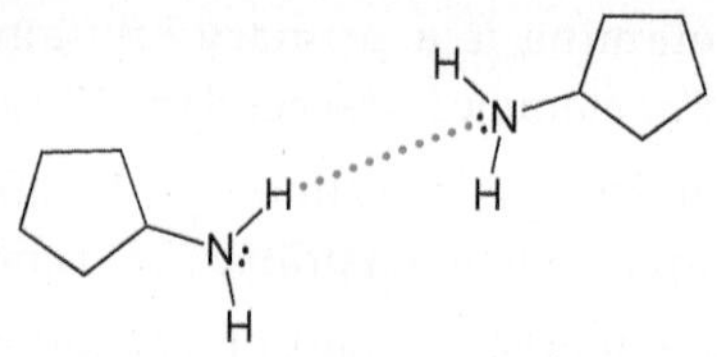

b)

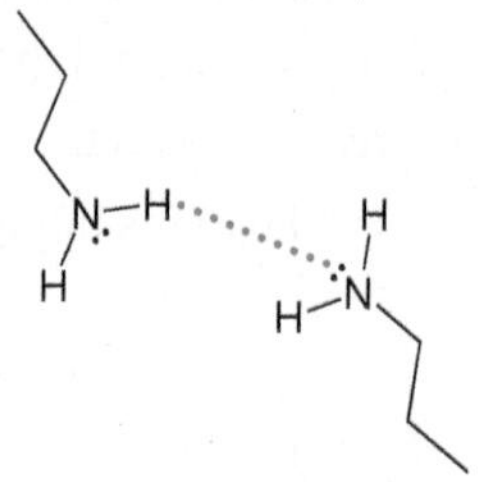

Radio buttons for: correct, incorrect

19.18 Rank these molecules in order of increasing boiling point.

Answer choices:

a)

b)

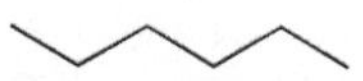

c)

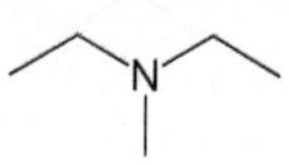

Target boxes: lowest boiling point, intermediate boiling point, highest boiling point

19.19 Rank these molecules in order of increasing boiling point.

Answer choices:

a)

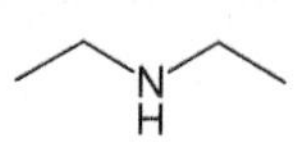

b)

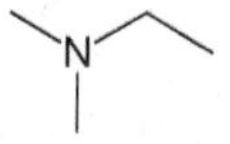

c)

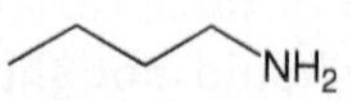

Target boxes: lowest boiling point, intermediate boiling point, highest boiling point

19.20 Rank these molecules in order of increasing boiling point.

Answer choices:

a)

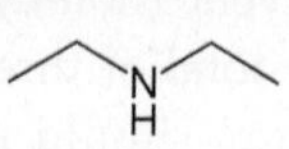

b)

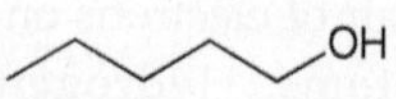

c)

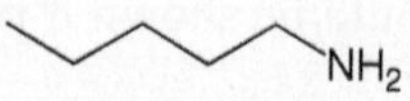

Target boxes: lowest boiling point, intermediate boiling point, highest boiling point

19.21 Rank these molecules in order of increasing solubility in water.

Answer choices:

a)

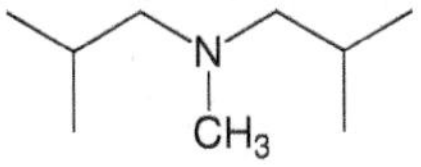

b)

c)

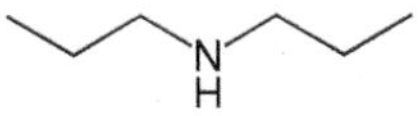

Target boxes: lowest water solubility, intermediate water solubility, greatest water solubility

19.22 Rank the molecules in order of increasing solubility in water.

Answer choices:

a)

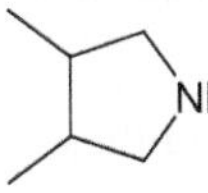

b)

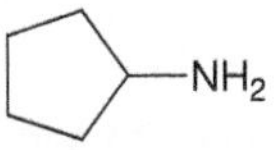

c)

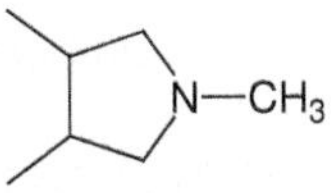

Target boxes: lowest water solubility, intermediate water solubility, greatest water solubility

19.23 Rank the molecules in order of increasing solubility in water.

Answer choices:

a)

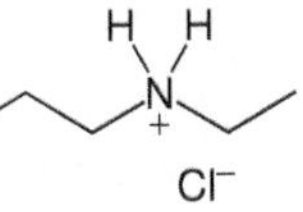

b)

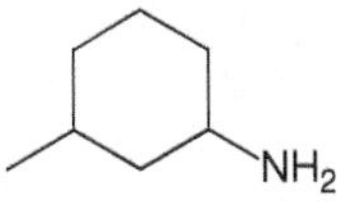

c)

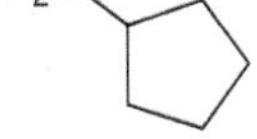

Target boxes: lowest water solubility, intermediate water solubility, greatest water solubility

19.24 Rank the molecules in order of increasing solubility in water.

Answer choices:

a)

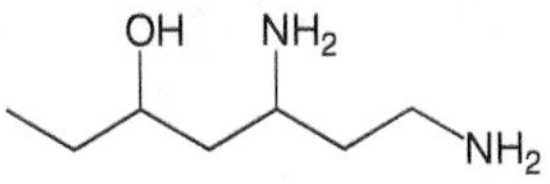

b)

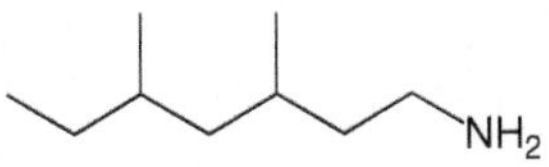

c)

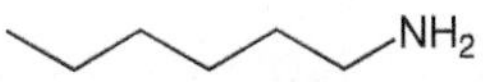

Target boxes: lowest water solubility, intermediate water solubility, greatest water solubility

19.25 Which of the following amine molecules are capable of forming intermolecular hydrogen bonds with other identical molecules?

Answer choices:

a)

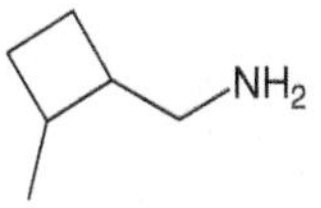

b)

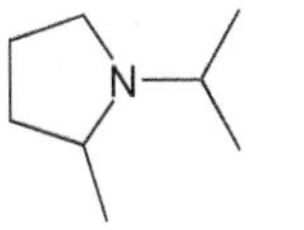

c)

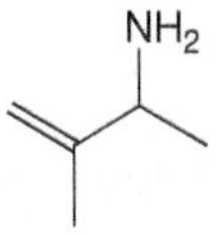

d)

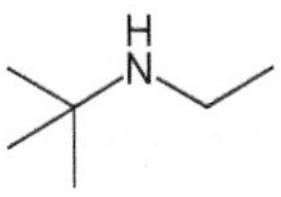

e)

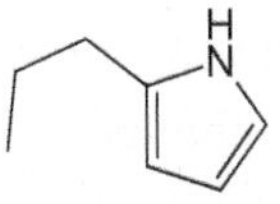

f)

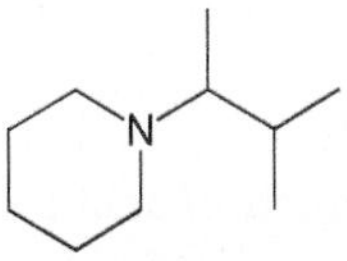

Target boxes: can form hydrogen bonds with other identical molecules, cannot form hydrogen bonds with other identical molecules

19.26 Which of these amine molecules are capable of forming hydrogen bonds with water?

Answer choices:

a)

b)

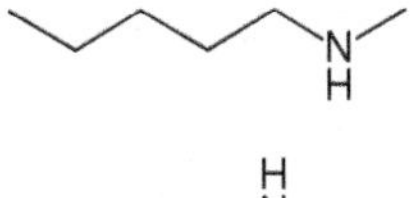

c)

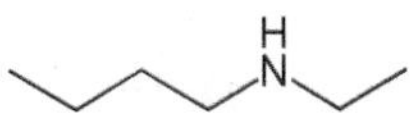

d)

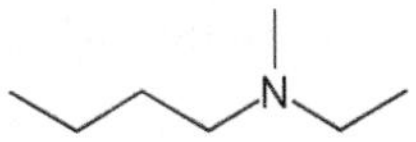

e)

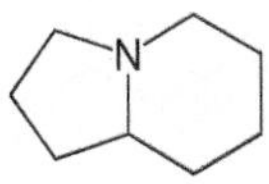

f)

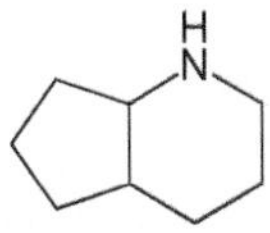

g)

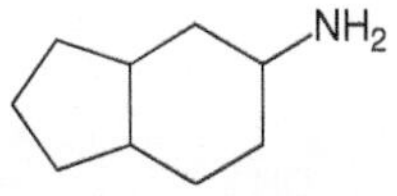

Target boxes: can form hydrogen bonds with water, cannot form hydrogen bonds with water

19.27 Hydrogen bonding between amine compounds plays a significant role in the structure of DNA. Hydrogen bonds form between the bases adenine (A) and thymine (T), and between the bases guanine (G) and cytosine (C). The two strands of DNA are held together by these hydrogen bonds, forming DNA's characteristic double helix. Examine the A—T and G—C hydrogen bonds in double stranded DNA. Which statement about separating strands in a DNA double helix is correct?

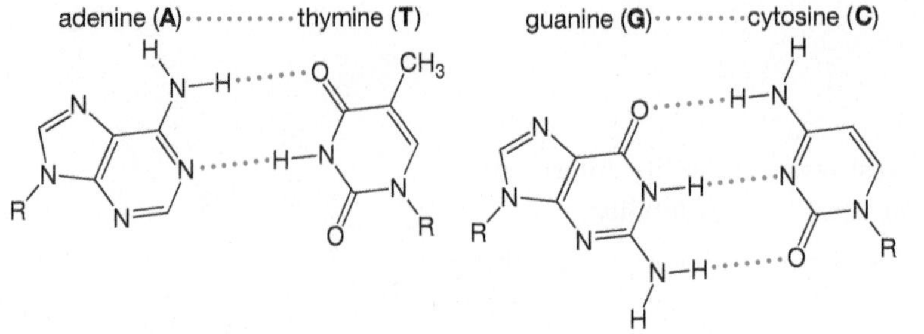

adenine (**A**)··········thymine (**T**)   guanine (**G**)········cytosine (**C**)

a) The two individual strands in double stranded DNA are harder to separate if they are composed mostly of A—T base pairing than if they are mostly composed of G—C base pairing.

b) The two individual strands in double stranded DNA are harder to separate if they are composed mostly of G—C base pairing than if they are mostly composed of A—T base pairing.

c) The two individual strands in double stranded DNA are equally difficult to whether they are composed mostly of G—C base pairing or mostly composed of A—T base pairing.

d) Double stranded DNA cannot be separated into individual strands because the A—T and G—C base pairs between the strands are held together too tightly by hydrogen bonding.

19.3 Reactions of Amines

LO 3: Predict and draw the products of acid-base reactions of amines.

19.28 What products are formed when an amine reacts with water?

   a) a ketone and the hydroxide ion

   b) an ammonium ion and the hydroxide ion

   c) an acetal and the hydroxide ion

   d) ammonia and the hydronium (H_3O^+) ion

   e) a primary alcohol and ammonia

19.29 What is the missing starting material in this reaction?

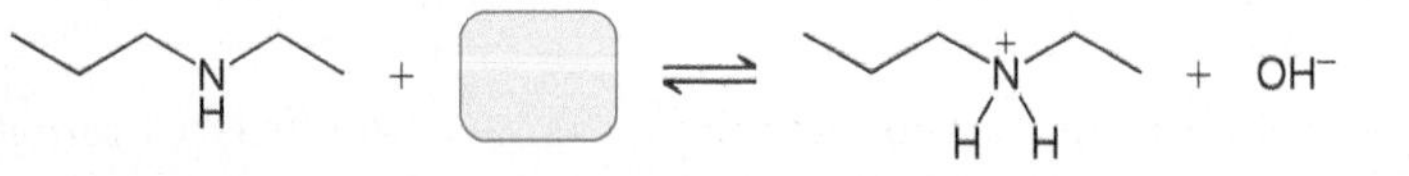

   a) NaOH   **b)** HCl   **c)** H_2O **d)** $H_2(g)$

19.30 Identify the products formed in this reaction,

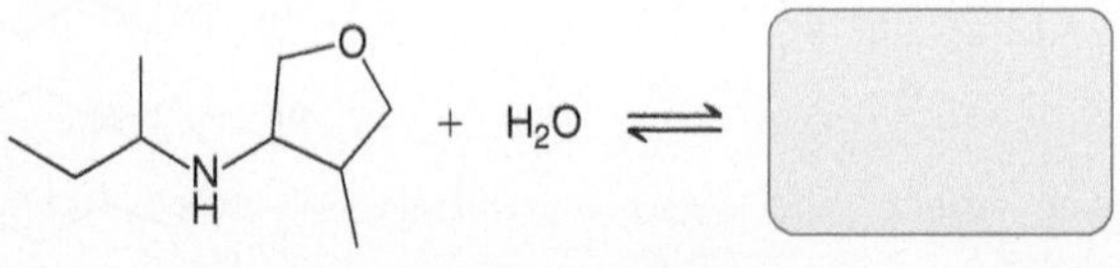

a)

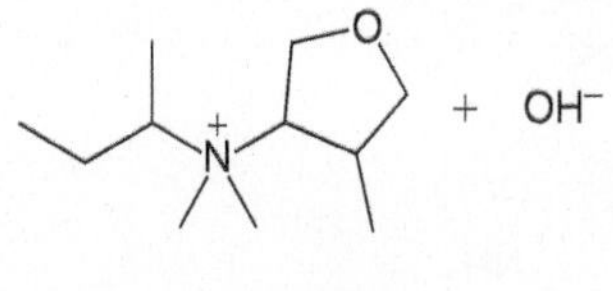

   + OH⁻

b)

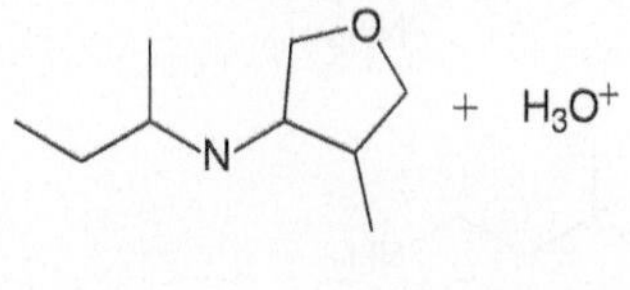

   + H_3O^+

c)

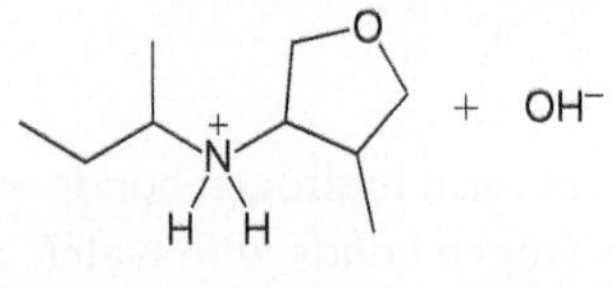

   + OH⁻

d)

   + H_3O^+

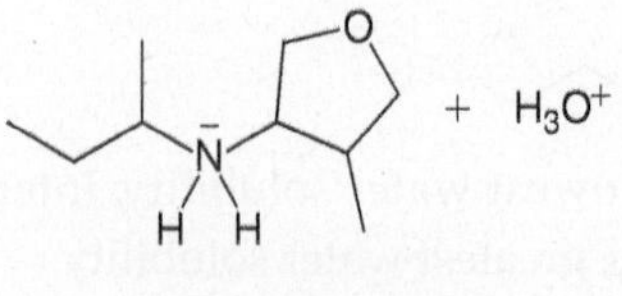

19.31 Identify the products formed in this reaction.

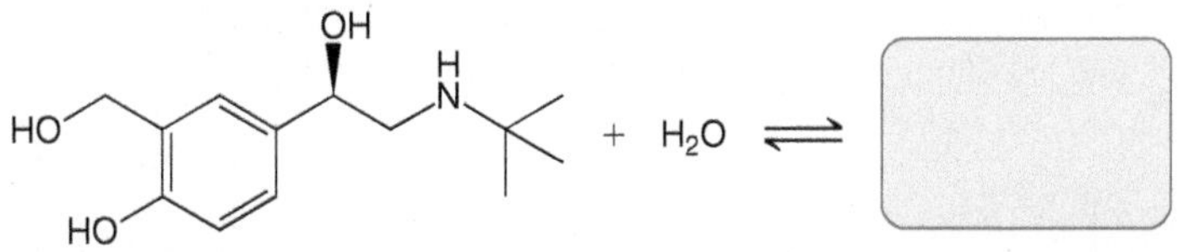

+ H_2O ⇌

a)

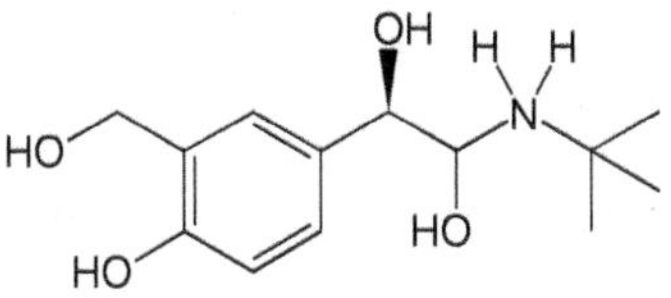

+ (reaction product structure)

b)

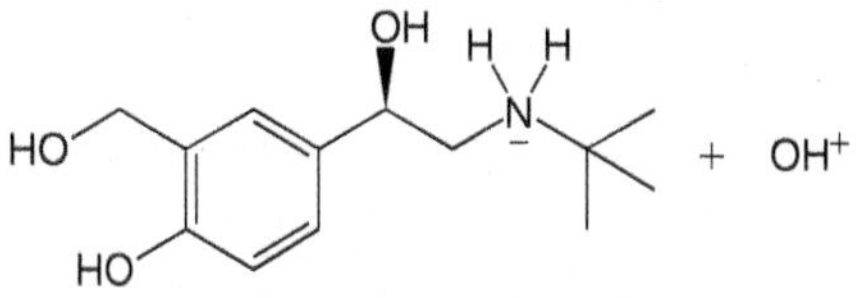

+ OH^+

c)

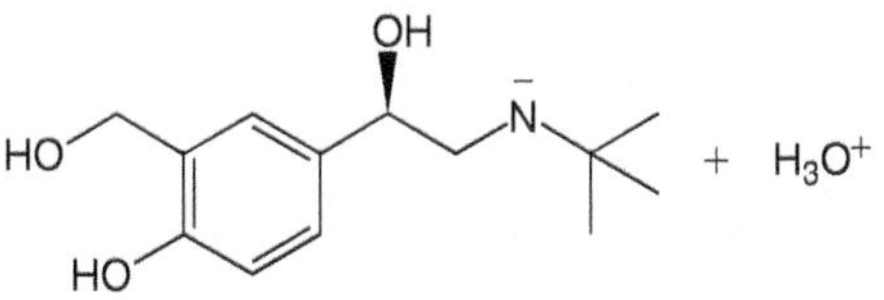

+ H_3O^+

d)

+ OH^-

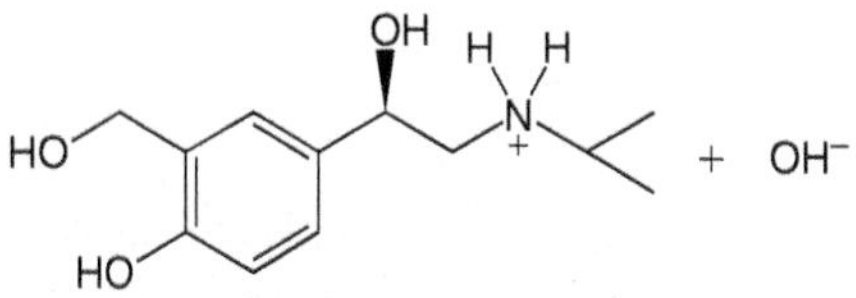

19.32 Identify the missing starting materials in this reaction.

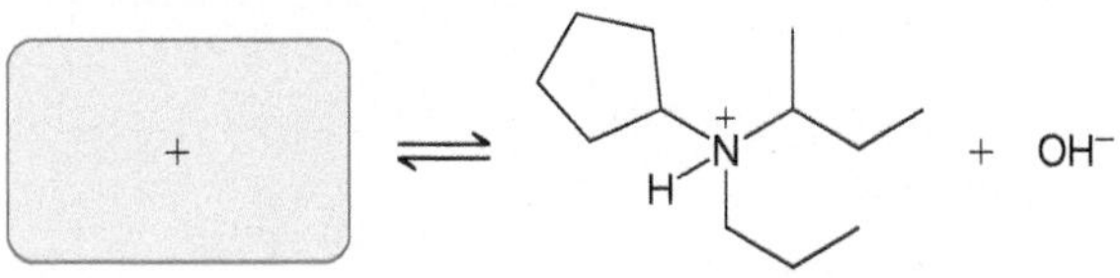

+ ⇌ + OH^-

a)

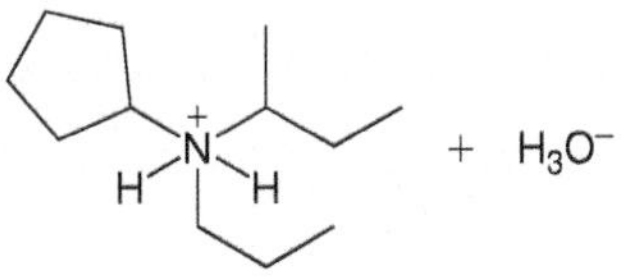

+ H_3O^-

b)

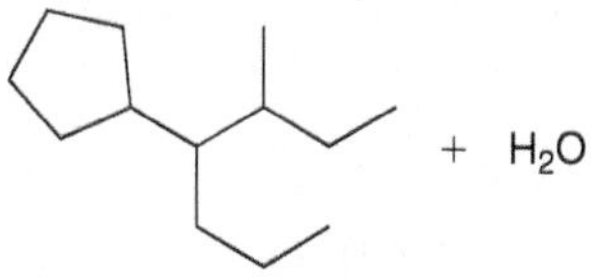

+ H_2O

c)

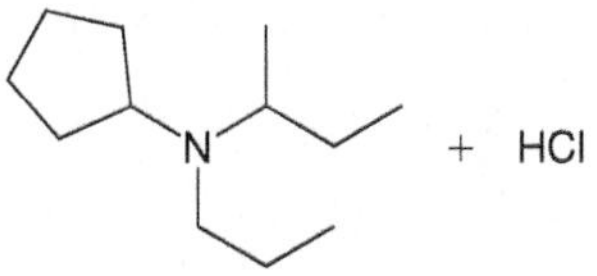

+ HCl

d)

+ H_2O

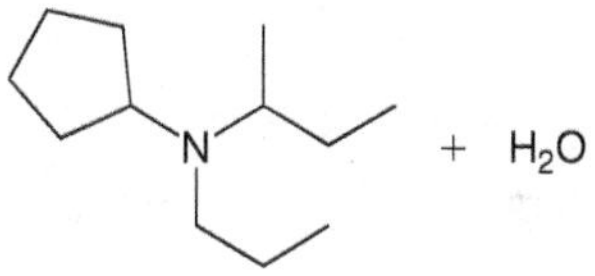

19.33 What product or products are formed when an amine reacts with an acid?

a) an amide and water **b)** a hemiacetal **c)** an ammonium salt

d) an ester **e)** ammonia and water

19.34 Sertraline, also known as Zoloft, is a medication used to treat depression, obsessive–compulsive disorder, panic disorder, and social anxiety disorder. It is a selective serotonin reuptake inhibitor (SSRI) and functions by increasing the amount of the neurotransmitter serotonin in the brain. What products are formed in the reaction when sertraline enters an acidic environment such as the digestive system?

+ HCl(aq) ⟶

a)

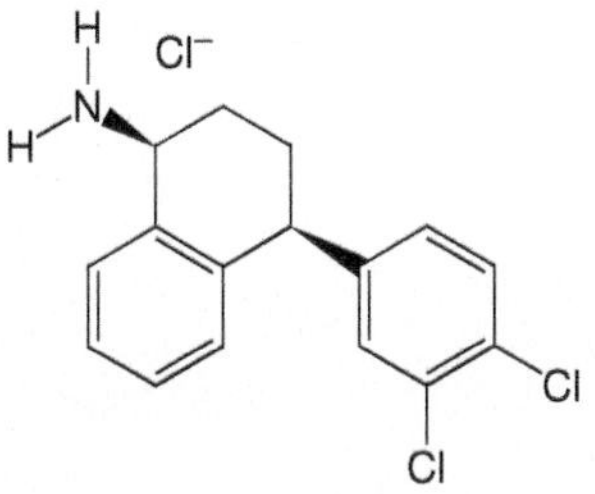

b)

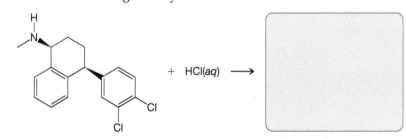

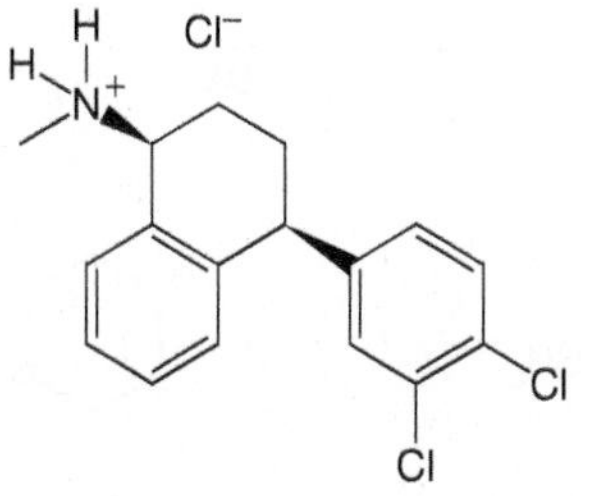

c)

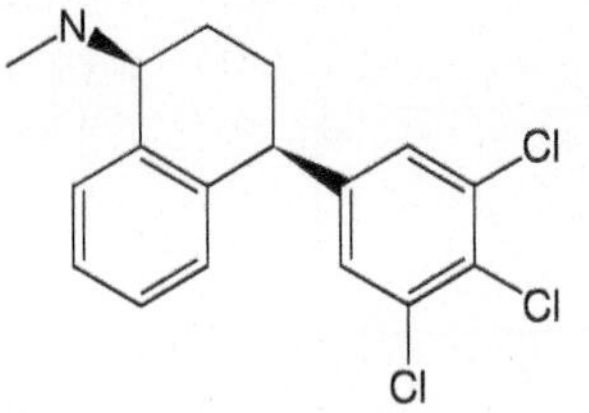

d)

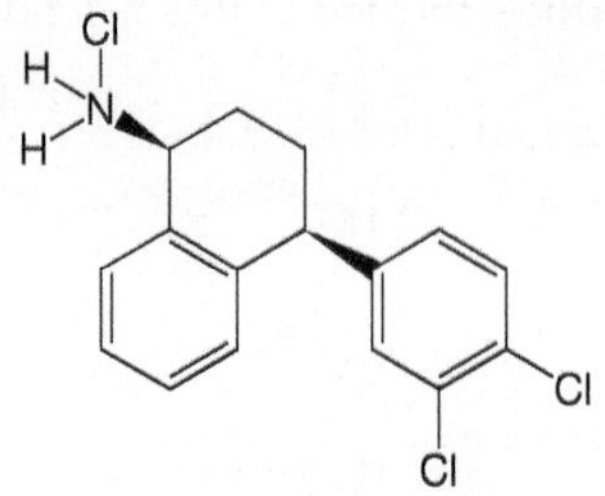

19.35 Drawing the starting material of a reaction: Use the drawing tool to build the *skeletal structure* of the missing starting material in the reaction shown. For this exercise, do not draw the lone pairs of electrons on nitrogen, but do include any hydrogen atoms bonded to nitrogen.

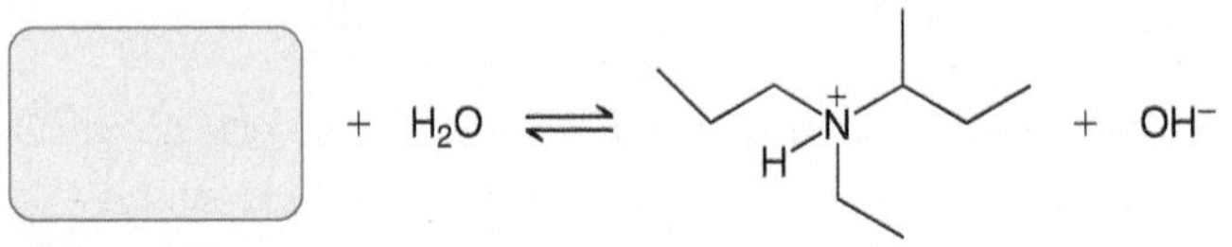

19.36 Amitriptyline, also known as Elavil, is a medication used to treat mental illness. What products are formed when amitriptyline enters an acidic environment such as the digestive system?

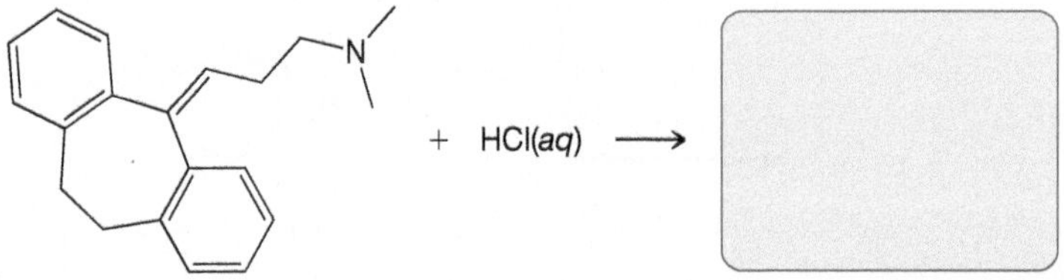

a)

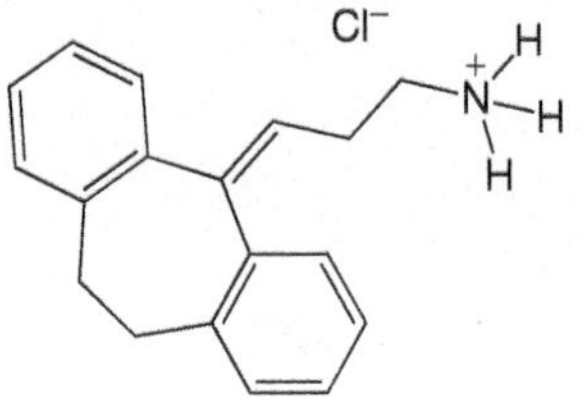

b)

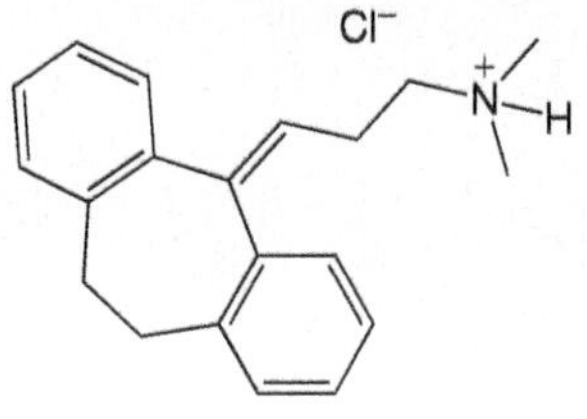

c)

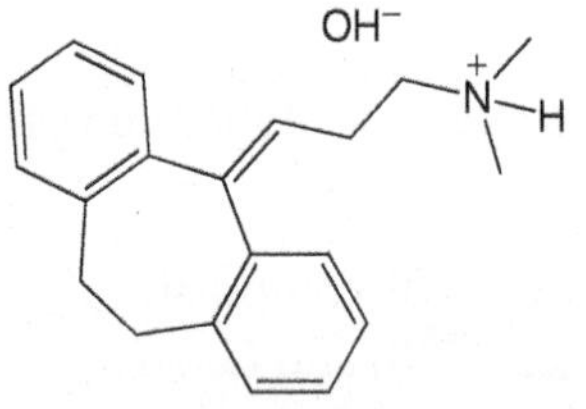

d)

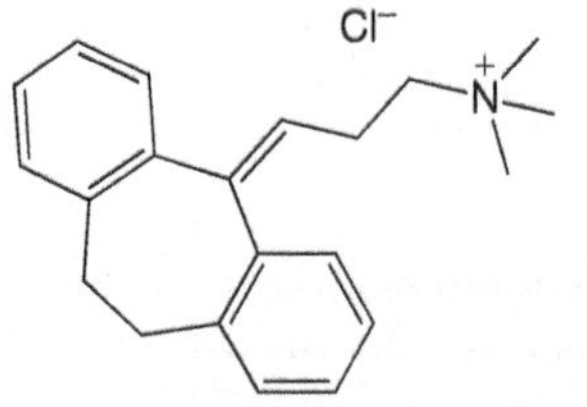

19.37 Ketamine, also known as Ketalar, is a medication used for pain relief, sedation, and maintaining anesthesia. When ketamine enters the acidic environment found in your digestive system, it undergoes a chemical reaction. What is the structure of ketamine?

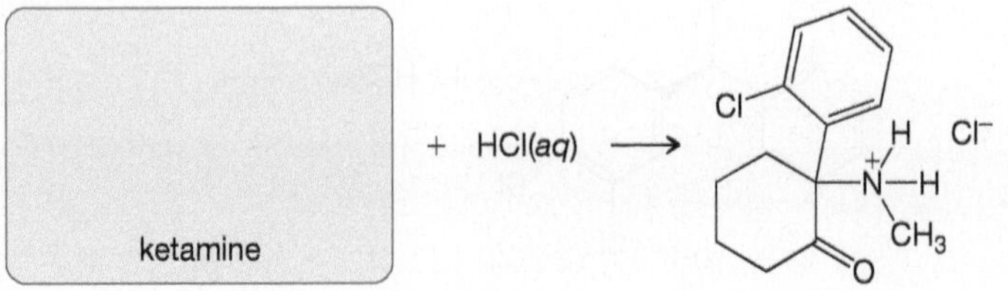

a)

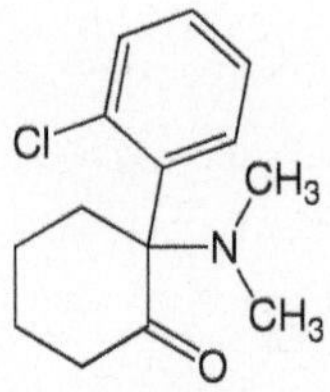

b)

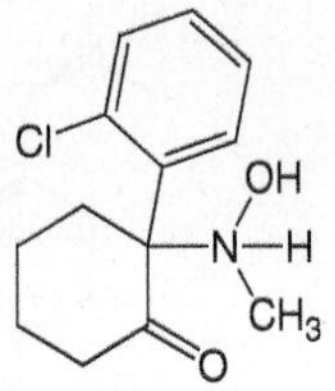

c)

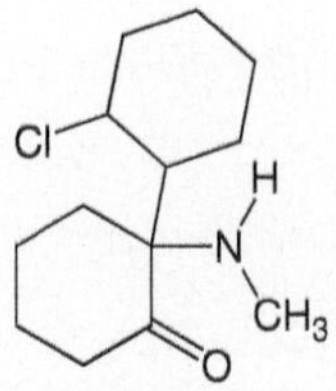

d)

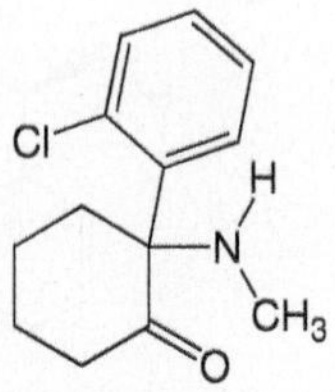

19.38 Drawing the starting material of a reaction: Gabapentin, also known as Neuronin, is a medication used to treat neuropathic pain, epilepsy, restless leg syndrome, and hot flashes. Use the drawing tool to build the *skeletal structure* of the missing gabapentin starting material in this reaction. For this exercise, do not draw the lone pairs of electrons on nitrogen or oxygen, but do include any hydrogen atoms bonded to nitrogen and/or oxygen if present on the starting molecule.

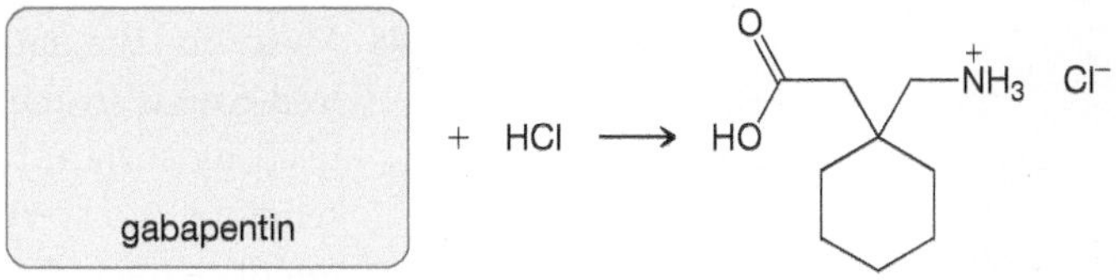

19.39 Drawing the starting material of a reaction: Diethylpropion, also known as Amfepramone, is a stimulant used to suppress appetite. Use the drawing tool to build the *skeletal structure* of the missing diethylpropion starting material in the reaction. For this exercise, do not draw the lone pairs of electrons on nitrogen or oxygen, but do include any hydrogen atoms bonded to nitrogen and/or oxygen if present on the starting material molecule.

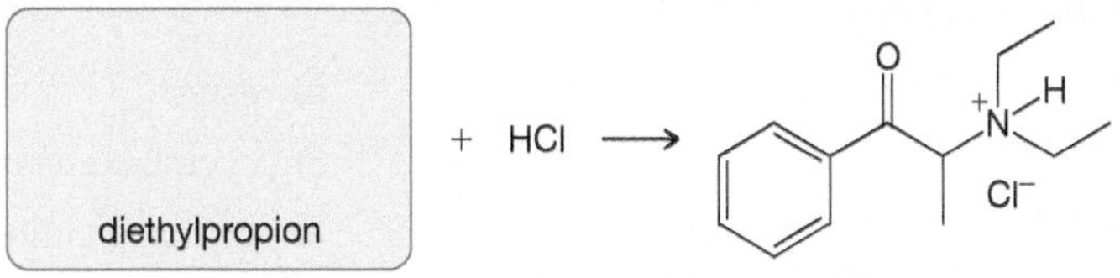

19.4 Alkaloids: Amines Found in Plants

LO 4: Describe the characteristics of alkaloids and provide examples.

19.40 Hygrine is an alkaloid present in the leaves of the coca plant, along with cocaine and other naturally occurring alkaloids. Identify *two* different characteristics of the hygrine molecule.

hygrine

a) ester
c) cyclohexane ring
e) primary amide
g) ketone
i) secondary amide
k) aromatic ring

b) tertiary amide
d) primary amine
f) alcohol
h) secondary amine
j) ether
l) tertiary amine

19.41 Both oxycodone, also known as OxyContin, and hydrocodone are addictive opioids used for pain management. Each of these drugs share very similar

chemical structures (shown below), and both are widely abused, leading to thousands of overdose deaths annually in the United States alone. Which statement correctly describes the difference(s) between these two opioid drugs?

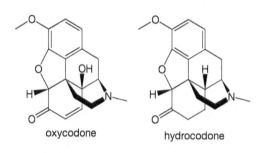

oxycodone   hydrocodone

a) Oxycodone contains a tertiary cyclic amine. Hydrocodone contains a secondary cyclic amine.

b) Oxycodone contains a ketone and two ether groups. Hydrocodone contains a ketone, an ether and a hydroxyl group.

c) Oxycodone contains two hydroxyl groups. Hydrocodone contains only one hydroxyl group.

d) Oxycodone contains a hydroxyl group. Hydrocodone does not contain a hydroxyl group.

19.42 Cathinone is a naturally occurring alkaloid present in the khat plant chewed in many parts of the world. Cathinone is a stimulant that produces feelings of excitement, loss of appetite, and euphoria. Which statement correctly describes the cathinone molecule?

cathinone

a) Cathinone contains a secondary amine, a ketone, and an aromatic (benzene) ring.

b) Cathinone contains a secondary amide, a ketone, and an aromatic (benzene) ring.

c) Cathinone contains a primary amine, a ketone, and an aromatic (benzene) ring.

d) Cathinone contains a primary amine, an ester, and a cyclohexane ring.

19.43 Vitamin B$_3$ (niacin) is an essential human nutrient present in a number of foods. Supplemental niacin is primarily used to treat niacin deficiency (pellagra) and high cholesterol. The molecule 4-aminobenzoic acid helps produce molecules known as pterines. Which statement correctly describes the characteristic similarities and differences between the chemical structures of niacin and 4-aminobenzoic acid?

vitamin B3 (niacin)   4-aminobenzoic acid

a) Both molecules contain an ester group branching from an aromatic ring. The nitrogen atom in niacin is part of a heterocyclic aromatic ring whereas the amine nitrogen in 4-aminobenzoic acid branches from the aromatic ring as an NH$_2$ group.

b) Both molecules contain a carboxylic acid group branching from an aromatic ring. The nitrogen atom in 4-aminobenzoic acid is part of a heterocyclic aromatic ring whereas the amine nitrogen in niacin branches from the aromatic ring as an NH$_2$ group.

c) Both molecules contain a carboxylic acid group branching from a cyclohexane ring. The nitrogen atom in niacin is part of a heterocyclic alkane ring whereas the amine nitrogen in 4-aminobenzoic acid branches from the alkane ring as an NH$_2$ group.

d) Both molecules contain a carboxylic acid group branching from an aromatic ring. The nitrogen atom in niacin is part of a heterocyclic aromatic ring whereas the amine nitrogen in 4-aminobenzoic acid branches from the aromatic ring as an NH$_2$ group.

19.44 Mescaline is a naturally occurring psychedelic alkaloid found in the peyote cactus. It has long been used by certain Native American communities in religious and spiritual ceremonies. Identify *three* different characteristics of the mescaline molecule.

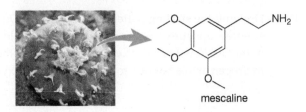

mescaline

a) ester

b) tertiary amide

c) cyclohexane ring

d) primary amine

e) primary amide

f) alcohol

g) ketone

h) secondary amine

i) secondary amide

j) ether

k) aromatic ring

l) tertiary amine

19.45 Vanillylamine is an alkaloid produced in the seed pods of the vanilla plant. Identify *four* different characteristics of the vanillylamine molecule.

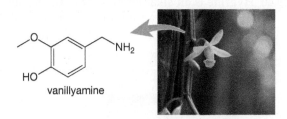

vanillyamine

a) ester

b) tertiary amide

c) cyclohexane ring

d) primary amine

e) primary amide

f) alcohol

g) ketone

h) secondary amine

i) secondary amide

j) ether

k) aromatic ring

l) tertiary amine

19.46 Lupinine is a toxin present in the seeds of lupine plants, the ingestion of which causes liver damage. Which correctly describes the lupinine molecule?

lupinine

a) Lupinine contains a secondary alcohol and an ammonium ion as part of a two-cyclohexane ring system.

b) Lupinine contains a primary alcohol and a tertiary amine as part of a two-cyclohexane ring system.

c) Lupinine contains a primary alcohol and a tertiary amine as part of a two-aromatic ring system.

d) Lupinine contains a primary alcohol and a tertiary amide as part of a two-cyclohexane ring system.

19.47 Caffeine is an alkaloid present in coffee and tea. Caffeine stimulates the central nervous system (CNS). The biosynthesis of caffeine in plants involves a multi-step conversion of xanthosine to caffeine by a series of enzymes. Which statement correctly describes the characteristic differences between the chemical structures of xanthosine and caffeine?

xanthosine   caffeine

a) Caffeine has three more methyl (CH_3) groups than xanthosine and one of the double bonds is in a different location in the ring. Xanthosine contains an additional carbohydrate ring not found on caffeine.

b) Caffeine has three more hydrogen atoms in the nitrogen containing ring system than xanthosine and one of the double bonds is in a different

location in the ring system. Xanthosine contains an additional carbohydrate ring not found on caffeine.

c) Caffeine has three more methyl (CH_3) groups than xanthosine and one of the double bonds is in a different location in the ring system. Caffeine contains an additional carbohydrate ring not found on xanthosine.

d) Caffeine has three secondary amine groups in the nitrogen containing ring system and xanthosine contains two primary amines. One of the double bonds is in a different location in the ring system and xanthosine contains an additional carbohydrate ring not found on caffeine.

19.48 Actinidine is a naturally occurring alkaloid found in the oil of valerian (*Valeriana officinalis*) and silver vine (*Actinidia polygama*) plants. Actinidine is a pheromone for a variety of insects and helps attract pollinators to the plants. Identify the *one* characteristic that best describes the actinidine molecule.

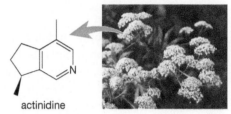

actinidine

a) ester   **b)** tertiary amide

c) cyclohexane ring   **d)** primary amine

e) primary amide   **f)** alcohol

g) ketone   **h)** aldehyde

i) secondary amide   **j)** ether

k) heterocyclic amine   **l)** tertiary amine

19.49 Heroin, morphine, and codeine are all opioid painkillers. The key molecules in each of these drugs contain a tertiary amine as part of a complex ring system. Which statement best describes the characteristic differences between the chemical structures of heroin, morphine, and codeine?

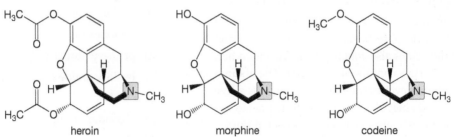

heroin   morphine   codeine

a) In addition to the complex ring system, heroin contains two ketone groups, morphine contains two hydroxyl groups, and codeine contains two ether groups.

b) In addition to the complex ring system, heroin contains two hydroxyl groups, morphine contains two ester groups, and codeine contains both an ether and a hydroxyl group.

c) In addition to the complex ring system, heroin contains two ester groups, morphine contains two hydroxyl groups, and codeine contains both an ether and a hydroxyl group.

d) In addition to the complex ring system, heroin contains two carboxylic acid groups, morphine contains two hydroxyl groups, and codeine contains both an ether and a hydroxyl group.

19.50 Papaverine is an alkaloid found in opium poppies. It is synthesized and used medically as a treatment to help improve blood flow in patients with circulation problems. It works by relaxing the blood vessels (vasodilation) so that blood can flow more easily to the heart and through the body. Study the skeletal structure of papaverine shown, then determine and enter the number of hydrogen atoms bonded at each site (i-iv).

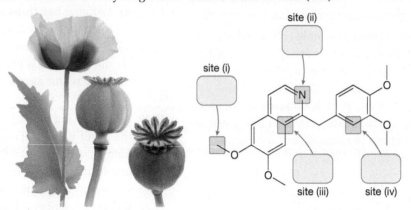

19.51 The molecules nornicotine and anabasine are both alkaloids present in tobacco plants. Each is similar in structure to nicotine, the primary addictive stimulant in tobacco products. Which statement best describes the characteristics of these two alkaloids?

nornicotine   anabasine

a) Both molecules have a nitrogen atom as part of an aromatic heterocyclic six-membered ring. Both molecules also contain an alkane-based heterocyclic ring containing nitrogen. The alkane-based heterocyclic amine in nornicotine is a six membered ring, and the alkane-based heterocyclic amine in anabasine is a five membered ring.

b) Both molecules have a nitrogen atom as part of an aromatic heterocyclic six-membered ring. Both molecules also contain an alkane-based heterocyclic ring containing nitrogen. The alkane-based heterocyclic amine in nornicotine is a five membered ring, and the alkane-based heterocyclic amine in anabasine is a six membered ring.

c) Both molecules contain a benzene ring. Both molecules also contain an alkane-based heterocyclic ring containing nitrogen. The alkane-based heterocyclic amine in nornicotine is a five membered ring, and the alkane-based heterocyclic amine in anabasine is a six membered ring.

d) Both molecules have a nitrogen atom as part of a cyclohexane ring. Both molecules also contain an alkane-based heterocyclic ring containing nitrogen. The alkane-based heterocyclic amine in nornicotine is a five membered ring, and the alkane-based heterocyclic amine in anabasine is a six membered ring.

19.52 Cuscohygrine occurs in the coca plant along with cocaine, hygrine, and other alkaloids. Identify *two* different characteristics of the cuscohygrine molecule.

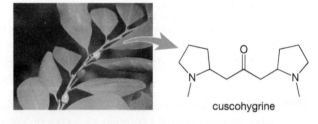

cuscohygrine

a) alkene

b) tertiary amide

c) cyclohexane ring

d) primary amine

e) tertiary amide

f) alcohol

g) secondary amine

h) aldehyde

i) heterocyclic amine

j) ether

k) ketone

l) ester

19.5 Neurotransmitters

LO 5: Describe and provide examples of the general structure and physiological function of neurotransmitters.

19.53 Norepinephrine is a neurotransmitter that plays a role in sleep, attention, and alertness. Dopamine is a neurotransmitter that helps regulate mood, sleep, and movement. These molecules are similar in both structure and biological function. In fact, dopamine is converted to norepinephrine in our bodies by the enzyme dopamine beta-hydroxylase (DBH). Which statement best describes in what way or ways the structure of dopamine differs from that of norepinephrine?

dopamine   DBH enzyme →   norepinephrine

a) Norepinephrine contains an ether group that is not present on the dopamine molecule.

b) Norepinephrine contains a secondary alcohol group that is not present on the dopamine molecule.

c) Norepinephrine contains a primary alcohol group that is not present on the dopamine molecule.

d) Norepinephrine contains an amide group that is not present on the dopamine molecule.

19.54 Dopamine is a neurotransmitter that increases pleasurable feelings and helps regulate movement, sleep, and mood. 3-methoxytyramine is produced when dopamine is metabolized by the enzyme catechol-O-methyl transferase (COMT). Which statement best describes the structural similarities and differences between these two alkaloids?

dopamine   enzyme →   3-methoxytyramine

a) Both molecules contain a primary amine and an aromatic ring. 3-methoxytyramine contains two hydroxyl groups bonded to the ring. Dopamine contains a methyl ether and a hydroxyl group.

b) Both molecules contain a primary amide and an aromatic ring. Dopamine contains two hydroxyl groups bonded to the ring. 3-methoxytyramine contains an oxygen with a negative charge and a hydroxyl group.

c) Both molecules contain a primary amine and a cyclohexane ring. Dopamine contains two hydroxyl groups bonded to the ring. 3-methoxytyramine contains a methyl ether and a hydroxyl group.

d) Both molecules contain a primary amine and an aromatic ring. Dopamine contains two hydroxyl groups bonded to the ring. 3-methoxytyramine contains a methyl ether and a hydroxyl group.

19.55 Glutamic acid is an amino acid used to make proteins in our bodies. It is also an abundant neurotransmitter used in the majority of the connections in the human brain. Identify *three* different characteristics of the glutamic acid molecule.

glutamic acid

a) alkene

b) primary amide

c) has formula $C_5H_9NO_4$

d) primary amine

e) tertiary amide

f) has formula $C_5H_8NO_4$

g) secondary amine

h) aldehyde

i) tertiary amine

j) secondary amide

k) ketone

l) carboxylic acid

19.56 Tetraethylammonium (TEA) is a molecule being investigated for its role in partially blocking the function of nerve cell clusters known as autonomic ganglia. Which statement best describes the structure of tetraethylammonium?

a) TEA is an ammonium anion having four ethyl groups bonded to nitrogen.

b) TEA is an ammonium cation having four propyl groups bonded to nitrogen.

c) TEA is a tertiary amine having four ethyl groups bonded to nitrogen.

d) TEA is an ammonium cation having four ethyl groups bonded to nitrogen.

19.57 Caramboxin (CBX) is found in star fruit (*Averrhoa carambola*) and can, in some cases, have a neurotoxic effect on individuals suffering from certain types of kidney disease. Identify *five* different characteristics of the caramboxin molecule.

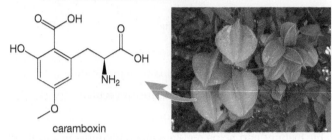

caramboxin

a) secondary amine

b) cyclohexene ring

c) cyclohexane ring

d) hydroxyl

e) tertiary amide

f) primary amine

g) carboxylic acid

h) aromatic ring

i) primary amide

j) ether

k) secondary amide

l) ester

m) tertiary amine

19.58 Phenethylamine (PEA) is an alkaloid found naturally in the body that acts as a central nervous system stimulant and a neurotransmitter. It is also used as a supplement to help treat depression and to improve mood, attention, and athletic performance. Identify *three* different characteristics of the phenethylamine molecule.

phenethylamine

a) has formula $C_8H_{16}N$

b) primary amide

c) secondary amide

d) primary amine

e) cyclohexane ring

f) heterocyclic amine

g) has formula $C_8H_{11}N$

h) secondary amine

i) tertiary amine

j) has formula $C_8H_{12}N$

k) aromatic ring

l) primary amine

19.59 Tryptamine is a naturally occurring alkaloid and neurotransmitter that is derived from the amino acid tryptophan. Which statement best describes the structural differences between these two molecules?

tryptophan   enzyme   tryptamine

a) Tryptamine is missing the carboxylic acid group that is found on tryptophan.

b) Tryptamine has a primary amine group and tryptophan does not.

c) Tryptophan is missing the carboxylic acid group that is found on tryptamine.

d) Tryptophan is an aromatic heterocyclic amine and tryptamine is not.

19.60 In the body, L-Dopa is converted into the neurotransmitter dopamine, which helps regulate mood, sleep, and movement. L-Dopa is also given as a medication to help treat Parkinson's disease. Which statement best describes how the chemical structure of dopamine differs from L-Dopa?

L-Dopa   enzyme   dopamine

a) Dopamine has a primary amine group and L-Dopa does not.

b) L-Dopa is missing the carboxylic acid group that is found on dopamine.

c) L-Dopa is an aromatic heterocyclic amine and dopamine is not.

d) Dopamine is missing the carboxylic acid group that is found on L-Dopa.

19.61 Comparing neurotransmitters and the effect of an enzyme-catalyzed reaction: Norepinephrine is a neurotransmitter that plays a role in sleep, attention, and alertness. Epinephrine (adrenaline) plays an important role in the fight-or-flight response in the body by increasing blood flow to muscles, heart rate, and blood sugar levels. The enzyme PNMT is responsible for converting norepinephrine to epinephrine in the body. Which of the following statements about the chemical change that occurs when the PNMT enzyme acts on norepinephrine is true?

norepinephrine
(noradrenaline)

epinephrine
(adrenaline)

a) The PNMT enzyme converts the primary amine in epinephrine into a secondary amine in norepinephrine by adding a methyl (CH_3) group to nitrogen.

b) The PNMT enzyme converts the secondary amine in norepinephrine into a primary amine in epinephrine by adding a methyl (CH_3) group to nitrogen.

c) The PNMT enzyme converts the secondary amide in norepinephrine into a primary amide in epinephrine by adding a methyl (CH_3) group to nitrogen.

d) The PNMT enzyme converts the primary amine in norepinephrine into a secondary amine in epinephrine by adding a methyl (CH_3) group to nitrogen.

19.62 The molecule 25I-NBOMe is a synthetic hallucinogen and stimulant that has been used in biomedical research for mapping the brain's use of serotonin receptors. It is also used as a recreational street drug. The World Health Organization (WHO) reports, however, that variations in formulations and dosage coupled with its potency results in health risks to consumers. Identify and select all characteristic features on the 25I-NBOMe molecule.

251-NBOMe

a) secondary amide	**b)** hydroxyl	**c)** tertiary amine	**d)** cyclohexane ring
e) primary amine	**f)** halogen	**g)** secondary amine	**h)** aromatic ring
i) primary amide	**j)** ether	**k)** cyclohexene ring	**l)** ester
m) tertiary amide			

19.63 Serotonin is a neurotransmitter that is involved in memory and mood as well as physiological processes such as vomiting and vasoconstriction. Melatonin is a hormone released in the pineal gland that regulates the sleep–wake cycle. Your body converts serotonin into melatonin through a two-step enzymatic process. Compare the similarities and differences between these two molecules. Identify *two* structural characteristics (functional groups) of the melatonin molecule that are not present on serotonin.

serotonin

melatonin

a) tertiary amide	**b)** cyclohexene ring	**c)** tertiary amine	**d)** cyclohexane ring
e) primary amine	**f)** cyclopentene	**g)** secondary amine	**h)** aromatic ring
i) primary amide	**j)** ether	**k)** hydroxyl	**l)** ester
m) secondary amide			

19.64 The molecule DSP-4 is a neurotoxin that is capable of crossing the blood-brain barrier and selectively impacting neurons that process norepinephrine (noradrenaline).

Use the drawing tool to build the *skeletal structure* of the DSP-4 molecule that matches the one shown. For this exercise, do not draw the lone pairs of electrons on nitrogen or the halogens, but do include hydrogen atom(s) bonded to nitrogen if appropriate.

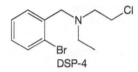

DSP-4

19.65 Translating a ball and stick model to a skeletal structure and drawing a neurotransmitter: The molecule gamma-aminobutyric acid (GABA) is a neurotransmitter made in the brain. GABA is also used as a medication for relieving anxiety, treating attention deficit-hyperactivity disorder (ADHD), and reducing symptoms of premenstrual syndrome (PMS).

Use the drawing tool to build the *skeletal structure* of the GABA molecule by interpreting the "ball-and-stick" model of GABA shown. For this exercise, do not draw the lone pairs of electrons on nitrogen or oxygen, but do include hydrogen atom(s) bonded to nitrogen and oxygen. Atom colors: Carbon (black), hydrogen (white), nitrogen (blue), oxygen (red).

gamma amino butyric acid (GABA)

19.6 Neurotransmitters

LO 6: Use the IUPAC system for naming organic compounds to convert from structure to name and from name to structure for amines and ammonium salts.

19.66 Drag the missing fragments into the spaces to complete the name of this amine molecule.

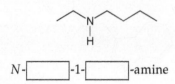

N-[_____]-1-[_____]-amine

Answer choices 1: methyl, ethyl, propyl, butyl, pentyl, hexyl

Answer boxes 2: methane, ethane, propane, butane, pentane, hexane

19.67 Which of the following molecules is 2-butanamine?

19.68 Drag the missing fragments into the spaces to complete the name of this amine molecule.

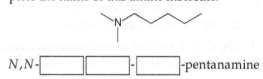

N,N-[_____][_____]-[_____]-pentanamine

Answer choices 1: mono, di, tri, tetra, penta, hexa

Answer choices 2: 1, 2, 3, 4, 5, 6

Answer choices 3: methyl, ethyl, propyl, butyl, pentyl, hexyl

19.69 What is the name of this molecule?

a) 2-aminohexanamine
b) 1-methyl-2-aminohexanamine
c) 2-methyl-1-hexanamine
d) 1-methyl-1-aminohexane

19.70 What is the name of this molecule?

a) 1-methyl-2-aminopropane
b) 2-ethyl-2-propanamine
c) 2-methyl-2-butanamine
d) 1,1-dimethyl-1-propanamine

19.71 What is the name of this molecule?

a) 5-octanamine
b) 1-propyl-1-pentanamine
c) 4-propyl-4-pentanamine
d) 4-octanamine

19.72 Drawing an amine: Draw the *skeletal structure* of diethylamine. Your skeletal structure should not show C—H bonds, lone pairs of electrons on nitrogen, or labels on carbon atoms. Hydrogen atom(s) bonded to nitrogen should be shown if present on the molecule.

19.73 What is the name of this molecule?

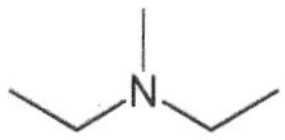

a) diethylmethylamine

b) *N,N*-diethylmethylamine

c) 2-ethyl-methylamine

d) *N*-ethyl-*N*-methylethanamine

19.74 Drawing an amine: Draw the *skeletal structure* of *N*-ethyl-4-octanamine. Your skeletal structure should not show C—H bonds, lone pairs of electrons on nitrogen, or labels on carbon atoms. Hydrogen atom(s) bonded to nitrogen should be shown if present on the molecule.

19.75 Which molecule is 2,2-dimethyl-1-butanamine?

a)

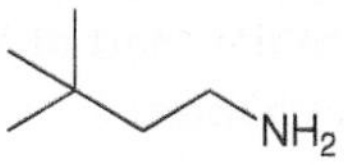

b)

c)

d)

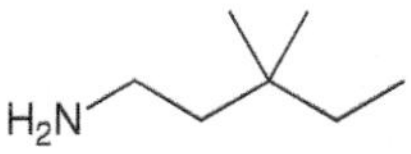

19.76 Which of the following molecules is tricyclopentyl-ammonium bromide?

a)

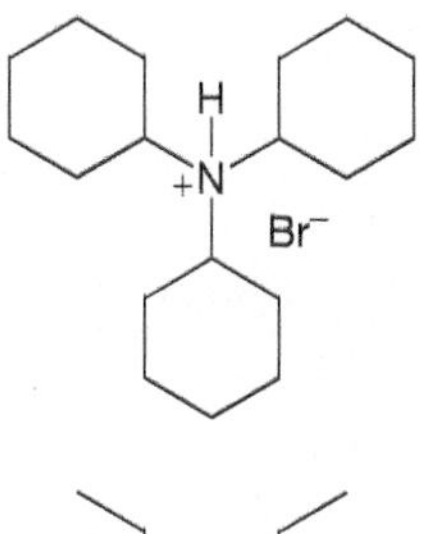

b)

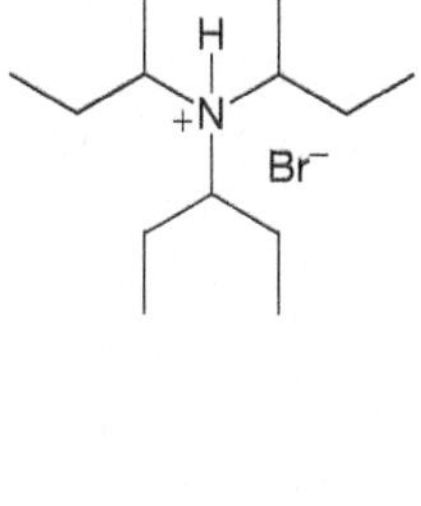

c)

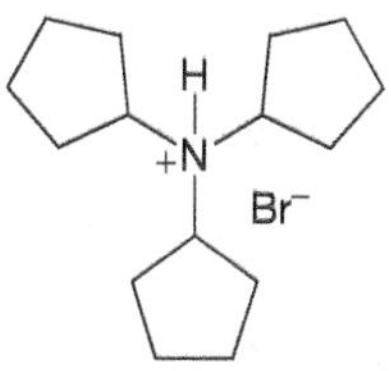

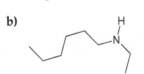

d)

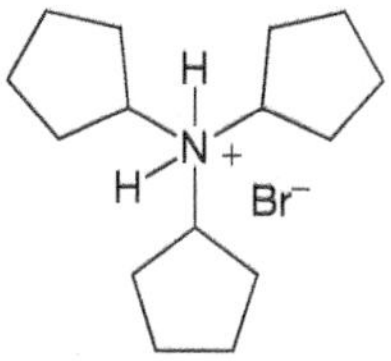

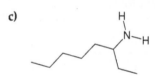

19.77 Which of the following molecules is *N*-ethyl-1-hexanamine?

a)

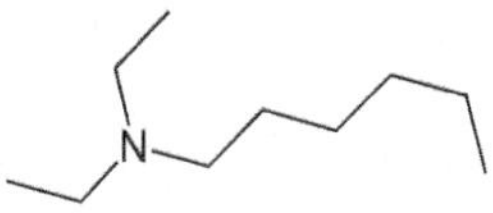

b)

c)

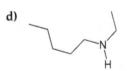

d)

19.78 What is the name of this molecule?

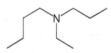

a) N-ethyl-N-propylbutanamine

b) *N,N*-diethylbutanamine

c) 4-aminoethylbutane

d) *N*-butyl-*N*-ethyl-*N*-propylamine

19.79 What is the name of the product formed in this reaction?

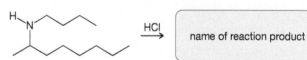

a) *N*-butyl-2-octylammonium chloride

b) 2-aminobutyloctane

c) *N*-butyl-2-octylamine

d) *N*-propyl-2-octylammonium chloride

Chapter 20

20.1 Introduction to Proteins

LO 20.1: **List the key functions that proteins carry out in the body.**

20.01 Which molecule type forms the building blocks of proteins?

   a) sugars

   b) amino acids

   c) nucleic acids

   d) fatty acids

20.02 Insulin is an example of which type of protein?

   a) structural

   b) denatured

   c) membrane

   d) regulatory

20.03 Aquaporins are multi-subunit proteins embedded in cell membranes that facilitate the movement of water in and out of cells. Aquaporins are an example of which type of protein?

   a) digestive

   b) membrane

   c) nuclear

   d) ribosomal

20.04 Which description best characterizes nonessential amino acids?

   a) amino acids that our bodies cannot use to build proteins

   b) amino acids that do not contain R group side chains

   c) amino acids that our bodies can make so do not need to come from the diet

   d) amino acids that contain amino and carboxyl groups separated by four or more carbon atoms in the chain

   e) amino acids that our bodies cannot make and must come from the diet

20.05 Which of the following statements is *not* a specific function of proteins?

   a) store the genetic information in cells

   b) provide structure and strength to certain tissues and hair

   c) catalyze enzymatic reactions in the cell

   d) transport molecules and ions across cell membranes

   e) assist with the movement of an organism

20.2 Amino Acids

LO 20.2: **Draw the charged forms of amino acids at a range of pH values and identify amino acid stereoisomers as D or L.**

20.06 In the structure of amino acids, what is the name of the carbon atom that the amino, carboxyl, and R groups are all bonded to?

   a) beta (β) carbon

   b) central carbon

   c) hydrocarbon

   d) alpha (α) carbon

20.07 Amino acid R groups (side chains) that are polar and attracted to water are_____.

   a) hydrophobic

   b) hydrophilic

   c) helical

   d) chiral

20.08 Sulfur-containing amino acids play important roles in metabolism and maintaining protein structure. Identify the sulfur-containing amino acids listed below. Try to answer this question from memory. If necessary, you may refer to the chart of amino acid structures presented in the chapter.

   Answer choices: threonine, proline, cysteine, asparagine, methionine

   Target boxes: contains sulfur, does not contain sulfur

20.09 The pH at which an amino acid has an overall net charge of zero is the _____.

   a) inflection point

   b) end point

   c) isoelectric point

   d) pH point

20.10 Identify the R group type on the amino acid isoleucine.

isoleucine

   a) polar acidic

   b) nonpolar

   c) polar neutral

   d) polar basic

20.11 Identify the R group type on the essential amino acid threonine.

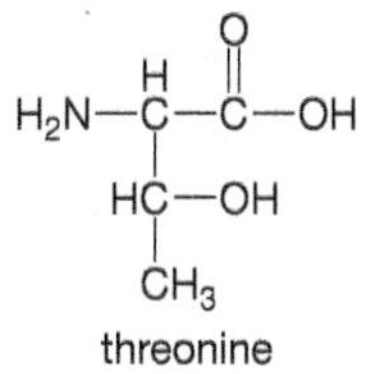

threonine

a) polar basic

b) nonpolar

c) polar acidic

d) polar neutral

20.12 Identify the R group type on the essential amino acid lysine.

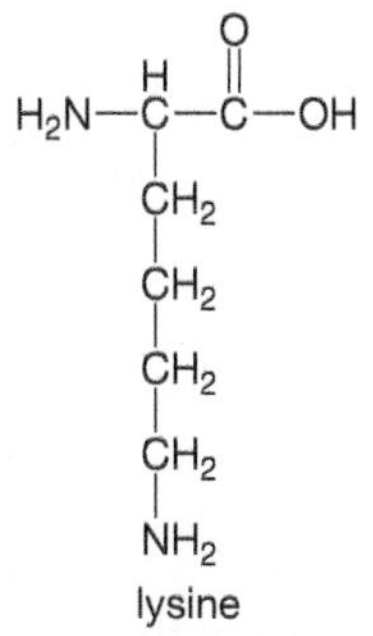

lysine

a) polar acidic

b) polar neutral

c) polar basic

d) nonpolar

20.13 When an amino acid is in the zwitterion form, the carboxylate group is _____.

a) positively charged

b) neutral

c) negatively charged

d) bonded to nitrogen

20.14 Which best describes the reaction in the *forward* direction from left to right?

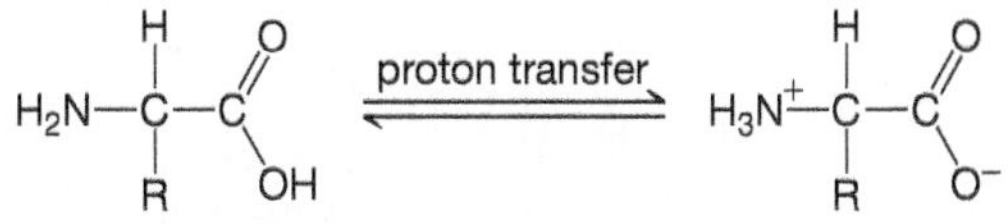

a) The carboxyl group accepts a proton to become the carboxylate anion and the amino group donates a proton to become an ammonium cation.

b) The ammonium cation donates a proton to become an amino group and the carboxylate anion accepts a proton to become a carboxyl group.

c) The carboxyl group donates a proton to become the carboxylate anion and the amino group accepts a proton to become an ammonium cation.

d) The amino group acts as an acid and the carboxyl group acts as a base.

20.15 Which statement best describes the reaction in the *reverse* direction from right to left?

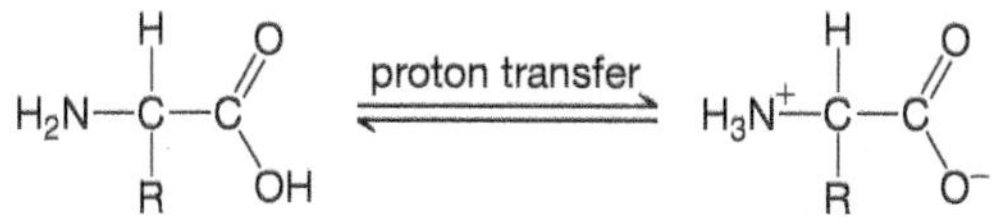

a) The carboxyl group donates a proton to become the carboxylate anion and the amino group accepts a proton to become an ammonium cation.

b) The amino group acts as a base and the carboxyl group acts as an acid.

c) The carboxyl group accepts a proton to become the carboxylate anion and the amino group donates a proton to become an ammonium cation.

d) The ammonium cation donates a proton to become an amino group and the carboxylate anion accepts a proton to become a carboxyl group.

20.16 Sort the amino acids into the bin with the appropriate polarity.

Answer choices:

a)

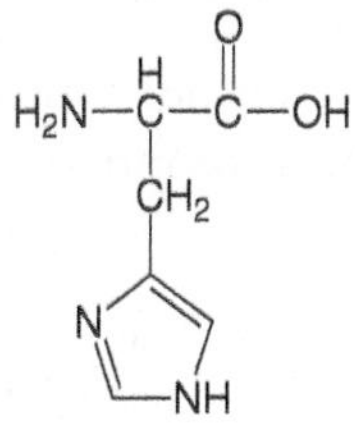

b)

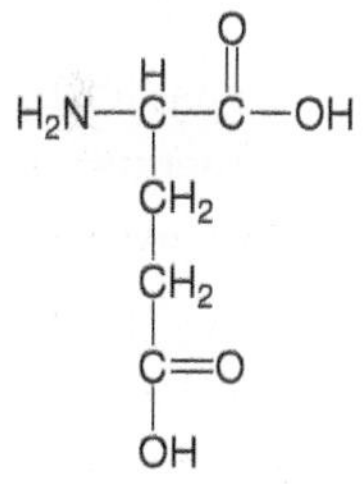

c)

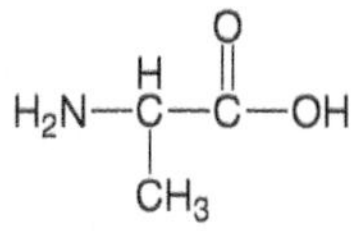

d)

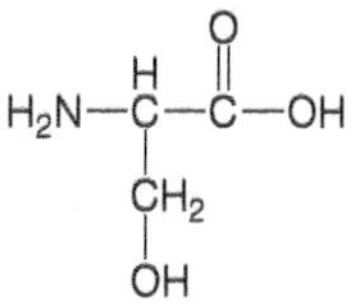

e)

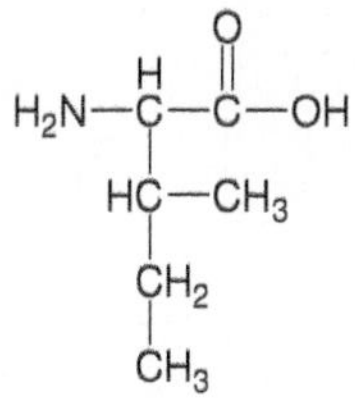

Target boxes: non-polar, polar (neutral), polar (acidic), polar (basic)

20.17 Identify the correct statement about the amino acid glycine.

   a) Glycine is the only naturally occurring amino acid that is non-chiral (achiral).

   b) Glycine is one of three naturally occurring amino acids that contains an acidic R group side chain.

   c) Glycine is the only naturally occurring beta (β) amino acid that exists as an equal mixture of the D and L forms at physiological pH.

   d) Glycine is one of four naturally occurring amino acids that does not ionize to form a zwitterion.

20.18 Study the structures of each amino acid shown. Identify those as positively charged, negatively charged, and those that have a zero-overall charge (neutral). Drag each amino acid into the bin with the correct electrical charge.

Answer choices:

a)

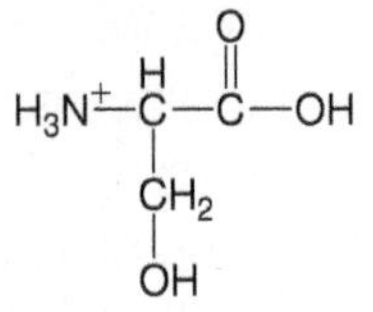

$H_3N^{\pm}$—C(H)—C(=O)—OH
CH₂
OH

b)

C(=O)—O⁻
H₂N⁺ (ring)

c)

H_2N—C(H)—C(=O)—O⁻
HC—CH₃
CH₃

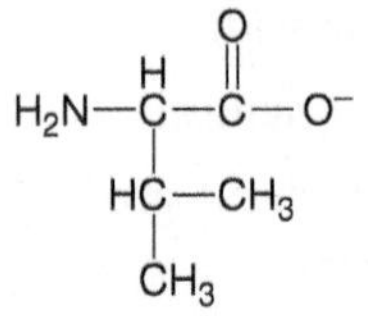

d)

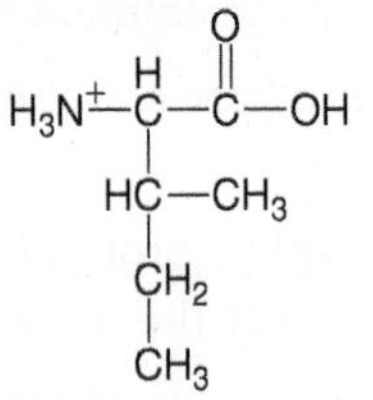

$H_3N^{\pm}$—C(H)—C(=O)—OH
HC—CH₃
CH₂
CH₃

e)

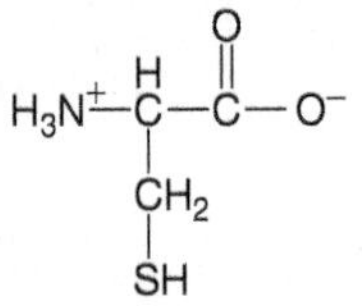

$H_3N^{\pm}$—C(H)—C(=O)—O⁻
CH₂
SH

f)

H_2N—C(H)—C(=O)—O⁻
CH₂
C=O
NH₂

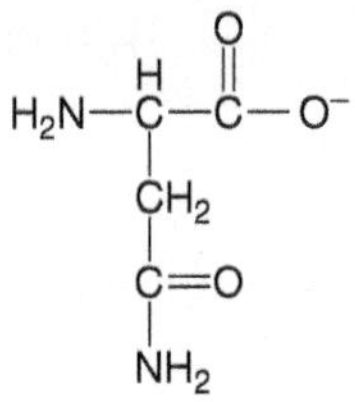

Target boxes: positively charged, negatively charged, overall neutral

20.19 Which of the illustrated functional groups that occur on amino acids would exist in the ionized state at high pH?

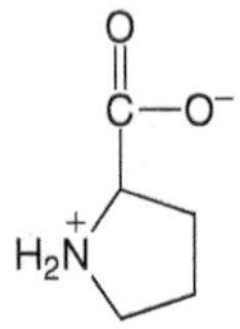

  a) H H
C—OH

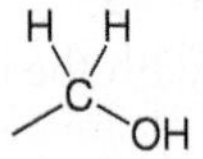

  b) (benzene ring)
C H H

  c) O
C—N(H)—H

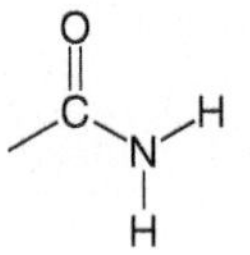

  d) O
C—O—H

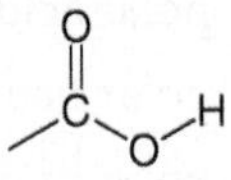

20.20 Consider this amino acid solution. Identify the reaction that takes place when the base NaOH is added to the aqueous solution. Drag the appropriate reactants and products into the boxes shown on each side of the reaction arrow.

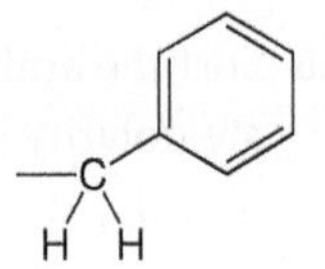

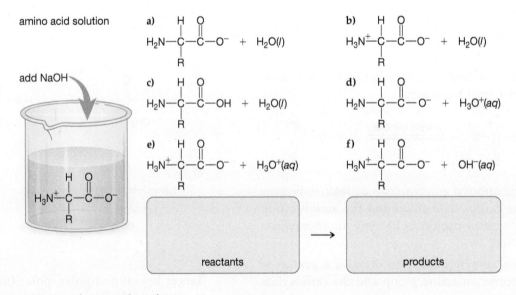

amino acid solution

a) H₂N—C(H)(R)—C(=O)—O⁻ + H₂O(l)

b) H₃N⁺—C(H)(R)—C(=O)—O⁻ + H₂O(l)

add NaOH

c) H₂N—C(H)(R)—C(=O)—OH + H₂O(l)

d) H₂N—C(H)(R)—C(=O)—O⁻ + H₃O⁺(aq)

e) H₃N⁺—C(H)(R)—C(=O)—O⁻ + H₃O⁺(aq)

f) H₃N⁺—C(H)(R)—C(=O)—O⁻ + OH⁻(aq)

H₃N⁺—C(H)(R)—C(=O)—O⁻

reactants → products

Target boxes: reactants box, products box

20.21 Consider this amino acid solution. Identify the reaction that takes place when the acid HCl is added to the aqueous solution. Drag the appropriate reactants and products into the boxes shown on each side of the reaction arrow.

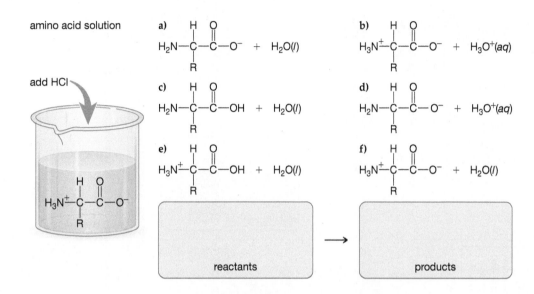

20.22 Examine the structures of each amino acid. Identify those that are in an aqueous solution with a pH greater than (>) the isoelectric point (pI), those that are at a pH equal to the pI, and those that are at a pH less than (<) the pI. Drag each structure into the correct bin.

Answer choices:

a)

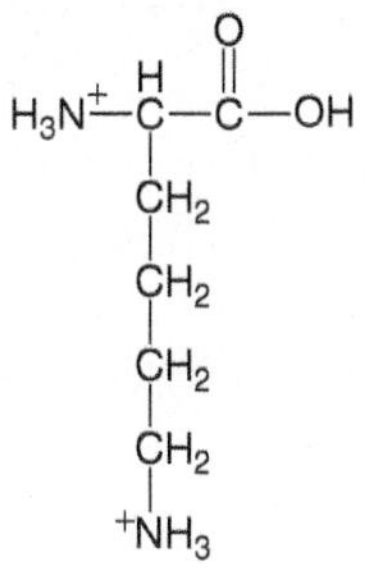

$H_3N^+-C-C-OH$
CH₂
CH₂
CH₂
CH₂
⁺NH₃

b)

$H_3N^+-C-C-O^-$
CH₂
CH₂
S
CH₃

c)

$H_3N^+-C-C-OH$
CH₂
C=O
OH

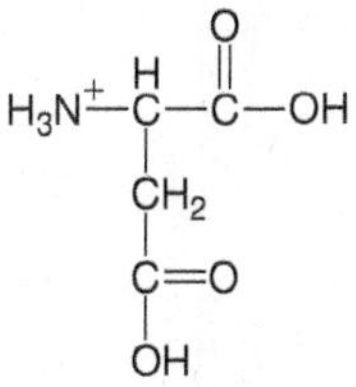

d)

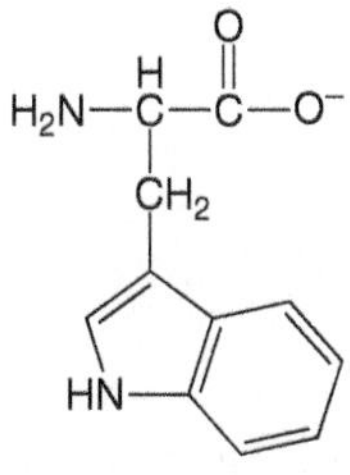

$H_2N-C-C-O^-$
CH₂
(indole ring, HN)

e)

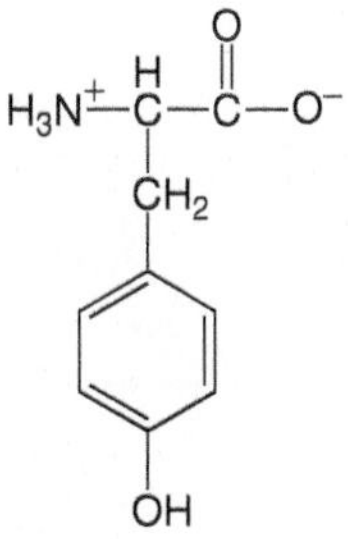

$H_3N^+-C-C-O^-$
CH₂
(phenol ring, OH)

f)

$H_2N-C-C-O^-$
CH₂
(imidazole ring, N, NH)

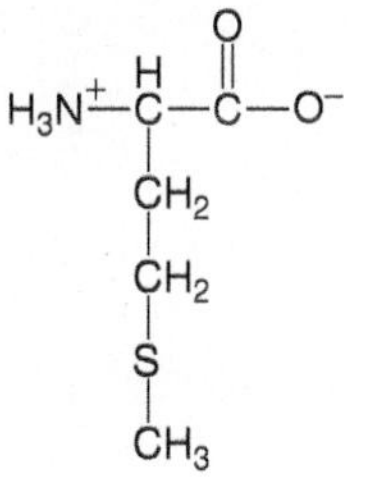

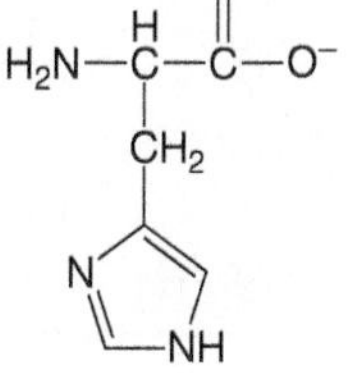

Target boxes: pH > pI, pH = pI, pH < pI

20.23 Study the structures of the 20 common amino acids shown. Identify each amino acid (using its one-letter abbreviation) that contains two chiral carbon atoms.

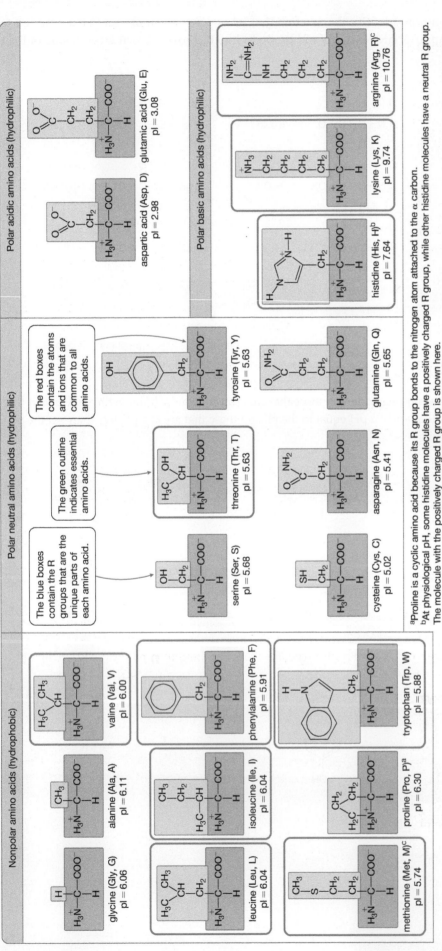

20.3 Peptides

LO 20.3: Draw simple peptides and identify peptide bonds.

20.24 Which arrow points to the peptide (amide) bond?

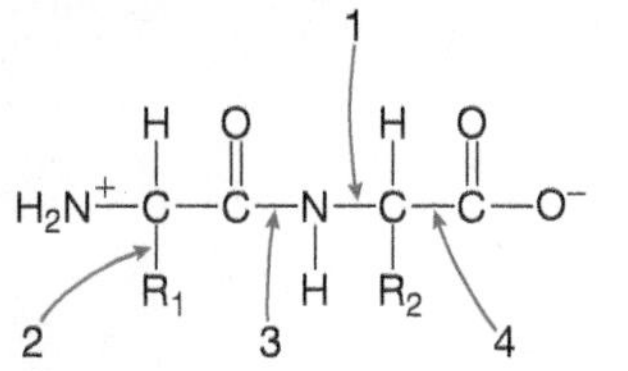

20.25 Which of the following best describes the role of enkephalins in the body?

a) pain regulation

b) blood clotting

c) cell growth

d) muscle contraction

e) bone regeneration

20.26 Identify the correctly drawn dipeptide.

a)

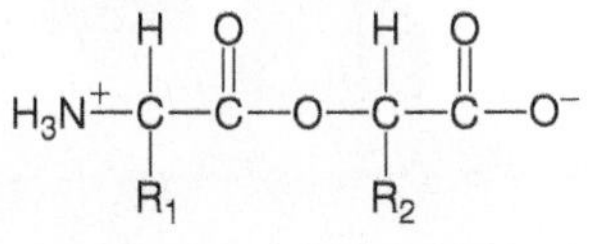

b)

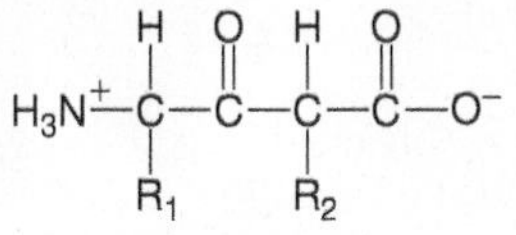

c)

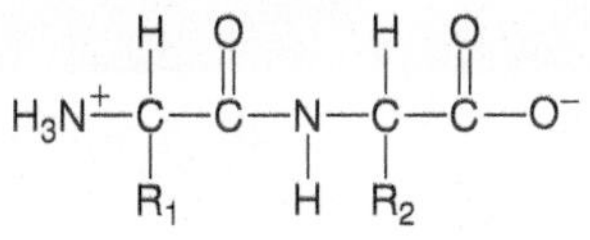

d)

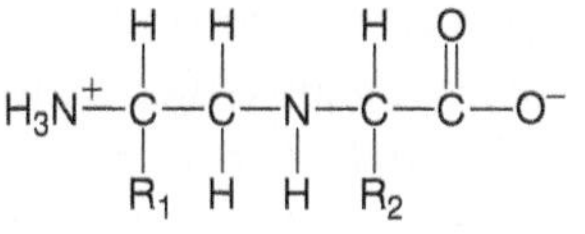

20.27 The peptide bonds that connect amino acids in a chain are known as _____.

a) ester bonds

b) hemiacetal bonds

c) aldehyde bonds

d) amide bonds

20.28 Which is the N-terminal amino acid in the peptide Ser-Ala-Met-Asn?

a) asparagine   b) alanine

c) ammonium   d) serine

e) cysteine

20.29 Which two groups are joined together as a peptide bond forms between amino acids?

a) ketone and alcohol

b) carboxylate and amino

c) amino and aldehyde

d) carboxylate and alcohol

e) ester and amide

20.30 Which of the following is the C-terminal amino acid in the peptide Glu-Leu-Cys-Tyr-Gln?

a) glutamic acid   b) glutamine

c) glycine   d) leucine

e) cysteine

20.31 Deltorphin is a naturally occurring peptide that occurs in the skin of some tropical frogs. The deltorphin peptide is able to cross the blood-brain barrier and produce similar effects as the opiates morphine and heroin. Which amino acid is *not* found in the sequence of the deltorphin structure? It may be helpful to refer to the table of amino acid structures when answering this question.

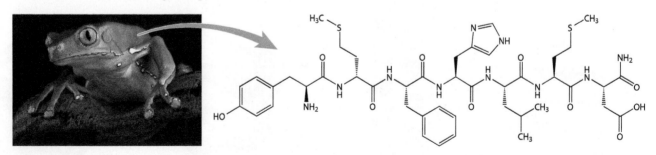

a) methionine   b) histidine   c) cysteine   d) tyrosine   e) leucine

20.32 How many unique tripeptides are possible?

a) 3   b) 6   c) 2   d) 9   e) 60

20.33 Spinorphin is a naturally occurring opioid peptide in the blood that helps regulate pain. Examine the structure of the spinorphin peptide shown then identify its correct amino acid sequence. It may be helpful to refer to the table of amino acid structures when answering this question.

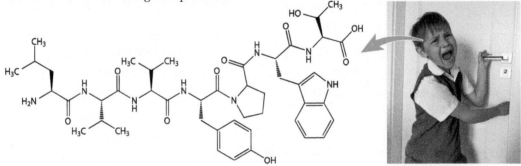

a) Thr-Trp-Pro-Tyr-Val-Val-Leu **b)** Ile-Val-Val-Phe-Pro-Trp-Thr **c)** Leu-Val-Val-Tyr-His-Trp-Val

d) Val-Leu-Leu-Tyr-Pro-Trp-Thr **e)** Leu-Val-Val-Tyr-Pro-Trp-Thr

20.34 Oxytocin is a naturally-occurring cyclic peptide containing a disulfide (S—S) bond between two cysteines in the sequence. It is a hormone released to help trigger contractions during childbirth and to trigger lactation. How many peptide bonds are in the oxytocin molecule?

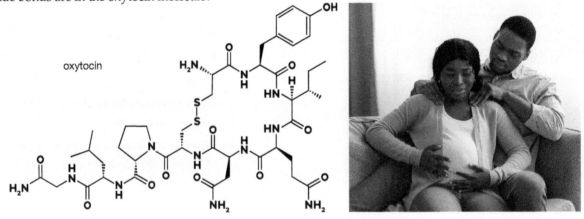

a) 7 peptide bonds **b)** 6 peptide bonds **c)** 9 peptide bonds **d)** 8 peptide bonds

20.4 Protein Structure

LO 20.4: Describe primary, secondary, tertiary, and quaternary structures of proteins.

20.35 In this chapter, we studied the different levels of protein structure. Identify the protein structure of each image.

Answer choices: tertiary structure, primary structure, quaternary structure, secondary structure

Target boxes:

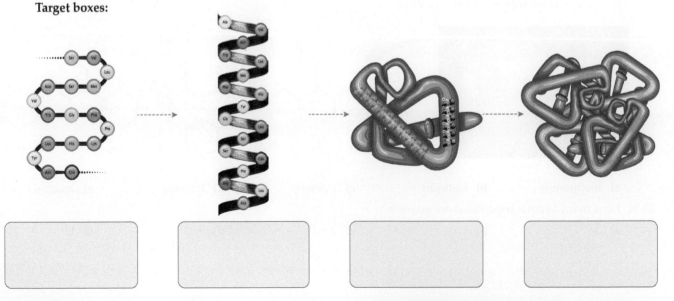

20.36 What type of protein secondary structure does this image represent?

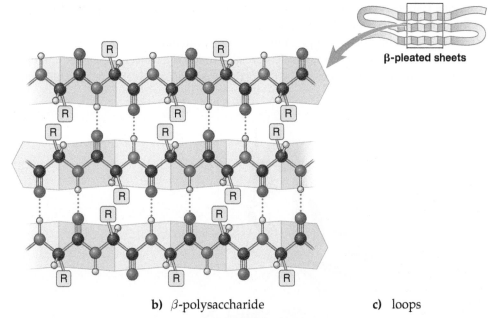

β-pleated sheets

a) α-helix   b) β-polysaccharide   c) loops

d) β-sheet   e) triple helix

20.37 Collagen is a structural protein that serves as a building block in bone, cartilage, tendons, teeth, and blood vessels. The collagen protein has which characteristic secondary structure?

a) beta sheet   b) alpha helix   c) double helix   d) triple helix

e) repeating disulfide bonds across beta sheets

20.38 Prion proteins (PrP) are associated with a variety of neurological diseases characterized by loss of motor control, dementia, and paralysis. A growing body of evidence suggests that misfolded prion proteins that have become altered in their 3-D structure play a role in these diseases. The structure of the human prion protein (hPrP) is shown below. This protein is mostly composed of which type of structural feature?

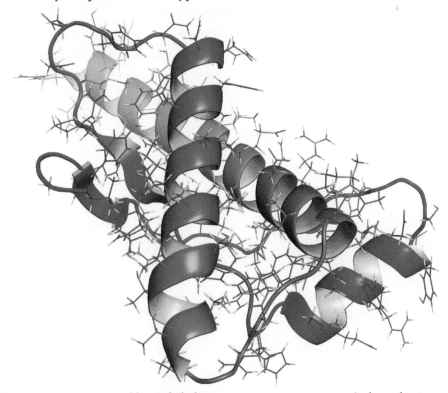

a) denatured proteins   b) triple helices   c) beta sheets

d) disulfide bonds   e) alpha helices

20.39 The programmed cell death protein 1 (PD-1) occurs on cells in the immune system where it helps regulate the body's immune response. PD-1 does this by binding to another receptor, called PD-L1, on other cells. This binding prevents the immune cells from destroying the second cell, even if it is cancerous. Researchers are developing anti-cancer drugs known as immune checkpoint inhibitors that can bind to PD-L1 and block binding between PD-1 and PD-L1. Without bound PD-1, the immune cells are able to kill the cancer cells. Examine the structure of the PD-1/PD-L1 complex below. This protein complex is mostly composed of which type of structural feature?

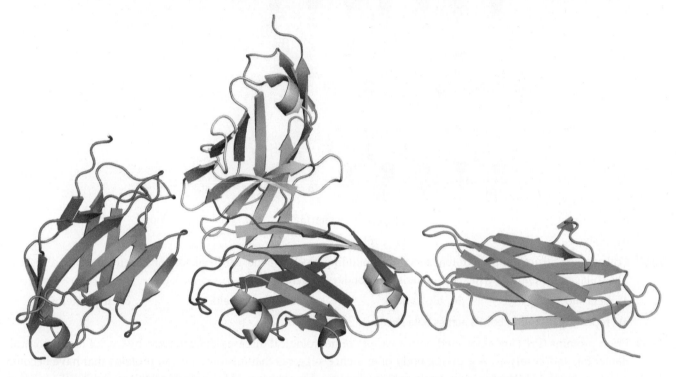

 a) alpha helix   **b)** beta sheet   **c)** triple helix

 d) unstructured loops   **e)** denatured proteins

20.40 What structural level results when two or more proteins combine to form an active larger protein?

 a) tertiary structure   **b)** secondary structure

 c) primary structure   **d)** quaternary structure

20.41 Salt bridges, also called electrostatic interactions or ion bridges, occur between the side chains of certain amino acids to help stabilize protein structure. Which pair of amino acids are most likely to form salt bridges between their R group side chains? It may be helpful to refer to the table of amino acid structures when answering this question.

20.42 Hydrogen bonding can occur between the R group side chains of some amino acids, which can help stabilize protein structure. Which pair of amino acids are most likely to form hydrogen bonds between their side chains? It may be helpful to refer to the table of amino acid structures when answering this question.

a) Glu and Val   b) Asn and Thr

c) Leu and Cys   d) Phe and Pro

e) His and Ala

20.43 London dispersion forces, also known as hydrophobic interactions, can occur between the side chains of specific amino acids to help stabilize protein structure. Which pair of amino acids is most likely to share London dispersion forces with each other? It may be helpful to refer to the table of amino acid structures when answering this question.

a) Gly and His   b) Asn and Asp

c) Thr and Lys   d) Phe and Val

e) Glu and Ile

20.44 What is the primary attractive force between these two amino acid side chains?

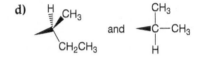

a) London dispersion

b) hydrogen bonding

c) disulfide bond

d) salt bridge

20.45 Determine the primary type of interaction that occurs between each of the pairs of amino acid R group side chains in tertiary protein structures. It may be helpful to refer to the table of amino acid structures when answering this question. Drag each pair of amino acid R group side chains into the correct bin.

Answer choices:

a) CH_2—⬡—OH and $\overset{H}{\underset{H}{C}}$—OH

b) CH_2SH and CH_2SH

c) $(CH_2)_4NH_3^+$ and $CH_2CH_2\overset{O}{C}$—O^-

d) $\overset{H}{\underset{CH_2CH_3}{C}}CH_3$ and $\overset{CH_3}{\underset{H}{C}}$—$CH_3$

Target boxes: London dispersion (hydrophobic), salt bridge, hydrogen bond, disulfide bond

---

20.46 Chlorotoxin is a peptide that occurs in the venom of the deathstalker scorpion. This peptide blocks chloride ion channels in cells. In recent years, scientists have learned that chlorotoxin also possesses targeting properties towards certain types of cancer cells. The fact that chlorotoxin binds preferentially to certain cells has allowed scientists to develop methods to diagnose and treat several types of cancer.

The single letter amino acid sequence of the chlorotoxin peptide is shown. Based on this sequence, determine the maximum number of disulfide bonds that are possible at any given time in a single folded protein structure of chlorotoxin. You may find it helpful to refer to the amino acid structures and one letter amino acid codes in Table 20.1 when answering this question.

MCMPCFTTDHQMARKCDDCCGGKGRGKCYGPQCLCR

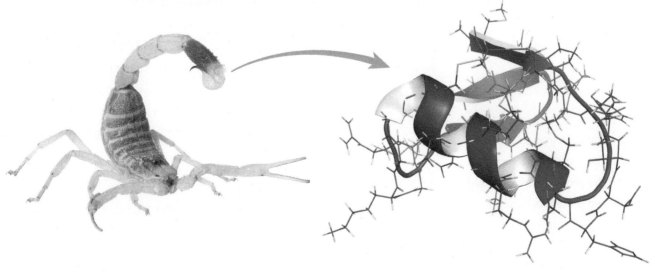

a) 3   b) 4   c) 8   d) 16

20.5 Protein Hydrolysis and Denaturation

LO 20.5: Draw the products of protein hydrolysis and describe protein denaturation.

20.47 Which statement best describes the overall process shown from left to right in the diagram?

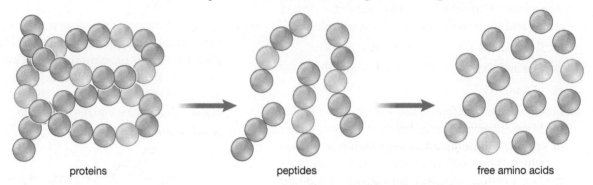

proteins   peptides   free amino acids

a) The protein is denatured.   **b)** The protein is synthesized.

c) The protein is hydrolyzed.   **d)** The protein is folding.

20.48 Which statement best describes the process in the diagram shown?

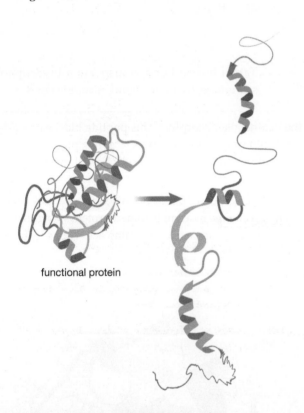

functional protein

a) The protein is folding.

b) The protein is hydrolyzed.

c) The protein is synthesized.

d) The protein is denatured.

20.49 Identify the numbered bond in the peptide backbone that is broken during a hydrolysis reaction.

a) The bond labeled 1 is broken during hydrolysis.

b) The bond labeled 2 is broken during hydrolysis.

c) The bond labeled 3 is broken during hydrolysis.

d) The bond labeled 4 is broken during hydrolysis.

20.50 Which environment is most likely to produce a protein in aqueous solution becoming denatured?

a) a buffered solution at pH 7.1

b) a temperature of 34 °C

c) a temperature of 26 °C

d) a buffered solution at pH 1.7

20.51 Which statement best describes protein denaturation?

a) The primary structure is changed.

b) Protein denaturation is always reversible.

c) The secondary, tertiary, or quaternary structure is changed.

d) It can only occur in proteins with quaternary structure.

e) It does not occur in a 90% alcohol solution.

20.52 A chaperone protein is one that _____.

   a) denatures mRNA to prevent disease transmission

   b) helps other proteins fold correctly correct

   c) changes the primary structure of a protein

   d) breaks down a protein into individual amino acids during digestion

20.53 Which condition would most likely *not* result in protein denaturation?

   a) an aqueous solution at pH 14 and 37 °C

   b) a soap solution at pH 7 and 55 °C

   c) a phosphate buffered saline solution at pH 7.4 and 32 °C

   d) a phosphate buffered saline solution at pH = 7 and 96 °C

   e) a 0.7 M aqueous solution of $AgNO_3$ at pH = 7 and 37 °C

20.54 What do protein denaturation and complete protein hydrolysis have in common?

   a) Both protein denaturation and complete protein hydrolysis result in the formation of additional alpha-helical structures.

   b) Both protein denaturation and complete protein hydrolysis cause the protein to no longer perform its original function.

   c) Both protein denaturation and complete protein hydrolysis result in the conversion of additional alpha-helical structures into beta-sheets.

   d) Both protein denaturation and complete protein hydrolysis result in the conversion of chaperone proteins to amyloid deposits.

20.55 Most correctly folded proteins are water soluble. Which statement best describes a correctly folded protein in aqueous solution?

   a) The nonpolar hydrophobic regions of the proteins are often in the center while the hydrophilic polar regions are exposed to the aqueous solvent.

   b) The hydrophilic polar regions of the proteins are often in the center while the nonpolar hydrophobic regions are exposed to the aqueous solvent.

   c) There is no difference between the center of a globular protein and the solvent exposed surface of the protein since it is dissolved in water.

   d) There is no difference between the hydrophobic and hydrophilic amino acid side chains when the protein is dissolved in water.

20.56 Casein is the primary protein in milk. Digesting milk protein produces peptides with biological activity. Casomorphins are a group of peptide fragments derived from the digestion of casein that may play a role in a range of biological activities including mucus production, insulin secretion, and hypoxia (low blood oxygen). The structure of one such peptide fragment (beta-casomorphin 7) is shown. What reaction products result from the complete hydrolysis of the peptide beta-casomorphin 7? It may be helpful to refer to the table of amino acid structures when answering this question.

beta-casomorphin 7

   a) Phe + Pro + Tyr + Pro + Gly + Pro + Ile

   b) Tyr + Pro + Phe + Pro + Gly + Pro + Leu

   c) Tyr + Pro + Phe + Pro + Pro + Ile

   d) Tyr + Pro + Phe + Pro + Gly + Pro + Ile

   e) Phe + Pro + Phe + Pro + Gly + Pro + Ile

Chapter 21

21.1 Introduction to Enzymes

LO 21.1: Describe the role enzymes play in biochemical reactions and recognize the six classes of enzyme function.

21.01 Lipases are biological molecules required for the metabolism of fats. Utilize your understanding of terminology discussed in this chapter to predict what type of biological macromolecule lipase is?

   a) lipid

   b) DNA

   c) polysaccharide

   d) enzyme

   e) RNA

21.02 The enzyme that breaks down the neurotransmitter acetylcholine is called _____.

   a) neurotransmitter synthase

   b) acetylcholine esterase

   c) acetylcholine mutase

   d) acetylcholine replicase

21.03 How do enzymes speed up the rate of reactions?

   a) Enzymes increase the activation energy.

   b) Enzymes increase the equilibrium constant K_{eq}.

   c) Enzymes lower the activation energy.

   d) Enzymes decrease the equilibrium constant K_{eq}.

   e) Enzymes increase the energy of the reactants.

21.04 The maximum number of substrate molecules converted to product by one enzyme molecule per unit of time is the _____.

   a) rate number

   b) activation energy

   c) kinetic number

   d) turnover energy

   e) turnover number

21.05 The proteins that form a network of stringy, insoluble proteins during blood clotting are called _____.

   a) fibrins   **b)** collagen

   c) hydrolase   **d)** plasmin

   e) urokinase

21.06 The enzyme in your blood that converts fibrin from its inactive form to its active form during blood clotting is called _____.

   a) urokinase   **b)** hemotransferase

   c) thrombin   **d)** fibrin   **e)** plasmin

21.07 What function do tissue plasminogen activator (t-PA) and urokinase both have in common?

   a) Both deactivate plasmin to help form clots and restrict blood flow.

   b) Both activate plasmin to help breakdown clots and restore blood flow.

   c) Both activate thrombin to help breakdown clots and restore blood flow.

   d) Both reduce the formation of red blood cells in the body and decrease blood pressure.

   e) Both stimulate the formation of fibrin which then helps breakdown clots and restore blood flow.

21.08 Maleate plays an important role in both metabolism and photosynthesis. The conversion of maleate to fumarate is catalyzed by an enzyme. What type of enzyme catalyzes this reaction?

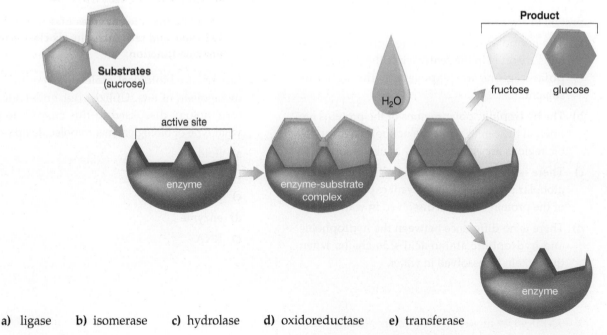

maleate   fumarate

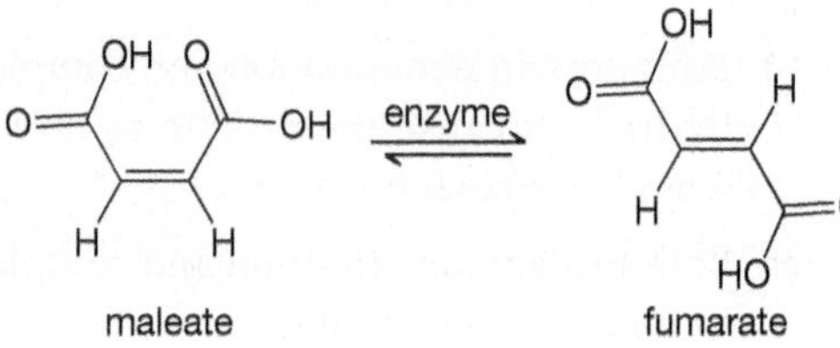

   a) transferase   **b)** oxidoreductase

   c) hydrolase   **d)** isomerase   **e)** ligase

21.09 Consider the diagram shown involving the conversion of sucrose (table sugar) to fructose (fruit sugar) and glucose (blood sugar). What type of enzyme catalyzes this reaction?

Product

Substrates
(sucrose)

fructose   glucose

H_2O

active site

enzyme

enzyme-substrate
complex

enzyme

   a) ligase   **b)** isomerase   **c)** hydrolase   **d)** oxidoreductase   **e)** transferase

21.10 Pyruvate and lactate are both important molecules in metabolic processes. Consider the enzyme-catalyzed reaction shown involving the conversion of pyruvate to lactate. What type of enzyme catalyzes this reaction?

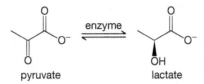

pyruvate   lactate

a) hydrolase   **b)** isomerase   **c)** ligase   **d)** transferase   **e)** oxidoreductase

21.11 A patient admitted to the emergency room in a hospital is believed to be suffering from severe liver disease. The attending doctor orders an "ALT" test to help diagnose the patient. The ALT enzyme catalyzes the reaction shown between the amino acid alanine (Ala) and α-ketoglutarate. This reaction is important for amino acid metabolism and proper liver function. What type of enzyme is ALT?

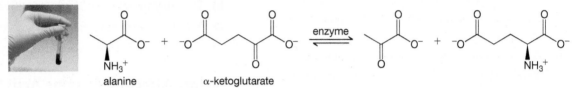

alanine α-ketoglutarate

a) isomerase   **b)** transferase   **c)** hydrolase   **d)** ligase

---

21.2 How Enzymes work

LO 21.2: Explain the two models of enzyme catalysis.

21.12 Sucrase catalyzes the hydrolysis of sucrose (table sugar) to fructose and glucose. Categorize each sugar as an enzyme, substrate, or product.

Answer choices: glucose, sucrase, fructose, sucrose

Target boxes: enzyme, substrate(s), product(s)

21.13 The region on an enzyme formed by the folds of the protein chains where a chemical reaction takes place is called the _____.

a) reaction center

b) substrate pocket

c) interaction site

d) active site

e) product formation site

21.14 The match between substrate and active site is referred to as _____.

a) enzyme specificity   **b)** enzyme inhibition

c) enzyme capacity   **d)** enzyme turnover number

e) enzyme regulation

21.15 Which statement best describes the lock-and-key model of enzyme activity?

a) The shape of the active site is flexible, but the shape of the substrate is not flexible.

b) The shape of the active site is nonflexible, but the shape of the substrate is flexible.

c) The shape of the active site is not flexible, and the shape of the substrate must exactly match the active site.

d) Both the size and shape of the active site are flexible so the intermolecular interactions between enzyme and substrate are noncompetitive.

21.16 Which best identifies the process shown in the diagram?

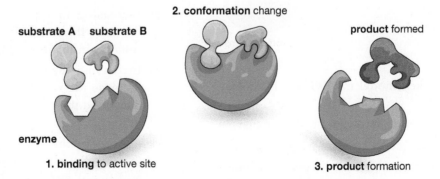

a) lock-and-key model   **b)** dispersion model   **c)** hydrolase model   **d)** induced-fit model

21.17 Select the statement that best describes an enzyme with stereochemical specificity.

a) The enzyme acts on all isomers of a substrate.

b) The enzyme reacts with specific functional groups.

c) The enzyme acts on a specific steric or optical isomer.

d) The enzyme acts on a specific bond type.

21.18 Which statement best describes the induced-fit model of enzyme activity?

a) Both the size and shape of the active site are flexible so the intermolecular interactions between enzyme and substrate switch from dipole-dipole to dispersion (hydrophobic).

b) The shape of the active site is nonflexible, and the shape of the substrate must exactly match the active site.

c) The shape of the active site is nonflexible, but the shape of the substrate is flexible.

d) The shape of the active site is flexible, but the shape of the substrate is nonflexible.

21.19 Which statement best describes an enzyme with group specificity?

a) The enzyme acts on a single, specific substrate.

b) The enzyme acts on a specific steric or optical isomer.

c) The enzyme acts on a specific bond type.

d) The enzyme reacts with specific functional groups.

21.20 Which description best identifies the process shown in the diagram?

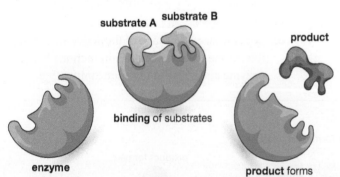

a) lock-and-key model involving a hydrolase enzyme

b) induced-fit model involving a hydrolase enzyme

c) lock-and-key model involving a ligase enzyme

d) allosteric control model involving a ligase enzyme

21.21 Select the statement that best describes an enzyme with bond specificity.

a) The enzyme acts on a specific steric or optical isomer.

b) The enzyme acts on a specific bond type.

c) The enzyme acts on a single, specific substrate.

d) The enzyme reacts with specific functional groups.

21.22 Which statement best describes an enzyme with absolute specificity?

a) The enzyme acts on a specific steric or optical isomer.

b) The enzyme acts on a single, specific substrate.

c) The enzyme reacts with specific functional groups.

d) The enzyme acts on a specific bond type.

21.3 Factors Affecting Enzyme Activity

LO 21.3: Describe the effects of temperature, pH, and reaction concentrations on enzyme activity and rate of reaction.

21.23 Lysozyme is an enzyme that occurs in tears, saliva, and mucus and helps defend against bacterial infections. It acts on the cell walls of bacteria to cleave (break apart) the peptidoglycan layer of the cell wall. Without an intact cell wall, the bacteria burst and die. The optimum pH for lysozyme is around 5. The activity of lysozyme is slowest at which pH?

a) pH 5.5   **b)** pH 4.8

c) pH 6.1   **d)** pH 2.5

21.24 The enzyme sucrase catalyzes the hydrolysis of table sugar (sucrose) to fructose and glucose. The optimum temperature for sucrase activity is 37 °C. The hydrolysis of sucrose is fastest at which temperature?

a) 35 °C   **b)** 27 °C

c) 47 °C   **d)** 98.6 °C

21.25 What is the predicted outcome of increasing the concentration of the enzyme when excess substrate is present in an enzyme-catalyzed reaction?

a) Increasing the enzyme concentration will decrease the turnover rate for the substrate resulting in an increase in product formation.

b) Increasing the enzyme concentration will increase the rate that the enzyme becomes denatured therefore decrease the rate of product formation.

c) Increasing the enzyme concentration will increase the rate of product formation since additional enzyme active sites have been introduced.

d) This change will have no effect since the rate of product formation is already at a maximum.

21.26 A student conducting undergraduate research is studying an enzyme in the laboratory. She begins an experiment in which the initial concentration of substrate is low. If she then increases the amount of substrate while keeping the amount of enzyme constant, what is the predicted impact on the rate of the enzyme-catalyzed reaction?

a) The rate will increase exponentially for as long as more substrate is being added.

b) The rate will increase rapidly at first and then gradually level off at a constant high rate.

c) The rate will remain constant since the amount of enzyme is being held constant.

d) The rate will decrease at first and then level off at a lower rate due to competitive inhibition.

e) The rate will decrease at first and then increase back to the original rate.

21.27 Examine the graph below showing reaction rate versus substrate concentration for an enzyme.

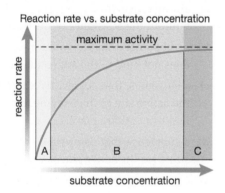

Reaction rate vs. substrate concentration

Drag each item onto the correct region(s) shown on the graph. A given item may be applied to more than one region. One or more items may also remain unassigned and unused.

Answer choices:

a) region in which the enzyme is not saturated with substrate

b) region in which the reaction rate remains constant (steady state)

c) region in which the enzyme is saturated with substrate

d) region in which the enzyme is denatured and becomes inactive

Target boxes: region A, region B, region C

21.28 Determine if each statement about enzyme activity is true or false.

Answer choices:

a) The activation energy of a reaction increases when an enzyme is used to catalyze a reaction.

b) Enzymes cannot be denatured because they are catalysts.

c) Enzymes are regenerated when a reaction is complete so they can be used again.

d) Enzymes speed up the reaction rate.

e) Enzymes must be at optimal pH, temperature, and substrate concentrations to function at all.

Target boxes: true, false

21.29 Determine if each statement about enzyme activity is true or false.

Answer choices:

a) Enzymes speed up the reaction rate by lowering the activation energy.

b) Enzymes are always very specific for the substrate they react with.

c) Enzymes, like other proteins, can be denatured.

d) Enzymes affect the reaction pathway by forming an enzyme-substrate complex.

Target boxes: true, false

21.30 A well-balanced diet combined with proper digestion is important for overall health and well-being. Chymotrypsin is an enzyme in the protease family that helps with digestion of protein. Chymotrypsin cleaves the peptide bonds that are on the C-terminal side of aromatic amino acids (Tyr, Phe, or Trp) as shown in the reaction below. The optimum pH for chymotrypsin is 7.8. Predict how each of the following will affect the rate of a chymotrypsin hydrolysis in a laboratory experiment conducted by a food scientist.

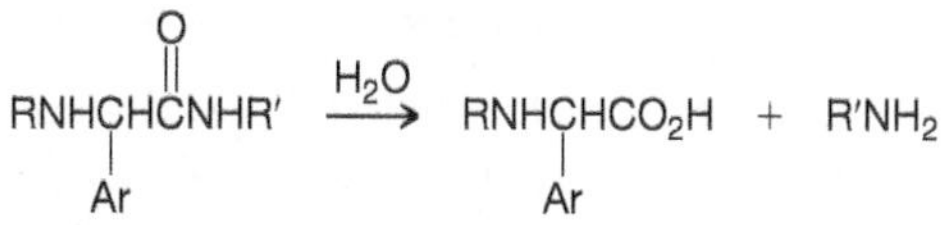

$$\underset{\underset{Ar}{|}}{RNHCHCNHR'} \xrightarrow{H_2O} \underset{\underset{Ar}{|}}{RNHCHCO_2H} + R'NH_2$$

Determine how each change in condition affects the reaction rate.

Answer choices:

a) increasing the pH to 12.6

b) adjust the temperature to 10 °C

c) decreasing the amount of chymotrypsin

d) lowering the pH to 3.5

Target boxes: increases the reaction rate, decreases the reaction rate

21.31 Lactose is a disaccharide that occurs in milk. Lactase is the enzyme that hydrolyzes the lactose into its component monosaccharides glucose and galactose. The optimal conditions for lactase activity are pH 6.6 – 6.8 and 35 – 40 °C. Assuming there is an excess of lactose substrate, predict how each of the following will affect the rate of a lactase catalyzed reaction that was originally at optimum conditions.

Determine how each change in condition affects the reaction rate.

Answer choices:

a) decreasing the concentration of lactose

b) lowering the pH to 4.2

c) adding more lactase

d) adjust the temperature to 25 °C

Target boxes: increases reaction rate, decreases reaction rate, no change in reaction rate

21.4 Enzyme Inhibition

LO 21.4: Differentiate between reversible and irreversible inhibition and describe the processes for competitive and noncompetitive enzyme inhibition.

21.32 How do ACE inhibitors help reduce blood pressure?

a) ACE inhibitors reduce the number of red blood cells resulting in lower blood volume and lower blood pressure.

b) ACE inhibitors catalyze specific enzymes that break down plaque inside blood vessels, thus lowering blood pressure.

c) ACE inhibitors increase the rate of the angiotensin-converting enzyme resulting in the breakdown of cholesterol in the arteries.

d) ACE inhibitors help relax and widen the arteries by blocking a signaling pathway that narrows blood vessels, which raises blood pressure.

21.33 Select the best description of a noncompetitive inhibitor.

a) a substance that competes with the natural substrate for the active site of the enzyme

b) a substance that slows the rate of reaction but does not bind to the active site of the enzyme

c) a substance that covalently attaches itself inside the active site of the enzyme to prevent the reaction from taking place

d) a substance that has no effect on the rate of the reaction when it binds to the enzyme

21.34 Select the best description of an irreversible inhibitor.

a) a substance that converts itself into product without the assistance of the enzyme

b) a substance that slows the rate of reaction but does not bind to the active site of the enzyme

c) a substance that covalently attaches itself inside the active site of the enzyme to prevent the reaction from taking place

d) a substance that competes with the natural substrate for the active site of the enzyme

21.35 Which statement best describes the drug methotrexate?

a) Methotrexate is an anticancer drug that acts as a noncompetitive inhibitor of the enzyme dihydrofolate reductase (DHFR).

b) Methotrexate is an anti-inflammatory drug that irreversibly inhibits the COX-2 enzyme.

c) Methotrexate is a non-competitive ACE inhibitor that helps relax arteries and reduce blood pressure.

d) Methotrexate is an anticancer drug that acts as a competitive inhibitor of the enzyme dihydrofolate reductase (DHFR).

21.36 Select the best description of a competitive inhibitor.

a) a substance that decreases the rate of the reverse reaction by increasing the equilibrium constant K for the forward reaction

b) a substance that covalently attaches itself inside the active site of the enzyme to prevent the reaction from taking place

c) a substance that slows the rate of reaction but does not bind to the active site of the enzyme

d) a substance that competes with the natural substrate for the active site of the enzyme

21.37 What does the abbreviation NSAID stand for?

a) noncompetitive systemic autoimmune diseases

b) nonsteroidal anti-inflammatory drugs

c) normalized secondary AIDS inhibiting drugs

d) non-treatable systemic autoinflammatory disease

21.38 Which is *not* a factor that affects enzyme reactivity in a controlled laboratory experiment?

a) the presence of an inhibitor

b) the pH of the reaction solution

c) the time of day the experiment is conducted

d) the temperature of the reaction temperature

e) the concentration of the substrate

21.39 An enzyme inhibitor that has a structure very similar to the natural enzyme substrate will most likely act as _____.

a) a non-competitive inhibitor

b) an additional catalyst to further accelerate the reaction

c) a competitive inhibitor

d) a zymogen

21.40 The action of an irreversible inhibitor _____.

a) can be reversed by the addition of a buffer that is at the optimum pH

b) can be reversed after two half-lives and the addition of a non-competitive inhibitor

c) can be reversed upon addition of a zymogen and a temperature shift to 37 °C

d) cannot be reversed

21.41 A student conducting undergraduate research is studying the characteristic of an enzyme believed to be important for cancer progression. In one experiment, she added an irreversible inhibitor to a test sample containing enzyme and substrate. She then wanted to allow the enzyme to become fully active again. What is the best way to restore enzyme activity in her test sample?

a) First add a competitive inhibitor that will compete out the first inhibitor, then adjust the pH and temperature to physiologic conditions.

b) Add more of the natural enzyme substrate.

c) Filter out the irreversible inhibitor.

d) The original enzyme has become inactivated so she can only add new enzyme.

e) Add more inhibitor and then adjust the pH and temperature to be optimum for the enzyme.

21.42 Which statement is *not* true for a competitive inhibitor?

a) The competitive inhibitor has a structure similar to the natural enzyme substrate.

b) The competitive inhibitor binds to the enzyme at a location other than the active site.

c) Increasing the substrate concentration can help reverse the effect of the competitive inhibitor.

d) The competitive inhibitor occupies the active site.

21.43 A team of students conducting a group project on enzyme activity have set up an enzymatic reaction that is running at the optimum pH and temperature for their enzyme. They then add a competitive inhibitor to the reaction and observe that the rate of the reaction has decreased as expected. They wish to speed up the reaction rate again. Which action is most likely to speed up the reaction?

a) Add more substrate so that it can out-compete the competitive inhibitor and increase the reaction rate.

b) Increase the temperature and mix the sample thoroughly.

c) Adjust the pH to 7.4, add more buffer then warm the sample to 37 °C.

d) Add more inhibitor, mix thoroughly, and allow the reaction time to speed up again.

21.44 Classify each item as typical of competitive or noncompetitive inhibition.

Answer choices:

a) The structure of the inhibitor is not similar to the substrate.

b) Adding more substrate reverses the inhibition.

c) The inhibitor has a structure very similar to the substrate.

d) The enzyme inhibition cannot be reversed by adding more substrate.

e) The inhibitor competes with the substrate for the active site.

Target boxes: competitive inhibition, noncompetitive inhibition

21.5 Regulation of Enzyme Activity

LO 21.5: **Identify the steps involved with allosteric control, feedback control, and covalent modification in regulating enzyme activity.**

21.45 Which statement best describes a zymogen?

a) Zymogens are irreversible inhibitors that use phosphate modification to inhibit a class of enzymes known as proteases.

b) Zymogens are proenzymes that are active until being deactivated by another enzyme.

c) Zymogens are proenzymes that are inactive until being activated by another enzyme.

d) Zymogens are proenzymes that act as negative regulators of phosphorylation enzymes.

21.46 Which of the following is another name for a proenzyme?

a) catalyst

b) inhibitor

c) regulator

d) zymogen

21.47 A student researcher has determined that the end-product of an enzyme-mediated reaction sequence is able to act as an inhibitor for an earlier step in the reaction sequence. What does this fact indicate about the process they are studying?

a) The end-product is a zymogen for the enzyme in the first reaction step.

b) The reaction sequence is under COX control that utilizes phosphorylation during the last reaction step.

c) The end-product acts as an irreversible inhibitor of the first reaction step.

d) The process is under feedback control by the end-product.

e) The enzyme in the first reaction step has more than one active site, one of which is the same as the active site of the last enzyme in the sequence.

21.48 How do allosteric enzymes control the rate that product is generated?

a) Allosteric enzymes bind a positive or negative regulator at a non-competitive site.

b) Allosteric enzymes change the shape of their active site when the substrate binds to the active site.

c) Allosteric enzymes bind an irreversible inhibitor in the active site.

d) Allosteric enzymes bind the substrate at a site away from the active site as well as within the active site.

e) Allosteric enzymes bind another identical enzyme to cover the active sites of both enzymes in the complex.

21.49 One type of enzyme regulation in nature results from a regulator binding to an allosteric enzyme. A regulator that speeds up the resulting reaction is known as a _____.

a) feedback regulator

b) non-competitive regulator

c) positive regulator

d) covalent regulator

e) zymogen regulator

21.50 Which is (or are) typically involved in allosteric regulation? Mark all correct answer options.

Answer choices:

a) allosteric enzyme

b) enzyme substrate

c) polyethylene glycol

d) regulator

e) reaction product(s)

21.51 In the feedback control model of enzyme regulation, which enzyme is most likely to be regulated?

a) the first enzyme in the sequence

b) the last enzyme in the sequence

c) the enzyme producing the buffer

d) the positive NSAID enzyme

e) the zymogen

21.52 Match each statement about enzyme regulation with the most appropriate term.

Answer choices:

a) addition of a phosphate activates an enzyme

b) fibrinogen is converted to fibrin by thrombin

c) a positive regulator increases enzyme activity

Target boxes: allosteric enzyme, covalent modification, zymogen

21.53 Match each statement about enzyme regulation with the most appropriate term.

Answer choices:

a) A protein is converted to an active enzyme when a covalent bond breaks and a portion of the polypeptide is removed.

b) The end product of a reaction sequence binds to the regulatory site of the first enzyme in the sequence.

c) A functional group is added or removed from an enzyme to regulate its activity.

Target boxes: covalent modification, allosteric enzyme, zymogen

21.54 In the feedback control model of enzyme regulation, which statement best describes an advantage to regulating an enzyme that is at or near the beginning of the reaction sequence?

a) This allows the end product to accumulate to high concentrations and act as a substrate for the first enzyme.

b) This prevents the last enzyme in the sequence to avoid being degraded into toxic zymogens.

c) This allows the last enzyme in the sequence to be converted to mRNA that can be stored in the nucleus and used later in cellular replication.

d) Little or no unneeded intermediate compounds are produced, saving cellular energy and materials.

21.6 Enzyme Cofactors and Vitamins

LO 21.6: Explain the role of enzyme cofactors and vitamins in enzyme function.

21.55 Which statement best describes enzyme cofactors?

a) organic molecules or metal ions that bind to enzymes and act as competitive inhibitors

b) multi-subunit proteins that bind with enzymes to form active quaternary structures

c) organic molecules or metal ions that bind to enzymes to help them function properly

d) segments of DNA that bind to enzyme active sites and act as positive allosteric regulators

21.56 A friend in your chemistry study group asks you what the difference is between a cofactor and a coenzyme. Which of the following is the best response?

a) Cofactors are a subset of coenzymes. Cofactors bind the regulatory sites on allosteric enzymes. Coenzymes bind noncompetitively to active sites to regulate enzyme activity.

b) Coenzymes are a specific type of cofactor. Coenzymes are organic molecules such as vitamins or modified vitamins. Cofactors also include metal ions such iron or zinc ions in the active site.

c) Both coenzymes and cofactors are enzyme inhibitors. Coenzymes are noncompetitive inhibitors whereas cofactors are competitive inhibitors. Both types of inhibitors can be reversible or irreversible, depending on the enzyme.

d) Coenzymes are zymogen activators whereas cofactors are allosteric regulators. Both types of molecules can increase or decrease rates of enzymatic reactions based on cellular needs.

21.57 What function do metal ions such as Fe^{2+} and Zn^{2+} serve for many enzymes?

a) isoenzymes

b) allosteric regulators

c) substrates

d) cofactors

e) non-competitive inhibitors

21.58 The enzyme carboxypeptidase helps with food digestion. What is the cofactor used by carboxypeptidase?

a) Fe^{3+}.

b) Vitamin B_{12}.

c) Vitamin D_3.

d) Zn^{2+}

21.59 A cofactor that is an organic molecule is known as _____.

a) an isoenzyme

b) a substrate

c) a zymogen

d) a fibrin

e) a coenzyme

21.60 Which of the following is most likely to be stored in the body?

a) water-soluble vitamins

b) fat-soluble vitamins

c) both water-soluble and fat-soluble vitamins

d) neither water-soluble nor fat-soluble vitamins

21.61 You and a classmate are studying for a chemistry quiz. Your study partner asks you which process coenzyme Vitamin K is involved in. Which is the best response?

a) blood clotting

b) metabolizing alcohol

c) DNA synthesis

d) protein hydrolysis

21.62 Categorize each statement based on whether or not it requires a cofactor

Answer choices:

a) contains Fe^{2+} in the active site

b) has desired activity at correct pH and temperature

c) uses vitamin B_1 (thiamine), which is important for energy production

Target boxes: no cofactor required, requires a cofactor

21.63 Select the most appropriate statement about water-soluble vitamins.

a) Water-soluble vitamins act as allosteric regulators of many enzymes.

b) Water-soluble vitamins are sources of essential amino acids.

c) Water-soluble vitamins become coenzymes required by some enzymes.

d) Water-soluble vitamins are irreversible inhibitors of quaternary enzymes.

e) Water-soluble vitamins denature enzymes to increased enzymatic activity.

Chapter 22

22.1 Building Blocks of DNA

LO 22.1: **Describe and draw the building blocks of nucleosides and nucleotides.**

22.01 A nitrogen-containing base that is connected to a sugar by an N-glycosidic linkage is called a _____.

a) base pair

b) nucleoside

c) histone

d) nucleotide

e) dipeptide

22.02 A nitrogen-containing base that is connected with an N-glycosidic linkage to a sugar containing a phosphate group is called a _____.

a) ribosome

b) base pair

c) nucleoside

d) disaccharide

e) nucleotide

22.03 What is the correct name for the nucleoside that contains the sugar ribose and the base uracil?

a) deoxy uracil   b) ribo uracil

c) deoxyuridine   d) uridine

22.04 Identify the components of the molecule shown below. The structures of the bases are provided for reference.

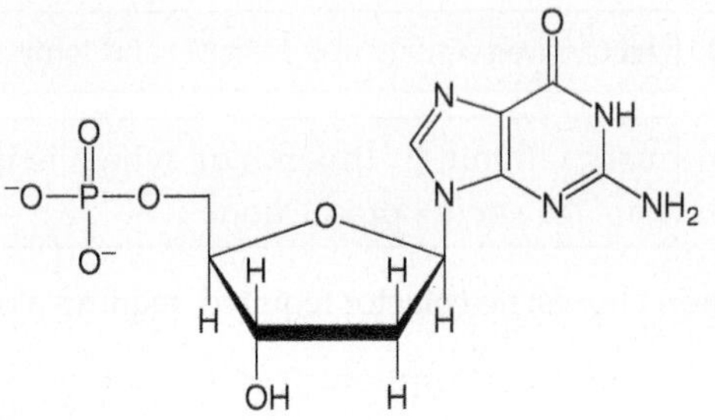

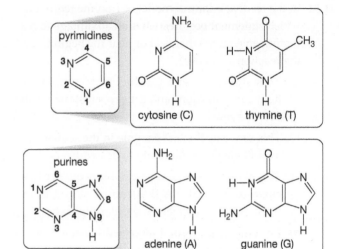

a) deoxyribose, guanine, phosphate

b) ribose, phosphate, guanine

c) deoxyribose, guanine, sulfate

d) deoxyribose, adenine, phosphate

e) ribose, adenine, phosphate

22.05 Identify the components of the molecule shown below. The structures of the bases are provided for reference.

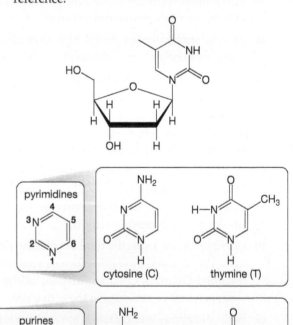

a) deoxyribose, thymine, phosphate

b) ribose, thymine   c) deoxyribose, cytosine

d) deoxyribose, cytosine, phosphate

e) deoxyribose, thymine

22.06 Consider the condensation reaction that forms a β-N-glycosidic bond between the ribose sugar and base shown. What is the missing product in this reaction?

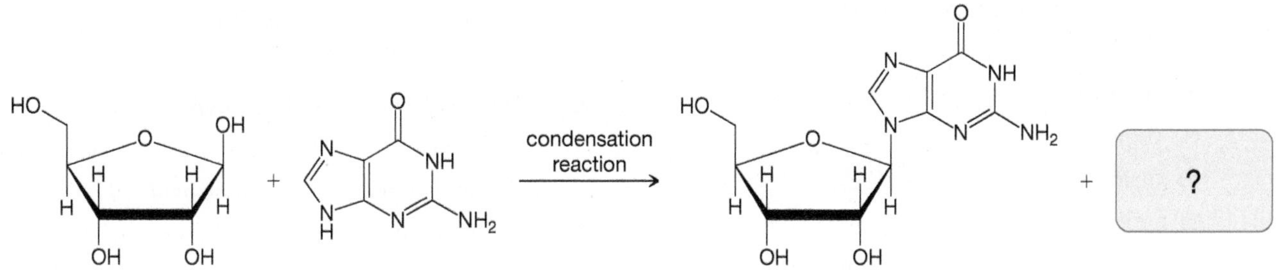

a) phosphate   **b)** NH_3 **c)** H_2O **d)** ribose   **e)** O_2

22.07 Consider the condensation reaction between the nucleoside and a phosphate group to form the nucleotide shown. What is the missing product in this reaction?

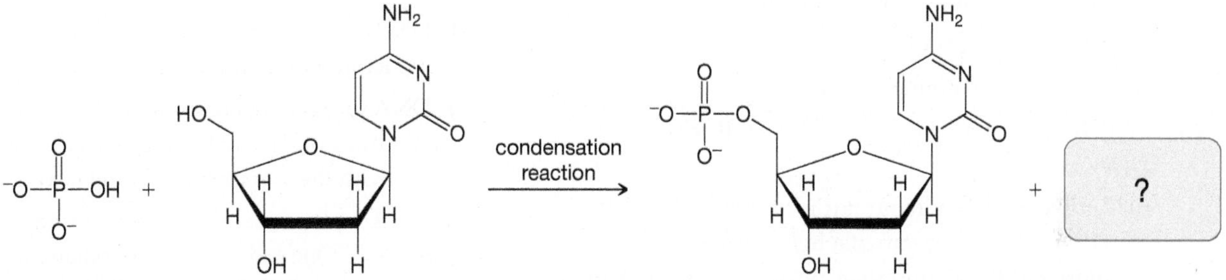

a) deoxribose   **b)** NH_3 **c)** CH_3OH **d)** H_2 **e)** H_2O

22.08 In a cell, nucleotides can contain either one, two, or three phosphate groups bonded to C5′ of the sugar ring. These are known as mono, di, and tri phosphates of a given nucleotide. Sort the molecules into the correct bin. Not all structures will be sorted into a bin.

Answer choices:

a)

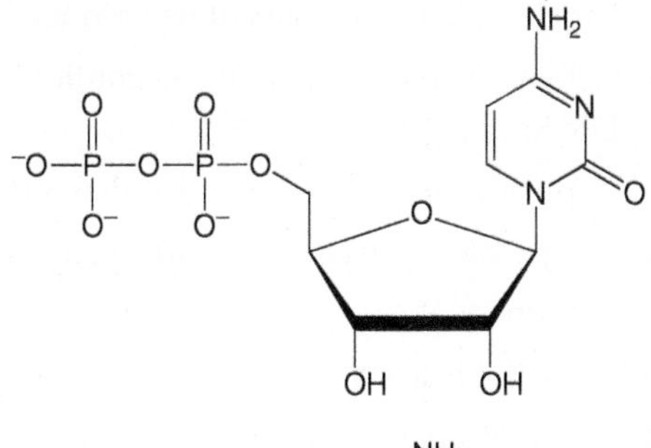

b)

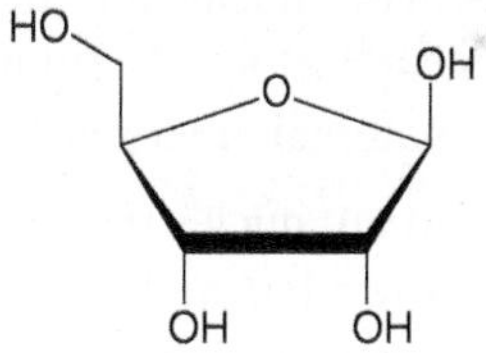

c)

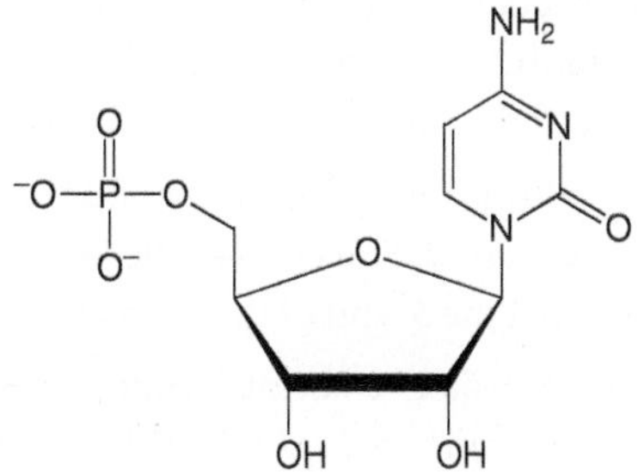

d)

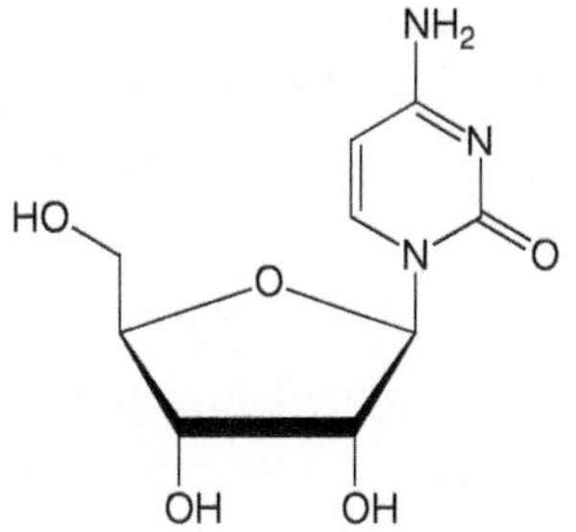

e)

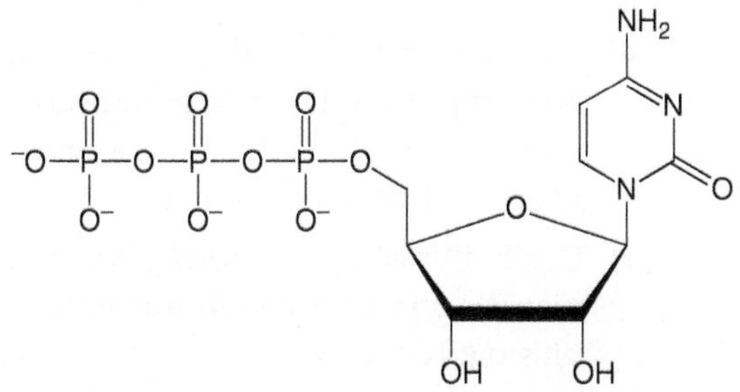

Target boxes: cytidine 5′-monophosphate (CMP), cytidine 5′-diphosphate (CDP), cytidine 5′-triphosphate (CTP)

22.09 In order to fit inside a cell, the extraordinarily long DNA molecules within eukaryotic cells are each coiled around what type of protein?

 a) ribosome

 b) chaperone

 c) protease

 d) histone

 e) proteome

22.10 What is the correct name for the nucleotide that contains the sugar ribose, a single phosphate group, and the base guanosine?

 a) guanodine 5′-monophosphate

 b) deoxyguanodine 5′-monophosphate

 c) guanosine 5′-triphosphate

 d) guanosine 5′-monophosphate

22.11 Which statement best describes mitochondrial DNA?

 a) Unlike the DNA in our nuclei, our mitochondrial DNA is based on a triple helix structure and is more tightly wound than chromosomal DNA in the nucleus.

 b) Unlike the DNA in our nuclei, our mitochondrial DNA contains uracil as a base that pairs with adenine (AU) instead of thymine pairing with adenine (AT).

 c) Unlike the DNA in our nuclei, our mitochondrial DNA comes almost exclusively from our mothers, following a maternal inheritance pattern.

 d) Unlike the DNA in our nuclei, our mitochondrial DNA is single stranded and is more tightly wound than chromosomal DNA in the nucleus.

 e) Unlike the DNA in our nuclei, our mitochondrial DNA contains 13 chromosomes instead of the 46 chromosomes found within the nucleus of each human cell.

22.12 Identify the item that is not part of a typical nucleotide.

 a) sugar ring

 b) base

 c) amino acid

 d) phosphate

22.13 What is the correct name for the nucleotide that contains the sugar deoxyribose, three phosphate groups, and the base thymine?

 a) thymine 5′-triphosphate

 b) deoxythymine 5′-triphosphate

 c) deoxyribose thymine 5′-triphosphate

 d) deoxythymine 5′-phosphate

22.2 Structure and Formation of Nucleic Acids

LO 22.2: Describe the structure and draw segments of a single strand of DNA including phosphodiester linkages.

22.14 What type of molecule is DNA?

 a) lipid   b) vitamin   c) protein

 d) nucleic acid   e) amino acid

22.15 Which is *not* found in RNA?

 a) ribose   b) a purine base

 c) deoxyribose   d) phosphate

 e) a pyrimidine base

22.16 Which statement about DNA is *not* true?

 a) DNA is a nucleic acid polymer made up of nucleotide monomers.

 b) DNA forms long chains with the 3′-OH group of one nucleotide joined by a phosphodiester linkage with the 5′-phosphate of the next nucleotide.

 c) DNA polynucleotides form in the direction $3′ \rightarrow 5′$. One end of the chain contains a phosphate group on carbon 3, and the other end of the chain contains a hydroxyl group (—OH) on carbon 5.

 d) DNA contains multiple nucleotides in an alternating sugar and phosphate pattern that forms a sugar-phosphate backbone.

 e) The sequence of the nucleotides in a DNA polynucleotide makes each of us unique.

22.17 Which of the following chemical entities is *not* found in DNA?

 a) a purine base   b) deoxyribose

 c) a pyrimidine base   d) phosphate

 e) ribose

22.18 Identify the true statement about cystic fibrosis.

 a) Cystic fibrosis is a serious genetic lung disease resulting from a 17 nucleotide GC rich nucleotide insert at the 3′ end of the human fibrosis gene.

 b) Cystic fibrosis is a serious genetic lung disease resulting from the deletion of the last four adenine (A) bases at the 3′ end of the human fibrosis gene.

 c) Cystic fibrosis is a serious genetic lung disease resulting from a poly nucleotide polymorphism (PNP).

 d) Cystic fibrosis is a serious genetic lung disease resulting from the reverse transcription of the human fibrosis gene that causes uracil (U) inserts to occur at thymine (T) sites.

 e) Cystic fibrosis is a serious genetic lung disease resulting from a single nucleotide polymorphism (SNP).

22.19 Determine whether or not each item is present in DNA.

Answer choices:

a) pyrimidine bases   b) ribose sugar rings

c) phosphate (phosphodiester linkages)

d) glucose sugar rings   e) purine bases

f) deoxyribose sugar rings

Target boxes: occurs in DNA, does not occur in DNA

22.20 How are the nucleotides in the backbone of DNA held together?

a) peptide bond linkages

b) phosphodiester linkages

c) glycosidic linkages

d) hemiacetal linkages

e) hydrogen bonding

22.21 Use the chemical constituents to complete the template below and build a short DNA strand.

Answer choices: free OH group, phosphate, sugar, base

Target boxes:

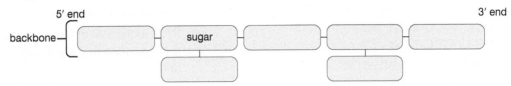

22.3 The DNA Double Helix

LO 22.3: Describe the structure and fundamental features of the DNA double helix.

22.22 What type of bonds supports base pairing between DNA strands in a double helix?

a) ionic bonds

b) phosphodiester bonds

c) triple bonds

d) hydrogen bonds

e) peptide bonds

22.23 Which of the following base pairings occurs in a double stranded DNA helix?

a) adenine - guanine   b) cytosine - guanine

c) uracil - adenine   d) adenine - cytosine

e) guanine - thymine

22.24 Which is *not* a typical base pairing in a double stranded DNA helix?

a) guanine - cytosine   b) adenine - thymine

c) cytosine - guanine   d) cytosine - adenine

e) thymine - adenine

22.25 Which of the following is a typical base pairing in a double stranded DNA helix?

a) Glycine and cytosine are a complementary base pair that form three hydrogen bonds together.

b) Adenine and thymine are a complementary base pair that form three hydrogen bonds together.

c) Cytosine and guanine are a complementary base pair that form two hydrogen bonds together.

d) Alanine and thymine are a complementary base pair that form two hydrogen bonds together.

22.26 Use the appropriate base letters to complete the set of complementary bases along this segment of double-stranded DNA.

Answer choices: A, T, G, C

Target boxes:

5′ – G – A – C –☐– G – A – T – C – G – 3′
3′ – C –☐– G – C –☐– T –☐– G – C – 5′

22.27 Use the appropriate base letters to complete the set of complementary bases along this segment of double-stranded DNA.

Answer choices: A, T, G, C

Target boxes:

5′ – T – C –☐– C – G – T –☐– C – G – 3′
3′ – A –☐– A – G –☐– A – T – G – C – 5′

22.28 Identify the DNA strand that is complementary to the one shown.

5′-T-G-C-G-A-3′

a) 3′-T-G-C-G-A-5′

b) 3′-U-C-G-C-A-5′

c) 5′-A-C-G-C-T-3′

d) 3′-A-C-G-C-T-5′

22.29 Identify the DNA strand that is complementary to the one shown.

3'-C-T-A-C-G-A-5'

a) 3'-G-A-T-G-C-T-5'

b) 5'-G-A-T-G-C-T-3'

c) 5'-C-T-A-C-G-A-3'

d) 5'-G-A-A-G-C-T-3'

22.30 Select the two complementary DNA strands.

a) 5'-C-G-T-T-A-G-A-3' and 3'-A-G-A-T-T-G-C-5'

b) 5'-T-T-A-G-C-G-A-3' and 5'-A-A-T-C-G-C-T-3'

c) 5'-T-A-C-G-A-C-C-3' and 3'-A-T-G-C-T-G-G-5'

d) 5'-C-C-G-A-T-C-A-3' and 3'-C-C-G-A-T-C-A-5'

22.31 Select the two complementary DNA strands.

a) 3'-T-A-C-C-T-A-G-A-C-5' and
   5'-A-T-G-G-A-T-C-T-G-3'

b) 5'-T-T-A-C-C-A-G-C-A-3' and
   5'-A-A-T-G-G-T-C-G-T-3'

c) 5'-C-C-A-T-T-A-G-C-G-3' and
   3'-G-G-T-A-T-T-C-G-C-5'

d) 3'-C-A-A-T-G-T-A-C-G-5' and
   5'-G-C-A-T-G-T-A-A-C-3'

22.32 Identify the segment of double stranded DNA that contains a base pair mismatch.

a) 5'-T-C-T-A-G-T-3' and 3'-A-G-A-T-C-A-5'

b) 5'-G-G-A-C-T-A-3' and 3'-C-C-T-G-A-T-5'

c) 5'-C-G-C-A-A-T-3' and 3'-G-G-G-T-T-A-5'

d) 5'-A-G-T-A-C-G-3' and 3'-T-C-A-T-G-C-5'

22.33 Which statement best describes gel electrophoresis of DNA?

a) Gel electrophoresis is used to attach DNA molecules together based on their size and charge.

b) Gel electrophoresis is used to separate DNA molecules based on the ratio of G:C base pairs found throughout a specific gene sequence.

c) Gel electrophoresis is used to group DNA molecules together based on the ratio of purine to pyrimidine bases.

d) Gel electrophoresis is used to separate DNA molecules based on their size and charge.

22.34 Which of the following is a true statement about DNA gel electrophoresis?

a) The positive charges on the DNA bases cause the DNA to flow through the gel toward the negative electrode.

b) Because the phosphate groups along the DNA backbone are negatively charged, DNA flows through the gel towards the positive electrode.

c) In gel electrophoresis, small DNA fragments move through the gel toward the positive electrode and the large DNA fragments move toward the negative electrode.

d) Gel electrophoresis separates DNA based on the percentage of G:C base pairs averaged against the net positive charge coefficient.

22.35 Which of the following is a true statement about DNA gel electrophoresis?

a) DNA molecules of opposite charges migrate to the same position in the gel, forming a visible band or line on the gel.

b) DNA molecules of different lengths migrate to the same position in the gel, forming a visible band or line on the gel.

c) DNA molecules of the same size migrate to the same position in the gel, forming a visible band or line on the gel.

d) DNA molecules of the same size migrate to opposite ends of the gel, forming two visible bands or lines on the gel.

22.4 DNA Replication

LO 22.4: Explain the process of DNA replication and the role of DNA polymerase.

22.36 Which enzyme in DNA replication is responsible for separating the two strands of the double helix?

a) primase   b) helicase

c) polymerase   d) ligase

e) replicase

22.37 Which best describes a DNA replication fork?

a) a short region of DNA that forms a triple helix with an Okasaki fragment

b) an open section of the RNA double helix

c) a long segment of double stranded DNA that contains the daughter strand

d) an open section of the DNA double helix

22.38 During DNA replication, the newly created DNA strand that grows continuously in the 5' to 3' direction is called the _____.

a) leading strand   b) lagging strand

c) Okazaki fragment   d) messenger DNA

22.39 What is the role of the enzyme primase in DNA replication?

a) The enzyme primase binds to double stranded DNA at the origin of replication and separates the two strands.

b) The enzyme primase joins the Okazaki fragments together, completing the complementary strand.

c) The enzyme primase binds at the primer site and begins attaching complementary bases to the 3′ end of the primer.

d) The enzyme primase binds to the single-stranded DNA and creates a short temporary single-stranded sequence of nucleotides called a primer.

22.40 Select the statement that best describes a DNA primer.

a) a short gene sequence that codes for the enzyme DNA polymerase, which is needed for the replication of new complementary strands

b) a short segment of DNA that provides a binding site for DNA polymerase so that it can begin synthesizing the new complementary strand

c) the region of DNA that bridges each Okazaki fragment in the leading strand of daughter DNA during the replication process

d) the gene sequence that codes for the enzyme primase, which is used to create Okazaki fragments along the lagging strand of DNA during replication

22.41 What is the sequence of a newly synthesized DNA strand whose template has the sequence 5′-CTAC-GTA-3′? Hint: pay special attention to the numbering at both ends of each sequence.

a) 5′-GATGCAT-3′   **b)** 3′-CTACGTA-5′

c) 3′-GATGCAT-5′   **d)** 5′-ATGCATC-3′

22.42 Which enzyme is *not* directly involved in DNA replication?

a) primase   **b)** lactase

c) DNA polymerase   **d)** helicase

e) ligase

22.5 DNA Technology Hide/Reveal

LO 22.5: Explain the mechanism and utility of several common DNA technologies.

22.43 Which of the following enzymes is used in CRISPR experiments?

a) DNA ligase   **b)** primase

c) PstIII   **d)** Cas9

e) PCR1

22.44 Which of the following would a DNA microarray be most useful for?

a) identifying the amino acid sequence of a short peptide

b) comparing DNA from a healthy tissue sample and a cancerous sample

c) sequencing the human genome

d) determining the turnover number of a specific enzyme

e) generating millions of copies of a gene sequence

22.45 A dideoxynucleotide lacks the 3′ OH group on the sugar ring. What impact does this have on the ability of DNA polymerase to lengthen a growing DNA strand?

a) The lack of the 3′ OH group increases the rate of DNA polymerase because the dideoxynucleotide is a competitive inhibitor of the Cas9 enzyme.

b) The lack of the 3′ OH group destabilizes the complex formed between helicase and lactase, halting DNA elongation.

c) The lack of the 3′ OH group prevents the attachment of the next nucleotide to the growing DNA strand.

d) The lack of the 3′ OH group causes a shift from double helical to triple helical DNA in the polymerase chain reaction (PCR).

Chapter 23

23.1 Structure of RNA

LO 23.1: Describe how RNA structure differs from DNA structure.

23.01 The process by which a protein is formed using the genetic information contained in RNA is called _____.

a) translocation   **b)** replication

c) transcription   **d)** translation

e) transesterification

23.02 The process of synthesizing an RNA molecule from a gene (DNA) is _____.

a) translocation   **b)** replication

c) transcription   **d)** translation

e) transformation

23.03 One difference between RNA and DNA is that _____.

a) DNA contains the base uracil and RNA does not

b) the sugar backbone in DNA is ribose whereas the sugar backbone in RNA is deoxyribose

c) in RNA, the base uracil replaces thymine

d) RNA generally forms a double helix whereas DNA is typically a triple helix

23.04 Select the base pairing that is found only in RNA.

a) T-A   **b)** C-G

c) A-U   **d)** A-T

e) G-C

23.05 Which base pairing is *not* found in RNA?

a) adenine-thymine   b) cytosine-guanine

c) uracil-adenine   d) guanine-cytosine

23.06 Select the correct difference between RNA and DNA.

a) RNA contains nitrogen bases bonded to the 2′ carbon on the sugar rings, whereas DNA contains bases attached to carbon 1′.

b) RNA is almost always single stranded whereas DNA is generally double stranded.

c) DNA has phosphate groups linking the 2′ carbon of one sugar ring with the 5′ carbon of the next sugar. The phosphate groups in RNA link the 3′ carbon of one sugar with the 5′ carbon of the next sugar.

d) DNA is a polynucleotide whereas RNA is a polypeptide.

e) RNA is stored only in the nucleus of the cell whereas DNA is typically found in the mitochondrion.

23.2 Transcription: RNA Synthesis

LO 23.2: Explain the key steps of transcription.

23.07 Messenger RNA (mRNA) is produced in the process of _____.

a) translation   b) DNA replication

c) transfusion   d) transmission

e) transcription

23.08 The enzyme required for DNA transcription is _____.

a) DNA polymerase   b) mRNAse

c) DNA transcriptase   d) RNA polymerase

e) RNA synthase

23.09 Which of the following is *not* a step in the process of transcription?

a) replication   b) termination

c) initiation   d) elongation

23.10 Which statement about transcription is correct?

a) During transcription, DNA is replicated, and the new copy contains one parent strand and one daughter strand.

b) The mRNA produced during transcription has the same sequence as the DNA template strand.

c) During transcription, uracil in the growing RNA base pairs with thymine on the DNA template strand.

d) The mRNA produced is complementary to the DNA template strand.

e) During transcription, both strands of DNA are used to produce two new complementary mRNA strands.

23.11 During the synthesis of mRNA, adenine in the DNA pairs with _____ on the growing RNA strand.

a) thymine   b) uracil

c) adenine   d) guanine

e) cytosine

23.12 Select the best description of the promoter's role in transcription.

a) a protein that attracts RNA polymerase so that the process of transcription can begin

b) a region of DNA at the beginning of a gene where transcription factors and RNA polymerase bind in order to initiate transcription

c) a region of DNA at the end of a gene that signals the RNA polymerase to release the newly constructed mRNA

d) a type of RNA that is responsible for promoting the transport of nucleotides to the transcription initiation site

e) a region of DNA generally located in the middle region of a gene where DNA polymerase binds to RNA polymerase, promoting mRNA translocation

23.13 Identify the correct mRNA sequence produced from a DNA template with the following sequence.

3′ G-T-A-C-T-T-A-G-T 5′

a) 5′ C-A-T-G-A-A-T-C-A 3′

b) 3′ C-A-U-G-A-A-U-C-A 5′

c) 5′ C-U-T-G-U-U-T-C-U 3′

d) 5′ C-A-U-G-A-A-U-C-A 3′

e) 5′ C-A-U-C-A-A-U-G-A 3′

23.14 Which sequence of mRNA is produced by transcription of the given DNA sequence?

Informational strand   5′ T-A-G-G-A-C-T-T-A 3′
Template strand   3′ A-T-C-C-T-G-A-A-T 5′

a) 5′ T-A-G-G-A-C-T-T-A 3′

b) 5′ A-U-U-C-A-G-G-A-U 3′

c) 5′ A-U-C-C-U-G-A-A-U 3′

d) 3′ A-U-C-C-U-G-A-A-U 5′

e) 5′ U-A-G-G-A-C-U-U-A 3′

23.15 Which sequence of mRNA is produced by transcription of the given DNA sequence?

Informational strand   5′ A-G-T-C-A-C-G-T 3′
Template strand   3′ T-C-A-G-T-G-C-A 5′

a) 3′ A-G-U-C-A-C-G-U 5′   b) 5′ A-G-T-C-A-C-G-T 3′

c) 5′ A-G-U-C-A-C-G-U 3′   d) 3′ T-C-A-G-T-G-C-A 5′

e) 5′ U-C-A-G-U-G-C-A 3′

23.16 Which sequence of double-stranded DNA produces the mRNA sequence shown?

mRNA sequence: 5′ C-U-A-G-U-A-C-C-A-U 3′

a) Informational strand   5′ G-A-T-C-A-T-G-G-T-A 3′
    Template strand   3′ C-T-A-G-T-A-C-C-A-T 5′

b) Informational strand   5′ C-T-A-G-T-A-C-C-A-T 3′
    Template strand   3′ G-A-T-C-A-T-G-G-T-A 5′

c) Informational strand   5′ C-U-A-G-U-A-C-C-A-U 3′
    Template strand   3′ G-A-T-C-A-T-G-G-T-A 5′

d) Informational strand   3′ C-T-A-G-T-A-C-C-A-T 5′
    Template strand   5′ G-A-T-C-A-T-G-G-T-A 3′

e) Informational strand   5′ C-U-A-G-U-A-C-C-A-U 3′
    Template strand   3′ G-A-U-C-A-U-G-G-U-A 5′

23.17 Identify the correct *informational* DNA strand that produces the mRNA sequence shown.

mRNA sequence: 5′ G-A-U-A-U-U-G-A-C 3′

a) Informational strand   3′ C-T-A-T-A-A-C-T-G 5′
b) Informational strand   5′ G-A-U-A-U-U-G-A-C 3′
c) Informational strand   3′ G-A-T-A-T-T-G-A-C 5′
d) Informational strand   5′ C-T-A-T-A-A-C-T-C 3′
e) Informational strand   5′ G-A-T-A-T-T-G-A-C 3′

23.18 Identify the correct *template* DNA strand that produces the mRNA sequence shown.

mRNA sequence: 5′ C-C-A-U-G-A-U-G-U 3′

a) Template strand   5′ G-G-T-A-C-T-A-C-A 3′
b) Template strand   5′ C-C-A-T-G-A-T-G-T 3′
c) Template strand   3′ G-G-T-A-C-T-A-C-A 5′
d) Template strand   3′ C-C-A-T-G-A-T-G-T 5′
e) Template strand   3′ G-G-A-T-C-A-T-C-T 5′

23.19 RNA viruses package their genetic information as RNA instead of DNA. These viruses can convert their RNA into viral DNA, which is then inserted into the DNA of the host cell. Part of this DNA codes for a special enzyme that allows for the conversion of viral RNA to viral DNA. Which special enzyme allows RNA to be converted to DNA?

a) RNA polymerase   b) DNA polymerase   c) viral replicase

d) reverse transcriptase   e) RNA transferase

23.20 Which process best outlines the viral life cycle?

  a) (1) Virus binds to proteins on host cell surface; (2) virus injects its genetic material into the host cell; (3) viral DNA or RNA uses host cell machinery to make more virus; (4) after replicating, the new viruses break free from the host cell to infect new cells.

  b) (1) Virus binds to lipids being transported into the host cell; (2) virus degrades host cell DNA; (3) viral DNA or RNA replaces host cell DNA; (4) host cell machinery makes more virus; (5) after replicating, the new viruses break free from the host cell to infect new cells.

  c) (1) T cells from the host recognize virus as foreign and attack viral particles; (2) virus responds by injecting its genetic material into the host cell; (3) viral enzyme degrades one strand of host cell genomic DNA then forms viral double stranded helix with host DNA; (4) virus is replicated when host cell divides; (5) after replicating, the new viruses break free from the host cell to infect new cells.

  d) (1) Virus binds to host red blood cell proteins; (2) virus injects its specialized enzymes that degrade host red blood cells; (3) virus attacks white blood cells and inject viral DNA or RNA host white blood cell; (4) viral DNA or RNA uses host cell machinery to make more virus; (5) after replicating, the new viruses break free from the host cell to infect new cells.

23.3 Translation: The Genetic Code

LO 23.3: **Use the genetic code to convert mRNA codons to a sequence of amino acids.**

23.21 Which type of RNA contains the genetic information from DNA that is needed for protein synthesis?

  a) rRNA
  b) tRNA
  c) sRNA
  d) mRNA
  e) dsRNA

23.22 The process by which messenger RNA (mRNA) is used as the template for protein synthesis is called _____.

  a) transcription
  b) transformation
  c) transfusion
  d) transmission
  e) translation

23.23 During protein synthesis, which molecule contains the codons that code for the amino acids?

  a) protease
  b) transferase
  c) ribosomal RNA
  d) reverse transcriptase
  e) messenger RNA

23.24 Identify the codon that signals the start of translation and codes for the amino acid methionine. Use the codon table (Table 23.1) to answer this question.

  a) AUC   **b)** UAG
  c) AGU   **d)** GUA
  e) AUG

23.25 Select the best description of translation.

  a) the process that uses DNA for mRNA synthesis
  b) the process that uses mRNA as a template for protein synthesis
  c) the process that converts mRNA to DNA
  d) the process that converts a protein sequence to mRNA
  e) the process that degrades proteins into amino acids

23.26 Select the best description of a codon.

  a) a set of three nucleotides on DNA that corresponds to a specific mRNA triplet sequence
  b) a set of complementary base pairs that signals viral replication within an infected host cell
  c) a set of three amino acids in a protein primary structure that signals the transition from an alpha helix to a beta sheet
  d) a set of three nucleotides on a mRNA that corresponds to a specific amino acid in a protein primary structure
  e) a set of three nucleotides on a mRNA sequence that codes for insulin to be released during a viral infection

23.27 Determine the appropriate classification for each codon; drag each codon into the correct classification bin. Use the codon table to complete this task.

  Answer choices: UAU, UAA, AUG UAC, CCA, UAG, UGA, UUU, AUC, ACG

  Target boxes: start/methionine, amino acid only, stop codon

23.28 Which codon is *not* a stop codon for translation? Use the codon table (Table 23.1) to answer this question.

  a) UAG   **b)** UGA
  c) UCA   **d)** UAA

23.29 Select the codon that does *not* code for the amino acid arginine (Arg) during translation. Use the codon table (Table 23.1) to answer this question.

a) CGA   b) AGG

c) CGG   d) CGU

e) CAG

23.30 How many codons signal for the amino acid valine (Val)? Use the codon table (Table 23.1) to answer this question.

a) 4   b) 3

c) 1   d) 2

23.31 How many codons signal for the amino acid isoleucine (Ile)? Use the codon table (Table 23.1) to answer this question.

a) 4   b) 2

c) 1   d) 3

23.32 The amino acid methionine has only one codon. Which other amino acid has only one codon? Use the codon table (Table 23.1) to answer this question.

a) cysteines (Cys)

b) leucine (Leu)

c) valine (Val)

d) glutamic acid (Glu)

e) tryptophan (Trp)

23.33 Match each mRNA sequence with the appropriate amino acid sequence that the mRNA codes for. Use the codon table (Table 23.1) to answer this question.

Answer choices:

a) Met Asn His Tyr Leu Val

b) Met Gln Cys Pro Ala Gly

c) Met Glu Arg Trp Ile Lys

Target boxes:

a) 5′ – AUG CAA UGC CCA GCA GGC UGA – 3′

b) 5′ – AUG GAA AGG UGG AUC AAG UGA – 3′

c) 5′ – AUG AAC CAU UAC UUG GUU UGA – 3′

23.34 Which amino acid sequence corresponds to the given messenger RNA (mRNA) sequence? Use the codon table (Table 23.1) to answer this question.

mRNA sequence: 5′-AUG CGA CAC GGA CUA UGG-3′

a) Trp-Leu-Gly-His-Arg-Met

b) Met-Arg-Gln-Gly-Val-Trp

c) Met-Gly-His-Pro-Leu-Trp

d) Met-Arg-His-Gly-Leu-Trp

e) Ile-Gln-His-Gly-Leu-Trp

23.35 Which mRNA could code for the peptide shown? Use the codon table (Table 23.1) to answer this question.

peptide sequence: Met-Ala-Pro-Asp-Met-Thr-Lys

a) AUG CGA CCG AAU AUG ACC AAA

b) AUG GCA CCG GAU AUG ACC AAA

c) AAA ACC AUG GAU CCG GCA AUG

d) AAA CCA GUA UAG GCC ACG GUA

e) AUG GCA GCC GAU AUG UAU AAA

23.36 Angiotensin II is a peptide that helps regulate blood pressure. It is also involved with inflammation and organ function. The mRNA sequence shown codes for the angiotensin II peptide sequence, Asp-Arg-Val-Tyr-Ile-His-Pro-Phe. Which *other* mRNA sequence also codes for this same peptide sequence? Use the codon table (Table 23.1) to answer this question.

One mRNA sequence that codes for Angiotensin II is:

GAU AGG GUA UAU AUU CAC CCA UUU

a) GAU CGG GAG UAU AGU CAC CCA UUU

b) GAC CGC GUA UAC AUU CAU CCG UUC

c) GAU AGG GUA UGG AUC CAU AUG UUC

d) GAC CGU GCU UGU AUU CAC CCU UUU

23.37 Some peptides, known as cell penetrating peptides (CPPs), are capable of passing through cell membranes. Researchers are exploring using CPPs as tools to deliver materials into cells to help treat a range of diseases and disorders. Examine the peptide sequence of the CPP peptide below and identify the mRNA sequence that could *not* be translated into this peptide sequence. Use the codon table (Table 23.1) to answer this question.

Tat peptide sequence: Gly-Arg-Lys-Lys-Arg-Arg-Gln-Arg-Arg-Arg-Pro-Pro-Gln

a) GGC CGC AAG AAA CGA CGC CAG CGU CGG AGA CCC CCG CAA

b) GGU AGG AAA AAG CGC AGG CAA AGA CGC CGU CCA CCU CAG

c) GGG CGA AAA AAC CGG CGG CAC AGA AGG CGA CCG CCU CAA

d) GGA AGA AAG AAG AGG CGC CAG CGC CGA AGA CCU CCC CAG

23.4 A Closer Look at Translation: Protein Synthesis

LO 23.4: Explain the key steps of translation.

23.38 A classmate in your study group asks you what an anticodon is. Select the best response.

a) a base triplet that is identical to the codon on DNA

b) a base triplet that is complementary to the codon on mRNA

c) a base triplet that hydrolyzes the codon on mRNA and delivers the correct amino acid coded for in mRNA

d) a base triplet that is identical to the codon on mRNA

e) a base triplet that is complementary to the codon on DNA

23.39 Which key player in the process of translation consists of a large subunit and a small subunit?

a) mRNA

b) tRNA

c) sRNA

d) ribosomes

e) none of the above

23.40 What is the major purpose of transfer RNA in translation?

a) Transfer RNAs deliver the correct amino acid to the ribosomes according to the sequence specified in the mRNA.

b) Transfer RNAs bind to specific sites coded for by the DNA sequence and deliver the correct codon to this location for mRNA synthesis.

c) Transfer RNAs hydrolyze the mRNA sequence at each codon site in order to release anticodons used to catalyze protein synthesis.

d) Transfer RNAs bind to specific sites coded for by the mRNA sequence which allows the enzyme reverse transcriptase to generate a DNA copy of the mRNA.

e) Transfer RNAs contain the template sequences that code for the synthesis of complete ribosomes.

23.41 Match each type of RNA with the appropriate description of its function.

Answer choices:

a) messenger RNA (mRNA)

b) transfer RNA (tRNA)

c) ribosomal RNA (rRNA)

Target boxes:

a) carries specific amino acids to the ribosomes for protein synthesis

b) found in the ribosomes where protein synthesis takes place

c) carries the information needed for protein synthesis from DNA in the nucleus to the ribosomes for protein synthesis

23.42 Match each nucleic acid with the appropriate description of its function.

Answer choices:

a) double stranded DNA

b) transfer RNA (tRNA)

c) messenger RNA (mRNA)

Target boxes:

a) contains the codons needed for translation

b) contains the template sequences needed for transcription

c) contains the anticodons needed for translation

23.43 Identify the term below that is *not* a step in protein synthesis.

a) elongation

b) transgression

c) initiation

d) termination

23.44 Identify the anticodon for AGU.

a) TCA

b) UCA

c) UCT

d) TGT

e) UGA

23.45 Which amino acid sequence results from translation of the given mRNA sequence? Use the codon table (Table 23.1) to answer this question.

mRNA: AUG-GUA-CAC-GAU-CGC

a) Met-Leu-His-Gln-Arg

b) Ile-Val-Glu-Asp-Arg

c) Met-Val-His-Asp-Arg

d) Tyr-His-Val-Leu-Ala

23.46 Proteins are synthesized during the process of translation. Complete the diagram shown by dragging each label into the correct empty box to complete the picture.

Answer choices:

a) ribosome

b) mRNA

c) peptide bond being formed

d) codon

e) polypeptide

f) amino acid

g) tRNA

h) anticodon

Target boxes:

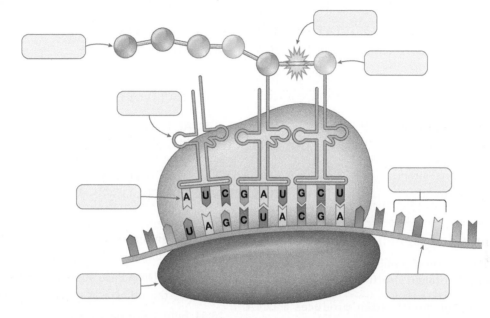

23.47 Which peptide sequence does this DNA code for? Use the codon table (Table 23.1) to answer this question.

Informational strand   5′ – ATG TTC CCA CTG TGT GCA – 3′

Template strand   3′ – TAC AAG GGT GAC ACA CGT – 5′

a) Phe-Lys-Gly-Asp-Thr-Arg

b) Cys-Thr-Gln-Trp-Glu-His

c) Met-Phe-Pro-Leu-Cys-Ala

d) Met-Phe-Arg-Leu-Cys-Gly

23.48 Which peptide sequence is coded for by this DNA? Use the codon table (Table 23.1) to answer this question.

Informational strand   5′ – ATG GGG CGT ATA AAA CAT GCA TAG – 3′

Template strand   3′ – TAC CCC GCA TAT TTT GTA CGT ATC – 5′

a) Asp-Thr-Tyr-Lys-Ile-Cys-Gly-Met

b) Met-Gly-Arg-Lys-Ile-His-Arg

c) Tyr-Pro-Ala-Tyr-Phe-Val-Arg-Ile

d) Met-Gly-Arg-Ile-Lys-His-Ala

23.49 Mesenchymal stem cells (MSCs) are stem cells in bone marrow that help make and repair cartilage and bone. Researchers are studying the peptide sequence Ser-Val-Val-Tyr-Gly-Leu-Arg because it may play a role in signaling the formation of new bone and blood vessels. Select the double-stranded DNA segment that could be transcribed and translated into the given peptide sequence. Use the codon table (Table 23.1) to answer this question.

Ser-Val-Val-Tyr-Gly-Leu-Arg

a)
Informational strand   5′ – CCT CAG TCC GTA TAC GAC GAA – 3′

Template strand   3′ – GGA GTC AGG CAT ATG CCT – 5′

b)
Informational strand   5′ – TCC GTC GTA TAC GGA CTG AGG – 3′

Template strand   3′ – AGG CAG CAT ATG CCT GAC TCC – 5′

c)
Informational strand   5′ – AGG CAG CAT ATG CCT GAC TCC – 3′

Template strand   3′ – TCC GTC GTA TAC GGA CTG AGG – 5′

d)
Informational strand   5′ – GGA GTC AGG CAT ATG CTG CCT – 3′

Template strand   3′ – CCT CAG TCC GTA TAC GAC GGA – 5′

23.50 Neuropeptide Y (NPY) is a 36 amino acid peptide in the brain and nervous system that is involved in cardiovascular function, blood pressure, appetite, sleep, pain processing, aggression, anxiety, and stress. Select the double-stranded DNA segment that codes for the first eight amino acids of the neuropeptide Y sequence shown. Use the codon table (Table 23.1) to answer this question.

Neuropeptide Y sequence: Tyr-Pro-Ser-Lys-Pro-Asp-Asn-Pro-Gly-Glu-Asp-Ala-Pro-Ala-Glu-Asp-Met-Ala-Arg-Tyr-Tyr-Ser-Ala-Leu-Arg-His-Tyr-Ile-Asn-Leu-Ile-Thr-Arg-Gln-Arg-Tyr

a)

Informational strand	5′ – TAT CCA AGT AAA CCG AAC GAT CCC – 3′
Template strand	3′ – ATA GGT TCA TTT GGC TTG CTA GGG – 5′

b)

Informational strand	5′ – ATA GGT TCA TTT GGC CTA TTA GGG – 3′
Template strand	3′ – TAT CCA AGT AAA CCG GAT AAT CCC – 5′

c)

Informational strand	5′ – GGG ATT ATC CGG TTT ACT TGG ATA – 3′
Template strand	3′ – CCC TAA TAG GCC AAA TGA ACC TAT – 5′

d)

Informational strand	5′ – TAT CCA AGT AAA CCG GAT AAT CCC – 3′
Template strand	3′ – ATA GGT TCA TTT GGC CTA TTA GGG – 5′

23.5 Mutations and Genetic Diseases

LO 23.5: Describe types of point mutations and how they affect protein structure.

23.51 Which type of modification produces a DNA mutation?

a) one or more changes to the DNA base sequence

b) conversion of one or more phosphate groups to nitrate groups

c) conversion of deoxyribose sugars to ribose sugars

d) conversion of alpha (α) glycosidic linkages to beta (β) glycosidic linkages

23.52 Which is *least* likely to be an environmental cause of DNA mutations?

a) prolonged exposure to nuclear waste materials

b) prolonged exposure to strong ultra-violet (UV) radiation

c) being near a person with a genetic disorder

d) exposure to high concentrations of carcinogenic chemicals

23.53 Select the best description of a silent substitution mutation.

a) a DNA base substitution that results in a frame shift to different start and stop codons

b) an mRNA base substitution that converts the DNA sequence of a gene so that the gene becomes silenced

c) an amino acid substitution that converts an enzyme to the inactive (silent) form

d) a DNA base substitution that does not change the amino acid sequence of a protein

23.54 Select the best description of a DNA missense mutation.

a) a base substitution that causes a codon to be missed during translation

b) a base substitution that changes an amino acid in a protein

c) a base substitution that causes RNA polymerase to miss three bases during transcription

d) a base substitution that allows DNA to be directly converted to protein

23.55 Consider each example of a substitution mutation found within an information DNA strand. Classify each mutation as either a silent mutation or a non-silent mutation. When answering this question, you may find it helpful to refer to the codon table (Table 23.1).

Answer choices:

a) TGC to TGA

b) CTG to TTA

c) CAC to CAG

d) CGG to AGA

Target boxes: silent mutation, non-silent mutation

23.56 Compare the original double-stranded DNA sequence with the mutated DNA shown. What type of mutation has occurred? When answering this question, you may find it helpful to refer to the codon table (Table 23.1).

Original double stranded DNA

Informational strand	5′ – ACT TGA **TAT** GAC ATG – 3′
Template strand	3′ – TGA ACT ATA CTG TAC – 5′

Mutated DNA

Informational strand	5′ – ACT TGA **GAT** GAC ATG – 3′
Template strand	3′ – TGA ACT CTA CTG TAC – 5′

a) missense mutation **b)** frameshift mutation **c)** silent substitution mutation

d) insertion mutation **e)** deletion mutation

23.57 Compare the original double-stranded DNA sequence with the mutated DNA shown. What type of mutation has occurred? When answering this question, you may find it helpful to refer to the codon table provided.

Original double stranded DNA

Informational strand	5′ – GGTTGGCACAACGCA – 3′
Template strand	3′ – CCAACCGTGTTGCGT – 5′

Mutated DNA

Informational strand	5′ – GGTTGCACAACGCA – 3′
Template strand	3′ – CCAACGTGTTGCGT – 5′

a) insertion mutation **b)** missense mutation **c)** silent substitution mutation

d) inverted mutation **e)** deletion mutation

23.58 Tay-Sachs disease is a fatal single-gene genetic disease. Which statement best describes Tay-Sachs disease?

a) DNA frameshift mutations produce additional copies of the enzyme acetylcholine esterase in the brain, resulting in rapid dementia, paralysis, and death.

b) DNA mutations produce faulty hexosaminidase A enzymes, causing fatty deposits to accumulate in the brain leading to rapid dementia, paralysis, and death.

c) Repeated DNA deletion mutations across the hexosaminidase A gene lead to misfolded hexosaminidase A enzymes that cannot metabolize fats properly. This leads to accumulation of plaque in the coronary arteries, heart disease and heart failure.

d) DNA insertion mutations in the ketoamidase B gene lead to tetrameric ketoamidase B enzymes that overproduce serotonin in the brain leading to blood clots, brain swelling and death.

23.59 Leukemia is a term used to describe a range of blood cancers in which the bone marrow produces too many white blood cells that crowd out normal cells in the blood. Which statement best describes chronic myeloid leukemia (CML)?

a) Chronic myeloid leukemia is caused by a rare missense point mutation in the primary white blood cell gene WBC1, leading to the overproduction of white blood cells.

b) Chronic myeloid leukemia is caused by a rare frame shift mutation in the myeloid C gene, leading to the overproduction of white blood cells.

c) Chronic myeloid leukemia is caused by a rare insertion mutation of a stop codon resulting in truncated myeloid proteins that lead to the overproduction of white blood cells.

d) Chronic myeloid leukemia is caused by a rare rearrangement of chromosomes, leading to the overproduction of white blood cells.

23.60 An undergraduate research student working in a virology lab is interested in a short segment of DNA with the following sequence: **5′-CAGGTCAACTGA-3′**. The student has identified four different mutations that occur in this sequence. Sort each of the DNA sequences as either resulting from a frameshift mutation or from a base substitution mutation of the original sequence.

Answer choices:

a) 5′-CAGGTCAACTCA-3′

b) 5′-CAGGTCACTGA-3′

c) 5′-CAGGTCAACCTCA-3′

d) 5′-CAGGTCAAGTGA-3′

Target boxes: frameshift mutation, base substitution mutation

23.61 A scientist working on vaccine development is studying the mRNA sequence 5′-ACG UUC GAU CCA AUG-3′. He recently identified a point mutation that changes CCA to GCA in the mRNA. Which is the amino acid sequence produced by the translation of the mutated mRNA? Use the codon table (Table 23.1) to create the correct amino acid sequence.

Answer choices:

a) Met   b) Asp   c) Arg   d) Phe

e) Val   f) Thr   g) Ala   h) Leu

Target boxes:

N-terminal ⬭—⬭—⬭—⬭—⬭

23.62 A medical researcher is interested in a genetic mutation that is thought to cause a structural change and malfunction of the protein it codes for. The short segment of DNA containing the mutation is shown below. Use the codon table (Table 23.1) along with your knowledge of transcription and translation to complete the statements below.

Original double stranded DNA

| Informational strand | 5′ – GCT AGC CAG TGG CGC – 3′ |
| Template strand | 3′ – CGA TCG GTC ACC **GCG** – 5′ |

Mutated DNA

| Informational strand | 5′ – GCT AGC CAG TGG CCC – 3′ |
| Template strand | 3′ – CGA TCG GTC ACC **GGG** – 5′ |

Answer choices:

a) Ser   b) Ala   c) Gly   d) His   e) Pro   f) Lys   g) Arg

Target boxes:

The base triplet GCG in the template strand of DNA produces the mRNA codon for ☐. A mutation in the template strand that produces the triplet GGG produces the mRNA codon for ☐. Since the R groups of these two amino acids are quite different, this mutation could cause structural changes to the new protein.

Chapter 24

24.1 Overview of Metabolism

LO 24.1: Distinguish between anabolic and catabolic pathways and describe where metabolic pathways occur in the body.

24.01 Which term is used to describe all of the reactions in the body that are involved in energy production and cell growth?

a) metastasis   b) glycolysis

c) anabolism   d) metabolism

e) catabolism

24.02 Most of the chemical reactions that generate energy from food happen in which organelle within cells?

a) nucleus   b) ribosomes

c) mitochondria

d) endoplasmic reticulum

e) chloroplasts

24.03 The process of breaking down large complex molecules into simpler ones for use in the body is _____.

a) anabolism   b) nucleation

c) gluconeogenesis   d) photosynthesis

e) catabolism

24.04 Which statement about catabolism is correct?

  a) The overall process of catabolism results in the absorption of energy.

  b) The overall process of catabolism results in the release of energy.

  c) The overall process of catabolism occurs in the cell nucleus.

  d) The overall process of catabolism requires the same amount of energy that is released.

  e) The overall process of catabolism results in the synthesis of new proteins.

24.05 The overall process by which large biomolecules are synthesized from smaller molecules is called _____.

  a) anabolism   **b)** retrosynthesis

  c) mitosis   **d)** catabolism

  e) saponification

24.06 Select the best description of a cyclic biochemical pathway.

  a) A cyclic pathway is a series of reactions that produces cyclic hemiacetals needed for metabolism.

  b) A cyclic pathway is a series of reactions that utilize cyclic adenosine monophosphase (cAMP) in the first and last step.

  c) A cyclic pathway is a series of reactions that regenerates the first reactant.

  d) A cyclic pathway is a series of reactions that are based on your regular sleep cycle.

  e) A cyclic pathway is a series of reactions that generates a final product.

24.07 While reviewing for an upcoming quiz, a classmate in your study group asks how many stages are there in catabolism. What should you tell them?

  a) There are three stages of catabolism.

  b) There are two stages of catabolism.

  c) There are five stages of catabolism.

  d) There are six stages of catabolism.

  e) There are eight stages of catabolism.

24.08 What occurs during the first stage of catabolism?

  a) Insulin is concentrated in the liver so that polysaccharides can be absorbed.

  b) Food is digested in the digestive tract to form small molecules such as sugars.

  c) ATP is generated and used to stimulate the synthesis of prostaglandins in the gallbladder.

  d) The citric acid cycle produces pyruvate for amino acid synthesis.

  e) Pyruvate is converted to citrate and lactate for the conversion of ADP to ATP.

24.09 Select the best description of the second stage of catabolism.

  a) The second stage of catabolism is the digestion of food to form small molecules such as sugars.

  b) The second stage of catabolism is oxidative phosphorylation.

  c) The second stage of catabolism is the citric acid cycle.

  d) The second stage of catabolism is pyruvate oxidation.

  e) The second stage of catabolism is the breakdown of monomers to produce ATP.

24.10 Determine whether each item is best described as anabolism or catabolism.

  Answer choices: breakdown of glycogen to glucose monosaccharide units, formation of the trisaccharide maltotriose from three glucose monomers, protein formation during translation, hydrolysis of a polypeptide into individual amino acids

  Target boxes: anabolism, catabolism

24.2 Important Components of Metabolic Pathways

LO 24.2: **Describe the basic structure and function of ATP, NAD$^+$, FAD, and coenzyme A.**

24.11 What are the components of the ADP molecule?

  a) ADP consists of three phosphate groups, a ribose sugar, and an adenine.

  b) ADP consists of two phosphate groups, a deoxyribose sugar, and an adenine.

  c) ADP consists of two phosphate groups, a ribose sugar, and an adenine.

  d) ADP consists of a phosphate group, a ribose sugar, and an adenine.

  e) ADP consists of three phosphate groups, a ribose sugar, and an alanine.

24.12 Which molecule is hydrolyzed to generate heat, contract muscles, and drive a wide array of chemical reactions in the cells of our bodies?

  a) cyclic AMP   **b)** NAD$^+$ **c)** ATP

  d) FAD   **e)** GTP

24.13 The addition of a phosphate group to a molecule is called _____.

  a) phosphonation

  b) dephosphorylation

  c) phosphor addition

  d) phosphotation

  e) phosphorylation

24.14 Select the correct structure of ATP.

a)

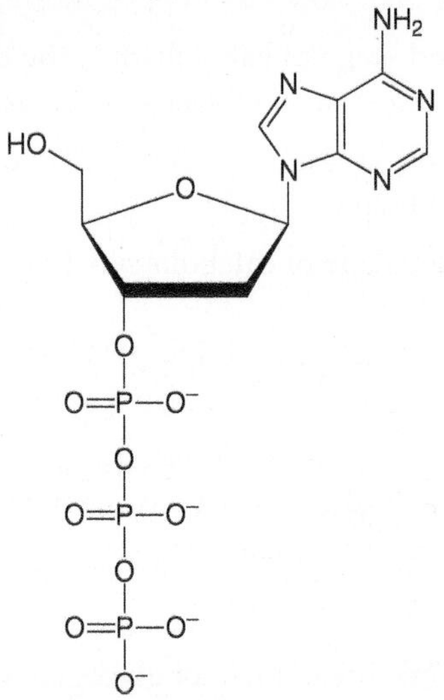

b)

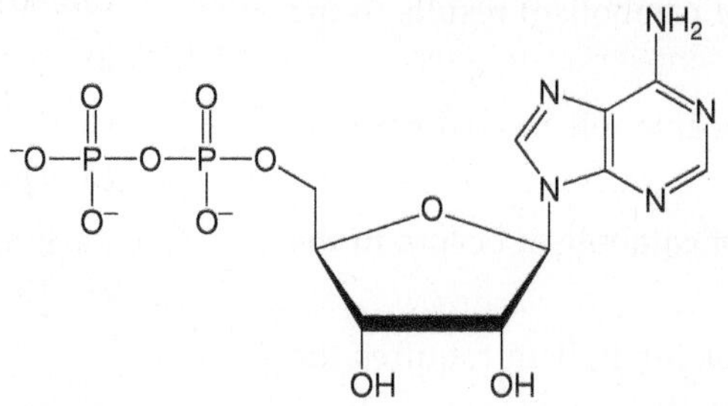

c)

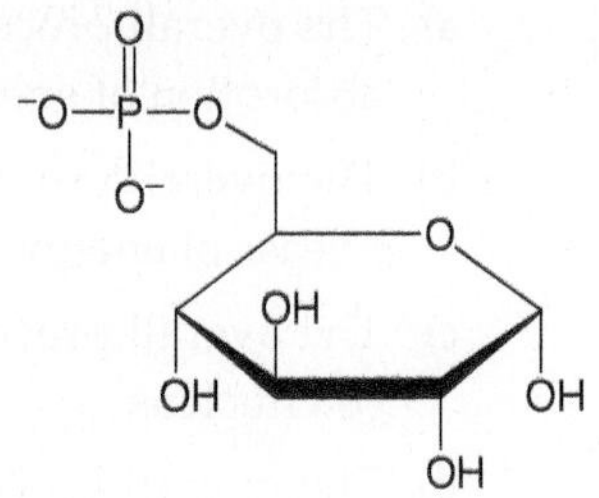

d)

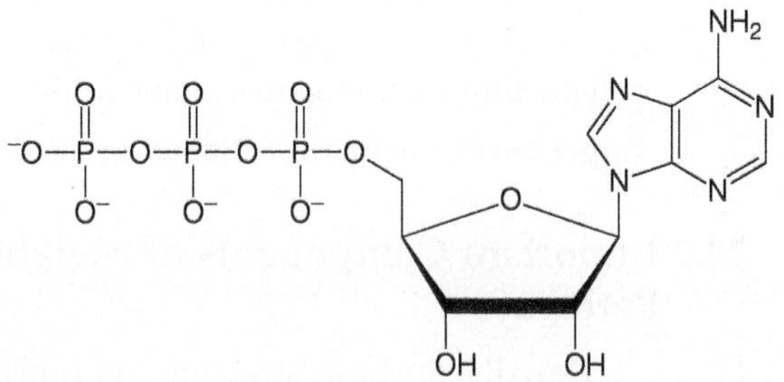

e)

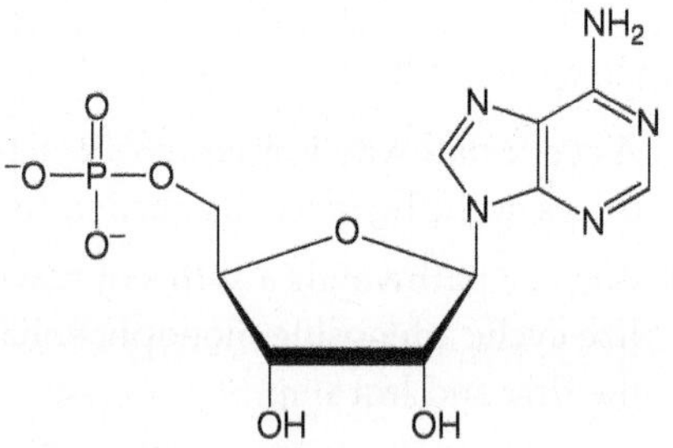

24.15 Complete the statement: The hydrolysis of ATP to form ADP is _____.

a) endothermic

b) a hydrogenation reaction

c) an isomerization reaction

d) isothermic

e) exothermic

24.16 Which equation best describes the hydrolysis of ATP to ADP?

a) $ADP + phosphate + 7.3 \text{ kcal/mol} \rightarrow ATP + H_2O$

b) $ATP + H_2O \rightarrow ADP + phosphate + 7.3 \text{ kcal/mol}$

c) $ATP + phosphate \rightarrow ADP + H_2O + 7.3 \text{ kcal/mol}$

d) $ADP + phosphate \rightarrow ATP + H_2O + 7.3 \text{ kcal/mol}$

e) $ADP + H_2O \rightarrow ATP + phosphate + 7.3 \text{ kcal/mol}$

24.17 Which coenzyme is most likely involved in a biochemical reaction that converts an alcohol group to an aldehyde?

a) NAD^+ b) $FADH_2$ c) CoA   d) FAD   e) acetyl-CoA

24.18 FAD is an important coenzyme that is derived from vitamin B_2 and helps shuttle electrons between molecules in metabolic pathways. What does the abbreviation FAD stand for?

a) folic acid dinucleotide

b) fumarate alkaline diphosphate

c) flavin alanine dinucleotide

d) flavin adenine dinucleotide

e) formic acid dehydrogenase

24.19 Select a correct function of coenzyme A.

a) to reduce $NADH_2$

b) to be a source of vitamin A

c) to oxidize FADH

d) to transfer phosphate groups

e) to transfer carbon atoms

24.20 In the cell, the phosphorylation of glucose is coupled to the hydrolysis of ATP. By using part of the energy released during ATP hydrolysis, the endothermic phosphorylation of glucose is achieved. Consider the two individual reactions shown then select the correct combined overall reaction.

Reaction 1: **ATP + H₂O → ADP + phosphate + 7.3 kcal/mol**

Reaction 2: **glucose + phosphate + 3.3 kJ/mol → glucose-6-phosphate + H₂O**

a) glucose + ATP → glucose-6-phosphate + ADP + 10.6 kJ/mol

b) glucose + phosphate + ATP → glucose-6-phosphate + ADP + 10.6 kcal/mol

c) glucose + ATP → glucose-6-phosphate + ADP + 4.0 kcal/mol

d) glucose + ATP + 10.6 kJ/mol → glucose-6-phosphate + ADP

e) glucose + phosphate → glucose-6-phosphate + ADP + 4.0 kJ/mol

24.21 In biological systems, glucose 1-phosphate can be converted into fructose 6-phosphate in two successive reactions. Consider the two individual reactions shown then select the correct combined overall reaction.

Reaction 1: **glucose 1-phosphate → glucose 6-phosphate + 7.3 kJ/mol**

Reaction 2: **glucose 6-phosphate + 1.7 kJ/mol → fructose-6-phosphate**

a) glucose 6-phosphate → fructose-6-phosphate + 5.6 kJ/mol

b) glucose 1-phosphate + 5.6 kJ/mol → fructose-6-phosphate

c) glucose 1-phosphate → fructose-6-phosphate + 9.0 kJ/mol

d) glucose 6-phosphate + 9.0 kJ/mol → fructose-6-phosphate

e) glucose 1-phosphate → fructose-6-phosphate + 5.6 kJ/mol

24.22 Phosphoenolpyruvate (PEP) is a key molecule in metabolism. The hydrolysis of PEP to pyruvate and phosphate releases 14.8 kcal/mol. The energy released in this reaction can be used to drive the synthesis of ATP from ADP and phosphate (an endothermic process requiring 7.3 kcal/mol). Identify the overall equation that best represents the combined reaction including the net energy change for the coupled reaction.

a) PEP + ADP + 7.5 kcal/mol → pyruvate + ATP

b) PEP + ADP → pyruvate + ATP + 7.5 kcal/mol

c) PEP + ADP + 14.8 kcal/mol → pyruvate + ATP

d) pyruvate + ADP + 7.5 kcal/mol → ATP + 14.8 kcal/mol

e) PEP + ATP → ADP + 14.8 kcal/mol

24.3 Glycolysis and Pyruvate Oxidation

LO 24.3: Describe the inputs, outputs, and role of glycolysis.

24.23 The overall process of glycolysis converts glucose into _____.

a) citrate   b) oxylate   c) pyruvate

d) FAD   e) lactate

24.24 Which step in the glycolysis pathway produces NADH?

a) the conversion of phosphoenolpyruvate (PEP) to pyruvate

b) the conversion of 3-phosphoglycerate to 2-phosphoglycerate

c) the conversion of glyceraldehyde 3-phosphate (G3P) to dihydroxyacetone phosphate (DHAP)

d) the conversion of glyceraldehyde 3-phosphate (G3P) to 1,3-bisphosphoglycerate

e) 1,3-bisphosphoglycerate to 3-phosphoglycerate

24.25 Which step in the glycolysis pathway hydrolyzes the first ATP?

a) the conversion of fructose 6-phosphate to fructose 1,6-bisphosphate

b) the conversion of ADP to ATP

c) the conversion of 1,3-bisphosphoglycerate to 3-phosphoglycerate

d) the conversion of phosphoenolpyruvate (PEP) to pyruvate

e) the conversion of glucose to glucose 6-phosphate

24.26 During the oxidation of pyruvate to form acetyl CoA, a carbon atom is removed in the form of carbon dioxide (CO_2). Which coenzymes are needed for this metabolic process?

a) ATP, CoA, and Vit B_{12} b) FAD and ATP

c) CoA and Niacin   d) PEP and CoA

e) NAD^+ and CoA

24.27 Select the correct overall (net) energy production in anaerobic glycolysis in terms of ATP molecules produced per molecule of glucose.

a) 2 ATP   b) 12 ATP   c) 8 ATP

d) 4 ATP   e) 6 ATP

24.28 In the presence of oxygen (aerobic conditions), the pyruvate formed during glycolysis is converted to _____.

a) ethanol   b) lactate

c) citrate   d) acetyl CoA

e) glyceraldehyde-3-phosphate (G3P)

24.29 The pyruvate generated during glycolysis is converted to lactate under what type of conditions?

a) high pH   b) aerobic

c) low pH   d) oxidative

e) anaerobic

24.30 During glycolysis, fructose-1,6-bisphosphate is split into _____.

a) glyceraldehyde 3-phosphate (G3P) and aldolase

b) dihydroxyacetone phosphate (DHAP) and glyceraldehyde 3-phosphate (G3P)

c) ATP and ADP

d) glyceraldehyde 3-phosphate (G3P) and isomerase

e) pyruvate and ATP

24.31 In step 3 of glycolysis, fructose 6-phosphate reacts with the enzyme phosphofructokinase and ATP. Which term best describes this type of reaction?

a) reduction   b) alkylation

c) phosphorylation   d) isomerization

e) cyclization

24.32 A researcher is studying metabolic pathways in yeast as a model to help understand biochemical pathways in other cells. She would like to stimulate the conversion of pyruvate to ethanol instead of acetyl CoA. Which environmental conditions would be best for the researcher to place her growing yeast cells into so that ethanol production is stimulated?

a) very low pH growth conditions

b) highly oxygenated growth conditions

c) very high pH growth conditions

d) very low oxygen growth conditions

e) 98 °C growth conditions

24.33 Our bodies metabolize sugars other than glucose (blood sugar) in order to provide the energy we need. These sugars must first, however, be converted to molecules that are able to enter somewhere in the glycolysis pathway. In muscle and kidney for example, fructose (fruit sugar) is converted into which molecule that then enters glycolysis at reaction 3?

a) fructose 1,6-bisphosphate

b) glucose 6-phosphate

c) fructose-6-phosphate

d) phosphofructokinase

e) ATP

24.34 Lactose is a disaccharide found primarily in milk and milk products. It is composed of galactose and glucose joined together by a $\beta - 1 \rightarrow 4$ glycosidic linkage. When lactose is broken down to its monosaccharide components, the galactose unit is converted to a metabolite that enters the glycolysis pathway. What molecule is galactose converted into so that it can enter glycolysis at reaction 2?

a) ATP

b) galactose-6-phosphate

c) fructose 6-phosphate

d) phosphoglucoisomerase

e) glucose 6-phosphate

24.35 Which step in the glycolysis pathway produces water as a side product?

a) the conversion of dihydroxyacetone phosphate (DHAP) to glyceraldehyde 3-phosphate (G3P)

b) the conversion of 3-phosphoglycerate to 2-phosphoglycerate

c) the conversion of 2-phosphoglycerate to phosphoenolpyruvate (PEP)

d) the conversion of phosphoenolpyruvate (PEP) to pyruvate

e) the conversion of 1,3-bisphosphoglycerate to 3-phosphoglycerate

24.36 What type of reaction is the conversion of dihydroxyacetone phosphate (DHAP) to glyceraldehyde 3-phosphate (G3P) in the glycolysis pathway?

a) cleavage   b) isomerization

c) dehydration   d) phosphate transfer

e) decarboxylation

24.37 What type of reaction is the conversion of 3-phosphoglycerate to 2-phosphoglycerate in the glycolysis pathway?

a) decarboxylation   b) phosphate transfer

c) cleavage   d) isomerization

e) dehydration

24.38 What is produced after one molecule of glucose has completed the glycolysis reaction sequence?

a) 2 ATP, 2 NADH, and 4 H^+ ions

b) 2 pyruvate, 2 NADH, and 4 H^+ ions

c) 2 ATP, 2 NADH, 2 pyruvate, and 4 H^+ ions

d) 6 ATP, 2 NADH, 2 pyruvate, and 4 H^+ ions

e) 4 ATP, 2 NADH, 2 pyruvate, and 4 H^+ ions

24.39 As the name suggests, glycolysis begins with the breakdown of glucose (blood sugar). A well-balanced diet contains a variety of foods including fruit, which contains fructose. Our bodies first convert fructose to fructose-1-phosphate in the liver. Which molecule is fructose-1-phosphate then converted into to serve as the starting material for the oxidation and phosphorylation step of glycolysis?

a) glyceraldehyde-3-phosphate

b) glucose 6-phosphate

c) 3-phospho-glycerate

d) phosphoenol-pyruvate (PEP)

e) fructose-1-phosphate

24.4 The Citric Acid Cycle

LO 24.4: Describe the inputs, outputs, and role of the citric acid cycle.

24.40 The citric acid cycle completes the breakdown of _____, releasing CO_2, ATP, and reducing NAD^+ and FAD.

a) lactate   b) citrate   c) ATP

d) glucose 6-phosphate   e) pyruvate

24.41 Which two compounds are necessary to start the citric acid cycle?

a) acetyl CoA and citrate

b) pyruvate and ATP

c) acetyl CoA and oxaloacetate

d) pyruvate and acetyl CoA

e) oxaloacetate and citrate

24.42 Which statement best describes the first step in the citric acid cycle?

a) Acetyl CoA reacts with oxaloacetate to produce citrate.

b) Acetyl CoA reacts with citrate to form isocitrate and water.

c) Acetyl CoA reacts with CoA-SH to produce citrate.

d) Oxaloacetate reacts with citrate to form isocitrate.

e) Acetyl CoA reacts with oxaloacetate to produce citrate.

24.43 Where inside the cell does the citric acid cycle take place?

a) nucleus

b) cytosol

c) endoplasmic reticulum (ER)

d) mitochondria

e) ribosome

24.44 What is needed for the conversion of succinate to fumarate in the citric acid cycle?

a) FAD

b) NAD^+ and CoA

c) ATP and CoA

d) acetyl CoA and pyruvate

e) NADH

24.45 What is needed for the conversion of α-ketoglutarate to succinyl CoA in the citric acid cycle?

a) NADH

b) NAD^+ and CoA

c) CO_2 and NADH

d) ATP and NAD

e) FAD

24.46 Which other products are formed as isocitrate is converted to α-ketoglutarate in the citric acid cycle?

a) O_2 and NAD^+

b) ADP and NADH

c) H^+ and CO_2

d) NADH and CO_2

e) CO_2, NADH, and H^+

24.47 Study the chemical structures of the coupled reactions in the citric acid cycle that involve the coenzyme NAD^+ as a reactant. What type of bond is formed in reactions involving NAD^+ as a reactant?

a) C—O   b) C=C

c) C=O   d) C—C

e) C—S

24.48 Study the chemical structures of the coupled reactions in the citric acid cycle that involve the coenzyme FAD as a reactant. Which description best characterizes reactions involving FAD as a reactant?

a) decarboxylation reactions (loss of CO_2)

b) the reduction of C=O bonds to alcohol groups

c) the formation of C=C bonds

d) the oxidation of alcohols to C=O bonds

e) the formation of new C—C single bonds

24.49 Identify the compound in the citric acid cycle that matches each description.

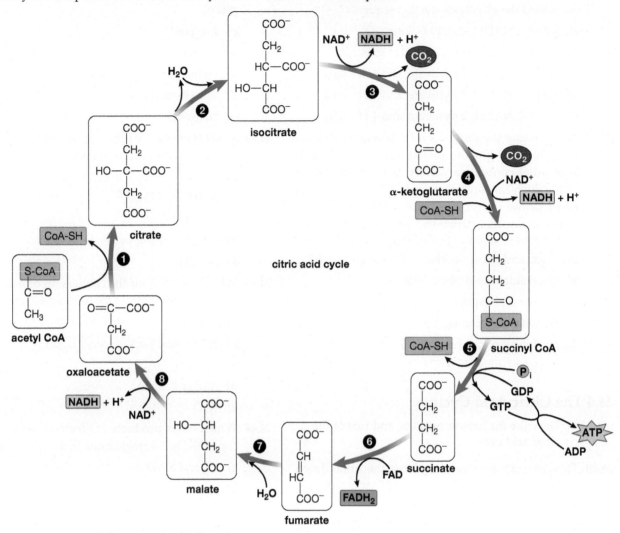

Answer choices: isocitrate, α-ketoglutarate, oxaloacetate, fumarate

Target boxes: has alkene C=C bond, has 4 carbons and a ketone group, has 5 carbon atoms, has an alcohol group

24.50 Identify the compound in the citric acid cycle that matches each description.

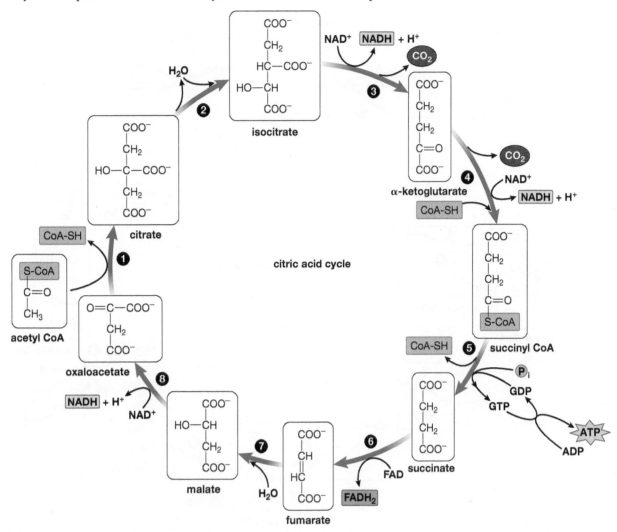

Answer choices: citrate, malate, succinyl-CoA, fumarate

Target boxes: is formed in a hydration reaction, has 6 carbons and an alcohol group, is formed in a reaction that also produces $FADH_2$, is attached to CoA

24.51 How many GTP molecules are formed in the citric acid cycle?

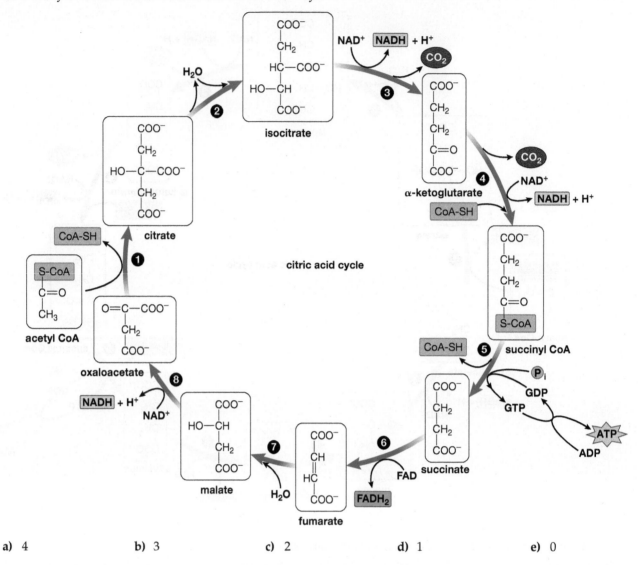

a) 4   b) 3   c) 2   d) 1   e) 0

24.52 How many molecules of carbon dioxide are produced in one turn of the citric acid cycle?

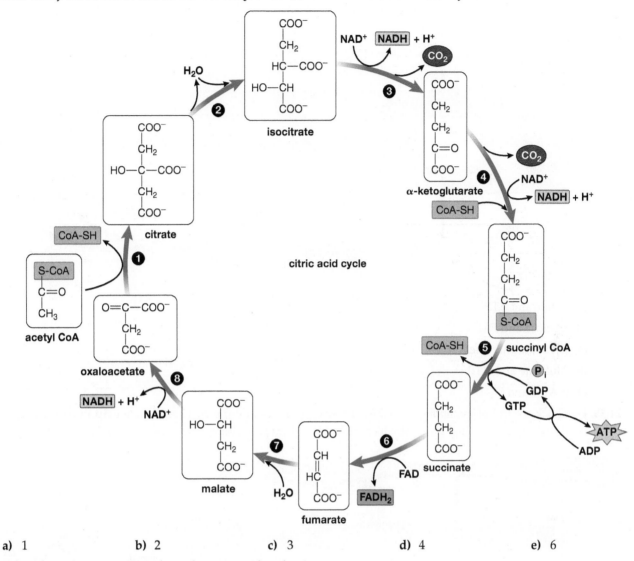

a) 1　　　　　　b) 2　　　　　　c) 3　　　　　　d) 4　　　　　　e) 6

24.53 Select the correct statement about the citric acid cycle.

$$\text{acetyl-CoA} + 3\text{NAD}^+ + \text{FAD} + \text{GDP} + \boxed{P} + 2\text{H}_2\text{O} \longrightarrow 2\text{CO}_2 + 3\boxed{\text{NADH}} + 3\text{H}^+ + \boxed{\text{FADH}_2} + \text{GTP} + \text{CoA}$$

a) The citric acid cycle produces $2\,\text{CO}_2$, 3 ATP, 3 H$^+$, FADH$_2$, GTP, and CoA during each turn.

b) The citric acid cycle produces $2\,\text{CO}_2$, 3 FAD, 3 H$^+$, 2 GTP, and CoA during each turn.

c) The citric acid cycle consumes Acetyl-CoA, 3 NADH, FAD, and GTP during each turn.

d) The citric acid cycle produces 3 NADH and 1 FADH$_2$ during each turn.

e) The citric acid cycle consumes Acetyl-CoA, 3 ATP, FAD, and GDP during each turn.

24.54 Glycolysis and the citric acid cycle must be coordinated through the use of feedback control in order to balance the energy needs of the cell. Glycolysis is inhibited by elevated levels of which two molecules?

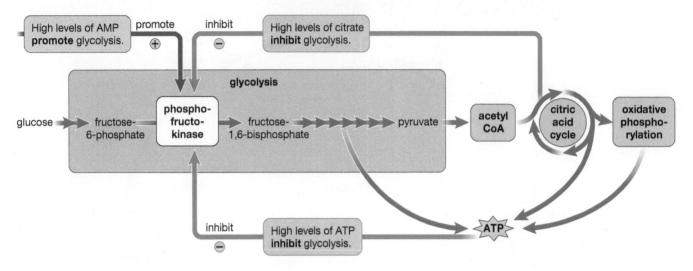

a) citrate and ATP

b) fructose and FAD

c) pyruvate and niacin

d) fumarate and GTP

e) NAD^+ and O_2

24.55 Feedback control of metabolic processes such as glycolysis and the citric acid cycle help the cell balance energy needs over time. Elevated levels of which molecule indicates an energy shortage in the cell, stimulating glycolysis?

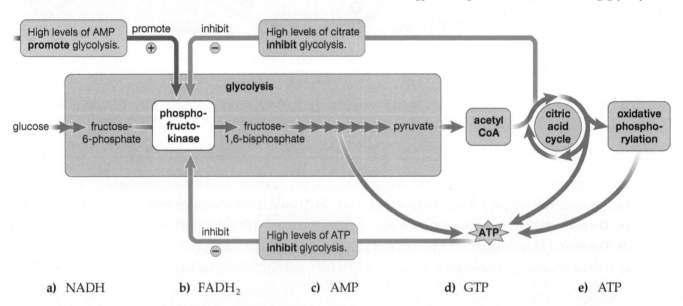

a) NADH   b) $FADH_2$ c) AMP   d) GTP   e) ATP

24.56 The citric acid cycle consists of eight steps. Several of these steps are coupled reactions that involve coenzymes and other important components in the cycle. Complete the citric acid cycle diagram shown by adding the appropriate missing item into each empty box.

Answer choices: NADH, FADH$_2$, GTP, CoA-SH

Target boxes:

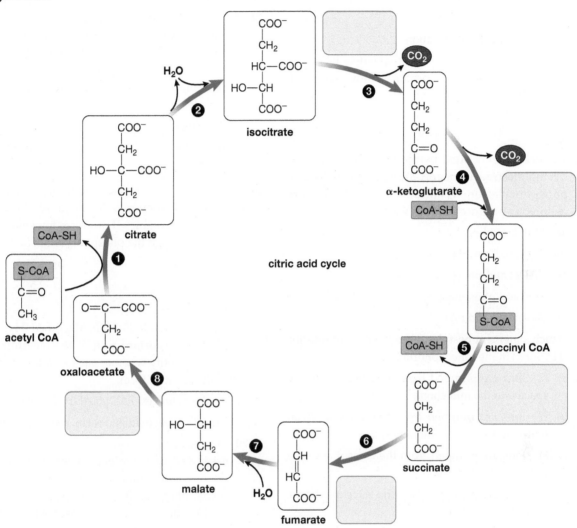

24.5 Oxidative Phosphorylation: The Electron Transport Chain and Chemiosmosis

LO 24.5: Explain the process of oxidative phosphorylation and the role of the electron transport chain.

24.57 Which molecule is produced using the energy released from the electron transport chain and chemiosmosis?

a) AMP

b) glucose

c) pyruvate

d) CO$_2$

e) ATP

24.58 In the electron transport chain, NADH and FADH$_2$ are sources of which of the following?

a) methyl groups and ATP

b) acetyl Co-A and H$^+$ ions

c) electrons and CO$_2$

d) H$^+$ ions and electrons

e) coenzyme Q and O$_2$

24.59 In chemiosmosis, hydrogen ions flow through a channel of which enzyme?

a) complex II

b) ATP reductase

c) cyt c

d) hydrolase

e) ATP synthase

24.60 The synthesis of ATP from ADP and phosphate during electron transport is known as _____.

a) phosphate isomerization

b) glycolysis

c) reductive deamination

d) hydrolysis

e) oxidative phosphorylation

24.61 The energy from each NADH that enters the transport chain at complex 1 produces how many ATP molecules?

a) 1   b) 2   c) 2.5

d) 3   e) 4.5

24.62 The energy generated by the oxidation reactions during electron transport are used for oxidative phosphorylation. What starting materials are required to produce ATP this way?

a) AMP and phosphate

b) GTP and CoA-SH

c) NADH and phosphate

d) ADP and phosphate

e) phosphate and $FADH_2$

24.63 Which statement best describes the flow of protons (H^+ ions) in the mitochondria?

a) H^+ ions are pumped from the intermembrane space into the mitochondrial matrix.

b) H^+ ions are pumped from the mitochondrial matrix to the intermembrane space.

c) H^+ ions are pumped from the ribosome to the mitochondrial matrix.

d) H^+ ions are pumped from the intermembrane space to the nucleus.

e) H^+ ions are pumped from the cytosol to the mitochondria matrix.

24.64 In electron transport, hydrogen ions and electrons from the oxidation of NADH and $FADH_2$ are passed from one electron carrier to the next until they combine with O_2 to form H_2O. Which molecule is an example of an electron carrier in this process?

a) coenzyme Q   b) ADP

c) H^+ d) acetyl CoA

e) H_2O

24.65 Which molecule in the electron transport chain is responsible for shuttling electrons from complex III to complex IV?

a) $FADH_2$ b) coenzyme Q

c) NADH   d) cytochrome C

e) acetyl CoA

24.66 Which of the following is *not* directly involved in the electron transport chain?

a) Cyt C   b) CTP synthase

c) complex I   d) O_2

e) coenzyme Q

24.67 The electron transport chain creates a proton gradient in cells that can be used by ATP synthase to produce ATP from ADP. Which molecule in the electron transport chain carries electrons between complex I and complex III and also between complex II and complex III?

a) oxygen (O_2) b) $FADH_2$

c) NADH   d) cytochrome C

e) coenzyme Q

24.68 $FADH_2$ enters the electron transport chain at complex II. The energy from the oxidation of each $FADH_2$ at complex II produces how many ATP molecules through the phosphorylation of ADP?

a) 1   b) 1.5

c) 2   d) 2.5

e) 4

24.69 The compounds FAD, NADH, $FADH_2$, and NAD play an important role in the electron transport chain. Identify whether each is in the oxidized form or the reduced form.

Answer choices: FAD, NADH, $FADH_2$, NAD^+

Target boxes: oxidized form, reduced form

24.70 The movement of electrons and protons (H^+ ions) is essential for the electron transport chain. This requires oxidation and reduction to occur at several points along the chain. Identify each reaction shown as either an oxidation or a reduction in the direction indicated by the reaction arrows.

Answer choices: reduction, oxidation

Target boxes:

$$FADH_2 \longrightarrow FAD + 2H^+ + 2e^-$$

$$CoQ + 2H^+ + 2e^- \longrightarrow CoQH_2$$

24.71 Select the correct name of fat cells.

a) granulocytes

b) lymphocytes

c) adipocytes

d) erythrocytes

e) hepatocytes

24.72 Cellular respiration in brown fat cells produces far less ATP than in other cells because the H^+ bypass ATP synthase. When the H^+ bypass ATP synthase and cross the membrane through an uncoupled protein, the H^+ is not used to generate ATP but is instead used to produce additional heat for the body. This means that these cells must metabolize far more glucose to generate the ATP they need. Select the statement about people living in cold climates that is most reasonable.

a) People living in cold climates are likely to have less brown fat than a person with a similar percent body fat that lives in a warm climate.

b) People living in cold climates are likely to have more white fat than a person with a similar percent body fat that lives in a warm climate.

c) People living in warm climates are likely to have more brown fat than a person with a similar percent body fat that lives in a cold climate.

d) People living in cold climates are likely to have more brown fat than a person with a similar percent body fat that lives in a warm climate.

24.73 Select the most appropriate statement about brown fat and the uncoupled protein (UCP).

a) Brown fat has an uncoupled protein (UCP) that allows H^+ to flow out of ATP synthase and generate more heat to warm the body.

b) Brown fat does not have an uncoupled protein (UCP) to allow H^+ to diffuse across the inner membrane without passing through ATP synthase.

c) Brown fat has an uncoupled protein (UCP) that allows H^+ to diffuse across the inner membrane without passing through ATP synthase.

d) Brown fat has an uncoupled protein (UCP) that allows NAD^+ to diffuse across the inner membrane to catalyze ATP synthase activity.

24.6 Synthesis of Glucose

LO 24.6: Describe the processes that produce glucose from lactate, triglycerides, and amino acids.

24.74 Select the best definition of gluconeogenesis.

a) the synthesis of glucose from glucagon

b) the breakdown of glucose through glycolysis

c) the conversion of glucose to glycogen under aerobic conditions

d) the synthesis of glucose from sources other than carbohydrates

e) the conversion of glucose to fructose and maltose for storage in adipose tissue

24.75 Which situation is most likely to activate gluconeogenesis?

a) a diet high in carbohydrates

b) a diet low in carbohydrates

c) a well-balanced diet

d) elevated choline levels in a diabetic individual

e) elevated serotonin levels in the brain

24.76 Our bodies can break down triacylglycerides that have been stored in fat cells into glycerol and fatty acids. The glycerol produced is then ultimately converted into _____.

a) amino acids   b) insulin   c) citrate

d) $FADH_2$ e) glucose

24.77 Which statement best describes gluconeogenesis?

a) Gluconeogenesis is an anabolic pathway that produces glucose from smaller molecules.

b) Gluconeogenesis is a catabolic pathway that produces glucose from glucagon.

c) Gluconeogenesis is a hydrolytic pathway that produces amino acids needed for protein synthesis.

d) Gluconeogenesis is a degradative pathway involving the breakdown of glycogen.

24.78 Where does gluconeogenesis occur?

a) large intestine   b) kidney

c) small intestine   d) liver   e) pancreas

24.79 Lactate produced by muscles working anaerobically is transported in the blood to the liver where it is first converted into which compound?

a) glycerol   b) citrate   c) glucose

d) oxylate   e) pyruvate

24.80 Fats can also serve as an important source of glucose. Our bodies can break down stored triacylglycerols into glycerol and fatty acids. The glycerol produced from triglycerides is first converted into which molecule?

a) glyceraldehyde   b) glycerol phosphate

c) lactate   d) adipic acid

e) dihydroxyacetone phosphate (DHAP)

24.81 The body can convert the glycerol component of triglycerides into glycolytic intermediates. Which of the following molecules is glycerol converted into that then enters glycolysis?

a) glycerol phosphate

b) 3-phosphoglycerate

c) dihydroxyacetone phosphate (DHAP)

d) glyceraldehyde

e) fumarate

24.82 Select the best description of the Cori cycle.

 a) A cyclic process in which pyruvate in muscles is transferred to the liver and converted to glucose. The glucose produced in the liver can then be used again by muscles in the body.

 b) A cyclic process in which lactate produced in muscles is transferred to the liver and converted to glucose. The glucose produced in the liver can then be used again by muscles in the body.

 c) A cyclic process in which lactate produced in the liver is transferred to the muscle where it is converted to pyruvate. The pyruvate produced in the muscle can then be used again by the liver.

 d) A cyclic process in which acetyl CoA produced in muscles is transferred to the liver and converted to oxaloacetate. The oxaloacetate produced in the liver can then be used by muscles in the body to produce more acetyl CoA.

24.83 Amino acids that our bodies can convert into glucose are known as _____.

 a) essential amino acids

 b) non-essential amino acids

 c) anabolic amino acids

 d) glucogenic amino acids

24.84 Which are two of the most common glucogenic amino acids?

 a) alanine and glutamine

 b) leucine and alanine

 c) phenylalanine and glutamine

 d) isoleucine and threonine

 e) tryptophan and tyrosine

24.85 Sort the compounds into those that are used directly as carbon sources for gluconeogenesis, and those that are not.

 Answer choices: CO_2, lactate, ATP, glycerol, alanine, NADH, $FADH_2$, glutamine

 Target boxes: used to make glucose, not used to make glucose

Chapter 25

25.1 Digestion of Fats and Cholesterol

LO 25.1: Describe how fats and cholesterol are digested in the body.

25.01 Triacylglycerols are composed of which combination of building blocks?

 a) glycine molecules covalently bound to three fatty acid chains through ether linkages

 b) glycerol molecules covalently bound to three amino acid side chains through ester linkages

 c) glycolate molecules covalently bound to two fatty acid chains through ester linkages

 d) glycerol molecules covalently bound to three fatty acid chains through ester linkages

 e) glucose molecules covalently bound to three fatty acid chains through ester linkages

25.02 Digesting and absorbing fats is challenging because lipids are not soluble in either the aqueous environment of our digestive tract nor in our blood. As a result, digestion of fats begins where in the body?

 a) pancreas b) small intestine c) gallbladder

 d) large intestine   e) stomach

25.03 Hydrophobic fat molecules clump together in the aqueous environment of the digestive tract, forming fat globules. Which of the following helps our bodies break down fat globules in order to make fat accessible to digestive enzymes?

 a) insulin b) phosphatase c) pyruvate

 d) polymerase e) bile salts

25.04 Once fat globules form micelles, the pancreas releases enzymes into the small intestine that help break down triacylglycerols. What type of enzyme performs this function?

 a) ligases b) hydrogenases c) lipases

 d) lyases   e) oxidases

25.05 Fatty acids and glycerol are released when _____ are metabolized in the small intestine.

 a) proteins b) glucose c) lipids

 d) amino acids e) nucleotides

25.06 After the micelles containing glycerol and fatty acids cross the cell membrane into the cells lining the small intestine, they recombine to reform triacylglycerols. These triacylglycerols are packaged together in large numbers with other molecules such as phospholipids, proteins, and cholesterol to form _____.

 a) nucleosomes   b) liposaccharides

 c) centromeres   d) lipoproteins

 e) ribosomes

25.07 Select the best description of the primary function of lipoproteins.

 a) Lipoproteins hydrolyze triacylglycerols to produce glycerol and long chain fatty acids that are readily absorbed into cells of the body where they can be stored or used to produce ATP.

 b) Lipoproteins transport the absorbed triacylglycerols to the cells of the body where the triacylglycerols can be stored or used to produce ATP.

 c) Lipoproteins transport ATP to the site of lipid hydrolysis and assist with the transport of fatty acids across the blood-brain barrier.

d) Lipoproteins transport the absorbed triacylglycerols into the electron transport chain where they are used to produce protons (H^+ ions), $FADH_2$, and electrons that drive ATP synthase to produce ATP for cellular energy.

e) Lipoproteins transport the absorbed triacylglycerols to the cells of the body where they enter the Cori cycle and produce acetyl CoA that enters the citric acid cycle.

24.08 Sort each process or structure into the correct bin based on whether or not it involves cholesterol.

Answer choices: protein degradation, cell membranes, hormone synthesis, triacylglycerol formation, DNA replication, synthesis of vitamin D

Target boxes: involves cholesterol, does *not* involve cholesterol

25.2 Fat Catabolism

LO 25.2: Describe oxidation of fatty acids and determine the ATP yield from fatty acid oxidation.

25.09 The process of removing 2-carbon segments of a fatty acid to use in additional metabolic steps is called _____.

a) fatty acid activation **b)** the Cori cycle

c) anabolic segregation **d)** fatty acid segmentation

e) β oxidation

25.10 Most of the glycerol that results from the breakdown of fats is metabolized in the liver. In the liver, there are two enzyme-mediated reactions that convert the glycerol into a molecule that can enter glycolysis and glucogenesis. What molecule is produced in the second enzyme-mediated reaction in the conversion of glycerol?

a) glycerol 3-phosphate **b)** acetyl CoA

c) pyruvate

d) dihydroxyacetone phosphate

e) phosphoenolpyruvate (PEP)

25.11 The glycerol produced during the breakdown of fats in the liver is converted to glycerol 3-phosphate by the enzyme glycerol kinase. Which reaction is coupled to this step?

a) the conversion of NADH to NAD^+

b) the conversion of acetyl CoA to CoA-SH

c) the conversion of $FADH_2$ to FAD

d) the conversion of O_2 to H_2O

e) the conversion of ATP to ADP

25.12 The breakdown of fats produces glycerol and fatty acids. Before the fatty acids can be broken down through β oxidation to produce energy for the cell, they must be transported through the mitochondrial membranes. What needs to occur before the fatty acids can be moved into the mitochondria?

a) Fatty acids are converted to waxes that bind to lipoproteins for transport through mitochondrial membranes.

b) Fatty acids are converted to sugar alcohols for transport through mitochondrial membranes.

c) Fatty acids are converted to fatty acyl CoA for transport through mitochondrial membranes.

d) Fatty acids are converted to micelles for transport through mitochondrial membranes.

25.13 The energy-consuming step of fatty acid catabolism requires the production of fatty acyl CoA. What process drives this energy-consuming step?

a) the conversion of ATP to AMP by acetyl CoA synthetase

b) the conversion of NADH to NAD^+ by lactate dehydrogenase

c) the conversion of glycerol to glycerol 3-phosphate by glycerol kinase

d) the conversion of glycerol 3-phosphate to dihydroxyacetone phosphate by glycerol 3-phosphate dehydrogenase

e) the conversion of FAD to $FADH_2$ by FAD synthase

25.14 What process carries fatty acyl CoA into the mitochondria matrix?

a) β oxidation **b)** oxidative phosphorylation

c) electron transport **d)** the carnitine shuttle

e) the Cori cycle

25.15 β oxidation removes two-carbon segments from the carboxyl end of fatty acids. This process produces a fatty acid molecule that is shorter by two carbon atoms. These segments are then further metabolized to produce energy for the cell. What metabolic process are the two-carbon segments used in?

a) protein synthesis **b)** the Cori cycle

c) the citric acid cycle

d) the production of bile salts

e) carnitine synthesis

25.16 What purpose does the formation of fatty acyl CoA serve in β oxidation?

a) to activate fatty acids for transport through the mitochondrial membranes and participate in the metabolic breakdown for energy production

b) to catalyze the two-step conversion of glycerol to dihydroxyacetone phosphate for metabolic breakdown for energy production

c) to enable the formation of activated lipoproteins that transport fatty acids into the liver for metabolic breakdown for energy production

d) to inhibit pyruvate oxidation and stimulate lipid production for hormone regulation in the body

e) to activate the fatty acid decarboxylation pathway that allow for CO_2 release during anabolic respiration

25.17 Fatty acyl CoA cannot cross into the mitochondrial matrix where oxidation occurs until which event takes place?

a) The fatty acyl CoA reacts with pyruvate produce ATP.

b) The fatty acyl CoA fragments into a free fatty acid and CoA-SH.

c) The fatty acyl CoA binds to the enzyme citrate dehydrogenate two NADH are produced.

d) The fatty acid binds to the carrier molecule carnitine.

e) The fatty acyl CoA binds to lipoproteins and a cholesterol molecule.

25.18 Where in the cell does β oxidation take place?

a) ribosome

b) nucleus

c) mitochondrial matrix

d) endoplasmic reticulum

e) Golgi apparatus

25.19 Identify the reaction type for each step in the β oxidation pathway. The structures of the starting material and product for each step is shown.

Answer choices: cleavage, oxidation, reduction, hydration, dehydration

Target boxes:

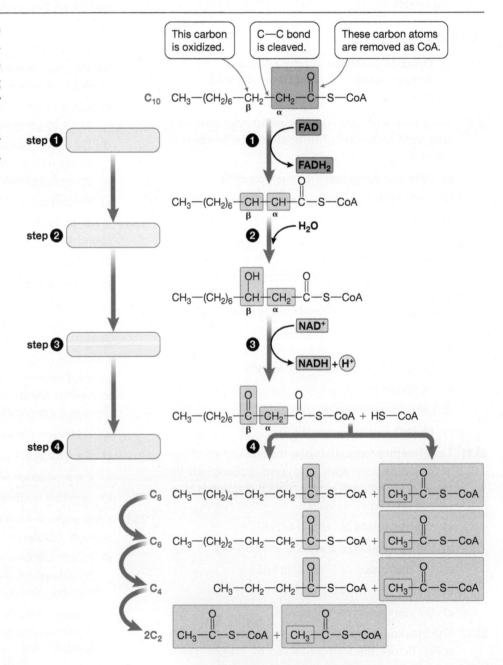

25.20 Reaction #1 in the beta oxidation pathway forms a carbon-carbon double bond between the alpha and beta carbon atoms on the fatty acid alkane chain. What type of reaction is this?

a) isomerization   b) cleavage

c) dehydration   d) oxidation

e) reduction

25.21 Reaction #2 in the beta oxidation pathway results in the conversion of an alkene to an alcohol group. What type of reaction is this?

a) cleavage   b) hydration

c) oxidation   d) dehydration

e) isomerization

25.22 Reaction #3 in the beta oxidation pathway converts a secondary alcohol group into a ketone group. What type of reaction is this?

a) isomerization   b) cleavage

c) hydration   d) dehydration

e) oxidation

25.23 Reaction #4 in the beta oxidation pathway forms acetyl CoA and an activated fatty acid that is two carbon atoms shorter than the reaction starting material. What type of reaction is this?

a) isomerization   b) oxidation

c) hydration   d) cleavage

e) dehydration

25.24 Select the correct statement about β oxidation.

a) Each four-step series of reactions forms one molecule each of acetyl CoA, NADH, and $FADH_2$.

b) Each four-step series of reactions forms one molecule of acetyl CoA, two molecules of NADH, and one molecule of $FADH_2$.

c) Each six-step series of reactions forms one molecule each of acetyl CoA, NADH, and $FADH_2$.

d) Each four-step series of reactions forms four molecules each of acetyl CoA, NADH, $FADH_2$.

e) Each four-step series of reactions forms one molecule each of acetyl CoA, NADH, pyruvate, and $FADH_2$.

24.25 Fatty acids from triacylglycerols undergo β oxidation to produce acetyl coenzyme A (acetyl CoA). Identify the alpha (α) and beta (β) carbon atoms on the activated fatty acid shown.

Answer choices: α, β

Target boxes:

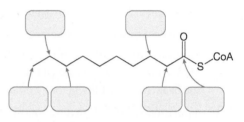

25.26 Lauric acid, $CH_3(CH_2)_{10}COOH$, is a fatty-acid found in coconut milk, human breast milk, cow's milk, and goat's milk. How many β oxidation cycles are required for the complete β oxidation of lauric acid?

a) 12   b) 10   c) 8   d) 6   e) 5

25.27 Stearic acid is one of the most common fatty acids in nature. Most people consume some of this fatty acid in their daily diet from both animal and plant fats. How many acetyl-CoA molecules are produced from the complete β oxidation of stearic acid?

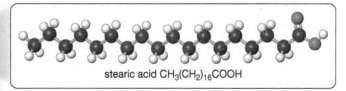

stearic acid $CH_3(CH_2)_{16}COOH$

a) 7   b) 8   c) 9   d) 17   e) 18

25.28 Oxidation of unsaturated fatty acids occurs in a similar way to oxidation of saturated fatty acids. However, an enzyme first converts a *cis* double bond to a *trans* double bond in the unsaturated fatty acid starting material. The product with the *trans* double bond can then enter the beta oxidation pathway at step 2. How many $FADH_2$ are produced from the complete β oxidation of an 8-carbon mono-unsaturated fatty acid?

a) 2   b) 3   c) 4   d) 7   e) 8

25.29 Which molecule is *not* a ketone body?

a) acetone   b) β-hydroxybutyrate

c) pyruvate   d) acetoacetate

25.30 Select the best description of ketoacidosis.

a) a potentially life-threatening condition associated with elevated blood pH that results from the basic nature of the ketone bodies

b) a potentially life-threatening condition associated with a low red blood cell (RBC) count that results from ketone bodies binding to lipoproteins

c) a potentially life-threatening condition associated with high cholesterol and low LDL values that results from the hydrophobic nature of ketone bodies

d) a potentially life-threatening condition associated with low blood pH that results from the acidic nature of the ketone bodies

25.3 Protein Catabolism

LO 25.3: Describe the catabolism of amino acids including the removal of the amino group and the pathways involved in the breakdown of the amino acid carbon skeleton.

25.31 Where in the body does the digestion of proteins begin?

a) small intestine   b) large intestine

c) liver   d) stomach

25.32 Identify the acid-tolerant stomach enzyme that breaks peptide bonds of a denatured polypeptide.

a) papain   b) isomerase

c) pepsin   d) thrombin

e) polymerase

24.33 Consider the enzyme coupled reaction of glutamate shown. Determine the missing reaction component.

Answer choices:

| $NADPH + H^+$ | $NADP^+$ |, | FAD | $FADH_2$ |,

| $NADH + H^+$ | NAD^+ |, | ATP | ADP |,

| NAD^+ | $NADH + H^+$ |

Target boxes:

25.34 In humans, the ammonium (NH_4^+) produced during oxidative deamination of amino acids enters which process?

a) glycolysis

b) the electron transport chain

c) Cori cycle

d) urea cycle

e) citric acid cycle

25.35 What type of reaction converts glutamate to α-ketoglutarate?

a) hydration

b) dehydration

c) hydrogenation

d) transamination

e) oxidative deamination

25.36 Which statement best describes the difference between oxidative deamination and transamination of amino acids?

a) Oxidative deamination transfers an amino group to an alpha-keto acid to form a new amino acid, whereas transamination removes an amino group to form an alpha-ketoacid.

b) Oxidative deamination removes an amino group to form an alpha-ketoacid, whereas transamination transfers an amino group to an alpha-keto acid to form a new amino acid.

c) Oxidative deamination removes an amino group to form pyruvate and NADH, whereas transamination transfers an amino group to a beta-keto acid to form a new amino acid.

d) Oxidative deamination removes an amino group to form the ammonium (NH_4^+) ion, phosphate, and a beta-ketoacid, whereas transamination transfers an amino group to an alpha-keto acid to form a new amino acid.

e) Oxidative deamination removes an amino group to form an alpha-ketoacid, whereas transamination transfers an amino group to another amino acid to form a beta-amino acid and pyruvate.

25.37 The ammonium ion (NH_4^+) produced by oxidative deamination reacts with carbon dioxide and ATP in the mitochondrial matrix to produce which molecule in the urea cycle?

a) α-ketoglutarate   **b)** pyruvate

c) carbamoyl phosphate

d) ornithine

e) urea

25.38 Which statement best describes the urea cycle?

a) a cycle of biochemical reactions that converts urea $(NH_2)_2 CO$ to ammonium ions (NH_4^+)

b) a cycle of biochemical reactions that converts nitrogen N_2 and pyruvate to urea, $(NH_2)_2 CO$

c) a cycle of biochemical reactions that converts glycerol and ammonium NH_4^+ ions to glycine and urea, $(NH_2)_2 CO$

d) a cycle of biochemical reactions that converts ammonium NH_4^+ ions to urea, $(NH_2)_2 CO$

e) a cycle of biochemical reactions that converts ammonium NH_4^+ ions and CO_2 to pyruvate, ATP, and urea, $(NH_2)_2 CO$

25.39 Which step in the urea cycle converts adenosine triphosphate (ATP) to adenosine monophosphate (AMP)?

a) step 1, transfer

b) step 2, condensation

c) step 3, cleavage

d) step 4, hydrolysis

e) the preparation step involving the formation of carbamoyl phosphate

25.40 Which is not a common fate of the carbon skeletons of amino acids during amino acid catabolism?

a) conversion to phosphate

b) conversion to pyruvate

c) conversion to acetyl-CoA

d) conversion to another intermediate in the citric acid cycle

25.41 Amino acids that break down to produce pyruvate or another metabolite that can then be converted to glucose are called _____.

a) glucogenic amino acids

b) glycemic amino acids

c) ketogenic amino acids

d) Zwitterionic amino acids

25.42 Many amino acid skeletons produce acetyl CoA and do not go on to produce glucose. Instead, they can produce ketone bodies. What is the name for this type of amino acid?

a) glucogenic amino acids

b) ornithinic amino acids

c) pyruvic amino acids

d) ketogenic amino acids

25.43 What product forms during the hydrolysis of arginine by the enzyme arginase in the urea cycle?

a) argininosuccinate and fumarate

b) fumarate and arginine

c) arginine and carbamoyl phosphate

d) ornithine and urea

25.4 Fatty Acid Synthesis

LO 25.4: Describe the synthesis of fatty acids from acetyl CoA.

25.44 What does the term lipogenesis mean?

a) the degradation of fatty acids two carbon atoms at a time

b) the synthesis of fatty acids two carbons at a time

c) the oxidation of fatty acids to form α-ketoacids and ATP

d) the conversion of fatty acids to NADPH and pyruvate

25.45 Which process uses the acyl carrier protein?

a) fatty acid synthesis

b) amino acid synthesis

c) fatty acid catabolism

d) glycolysis

e) gluconeogenesis

25.46 Malonyl CoA is decarboxylated while being used in which biochemical processes?

a) fatty acid catabolism

b) glycolysis

c) citric acid cycle

d) gluconeogenesis

e) fatty acid synthesis

25.47 What type of reaction does acetoacetyl-ACP undergo in reaction 2 of the fatty acid synthesis pathway?

a) acetoacetyl-ACP undergoes oxidation

b) acetoacetyl-ACP undergoes hydration

c) acetoacetyl-ACP undergoes dehydration

d) acetoacetyl-ACP undergoes reduction

e) acetoacetyl-ACP undergoes isomerization

25.48 What type of chemical reaction forms *trans*-2-enoyl-ACP from 3-hydroxy-ACP in reaction 3 of the fatty acid synthesis?

a) reduction   **b)** hydration

c) oxidation   **d)** condensation

e) dehydration

25.49 In reaction 4 of the fatty acid synthesis pathway, *trans*-2-enoyl-ACP is converted to butyryl-ACP. What type of chemical reaction is this conversion?

a) reduction   b) dehydration

c) condensation   d) oxidation

e) hydration

25.50 Acetyl-ACP and malonyl-ACP reaction in reaction 1 of the fatty acid synthesis pathway to form acetoacetyl-ACP. What type of chemical reaction is this?

a) dehydration   b) oxidation

c) condensation   d) reduction

e) hydration

24.51 Pair each enzyme with the correct reaction that it catalyzes during fatty acid synthesis.

Answer choices: acetyl-CoA transacylase, malonyl-CoA transacylase, β-ketoacyl-ACP reductase

Target boxes: converts malonyl-CoA to malonyl-ACP, reduces a ketone group to a hydroxyl group, converts acetyl-CoA to acetyl-ACP

24.52 Pair each enzyme with the correct reaction that it catalyzes during fatty acid synthesis.

Answer choices: enoyl-ACP reductase, β-ketoacyl-ACP synthase, 3-hydroxyacyl-ACP dehydrase

Target boxes: catalyzes the formation of an alkene C=C from the dehydration of an OH group, converts an alkene C=C bond to an alkane C—C bond, combines a two-carbon acetyl group with a three-carbon acetyl group and CO_2 is released

24.53 Identify the items involved in the breakdown of fat (catabolism) and those involved in fatty acid synthesis.

Answer choices: dehydration of an OH group, hydration of a C=C bond, FAD/$FADH_2$, NADPH/$NADP^+$, decarboxylation releases CO_2, ACP, oxidation of an OH group, coenzyme A

Target boxes: fat catabolism, fatty acid synthesis

25.5 Amino Acid Synthesis

LO 25.5: Describe the general pathways involved with the synthesis of nonessential amino acids from the intermediates of glycolysis and citric acid cycle.

25.54 Which molecule provides the amino group needed for transamination as the body synthesizes nonessential amino acids?

a) citrate   b) carnitine

c) glutamate   d) pyruvate

e) oxaloacetate

25.55 Identify the amino acid that is produced during the transamination reaction shown? It may be helpful to refer to the amino acid structures (Table 20.1).

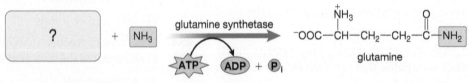

a) glutamine   b) lysine   c) alanine   d) asparagine   e) aspartate

25.56 Identify the missing starting material in the amino acid synthesis reaction shown. It may be helpful to refer to the amino acid structures (Table 20.1).

a) alanine   b) aspartate   c) glutamate   d) fumarate   e) asparagine

---

25.57 Which type of reaction is most used by the body as it synthesizes nonessential amino acids?

a) hydrogenation   b) dehydration

c) acetal formation   d) transamination

25.58 Identify the nonessential amino acid that the body produces using oxaloacetate from the citric acid cycle. It may be helpful to refer to Figure 25.37.

a) tyrosine   b) glutamate

c) glutamine   d) aspartate

25.59 Identify the nonessential amino acid that the body uses to produce cysteine. It may be helpful to refer to Figure 25.37.

a) 3-phosphoglycerate

b) serine

c) alanine

d) tyrosine

Appendix B
Visible Chem Videos and Learn Interactives by Concepts or Skill

Physical Changes (VisibleChem Video 1.1)

Chemical Changes (VisibleChem Video 1.2)

Identifying Elements in Chemical Formulas (Learn 1.1)

Tour of the Periodic Table (VisibleChem Video 1.3)

Measuring Length, Volume, and Mass (VisibleChem Video 2.1)

Converting Large and Small Numbers to Scientific Notation (Learn 2.1)

Determining Significant Figures in Calculations – Multiplication and Division (Learn 2.2)

Determining Significant Figures in Calculations – Addition and Subtraction (Learn 2.3)

Metric System Unit Conversion Problem Solving (VisibleChem Video 2.2)

Metric-English System Unit Conversion Problem Solving (VisibleChem Video 2.3)

Problem Solving Using Conversion Factors Composed of Two Units (VisibleChem Video 2.4)

Solving Unit Conversion Problems (Learn 2.4)

Using Two or More Conversion Factors When Converting Units (Learn 2.5)

Calculating Dosage of an Oral Tablet (Learn 2.6)

Calculating Dosage of Liquid Medication Based on Body Weight (Learn 2.7)

Calculating the Amount of a Toxin in a Liter of Water (Learn 2.8)

Converting Temperatures (Learn 2.9)

Problem Solving with Density (Learn 2.10)

Calculating Atomic Mass (Learn 3.1)

The Atomic Structure of Common Elements (VisibleChem Video 3.1)

Organization of Electrons into Energy Levels, Sublevels, and Orbitals (VisibleChem Video 3.2)

Writing Electron-dot Symbols (Learn 3.2)

Electron Arrangements (VisibleChem Video 3.3)

Orbital Diagrams and Electron Configurations (Learn 3.3)

Electron Configurations and the Periodic Table (Learn 3.4)

Identifying Valence Electrons from Electron Configurations (Learn 3.5)

Writing a Nuclear Equation (Learn 4.1)

Nuclear Reactions (VisibleChem Video 4.1)

Radiation Dosage (Learn 4.2)

Half-Life Calculations (VisibleChem Video 4.2)

Carbon Dating (VisibleChem Video 4.3)

Determining the Number of Protons and Electrons from Ion Symbols (Learn 5.1)

Formation of Ions (VisibleChem Video 5.1)

Representing Ions (Learn 5.2)

Using the Periodic Table to Determine Ionic Charges (Learn 5.3)

Formation of Ionic Compounds (VisibleChem Video 5.2)

Writing Formulas for Ionic Compounds from Ions (Learn 5.4)

Writing the Name of Ionic Compounds (Learn 5.5)

Naming Ionic Compounds with Cations that Have Variable Charges (Learn 5.6)

Determining the Chemical Formula of an Ionic Compound from Its Name (Learn 5.7)

Providing the Chemical Formula of an Ionic Compound that includes a Polyatomic Ion (Learn 5.8)

Drawing the Lewis Structure of Methane (VisibleChem Video 6.1)

Drawing the Lewis Structure of Water (VisibleChem Video 6.2)

Drawing the Lewis Structure of Carbon Tetrachloride (VisibleChem Video 6.3)

Drawing Lewis Structures of Small Molecules (Learn 6.1)

Drawing Lewis Structures for Molecules with Multiple Bonds (Learn 6.2)

Drawing Lewis Structures for Molecules with More Than One Central Atom (Learn 6.3)

Shapes of Molecules (VisibleChem Video 6.4)

Using VSEPR Theory to Predict the Shapes of Molecules (VisibleChem Video 6.5)

Using VSEPR to Predict the Shape of Small Molecules (Learn 6.4)

Naming Binary Covalent Compounds (Learn 6.5)

Writing the Chemical Formula from the Name of a Covalent Compound (Learn 6.6)

Comparing Electronegativity Values for Elements Across the Periodic Table (Learn 7.1)

Predicting Bond Type and Assigning Partial Charges (Learn 7.2)

Exploring the Polarity of Molecules (VisibleChem Video 7.1)

Predicting Whether a Small Molecule is Polar or Nonpolar (Learn 7.3)

Identifying Polar and Nonpolar Regions of Large Molecules (Learn 7.4)

Forces Between Molecules (VisibleChem Video 7.2)

Identifying Intermolecular Forces (Learn 7.5)

Writing and Balancing Chemical Equations (VisibleChem Video 8.1)

Balancing Chemical Equations (VisibleChem Video 8.2)

Converting Between Molecules and Moles (Learn 8.1)

Calculating Molar Mass (Learn 8.2)

Converting Between Mass and Moles (VisibleChem Video 8.3)

Converting Between Moles and Mass (VisibleChem Video 8.4)

Converting Between Mass and Number of Molecules (VisibleChem Video 8.5)

Converting Between Number of Molecules and Mass (VisibleChem Video 8.6)

Calculating Moles Using Mole Ratios (Learn 8.3)

Converting Grams of Reactant to Grams of Product (Learn 8.4)

Converting Grams of One Reactant to Grams of Another Reactant (Learn 8.5)

Determining the Limiting Reactant and Calculating the Amount of Product That Forms (Learn 8.6)

Determining the Limiting Reactant and Calculating the Mass of Product (Learn 8.7)

Calculating the Amount of Heat Generated by a Reaction from Mass of Reactant (Learn 9.1)

Calculating the Amount of Heat Generated by a Reaction from Mass of Product (Learn 9.2)

Energy Diagrams and Activation Energy (VisibleChem Video 9.1)

Molecular Collisions That Lead to Products (VisibleChem Video 9.2)

The Significance of the Equilibrium Constant (VisibleChem Video 9.3)

Le Chatelier's Principle (VisibleChem Video 9.4)

Calculating the Equilibrium Constant (Learn 9.3)

Converting Between Pressure Units (Learn 10.1)

Gas Laws (VisibleChem Video 10.1)

Using Avogadro's Law to Determine Amounts of Gas at STP (Learn 10.2)

Intermolecular Forces and the Relationship to Boiling and Melting Points (VisibleChem Video 10.2)

Using Dalton's Law to Determine Partial Pressures (Learn 10.3)

Predicting Relative Boiling Points (VisibleChem Video 10.3)

Using Heat of Vaporization to Determine Energy Amounts (Learn 10.4)

Using Heat of Fusion to Determine Energy Amounts (Learn 10.5)

Ionic Compounds Dissociate into Ions in Water (VisibleChem Video 11.1)

Compounds that are Soluble in Water (VisibleChem Video 11.2)

Nonpolar Compounds and Nonpolar Solvents (VisibleChem Video 11.3)

Reporting Solution Concentration as Percent (VisibleChem Video 11.4)

Reporting Solution Concentration as Molarity (M) (VisibleChem Video 11.5)

Solution Dilution Calculations (VisibleChem Video 11.6)

Boiling Point Elevation (Learn 11.1)

Freezing Point Depression (Learn 11.2)

Identifying Conjugate Acid-Base Pairs (Learn 12.1)

Strong vs. Weak Acids and Bases (VisibleChem Video 12.1)

Predicting the Direction of Equilibrium Using Acid and Base Strength (VisibleChem Video 12.2)

Writing an Acid Dissociation Constant (K_a) Expression (Learn 12.2)

Using Ka Values to Determine Relative Acid Strength (Learn 12.3)

Using Kw to Calculate [H_3O^+] and [OH^-] (Learn 12.4)

Calculating pH and Hydronium Ion Concentration (VisibleChem Video 12.3)

Small Changes in pH Indicate Large Changes in Hydronium Ion Concentration (VisibleChem Video 12.4)

Balancing Neutralization Reactions (Learn 12.5)

Titration of HCl with NaOH (VisibleChem Video 12.5)

Determining Acid Molarity from a Titration (Learn 12.6)

How a Buffer Maintains pH (VisibleChem Video 12.6)

Calculating the pH of a Buffer (Learn 12.7)

Drawing Wedge-Dash Structures of Molecules (Learn 13.1)

Drawing Condensed Structures (Learn 13.2)

Interpreting Skeletal Structures (Learn 13.3)

Rotation Around Carbon-Carbon Single Bonds (VisibleChem Video 13.1)

Drawing Structural Isomers (VisibleChem Video 13.2)

Interpreting Skeletal Structures of Large Organic Molecules (VisibleChem Video 13.3)

Recognizing and Drawing *Cis* and *Trans* Isomers (VisibleChem Video 13.4)

Predicting Products of Alkene Addition Reactions (VisibleChem Video 13.5)

Understanding Polymerization Reactions of Alkenes (VisibleChem Video 13.6)

Classifying Alcohols as 1°, 2°, or 3° (Learn 14.1)

Dehydration Reactions of Alcohols (VisibleChem Video 14.1)

Oxidation Reactions of Alcohols (VisibleChem Video 14.2)

Oxidation Reactions of Thiols to Produce Disulfides (VisibleChem Video 14.3)

Chirality of Objects (VisibleChem Video 14.4)

Chiral Compounds (VisibleChem Video 14.5)

Oxidation Reactions of Aldehydes (VisibleChem Video 15.1)

Reduction Reactions of Aldehydes and Ketones (VisibleChem Video 15.2)

Forming Acetals and Hemiacetals from Aldehydes and Ketones (VisibleChem Video 15.3)

The Formation of Cyclic Hemiacetals and Cyclic Acetals (VisibleChem Video 15.4)

Classifying Monosaccharides (Learn 16.1)

Determining the Stereochemistry of Monosaccharides (Learn 16.2)

Drawing the Haworth Cyclic Structure from an Acyclic Aldohexose (VisibleChem Video 16.1)

Drawing the Haworth Cyclic Structure from an Acyclic Ketohexose (VisibleChem Video 16.2)

The Structural Features of Disaccharides (VisibleChem Video 16.3)

Carboxylic Acids are Weak Acids (VisibleChem Video 17.1)

Soaps (VisibleChem Video 17.2)

Esterification and Amide Formation (VisibleChem Video 17.3)

Ester and Amide Hydrolysis (VisibleChem Video 17.4)

Structure of a Triacylglycerol (Learn 18.1)

Reactions of Triacylglycerols (VisibleChem Video 18.1)

Metabolism of Triacylglycerols (VisibleChem Video 18.2)

Structure and Function of Phosphoacylglycerols (VisibleChem Video 18.3)

Structure and Function of Sphingomyelin (VisibleChem Video 18.4)

Classifying Amines as 1°, 2°, or 3° (Learn 19.1)

Hydrogen Bonds Between Amine Molecules (VisibleChem Video 19.1)

Reactions of Amines (VisibleChem Video 19.2)

Formation of a Peptide Bond (VisibleChem Video 20.1)

Drawing Peptide Bond Formation (Learn 20.1)

Overview of Protein Structure (VisibleChem Video 20.2)

Stabilizing Interactions in Protein Folding (VisibleChem Video 20.3)

Enzyme Inhibition (VisibleChem Video 21.1)

Enzyme Regulation (VisibleChem Video 21.2)

Forming and Naming Nucleosides (Learn 22.1)

Linking Nucleotides (VisibleChem Video 22.1)

DNA Double Helix (VisibleChem Video 22.2)

DNA Replication (VisibleChem Video 22.3)

Overview of Transcription (VisibleChem Video 23.1)

A Closer Look at Transcription (VisibleChem Video 23.2)

Using the Genetic Code to Determine an Amino Acid Sequence from mRNA (Learn 23.1)

Translation and Protein Synthesis (VisibleChem Video 23.3)

The Energy-Consuming Reactions of Glycolysis (VisibleChem Video 24.1)

The Energy-Generating Reactions of Glycolysis (VisibleChem Video 24.2)

The Reactions of the Citric Acid Cycle (VisibleChem Video 24.3)

Oxidative Phosphorylation (VisibleChem Video 24.4)

Beta Oxidation of Fatty Acids (VisibleChem Video 25.1)

Determining the Number of ATP Molecules Produced from a Fatty Acid (Learn 25.1)

Removing Amino Groups from Amino Acids (VisibleChem Video 25.2)

The Fate of the Carbon Skeletons from Amino Acids (VisibleChem Video 25.3)

Credits

Cover watchara/Shutterstock.

Front Matter Nik Merkulov/Shutterstock.

Unit 1 Figure U1.3: SciePro/Shutterstock; U1.5: Dmitry Kalinovsky/Shutterstock; U1.7: springsky/Shutterstock; U1.8: qvist/Shutterstock

Chapter 1 Chapter Opener: SUWIT NGAOKAEW/Shutterstock, Blend Images/Shutterstock; Figure 1.1a: Roman Zaiets/Shutterstock; 1.1b: Kessudap/123rf.com; 1.1c: Riccardo Mayer/Shutterstock; 1.2a: Image Source Trading Ltd/Shutterstock; 1.2b: Prostock-studio/Shutterstock; 1.5a: Charles Darwin 1837; 1.5b: Courtesy Ava Helen and Linus Pauling Papers, Oregon State University Libraries; 1.6: "Gold Nanoparticle" image courtesy of the Electronic Visualization Laboratory at the University of Illinois Chicago (UIC), UIC Department of Chemistry's Petr Král Research Group, and University of Massachusetts, Amherst's Vincent M. Rotello Research Group; 1.16 (clockwise from top left): gcpics/Shutterstock, Sebastian Kaulitzki/123rf.com, Africa Studio/Shutterstock, Nenad.C/Shutterstock, Scott A. Frangos/Shutterstock, Dariush M/Shutterstock; 1.17 (left to right): TATIANA MAKOTRA/123rf.com, LP2 Studio/Shutterstock; 1.18a: Kelly Headrick/Shutterstock; 1.18b: Tigergallery/Shutterstock; 1.19: Monthon Wachirasettakul/123rf.com; 1.20 (left to right): Jelli Márk/123rf.com, Konstantin Chagin/123rf.com, Ewa Studio/Shutterstock, Eric Krouse/Shutterstock; 1.21: robert mcgillivray/Shutterstock; 1.22: Yuangeng Zhang/Shutterstock; 1.23: Africa Studio/Shutterstock; 1.26 (clockwise from top): Johan Swanepoel/Shutterstock, Randy Hergenrether. Shutterstock, Katrina Brown/Shutterstock, Gorodenkoff/Shutterstock, Triff/Shutterstock, alekleks/Shutterstock; 1.27: belchonock/123rf.com; 1.28: Miro Novak/Shutterstock; 1.29: Steven Heap/123rf.com; 1.35: Vera Kalyuzhnaya/Shutterstock; 1.37 (left to right, top to bottom): Trevor Clifford/Pearson Education Ltd., Bjoern Wylezich/Shutterstock, grenadier/Wikimedia Commons, Rvkamalov gmail.com/Shutterstock, jiangdi/Shutterstock, Robert Kyllo/Shutterstock, mikeledray/Shutterstock

Chapter 2 Chapter Opener: Sasi Ponchaisan/123rf.com; Figure 2.1a: Antonio Guillem/123rf.com; 2.1b: NikoNomad/Shutterstock; 2.1c: toysf400/Shutterstock; 2.2: Brian A Jackson/Shutterstock; 2.3: Michaeljung/Shutterstock; 2.4: sirtravelalot/Shutterstock; 2.5: JaturunThakard; 2.6: wawritto/Shutterstock; 2.7: Ivan Hoermann/Shutterstock; 2.8: Beneda Miroslav/Shutterstock; 2.9: schlyx/Shutterstock; 2.10: Australis Photography/Shutterstock; 2.11a: Alexey Repka/123rf.com; 2.11b: P A/Shutterstock; 2.12: xrender/Shutterstock; 2-13: pefostudio5/Shutterstock; 2.14 (left to right): Gorlov-KV/Shutterstock, Tyler Olson/Shutterstock; 2.22: Monika Wisniewska/123rf.com; 2.23: Aline Tong/Shutterstock; 2.24: Cavan Images/Alamy Stock Photo; 2.25: Supitcha McAdam/Shutterstock; 2.27: Dr Juerg Alean/Science Source; 2.35a: jovannig/123rf.com; 2.35b: lightwise/123rf.com; 2.36: Rob Byron/Shutterstock

Chapter 3 Chapter Opener: adison pangchai/Shutterstock; Figure 3.1a: Maor_Winetrob/Shutterstock; 3.1b: Djomas/Shutterstock; 3.2: ruzanna/Shutterstock; 3.4 (left to right): Marcel Mooij/Shutterstock, Kostyantine Pankin/123rf.com; 3.5: Turtle Rock Scientific/Science Source; 3.8: robertharding/Alamy Stock Photo; 3.29: Edward Haylan/Shutterstock

Chapter 4 Chapter Opener: agsandrew/Shutterstock; Figure 4.1a: Alexander Raths/Shutterstock; 4.1b: Petr Smagin/Shutterstock; 4.1c: sfam_photo/Shutterstock; 4.2: Pictorial Press Ltd/Alamy Stock Photo; 4.3: sirtravelalot/Shutterstock; 4.4: gokturk_06/Shutterstock; 4.5: REUTERS/Alamy Stock Photo; 4.6: METAS, Switzerland; 4.15: sciencepics/Shutterstock; 4.20: Tyler Olson/123rf.com; 4.21: Hank Frentz/123rf.com; 4.27: Zhejiang Daily - Imaginechina/AP Images

Unit 2 Figure U2.1: Huen Structure Bio/Shutterstock; U2.2: auremar/123rf.com; U2.3: Alex_Traksel/Shutterstock; U2.6: Huen Structure Bio/Shutterstock; U2.7: Tyler Olson/Shutterstock

Chapter 5 Chapter Opener: Zastolskiy Victor/Shutterstock; Figure 5.1a: Bill45/Shutterstock; 5.1b: Prostock-studio/Shutterstock; 5.1c: Brian A Jackson/Shutterstock; 5.2: Motortion Films/Shutterstock; 5.13: Levent Konuk/Shutterstock; 5.14 (clockwise from top left): Gareth Boden/Pearson Education Ltd., Rvkamalov gmail.com/Shutterstock, oNabby/Shutterstock, Krakenimages.com/Shutterstock; 5.15: oNabby/Shutterstock; 5.16: noomhh/123rf.com; 5.17a: Aumm graphixphoto/Shutterstock; 5.17b: Lubo Ivanko/Shutterstock; 5.18: chuyuss/Shutterstock; 5.20: Corepics VOF/Shutterstock; 5.21: stockcreations/Shutterstock; 5.22: GVictoria/Shutterstock; 5.23: pedalist/Shutterstock; 5.24a: tanyapuntti/123rf.com; 5.24b: rafaelbenari/123rf.com; 5.25: Fotokostic/Shutterstock

Chapter 6 Chapter Opener: Forance/Shutterstock; Figure 6.1: Alpha Tauri 3D Graphics/Shutterstock; 6.2: dpa picture alliance/Alamy Stock Photo; 6.3 (left to right): Science History Images/Alamy Stock Photo, Gilbert Newton Lewis; 6.8: anny Studio/Shutterstock; 6.11a: Shawn Hempel/123rf.com; 6.11b: Shi Yali/Shutterstock; 6.11c: Nicha/Shutterstock; 6.13: MarcelClemens/Shutterstock; 6.15a: Andraž Cerar/Shutterstock; 6.15b: Alim Yakubov/Shutterstock; 6.17a: Smereka/Shutterstock; 6.17b: Ulrich Baumgarten/Getty Images; 6.31: R. Gino Santa Maria/Shutterstock; 6.34a (top to bottom): BW Folsom/Shutterstock, Stillfx/123rf.com

Chapter 7 Chapter Opener: somersault1824/Shutterstock; Figure 7.1a: Thinnapob Proongsak/Shutterstock; 7.1b: Arun Roisri/Shutterstock; 7.1c: TinnaPong/Shutterstock; 7.11: T.W./Shutterstock; 7.12: sirtravelalot/Shutterstock; 7.13: defpicture/Shutterstock; 7.22: paytai/Shutterstock

Unit 3 Figure U3.1a: Randy L. Jirtle; U3.1b: Mopic/Shutterstock; U3.2a: fancystudio/123rf.com; U3.2b: Atthapon Raksthaput/Shutterstock; U3.2c: MBI/Shutterstock; U3.6: Stockbroker/123rf.com

13.23: MIA Studio/Shutterstock; 13.24: SasinT/Shutterstock; 13.35 (left to right): ghenadie/Shutterstock, fermate/123rf.com, Yellow Cat/Shutterstock; 13.39a: sirtravelalot/Shutterstock; 13.40 (left to right): Toa55/Shutterstock, Korionov/Shutterstock, Denis Torkhov/Shutterstock

Chapter 14 Chapter Opener: StudioMolekuul/Shutterstock; Figure 14.1a: Aleksandar Malivuk/Shutterstock; 14.1b: herjua/Shutterstock; 14.1c: airdone/Shutterstock; 14.2a: Photographee.eu/Shutterstock; 14.2b: lsantilli/123rf.com; 14.2c: Alexander Oganezov/Shutterstock; 14.5: David Ridley/Shutterstock; 14.12 (left to right): Liv Friis-Larsen/123rf.com, Rob Marmion/Shutterstock: 14.13a: Geoffrey Kuchera/Shutterstock; 14.13b: UPI/Alamy Stock Photo; 14.13c: airdone/Shutterstock; 14.14 (left to right): Sea Wave/Shutterstock, Natthawon Chaosakun/Shutterstock; 14.22: Andrew Aitchison/Alamy Stock Photo; 14.25: royaltystockphoto/123rf.com; 14.26: Tyler Olson/Shutterstock; End of Chapter Quiz 14.8: airdone/Shutterstock; End of Chapter Quiz 14.12: fotovapl/Shutterstock

Unit 6 Figure U6.1: Click and Photo/Shutterstock; U6.4 (left to right): Andrey_Popov/Shutterstock, Click and Photo/Shutterstock; U6.5: santypan/Shutterstock; U6.6: Marcin Ciesielski/123rf.com; U6.7: Jarun Ontakrai/Shutterstock; U6.8: CGN089/Shutterstock; U6.9: PhotoStock10/Shutterstock; U6.10: McGlacken-Byrne, S. M., Drew, S. E., Turner, K., Peters, C., & Amin, R. (2021). The SARS-CoV-2 pandemic is associated with increased severity of presentation of childhood onset type 1 diabetes mellitus: A multi-centre study of the first COVID-19 wave. *Diabetic Medicine*, 38(9), e14640

Chapter 15 Chapter Opener: Kateryna Kon/Shutterstock; Figure 15.1a: Marc Bruxelle/Shutterstock ; 15.1b: memorisz/Shutterstock; 15.1c: Puwadol Jaturawutthichai/Shutterstock; 15.2: Tyler Olson/Shutterstock; 15.3: xpixel/Shutterstock; 15.5: Jaroslaw Grudzinski/Shutterstock; 15.6: MBI/Shutterstock; 15.7: GOIMAGES/Alamy Stock Photo; 15.8: PureRadiancePhoto/Shutterstock; 15.26: Ian Yefimkin/123rf.com; 15.27: Billion Photos/Shutterstock; 15.28: mailsonpignata/Shutterstock

Chapter 16 Chapter Opener: Peter Waters/Shutterstock; Figure 16.1a: Smileus/Shutterstock; 16.1b: Piotr Adamowicz/Shutterstock; 16.1c: Sherry Yates Young/Shutterstock; 16.2a: Siegfried Kopp/123rf.com; 16.2b: Billion Photos/Shutterstock; 16.3: Sea Wave/Shutterstock; 16.4: Bitt24/Shutterstock; 16.5 (left to right): Topseller/Shutterstock, Michaeljung/Shutterstock; 16.6a: Kurhan/Shutterstock; 16.6b: Wavebreakmedia/Shutterstock; 16.8: Helder Almeida/Shutterstock; 16.10: Room's Studio/Shutterstock; 16.14: Thammasak Lek/Shutterstock; 16.15b: Serg64/Shutterstock; 16.15c: Margouillat photo/Shutterstock; 16.18: Prasit Rodphan/123rf.com; 16.19: Dmitry Lobanov/Shutterstock; 16.20: Alexander Raths/Shutterstock; 16.21: Coleman Yuen/Pearson Education Asia Ltd.; 16.23: 0833379753/Shutterstock; 16.24 (top to bottom): Africa Studio/Shutterstock, SciePro/Shutterstock; 16.25 (top to bottom): smereka/Shutterstock, beats1/Shutterstock; 16.26: M. Unal Ozmen/Shutterstock; 16.27: Biophoto Associates/Science Source; 16.28: TinyPhoto/Shutterstock; 16.29: ultimathule/Shutterstock; 16.38: Dirima/Shutterstock, (inset) SlayStorm/Shutterstock; 16.39: Sherry Yates Young/Shutterstock

Unit 7 Figure U7.1: Mangostar/Shutterstock; U7.3: rido/123rf.com; U7.4: Esan Indy Studios/Shutterstock; U7.5: Konektus Photo/Shutterstock; U7.6: Gleb Usovich/Shutterstock; U7.7: Mas Dafi/Shutterstock; U7.8: somkku9kanokwan/123rf.com

Chapter 17 Chapter Opener: Maria Uspenskaya/Shutterstock; Figure 17.1a: SofikoS/Shutterstock; 17.1b: Julia Hiebaum/Alamy Stock Photo; 17.1c: Sergey Novikov/Shutterstock; 17.3 (left to right): Jenoche/Shutterstock, Igor Boldyrev/Shutterstock, Maria Uspenskaya/Shutterstock; 17.4 (clockwise from top left): Maria Uspenskaya/Shutterstock, Jeannette Lambert/Shutterstock, Trendsetter Images/123rf.com, Riccardo Mayer/Shutterstock, pixs4u/Shutterstock, margouillat photo/Shutterstock; 17.15: Milos Vucicevic/Shutterstock; 17.16: ang intaravichian/Shutterstock; 17.25: Roman.S-Photographer/Shutterstock; 17.26: Witsawat.S/Shutterstock; 17.27: Nicole Ciscato/Shutterstock; 17.28: photokup/Shutterstock; 17.29: chaiyapruek youprasert/Shutterstock; 17.30: littleny/Shutterstock; 17.31 (left to right): Alba_alioth/Shutterstock, Евгений Вершинин/Alamy Stock Photo; 17.32: Dalibor Sevaljevic/123rf.com; 17.33: Elnur/Shutterstock

Chapter 18 Chapter Opener: Kateryna Kon/Shutterstock; Figure 18.1a: Jarun Ontakrai/123rf.com; 18.1b: Stephen VanHorn/Shutterstock; 18.1c: fongbeerredhot/Shutterstock; 18.2: Lightspring/Shutterstock; 18.3 (clockwise from top): MilanMarkovic78/Shutterstock, Iakov Filimonov/Shutterstock, Phonlamai Photo/Shutterstock, Peter Bernik/Shutterstock, Diego Cardini/123rf.com; 18.4 (left to right): MBI/Shutterstock, Ron Dale/Shutterstock; 18.5 (top to bottom): Kateryna Bibro/123rf.com, Ekkachai/Shutterstock, natika/123rf.com, Valentyn Volkov/Shutterstock, Lillac/Shutterstock, Elena Shashkina/123rf.com; 18.13a: StudioSmart/Shutterstock; 18.13b: apiguide/Shutterstock; 18.13c: Shane Gross/Shutterstock; 18.14: nickdale/123rf.com; 18.16 (left to right): subbotina/123rf.com, MaraZe/Shutterstock; 18.17 (left to right): Oleksiy Mark/Shutterstock, mipan/Shutterstock; 18.28 (left to right): Mark Adams/123rf.com, Sherry Yates Young/123rf.com; 18.30: Lightspring/Shutterstock; 18.31: Volt Collection/Shutterstock; 18.32: Asia Images Group/Shutterstock; 18.34a: Kamira/Shutterstock; 18.34b: Nattakorn Maneerat/123rf.com; 18.34c: MBI/Shutterstock; 18.34d: Pete Saloutos/Shutterstock; 18.35: Suwannee Ngoenklan/Shutterstock; 18.36 (left to right): Sherry Yates Young/123rf.com, Antonio Guillem/123rf.com; 18.37 (left to right): BlueRingMedia/Shutterstock, Image Point Fr/Shutterstock

Unit 8 Figure U8.1: Andriy Blokhin/Shutterstock; U8.2: Eraxion/123rf.com; U8.3: U.S. DEA; U8.4: Hanson L/Shutterstock; U8.5: New2me86/Shutterstock; U8.7: Che, T., Majumdar, S., Zaidi, S.A., Ondachi, P., McCorvy, J.D., Wang, S., Mosier, P.D., Uprety, R., Vardy, E., Krumm, B.E., Han, G.W., Lee, M.Y., Pardon, E., Steyaert, J., Huang, X.P., Strachan, R.T., Tribo, A.R., Pasternak, G.W., Carroll, F.I., Stevens, R.C., Cherezov, V., Katritch, V., Wacker, D., Roth, B.L. (2018) *Cell* 172: 55-67.e15; U8.8: Gorodenkoff/Shutterstock

Chapter 19 Chapter Opener: nobeastsofierce/123rf.com; Figure 19.1a: Franck Boston/Shutterstock; 19.1b: Pics-xl/Shutterstock; 19.1c: isak55/Shutterstock; 19.2: Africa Studio/Shutterstock; 19.3 (left to right): Kamonrat Meunklad/123rf.

Unit 10 Figure U10.1 (top to bottom): Ministr-84/Shutterstock, Trueffelpix/Shutterstock; U10.2: Pikovit/Shutterstock; U10.3: darko m/Shutterstock, Pikovit/Shutterstock, (insets, clockwise from top) MinDof/Shutterstock, Sean Pavone/Shutterstock, Africa Studio/Shutterstock, simonalvinge/Shutterstock, Rawpixel.com/Shutterstock; U10.4: Creativa Images/Shutterstock; U10.5: New Africa/Shutterstock; U10.6: Shidlovski/Shutterstock; U10.7 (left to right): Bildagentur Zoonar GmbH, MedstockPhotos/Shutterstock

Chapter 24 Chapter Opener: Science Photo Library/Alamy Stock Photo; Figure 24.1a: SVRSLYIMAGE/Shutterstock; 24.1b: Science History Images/Alamy Stock Photo; 24.1c: Alexander Raths/Shutterstock; 24.2: fizkes/Shutterstock; 24.3 (left to right): Josep Suria/Shutterstock, Tada Images/Shutterstock; 24.5 (top to bottom): PhotoSGH/Shutterstock, marilyn barbone/Shutterstock, Jean-Paul CHASSENET/123rf.com; 24.10: Paul Matthew Photography/Shutterstock; 24.12: Shawn Pecor/Shutterstock; 24.13a: SCIENCE PHOTO LIBRARY/Science Source; 24.13b: Anita Patterson Peppers/Shutterstock; 24.14b: Science History Images/Alamy Stock Photo; 24.16: piotr_pabijan/Shutterstock; 24.17: facai/Shutterstock; 24.20 (left to right): Rob Byron/Shutterstock, Africa Studio/Shutterstock; 24.23: Andrea Izzotti/Shutterstock; 24.24: Joshua Resnick/Shutterstock; 24.29a: john michael evan potter/Shutterstock; 24.31 (left to right): Alexandr Zadiraka/Shutterstock, MBI/Shutterstock; 24.39: Naufal MQ/Shutterstock; 24.40: Jarun Ontakrai/Shutterstock; 24.42: Wallace Kirkland/The LIFE Picture Collection/Shutterstock

Chapter 25 Chapter Opener: Juan Gaertner/Shutterstock; Figure 25.1a: Cathy Yeulet/123rf.com; 25.1b: Fortyforks/Shutterstock; 25.1c: Africa Studio/Shutterstock; 25.2 (top to bottom): PhotoSGH/Shutterstock, marilyn barbone/Shutterstock, Jean-Paul CHASSENET/123rf.com; 25.3: Cathy Yeulet/123rf.com; 25.4: kerale/Shutterstock; 25.5: JulijaDmitrijeva/Shutterstock; 25.6: Jarun Ontakrai/123rf.com; 25.14 (top to bottom): PhotoSGH/Shutterstock, marilyn barbone/Shutterstock, Jean-Paul CHASSENET/123rf.com; 25.14b: Rafa Irusta/Shutterstock; 25.15: Helen Sushitskaya/Shutterstock; 25.19: XiXinXIng/Shutterstock; 25.20: memorisz/Shutterstock; 25.21 (top to bottom): PhotoSGH/Shutterstock, marilyn barbone/Shutterstock, Jean-Paul CHASSENET/123rf.com; 25.22: Africa Studio/Shutterstock; 25.30: Chubykin Arkady/Shutterstock; 25.31 (left to right): Cuson/Shutterstock, EvgeniiAnd/Shutterstock, Henk Bentlage/Shutterstock; 25.32: Africa Studio/Shutterstock; 25.33: Chubykin Arkady/Shutterstock; 25.34: Scio21/Shutterstock; 25.36: CDC

Appendix A Problem 2.11 (clockwise from top left): iofoto/Shutterstock, Andreypopov/123rf.com, Marlon Lopez MMG1 Design/Shutterstock, gajus/123rf.com; 2.106: Andrey Armyagov/Shutterstock; 2.107: ucchie79/Shutterstock; 2.111: Breck P. Kent/Shutterstock; 2.121: Dmitry Kalinovsky/Shutterstock; 2.122: Pius Lee/Shutterstock; 2.123: Suphatthra China/Shutterstock; 2.124: MBI/Shutterstock; 4.34: New Africa/Shutterstock; 4.43 (top to bottom): Photographee.eu/Shutterstock, SciePro/Shutterstock; 4.44: aniphaes/123rf.com; 4.64: Gorodenkoff/Shutterstock; 8.31 (left to right): Picsfive/Shutterstock, Kasa1982/Shutterstock; 8.40: Tyler Olson/Shutterstock; 8.65: Mary Terriberry/Shutterstock; 8.67: Oleg_Yakovlev/Shutterstock; 8.69: oticki/Shutterstock; 8.70: plepraisaeng/123rf.com; 9.01a: StudioByTheSea/Shutterstock; 9.01b: Orla/Shutterstock; 9.01c: Giuliano Del Moretto/Shutterstock; 9.01d: Jacek Chabraszewski/Shutterstock; 9.01e: Vivek BR/Shutterstock; 9.06: New Africa/Shutterstock; 9.09: EyeEm/Alamy Stock Photo; 9.10 (left to right): Nitr/Shutterstock, Jiri Hera/Shutterstock; 9.11 (left to right): M. Unal Ozmen/Shutterstock, luckyraccoon/Shutterstock; 9.63: Tom Grundy/123rf.com; 10.14: VideoFort/Shutterstock; 10.28: DECHA CHAIYARAT/Shutterstock; 10.29: Benny Marty/Shutterstock; 10.31: Moish Studio/Shutterstock; 10.41: Tudor Photography/Pearson Education Ltd.; 10.45: Anton Zhigayev/123rf.com; 10.71-10.75 (left to right): givaga/Shutterstock, Adisa/Shutterstock, CAN BALCIOGLU/Shutterstock; 11.25: Breck P. Kent/Shutterstock; 11.33: Mongkolchon Akesin/Shutterstock; 11.60: MBLifestyle/Shutterstock; 11.64: Wade H. Massie/Shutterstock; 11.69: sirtravelalot/Shutterstock; 12.51: PhotoSky/Shutterstock; 12.58: atic12/123rf.com; 12.60: imging/Shutterstock; 12.62: cubephoto/Shutterstock; 12.73: Decha Thapanya/Shutterstock; 12.89: Swapan Photography/Shutterstock; 14.6: vanillaechoes/Shutterstock; 14.7: michaeljung/Shutterstock; 14.8: imageBROKER.com/Shutterstock; 14.26: jeep5d/Shutterstock; 14.62: Scorpp/Shutterstock; 19.40: LIKIT SUPASAI/Shutterstock; 19.42: JOHN MUCHANGI M/Shutterstock; 19.44: Charlie Edward/Shutterstock; 19.45: SIRIMAT KAMSAIIN/Shutterstock; 19.46: Dominator/Shutterstock; 19.48: JurateBuiviene/Shutterstock; 19.50: Aniko Gerendi Enderle/Shutterstock; 19.52: LIKIT SUPASAI/Shutterstock; 19.57: guentermanaus/Shutterstock; 20.31 (left to right): reptiles4all/Shutterstock, chromatos/Shutterstock; 20.33 (left to right): chromatos/Shutterstock, Sh_olya/Shutterstock; 20.34 (left to right): EshanaPhoto/Shutterstock, Prostock-studio/Shutterstock; 20.35: N.Vinoth Narasingam/Shutterstock; 20.38: StudioMolekuul/Shutterstock; 20.39: IT Tech Science/Shutterstock; 20.46 (left to right): Protasov AN/Shutterstock, StudioMolekuul/Shutterstock; 20.48: Aldona Griskeviciene/Shutterstock; 20.56: molekuul/123rf.com; 21.09: Designua/Shutterstock; 21.11: phloxii/Shutterstock; 21.16: Art of Science/Shutterstock; 21.20: Art of Science/Shutterstock; 21.31: shurkin_son/Shutterstock; 23.60: antoniodiaz/Shutterstock; 25.26: Kingspirit Image Room/Shutterstock; 25.27: Andrei Iakhniuk/Shutterstock

Glossary/Index

A

Abbreviated electron configuration, 58–59

ABO blood types, 407, 407f

Absolute specificity, 534, 535t

Absolute zero The coldest possible temperature, which is equivalent to 0 K and −273.15 °C, 39, 39f

Absorbed dose A measurement that indicates the energy of radiation absorbed per mass of tissue, 70–71, 70t

Acetal A functional group that contains two alkoxy groups (OR) bonded to the same carbon, 375–378, 376f, 377f, 378t

Acetaldehyde, 125, 125f, 370, 370f

Acetamide, 425f

Acetaminophen, 48, 48f

Acetate, polyatomic ions, 105–107, 105t, 106ft, 107ft

Acetic acid, 269, 269f, 273f, 274t, 425f
  buffers, 283–286, 284f, 285t
  dissociation constant, 277t

Acetoacetate, 416, 416f, 660–661, 660f

Acetone, 234, 234f, 239t, 370, 370f

Acetylation Chemical reactions in which an acetyl group (CH_3CO) is transferred to a molecule. Acetylation of the proteins that DNA coils around helps with gene regulation by controlling the condensation of DNA. These acetyl groups leave DNA loosely coiled and available for use.

Acetylcholine, 494–495, 494f, 495t, 529f

Acetylcholinesterase, 529, 529f, 530, 530t

Acetyl-CoA (acetyl coenzyme A) The compound formed when an acetyl group (CH_3CO) bonds to CoA. Many different types of molecules are converted to acetyl-CoA before being metabolized in mitochondria, 624–625, 624f, 625f
  beta oxidation (fatty acid oxidation), 656–660, 657f, 658f, 659f
  citric acid cycle, 631–634, 632f, 633f, 634f
  glucose, energy production from, 637, 638f
  ketone bodies and ketogenesis, 660–661, 660f
  lipogenesis, 668, 669f
  pyruvate oxidation and reduction, 629–631, 629f, 630f, 631f

Acetylene, 319, 319f

Acetyl group A group of atoms on organic molecules with the formula CH_3CO. The central carbonyl carbon atom on the acetyl group is the atom that connects to the organic molecule through a covalent bond.

Acetyl transacylase, 668, 669f

Achilles tendon, 502f

Achiral A molecule or object that is superimposable with its mirror image, 347, 347f

Acid A substance that produces hydrogen ions (H^+) when dissolved in water, 268f, 269, 269f

See also Acids and bases

Acid-base reactions A chemical reaction that involves the reaction of an acid with a base. A hydrogen ion (H^+) is transferred from an acid to a base in these reactions, 280–283, 281f, 282f

See also Acids and bases

Acid dissociation constant (K_a) The equilibrium constant for the dissociation reaction of an acid, represented with K_a, 276–277, 277ft
  buffers and, 285–286, 285t
  carboxylic acids, 430–432, 431f

Acid rain Precipitation that contains acidic compounds dissolved in the water droplets, 281–282, 282f, 287, 287f

Acids and bases, 268, 268f
  acid dissociation constant (K_a), 276–277, 277ft
  acidic and basic solutions, 279, 279f
  acids, overview of, 269, 269f
  amino acids, 506–507, 508t, 509, 509f
  bases, overview of, 270–271, 270f
  bicarbonate reactions, 282–283, 282f
  Brønsted-Lowry definition of, 270–271, 271f
  buffers, 283–287, 284f, 285t, 286f, 287f
  carbonate reactions, 282–283, 282f
  carboxylate ions, 430–432, 431f
  carboxylic acid group, 272, 273f
  conjugate acid-base pairs, 271–272, 271f
  COVID-19 and silent hypoxia, 295–298, 295f, 296f, 297f
  diprotic acids, 275–276, 276f, 281–282, 282f
  neutralization reactions, 281–282, 281f, 282f

neutral solutions, 279, 279f
  pH, 280, 280f
  protein hydrolysis and denaturation, 519–521, 520f, 521f
  salts, 281, 281f
  spectator ions, 281, 281f
  strong and weak acids and bases, 273–276, 274ft, 275t, 276f
  titration, 283
  water dissociation constant (K_w), 278–279, 278f

ACP-activated acetyl group (acetyl ACP), 668, 669f

ACP-activated acyl group (malonyl ACP), 668, 669f

Acquired mutations, 598, 598f

Actin, 503f

Activation energy (E_a) The minimum amount of energy that colliding reactants must possess in order for their collisions to result in a chemical reaction. Every chemical reaction has a specific activation energy, 186f, 187
  catalysts and, 189, 189f
  enzymes and, 529, 530f

See also Catalyst; Enzyme

Active site A region of an enzyme formed by the folds of the protein chains where a chemical reaction takes place. Each active site has a specific size, shape, and charge that allows a substrate, or possibly several substrates, to fit correctly, 532–535, 533f, 534f, 535t

Actual yield The amount of product obtained in a real chemical reaction conducted in a laboratory, biological setting, or manufacturing environment, 172

Acyclic alkane Alkanes that can be either straight-chains or branched chains, but do not contain cyclic (ring) structures, 310

Acyclic carbohydrate, 387, 387f

Acyl carrier protein (ACP) A cofactor required for lipogenesis. Acetyl CoA and malonyl CoA are activated when an acyl carrier protein (ACP) is transferred, forming acetyl ACP and malonyl ACP respectively. The enzymes acetyl transacylase and malonyl transacylase catalyze these reactions, 668, 669f